Standard Mathematical
Tables

Standard Mathematical Tables

Tables

Twenty-third Edition

Editor-in-chief of Mathematics

SAMUEL M. SELBY, Ph.D. Sc.D.

Distinguished Professor Emeritus of Mathematics and formerly Chairman,
Mathematics Department, University of Akron.
Emeritus Professor of Mathematics, Hiram College, Hiram, Ohio

published by:

CRC PRESS, INC.
18901 Cranwood Parkway · Cleveland, Ohio 44128

PREFACE

In keeping abreast of the times, the CRC *Standard Mathematical Tables* is responding to requests of users who have indicated a need for an upgrading of interest rate information in its financial section. This 23rd edition features compound interest and associated material from ¼% to 20% in intervals of ¼%.

It is, as always, the purpose of the CRC Tables to service all facets of the scientific, engineering, industrial, and educational personnel and as a consequence includes in its customary contents information pertaining to metric conversion tables, octo-decimal tables, an extensive set of integral tables, tables for differential equations, trigonometric and hyperbolic functions, algebra, vector analysis, statistics, tables of indices and power residues, the totient function, primitive roots for primes, and several other tables of practical and mathematical interest.

It is hoped that this 23rd edition will enjoy the same popular acceptance as its predecessors. The editorial staff wishes to express its sincere appreciation to Kathleen Mills, administrative editor and Paula Osborne, production editor, for their meticulous handling of details so as to make final production of this 23rd edition possible.

Constructive suggestions are always welcome from users of the tables, as improvement of contents follows if and only if close contacts are maintained between them and the editorial staff. All inquiries may be sent to either the editor or the publishers at the Cleveland address.

Samuel M. Selby, Editor-in-chief, Mathematics
Robert C. Weast, Editor-in-chief

CONTENTS

SI SYSTEM OF MEASUREMENT

SI, which is the abbreviation of the French words "Système Internationale d'Unites," is the accepted abbreviation for the International Metric System, which has seven base units, as shown below.

UNITS FOR A SYSTEM OF MEASURES AS USED INTERNATIONALLY

Quantity measured	Unit	Abbreviation
Length	meter	m
Mass	kilogram	kg
Time	second	s
Electric current	ampere	A
Temperature	degree Kelvin	K
Luminous intensity	candela	cd
Amount of substance	mole	mol

Supplementary and Derived Units from Base Units as Used Internationally

Supplementary Units

Plane angle	radian	rad
Solid angle	steradian	sr

SI Derived Units with Special Names

Quantity	Name	Symbol	Expressed in terms of other units	Expressed in terms of base units*
Frequency[†]	hertz	Hz		s^{-1}
Force	newton	N		$m \cdot kg \cdot s^{-2}$
Pressure, stress	pascal	Pa	N/m^2	$m^{-1} \cdot kg \cdot s^{-2}$
Energy, work, quantity of heat	joule	J	$N \cdot m$	$m^2 \cdot kg \cdot s^{-2}$
Power, radiant flux	watt	W	J/s	$m^2 \cdot kg \cdot s^{-3}$
Quantity of electricity, electric charge	coulomb	C		$s \cdot A$
Electric potential, potential difference, electromotive force	volt	V	W/A	$m^2 \cdot kg \cdot s^{-3} \cdot A^{-1}$
Electric capacitance	farad	F	C/V	$m^{-2} \cdot kg^{-1} \cdot s^4 \cdot A^2$
Electric resistance	ohm	Ω	V/A	$m^2 \cdot kg \cdot s^{-3} \cdot A^{-2}$
Electric conductance	siemens	S	A/V	$m^{-2} \cdot kg^{-1} \cdot s^3 \cdot A^2$
Magnetic flux	weber	Wb	$V \cdot s$	$m^2 \cdot kg \cdot s^{-2} \cdot A^{-1}$
Magnetic flux density	tesla	T	Wb/m^2	$kg \cdot s^{-2} \cdot A^{-1}$
Inductance	henry	H	Wb/A	$m^2 \cdot kg \cdot s^{-2} \cdot A^{-2}$
Luminous flux	lumen	lm		$cd \cdot sr^{‡}$
Illuminance	lux	lx	lm/m^2	$m^{-2} \cdot cd \cdot sr^{‡}$

*The formulas for derived units are not necessarily unique. For example, the volt may be defined as 1 joule per coulomb.

[†]The SI unit of frequency, the hertz, is one cycle per second. The reciprocal of the frequency is the period. The hertz is not recommended for use as a measure of discrete items per unit of time; e.g., 5 boxes per second on an assembly line would not be referred to as 5 hertz.

[‡]In this expression the steradian (sr) is treated as a base unit.

Examples of SI Derived Units Expressed in Terms of Other Units and the Base Units

Quantity	Description	Expressed in terms of other units	Expressed in terms of base or supplementary units
Area	square meter		m^2
Volume	cubic meter		m^3
Speed			
linear	meter per second		m/s
angular	radian per second		rad/s
Acceleration			
linear	meter per second squared		m/s^2
angular	radian per second squared		rad/s^2
Wave number*	1 per meter		m^{-1}
Density, mass density	kilogram per cubic meter		kg/m^3
Concentration (of amount of substance)	mole per cubic meter		mol/m^3
Activity (radioactive)[†]	1 per second		s^{-1}
Specific volume	cubic meter per kilogram		m^3/kg
Luminance	candela per square meter		cd/m^3
Dynamic viscosity	pascal second	Pa·s	$m^{-1} \cdot kg \cdot s^{-1}$
Moment of force	newton meter	N·m	$m^2 \cdot kg \cdot s^{-2}$
Surface tension	newton per meter	N/m	$kg \cdot s^{-2}$
Heat flux density, irradiance	watt per square meter	W/m^2	$kg \cdot s^{-3}$
Heat capacity, entropy	joule per kelvin	J/K	$m^2 \cdot kg \cdot s^{-2} \cdot K^{-1}$
Specific heat capacity, specific entropy	joule per kilogram kelvin	J/(kg·K)	$m^2 \cdot s^{-2} \cdot K^{-1}$
Specific energy	joule per kilogram	J/kg	$m^2 \cdot s^{-2}$
Thermal conductivity	watt per meter kelvin	W/(m·K)	$m \cdot kg \cdot s^{-3} \cdot K^{-1}$
Energy density	joule per cubic meter	J/m^3	$m^{-1} \cdot kg \cdot s^{-2}$
Electric field strength	volt per meter	V/m	$m \cdot kg \cdot s^{-3} \cdot A^{-1}$
Electric charge density	coulomb per cubic meter	C/m^3	$m^{-3} \cdot s \cdot A$
Surface density of charge, flux density	coulomb per square meter	C/m^2	$m^{-2} \cdot s \cdot A$
Permittivity	farad per meter	F/m	$m^{-3} \cdot kg^{-1} \cdot s^4 \cdot A^2$
Current density	ampere per square meter		$A \cdot m^{-2}$
Magnetic field strength	ampere per meter		$A \cdot m^{-1}$
Permeability	henry per meter	H/m	$m \cdot kg \cdot s^{-2} \cdot A^{-2}$
Molar energy	joule per mole	J/mole	$m^2 \cdot kg \cdot s^{-2} \cdot mol^{-1}$
Molar entropy, molar heat capacity	joule per mole kelvin	J/(mol·K)	$m^2 \cdot kg \cdot s^{-2} \cdot K^{-1} \cdot mol^{-1}$
Radiant intensity	watt per steradian	W/sr	$m^2 \cdot kg \cdot s^{-3} \cdot sr^{-1}$

*The wave number is the reciprocal of the wavelength, expressed in meters, of an electromagnetic radiation.

[†]Activity is the intensity of a radioactive source. It can be expressed as the number of atoms disintegrating in unit time, the number of scintillations, or other effects per unit time. The unit hertz is not used for this quantity although its dimensions are the same.

NOTE: The values of certain so-called dimensionless quantities, as for example refractive index, relative permeability, or relative permittivity, are expressed by pure numbers.

RECOMMENDED DECIMAL MULTIPLES
AND SUBMULTIPLES

Multiples and submultiples	Prefixes	Symbols
10^{12}	tera	T
10^9	giga	G
10^6	mega	M
10^3	kilo	k
10^2	hecto	h
10	deca	da
10^{-1}	deci	d
10^{-2}	centi	c
10^{-3}	milli	m
10^{-6}	micro	μ (greek mu)
10^{-9}	nano	n
10^{-12}	pico	p
10^{-15}	femto	f
10^{-18}	atto	a

DEFINED VALUES AND EQUIVALENTS

Meter	m	1 650 763.73 wavelengths in vacuo of the unperturbed transition $2_{p_{10}} - 5_{d_5}$ in ^{86}Kr
Kilogram	kg	Mass of the international kilgram at Sèvres, France
Second	s	The unit of time is based on the transition between the two hyperfine levels of the ground state of the atom of the pure nuclide Cesium-133, undisturbed by external fields, with the value 9,192,631,770 cycles taken as exactly 1 s (1964 definition)
Degree Kelvin	K	Defined in the thermodynamic scale by assigning 273.16 K to the triple point of water (freezing point, 273.15 K = 0°C)
Unified atomic mass unit	u	1/12 the mass of an atom of the ^{12}C nuclide
Mole	mol	Amount of substance containing the same number of atoms as 12 g of pure ^{12}C
Standard acceleration of free fall	g_n	9.806 65 ms^{-2}, 980.665 cm s^{-2}
Normal atmospheric pressure	atm	101 325 N m^{-2}, 1 013 250 dyn cm^{-2} (exactly)
Thermochemical calorie	cal$_{th}$	4.1840 J, 4.1840 × 10^7 erg (exactly)
International Steam Table calorie	cal$_{IT}$	4.1868 J, 4.1868 × 10^7 erg (exactly)
Liter	l	0.001 m^3, 1000 cm^3 (exactly)
Inch	in	0.0254 m, 2.54 cm (exactly)
Pound (avdp)	lb	0.453 592 37 kg, 453.592 37 g (exactly)

CONVERSION FACTORS

Conversion Factors – Metric to English

To obtain	Multiply	By
Inches	Centimeters	0.3937007874
Feet	Meters	3.280839895
Yards	Meters	1.093613298
Miles	Kilometers	0.6213711922
Ounces	Grams	$3.527396195 \times 10^{-2}$
Pounds	Kilograms	2.204622622
Gallons	Liters	0.2641720524
Fluid ounces	Milliliters (cc)	$3.381402270 \times 10^{-2}$
Square inches	Square centimeters	0.1550003100
Square feet	Square meters	10.76391042
Square yards	Square meters	1.195990046
Cubic inches	Milliliters (cc)	$6.102374409 \times 10^{-2}$
Cubic feet	Cubic meters	35.31466672
Cubic yards	Cubic meters	1.307950619

Conversion Factors – English to Metric*

To obtain	Multiply	By
Microns	Mils	**25.4**
Centimeters	Inches	**2.54**
Meters	Feet	**0.3048**
Meters	Yards	**0.9144**
Kilometers	Miles	**1.609344**
Grams	Ounces	28.34952313
Kilograms	Pounds	**0.45359237**
Liters	Gallons	**3.785411784**
Milliliters (cc)	Fluid ounces	29.57352956
Square centimeters	Square inches	**6.4516**
Square meters	Square feet	**0.09290304**
Square meters	Square yards	**0.83612736**
Milliliters (cc)	Cubic inches	**16.387064**
Cubic meters	Cubic feet	$2.831684659 \times 10^{-2}$
Cubic meters	Cubic yards	0.764554858

*Boldface numbers are exact; others are given to ten significant figures where so indicated by the multiplier factor.

Conversion Factors – General*

To obtain	Multiply	By
Atmospheres	Feet of water @ 4°C	2.950×10^{-5}
Atmospheres	Inches of mercury @ 0°C	3.342×10^{-2}
Atmospheres	Pounds per square inch	6.804×10^{-2}
BTU	Food-pounds	1.285×10^{-3}
BTU	Joules	9.480×10^{-4}
Cords	Cubic feet	**128**

To obtain	Multiply	By
Degree (angle)	Radians	57.2958
Ergs	Foot-pounds	1.356×10^7
Feet	Miles	**5280**
Feet of water @ 4°C	Atmospheres	33.90
Foot-pounds	Horsepower-hours	1.98×10^6
Foot-pounds	Kilowatt-hours	2.655×10^6
Food-pounds per min	Horsepower	3.3×10^4
Horsepower	Foot-pounds per sec	1.818×10^{-3}
Inches of mercury @ 0°C	Pounds per square inch	2.036
Joules	BTU	1054.8
Joules	Foot-pounds	1.35582
Kilowatts	BTU per min	1.758×10^{-2}
Kilowatts	Foot-pounds per min	2.26×10^{-5}
Kilowatts	Horsepower	0.745712
Knots	Miles per hour	0.86897624
Miles	Feet	1.894×10^{-4}
Nautical miles	Miles	0.86897624
Radians	Degrees	1.745×10^{-2}
Square feet	Acres	**43560**
Watts	BTU per min	17.5796

*Boldface numbers are exact; others are given to ten significant figures where so indicated by the multiplier factor.

Temperature Factors

$$°F = 9/5 \ (°C) + 32$$

Fahrenheit temperature = 1.8 (temperature in kelvins) −459.67

$$°C = 5/9 \ (°F) - 32$$

Celsius temperature = temperature in kelvins −273.15
Fahrenheit temperature = 1.8 (Celsius temperature) +32

PHYSICAL CONSTANTS

Equatorial radius of the earth = 6378.388 km = 3963.34 miles (statute).
Polar radius of the earth, 6356.912 km = 3949.99 miles (statute).
1 degree of latitude at 40° = 69 miles.
1 international nautical mile = 1.15078 miles (statute) = 1852 m = 6076.115 ft.
Mean density of the earth = 5.522 g/cm³ = 344.7 lb/ft³.
Constant of gravitation, $(6.673 \pm 0.003) \times 10^3$ cm³ gm⁻¹ s⁻².
Acceleration due to gravity at sea level, latitude 45° = 980.665 cm/s² = 32.1740 ft/sec².
Length of seconds pendulum at sea level, latitude 45° = 99.3574 cm = 39.1171 in.
1 knot (international) = 101.269 ft/min = 1.6878 ft/sec = 1.1508 miles (statute)/hr.
1 micron = 10^{-4} cm.
1 ångstrom = 10^{-8} cm.
Mass of hydrogen atom = $(1.67339 \pm 0.00031) \times 10^{-24}$ g.
Density of mercury at 0°C = 13.5955 g/ml.
Density of water at 3.98°C = 1.000000 g/ml.
Density, maximum, of water, at 3.98°C = 0.999973 g/cm³.
Density of dry air at 0°C, 760 mm = 1.2929 g/liter.
Velocity of sound in dry air at 0°C = 331.36 m/s = 1087.1 ft/sec.
Velocity of light in vacuum = $(2.997925 \pm 0.000002) \times 10^{10}$ cm/s.
Heat of fusion of water 0°C = 79.71 cal/g.
Heat of vaporization of water 100°C = 539.55 cal/g.
Electrochemical equivalent of silver 0.001118 g/sec international amp.
Absolute wave length of red cadmium light in air at 15°C, 760 mm pressure = 6438.4696 A.
Wave length of orange-red line of krypton 86 = 6057.802 A.

NUMBERS CONTAINING π

	Number	Logarithm		Number	Logarithm
π	3.1415 927	0.4971 499	$2\pi^2$	19.7392 088	1.2953 297
2π	6.2831 853	0.7981 799	$\pi/180$	0.0174 533	8.2418 774 − 10
3π	9.4247 780	0.9742 711	$180/\pi$	57.2957 795	1.7581 226
4π	12.5663 706	1.0992 099	$4\pi^2$	39.4784 176	1.5963 597
8π	25.1327 412	1.4002 399	$1/\pi^2$	0.1013 212	9.0057 003 − 10
$\pi/2$	1.5707 963	0.1961 199	$1/(2\pi^2)$	0.0506 606	8.7046 703 − 10
$\pi/3$	1.0471 976	0.0200 286	$1/(4\pi^2)$	0.0253 303	8.4036 403 − 10
$\pi/4$	0.7853 982	9.8950 899 − 10	$\sqrt{\pi}$	1.7724 539	0.2485 749
$\pi/6$	0.5235 988	9.7189 986 − 10	$\dfrac{\sqrt{\pi}}{2}$	0.8862 269	9.9475 449 − 10
$\pi/8$	0.3926 991	9.5940 599 − 10	$\sqrt{\frac{\pi}{3}}$	0.4431 135	9.6465 149 − 10
$2\pi/3$	2.0943 951	0.3210 586	$\sqrt{\frac{\pi}{2}}$	1.2533 141	0.0980 599
$4\pi/3$	4.1887 902	0.6220 886	$\sqrt{\frac{2}{\pi}}$	0.7978 846	9.9019 401 − 10
$1/\pi$	0.3183 099	9.5028 501 − 10	π^3	31.0062 767	1.4914 496
$2/\pi$	0.6366 198	9.8038 801 − 10	$\sqrt[3]{\pi}$	1.4645 919	0.1657 166
$4/\pi$	1.2732 395	0.1049 101	$1/\sqrt[3]{\pi}$	0.6827 841	9.8342 834 − 10
$1/(2\pi)$	0.1591 549	9.2018 201 − 10	$\sqrt[3]{\pi^2}$	2.1450 294	0.3314 332
$1/(4\pi)$	0.0795 775	8.9007 901 − 10	$1/\sqrt{\pi}$	0.5641 896	9.7514 251 − 10
$1/(6\pi)$	0.0530 516	8.7246 989 − 10	$1/\sqrt{2\pi}$	0.3989 423	9.6009 101 − 10
$1/(8\pi)$	0.0397 887	8.5997 601 − 10	$2/\sqrt{\pi}$	1.1283 792	0.0524 551
π^2	9.8696 044	0.9942 997			

MULTIPLES OF $\dfrac{\pi}{2}$

n	$n\dfrac{\pi}{2}$	n	$n\dfrac{\pi}{2}$	n	$n\dfrac{\pi}{2}$	n	$n\dfrac{\pi}{2}$
1	1.57079 63268	26	40.84070 44967	51	80.11061 26665	76	119.38052 08364
2	3.14159 26536	27	42.41150 08235	52	81.68140 89933	77	120.95131 71632
3	4.71238 89804	28	43.98229 71503	53	83.25220 53201	78	122.52211 34900
4	6.28318 53072	29	45.55309 34771	54	84.82300 16469	79	124.09290 98168
5	7.85398 16340	30	47.12388 98038	55	86.39379 79737	80	125.66370 61436
6	9.42477 79608	31	48.69468 61306	56	87.96459 43005	81	127.23450 24704
7	10.99557 42876	32	50.26548 24574	57	89.53539 06273	82	128.80529 87972
8	12.56637 06144	33	51.83627 87842	58	91.10618 69541	83	130.37609 51240
9	14.13716 69412	34	53.40707 51110	59	92.67698 32809	84	131.94689 14508
10	15.70796 32679	35	54.97787 14378	60	94.24777 96077	85	133.51768 77776
11	17.27875 95947	36	56.54866 77646	61	95.81857 59345	86	135.08848 41044
12	18.84955 59215	37	58.11946 40914	62	97.38937 22613	87	136.65928 04312
13	20.42035 22483	38	59.69026 04182	63	98.96016 85881	88	138.23007 67580
14	21.99114 85751	39	61.26105 67450	64	100.53096 49149	89	139.80087 30847
15	23.56194 49019	40	62.83185 30718	65	102.10176 12417	90	141.37166 94115
16	25.13274 12287	41	64.40264 93986	66	103.67255 75685	91	142.94246 57383
17	26.70353 75555	42	65.97344 57254	67	105.24335 38953	92	144.51326 20651
18	28.27433 38823	43	67.54424 20522	68	106.81415 02221	93	146.08405 83919
19	29.84513 02091	44	69.11503 83790	69	108.38494 65488	94	147.65485 47187
20	31.41592 65359	45	70.68583 47058	70	109.95574 28756	95	149.22565 10455
21	32.98672 28627	46	72.25663 10326	71	111.52653 92024	96	150.79644 73723
22	34.55751 91895	47	73.82742 73594	72	113.09733 55292	97	152.36724 36991
23	36.12831 55163	48	75.39822 36862	73	114.66813 18560	98	153.93804 00259
24	37.69911 18431	49	76.96902 00129	74	116.23892 81828	99	155.50883 63527
25	39.26990 81699	50	78.53981 63397	75	117.80972 45096	100	157.07963 26795

MOMENT OF INERTIA FOR VARIOUS BODIES OF MASS

The mass of the body is indicated by m.

Body	Axis	Moment of inertia
Uniform thin rod	Normal to the length, at one end	$m\dfrac{l^2}{3}$
Uniform thin rod	Normal to the length, at the center	$m\dfrac{l^2}{12}$
Thin rectangular sheet, sides a and b	Through the center parallel to b	$m\dfrac{a^2}{12}$
Thin rectangular sheet, sides a and b	Through the center perpendicular to the sheet	$m\dfrac{a^2 + b^2}{12}$
Thin circular sheet of radius r	Normal to the plate through the center	$m\dfrac{r^2}{2}$
Thin circular sheet of radius r	Along any diameter	$m\dfrac{r^2}{4}$
Thin circular ring. Radii r_1 and r_2	Through center normal to plane of ring	$m\dfrac{r_1^2 + r_2^2}{2}$
Thin circular ring. Radii r_1 and r_2	Any diameter	$m\dfrac{r_1^2 + r_2^2}{4}$
Rectangular parallelopiped, edges a, b, and c	Through center perpendicular to face ab, (parallel to edge c)	$m\dfrac{a^2 + b^2}{12}$
Sphere, radius r	Any diameter	$m\dfrac{2}{5}r^2$
Spherical shell, external radius r_1, internal radius r_2	Any diameter	$m\dfrac{2}{5}\dfrac{(r_1^5 - r_2^5)}{(r_1^3 - r_2^3)}$
Spherical shell, very thin, mean radius, r	Any diameter	$m\dfrac{2}{3}r^2$
Right circular cylinder of radius r, length l	The longitudinal axis of the solid	$m\dfrac{r^2}{2}$
Right circular cylinder of radius r, length l	Transverse diameter	$m\left(\dfrac{r^2}{4} + \dfrac{l^2}{12}\right)$
Hollow circular cylinder, length l, radii r_1 and r_2	The longitudinal axis of the figure	$m\dfrac{(r_1^2 + r_2^2)}{2}$
Thin cylindrical shell, length l, mean radius, r	The longitudinal axis of the figure	mr^2
Hollow circular cylinder, length l, radii r_1 and r_2	Transverse diameter	$m\left[\dfrac{r_1^2 + r_2^2}{4} + \dfrac{l^2}{12}\right]$
Hollow circular cylinder, length l, very thin, mean radius	Transverse diameter	$m\left(\dfrac{r^2}{2} + \dfrac{l^2}{12}\right)$
Elliptic cylinder, length l, transverse semiaxes a and b	Longitudinal axis	$m\left(\dfrac{a^2 + b^2}{4}\right)$
Right cone, altitude h, radius of base r	Axis of the figure	$m\dfrac{3}{10}r^2$
Spheroid of revolution, equatorial radius r	Polar axis	$m\dfrac{2r^2}{5}$
Ellipsoid, axes $2a$, $2b$, $2c$	Axis $2a$	$m\dfrac{(b^2 + c^2)}{5}$

MENSURATION FORMULAS

Dr. Howard Eves

TRIANGLES

In the following: K = area, r = radius of the inscribed circle, R = radius of the circumscribed circle.

Right Triangle

$A + B = C = 90°$
$c^2 = a^2 + b^2$ (*Pythagorean relation*)
$a = \sqrt{(c + b)(c - b)}$
$K = \frac{1}{2}ab$

$r = \dfrac{ab}{a + b + c}$, $R = \frac{1}{2}c$

$h = \dfrac{ab}{c}$, $m = \dfrac{b^2}{c}$, $n = \dfrac{a^2}{c}$

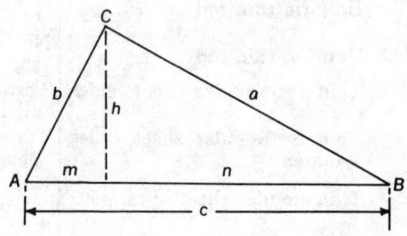

Equilateral Triangle

$A = B = C = 60°$
$K = \frac{1}{4}a^2\sqrt{3}$
$r = \frac{1}{6}a\sqrt{3}$, $R = \frac{1}{3}a\sqrt{3}$
$h = \frac{1}{2}a\sqrt{3}$

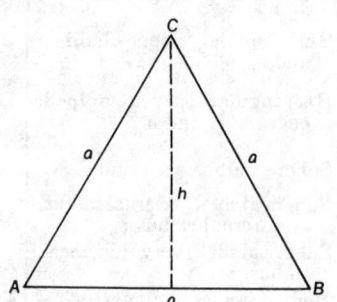

General Triangle

Let $s = \frac{1}{2}(a + b + c)$, h_c = length of altitude on side c, t_c = length of bisector of angle C, m_c = length of median to side c.

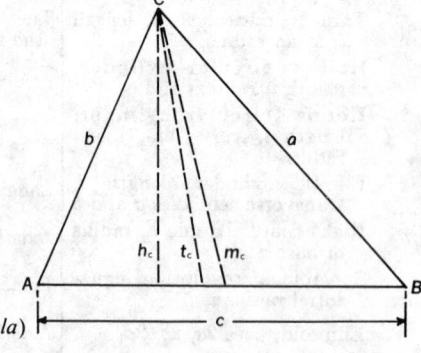

$A + B + C = 180°$
$c^2 = a^2 + b^2 - 2ab \cos C$
$\qquad$ (*law of cosines*)
$K = \frac{1}{2}h_c c = \frac{1}{2}ab \sin C$
$\quad = \dfrac{c^2 \sin A \sin B}{2 \sin C}$
$\quad = rs = \dfrac{abc}{4R}$
$\quad = \sqrt{s(s - a)(s - b)(s - c)}$ (*Heron's formula*)

8

$$r = c \sin \frac{A}{2} \sin \frac{B}{2} \sec \frac{C}{2} = \frac{ab \sin C}{2s} = (s - c) \tan \frac{C}{2}$$

$$= \sqrt{\frac{(s - a)(s - b)(s - c)}{s}} = \frac{K}{s} = 4R \sin \frac{A}{2} \sin \frac{B}{2} \sin \frac{C}{2}$$

$$R = \frac{c}{2 \sin C} = \frac{abc}{4\sqrt{s(s - a)(s - b)(s - c)}} = \frac{abc}{4K}$$

$$h_c = a \sin B = b \sin A = \frac{2K}{c}$$

$$t_c = \frac{2ab}{a + b} \cos \frac{C}{2} = \sqrt{ab \left\{ 1 - \frac{c^2}{(a + b)^2} \right\}}$$

$$m_c = \sqrt{\frac{a^2}{2} + \frac{b^2}{2} - \frac{c^2}{4}}$$

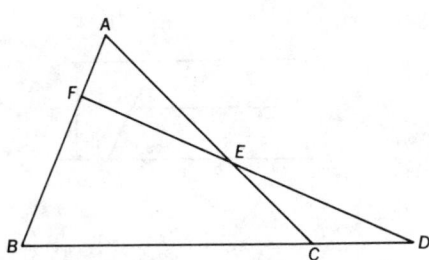 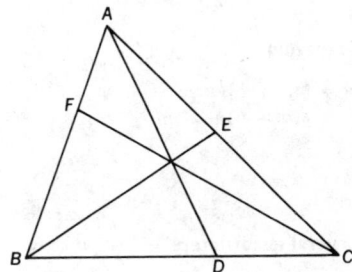

Menelaus' Theorem. A necessary and sufficient condition for points D, E, F on the respective side lines BC, CA, AB of a triangle ABC to be collinear is that

$$BD \cdot CE \cdot AF = - DC \cdot EA \cdot FB,$$

where all segments in the formula are directed segments.

Ceva's Theorem. A necessary and sufficient condition for AD, BE, CF, where D, E, F are points on the respective side lines BC, CA, AB of a triangle ABC, to be concurrent is that

$$BD \cdot CE \cdot AF = + DC \cdot EA \cdot FB,$$

where all segments in the formula are directed segments.

QUADRILATERALS

In the following: K = area, p and q are diagonals.

Rectangle

$A = B = C = D = 90°$
$K = ab,\quad p = \sqrt{a^2 + b^2}$

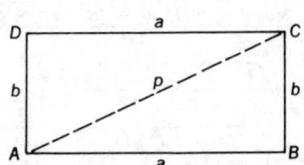

Parallelogram

$A = C, \quad B = D, \quad A + B = 180°$
$K = bh = ab \sin A = ab \sin B$
$h = a \sin A = a \sin B$
$p = \sqrt{a^2 + b^2 - 2ab \cos A}$
$q = \sqrt{a^2 + b^2 - 2ab \cos B} = \sqrt{a^2 + b^2 + 2ab \cos A}$

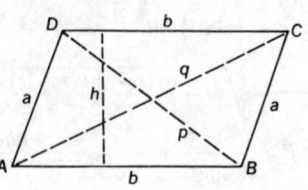

Rhombus

$p^2 + q^2 = 4a^2$
$K = \frac{1}{2}pq$

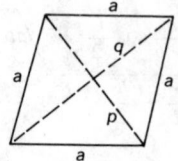

Trapezoid

$m = \frac{1}{2}(a + b)$
$K = \frac{1}{2}(a + b)h = mh$

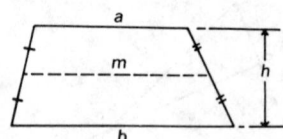

General quadrilateral

Let $s = \frac{1}{2}(a + b + c + d)$.
$$
\begin{aligned}
K &= \tfrac{1}{2}pq \sin \theta \\
&= \tfrac{1}{4}(b^2 + d^2 - a^2 - c^2) \tan \theta \\
&= \tfrac{1}{4}\sqrt{4p^2q^2 - (b^2 + d^2 - a^2 - c^2)^2} \\
&\qquad (Bretschneider's \ formula) \\
&= \sqrt{(s - a)(s - b)(s - c)(s - d) - abcd \cos^2 \left(\frac{A + B}{2}\right)}
\end{aligned}
$$

Theorem. The diagonals of a quadrilateral with consecutive sides a, b, c, d are perpendicular if and only if $a^2 + c^2 = b^2 + d^2$.

Cyclic Quadrilateral

Let R = radius of the circumscribed circle.
$$
A + C = B + D = 180°
$$
$$
K = \sqrt{(s - a)(s - b)(s - c)(s - d)}
$$
$$
(Brahmagupta's \ formula)
$$
$$
= \frac{\sqrt{(ac + bd)(ad + bc)(ab + cd)}}{4R}
$$
$$
p = \sqrt{\frac{(ac + bd)(ab + cd)}{ad + bc}}, \quad q = \sqrt{\frac{(ac + bd)(ad + bc)}{ab + cd}}
$$
$$
R = \frac{1}{2}\sqrt{\frac{(ac + bd)(ad + bc)(ab + cd)}{(s - a)(s - b)(s - c)(s - d)}}, \quad \sin \theta = \frac{2K}{ac + bd}
$$

Ptolemy's Theorem. A convex quadrilateral with consecutive sides a, b, c, d and diagonals p and q is cyclic if and only if $ac + bd = pq$.

Cyclic-inscriptable Quadrilateral

Let r = radius of the inscribed circle, R = radius of the circumscribed circle, m = distance between the centers of the inscribed and the circumscribed circles.

$$A + C = B + D = 180°$$

$$a + c = b + d$$

$$K = \sqrt{abcd}$$

$$\frac{1}{(R - m)^2} + \frac{1}{(R + m)^2} = \frac{1}{r^2}$$

$$r = \frac{\sqrt{abcd}}{s}$$

$$R = \tfrac{1}{2} \sqrt{\frac{(ac + bd)(ad + bc)(ab + cd)}{abcd}}$$

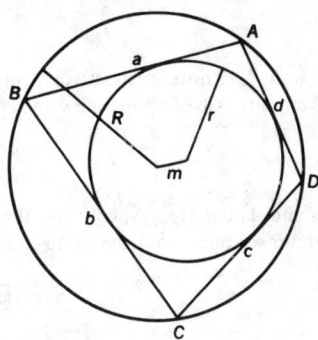

REGULAR POLYGONS

In the following: n = number of sides, s = length of each side, p = perimeter, θ = one of the vertex angles, r = radius of the inscribed circle, R = radius of the circumscribed circle, K = area.

$$\theta = \left(\frac{n - 2}{n}\right) 180°$$

$$s = 2r \tan \frac{180°}{n} = 2R \sin \frac{180°}{n}$$

$$p = ns$$

$$K = \tfrac{1}{4} n s^2 \cot \frac{180°}{n}$$

$$= n r^2 \tan \frac{180°}{n}$$

$$= \tfrac{1}{2} n R^2 \sin \frac{360°}{n}$$

$$r = \tfrac{1}{2} s \cot \frac{180°}{n}, \quad R = \tfrac{1}{2} s \csc \frac{180°}{n}$$

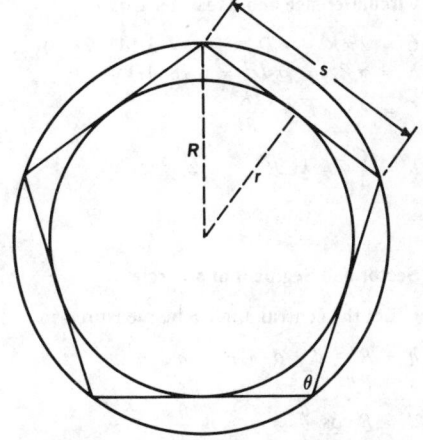

Polygon	n	K	r	R
Triangle (equilateral)	3	$0.43301s^2$	$0.28868s$	$0.57735s$
Square	4	$1.00000s^2$	$0.50000s$	$0.70711s$
Pentagon	5	$1.72048s^2$	$0.68819s$	$0.85065s$
Hexagon	6	$2.59808s^2$	$0.86603s$	$1.00000s$
Heptagon	7	$3.63391s^2$	$1.0383s$	$1.1524s$
Octagon	8	$4.82843s^2$	$1.2071s$	$1.3066s$
Nonagon	9	$6.18182s^2$	$1.3737s$	$1.4619s$
Decagon	10	$7.69421s^2$	$1.5388s$	$1.6180s$
Undecagon	11	$9.36564s^2$	$1.7028s$	$1.7747s$
Dodecagon	12	$11.19615s^2$	$1.8660s$	$1.9319s$

If s_k denotes the side of a regular polygon of k sides inscribed in a circle of radius R, then

$$s_{2n} = \sqrt{2R^2 - R\sqrt{4R^2 - s_n^2}}.$$

If S_k denotes the side of a regular polygon of k sides circumscribed about a circle of radius r, then

$$S_{2n} = \frac{2rS_n}{2r + \sqrt{4r^2 + S_n^2}}$$

If p_k and P_k denote, respectively, the perimeters of regular polygons of k sides inscribed in and circumscribed about the same circle, then

$$P_{2n} = \frac{2p_n P_n}{p_n + P_n} \quad \text{and} \quad p_{2n} = \sqrt{p_n P_{2n}}.$$

If a_k and A_k denote, respectively, the areas of regular polygons of k sides inscribed in and circumscribed about the same circle, then

$$a_{2n} = \sqrt{a_n A_n} \quad \text{and} \quad A_{2n} = \frac{2a_{2n} A_n}{a_{2n} + A_n}.$$

CIRCLES

In the following: R = radius, D = diameter, C = circumference, K = area.

Circumference and Area of a Circle

$$C = 2\pi R = \pi D \quad (\pi = 3.14159\cdots)$$
$$K = \pi R^2 = \tfrac{1}{4}\pi D^2 = 0.7854 D^2$$
$$C = 2\sqrt{\pi K} = \frac{2K}{R}$$

$$K = \frac{C^2}{4\pi} = \tfrac{1}{2}CR$$

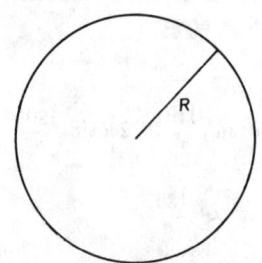

Sector and Segment of a Circle

Let the central angle θ be measured in radians ($\theta < \pi$).

$$h = R - d, \quad d = R - h$$
$$s = R\theta$$
$$d = R\cos\frac{\theta}{2} = \tfrac{1}{2}c\cot\frac{\theta}{2}$$
$$\quad = \tfrac{1}{2}\sqrt{4R^2 - c^2}$$
$$c = 2R\sin\frac{\theta}{2} = 2d\tan\frac{\theta}{2}$$
$$\quad = 2\sqrt{R^2 - d^2} = \sqrt{4h(2R - h)}$$
$$\theta = \frac{s}{R} = 2\,\mathrm{Cos}^{-1}\frac{d}{R} = 2\,\mathrm{Tan}^{-1}\frac{c}{2d} = 2\,\mathrm{Sin}^{-1}\frac{c}{2R}$$

$$K \text{ (sector)} = \tfrac{1}{2}Rs = \tfrac{1}{2}R^2\theta$$

$$K \text{ (segment)} = \tfrac{1}{2}R^2(\theta - \sin\theta) = \tfrac{1}{2}(Rs - cd) = R^2\,\mathrm{Cos}^{-1}\frac{d}{R} - d\sqrt{R^2 - d^2}$$

$$\quad = R^2\,\mathrm{Cos}^{-1}\frac{R - h}{R} - (R - h)\sqrt{2Rh - h^2}$$

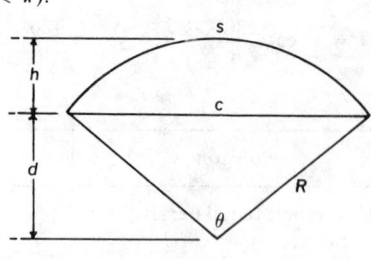

Sector of an Annulus

$h = R_1 - R_2$
$K = \frac{1}{2}\theta(R_1 + R_2)(R_1 - R_2)$
$\quad = \frac{1}{2}\theta h(R_1 + R_2)$
$\quad = \frac{1}{2}h(s_1 + s_2)$

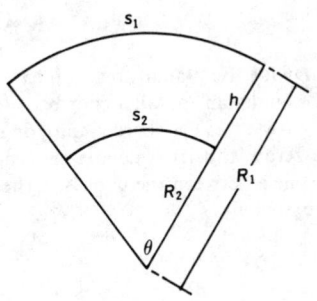

CONIC SECTIONS

Ellipse

Let p = circumference, K = area

$p = 2\pi \sqrt{\dfrac{a^2 + b^2}{2}}$ (approximately)

$\quad = 4aE$ (exactly)   See table of elliptic integral for E, using $k = \sqrt{a^2 - b^2}/a$.

$K = \pi ab$

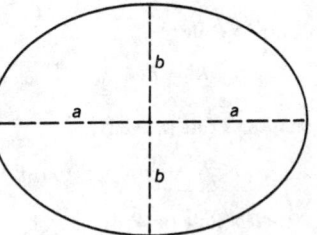

Parabolic Segment

$$s = \sqrt{4x^2 + y^2} + \frac{y^2}{2x}\log_e\left[\frac{2x + \sqrt{4x^2 + y^2}}{y}\right]$$

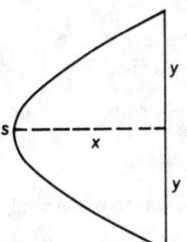

K (right segment) $= \frac{4}{3}xy$
K (oblique segment) $= \frac{4}{3}T$, where T is the area of the triangle with base along the chord of the segment and with opposite vertex at the point on the parabola at which the tangent to the parabola is parallel to the chord of the segment.

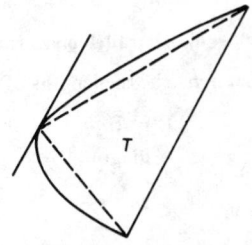

CAVALIERI'S THEOREM FOR THE PLANE

If two planar areas are included between a pair of parallel lines, and if the two segments cut off by the areas on any line parallel to the including lines are equal in length, then the two planar areas are equal.

PLANAR AREAS BY APPROXIMATION

Divide the planar area K into n strips by equidistant parallel chords of lengths $y_0, y_1, y_2, \ldots, y_n$ (where y_0 and/or y_n may be zero), and let h denote the common distance between the chords. Then, approximately:

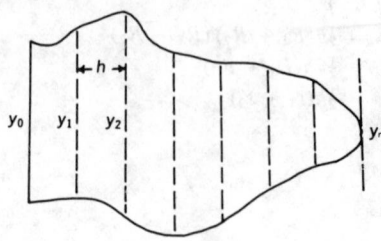

Trapezoidal Rule

$$K = h(\tfrac{1}{2}y_0 + y_1 + y_2 + \cdots + y_{n-1} + \tfrac{1}{2}y_n)$$

Durand's Rule

$$K = h(\tfrac{4}{10}y_0 + \tfrac{11}{10}y_1 + y_2 + y_3 + \cdots + y_{n-2} + \tfrac{11}{10}y_{n-1} + \tfrac{4}{10}y_n)$$

Simpson's rule (n even)

$$K = \tfrac{1}{3}h(y_0 + 4y_1 + 2y_2 + 4y_3 + 2y_4 + \cdots + 2y_{n-2} + 4y_{n-1} + y_n)$$

Weddle's Rule ($n = 6$)

$$K = \tfrac{3}{10}h(y_0 + 5y_1 + y_2 + 6y_3 + y_4 + 5y_5 + y_6)$$

SOLIDS BOUNDED BY PLANES

In the following: S = lateral surface, T = total surface, V = volume.

Cube

Let a = length of each edge.

$$T = 6a^2, \quad \text{diagonal of face} = a\sqrt{2}$$
$$V = a^3, \quad \text{diagonal of cube} = a\sqrt{3}$$

Rectangular Parallelepiped (or box)

Let a, b, c be the lengths of its edges.

$$T = 2(ab + bc + ca), \quad V = abc$$
$$\text{diagonal} = \sqrt{a^2 + b^2 + c^2}$$

Prism

$$S = \text{(perimeter of right section)} \times \text{(lateral edge)}$$
$$V = \text{(area of right section)} \times \text{(lateral edge)}$$
$$= \text{(area of base)} \times \text{(altitude)}$$

Truncated Triangular Prism

$$V = \text{(area of right section)} \times \tfrac{1}{3}\text{(sum of the three lateral edges)}$$

Pyramid

S of regular pyramid = $\frac{1}{2}$ (perimeter of base) × (slant height)

$V = \frac{1}{3}$ (area of base) × (altitude)

Frustum of Pyramid

Let B_1 = area of lower base, B_2 = area of upper base, h = altitude.

S of regular figure = $\frac{1}{2}$ (sum of perimeters of bases) × (slant height)

$V = \frac{1}{3}h(B_1 + B_2 + \sqrt{B_1B_2})$

Prismatoid

A *prismatoid* is a polyhedron having for bases two polygons in parallel planes, and for lateral faces triangles or trapezoids with one side lying in one base, and the opposite vertex or side lying in the other base, of the polyhedron. Let B_1 = area of lower base, M = area of midsection, B_2 = area of upper base, h = altitude.

$$V = \frac{1}{6}h(B_1 + 4M + B_2) \quad \text{(the } prismoidal \ formula)$$

Note: Since cubes, rectangular parallelepipeds, prisms, pyramids, and frustums of pyramids are all examples of prismatoids, the formula for the volume of a prismatoid subsumes most of the above volume formulae.

Regular Polyhedra

Let v = number of vertices, e = number of edges, f = number of faces, α = each dihedral angle, a = length of each edge, r = radius of the inscribed sphere, R = radius of the circumscribed sphere, A = area of each face, T = total area, V = volume.

$v - e + f = 2$ (the *Euler-Descartes formula*—actually holds for *any* convex polyhedron)

$$T = fA$$
$$V = \frac{1}{3}rfA = \frac{1}{3}rT$$

Name	Nature of Surface	T	V
Tetrahedron	4 equilateral triangles	$1.73205a^2$	$0.11785a^3$
Hexahedron (cube)	6 squares	$6.00000a^2$	$1.00000a^3$
Octahedron	8 equilateral triangles	$3.46410a^2$	$0.47140a^3$
Dodecahedron	12 regular pentagons	$20.64573a^2$	$7.66312a^3$
Icosahedron	20 equilateral triangles	$8.66025a^2$	$2.18169a^3$

Name	v	e	f	α	a	r
Tetrahedron	4	6	4	70° 32′	$1.633R$	$0.333R$
Hexahedron	8	12	6	90°	$1.155R$	$0.577R$
Octahedron	6	12	8	109° 28′	$1.414R$	$0.577R$
Dodecahedron	20	30	12	116° 34′	$0.714R$	$0.795R$
Icosahedron	12	30	20	138° 11′	$1.051R$	$0.795R$

Name	A	r	R	V
Tetrahedron	$\frac{1}{4}a^2\sqrt{3}$	$\frac{1}{12}a\sqrt{6}$	$\frac{1}{4}a\sqrt{6}$	$\frac{1}{12}a^3\sqrt{2}$
Hexahedron	a^2	$\frac{1}{2}a$	$\frac{1}{2}a\sqrt{3}$	a^3
Octahedron	$\frac{1}{4}a^2\sqrt{3}$	$\frac{1}{6}a\sqrt{6}$	$\frac{1}{2}a\sqrt{2}$	$\frac{1}{3}a^3\sqrt{2}$
Dodecahedron	$\frac{1}{4}a^2\sqrt{25+10\sqrt{5}}$	$\frac{1}{20}a\sqrt{250+110\sqrt{5}}$	$\frac{1}{4}a(\sqrt{15}+\sqrt{3})$	$\frac{1}{4}a^3(15+7\sqrt{5})$
Icosahedron	$\frac{1}{4}a^2\sqrt{3}$	$\frac{1}{12}a\sqrt{42+18\sqrt{5}}$	$\frac{1}{4}a\sqrt{10+2\sqrt{5}}$	$\frac{5}{12}a^3(3+\sqrt{5})$

CYLINDERS AND CONES

In the following: B_1 = area of lower base, B_2 = area of upper base, h = altitude, S = lateral surface, T = total surface, V = volume.

Cylinder

S = (perimeter of right section) × (lateral edge)
V = (area of right section) × (lateral edge)

Right Circular Cylinder

Let R = radius of base.

$$S = 2\pi Rh, \quad T = 2\pi R(R+h), \quad V = \pi R^2 h$$

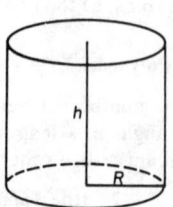

Cone

$$V = \tfrac{1}{3}B_1 h$$

Right Circular Cone

Let R = radius of base, s = slant height.

$$s = \sqrt{R^2 + h^2}$$
$$S = \pi Rs = \pi R\sqrt{R^2 + h^2}$$
$$T = \pi R(R + s) = \pi R(R + \sqrt{R^2 + h^2})$$
$$V = \tfrac{1}{3}\pi R^2 h$$

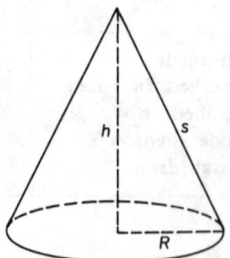

Frustum of Cone

$V = \frac{1}{3}h(B_1 + B_2 + \sqrt{B_1 B_2})$, where B_1 and B_2 are the areas of the bases.

Frustum of Right Circular Cone

Let R_1 = radius of lower base, R_2 = radius of upper base, s = slant height.

$$s = \sqrt{(R_1 - R_2)^2 + h^2}$$
$$S = \pi(R_1 + R_2)\,s$$
$$\quad = \pi(R_1 + R_2)\sqrt{(R_1 - R_2)^2 + h^2}$$
$$T = \pi[R_1^2 + R_2^2 + (R_1 + R_2)\,s]$$
$$\quad = \pi[R_1^2 + R_2^2 + (R_1 + R_2)\sqrt{(R_1 - R_2)^2 + h^2}]$$
$$V = \tfrac{1}{3}\pi h(R_1^2 + R_2^2 + R_1 R_2)$$

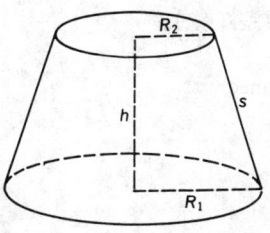

SPHERICAL FIGURES

In the following: R = radius of sphere, D = diameter of sphere, S = surface area, V = volume.

Sphere

$$D = 2R$$
$$S = 4\pi R^2 = \pi D^2 = 12.57 R^2$$
$$V = \tfrac{4}{3}\pi R^3 = \tfrac{1}{6}\pi D^3 = 4.189 R^3$$

Zone and Segment of One Base

$$S = 2\pi Rh = \pi Dh = \pi p^2$$
$$V = \tfrac{1}{3}\pi h^2(3R - h) = \tfrac{1}{6}\pi h(3a^2 + h^2)$$

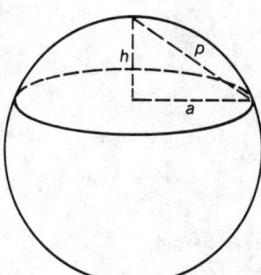

Zone and Segment of Two Bases

$$S = 2\pi Rh = \pi Dh$$
$$V = \tfrac{1}{6}\pi h(3a^2 + 3b^2 + h^2)$$

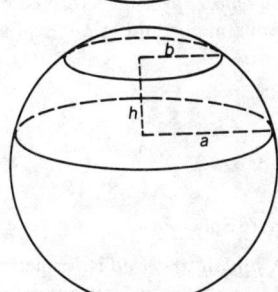

Lune

$$S = 2R^2\theta, \quad \theta \text{ in radians}$$

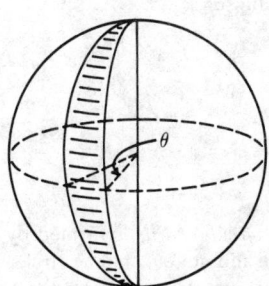

Spherical Sector

$$V = \tfrac{2}{3}\pi R^2 h = \tfrac{1}{6}\pi D^2 h$$

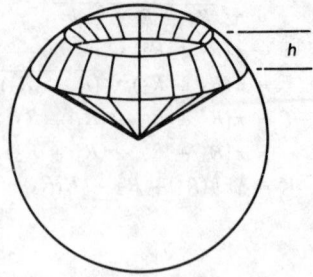

Spherical Triangle and Polygon

Let A, B, C be the angles, in radians, of the triangle; let θ = sum of angles, in radians, of a spherical polygon of n sides.

$$S = (A + B + C - \pi)R^2$$
$$S = [\theta - (n - 2)\pi]R^2$$

SPHEROIDS

Ellipsoid

Let a, b, c be the lengths of the semiaxes.

$$V = \tfrac{4}{3}\pi abc$$

Oblate Spheroid

An *oblate spheroid* is formed by the rotation of an ellipse about its minor axis. Let a and b be the major and minor semiaxes, respectively, and ϵ the eccentricity, of the revolving ellipse.

$$S = 2\pi a^2 + \pi \frac{b^2}{\epsilon}\log_e \frac{1 + \epsilon}{1 - \epsilon}$$
$$V = \tfrac{4}{3}\pi a^2 b$$

Prolate Spheroid

A *prolate spheroid* is formed by the rotation of an ellipse about its major axis. Let a and b be the major and minor semiaxes, respectively, and ϵ the eccentricity, of the revolving ellipse.

$$S = 2\pi b^2 + 2\pi \frac{ab}{\epsilon}\sin^{-1}\epsilon$$
$$V = \tfrac{4}{3}\pi ab^2$$

CIRCULAR TORUS

A *circular torus* is formed by the rotation of a circle about an axis in the plane of the circle and not cutting the circle. Let r be the radius of the revolving circle and let R be the distance of its center from the axis of rotation.

$$S = 4\pi^2 Rr$$
$$V = 2\pi^2 Rr^2$$

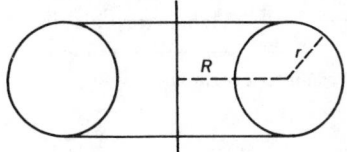

PAPPUS-GULDINUS THEOREMS

1. If a planar arc be revolved about an axis in its plane, but not cutting the arc, the area of the surface of revolution so formed is equal to the product of the length of the arc and the length of the path traced by the centroid of the arc.

2. If a planar area be revolved about an axis in its plane, but not intersecting the area, the volume of the solid of revolution so formed is equal to the product of the area and the length of the path traced by the centroid of the area.

CAVALIERI'S THEOREM FOR SPACE

If two solids are included between a pair of parallel planes, and if the two sections cut by them on any plane parallel to the including planes are equal in area, then the volumes of the solids are equal.

GENERAL PRISMATOID

A *general prismatoid* is a solid such that the area A_y of any section parallel to and distant y from a fixed plane can be expressed as a polynomial in y of degreee not higher than the third. That is,

$$A_y = ay^3 + by^2 + cy + d,$$

where a, b, c, d are constants which may be positive, zero, or negative. Let B_1 = area of lower base, M = area of midsection, B_2 = area of upper base, h = altitude.

$$V = \tfrac{1}{6}h(B_1 + 4M + B_2)$$

Note. All prismatoids, cylinders, cones, spheres, spheroids, and many other solids are general prismatoids.

CENTROIDS

If a geometrical figure possesses a center of symmetry, that point is the centroid of the figure.

If a geometrical figure possesses an axis of symmetry, the centroid of the figure lies on that axis.

Geometrical Figure	Location of Centroid
Perimeter of triangle	Center of the inscribed circle of the triangle whose vertices are the midpoints of the sides of the given triangle.
Arc of semicircle of radius R	Distance from diameter $= \dfrac{2R}{\pi}$
Arc of 2α radians of a circle of radius R	Distance from center of circle $= \dfrac{R\sin\alpha}{\alpha}$
Area of triangle	Intersection of the medians
Area of quadrilateral	Intersection of the diagonals of the parallelogram whose sides pass through adjacent trisection points of pairs of consecutive sides of the quadrilateral
Area of semicircle of radius R	Distance from diameter $= \dfrac{4R}{3\pi}$
Area of circular sector of radius R and central angle 2α radians	Distance from center of circle $= \dfrac{2R\sin\alpha}{3\alpha}$
Area of semiellipse of altitude h	Distance from base $= \dfrac{4h}{3\pi}$
Area of a quadrant of an ellipse of major and minor semiaxes a and b	Distance from minor axis $= \dfrac{4a}{3\pi}$, distance from major axis $= \dfrac{4b}{3\pi}$
Area of right parabolic segment of altitude h	Distance from base $= \frac{2}{5}h$
Lateral area of regular pyramid or right circular cone	Distance from base $= \frac{1}{3}h$
Area of hemisphere of radius R	Distance from base $= \frac{1}{2}R$
Volume of pyramid or cone	One fourth the way from the centroid of the base to the vertex of the pyramid or cone
Volume of frustum of pyramid or cone with d as the distance between the centroids of its bases and k as the ratio of similarity of the upper base to the lower base	On the line joining the centroids of the two bases at a distance from the centroid of the lower base $= \frac{1}{4}d\left(\dfrac{1 + 2k + 3k^2}{1 + k + k^2}\right)$
Volume of hemisphere of radius R	Distance from base $= \frac{3}{8}R$
Volume of revolution of altitude h obtained by revolving a semiellipse about its axis of symmetry	Distance from base $= \frac{3}{8}h$
Volume of paraboloid of revolution of altitude h	Distance from base $= \frac{1}{3}h$

RECIPROCALS, CIRCUMFERENCE AND AREA OF CIRCLES

As a matter of convenience, the values of $1000 \times (1/n)$ are given in the table. To obtain the actual value of the reciprocal, shift the decimal point three places to the left.
Circumferences and areas of circles are given for the values of n as the diameter.

$n=$ dia	$1000\dfrac{1}{n}$	Circumference πn	Area $\dfrac{\pi n^2}{4}$	$n=$ dia	$1000\dfrac{1}{n}$	Circumference πn	Area $\dfrac{\pi n^2}{4}$
0	∞	0.000000	.0000000	50	20.00000	157.0796	1963.495
1	1000.000	3.141593	.7853982	51	19.60784	160.2212	2042.821
2	500.0000	6.283185	3.141593	52	19.23077	163.3628	2123.717
3	333.3333	9.424778	7.068583	53	18.86792	166.5044	2206.183
4	250.0000	12.56637	12.56637	54	18.51852	169.6460	2290.221
5	200.0000	15.70796	19.63495	55	18.18182	172.7876	2375.829
6	166.6667	18.84956	28.27433	56	17.85714	175.9292	2463.009
7	142.8571	21.99115	38.48451	57	17.54386	179.0708	2551.759
8	125.0000	25.13274	50.26548	58	17.24138	182.2124	2642.079
9	111.1111	28.27433	63.61725	59	16.94915	185.3540	2733.971
10	100.0000	31.41593	78.53982	60	16.66667	188.4956	2827.433
11	90.90909	34.55752	95.03318	61	16.39344	191.6372	2922.467
12	83.33333	37.69911	113.0973	62	16.12903	194.7787	3019.071
13	76.92308	40.84070	132.7323	63	15.87302	197.9203	3117.245
14	71.42857	43.98230	153.9380	64	15.62500	201.0619	3216.991
15	66.66667	47.12389	176.7146	65	15.38462	204.2035	3318.307
16	62.50000	50.26548	201.0619	66	15.15152	207.3451	3421.194
17	58.82353	53.40708	226.9801	67	14.92537	210.4867	3525.652
18	55.55556	56.54867	254.4690	68	14.70588	213.6283	3631.681
19	52.63158	59.69026	283.5287	69	14.49275	216.7699	3739.281
20	50.00000	62.83185	314.1593	70	14.28571	219.9115	3848.451
21	47.61905	65.97345	346.3606	71	14.08451	223.0531	3959.192
22	45.45455	69.11504	380.1327	72	13.88889	226.1947	4071.504
23	43.47826	72.25663	415.4756	73	13.69863	229.3363	4185.387
24	41.66667	75.39822	452.3893	74	13.51351	232.4779	4300.840
25	40.00000	78.53982	490.8739	75	13.33333	235.6194	4417.865
26	38.46154	81.68141	530.9292	76	13.15789	238.7610	4536.460
27	37.03704	84.82300	572.5553	77	12.98701	241.9026	4656.626
28	35.71429	87.96459	615.7522	78	12.82051	245.0442	4778.362
29	34.48276	91.10619	660.5199	79	12.65823	248.1858	4901.670
30	33.33333	94.24778	706.8583	80	12.50000	251.3274	5026.548
31	32.25806	97.38937	754.7676	81	12.34568	254.4690	5152.997
32	31.25000	100.5310	804.2477	82	12.19512	257.6106	5281.017
33	30.30303	103.6726	855.2986	83	12.04819	260.7522	5410.608
34	29.41176	106.8142	907.9203	84	11.90476	263.8938	5541.769
35	28.57143	109.9557	962.1128	85	11.76471	267.0354	5674.502
36	27.77778	113.0973	1017.876	86	11.62791	270.1770	5808.805
37	27.02703	116.2389	1075.210	87	11.49425	273.3186	5944.679
38	26.31579	119.3805	1134.115	88	11.36364	276.4602	6082.123
39	25.64103	122.5221	1194.591	89	11.23596	279.6017	6221.139
40	25.00000	125.6637	1256.637	90	11.11111	282.7433	6361.725
41	24.39024	128.8053	1320.254	91	10.98901	285.8849	6503.882
42	23.80952	131.9469	1385.442	92	10.86957	289.0265	6647.610
43	23.25581	135.0885	1452.201	93	10.75269	292.1681	6792.909
44	22.72727	138.2301	1520.531	94	10.63830	295.3097	6939.778
45	22.22222	141.3717	1590.431	95	10.52632	298.4513	7088.218
46	21.73913	144.5133	1661.903	96	10.41667	301.5929	7238.229
47	21.27660	147.6549	1734.945	97	10.30928	304.7345	7389.811
48	20.83333	150.7964	1809.557	98	10.20408	307.8761	7542.964
49	20.40816	153.9380	1885.741	99	10.10101	311.0177	7697.687
50	20.00000	157.0796	1963.495	100	10.00000	314.1593	7853.982

RECIPROCALS, CIRCUMFERENCE AND AREA OF CIRCLES (Continued)

n = dia	$1000\dfrac{1}{n}$	Circumference πn	Area $\dfrac{\pi n^2}{4}$	n = dia	$1000\dfrac{1}{n}$	Circumference πn	Area $\dfrac{\pi n^2}{4}$
100	10.00000	314.1593	7853.982	**150**	6.666 667	471.2389	17671.46
101	9.900 990	317.3009	8011.847	151	6.622 517	474.3805	17907.86
102	9.803 922	320.4425	8171.282	152	6.578 947	477.5221	18145.84
103	9.708 738	323.5840	8332.289	153	6.535 948	480.6637	18385.39
104	9.615 385	326.7256	8494.867	154	6.493 506	483.8053	18626.50
105	9.523 810	329.8672	8659.015	155	6.451 613	486.9469	18869.19
106	9.433 962	333.0088	8824.734	156	6.410 256	490.0885	19113.45
107	9.345 794	336.1504	8992.024	157	6.369 427	493.2300	19359.28
108	9.259 259	339.2920	9160.884	158	6.329 114	496.3716	19606.68
109	9.174 312	342.4336	9331.316	159	6.289 308	499.5132	19855.65
110	9.090 909	345.5752	9503.318	**160**	6.250 000	502.6548	20106.19
111	9.009 009	348.7168	9676.891	161	6.211 180	505.7964	20358.31
112	8.928 571	351.8584	9852.035	162	6.172 840	508.9380	20611.99
113	8.849 558	355.0000	10028.75	163	6.134 969	512.0796	20867.24
114	8.771 930	358.1416	10207.03	164	6.097 561	515.2212	21124.07
115	8.695 652	361.2832	10386.89	165	6.060 606	518.3628	21382.46
116	8.620 690	364.4247	10568.32	166	6.024 096	521.5044	21642.43
117	8.547 009	367.5663	10751.32	167	5.988 024	524.6460	21903.97
118	8.474 576	370.7079	10935.88	168	5.952 381	527.7876	22167.08
119	8.403 361	373.8495	11122.02	169	5.917 160	530.9292	22431.76
120	8.333 333	376.9911	11309.73	**170**	5.882 353	534.0708	22698.01
121	8.264 463	380.1327	11499.01	171	5.847 953	537.2123	22965.83
122	8.196 721	383.2743	11689.87	172	5.813 953	540.3539	23235.22
123	8.130 081	386.4159	11882.29	173	5.780 347	543.4955	23506.18
124	8.064 516	389.5575	12076.28	174	5.747 126	546.6371	23778.71
125	8.000 000	392.6991	12271.85	175	5.714 286	549.7787	24052.82
126	7.936 508	395.8407	12468.98	176	5.681 818	552.9203	24328.49
127	7.874 016	398.9823	12667.69	177	5.649 718	556.0619	24605.74
128	7.812 500	402.1239	12867.96	178	5.617 978	559.2035	24884.56
129	7.751 938	405.2655	13069.81	179	5.586 592	562.3451	25164.94
130	7.692 308	408.4070	13273.23	**180**	5.555 556	565.4867	25446.90
131	7.633 588	411.5486	13478.22	181	5.524 862	568.6283	25730.43
132	7.575 758	414.6902	13684.78	182	5.494 505	571.7699	26015.53
133	7.518 797	417.8318	13892.91	183	5.464 481	574.9115	26302.20
134	7.462 687	420.9734	14102.61	184	5.434 783	578.0530	26590.44
135	7.407 407	424.1150	14313.88	185	5.405 405	581.1946	26880.25
136	7.352 941	427.2566	14526.72	186	5.376 344	584.3362	27171.63
137	7.299 270	430.3982	14741.14	187	5.347 594	587.4778	27464.59
138	7.246 377	433.5398	14957.12	188	5.319 149	590.6194	27759.11
139	7.194 245	436.6814	15174.68	189	5.291 005	593.7610	28055.21
140	7.142 857	439.8230	15393.80	**190**	5.263 158	596.9026	28352.87
141	7.092 199	442.9646	15614.50	191	5.235 602	600.0442	28652.11
142	7.042 254	446.1062	15836.77	192	5.208 333	603.1858	28952.92
143	6.993 007	449.2477	16060.61	193	5.181 347	606.3274	29255.30
144	6.944 444	452.3893	16286.02	194	5.154 639	609.4690	29559.25
145	6.896 552	455.5309	16513.00	195	5.128 205	612.6106	29864.77
146	6.849 315	458.6725	16741.55	196	5.102 041	615.7522	30171.86
147	6.802 721	461.8141	16971.67	197	5.076 142	618.8938	30480.52
148	6.756 757	464.9557	17203.36	198	5.050 505	622.0353	30790.75
149	6.711 409	468.0973	17436.62	199	5.025 126	625.1769	31102.55
150	6.666 667	471.2389	17671.46	**200**	5.000 000	628.3185	31415.93

RECIPROCALS, CIRCUMFERENCE AND AREA OF CIRCLES (Continued)

$n = $ dia	$1000\dfrac{1}{n}$	Circum- ference πn	Area $\dfrac{\pi n^2}{4}$	$n = $ dia	$1000\dfrac{1}{n}$	Circum- ference πn	Area $\dfrac{\pi n^2}{4}$
200	5.000 000	628.3185	31415.93	**250**	4.000 000	785.3982	49087.39
201	4.975 124	631.4601	31730.87	251	3.984 064	788.5398	49480.87
202	4.950 495	634.6017	32047.39	252	3.968 254	791.6813	49875.92
203	4.926 108	637.7433	32365.47	253	3.952 569	794.8229	50272.55
204	4.901 961	640.8849	32685.13	254	3.937 008	797.9645	50670.75
205	4.878 049	644.0265	33006.36	255	3.921 569	801.1061	51070.52
206	4.854 369	647.1681	33329.16	256	3.906 250	804.2477	51471.85
207	4.830 918	650.3097	33653.53	257	3.891 051	807.3893	51874.76
208	4.807 692	653.4513	33979.47	258	3.875 969	810.5309	52279.24
209	4.784 689	656.5929	34306.98	259	3.861 004	813.6725	52685.29
210	4.761 905	659.7345	34636.06	**260**	3.846 154	816.8141	53092.92
211	4.739 336	662.8760	34966.71	261	3.831 418	819.9557	53502.11
212	4.716 981	666.0176	35298.94	262	3.816 794	823.0973	53912.87
213	4.694 836	669.1592	35632.73	263	3.802 281	826.2389	54325.21
214	4.672 897	672.3008	35968.09	264	3.787 879	829.3805	54739.11
215	4.651 163	675.4424	36305.03	265	3.773 585	832.5221	55154.59
216	4.629 630	678.5840	36643.54	266	3.759 398	835.6636	55571.63
217	4.608 295	681.7256	36983.61	267	3.745 318	838.8052	55990.25
218	4.587 156	684.8672	37325.26	268	3.731 343	841.9468	56410.44
219	4.566 210	688.0088	37668.48	269	3.717 472	845.0884	56832.20
220	4.545 455	691.1504	38013.27	**270**	3.703 704	848.2300	57255.53
221	4.524 887	694.2920	38359.63	271	3.690 037	851.3716	57680.43
222	4.504 505	697.4336	38707.56	272	3.676 471	854.5132	58106.90
223	4.484 305	700.5752	39057.07	273	3.663 004	857.6548	58534.94
224	4.464 286	703.7168	39408.14	274	3.649 635	860.7964	58964.55
225	4.444 444	706.8583	39760.78	275	3.636 364	863.9380	59395.74
226	4.424 779	709.9999	40115.00	276	3.623 188	867.0796	59828.49
227	4.405 286	713.1415	40470.78	277	3.610 108	870.2212	60262.82
228	4.385 965	716.2831	40828.14	278	3.597 122	873.3628	60698.71
229	4.366 812	719.4247	41187.07	279	3.584 229	876.5044	61136.18
230	4.347 826	722.5663	41547.56	**280**	3.571 429	879.6459	61575.22
231	4.329 004	725.7079	41909.63	281	3.558 719	882.7875	62015.82
232	4.310 345	728.8495	42273.27	282	3.546 099	885.9291	62458.00
233	4.291 845	731.9911	42638.48	283	3.533 569	889.0707	62901.75
234	4.273 504	735.1327	43005.26	284	3.521 127	892.2123	63347.07
235	4.255 319	738.2743	43373.61	285	3.508 772	895.3539	63793.97
236	4.237 288	741.4159	43743.54	286	3.496 503	898.4955	64242.43
237	4.219 409	744.5575	44115.03	287	3.484 321	901.6371	64692.46
238	4.201 681	747.6991	44488.09	288	3.472 222	904.7787	65144.07
239	4.184 100	750.8406	44862.73	289	3.460 208	907.9203	65597.24
240	4.166 667	753.9822	45238.93	**290**	3.448 276	911.0619	66051.99
241	4.149 378	757.1238	45616.71	291	3.436 426	914.2035	66508.30
242	4.132 231	760.2654	45996.06	292	3.424 658	917.3451	66966.19
243	4.115 226	763.4070	46376.98	293	3.412 969	920.4866	67425.65
244	4.098 361	766.5486	46759.47	294	3.401 361	923.6282	67886.68
245	4.081 633	769.6902	47143.52	295	3.389 831	926.7698	68349.28
246	4.065 041	772.8318	47529.16	296	3.378 378	929.9114	68813.45
247	4.048 583	775.9734	47916.36	297	3.367 003	933.0530	69279.19
248	4.032 258	779.1150	48305.13	298	3.355 705	936.1946	69746.50
249	4.016 064	782.2566	48695.47	299	3.344 482	939.3362	70215.38
250	4.000 000	785.3982	49087.39	**300**	3.333 333	942.4778	70685.83

Numerical Tables

RECIPROCALS, CIRCUMFERENCE AND AREA OF CIRCLES (Continued)

n = dia	$1000\dfrac{1}{n}$	Circumference πn	Area $\dfrac{\pi n^2}{4}$	n = dia	$1000\dfrac{1}{n}$	Circumference πn	Area $\dfrac{\pi n^2}{4}$
300	3.333 333	942.4778	70685.83	**350**	2.857 143	1099.557	96211.28
301	3.322 259	945.6194	71157.86	351	2.849 003	1102.699	96761.84
302	3.311 258	948.7610	71631.45	352	2.840 909	1105.841	97313.97
303	3.300 330	951.9026	72106.62	353	2.832 861	1108.982	97867.68
304	3.289 474	955.0442	72583.36	354	2.824 859	1112.124	98422.96
305	3.278 689	958.1858	73061.66	355	2.816 901	1115.265	98979.80
306	3.267 974	961.3274	73541.54	356	2.808 989	1118.407	99538.22
307	3.257 329	964.4689	74022.99	357	2.801 120	1121.549	100 098.2
308	3.246 753	967.6105	74506.01	358	2.793 296	1124.690	100 659.8
309	3.236 246	970.7521	74990.60	359	2.785 515	1127.832	101 222.9
310	3.225 806	973.8937	75476.76	**360**	2.777 778	1130.973	101 787.6
311	3.215 434	977.0353	75964.50	361	2.770 083	1134.115	102 353.9
312	3.205 128	980.1769	76453.80	362	2.762 431	1137.257	102 921.7
313	3.194 888	983.3185	76944.67	363	2.754 821	1140.398	103 491.1
314	3.184 713	986.4601	77437.12	364	2.747 253	1143.540	104 062.1
315	3.174 603	989.6017	77931.13	365	2.739 726	1146.681	104 634.7
316	3.164 557	992.7433	78426.72	366	2.732 240	1149.823	105 208.8
317	3.154 574	995.8849	78923.88	367	2.724 796	1152.965	105 784.5
318	3.144 654	999.0265	79422.60	368	2.717 391	1156.106	106 361.8
319	3.134 796	1002.168	79922.90	369	2.710 027	1159.248	106 940.6
320	3.125 000	1005.310	80424.77	**370**	2.702 703	1162.389	107 521.0
321	3.115 265	1008.451	80928.21	371	2.695 418	1165.531	108 103.0
322	3.105 590	1011.593	81433.22	372	2.688 172	1168.672	108 686.5
323	3.095 975	1014.734	81939.80	373	2.680 965	1171.814	109 271.7
324	3.086 420	1017.876	82447.96	374	2.673 797	1174.956	109 858.4
325	3.076 923	1021.018	82957.68	375	2.666 667	1178.097	110 446.6
326	3.067 485	1024.159	83468.98	376	2.659 574	1181.239	111 036.5
327	3.058 104	1027.301	83981.84	377	2.652 520	1184.380	111 627.9
328	3.048 780	1030.442	84496.28	378	2.645 503	1187.522	112 220.8
329	3.039 514	1033.584	85012.28	379	2.638 522	1190.664	112 815.4
330	3.030 303	1036.726	85529.86	**380**	2.631 579	1193.805	113 411.5
331	3.021 148	1039.867	86049.01	381	2.624 672	1196.947	114 009.2
332	3.012 048	1043.009	86569.73	382	2.617 801	1200.088	114 608.4
333	3.003 003	1046.150	87092.02	383	2.610 966	1203.230	115 209.3
334	2.994 012	1049.292	87615.88	384	2.604 167	1206.372	115 811.7
335	2.985 075	1052.434	88141.31	385	2.597 403	1209.513	116 415.6
336	2.976 190	1055.575	88668.31	386	2.590 674	1212.655	117 021.2
337	2.967 359	1058.717	89196.88	387	2.583 979	1215.796	117 628.3
338	2.958 580	1061.858	89727.03	388	2.577 320	1218.938	118 237.0
339	2.949 853	1065.000	90258.74	389	2.570 694	1222.080	118 847.2
340	2.941 176	1068.142	90792.03	**390**	2.564 103	1225.221	119 459.1
341	2.932 551	1071.283	91326.88	391	2.557 545	1228.363	120 072.5
342	2.923 977	1074.425	91863.31	392	2.551 020	1231.504	120 687.4
343	2.915 452	1077.566	92401.31	393	2.544 529	1234.646	121 304.0
344	2.906 977	1080.708	92940.88	394	2.538 071	1237.788	121 922.1
345	2.898 551	1083.849	93482.02	395	2.531 646	1240.929	122 541.7
346	2.890 173	1086.991	94024.73	396	2.525 253	1244.071	123 163.0
347	2.881 844	1090.133	94569.01	397	2.518 892	1247.212	123 785.8
348	2.873 563	1093.274	95114.86	398	2.512 563	1250.354	124 410.2
349	2.865 330	1096.416	95662.28	399	2.506 266	1253.495	125 036.2
350	2.857 143	1099.557	96211.28	**400**	2.500 000	1256.637	125 663.7

RECIPROCALS, CIRCUMFERENCE AND AREA OF CIRCLES (Continued)

n = dia	$1000\dfrac{1}{n}$	Circum- ference πn	Area $\dfrac{\pi n^2}{4}$	n = dia	$1000\dfrac{1}{n}$	Circum- ference πn	Area $\dfrac{\pi n^2}{4}$
400	2.500 000	1256.637	125 663.7	**450**	2.222 222	1413.717	159 043.1
401	2.493 766	1259.779	126 292.8	451	2.217 295	1416.858	159 750.8
402	2.487 562	1262.920	126 923.5	452	2.212 389	1420.000	160 460.0
403	2.481 390	1266.062	127 555.7	453	2.207 506	1423.141	161 170.8
404	2.475 248	1269.203	128 189.5	454	2.202 643	1426.283	161 883.1
405	2.469 136	1272.345	128 824.9	455	2.197 802	1429.425	162 597.1
406	2.463 054	1275.487	129 461.9	456	2.192 982	1432.566	163 312.6
407	2.457 002	1278.628	130 100.4	457	2.188 184	1435.708	164 029.6
408	2.450 980	1281.770	130 740.5	458	2.183 406	1438.849	164 748.3
409	2.444 988	1284.911	131 382.2	459	2.178 649	1441.991	165 468.5
410	2.439 024	1288.053	132 025.4	**460**	2.173 913	1445.133	166 190.3
411	2.433 090	1291.195	132 670.2	461	2.169 197	1448.274	166 913.6
412	2.427 184	1294.336	133 316.6	462	2.164 502	1451.416	167 638.5
413	2.421 308	1297.478	133 964.6	463	2.159 827	1454.557	168 365.0
414	2.415 459	1300.619	134 614.1	464	2.155 172	1457.699	169 093.1
415	2.409 639	1303.761	135 265.2	465	2.150 538	1460.841	169 822.7
416	2.403 846	1306.903	135 917.9	466	2.145 923	1463.982	170 553.9
417	2.398 082	1310.044	136 572.1	467	2.141 328	1467.124	171 286.7
418	2.392 344	1313.186	137 227.9	468	2.136 752	1470.265	172 021.0
419	2.386 635	1316.327	137 885.3	469	2.132 196	1473.407	172 757.0
420	2.380 952	1319.469	138 544.2	**470**	2.127 660	1476.549	173 494.5
421	2.375 297	1322.611	139 204.8	471	2.123 142	1479.690	174 233.5
422	2.369 668	1325.752	139 866.8	472	2.118 644	1482.832	174 974.1
423	2.364 066	1328.894	140 530.5	473	2.114 165	1485.973	175 716.3
424	2.358 491	1332.035	141 195.7	474	2.109 705	1489.115	176 460.1
425	2.352 941	1335.177	141 862.5	475	2.105 263	1492.257	177 205.5
426	2.347 418	1338.318	142 530.9	476	2.100 840	1495.398	177 952.4
427	2.341 920	1341.460	143 200.9	477	2.096 436	1498.540	178 700.9
428	2.336 449	1344.602	143 872.4	478	2.092 050	1501.681	179 450.9
429	2.331 002	1347.743	144 545.5	479	2.087 683	1504.823	180 202.5
430	2.325 581	1350.885	145 220.1	**480**	2.083 333	1507.964	180 955.7
431	2.320 186	1354.026	145 896.3	481	2.079 002	1511.106	181 710.5
432	2.314 815	1357.168	146 574.1	482	2.074 689	1514.248	182 466.8
433	2.309 469	1360.310	147 253.5	483	2.070 393	1517.389	183 224.8
434	2.304 147	1363.451	147 934.5	484	2.066 116	1520.531	183 984.2
435	2.298 851	1366.593	148 617.0	485	2.061 856	1523.672	184 745.3
436	2.293 578	1369.734	149 301.0	486	2.057 613	1526.814	185 507.9
437	2.288 330	1372.876	149 986.7	487	2.053 388	1529.956	186 272.1
438	2.283 105	1376.018	150 673.9	488	2.049 180	1533.097	187 037.9
439	2.277 904	1379.159	151 362.7	489	2.044 990	1536.239	187 805.2
440	2.272 727	1382.301	152 053.1	**490**	2.040 816	1539.380	188 574.1
441	2.267 574	1385.442	152 745.0	491	2.036 660	1542.522	189 344.6
442	2.262 443	1388.584	153 438.5	492	2.032 520	1545.664	190 116.6
443	2.257 336	1391.726	154 133.6	493	2.028 398	1548.805	190 890.2
444	2.252 252	1394.867	154 830.3	494	2.024 291	1551.947	191 665.4
445	2.247 191	1398.009	155 528.5	495	2.020 202	1555.088	192 442.2
446	2.242 152	1401.150	156 228.3	496	2.016 129	1558.230	193 220.5
447	2.237 136	1404.292	156 929.6	497	2.012 072	1561.372	194 000.4
448	2.232 143	1407.434	157 632.6	498	2.008 032	1564.513	194 781.9
449	2.227 171	1410.575	158 337.1	499	2.004 008	1567.655	195 564.9
450	2.222 222	1413.717	159 043.1	**500**	2.000 000	1570.796	196 349.5

RECIPROCALS, CIRCUMFERENCE AND AREA OF CIRCLES (Continued)

$n=$ dia	$1000\dfrac{1}{n}$	Circum- ference πn	Area $\dfrac{\pi n^2}{4}$	$n=$ dia	$1000\dfrac{1}{n}$	Circum- ference πn	Area $\dfrac{\pi n^2}{4}$
500	2.000 000	1570.796	196 349.5	**550**	1.818 182	1727.876	237 582.9
501	1.996 008	1573.938	197 135.7	551	1.814 882	1731.018	238 447.7
502	1.992 032	1577.080	197 923.5	552	1.811 594	1734.159	239 314.0
503	1.988 072	1580.221	198 712.8	553	1.808 318	1737.301	240 181.8
504	1.984 127	1583.363	199 503.7	554	1.805 054	1740.442	241 051.3
505	1.980 198	1586.504	200 296.2	555	1.801 802	1743.584	241 922.3
506	1.976 285	1589.646	201 090.2	556	1.798 561	1746.726	242 794.8
507	1.972 387	1592.787	201 885.8	557	1.795 332	1749.867	243 669.0
508	1.968 504	1595.929	202 683.0	558	1.792 115	1753.009	244 544.7
509	1.964 637	1599.071	203 481.7	559	1.788 909	1756.150	245 422.0
510	1.960 784	1602.212	204 282.1	**560**	1.785 714	1759.292	246 300.9
511	1.956 947	1605.354	205 084.0	561	1.782 531	1762.433	247 181.3
512	1.953 125	1608.495	205 887.4	562	1.779 359	1765.575	248 063.3
513	1.949 318	1611.637	206 692.4	563	1.776 199	1768.717	248 946.9
514	1.945 525	1614.779	207 499.1	564	1.773 050	1771.858	249 832.0
515	1.941 748	1617.920	208 307.2	565	1.769 912	1775.000	250 718.7
516	1.937 984	1621.062	209 117.0	566	1.766 784	1778.141	251 607.0
517	1.934 236	1624.203	209 928.3	567	1.763 668	1781.283	252 496.9
518	1.930 502	1627.345	210 741.2	568	1.760 563	1784.425	253 388.3
519	1.926 782	1630.487	211 555.6	569	1.757 469	1787.566	254 281.3
520	1.923 077	1633.628	212 371.7	**570**	1.754 386	1790.708	255 175.9
521	1.919 386	1636.770	213 189.3	571	1.751 313	1793.849	256 072.0
522	1.915 709	1639.911	214 008.4	572	1.748 252	1796.991	256 969.7
523	1.912 046	1643.053	214 829.2	573	1.745 201	1800.133	257 869.0
524	1.908 397	1646.195	215 651.5	574	1.742 160	1803.274	258 769.8
525	1.904 762	1649.336	216 475.4	575	1.739 130	1806.416	259 672.3
526	1.901 141	1652.478	217 300.8	576	1.736 111	1809.557	260 576.3
527	1.897 533	1655.619	218 127.8	577	1.733 102	1812.699	261 481.8
528	1.893 939	1658.761	218 956.4	578	1.730 104	1815.841	262 389.0
529	1.890 359	1661.903	219 786.6	579	1.727 116	1818.982	263 297.7
530	1.886 792	1665.044	220 618.3	**580**	1.724 138	1822.124	264 207.9
531	1.883 239	1668.186	221 451.7	581	1.721 170	1825.265	265 119.8
532	1.879 699	1671.327	222 286.5	582	1.718 213	1828.407	266 033.2
533	1.876 173	1674.469	223 123.0	583	1.715 266	1831.549	266 948.2
534	1.872 659	1677.610	223 961.0	584	1.712 329	1834.690	267 864.8
535	1.869 159	1680.752	224 800.6	585	1.709 402	1837.832	268 782.9
536	1.865 672	1683.894	225 641.8	586	1.706 485	1840.973	269 702.6
537	1.862 197	1687.035	226 484.5	587	1.703 578	1844.115	270 623.9
538	1.858 736	1690.177	227 328.8	588	1.700 680	1847.256	271 546.7
539	1.855 288	1693.318	228 174.7	589	1.697 793	1850.398	272 471.1
540	1.851 852	1696.460	229 022.1	**590**	1.694 915	1853.540	273 397.1
541	1.848 429	1699.602	229 871.1	591	1.692 047	1856.681	274 324.7
542	1.845 018	1702.743	230 721.7	592	1.689 189	1859.823	275 253.8
543	1.841 621	1705.885	231 573.9	593	1.686 341	1862.964	276 184.5
544	1.838 235	1709.026	232 427.6	594	1.683 502	1866.106	277 116.7
545	1.834 862	1712.168	233 282.9	595	1.680 672	1869.248	278 050.6
546	1.831 502	1715.310	234 139.8	596	1.677 852	1872.389	278 986.0
547	1.828 154	1718.451	234 998.2	597	1.675 042	1875.531	279 923.0
548	1.824 818	1721.593	235 858.2	598	1.672 241	1878.672	280 861.5
549	1.821 494	1724.734	236 719.8	599	1.669 449	1881.814	281 801.6
550	1.818 182	1727.876	237.582.9	**600**	1.666 667	1884.956	282 743.3

RECIPROCALS, CIRCUMFERENCE AND AREA OF CIRCLES (Continued)

n = dia	$1000\frac{1}{n}$	Circum- ference πn	Area $\frac{\pi n^2}{4}$	n = dia	$1000\frac{1}{n}$	Circum- ference πn	Area $\frac{\pi n^2}{4}$
600	1.666 667	1884.956	282 743.3	**650**	1.538 462	2042.035	331 830.7
601	1.663 894	1888.097	283 686.6	651	1.536 098	2045.177	332 852.5
602	1.661 130	1891.239	284 631.4	652	1.533 742	2048.318	333 875.9
603	1.658 375	1894.380	285 577.8	653	1.531 394	2051.460	334 900.8
604	1.655 629	1897.522	286 525.8	654	1.529 052	2054.602	335 927.4
605	1.652 893	1900.664	287 475.4	655	1.526 718	2057.743	336 955.4
606	1.650 165	1903.805	288 426.5	656	1.524 390	2060.885	337 985.1
607	1.647 446	1906.947	289 379.2	657	1.522 070	2064.026	339 016.3
608	1.644 737	1910.088	290 333.4	658	1.519 757	2067.168	340 049.1
609	1.642 036	1913.230	291 289.3	659	1.517 451	2070.310	341 083.5
610	1.639 344	1916.372	292 246.7	**660**	1.515 152	2073.451	342 119.4
611	1.636 661	1919.513	293 205.6	661	1.512 859	2076.593	343 157.0
612	1.633 987	1922.655	294 166.2	662	1.510 574	2079.734	344 196.0
613	1.631 321	1925.796	295 128.3	663	1.508 296	2082.876	345 236.7
614	1.628 664	1928.938	296 092.0	664	1.506 024	2086.018	346 278.9
615	1.626 016	1932.079	297 057.2	665	1.503 759	2089.159	347 322.7
616	1.623 377	1935.221	298 024.0	666	1.501 502	2092.301	348 368.1
617	1.620 746	1938.363	298 992.4	667	1.499 250	2095.442	349 415.0
618	1.618 123	1941.504	299 962.4	668	1.497 006	2098.584	350 463.5
619	1.615 509	1944.646	300 933.9	669	1.494 768	2101.725	351 513.6
620	1.612 903	1947.787	301 907.1	**670**	1.492 537	2104.867	352 565.2
621	1.610 306	1950.929	302 881.7	671	1.490 313	2108.009	353 618.5
622	1.607 717	1954.071	303 858.0	672	1.488 095	2111.150	354 673.2
623	1.605 136	1957.212	304 835.8	673	1.485 884	2114.292	355 729.6
624	1.602 564	1960.354	305 815.2	674	1.483 680	2117.433	356 787.5
625	1.600 000	1963.495	306 796.2	675	1.481 481	2120.575	357 847.0
626	1.597 444	1966.637	307 778.7	676	1.479 290	2123.717	358 908.1
627	1.594 896	1969.779	308 762.8	677	1.477 105	2126.858	359 970.8
628	1.592 357	1972.920	309 748.5	678	1.474 926	2130.000	361 035.0
629	1.589 825	1976.062	310 735.7	679	1.472 754	2133.141	362 100.8
630	1.587 302	1979.203	311 724.5	**680**	1.470 588	2136.283	363 168.1
631	1.584 786	1982.345	312 714.9	681	1.468 429	2139.425	364 237.0
632	1.582 278	1985.487	313 706.9	682	1.466 276	2142.566	365 307.5
633	1.579 779	1988.628	314 700.4	683	1.464 129	2145.708	366 379.6
634	1.577 287	1991.770	315 695.5	684	1.461 988	2148.849	367 453.2
635	1.574 803	1994.911	316 692.2	685	1.459 854	2151.991	368 528.5
636	1.572 327	1998.053	317 690.4	686	1.457 726	2155.133	369 605.2
637	1.569 859	2001.195	318 690.2	687	1.455 604	2158.274	370 683.6
638	1.567 398	2004.336	319 691.6	688	1.453 488	2161.416	371 763.5
639	1.564 945	2007.478	320 694.6	689	1.451 379	2164.557	372 845.0
640	1.562 500	2010.619	321 699.1	**690**	1.449 275	2167.699	373 928.1
641	1.560 062	2013.761	322 705.2	691	1.447 178	2170.841	375 012.7
642	1.557 632	2016.902	323 712.8	692	1.445 087	2173.982	376 098.9
643	1.555 210	2020.044	324 722.1	693	1.443 001	2177.124	377 186.7
644	1.552 795	2023.186	325 732.9	694	1.440 922	2180.265	378 276.0
645	1.550 388	2026.327	326 745.3	695	1.438 849	2183.407	379 366.9
646	1.547 988	2029.469	327 759.2	696	1.436 782	2186.548	380 459.4
647	1.545 595	2032.610	328 774.7	697	1.434 720	2189.690	381 553.5
648	1.543 210	2035.752	329 791.8	698	1.432 665	2192.832	382 649.1
649	1.540 832	2038.894	330 810.5	699	1.430 615	2195.973	383 746.3
650	1.538 462	2042.035	331 830.7	**700**	1.428 571	2199.115	384 845.1

RECIPROCALS, CIRCUMFERENCE AND AREA OF CIRCLES (Continued)

$n = $ dia	$1000\dfrac{1}{n}$	Circum-ference πn	Area $\dfrac{\pi n^2}{4}$	$n = $ dia	$1000\dfrac{1}{n}$	Circum-ference πn	Area $\dfrac{\pi n^2}{4}$
700	1.428 571	2199.115	384 845.1	750	1.333 333	2356.194	441 786.5
701	1.426 534	2202.256	385 945.4	751	1.331 558	2359.336	442 965.3
702	1.424 501	2205.398	387 047.4	752	1.329 787	2362.478	444 145.8
703	1.422 475	2208.540	388 150.8	753	1.328 021	2365.619	445 327.8
704	1.420 455	2211.681	389 255.9	754	1.326 260	2368.761	446 511.4
705	1.418 440	2214.823	390 362.5	755	1.324 503	2371.902	447 696.6
706	1.416 431	2217.964	391 470.7	756	1.322 751	2375.044	448 883.3
707	1.414 427	2221.106	392 580.5	757	1.321 004	2378.186	450 071.6
708	1.412 429	2224.248	393 691.8	758	1.319 261	2381.327	451 261.5
709	1.410 437	2227.389	394 804.7	759	1.317 523	2384.469	452 453.0
710	1.408 451	2230.531	395 919.2	760	1.315 789	2387.610	453 646.0
711	1.406 470	2233.672	397 035.3	761	1.314 060	2390.752	454 840.6
712	1.404 494	2236.814	398 152.9	762	1.312 336	2393.894	456 036.7
713	1.402 525	2239.956	399 272.1	763	1.310 616	2397.035	457 234.5
714	1.400 560	2243.097	400 392.8	764	1.308 901	2400.177	458 433.8
715	1.398 601	2246.239	401 515.2	765	1.307 190	2403.318	459 634.6
716	1.396 648	2249.380	402 639.1	766	1.305 483	2406.460	460 837.1
717	1.394 700	2252.522	403 764.6	767	1.303 781	2409.602	462 041.1
718	1.392 758	2255.664	404 891.6	768	1.302 083	2412.743	463 246.7
719	1.390 821	2258.805	406 020.2	769	1.300 390	2415.885	464 453.8
720	1.388 889	2261.947	407 150.4	770	1.298 701	2419.026	465 662.6
721	1.386 963	2265.088	408 282.2	771	1.297 017	2422.168	466 872.9
722	1.385 042	2268.230	409 415.5	772	1.295 337	2425.310	468 084.7
723	1.383 126	2271.371	410 550.4	773	1.293 661	2428.451	469 298.2
724	1.381 215	2274.513	411 686.9	774	1.291 990	2431.593	470 513.2
725	1.379 310	2277.655	412 824.9	775	1.290 323	2434.734	471 729.8
726	1.377 410	2280.796	413 964.5	776	1.288 660	2437.876	472 947.9
727	1.375 516	2283.938	415 105.7	777	1.287 001	2441.017	474 167.6
728	1.373 626	2287.079	416 248.5	778	1.285 347	2444.159	475 388.9
729	1.371 742	2290.221	417 392.8	779	1.283 697	2447.301	476 611.8
730	1.369 863	2293.363	418 538.7	780	1.282 051	2450.442	477 836.2
731	1.367 989	2296.504	419 686.1	781	1.280 410	2453.584	479 062.2
732	1.366 120	2299.646	420 835.2	782	1.278 772	2456.725	480 289.8
733	1.364 256	2302.787	421 985.8	783	1.277 139	2459.867	481 519.0
734	1.362 398	2305.929	423 138.0	784	1.275 510	2463.009	482 749.7
735	1.360 544	2309.071	424 291.7	785	1.273 885	2466.150	483 982.0
736	1.358 696	2312.212	425 447.0	786	1.272 265	2469.292	485 215.8
737	1.356 852	2315.354	426 603.9	787	1.270 648	2472.433	486 451.3
738	1.355 014	2318.495	427 762.4	788	1.269 036	2475.575	487 688.3
739	1.353 180	2321.637	428 922.4	789	1.267 427	2478.717	488 926.9
740	1.351 351	2324.779	430 084.0	790	1.265 823	2481.858	490 167.0
741	1.349 528	2327.920	431 247.2	791	1.264 223	2485.000	491 408.7
742	1.347 709	2331.062	432 412.0	792	1.262 626	2488.141	492 652.0
743	1.345 895	2334.203	433 578.3	793	1.261 034	2491.283	493 896.8
744	1.344 086	2337.345	434 746.2	794	1.259 446	2494.425	495 143.3
745	1.342 282	2340.487	435 915.6	795	1.257 862	2497.566	496 391.3
746	1.340 483	2343.628	437 086.6	796	1.256 281	2500.708	497 640.8
747	1.338 688	2346.770	438 259.2	797	1.254 705	2503.849	498 892.0
748	1.336 898	2349.911	439 433.4	798	1.253 133	2506.991	500 144.7
749	1.335 113	2353.053	440 609.2	799	1.251 564	2510.133	501 399.0
750	1.333 333	2356.194	441 786.5	800	1.250 000	2513.274	502 654.8

RECIPROCALS, CIRCUMFERENCE AND AREA OF CIRCLES (Continued)

n = dia	$1000\dfrac{1}{n}$	Circumference πn	Area $\dfrac{\pi n^2}{4}$	n = dia	$1000\dfrac{1}{n}$	Circumference πn	Area $\dfrac{\pi n^2}{4}$
800	1.250 000	2513.274	502 654.8	**850**	1.176 471	2670.354	567 450.2
801	1.248 439	2516.416	503 912.2	851	1.175 088	2673.495	568 786.1
802	1.246 883	2519.557	505 171.2	852	1.173 709	2676.637	570 123.7
803	1.245 330	2522.699	506 431.8	853	1.172 333	2679.779	571 462.8
804	1.243 781	2525.840	507 693.9	854	1.170 960	2682.920	572 803.4
805	1.242 236	2528.982	508 957.6	855	1.169 591	2686.062	574 145.7
806	1.240 695	2532.124	510 222.9	856	1.168 224	2689.203	575 489.5
807	1.239 157	2535.265	511 489.8	857	1.166 861	2692.345	576 834.9
808	1.237 624	2538.407	512 758.2	858	1.165 501	2695.486	578 181.9
809	1.236 094	2541.548	514 028.2	859	1.164 144	2698.628	579 530.4
810	1.234 568	2544.690	515 299.7	**860**	1.162 791	2701.770	580 880.5
811	1.233 046	2547.832	516 572.9	861	1.161 440	2704.911	582 232.2
812	1.231 527	2550.973	517 847.6	862	1.160 093	2708.053	583 585.4
813	1.230 012	2554.115	519 123.8	863	1.158 749	2711.194	584 940.2
814	1.228 501	2557.256	520 401.7	864	1.157 407	2714.336	586 296.6
815	1.226 994	2560.398	521 681.1	865	1.156 069	2717.478	587 654.5
816	1.225 490	2563.540	522 962.1	866	1.154 734	2720.619	589 014.1
817	1.223 990	2566.681	524 244.6	867	1.153 403	2723.761	590 375.2
818	1.222 494	2569.823	525 528.8	868	1.152 074	2726.902	591 737.8
819	1.221 001	2572.964	526 814.5	869	1.150 748	2730.044	593 102.1
820	1.219 512	2576.106	528 101.7	**870**	1.149 425	2733.186	594 467.9
821	1.218 027	2579.248	529 390.6	871	1.148 106	2736.327	595 835.2
822	1.216 545	2582.389	530 681.0	872	1.146 789	2739.469	597 204.2
823	1.215 067	2585.531	531 973.0	873	1.145 475	2742.610	598 574.7
824	1.213 592	2588.672	533 266.5	874	1.144 165	2745.752	599 946.8
825	1.212 121	2591.814	534 561.6	875	1.142 857	2748.894	601 320.5
826	1.210 654	2594.956	535 858.3	876	1.141 553	2752.035	602 695.7
827	1.209 190	2598.097	537 156.6	877	1.140 251	2755.177	604 072.5
828	1.207 729	2601.239	538 456.4	878	1.138 952	2758.318	605 450.9
829	1.206 273	2604.380	539 757.8	879	1.137 656	2761.460	606 830.8
830	1.204 819	2607.522	541 060.8	**880**	1.136 364	2764.602	608 212.3
831	1.203 369	2610.663	542 365.3	881	1.135 074	2767.743	609 595.4
832	1.201 923	2613.805	543 671.5	882	1.133 787	2770.885	610 980.1
833	1.200 480	2616.947	544 979.1	883	1.132 503	2774.026	612 366.3
834	1.199 041	2620.088	546 288.4	884	1.131 222	2777.168	613 754.1
835	1.197 605	2623.230	547 599.2	885	1.129 944	2780.309	615 143.5
836	1.196 172	2626.371	548 911.6	886	1.128 668	2783.451	616 534.4
837	1.194 743	2629.513	550 225.6	887	1.127 396	2786.593	617 926.9
838	1.193 317	2632.655	551 541.1	888	1.126 126	2789.734	619 321.0
839	1.191 895	2635.796	552 858.3	889	1.124 859	2792.876	620 716.7
840	1.190 476	2638.938	554 176.9	**890**	1.123 596	2796.017	622 113.9
841	1.189 061	2642.079	555 497.2	891	1.122 334	2799.159	623 512.7
842	1.187 648	2645.221	556 819.0	892	1.121 076	2802.301	624 913.0
843	1.186 240	2648.363	558 142.4	893	1.119 821	2805.442	626 315.0
844	1.184 834	2651.504	559 467.4	894	1.118 568	2808.584	627 718.5
845	1.183 432	2654.646	560 793.9	895	1.117 318	2811.725	629 123.6
846	1.182 033	2657.787	562 122.0	896	1.116 071	2814.867	630 530.2
847	1.180 638	2660.929	563 451.7	897	1.114 827	2818.009	631 938.4
848	1.179 245	2664.071	564 783.0	898	1.113 586	2821.150	633 348.2
849	1.177 856	2667.212	566 115.8	899	1.112 347	2824.292	634 759.6
850	1.176 471	2670.354	567 450.2	**900**	1.111 111	2827.433	636 172.5

Numerical Tables

RECIPROCALS, CIRCUMFERENCE AND AREA OF CIRCLES (Continued)

n = dia	$1000\dfrac{1}{n}$	Circum-ference πn	Area $\dfrac{\pi n^2}{4}$	n = dia	$1000\dfrac{1}{n}$	Circum-ference πn	Area $\dfrac{\pi n^2}{4}$
900	1.111 111	2827.433	636 172.5	**950**	1.052 632	2984.513	708 821.8
901	1.109 878	2830.575	637 587.0	951	1.051 525	2987.655	710 314.9
902	1.108 647	2833.717	639 003.1	952	1.050 420	2990.796	711 809.5
903	1.107 420	2836.858	640 420.7	953	1.049 318	2993.938	713 305.7
904	1.106 195	2840.000	641 839.9	954	1.048 218	2997.079	714 803.4
905	1.104 972	2843.141	643 260.7	955	1.047 120	3000.221	716 302.8
906	1.103 753	2846.283	644 683.1	956	1.046 025	3003.363	717 803.7
907	1.102 536	2849.425	646 107.0	957	1.044 932	3006.504	719 306.1
908	1.101 322	2852.566	647 532.5	958	1.043 841	3009.646	720 810.2
909	1.100 110	2855.708	648 959.6	959	1.042 753	3012.787	722 315.8
910	1.098 901	2858.849	650 388.2	**960**	1.041 667	3015.929	723 822.9
911	1.097 695	2861.991	651 818.4	961	1.040 583	3019.071	725 331.7
912	1.096 491	2865.133	653 250.2	962	1.039 501	3022.212	726 842.0
913	1.095 290	2868.274	654 683.6	963	1.038 422	3025.354	728 353.9
914	1.094 092	2871.416	656 118.5	964	1.037 344	3028.495	729 867.4
915	1.092 896	2874.557	657 555.0	965	1.036 269	3031.637	731 382.4
916	1.091 703	2877.699	658 993.0	966	1.035 197	3034.779	732 899.0
917	1.090 513	2880.840	660 432.7	967	1.034 126	3037.920	734 417.2
918	1.089 325	2883.982	661 873.9	968	1.033 058	3041.062	735 936.9
919	1.088 139	2887.124	663 316.7	969	1.031 992	3044.203	737 458.2
920	1.086 957	2890.265	664 761.0	**970**	1.030 928	3047.345	738 981.1
921	1.085 776	2893.407	666 206.9	971	1.029 866	3050.486	740 505.6
922	1.084 599	2896.548	667 654.4	972	1.028 807	3053.628	742 031.6
923	1.083 424	2899.690	669 103.5	973	1.027 749	3056.770	743 559.2
924	1.082 251	2902.832	670 554.1	974	1.026 694	3059.911	745 088.4
925	1.081 081	2905.973	672 006.3	975	1.025 641	3063.053	746 619.1
926	1.079 914	2909.115	673 460.1	976	1.024 590	3066.194	748 151.4
927	1.078 749	2912.256	674 915.4	977	1.023 541	3069.336	749 685.3
928	1.077 586	2915.398	676 372.3	978	1.022 495	3072.478	751 220.8
929	1.076 426	2918.540	677 830.8	979	1.021 450	3075.619	752 757.8
930	1.075 269	2921.681	679 290.9	**980**	1.020 408	3078.761	754 296.4
931	1.074 114	2924.823	680 752.5	981	1.019 368	3081.902	755 836.6
932	1.072 961	2927.964	682 215.7	982	1.018 330	3085.044	757 378.3
933	1.071 811	2931.106	683 680.5	983	1.017 294	3088.186	758 921.6
934	1.070 664	2934.248	685 146.8	984	1.016 260	3091.327	760 466.5
935	1.069 519	2937.389	686 614.7	985	1.015 228	3094.469	762 012.9
936	1.068 376	2940.531	688 084.2	986	1.014 199	3097.610	763 561.0
937	1.067 236	2943.672	689 555.2	987	1.013 171	3100.752	765 110.5
938	1.066 098	2946.814	691 027.9	988	1.012 146	3103.894	766 661.7
939	1.064 963	2949.956	692 502.1	989	1.011 122	3107.035	768 214.4
940	1.063 830	2953.097	693 977.8	**990**	1.010 101	3110.177	769 768.7
941	1.062 699	2956.239	695 455.2	991	1.009 082	3113.318	771 324.6
942	1.061 571	2959.380	696 934.1	992	1.008 065	3116.460	772 882.1
943	1.060 445	2962.522	698 414.5	993	1.007 049	3119.602	774 441.1
944	1.059 322	2965.663	699 896.6	994	1.006 036	3122.743	776 001.7
945	1.058 201	2968.805	701 380.2	995	1.005 025	3125.885	777 563.8
946	1.057 082	2971.947	702 865.4	996	1.004 016	3129.026	779 127.5
947	1.055 966	2975.088	704 352.1	997	1.003 009	3132.168	780 692.8
948	1.054 852	2978.230	705 840.5	998	1.002 004	3135.309	782 259.7
949	1.053 741	2981.371	707 330.4	999	1.001 001	3138.451	783 828.2
950	1.052 632	2984.513	708 821.8	**1000**	1.000 000	3141.593	785 398.2

POWERS OF NUMBERS

This table contains the fourth through ninth power of the numbers from 1 to 100. Second and third powers will be found in the tables headed "Squares, Square Root, and Cube and Cube Root."

The larger numbers are expressed exponentially to at least seven significant figures.

The approximate value written as a whole number may be obtained by shifting the decimal point to the right by the number of places indicated in the exponent of 10 shown at the head of each group of values. For example: the approximate value of 33^8 is found in the table as 14.064086×10^{11}. Written as a whole number it is 1 406 408 600 000.

Numerical Tables

POWERS OF NUMBERS

n	n^4	n^5	n^6	n^7	n^8	n^9
1	1	1	1	1	1	1
2	16	32	64	128	256	512
3	81	243	729	2187	6561	19683
4	256	1024	4096	16384	65536	262144
5	625	3125	15625	78125	390625	1953125
6	1296	7776	46656	279936	1679616	10077696
7	2401	16807	117649	823543	5764801	40353607
8	4096	32768	262144	2097152	16777216	134217728
9	6561	59049	531441	4782969	43046721	387420489
					$\times 10^8$	$\times 10^9$
10	10000	100000	1000000	10000000	1.000000	1.000000
11	14641	161051	1771561	19487171	2.143589	2.357948
12	20736	248832	2985984	35831808	4.299817	5.159780
13	28561	371293	4826809	62748517	8.157307	10.604499
14	38416	537824	7529536	105413504	14.757891	20.661047
15	50625	759375	11390625	170859375	25.628906	38.443359
16	65536	1048576	16777216	268435456	42.949673	68.719477
17	83521	1419857	24137569	410338673	69.757574	118.587876
18	104976	1889568	34012224	612220032	110.199606	198.359290
19	130321	2476099	47045881	893871739	169.835630	322.687698
				$\times 10^9$	$\times 10^{10}$	$\times 10^{11}$
20	160000	3200000	64000000	1.280000	2.560000	5.120000
21	194481	4084101	85766121	1.801089	3.782286	7.942800
22	234256	5153632	113379904	2.494358	5.487587	12.072692
23	279841	6436343	148035889	3.404825	7.831099	18.011527
24	331776	7962624	191102976	4.586471	11.007531	26.418075
25	390625	9765625	244140625	6.103516	15.258789	38.146973
26	456976	11881376	308915776	8.031810	20.882706	54.295037
27	531441	14348907	387420489	10.460353	28.242954	76.255975
28	614656	17210368	481890304	13.492929	37.780200	105.784560
29	707281	20511149	594823321	17.249876	50.024641	145.071460
			$\times 10^8$	$\times 10^{10}$	$\times 10^{11}$	$\times 10^{13}$
30	810000	24300000	7.290000	2.187000	6.561000	1.968300
31	923521	28629151	8.875037	2.751261	8.528910	2.643962
32	1048576	33554432	10.737418	3.435974	10.995116	3.518437
33	1185921	39135393	12.914680	4.261844	14.064086	4.641148
34	1336336	45435424	15.448044	5.252335	17.857939	6.071699
35	1500625	52521875	18.382656	6.433930	22.518754	7.881564
36	1679616	60466176	21.767823	7.836416	28.211099	10.155996
37	1874161	69343957	25.657264	9.493188	35.124795	12.996174
38	2085136	79235168	30.109364	11.441558	43.477921	16.521610
39	2313441	90224199	35.187438	13.723101	53.520093	20.872836
			$\times 10^9$	$\times 10^{10}$	$\times 10^{12}$	$\times 10^{14}$
40	2560000	102400000	4.096000	16.384000	6.553600	2.621440
41	2825761	115856201	4.750104	19.475427	7.984925	3.273819
42	3111696	130691232	5.489032	23.053933	9.682652	4.066714
43	3418801	147008443	6.321363	27.181861	11.688200	5.025926
44	3748096	164916224	7.256314	31.927781	14.048224	6.181218
45	4100625	184528125	8.303766	37.366945	16.815125	7.566806
46	4477456	205962976	9.474297	43.581766	20.047612	9.221902
47	4879681	229345007	10.779215	50.662312	23.811287	11.191305
48	5308416	254803968	12.230590	58.706834	28.179280	13.526055
49	5764801	282475249	13.841287	67.822307	33.232931	16.284136
50	6250000	312500000	15.625000	78.125000	39.062500	19.531250

POWERS OF NUMBERS (Continued)

n	n^4	n^5	n^6	n^7	n^8	n^9
			$\times 10^9$	$\times 10^{11}$	$\times 10^{13}$	$\times 10^{14}$
50	6250000	312500000	15.625000	7.812500	3.906250	19.531250
51	6765201	345025251	17.596288	8.974107	4.576794	23.341652
52	7311616	380204032	19.770610	10.280717	5.345973	27.799059
53	7890481	418195493	22.164361	11.747111	6.225969	32.997636
54	8503056	459165024	24.794911	13.389252	7.230196	39.043059
55	9150625	503284375	27.680641	15.224352	8.373394	46.053666
56	9834496	550731776	30.840979	17.270948	9.671731	54.161694
57	10556001	601692057	34.296447	19.548975	11.142916	63.514620
58	11316496	656356768	38.068693	22.079842	12.806308	74.276587
59	12117361	714924299	42.180534	24.886515	14.683044	86.629958
		$\times 10^8$	$\times 10^{10}$	$\times 10^{11}$	$\times 10^{13}$	$\times 10^{16}$
60	12960000	7.776000	4.665600	27.993600	16.796160	1.007770
61	13845841	8.445963	5.152037	31.427428	19.170731	1.169415
62	14776336	9.161328	5.680024	35.216146	21.834011	1.353709
63	15752961	9.924365	6.252350	39.389806	24.815578	1.563381
64	16777216	10.737418	6.871948	43.980465	28.147498	1.801440
65	17850625	11.602906	7.541889	49.022279	31.864481	2.071191
66	18974736	12.523326	8.265395	54.551607	36.004061	2.376268
67	20151121	13.501251	9.045838	60.607116	40.606768	2.720653
68	21381376	14.539336	9.886748	67.229888	45.716324	3.108710
69	22667121	15.640313	10.791816	74.463533	51.379837	3.545209
		$\times 10^8$	$\times 10^{10}$	$\times 10^{12}$	$\times 10^{14}$	$\times 10^{16}$
70	24010000	16.807000	11.764900	8.235430	5.764801	4.035361
71	25411681	18.042294	12.810028	9.095120	6.457535	4.584850
72	26873856	19.349176	13.931407	10.030613	7.222041	5.199870
73	28398241	20.730716	15.133423	11.047399	8.064601	5.887159
74	29986576	22.190066	16.420649	12.151280	8.991947	6.654041
75	31640625	23.730469	17.797952	13.348389	10.011292	7.508469
76	33362176	25.355254	19.269993	14.645195	11.130348	8.459064
77	35153041	27.067842	20.842238	16.048523	12.357363	9.515169
78	37015056	28.871744	22.519960	17.565569	13.701144	10.686892
79	38950081	30.770564	24.308746	19.203909	15.171088	11.985160
		$\times 10^8$	$\times 10^{10}$	$\times 10^{12}$	$\times 10^{14}$	$\times 10^{16}$
80	40960000	32.768000	26.214400	20.971520	16.777216	13.421773
81	43046721	34.867844	28.242954	22.876792	18.530202	15.009464
82	45212176	37.073984	30.400667	24.928547	20.441409	16.761955
83	47458321	39.390406	32.694037	27.136051	22.522922	18.694026
84	49787136	41.821194	35.129803	29.509035	24.787589	20.821575
85	52200625	44.370531	37.714952	32.057709	27.249053	23.161695
86	54700816	47.042702	40.456724	34.792782	29.921793	25.732742
87	57289761	49.842092	43.362620	37.725479	32.821167	28.554415
88	59969536	52.773192	46.440409	40.867560	35.963452	31.647838
89	62742241	55.840594	49.698129	44.231335	39.365888	35.035640
		$\times 10^9$	$\times 10^{11}$	$\times 10^{13}$	$\times 10^{15}$	$\times 10^{17}$
90	65610000	5.904900	5.314410	4.782969	4.304672	3.874205
91	68574961	6.240321	5.678693	5.167610	4.702525	4.279298
92	71639296	6.590815	6.063550	5.578466	5.132189	4.721614
93	74805201	6.956884	6.469902	6.017009	5.595818	5.204111
94	78074896	7.339040	6.898698	6.484776	6.095689	5.729948
95	81450625	7.737809	7.350919	6.983373	6.634204	6.302494
96	84934656	8.153727	7.827798	7.514475	7.213896	6.925340
97	88529281	8.587340	8.329720	8.079828	7.837434	7.602311
98	92236816	9.039208	8.858424	8.681255	8.507630	8.337478
99	96059601	9.509900	9.414801	9.320653	9.227447	9.135172
100	100000000	10.000000	10.000000	10.000000	10.000000	10.000000

POSITIVE POWERS OF TWO

n	2ⁿ			
1	2			
2	4			
3	8			
4	16			
5	32			
6	64			
7	128			
8	256			
9	512			
10	1024			
11	2048			
12	4096			
13	8192			
14	16384			
15	32768			
16	65536			
17	13107	2		
18	26214	4		
19	52428	8		
20	10485	76		
21	20971	52		
22	41943	04		
23	83886	08		
24	16777	216		
25	33554	432		
26	67108	864		
27	13421	7728		
28	26843	5456		
29	53687	0912		
30	10737	41824		
31	21474	83648		
32	42949	67296		
33	85899	34592		
34	17179	86918	4	
35	34359	73836	8	
36	68719	47673	6	
37	13743	89534	72	
38	27487	79069	44	
39	54975	58138	88	
40	10995	11627	776	
41	21990	23255	552	
42	43980	46511	104	
43	87960	93022	208	
44	17592	18604	4416	
45	35184	37208	8832	
46	70368	74417	7664	
47	14073	74883	55328	
48	28147	49767	10656	
49	56294	99534	21312	
50	11258	99906	84262	4

n	2ⁿ					
51	22517	99813	68524	8		
52	45035	99627	37049	6		
53	90071	99254	74099	2		
54	18014	39850	94819	84		
55	36028	79701	89639	68		
56	72057	59403	79279	36		
57	14411	51880	75855	872		
58	28823	03761	51711	744		
59	57646	07523	03423	488		
60	11529	21504	60684	6976		
61	23058	43009	21369	3952		
62	46116	86018	42738	7904		
63	92233	72036	85477	5808		
64	18446	74407	37095	51616		
65	36893	48814	74191	03232		
66	73786	97629	48382	06464		
67	14757	39525	89676	41292	8	
68	29514	79051	79352	82585	6	
69	59029	58103	58705	65171	2	
70	11805	91620	71741	13034	24	
71	23611	83241	43482	26068	48	
72	47223	66482	86964	52136	96	
73	94447	32965	73929	04273	92	
74	18889	46593	14785	80854	784	
75	37778	93186	29571	61709	568	
76	75557	86372	59143	23419	136	
77	15111	57274	51828	64683	8272	
78	30223	14549	03657	29367	6544	
79	60446	29098	07314	58735	3088	
80	12089	25819	61462	91747	06176	
81	24178	51639	22925	83494	12352	
82	48357	03278	45851	66988	24704	
83	96714	06556	91703	33976	49408	
84	19342	81311	38340	66795	29881	6
85	38685	62622	76681	33590	59763	2
86	77371	25245	53362	67181	19526	4
87	15474	25049	10672	53436	23905	28
88	30948	50098	21345	06872	47810	56
89	61897	00196	42690	13744	95621	12
90	12379	40039	28538	02748	99124	224
91	24758	80078	57076	05497	98248	448
92	49517	60157	14152	10995	96496	896
93	99035	20314	28304	21991	92993	792
94	19807	04062	85660	84398	38598	7584
95	39614	08125	71321	68796	77197	5168
96	79228	16251	42643	37593	54395	0336
97	15845	63250	28528	67518	70879	00672
98	31691	26500	57057	35037	41758	01344
99	63382	53001	14114	70074	83516	02688
100	12676	50600	22822	94014	96703	20537 6
101	25353	01200	45645	88029	93406	41075 2

NEGATIVE POWERS OF TWO

n	2^{-n}							
0	1.0							
1	0.5							
2	0.25							
3	0.125							
4	0.0625							
5	0.03125							
6	0.01562	5						
7	0.00781	25						
8	0.00390	625						
9	0.00195	3125						
10	0.00097	65625						
11	0.00048	82812	5					
12	0.00024	41406	25					
13	0.00012	20703	125					
14	0.00006	10351	5625					
15	0.00003	05175	78125					
16	0.00001	52587	89062	5				
17	0.00000	76293	94531	25				
18	0.00000	38146	97265	625				
19	0.00000	19073	48632	8125				
20	0.00000	09536	74316	40625				
21	0.00000	04768	37158	20312	5			
22	0.00000	02384	18579	10156	25			
23	0.00000	01192	09289	55078	125			
24	0.00000	00596	04644	77539	0625			
25	0.00000	00298	02322	38769	53125			
26	0.00000	00149	01161	19384	76562	5		
27	0.00000	00074	50580	59692	38281	25		
28	0.00000	00037	25290	29846	19140	625		
29	0.00000	00018	62645	14923	09570	3125		
30	0.00000	00009	31322	57461	54785	15625		
31	0.00000	00004	65661	28730	77392	57812	5	
32	0.00000	00002	32830	64365	38696	28906	25	
33	0.00000	00001	16415	32182	69348	14453	125	
34	0.00000	00000	58207	66091	34674	07226	5625	
35	0.00000	00000	29103	83045	67337	03613	28125	
36	0.00000	00000	14551	91522	83668	51806	64062	5
37	0.00000	00000	07275	95761	41834	25903	32031	25
38	0.00000	00000	03637	97880	70917	12951	66015	625
39	0.00000	00000	01818	98940	35458	56475	83007	8125
40	0.00000	00000	00909	49470	17729	28237	91503	90625
41	0.00000	00000	00454	74735	08864	64118	95751	95312	5
42	0.00000	00000	00227	37367	54432	32059	47875	97656	25
43	0.00000	00000	00113	68683	77216	16029	73937	98828	125
44	0.00000	00000	00056	84341	88608	08014	86968	99414	0625
45	0.00000	00000	00028	42170	94304	04007	43484	49707	03125
46	0.00000	00000	00014	21085	47152	02003	71742	24853	51562	5
47	0.00000	00000	00007	10542	73576	01001	85871	12426	75781	25
48	0.00000	00000	00003	55271	36788	00500	92935	56213	37890	625
49	0.00000	00000	00001	77635	68394	00250	46467	78106	68945	3125
50	0.00000	00000	00000	88817	84197	00125	23233	89053	34472	65625

SUMS OF POWERS OF INTEGERS, $\displaystyle\sum_{k=1}^{n} k^m$

$(m = 1, 2, 3, 4); 1 \le n \le 40$

n	Σk	Σk^2	Σk^3	Σk^4
1	1	1	1	1
2	3	5	9	17
3	6	14	36	98
4	10	30	100	354
5	15	55	225	979
6	21	91	441	2275
7	28	140	784	4676
8	36	204	1296	8772
9	45	285	2025	15333
10	55	385	3025	25333
11	66	506	4356	39974
12	78	650	6084	60710
13	91	819	8281	89271
14	105	1015	11025	127687
15	120	1240	14400	178312
16	136	1496	18496	243848
17	153	1785	23409	327369
18	171	2109	29241	432345
19	190	2470	36100	562666
20	210	2870	44100	722666
21	231	3311	53361	917147
22	253	3795	64009	1151403
23	276	4324	76176	1431244
24	300	4900	90000	1763020
25	325	5525	105625	2153645
26	351	6201	123201	2610621
27	378	6930	142884	3142062
28	406	7714	164836	3756718
29	435	8555	189225	4463999
30	465	9455	216225	5273999
31	496	10416	246016	6197520
32	528	11440	278784	7246096
33	561	12529	314721	8432017
34	595	13685	354025	9768353
35	630	14910	396900	11268978
36	666	16206	443556	12948594
37	703	17575	494209	14822755
38	741	19019	549081	16907891
39	780	20540	608400	19221332
40	820	22140	672400	21781332

*SUMS OF POWERS OF THE FIRST *n* INTEGERS

$$\sum_{k=1}^{n} k = 1 + 2 + 3 + \cdots + n = \frac{n(n+1)}{2}$$

$$\sum_{k=1}^{n} k^2 = 1^2 + 2^2 + 3^2 + \cdots + n^2 = \frac{n(n+1)(2n+1)}{6}$$

$$\sum_{k=1}^{n} k^3 = \frac{n^2(n+1)^2}{4}$$

$$\sum_{k=1}^{n} k^4 = \frac{n}{30}(n+1)(2n+1)(3n^2 + 3n - 1).$$

$$\sum_{k=1}^{n} k^5 = \frac{n^2}{12}(n+1)^2(2n^2 + 2n - 1).$$

$$\sum_{k=1}^{n} k^6 = \frac{n}{42}(n+1)(2n+1)(3n^4 + 6n^3 - 3n + 1).$$

$$\sum_{k=1}^{n} k^7 = \frac{n^2}{24}(n+1)^2(3n^4 + 6n^3 - n^2 - 4n + 2).$$

$$\sum_{k=1}^{n} k^8 = \frac{n}{90}(n+1)(2n+1)(5n^6 + 15n^5 + 5n^4 - 15n^3 - n^2 + 9n - 3).$$

$$\sum_{k=1}^{n} k^9 = \frac{n^2}{20}(n+1)^2(2n^6 + 6n^5 + n^4 - 8n^3 + n^2 + 6n - 3).$$

$$\sum_{k=1}^{n} k^{10} = \frac{n}{66}(n+1)(2n+1)(3n^8 + 12n^7 + 8n^6 - 18n^5$$
$$- 10n^4 + 24n^3 + 2n^2 - 15n + 5).$$

* See page 70 for generating formula.

FACTORS AND PRIMES

The table presents the prime factors of *all* factorable numbers and the mantissas of the common logarithms of all prime numbers from 1 to 2000.

It should be noted that the third digit of the number is given at the top of the page and that the table runs across two facing pages. Thus, the factors of 258 are found, on the right hand page, on a line with 25 and under vertical column 8 to be $2 \cdot 3 \cdot 43$.

FACTORS AND PRIMES

If n is prime the mantissa of its common logarithm is given. If n is not prime its prime factors are given.

n	0	1	2	3	4
0	....	0000000	3010300	4771213	2^2
1	$2 \cdot 5$	0413927	$2^2 \cdot 3$	1139434	$2 \cdot 7$
2	$2^2 \cdot 5$	$3 \cdot 7$	$2 \cdot 11$	3617278	$2^3 \cdot 3$
3	$2 \cdot 3 \cdot 5$	4913617	2^5	$3 \cdot 11$	$2 \cdot 17$
4	$2^3 \cdot 5$	6127839	$2 \cdot 3 \cdot 7$	6334685	$2^2 \cdot 11$
5	$2 \cdot 5^2$	$3 \cdot 17$	$2^2 \cdot 13$	7242759	$2 \cdot 3^3$
6	$2^2 \cdot 3 \cdot 5$	7853298	$2 \cdot 31$	$3^2 \cdot 7$	2^6
7	$2 \cdot 5 \cdot 7$	8512583	$2^3 \cdot 3^2$	8633229	$2 \cdot 37$
8	$2^4 \cdot 5$	3^4	$2 \cdot 41$	9190781	$2^2 \cdot 3 \cdot 7$
9	$2 \cdot 3^2 \cdot 5$	$7 \cdot 13$	$2^2 \cdot 23$	$3 \cdot 31$	$2 \cdot 47$
10	$2^2 \cdot 5^2$	0043214	$2 \cdot 3 \cdot 17$	0128372	$2^3 \cdot 13$
11	$2 \cdot 5 \cdot 11$	$3 \cdot 37$	$2^4 \cdot 7$	0530784	$2 \cdot 3 \cdot 19$
12	$2^3 \cdot 3 \cdot 5$	11^2	$2 \cdot 61$	$3 \cdot 41$	$2^2 \cdot 31$
13	$2 \cdot 5 \cdot 13$	1172713	$2^2 \cdot 3 \cdot 11$	$7 \cdot 19$	$2 \cdot 67$
14	$2^2 \cdot 5 \cdot 7$	$3 \cdot 47$	$2 \cdot 71$	$11 \cdot 13$	$2^4 \cdot 3^2$
15	$2 \cdot 3 \cdot 5^2$	1789769	$2^3 \cdot 19$	$3^2 \cdot 17$	$2 \cdot 7 \cdot 11$
16	$2^5 \cdot 5$	$7 \cdot 23$	$2 \cdot 3^4$	2121876	$2^3 \cdot 41$
17	$2 \cdot 5 \cdot 17$	$3^2 \cdot 19$	$2^2 \cdot 43$	2380461	$2 \cdot 3 \cdot 29$
18	$2^2 \cdot 3^2 \cdot 5$	2576786	$2 \cdot 7 \cdot 13$	$3 \cdot 61$	$2^3 \cdot 23$
19	$2 \cdot 5 \cdot 19$	2810334	$2^6 \cdot 3$	2855573	$2 \cdot 97$
20	$2^3 \cdot 5^2$	$3 \cdot 67$	$2 \cdot 101$	$7 \cdot 29$	$2^2 \cdot 3 \cdot 17$
21	$2 \cdot 3 \cdot 5 \cdot 7$	3242825	$2^2 \cdot 53$	$3 \cdot 71$	$2 \cdot 107$
22	$2^2 \cdot 5 \cdot 11$	$13 \cdot 17$	$2 \cdot 3 \cdot 37$	3483049	$2^5 \cdot 7$
23	$2 \cdot 5 \cdot 23$	$3 \cdot 7 \cdot 11$	$2^2 \cdot 29$	3673559	$2 \cdot 3^2 \cdot 13$
24	$2^4 \cdot 3 \cdot 5$	3820170	$2 \cdot 11^2$	3^5	$2^2 \cdot 61$
25	$2 \cdot 5^3$	3996737	$2^2 \cdot 3^2 \cdot 7$	$11 \cdot 23$	$2 \cdot 127$
26	$2^2 \cdot 5 \cdot 13$	$3^2 \cdot 29$	$2 \cdot 131$	4199557	$2^3 \cdot 3 \cdot 11$
27	$2 \cdot 3^3 \cdot 5$	4329693	$2^4 \cdot 17$	$3 \cdot 7 \cdot 13$	$2 \cdot 137$
28	$2^3 \cdot 5 \cdot 7$	4487063	$2 \cdot 3 \cdot 47$	4517864	$2^2 \cdot 71$
29	$2 \cdot 5 \cdot 29$	$3 \cdot 97$	$2^2 \cdot 73$	4668676	$2 \cdot 3 \cdot 7^2$
30	$2^2 \cdot 3 \cdot 5^2$	$7 \cdot 43$	$2 \cdot 151$	$3 \cdot 101$	$2^4 \cdot 19$
31	$2 \cdot 5 \cdot 31$	4927604	$2^3 \cdot 3 \cdot 13$	4955443	$2 \cdot 157$
32	$2^6 \cdot 5$	$3 \cdot 107$	$2 \cdot 7 \cdot 23$	$17 \cdot 19$	$2^3 \cdot 3^4$
33	$2 \cdot 3 \cdot 5 \cdot 11$	5198280	$2^2 \cdot 83$	$3^2 \cdot 37$	$2 \cdot 167$
34	$2^2 \cdot 5 \cdot 17$	$11 \cdot 31$	$2 \cdot 3^2 \cdot 19$	7^3	$2^3 \cdot 43$
35	$2 \cdot 5^2 \cdot 7$	$3^3 \cdot 13$	$2^5 \cdot 11$	5477747	$2 \cdot 3 \cdot 59$
36	$2^3 \cdot 3^2 \cdot 5$	19^2	$2 \cdot 181$	$3 \cdot 11^2$	$2^2 \cdot 7 \cdot 13$
37	$2 \cdot 5 \cdot 37$	$7 \cdot 53$	$2^3 \cdot 3 \cdot 31$	5717088	$2 \cdot 11 \cdot 17$
38	$2^2 \cdot 5 \cdot 19$	$3 \cdot 127$	$2 \cdot 191$	5831988	$2^7 \cdot 3$
39	$2 \cdot 3 \cdot 5 \cdot 13$	$17 \cdot 23$	$2^3 \cdot 7^2$	$3 \cdot 131$	$2 \cdot 197$
40	$2^4 \cdot 5^2$	6031444	$2 \cdot 3 \cdot 67$	$13 \cdot 31$	$2^2 \cdot 101$
41	$2 \cdot 5 \cdot 41$	$3 \cdot 137$	$2^3 \cdot 103$	$7 \cdot 59$	$2 \cdot 3^2 \cdot 23$
42	$2^2 \cdot 3 \cdot 5 \cdot 7$	6242821	$2 \cdot 211$	$3^2 \cdot 47$	$2^3 \cdot 53$
43	$2 \cdot 5 \cdot 43$	6344773	$2^4 \cdot 3^3$	6364879	$2 \cdot 7 \cdot 31$
44	$2^3 \cdot 5 \cdot 11$	$3^3 \cdot 7^2$	$2 \cdot 13 \cdot 17$	6464037	$2^2 \cdot 3 \cdot 37$
45	$2 \cdot 3^2 \cdot 5^2$	$11 \cdot 41$	$2^2 \cdot 113$	$3 \cdot 151$	$2 \cdot 227$
46	$2^2 \cdot 5 \cdot 23$	6637009	$2 \cdot 3 \cdot 7 \cdot 11$	6655810	$2^4 \cdot 29$
47	$2 \cdot 5 \cdot 47$	$3 \cdot 157$	$2^5 \cdot 59$	$11 \cdot 43$	$2 \cdot 3 \cdot 79$
48	$2^5 \cdot 3 \cdot 5$	$13 \cdot 37$	$2 \cdot 241$	$3 \cdot 7 \cdot 23$	$2^2 \cdot 11^2$
49	$2 \cdot 5 \cdot 7^2$	6910815	$2^2 \cdot 3 \cdot 41$	$17 \cdot 29$	$2 \cdot 13 \cdot 19$
50	$2^2 \cdot 5^3$	$3 \cdot 167$	$2 \cdot 251$	7015680	$2^3 \cdot 3^2 \cdot 7$

FACTORS AND PRIMES (Continued)

n	5	6	7	8	9
0	6989700	$2 \cdot 3$	8450980	2^3	3^2
1	$3 \cdot 5$	2^4	2304489	$2 \cdot 3^2$	2787536
2	5^2	$2 \cdot 13$	3^3	$2^2 \cdot 7$	4623980
3	$5 \cdot 7$	$2^2 \cdot 3^2$	5682017	$2 \cdot 19$	$3 \cdot 13$
4	$3^2 \cdot 5$	$2 \cdot 23$	6720979	$2^4 \cdot 3$	7^2
5	$5 \cdot 11$	$2^3 \cdot 7$	$3 \cdot 19$	$2 \cdot 29$	7708520
6	$5 \cdot 13$	$2 \cdot 3 \cdot 11$	8260748	$2^2 \cdot 17$	$3 \cdot 23$
7	$3 \cdot 5^2$	$2^2 \cdot 19$	$7 \cdot 11$	$2 \cdot 3 \cdot 13$	8976271
8	$5 \cdot 17$	$2 \cdot 43$	$3 \cdot 29$	$2^3 \cdot 11$	9493900
9	$5 \cdot 19$	$2^5 \cdot 3$	9867717	$2 \cdot 7^2$	$3^2 \cdot 11$
10	$3 \cdot 5 \cdot 7$	$2 \cdot 53$	0293838	$2^2 \cdot 3^3$	0374265
11	$5 \cdot 23$	$2^2 \cdot 29$	$3^2 \cdot 13$	$2 \cdot 59$	$7 \cdot 17$
12	5^3	$2 \cdot 3^2 \cdot 7$	1038037	2^7	$3 \cdot 43$
13	$3^3 \cdot 5$	$2^3 \cdot 17$	1367206	$2 \cdot 3 \cdot 23$	1430148
14	$5 \cdot 29$	$2 \cdot 73$	$3 \cdot 7^2$	$2^2 \cdot 37$	1731863
15	$5 \cdot 31$	$2^2 \cdot 3 \cdot 13$	1958997	$2 \cdot 79$	$3 \cdot 53$
16	$3 \cdot 5 \cdot 11$	$2 \cdot 83$	2227165	$2^3 \cdot 3 \cdot 7$	13^2
17	$5^2 \cdot 7$	$2^4 \cdot 11$	$3 \cdot 59$	$2 \cdot 89$	2528530
18	$5 \cdot 37$	$2 \cdot 3 \cdot 31$	$11 \cdot 17$	$2^2 \cdot 47$	$3^3 \cdot 7$
19	$3 \cdot 5 \cdot 13$	$2^2 \cdot 7^2$	2944662	$2 \cdot 3^2 \cdot 11$	2988531
20	$5 \cdot 41$	$2 \cdot 103$	$3^2 \cdot 23$	$2^4 \cdot 13$	$11 \cdot 19$
21	$5 \cdot 43$	$2^3 \cdot 3^3$	$7 \cdot 31$	$2 \cdot 109$	$3 \cdot 73$
22	$3^2 \cdot 5^2$	$2 \cdot 113$	3560259	$2^2 \cdot 3 \cdot 19$	3598355
23	$5 \cdot 47$	$2^2 \cdot 59$	$3 \cdot 79$	$2 \cdot 7 \cdot 17$	3783979
24	$5 \cdot 7^2$	$2 \cdot 3 \cdot 41$	$13 \cdot 19$	$2^3 \cdot 31$	$3 \cdot 83$
25	$3 \cdot 5 \cdot 17$	2^8	4099331	$2 \cdot 3 \cdot 43$	$7 \cdot 37$
26	$5 \cdot 53$	$2 \cdot 7 \cdot 19$	$3 \cdot 89$	$2^2 \cdot 67$	4297523
27	$5^2 \cdot 11$	$2^2 \cdot 3 \cdot 23$	4424798	$2 \cdot 139$	$3^2 \cdot 31$
28	$3 \cdot 5 \cdot 19$	$2 \cdot 11 \cdot 13$	$7 \cdot 41$	$2^5 \cdot 3^2$	17^2
29	$5 \cdot 59$	$2^3 \cdot 37$	$3^3 \cdot 11$	$2 \cdot 149$	$13 \cdot 23$
30	$5 \cdot 61$	$2 \cdot 3^2 \cdot 17$	4871384	$2^2 \cdot 7 \cdot 11$	$3 \cdot 103$
31	$3^2 \cdot 5 \cdot 7$	$2^2 \cdot 79$	5010593	$2 \cdot 3 \cdot 53$	$11 \cdot 29$
32	$5^2 \cdot 13$	$2 \cdot 163$	$3 \cdot 109$	$2^3 \cdot 41$	$7 \cdot 47$
33	$5 \cdot 67$	$2^4 \cdot 3 \cdot 7$	5276299	$2 \cdot 13^2$	$3 \cdot 113$
34	$3 \cdot 5 \cdot 23$	$2 \cdot 173$	5403295	$2^2 \cdot 3 \cdot 29$	5428254
35	$5 \cdot 71$	$2^2 \cdot 89$	$3 \cdot 7 \cdot 17$	$2 \cdot 179$	5550944
36	$5 \cdot 73$	$2 \cdot 3 \cdot 61$	5646661	$2^4 \cdot 23$	$3^2 \cdot 41$
37	$3 \cdot 5^3$	$2^3 \cdot 47$	$13 \cdot 29$	$2 \cdot 3^3 \cdot 7$	5786392
38	$5 \cdot 7 \cdot 11$	$2 \cdot 193$	$3^2 \cdot 43$	$2^2 \cdot 97$	5899496
39	$5 \cdot 79$	$2^2 \cdot 3^2 \cdot 11$	5987905	$2 \cdot 199$	$3 \cdot 7 \cdot 19$
40	$3^4 \cdot 5$	$2 \cdot 7 \cdot 29$	$11 \cdot 37$	$2^3 \cdot 3 \cdot 17$	6117233
41	$5 \cdot 83$	$2^5 \cdot 13$	$3 \cdot 139$	$2 \cdot 11 \cdot 19$	6222140
42	$5^2 \cdot 17$	$2 \cdot 3 \cdot 71$	$7 \cdot 61$	$2^2 \cdot 107$	$3 \cdot 11 \cdot 13$
43	$3 \cdot 5 \cdot 29$	$2^2 \cdot 109$	$19 \cdot 23$	$2 \cdot 3 \cdot 73$	6424645
44	$5 \cdot 89$	$2 \cdot 223$	$3 \cdot 149$	$2^6 \cdot 7$	6522463
45	$5 \cdot 7 \cdot 13$	$2^2 \cdot 3 \cdot 19$	6599162	$2 \cdot 229$	$3^3 \cdot 17$
46	$3 \cdot 5 \cdot 31$	$2 \cdot 233$	6693169	$2^2 \cdot 3^2 \cdot 13$	$7 \cdot 67$
47	$5^2 \cdot 19$	$2^2 \cdot 7 \cdot 17$	$3^2 \cdot 53$	$2 \cdot 239$	6803355
48	$5 \cdot 97$	$2 \cdot 3^5$	6875290	$2^3 \cdot 61$	$3 \cdot 163$
49	$3^2 \cdot 5 \cdot 11$	$2^4 \cdot 31$	$7 \cdot 71$	$2 \cdot 3 \cdot 83$	6981005
50	$5 \cdot 101$	$2 \cdot 11 \cdot 23$	$3 \cdot 13^2$	$2^2 \cdot 127$	7067178

FACTORS AND PRIMES (Continued)

n	0	1	2	3	4
50	$2^2 \cdot 5^3$	$3 \cdot 167$	$2 \cdot 251$	7015680	$2^3 \cdot 3^2 \cdot 7$
51	$2 \cdot 3 \cdot 5 \cdot 17$	$7 \cdot 73$	2^9	$3^3 \cdot 19$	$2 \cdot 257$
52	$2^3 \cdot 5 \cdot 13$	7168377	$2 \cdot 3^2 \cdot 29$	7185017	$2^2 \cdot 131$
53	$2 \cdot 5 \cdot 53$	$3^2 \cdot 59$	$2^2 \cdot 7 \cdot 19$	$13 \cdot 41$	$2 \cdot 3 \cdot 89$
54	$2^2 \cdot 3^3 \cdot 5$	7331973	$2 \cdot 271$	$3 \cdot 181$	$2^5 \cdot 17$
55	$2 \cdot 5^2 \cdot 11$	$19 \cdot 29$	$2^3 \cdot 3 \cdot 23$	$7 \cdot 79$	$2 \cdot 277$
56	$2^4 \cdot 5 \cdot 7$	$3 \cdot 11 \cdot 17$	$2 \cdot 281$	7505084	$2^2 \cdot 3 \cdot 47$
57	$2 \cdot 3 \cdot 5 \cdot 19$	7566361	$2^2 \cdot 11 \cdot 13$	$3 \cdot 191$	$2 \cdot 7 \cdot 41$
58	$2^2 \cdot 5 \cdot 29$	$7 \cdot 83$	$2 \cdot 3 \cdot 97$	$11 \cdot 53$	$2^3 \cdot 73$
59	$2 \cdot 5 \cdot 59$	$3 \cdot 197$	$2^4 \cdot 37$	7730547	$2 \cdot 3^3 \cdot 11$
60	$2^3 \cdot 3 \cdot 5^2$	7788745	$2 \cdot 7 \cdot 43$	$3^2 \cdot 67$	$2^2 \cdot 151$
61	$2 \cdot 5 \cdot 61$	$13 \cdot 47$	$2^2 \cdot 3^2 \cdot 17$	7874605	$2 \cdot 307$
62	$2^2 \cdot 5 \cdot 31$	$3^3 \cdot 23$	$2 \cdot 311$	$7 \cdot 89$	$2^4 \cdot 3 \cdot 13$
63	$2 \cdot 3^2 \cdot 5 \cdot 7$	8000294	$2^3 \cdot 79$	$3 \cdot 211$	$2 \cdot 317$
64	$2^7 \cdot 5$	8068580	$2 \cdot 3 \cdot 107$	8082110	$2^2 \cdot 7 \cdot 23$
65	$2 \cdot 5^2 \cdot 13$	$3 \cdot 7 \cdot 31$	$2^2 \cdot 163$	8149132	$2 \cdot 3 \cdot 109$
66	$2^2 \cdot 3 \cdot 5 \cdot 11$	8202015	$2 \cdot 331$	$3 \cdot 13 \cdot 17$	$2^3 \cdot 83$
67	$2 \cdot 5 \cdot 67$	$11 \cdot 61$	$2^5 \cdot 3 \cdot 7$	8280151	$2 \cdot 337$
68	$2^3 \cdot 5 \cdot 17$	$3 \cdot 227$	$2 \cdot 11 \cdot 31$	8344207	$2^2 \cdot 3^2 \cdot 19$
69	$2 \cdot 3 \cdot 5 \cdot 23$	8394780	$2^2 \cdot 173$	$3^2 \cdot 7 \cdot 11$	$2 \cdot 347$
70	$2^2 \cdot 5^2 \cdot 7$	8457180	$2 \cdot 3^3 \cdot 13$	$19 \cdot 37$	$2^6 \cdot 11$
71	$2 \cdot 5 \cdot 71$	$3^2 \cdot 79$	$2^3 \cdot 89$	$23 \cdot 31$	$2 \cdot 3 \cdot 7 \cdot 17$
72	$2^4 \cdot 3^2 \cdot 5$	$7 \cdot 103$	$2 \cdot 19^2$	$3 \cdot 241$	$2^2 \cdot 181$
73	$2 \cdot 5 \cdot 73$	$17 \cdot 43$	$2^2 \cdot 3 \cdot 61$	8651040	$2 \cdot 367$
74	$2^2 \cdot 5 \cdot 37$	$3 \cdot 13 \cdot 19$	$2 \cdot 7 \cdot 53$	8709888	$2^3 \cdot 3 \cdot 31$
75	$2 \cdot 3 \cdot 5^3$	8756399	$2^4 \cdot 47$	$3 \cdot 251$	$2 \cdot 13 \cdot 29$
76	$2^3 \cdot 5 \cdot 19$	8813847	$2 \cdot 3 \cdot 127$	$7 \cdot 109$	$2^2 \cdot 191$
77	$2 \cdot 5 \cdot 7 \cdot 11$	$3 \cdot 257$	$2^2 \cdot 193$	8881795	$2 \cdot 3^2 \cdot 43$
78	$2^2 \cdot 3 \cdot 5 \cdot 13$	$11 \cdot 71$	$2 \cdot 17 \cdot 23$	$3^3 \cdot 29$	$2^4 \cdot 7^2$
79	$2 \cdot 5 \cdot 79$	$7 \cdot 113$	$2^3 \cdot 3^2 \cdot 11$	$13 \cdot 61$	$2 \cdot 397$
80	$2^5 \cdot 5^2$	$3^2 \cdot 89$	$2 \cdot 401$	$11 \cdot 73$	$2^2 \cdot 3 \cdot 67$
81	$2 \cdot 3^4 \cdot 5$	9090209	$2^2 \cdot 7 \cdot 29$	$3 \cdot 271$	$2 \cdot 11 \cdot 37$
82	$2^2 \cdot 5 \cdot 41$	9143432	$2 \cdot 3 \cdot 137$	9153998	$2^3 \cdot 103$
83	$2 \cdot 5 \cdot 83$	$3 \cdot 277$	$2^6 \cdot 13$	$7^2 \cdot 17$	$2 \cdot 3 \cdot 139$
84	$2^3 \cdot 3 \cdot 5 \cdot 7$	29^2	$2 \cdot 421$	$3 \cdot 281$	$2^2 \cdot 211$
85	$2 \cdot 5^2 \cdot 17$	$23 \cdot 37$	$2^2 \cdot 3 \cdot 71$	9309490	$2 \cdot 7 \cdot 61$
86	$2^2 \cdot 5 \cdot 43$	$3 \cdot 7 \cdot 41$	$2 \cdot 431$	9360108	$2^5 \cdot 3^3$
87	$2 \cdot 3 \cdot 5 \cdot 29$	$13 \cdot 67$	$2^3 \cdot 109$	$3^2 \cdot 97$	$2 \cdot 19 \cdot 23$
88	$2^4 \cdot 5 \cdot 11$	9449759	$2 \cdot 3^2 \cdot 7^2$	9459607	$2^2 \cdot 13 \cdot 17$
89	$2 \cdot 5 \cdot 89$	$3^4 \cdot 11$	$2^2 \cdot 223$	$19 \cdot 47$	$2 \cdot 3 \cdot 149$
90	$2^2 \cdot 3^2 \cdot 5^2$	$17 \cdot 53$	$2 \cdot 11 \cdot 41$	$3 \cdot 7 \cdot 43$	$2^3 \cdot 113$
91	$2 \cdot 5 \cdot 7 \cdot 13$	9595184	$2^4 \cdot 3 \cdot 19$	$11 \cdot 83$	$2 \cdot 457$
92	$2^3 \cdot 5 \cdot 23$	$3 \cdot 307$	$2 \cdot 461$	$13 \cdot 71$	$2^2 \cdot 3 \cdot 7 \cdot 11$
93	$2 \cdot 3 \cdot 5 \cdot 31$	$7^2 \cdot 19$	$2^2 \cdot 233$	$3 \cdot 311$	$2 \cdot 467$
94	$2^2 \cdot 5 \cdot 47$	9735896	$2 \cdot 3 \cdot 157$	$23 \cdot 41$	$2^4 \cdot 59$
95	$2 \cdot 5^2 \cdot 19$	$3 \cdot 317$	$2^3 \cdot 7 \cdot 17$	9790929	$2 \cdot 3^2 \cdot 53$
96	$2^6 \cdot 3 \cdot 5$	31^2	$2 \cdot 13 \cdot 37$	$3^2 \cdot 107$	$2^2 \cdot 241$
97	$2 \cdot 5 \cdot 97$	9872192	$2^2 \cdot 3^5$	$7 \cdot 139$	$2 \cdot 487$
98	$2^2 \cdot 5 \cdot 7^2$	$3^2 \cdot 109$	$2 \cdot 491$	9925535	$2^3 \cdot 3 \cdot 41$
99	$2 \cdot 3^2 \cdot 5 \cdot 11$	9960737	$2^5 \cdot 31$	$3 \cdot 331$	$2 \cdot 7 \cdot 71$
100	$2^3 \cdot 5^3$	$7 \cdot 11 \cdot 13$	$2 \cdot 3 \cdot 167$	$17 \cdot 59$	$2^2 \cdot 251$

FACTORS AND PRIMES (Continued)

n	5	6	7	8	9
50	$5 \cdot 101$	$2 \cdot 11 \cdot 23$	$3 \cdot 13^2$	$2^2 \cdot 127$	7067178
51	$5 \cdot 103$	$2^2 \cdot 3 \cdot 43$	$11 \cdot 47$	$2 \cdot 7 \cdot 37$	$3 \cdot 173$
52	$3 \cdot 5^2 \cdot 7$	$2 \cdot 263$	$17 \cdot 31$	$2^4 \cdot 3 \cdot 11$	23^2
53	$5 \cdot 107$	$2^3 \cdot 67$	$3 \cdot 179$	$2 \cdot 269$	$7^2 \cdot 11$
54	$5 \cdot 109$	$2 \cdot 3 \cdot 7 \cdot 13$	7379873	$2^2 \cdot 137$	$3^2 \cdot 61$
55	$3 \cdot 5 \cdot 37$	$2^2 \cdot 139$	7458552	$2 \cdot 3^2 \cdot 31$	$13 \cdot 43$
56	$5 \cdot 113$	$2 \cdot 283$	$3^4 \cdot 7$	$2^3 \cdot 71$	7551123
57	$5^2 \cdot 23$	$2^6 \cdot 3^2$	7611758	$2 \cdot 17^2$	$3 \cdot 193$
58	$3^2 \cdot 5 \cdot 13$	$2 \cdot 293$	7686381	$2^2 \cdot 3 \cdot 7^2$	$19 \cdot 31$
59	$5 \cdot 7 \cdot 17$	$2^2 \cdot 149$	$3 \cdot 199$	$2 \cdot 13 \cdot 23$	7774268
60	$5 \cdot 11^2$	$2 \cdot 3 \cdot 101$	7831887	$2^5 \cdot 19$	$3 \cdot 7 \cdot 29$
61	$3 \cdot 5 \cdot 41$	$2^3 \cdot 7 \cdot 11$	7902852	$2 \cdot 3 \cdot 103$	7916906
62	5^4	$2 \cdot 313$	$3 \cdot 11 \cdot 19$	$2^2 \cdot 157$	$17 \cdot 37$
63	$5 \cdot 127$	$2^2 \cdot 3 \cdot 53$	$7^2 \cdot 13$	$2 \cdot 11 \cdot 29$	$3^2 \cdot 71$
64	$3 \cdot 5 \cdot 43$	$2 \cdot 17 \cdot 19$	8109043	$2^3 \cdot 3^4$	$11 \cdot 59$
65	$5 \cdot 131$	$2^4 \cdot 41$	$3^2 \cdot 73$	$2 \cdot 7 \cdot 47$	8188854
66	$5 \cdot 7 \cdot 19$	$2 \cdot 3^2 \cdot 37$	$23 \cdot 29$	$2^2 \cdot 167$	$3 \cdot 223$
67	$3^3 \cdot 5^2$	$2^2 \cdot 13^2$	8305887	$2 \cdot 3 \cdot 113$	$7 \cdot 97$
68	$5 \cdot 137$	$2 \cdot 7^3$	$3 \cdot 229$	$2^4 \cdot 43$	$13 \cdot 53$
69	$5 \cdot 139$	$2^3 \cdot 3 \cdot 29$	$17 \cdot 41$	$2 \cdot 349$	$3 \cdot 233$
70	$3 \cdot 5 \cdot 47$	$2 \cdot 353$	$7 \cdot 101$	$2^2 \cdot 3 \cdot 59$	8506462
71	$5 \cdot 11 \cdot 13$	$2^2 \cdot 179$	$3 \cdot 239$	$2 \cdot 359$	8567289
72	$5^2 \cdot 29$	$2 \cdot 3 \cdot 11^2$	8615344	$2^3 \cdot 7 \cdot 13$	3^6
73	$3 \cdot 5 \cdot 7^2$	$2^5 \cdot 23$	$11 \cdot 67$	$2 \cdot 3^2 \cdot 41$	8686444
74	$5 \cdot 149$	$2 \cdot 373$	$3^2 \cdot 83$	$2^2 \cdot 11 \cdot 17$	$7 \cdot 107$
75	$5 \cdot 151$	$2^2 \cdot 3^3 \cdot 7$	8790959	$2 \cdot 379$	$3 \cdot 11 \cdot 23$
76	$3^2 \cdot 5 \cdot 17$	$2 \cdot 383$	$13 \cdot 59$	$2^8 \cdot 3$	8859263
77	$5^2 \cdot 31$	$2^3 \cdot 97$	$3 \cdot 7 \cdot 37$	$2 \cdot 389$	$19 \cdot 41$
78	$5 \cdot 157$	$2 \cdot 3 \cdot 131$	8959747	$2^2 \cdot 197$	$3 \cdot 263$
79	$3 \cdot 5 \cdot 53$	$2^2 \cdot 199$	9014583	$2 \cdot 3 \cdot 7 \cdot 19$	$17 \cdot 47$
80	$5 \cdot 7 \cdot 23$	$2 \cdot 13 \cdot 31$	$3 \cdot 269$	$2^2 \cdot 101$	9079485
81	$5 \cdot 163$	$2^4 \cdot 3 \cdot 17$	$19 \cdot 43$	$2 \cdot 409$	$3^2 \cdot 7 \cdot 13$
82	$3 \cdot 5^2 \cdot 11$	$2 \cdot 7 \cdot 59$	9175055	$2^3 \cdot 3^2 \cdot 23$	9185545
83	$5 \cdot 167$	$2^2 \cdot 11 \cdot 19$	$3^3 \cdot 31$	$2 \cdot 419$	9237620
84	$5 \cdot 13^2$	$2 \cdot 3^2 \cdot 47$	$7 \cdot 11^2$	$2^4 \cdot 53$	$3 \cdot 283$
85	$3^2 \cdot 5 \cdot 19$	$2^3 \cdot 107$	9329808	$2 \cdot 3 \cdot 11 \cdot 13$	9339932
86	$5 \cdot 173$	$2 \cdot 433$	$3 \cdot 17^2$	$2^2 \cdot 7 \cdot 31$	$11 \cdot 79$
87	$5^3 \cdot 7$	$2^2 \cdot 3 \cdot 73$	9429996	$2 \cdot 439$	$3 \cdot 293$
88	$3 \cdot 5 \cdot 59$	$2 \cdot 443$	9479236	$2^3 \cdot 3 \cdot 37$	$7 \cdot 127$
89	$5 \cdot 179$	$2^7 \cdot 7$	$3 \cdot 13 \cdot 23$	$2 \cdot 449$	$29 \cdot 31$
90	$5 \cdot 181$	$2 \cdot 3 \cdot 151$	9576073	$2^2 \cdot 227$	$3^2 \cdot 101$
91	$3 \cdot 5 \cdot 61$	$2^2 \cdot 229$	$7 \cdot 131$	$2 \cdot 3^3 \cdot 17$	9633155
92	$5^2 \cdot 37$	$2 \cdot 463$	$3^2 \cdot 103$	$2^5 \cdot 29$	9680157
93	$5 \cdot 11 \cdot 17$	$2^3 \cdot 3^2 \cdot 13$	9717396	$2 \cdot 7 \cdot 67$	$3 \cdot 313$
94	$3^3 \cdot 5 \cdot 7$	$2 \cdot 11 \cdot 43$	9763500	$2^2 \cdot 3 \cdot 79$	$13 \cdot 73$
95	$5 \cdot 191$	$2^2 \cdot 239$	$3 \cdot 11 \cdot 29$	$2 \cdot 479$	$7 \cdot 137$
96	$5 \cdot 193$	$2 \cdot 3 \cdot 7 \cdot 23$	9854265	$2^3 \cdot 11^2$	$3 \cdot 17 \cdot 19$
97	$3 \cdot 5^2 \cdot 13$	$2^4 \cdot 61$	9898946	$2 \cdot 3 \cdot 163$	$11 \cdot 89$
98	$5 \cdot 197$	$2 \cdot 17 \cdot 29$	$3 \cdot 7 \cdot 47$	$2^2 \cdot 13 \cdot 19$	$23 \cdot 43$
99	$5 \cdot 199$	$2^2 \cdot 3 \cdot 83$	9986952	$2 \cdot 499$	$3^3 \cdot 37$
100	$3 \cdot 5 \cdot 67$	$2 \cdot 503$	$19 \cdot 53$	$2^4 \cdot 3^2 \cdot 7$	0038912

FACTORS AND PRIMES (Continued)

n	0	1	2	3	4
100	$2^3 \cdot 5^3$	$7 \cdot 11 \cdot 13$	$2 \cdot 3 \cdot 167$	$17 \cdot 59$	$2^2 \cdot 251$
101	$2 \cdot 5 \cdot 101$	$3 \cdot 337$	$2^2 \cdot 11 \cdot 23$	0056094	$2 \cdot 3 \cdot 13^2$
102	$2^2 \cdot 3 \cdot 5 \cdot 17$	0090257	$2 \cdot 7 \cdot 73$	$3 \cdot 11 \cdot 31$	2^{10}
103	$2 \cdot 5 \cdot 103$	0132587	$2^3 \cdot 3 \cdot 43$	0141003	$2 \cdot 11 \cdot 47$
104	$2^4 \cdot 5 \cdot 13$	$3 \cdot 347$	$2 \cdot 521$	$7 \cdot 149$	$2^2 \cdot 3^2 \cdot 29$
105	$2 \cdot 3 \cdot 5^2 \cdot 7$	0216027	$2^2 \cdot 263$	$3^4 \cdot 13$	$2 \cdot 17 \cdot 31$
106	$2^2 \cdot 5 \cdot 53$	0257154	$2 \cdot 3^2 \cdot 59$	0265333	$2^3 \cdot 7 \cdot 19$
107	$2 \cdot 5 \cdot 107$	$3^2 \cdot 7 \cdot 17$	$2^4 \cdot 67$	$29 \cdot 37$	$2 \cdot 3 \cdot 179$
108	$2^3 \cdot 3^3 \cdot 5$	$23 \cdot 47$	$2 \cdot 541$	$3 \cdot 19^2$	$2^2 \cdot 271$
109	$2 \cdot 5 \cdot 109$	0378248	$2^2 \cdot 3 \cdot 7 \cdot 13$	0386202	$2 \cdot 547$
110	$2^2 \cdot 5^2 \cdot 11$	$3 \cdot 367$	$2 \cdot 19 \cdot 29$	0425755	$2^4 \cdot 3 \cdot 23$
111	$2 \cdot 3 \cdot 5 \cdot 37$	$11 \cdot 101$	$2^3 \cdot 139$	$3 \cdot 7 \cdot 53$	$2 \cdot 557$
112	$2^5 \cdot 5 \cdot 7$	$19 \cdot 59$	$2 \cdot 3 \cdot 11 \cdot 17$	0503798	$2^2 \cdot 281$
113	$2 \cdot 5 \cdot 113$	$3 \cdot 13 \cdot 29$	$2^2 \cdot 283$	$11 \cdot 103$	$2 \cdot 3^4 \cdot 7$
114	$2^2 \cdot 3 \cdot 5 \cdot 19$	$7 \cdot 163$	$2 \cdot 571$	$3^2 \cdot 127$	$2^3 \cdot 11 \cdot 13$
115	$2 \cdot 5^2 \cdot 23$	0610753	$2^7 \cdot 3^2$	0618293	$2 \cdot 577$
116	$2^3 \cdot 5 \cdot 29$	$3^3 \cdot 43$	$2 \cdot 7 \cdot 83$	0655797	$2^2 \cdot 3 \cdot 97$
117	$2 \cdot 3^2 \cdot 5 \cdot 13$	0685569	$2^2 \cdot 293$	$3 \cdot 17 \cdot 23$	$2 \cdot 587$
118	$2^2 \cdot 5 \cdot 59$	0722499	$2 \cdot 3 \cdot 197$	$7 \cdot 13^2$	$2^5 \cdot 37$
119	$2 \cdot 5 \cdot 7 \cdot 17$	$3 \cdot 397$	$2^3 \cdot 149$	0766404	$2 \cdot 3 \cdot 199$
120	$2^4 \cdot 3 \cdot 5^2$	0795430	$2 \cdot 601$	$3 \cdot 401$	$2^2 \cdot 7 \cdot 43$
121	$2 \cdot 5 \cdot 11^2$	$7 \cdot 173$	$2^2 \cdot 3 \cdot 101$	0838608	$2 \cdot 607$
122	$2^2 \cdot 5 \cdot 61$	$3 \cdot 11 \cdot 37$	$2 \cdot 13 \cdot 47$	0874265	$2^3 \cdot 3^2 \cdot 17$
123	$2 \cdot 3 \cdot 5 \cdot 41$	0902581	$2^4 \cdot 7 \cdot 11$	$3^2 \cdot 137$	$2 \cdot 617$
124	$2^3 \cdot 5 \cdot 31$	$17 \cdot 73$	$2 \cdot 3^3 \cdot 23$	$11 \cdot 113$	$2^2 \cdot 311$
125	$2 \cdot 5^4$	$3^2 \cdot 139$	$2^2 \cdot 313$	$7 \cdot 179$	$2 \cdot 3 \cdot 11 \cdot 19$
126	$2^2 \cdot 3^2 \cdot 5 \cdot 7$	$13 \cdot 97$	$2 \cdot 631$	$3 \cdot 421$	$2^4 \cdot 79$
127	$2 \cdot 5 \cdot 127$	$31 \cdot 41$	$2^3 \cdot 3 \cdot 53$	$19 \cdot 67$	$2 \cdot 7^2 \cdot 13$
128	$2^8 \cdot 5$	$3 \cdot 7 \cdot 61$	$2 \cdot 641$	1082267	$2^2 \cdot 3 \cdot 107$
129	$2 \cdot 3 \cdot 5 \cdot 43$	1109262	$2^2 \cdot 17 \cdot 19$	$3 \cdot 431$	$2 \cdot 647$
130	$2^2 \cdot 5^2 \cdot 13$	1142773	$2 \cdot 3 \cdot 7 \cdot 31$	1149444	$2^3 \cdot 163$
131	$2 \cdot 5 \cdot 131$	$3 \cdot 19 \cdot 23$	$2^5 \cdot 41$	$13 \cdot 101$	$2 \cdot 3^2 \cdot 73$
132	$2^3 \cdot 3 \cdot 5 \cdot 11$	1209028	$2 \cdot 661$	$3^3 \cdot 7^2$	$2^2 \cdot 331$
133	$2 \cdot 5 \cdot 7 \cdot 19$	11^3	$2^3 \cdot 3^2 \cdot 37$	$31 \cdot 43$	$2 \cdot 23 \cdot 29$
134	$2^2 \cdot 5 \cdot 67$	$3^2 \cdot 149$	$2 \cdot 11 \cdot 61$	$17 \cdot 79$	$2^6 \cdot 3 \cdot 7$
135	$2 \cdot 3^3 \cdot 5^2$	$7 \cdot 193$	$2^3 \cdot 13^2$	$3 \cdot 11 \cdot 41$	$2 \cdot 677$
136	$2^4 \cdot 5 \cdot 17$	1338581	$2 \cdot 3 \cdot 227$	$29 \cdot 47$	$2^2 \cdot 11 \cdot 31$
137	$2 \cdot 5 \cdot 137$	$3 \cdot 457$	$2^2 \cdot 7^3$	1376705	$2 \cdot 3 \cdot 229$
138	$2^2 \cdot 3 \cdot 5 \cdot 23$	1401937	$2 \cdot 691$	$3 \cdot 461$	$2^3 \cdot 173$
139	$2 \cdot 5 \cdot 139$	$13 \cdot 107$	$2^4 \cdot 3 \cdot 29$	$7 \cdot 199$	$2 \cdot 17 \cdot 41$
140	$2^3 \cdot 5^2 \cdot 7$	$3 \cdot 467$	$2 \cdot 701$	$23 \cdot 61$	$2^2 \cdot 3^3 \cdot 13$
141	$2 \cdot 3 \cdot 5 \cdot 47$	$17 \cdot 83$	$2^2 \cdot 353$	$3^2 \cdot 157$	$2 \cdot 7 \cdot 101$
142	$2^2 \cdot 5 \cdot 71$	$7^2 \cdot 29$	$2 \cdot 3^2 \cdot 79$	1532049	$2^4 \cdot 89$
143	$2 \cdot 5 \cdot 11 \cdot 13$	$3^3 \cdot 53$	$2^3 \cdot 179$	1562462	$2 \cdot 3 \cdot 239$
144	$2^5 \cdot 3^2 \cdot 5$	$11 \cdot 131$	$2 \cdot 7 \cdot 103$	$3 \cdot 13 \cdot 37$	$2^2 \cdot 19^2$
145	$2 \cdot 5^2 \cdot 29$	1616674	$2^2 \cdot 3 \cdot 11^2$	1622656	$2 \cdot 727$
146	$2^2 \cdot 5 \cdot 73$	$3 \cdot 487$	$2 \cdot 17 \cdot 43$	$7 \cdot 11 \cdot 19$	$2^3 \cdot 3 \cdot 61$
147	$2 \cdot 3 \cdot 5 \cdot 7^2$	1676127	$2^6 \cdot 23$	$3 \cdot 491$	$2 \cdot 11 \cdot 67$
148	$2^3 \cdot 5 \cdot 37$	1705551	$2 \cdot 3 \cdot 13 \cdot 19$	1711412	$2^2 \cdot 7 \cdot 53$
149	$2 \cdot 5 \cdot 149$	$3 \cdot 7 \cdot 71$	$2^3 \cdot 373$	1740598	$2 \cdot 3^2 \cdot 83$
150	$2^2 \cdot 3 \cdot 5^3$	$19 \cdot 79$	$2 \cdot 751$	$3^2 \cdot 167$	$2^5 \cdot 47$

FACTORS AND PRIMES (Continued)

n	5	6	7	8	9
100	$3 \cdot 5 \cdot 67$	$2 \cdot 503$	$19 \cdot 53$	$2^4 \cdot 3^2 \cdot 7$	0038912
101	$5 \cdot 7 \cdot 29$	$2^3 \cdot 127$	$3^2 \cdot 113$	$2 \cdot 509$	0081742
102	$5^2 \cdot 41$	$2 \cdot 3^3 \cdot 19$	$13 \cdot 79$	$2^2 \cdot 257$	$3 \cdot 7^3$
103	$3^2 \cdot 5 \cdot 23$	$2^2 \cdot 7 \cdot 37$	$17 \cdot 61$	$2 \cdot 3 \cdot 173$	0166155
104	$5 \cdot 11 \cdot 19$	$2 \cdot 523$	$3 \cdot 349$	$2^3 \cdot 131$	0207755
105	$5 \cdot 211$	$2^5 \cdot 3 \cdot 11$	$7 \cdot 151$	$2 \cdot 23^2$	$3 \cdot 353$
106	$3 \cdot 5 \cdot 71$	$2 \cdot 13 \cdot 41$	$11 \cdot 97$	$2^2 \cdot 3 \cdot 89$	0289777
107	$5^2 \cdot 43$	$2^2 \cdot 269$	$3 \cdot 359$	$2 \cdot 7^2 \cdot 11$	$13 \cdot 83$
108	$5 \cdot 7 \cdot 31$	$2 \cdot 3 \cdot 181$	0362295	$2^6 \cdot 17$	$3^2 \cdot 11^2$
109	$3 \cdot 5 \cdot 73$	$2^3 \cdot 137$	0402066	$2 \cdot 3^2 \cdot 61$	$7 \cdot 157$
110	$5 \cdot 13 \cdot 17$	$2 \cdot 7 \cdot 79$	$3^3 \cdot 41$	$2^2 \cdot 277$	0449315
111	$5 \cdot 223$	$2^2 \cdot 3^2 \cdot 31$	0480532	$2 \cdot 13 \cdot 43$	$3 \cdot 373$
112	$3^2 \cdot 5^3$	$2 \cdot 563$	$7^2 \cdot 23$	$2^3 \cdot 3 \cdot 47$	0526939
113	$5 \cdot 227$	$2^4 \cdot 71$	$3 \cdot 379$	$2 \cdot 569$	$17 \cdot 67$
114	$5 \cdot 229$	$2 \cdot 3 \cdot 191$	$31 \cdot 37$	$2^2 \cdot 7 \cdot 41$	$3 \cdot 383$
115	$3 \cdot 5 \cdot 7 \cdot 11$	$2^2 \cdot 17^2$	$13 \cdot 89$	$2 \cdot 3 \cdot 193$	$19 \cdot 61$
116	$5 \cdot 233$	$2 \cdot 11 \cdot 53$	$3 \cdot 389$	$2^4 \cdot 73$	$7 \cdot 167$
117	$5^2 \cdot 47$	$2^3 \cdot 3 \cdot 7^2$	$11 \cdot 107$	$2 \cdot 19 \cdot 31$	$3^2 \cdot 131$
118	$3 \cdot 5 \cdot 79$	$2 \cdot 593$	0744507	$2^2 \cdot 3^3 \cdot 11$	$29 \cdot 41$
119	$5 \cdot 239$	$2^3 \cdot 13 \cdot 23$	$3^2 \cdot 7 \cdot 19$	$2 \cdot 599$	$11 \cdot 109$
120	$5 \cdot 241$	$2 \cdot 3^2 \cdot 67$	$17 \cdot 71$	$2^3 \cdot 151$	$3 \cdot 13 \cdot 31$
121	$3^6 \cdot 5$	$2^6 \cdot 19$	0852906	$2 \cdot 3 \cdot 7 \cdot 29$	$23 \cdot 53$
122	$5^2 \cdot 7^2$	$2 \cdot 613$	$3 \cdot 409$	$2^2 \cdot 307$	0895519
123	$5 \cdot 13 \cdot 19$	$2^2 \cdot 3 \cdot 103$	0923697	$2 \cdot 619$	$3 \cdot 7 \cdot 59$
124	$3 \cdot 5 \cdot 83$	$2 \cdot 7 \cdot 89$	$29 \cdot 43$	$2^5 \cdot 3 \cdot 13$	0965624
125	$5 \cdot 251$	$2^3 \cdot 157$	$3 \cdot 419$	$2 \cdot 17 \cdot 37$	1000257
126	$5 \cdot 11 \cdot 23$	$2 \cdot 3 \cdot 211$	$7 \cdot 181$	$2^2 \cdot 317$	$3^3 \cdot 47$
127	$3 \cdot 5^2 \cdot 17$	$2^2 \cdot 11 \cdot 29$	1061909	$2 \cdot 3^2 \cdot 71$	1068705
128	$5 \cdot 257$	$2 \cdot 643$	$3^2 \cdot 11 \cdot 13$	$2^3 \cdot 7 \cdot 23$	1102529
129	$5 \cdot 7 \cdot 37$	$2^4 \cdot 3^4$	1129400	$2 \cdot 11 \cdot 59$	$3 \cdot 433$
130	$3^2 \cdot 5 \cdot 29$	$2 \cdot 653$	1162756	$2^2 \cdot 3 \cdot 109$	$7 \cdot 11 \cdot 17$
131	$5 \cdot 263$	$2^2 \cdot 7 \cdot 47$	$3 \cdot 439$	$2 \cdot 659$	1202448
132	$5^2 \cdot 53$	$2 \cdot 3 \cdot 13 \cdot 17$	1228709	$2^4 \cdot 83$	$3 \cdot 443$
133	$3 \cdot 5 \cdot 89$	$2^3 \cdot 167$	$7 \cdot 191$	$2 \cdot 3 \cdot 223$	$13 \cdot 103$
134	$5 \cdot 269$	$2 \cdot 673$	$3 \cdot 449$	$2^2 \cdot 337$	$19 \cdot 71$
135	$5 \cdot 271$	$2^2 \cdot 3 \cdot 113$	$23 \cdot 59$	$2 \cdot 7 \cdot 97$	$3^2 \cdot 151$
136	$3 \cdot 5 \cdot 7 \cdot 13$	$2 \cdot 683$	1357685	$2^3 \cdot 3^2 \cdot 19$	37^2
137	$5^3 \cdot 11$	$2^5 \cdot 43$	$3^4 \cdot 17$	$2 \cdot 13 \cdot 53$	$7 \cdot 197$
138	$5 \cdot 277$	$2 \cdot 3^2 \cdot 7 \cdot 11$	$19 \cdot 73$	$2^3 \cdot 347$	$3 \cdot 463$
139	$3^2 \cdot 5 \cdot 31$	$2^2 \cdot 349$	$11 \cdot 127$	$2 \cdot 3 \cdot 233$	1458177
140	$5 \cdot 281$	$2 \cdot 19 \cdot 37$	$3 \cdot 7 \cdot 67$	$2^7 \cdot 11$	1489110
141	$5 \cdot 283$	$2^3 \cdot 3 \cdot 59$	$13 \cdot 109$	$2 \cdot 709$	$3 \cdot 11 \cdot 43$
142	$3 \cdot 5^2 \cdot 19$	$2 \cdot 23 \cdot 31$	1544240	$2^2 \cdot 3 \cdot 7 \cdot 17$	1550322
143	$5 \cdot 7 \cdot 41$	$2^2 \cdot 359$	$3 \cdot 479$	$2 \cdot 719$	1580608
144	$5 \cdot 17^2$	$2 \cdot 3 \cdot 241$	1604685	$2^3 \cdot 181$	$3^2 \cdot 7 \cdot 23$
145	$3 \cdot 5 \cdot 97$	$2^4 \cdot 7 \cdot 13$	$31 \cdot 47$	$2 \cdot 3^6$	1640553
146	$5 \cdot 293$	$2 \cdot 733$	$3^2 \cdot 163$	$2^2 \cdot 367$	$13 \cdot 113$
147	$5^2 \cdot 59$	$2^2 \cdot 3^2 \cdot 41$	$7 \cdot 211$	$2 \cdot 739$	$3 \cdot 17 \cdot 29$
148	$3^3 \cdot 5 \cdot 11$	$2 \cdot 743$	1723110	$2^4 \cdot 3 \cdot 31$	1728947
149	$5 \cdot 13 \cdot 23$	$2^3 \cdot 11 \cdot 17$	$3 \cdot 499$	$2 \cdot 7 \cdot 107$	1758016
150	$5 \cdot 7 \cdot 43$	$2 \cdot 3 \cdot 251$	$11 \cdot 137$	$2^2 \cdot 13 \cdot 29$	$3 \cdot 503$

FACTORS AND PRIMES (Continued)

n	0	1	2	3	4
150	$2^2 \cdot 3 \cdot 5^3$	$19 \cdot 79$	$2 \cdot 751$	$3^2 \cdot 167$	$2^5 \cdot 47$
151	$2 \cdot 5 \cdot 151$	1792645	$2^3 \cdot 3^3 \cdot 7$	$17 \cdot 89$	$2 \cdot 757$
152	$2^4 \cdot 5 \cdot 19$	$3^2 \cdot 13^2$	$2 \cdot 761$	1826999	$2^2 \cdot 3 \cdot 127$
153	$2 \cdot 3^2 \cdot 5 \cdot 17$	1849752	$2^2 \cdot 383$	$3 \cdot 7 \cdot 73$	$2 \cdot 13 \cdot 59$
154	$2^2 \cdot 5 \cdot 7 \cdot 11$	$23 \cdot 67$	$2 \cdot 3 \cdot 257$	1883659	$2^3 \cdot 193$
155	$2 \cdot 5^2 \cdot 31$	$3 \cdot 11 \cdot 47$	$2^4 \cdot 97$	1911715	$2 \cdot 3 \cdot 7 \cdot 37$
156	$2^3 \cdot 3 \cdot 5 \cdot 13$	$7 \cdot 223$	$2 \cdot 11 \cdot 71$	$3 \cdot 521$	$2^2 \cdot 17 \cdot 23$
157	$2 \cdot 5 \cdot 157$	1961762	$2^2 \cdot 3 \cdot 131$	$11^2 \cdot 13$	$2 \cdot 787$
158	$2^2 \cdot 5 \cdot 79$	$3 \cdot 17 \cdot 31$	$2 \cdot 7 \cdot 113$	1994809	$2^4 \cdot 3^2 \cdot 11$
159	$2 \cdot 3 \cdot 5 \cdot 53$	$37 \cdot 43$	$2^3 \cdot 199$	$3^3 \cdot 59$	$2 \cdot 797$
160	$2^6 \cdot 5^2$	2043913	$2 \cdot 3^2 \cdot 89$	$7 \cdot 229$	$2^2 \cdot 401$
161	$2 \cdot 5 \cdot 7 \cdot 23$	$3^2 \cdot 179$	$2^2 \cdot 13 \cdot 31$	2076344	$2 \cdot 3 \cdot 269$
162	$2 \cdot 3^4 \cdot 5$	2097830	$2 \cdot 811$	$3 \cdot 541$	$2^3 \cdot 7 \cdot 29$
163	$2 \cdot 5 \cdot 163$	$7 \cdot 233$	$2^5 \cdot 3 \cdot 17$	$23 \cdot 71$	$2 \cdot 19 \cdot 43$
164	$2^3 \cdot 5 \cdot 41$	$3 \cdot 547$	$2 \cdot 821$	$31 \cdot 53$	$2^2 \cdot 3 \cdot 137$
165	$2 \cdot 3 \cdot 5^2 \cdot 11$	$13 \cdot 127$	$2^2 \cdot 7 \cdot 59$	$3 \cdot 19 \cdot 29$	$2 \cdot 827$
166	$2^2 \cdot 5 \cdot 83$	$11 \cdot 151$	$2 \cdot 3 \cdot 277$	2208922	$2^7 \cdot 13$
167	$2 \cdot 5 \cdot 167$	$3 \cdot 557$	$2^3 \cdot 11 \cdot 19$	$7 \cdot 239$	$2 \cdot 3^3 \cdot 31$
168	$2^4 \cdot 3 \cdot 5 \cdot 7$	41^2	$2 \cdot 29^2$	$3^2 \cdot 11 \cdot 17$	$2^2 \cdot 421$
169	$2 \cdot 5 \cdot 13^2$	$19 \cdot 89$	$2^2 \cdot 3^2 \cdot 47$	2286570	$2 \cdot 7 \cdot 11^2$
170	$2^2 \cdot 5^2 \cdot 17$	$3^5 \cdot 7$	$2 \cdot 23 \cdot 37$	$13 \cdot 131$	$2^3 \cdot 3 \cdot 71$
171	$2 \cdot 3^2 \cdot 5 \cdot 19$	$29 \cdot 59$	$2^4 \cdot 107$	$3 \cdot 571$	$2 \cdot 857$
172	$2^3 \cdot 5 \cdot 43$	2357809	$2 \cdot 3 \cdot 7 \cdot 41$	2362853	$2^2 \cdot 431$
173	$2 \cdot 5 \cdot 173$	$3 \cdot 577$	$2^2 \cdot 433$	2387986	$2 \cdot 3 \cdot 17^2$
174	$2^2 \cdot 3 \cdot 5 \cdot 29$	2407988	$2 \cdot 13 \cdot 67$	$3 \cdot 7 \cdot 83$	$2^4 \cdot 109$
175	$2 \cdot 5^3 \cdot 7$	$17 \cdot 103$	$2^3 \cdot 3 \cdot 73$	2437819	$2 \cdot 877$
176	$2^5 \cdot 5 \cdot 11$	$3 \cdot 587$	$2 \cdot 881$	$41 \cdot 43$	$2^2 \cdot 3^2 \cdot 7^2$
177	$2 \cdot 3 \cdot 5 \cdot 59$	$7 \cdot 11 \cdot 23$	$2^2 \cdot 443$	$3^2 \cdot 197$	$2 \cdot 887$
178	$2^2 \cdot 5 \cdot 89$	$13 \cdot 137$	$2 \cdot 3^4 \cdot 11$	2511513	$2^3 \cdot 223$
179	$2 \cdot 5 \cdot 179$	$3^2 \cdot 199$	$2^8 \cdot 7$	$11 \cdot 163$	$2 \cdot 3 \cdot 13 \cdot 23$
180	$2^3 \cdot 3^2 \cdot 5^2$	2555137	$2 \cdot 17 \cdot 53$	$3 \cdot 601$	$2^2 \cdot 11 \cdot 41$
181	$2 \cdot 5 \cdot 181$	2579185	$2^2 \cdot 3 \cdot 151$	$7^2 \cdot 37$	$2 \cdot 907$
182	$2^2 \cdot 5 \cdot 7 \cdot 13$	$3 \cdot 607$	$2 \cdot 911$	2607867	$2^5 \cdot 3 \cdot 19$
183	$2 \cdot 3 \cdot 5 \cdot 61$	2626883	$2^3 \cdot 229$	$3 \cdot 13 \cdot 47$	$2 \cdot 7 \cdot 131$
184	$2^4 \cdot 5 \cdot 23$	$7 \cdot 263$	$2 \cdot 3 \cdot 307$	$19 \cdot 97$	$2^2 \cdot 461$
185	$2 \cdot 5^2 \cdot 37$	$3 \cdot 617$	$2^2 \cdot 463$	$17 \cdot 109$	$2 \cdot 3^2 \cdot 103$
186	$2^2 \cdot 3 \cdot 5 \cdot 31$	2697464	$2 \cdot 7^2 \cdot 19$	$3^4 \cdot 23$	$2^3 \cdot 233$
187	$2 \cdot 5 \cdot 11 \cdot 17$	2720738	$2^4 \cdot 3^2 \cdot 13$	2725378	$2 \cdot 937$
188	$2^3 \cdot 5 \cdot 47$	$3^2 \cdot 11 \cdot 19$	$2 \cdot 941$	$7 \cdot 269$	$2^2 \cdot 3 \cdot 157$
189	$2 \cdot 3^3 \cdot 5 \cdot 7$	$31 \cdot 61$	$2^2 \cdot 11 \cdot 43$	$3 \cdot 631$	$2 \cdot 947$
190	$2^2 \cdot 5^2 \cdot 19$	2789821	$2 \cdot 3 \cdot 317$	$11 \cdot 173$	$2^4 \cdot 7 \cdot 17$
191	$2 \cdot 5 \cdot 191$	$3 \cdot 7^2 \cdot 13$	$2^3 \cdot 239$	2817150	$2 \cdot 3 \cdot 11 \cdot 29$
192	$2^7 \cdot 3 \cdot 5$	$17 \cdot 113$	$2 \cdot 31^2$	$3 \cdot 641$	$2^2 \cdot 13 \cdot 37$
193	$2 \cdot 5 \cdot 193$	2857823	$2^2 \cdot 3 \cdot 7 \cdot 23$	2862319	$2 \cdot 967$
194	$2^2 \cdot 5 \cdot 97$	$3 \cdot 647$	$2 \cdot 971$	$29 \cdot 67$	$2^3 \cdot 3^5$
195	$2 \cdot 3 \cdot 5^2 \cdot 13$	2902573	$2^5 \cdot 61$	$3^2 \cdot 7 \cdot 31$	$2 \cdot 977$
196	$2 \cdot 5 \cdot 7^2$	$37 \cdot 53$	$2 \cdot 3^2 \cdot 109$	$13 \cdot 151$	$2^2 \cdot 491$
197	$2 \cdot 5 \cdot 197$	$3^3 \cdot 73$	$2^2 \cdot 17 \cdot 29$	2951271	$2 \cdot 3 \cdot 7 \cdot 47$
198	$2^2 \cdot 3^2 \cdot 5 \cdot 11$	$7 \cdot 283$	$2 \cdot 991$	$3 \cdot 661$	$2^6 \cdot 31$
199	$2 \cdot 5 \cdot 199$	$11 \cdot 181$	$2^3 \cdot 3 \cdot 83$	2995073	$2 \cdot 997$
200	$2^4 \cdot 5^3$	$3 \cdot 23 \cdot 29$	$2 \cdot 7 \cdot 11 \cdot 13$	3016809	$2^2 \cdot 3 \cdot 167$

FACTORS AND PRIMES (Continued)

n	5	6	7	8	9
150	$5 \cdot 7 \cdot 43$	$2 \cdot 3 \cdot 251$	$11 \cdot 137$	$2^2 \cdot 13 \cdot 29$	$3 \cdot 503$
151	$3 \cdot 5 \cdot 101$	$2^2 \cdot 379$	$37 \cdot 41$	$2 \cdot 3 \cdot 11 \cdot 23$	$7^2 \cdot 31$
152	$5^2 \cdot 61$	$2 \cdot 7 \cdot 109$	$3 \cdot 509$	$2^3 \cdot 191$	$11 \cdot 139$
153	$5 \cdot 307$	$2^9 \cdot 3$	$29 \cdot 53$	$2 \cdot 769$	$3^4 \cdot 19$
154	$3 \cdot 5 \cdot 103$	$2 \cdot 773$	$7 \cdot 13 \cdot 17$	$2^2 \cdot 3^2 \cdot 43$	1900514
155	$5 \cdot 311$	$2^2 \cdot 389$	$3^2 \cdot 173$	$2 \cdot 19 \cdot 41$	1928461
156	$5 \cdot 313$	$2 \cdot 3^3 \cdot 29$	1950690	$2^5 \cdot 7^2$	$3 \cdot 523$
157	$3^2 \cdot 5^2 \cdot 7$	$2^3 \cdot 197$	$19 \cdot 83$	$2 \cdot 3 \cdot 263$	1983821
158	$5 \cdot 317$	$2 \cdot 13 \cdot 61$	$3 \cdot 23^2$	$2^2 \cdot 397$	$7 \cdot 227$
159	$5 \cdot 11 \cdot 29$	$2^3 \cdot 3 \cdot 7 \cdot 19$	2033049	$2 \cdot 17 \cdot 47$	$3 \cdot 13 \cdot 41$
160	$3 \cdot 5 \cdot 107$	$2 \cdot 11 \cdot 73$	2060159	$2^3 \cdot 3 \cdot 67$	2065560
161	$5 \cdot 17 \cdot 19$	$2^4 \cdot 101$	$3 \cdot 7^2 \cdot 11$	$2 \cdot 809$	2092468
162	$5^2 \cdot 13$	$2 \cdot 3 \cdot 271$	2113876	$2^2 \cdot 11 \cdot 37$	$3^2 \cdot 181$
163	$3 \cdot 5 \cdot 109$	$2^2 \cdot 409$	2140487	$2 \cdot 3^2 \cdot 7 \cdot 13$	$11 \cdot 149$
164	$5 \cdot 7 \cdot 47$	$2 \cdot 823$	$3^3 \cdot 61$	$2^4 \cdot 103$	$17 \cdot 97$
165	$5 \cdot 331$	$2^3 \cdot 3^2 \cdot 23$	2193225	$2 \cdot 829$	$3 \cdot 7 \cdot 79$
166	$3^2 \cdot 5 \cdot 37$	$2 \cdot 7^2 \cdot 17$	2219356	$2^2 \cdot 3 \cdot 139$	2224563
167	$5^2 \cdot 67$	$2^2 \cdot 419$	$3 \cdot 13 \cdot 43$	$2 \cdot 839$	$23 \cdot 73$
168	$5 \cdot 337$	$2 \cdot 3 \cdot 281$	$7 \cdot 241$	$2^3 \cdot 211$	$3 \cdot 563$
169	$3 \cdot 5 \cdot 113$	$2^5 \cdot 53$	2296818	$2 \cdot 3 \cdot 283$	2301934
170	$5 \cdot 11 \cdot 31$	$2 \cdot 853$	$3 \cdot 569$	$2^2 \cdot 7 \cdot 61$	2327421
171	$5 \cdot 7^3$	$2^2 \cdot 3 \cdot 11 \cdot 13$	$17 \cdot 101$	$2 \cdot 859$	$3^2 \cdot 191$
172	$3 \cdot 5^2 \cdot 23$	$2 \cdot 863$	$11 \cdot 157$	$2^6 \cdot 3^3$	$7 \cdot 13 \cdot 19$
173	$5 \cdot 347$	$2^3 \cdot 7 \cdot 31$	$3^2 \cdot 193$	$2 \cdot 11 \cdot 79$	$37 \cdot 47$
174	$5 \cdot 349$	$2 \cdot 3^2 \cdot 97$	2422929	$2^2 \cdot 19 \cdot 23$	$3 \cdot 11 \cdot 53$
175	$3^2 \cdot 5 \cdot 13$	$2^2 \cdot 439$	$7 \cdot 251$	$2 \cdot 3 \cdot 293$	2452658
176	$5 \cdot 353$	$2 \cdot 883$	$3 \cdot 19 \cdot 31$	$2^3 \cdot 13 \cdot 17$	$29 \cdot 61$
177	$5^2 \cdot 71$	$2^4 \cdot 3 \cdot 37$	2496874	$2 \cdot 7 \cdot 127$	$3 \cdot 593$
178	$3 \cdot 5 \cdot 7 \cdot 17$	$2 \cdot 19 \cdot 47$	2521246	$2^3 \cdot 3 \cdot 149$	2526103
179	$5 \cdot 359$	$2^2 \cdot 449$	$3 \cdot 599$	$2 \cdot 29 \cdot 31$	$7 \cdot 257$
180	$5 \cdot 19^2$	$2 \cdot 3 \cdot 7 \cdot 43$	$13 \cdot 139$	$2^4 \cdot 113$	$3^3 \cdot 67$
181	$3 \cdot 5 \cdot 11^2$	$2^3 \cdot 227$	$23 \cdot 79$	$2 \cdot 3^2 \cdot 101$	$17 \cdot 107$
182	$5^2 \cdot 73$	$2 \cdot 11 \cdot 83$	$3^2 \cdot 7 \cdot 29$	$2^2 \cdot 457$	$31 \cdot 59$
183	$5 \cdot 367$	$2^2 \cdot 3^2 \cdot 17$	$11 \cdot 167$	$2 \cdot 919$	$3 \cdot 613$
184	$3^2 \cdot 5 \cdot 41$	$2 \cdot 13 \cdot 71$	2664669	$2^3 \cdot 3 \cdot 7 \cdot 11$	43^2
185	$5 \cdot 7 \cdot 53$	$2^6 \cdot 29$	$3 \cdot 619$	$2 \cdot 929$	$11 \cdot 13^2$
186	$5 \cdot 373$	$2 \cdot 3 \cdot 311$	2711443	$2^2 \cdot 467$	$3 \cdot 7 \cdot 89$
187	$3 \cdot 5^4$	$2^2 \cdot 7 \cdot 67$	2734643	$2 \cdot 3 \cdot 313$	2739268
188	$5 \cdot 13 \cdot 29$	$2 \cdot 23 \cdot 41$	$3 \cdot 17 \cdot 37$	$2^5 \cdot 59$	2762320
189	$5 \cdot 379$	$2^3 \cdot 3 \cdot 79$	$7 \cdot 271$	$2 \cdot 13 \cdot 73$	$3^2 \cdot 211$
190	$3 \cdot 5 \cdot 127$	$2 \cdot 953$	2803507	$2^2 \cdot 3^2 \cdot 53$	$23 \cdot 83$
191	$5 \cdot 383$	$2^2 \cdot 479$	$3^3 \cdot 71$	$2 \cdot 7 \cdot 137$	$19 \cdot 101$
192	$5^2 \cdot 7 \cdot 11$	$2 \cdot 3^2 \cdot 107$	$41 \cdot 47$	$2^3 \cdot 241$	$3 \cdot 643$
193	$3^2 \cdot 5 \cdot 43$	$2^4 \cdot 11^2$	$13 \cdot 149$	$2 \cdot 3 \cdot 17 \cdot 19$	$7 \cdot 277$
194	$5 \cdot 389$	$2 \cdot 7 \cdot 139$	$3 \cdot 11 \cdot 59$	$2^2 \cdot 487$	2898118
195	$5 \cdot 17 \cdot 23$	$2^2 \cdot 3 \cdot 163$	$19 \cdot 103$	$2 \cdot 11 \cdot 89$	$3 \cdot 653$
196	$3 \cdot 5 \cdot 131$	$2 \cdot 983$	$7 \cdot 281$	$2^4 \cdot 3 \cdot 41$	$11 \cdot 179$
197	$5^2 \cdot 79$	$2^3 \cdot 13 \cdot 19$	$3 \cdot 659$	$2 \cdot 23 \cdot 43$	2964458
198	$5 \cdot 397$	$2 \cdot 3 \cdot 331$	2981979	$2^2 \cdot 7 \cdot 71$	$3^2 \cdot 13 \cdot 17$
199	$3 \cdot 5 \cdot 7 \cdot 19$	$2^2 \cdot 499$	3003781	$2 \cdot 3^3 \cdot 37$	3008128
200	$5 \cdot 401$	$2 \cdot 17 \cdot 59$	$3^2 \cdot 223$	$2^3 \cdot 251$	$7^2 \cdot 41$

EXTENDED TABLES OF FACTORS AND PRIMES

The following procedure makes possible the determination of a number between 2009 and 19,949 as being either prime, or if not, what its factors will be. It is herewith included with the kind permission of its author, Professor Leonard Caners.

The following symbols will be used:

N is the number whose factors, if any, are to be determined.
A is N with the last digit dropped. Thus if $N = 17,873$, $A = 1787$.
R is the range and is the integral part of the square root of N with its last two digits dropped. Thus R of $17,873 = 13$.
K is the key number and is found in the table below.
P_1 is a possible factor corresponding to K.
The twin series are given in the table for the sake of completeness but are not written down in actual practice.
There are two steps as outlined below.

Step I

N	K	P_1	Series	Procedure
Any number ending in 1, 3, 7, or 9, within limits stated above	$A - R$	$10R +$ last digit	$K + n; P_1 - 10n$ $n = 0, 1, \ldots, 2R + 1$	Beginning with K read table of Factors and Primes from left to right and look for corresponding possible factors

Step II

N ending in	K	P_1	Series	Procedure
1	$(A - 2) - 3R$	$10R + 7$	$K + 3n; P_1 - 10n$ $n = 0, 1, \ldots, 2R + 1$	Same as in Step I except that only every *third* entry in table of Factors and Primes is examined for corresponding possible factors
3	$A - 3R$	$10R + 1$	$n = 0, 1, \ldots, 2R + 1$	
7	$(A - 2) - 3R$	$10R + 9$	$n = 0, 1, \ldots, 2R + 1$	
9	$A - 3R$	$10R + 3$	$n = 0, 1, \ldots, 2R + 1$	

As an example consider 7519. Using tables on preceding pages proceed as follows:

Step I

From Table $N = 7519$; $A = 751$; $R = 8$, $K = 743$; $P_1 = 89$ and the series obtained:

743	89
744	79
745	69
746	59
—	—
751	9
752	1
753	11
—	—
760	81

EXTENDED TABLES OF FACTORS AND PRIMES (Continued)

Examining the Table of Factors and Primes beginning with 743 note whether 743 has 89 as a factor; whether 744 has 79 as a factor, etc. Then continue to read from left to right keeping in mind the possible factors 69, 59, . . . 81.

Since none are found one concludes that 7519 has no factors within the given range ending in 9 or 1.

Step II

From Table $K = 727$ and $P_1 = 83$; the series obtained is:

727	83
730	73
733	63
—	—
751	3
754	7
—	—
778	87

Proceed exactly as in Step I. Begin with 727 and note whether it has 83 as a factor. Thereafter examine every *third* entry for the remaining corresponding possible factors 73, 63 . . . 3, 7, . . . 87. Since 730 yields the factor 73 one concludes that 73 is the factor of 7519. By division $7519 = 73 \times 103$. Had no factor been found in either Step I or Step II the conclusion would be that the number under consideration was prime.

Proof for Step I

Let N end in 1. Then, if N has a factor ending in 1, write

$$(10a + 1)(10b + 1) = N = 10A + 1$$
$$10ab + a + b = A$$

or

$$b(10a + 1) = (A - a)$$

This proves that any factor $10a + 1$ of N is also a factor of $A - a$. Let $a = (R - n)$, then $(10a + 1)$ becomes $(10R + 1) - 10n$ and $(A - a)$ becomes $(A - R) + n$, i.e., $P_1 - 10n$ and $K + n$ respectively as given in the table. Since $P_1 - 10n$ becomes a number ending in 9 when $P_1 < 10n$, all possible factors ending in 9 are also provided for.

The proof for Step II is similar. For possible factors ending in 3 or 7 write

$$(10a + 7)(10b + 3) = N = 10A + 1.$$

By identical reasoning this results in $P_1 - 10n$ and $K + 3n$ respectively given in the table. This completes the proof for numbers ending in 1.

Identical reasoning establishes the key numbers and series for ending in 3, 7, or 9.

A separate table giving primes from 1 to 100,000 is included on pages 172 to 179.

Numerical Tables

FACTORIALS, EXACT VALUES

n	$n!$	n	$n!$
1	1	11	399 16800
2	2	12	4790 01600
3	6	13	62270 20800
4	24	14	8 71782 91200
5	120	15	130 76743 68000
6	720	16	2092 27898 88000
7	5040	17	35568 74280 96000
8	40320	18	6 40237 37057 28000
9	3 62880	19	121 64510 04088 32000
10	36 28800	20	2432 90200 81766 40000

FACTORIALS AND THEIR COMMON LOGARITHMS

The product $n \times (n - 1) \times (n - 2) \times \cdots \times 1$ is called factorial n, expressed as $n!$ For example: *factorial* $5 = 5! = 5 \times 4 \times 3 \times 2 \times 1 = 120$. Factorials are very often met with in series. For purposes of computation in such cases the table giving the values of the factorials and of their logarithms for numbers from 1 to 100 is provided. The values of the factorials are expressed exponentially to 5 significant figures.

The following table gives the reciprocals of the factorials and their logarithms for numbers from 1 to 100.

Above is a short table giving the exact values of the factorials of the numbers from 1 to 20.

FACTORIALS AND THEIR COMMON LOGARITHMS

n	$n!$	$\log n!$	n	$n!$	$\log n!$
			50	3.0414×10^{64}	64.48307
1	1.0000	0.00000	51	1.5511×10^{66}	66.19065
2	2.0000	0.30103	52	8.0658×10^{67}	67.90665
3	6.0000	0.77815	53	4.2749×10^{69}	69.63092
4	2.4000×10	1.38021	54	2.3084×10^{71}	71.36332
5	1.2000×10^2	2.07918	55	1.2696×10^{73}	73.10368
6	7.2000×10^2	2.85733	56	7.1100×10^{74}	74.85187
7	5.0400×10^3	3.70243	57	4.0527×10^{76}	76.60774
8	4.0320×10^4	4.60552	58	2.3506×10^{78}	78.37117
9	3.6288×10^5	5.55976	59	1.3868×10^{80}	80.14202
10	3.6288×10^6	6.55976	60	8.3210×10^{81}	81.92017
11	3.9917×10^7	7.60116	61	5.0758×10^{83}	83.70550
12	4.7900×10^8	8.68034	62	3.1470×10^{85}	85.49790
13	6.2270×10^9	9.79428	63	1.9826×10^{87}	87.29724
14	8.7178×10^{10}	10.94041	64	1.2689×10^{89}	89.10342
15	1.3077×10^{12}	12.11650	65	8.2477×10^{90}	90.91633
16	2.0923×10^{13}	13.32062	66	5.4434×10^{92}	92.73587
17	3.5569×10^{14}	14.55107	67	3.6471×10^{94}	94.56195
18	6.4024×10^{15}	15.80634	68	2.4800×10^{96}	96.39446
19	1.2165×10^{17}	17.08509	69	1.7112×10^{98}	98.23331
20	2.4329×10^{18}	18.38612	70	1.1979×10^{100}	100.07841
21	5.1091×10^{19}	19.70834	71	8.5048×10^{101}	101.92966
22	1.1240×10^{21}	21.05077	72	6.1234×10^{103}	103.78700
23	2.5852×10^{22}	22.41249	73	4.4701×10^{105}	105.65032
24	6.2045×10^{23}	23.79271	74	3.3079×10^{107}	107.51955
25	1.5511×10^{25}	25.19065	75	2.4809×10^{109}	109.39461
26	4.0329×10^{26}	26.60562	76	1.8855×10^{111}	111.27543
27	1.0889×10^{28}	28.03698	77	1.4518×10^{113}	113.16192
28	3.0489×10^{29}	29.48414	78	1.1324×10^{115}	115.05401
29	8.8418×10^{30}	30.94654	79	8.9462×10^{116}	116.95164
30	2.6525×10^{32}	32.42366	80	7.1569×10^{118}	118.85473
31	8.2228×10^{33}	33.91502	81	5.7971×10^{120}	120.76321
32	2.6313×10^{35}	35.42017	82	4.7536×10^{122}	122.67703
33	8.6833×10^{36}	36.93869	83	3.9455×10^{124}	124.59610
34	2.9523×10^{38}	38.47016	84	3.3142×10^{126}	126.52038
35	1.0333×10^{40}	40.01423	85	2.8171×10^{128}	128.44980
36	3.7199×10^{41}	41.57054	86	2.4227×10^{130}	130.38430
37	1.3764×10^{43}	43.13874	87	2.1078×10^{132}	132.32382
38	5.2302×10^{44}	44.71852	88	1.8548×10^{134}	134.26830
39	2.0398×10^{46}	46.30959	89	1.6508×10^{136}	136.21769
40	8.1592×10^{47}	47.91165	90	1.4857×10^{138}	138.17194
41	3.3453×10^{49}	49.52443	91	1.3520×10^{140}	140.13098
42	1.4050×10^{51}	51.14768	92	1.2438×10^{142}	142.09476
43	6.0415×10^{52}	52.78115	93	1.1568×10^{144}	144.06325
44	2.6583×10^{54}	54.42460	94	1.0874×10^{146}	146.03638
45	1.1962×10^{56}	56.07781	95	1.0330×10^{148}	148.01410
46	5.5026×10^{57}	57.74057	96	9.9168×10^{149}	149.99637
47	2.5862×10^{59}	59.41267	97	9.6193×10^{151}	151.98314
48	1.2414×10^{61}	61.09391	98	9.4269×10^{153}	153.97437
49	6.0828×10^{62}	62.78410	99	9.3326×10^{155}	155.97000
50	3.0414×10^{64}	64.48307	100	9.3326×10^{157}	157.97000

$$n! = \left(\frac{n}{e}\right)^n \sqrt{2\pi n} + h; \; n = 1, 2, 3, \ldots \left[0 < \frac{h}{n!} < \frac{1}{12n}\right]$$

$$\lim_{n \to \infty} \frac{n! e^n}{n^{n+\frac{1}{2}}} = \sqrt{2\pi} \qquad \lim_{n \to \infty} \frac{(n!)^{\frac{1}{n}}}{n} = \frac{1}{e}$$

RECIPROCALS OF FACTORIALS AND THEIR COMMON LOGARITHMS

n	$1/n!$	$\log(1/n!)$	n	$1/n!$	$\log(1/n!)$
1	$1.$	$.00000$	51	$.64470 \times 10^{-66}$	$\overline{67}.80935$
2	0.5	$\overline{1}.69897$	52	$.12398 \times 10^{-67}$	$\overline{68}.09335$
3	$.16667$	$\overline{1}.22185$	53	$.23392 \times 10^{-69}$	$\overline{70}.36908$
*4	$.41667 \times 10^{-1}$	$\overline{2}.61979$	54	$.43319 \times 10^{-71}$	$\overline{72}.63668$
5	$.83333 \times 10^{-2}$	$\overline{3}.92082$	55	$.78762 \times 10^{-73}$	$\overline{74}.89632$
6	$.13889 \times 10^{-2}$	$\overline{3}.14267$	56	$.14065 \times 10^{-74}$	$\overline{75}.14813$
7	$.19841 \times 10^{-3}$	$\overline{4}.29757$	57	$.24675 \times 10^{-76}$	$\overline{77}.39226$
8	$.24802 \times 10^{-4}$	$\overline{5}.39448$	58	$.42543 \times 10^{-78}$	$\overline{79}.62883$
9	$.27557 \times 10^{-5}$	$\overline{6}.44024$	59	$.72107 \times 10^{-80}$	$\overline{81}.85798$
10	$.27557 \times 10^{-6}$	$\overline{7}.44024$	60	$.12018 \times 10^{-81}$	$\overline{82}.07983$
11	$.25052 \times 10^{-7}$	$\overline{8}.39884$	61	$.19701 \times 10^{-83}$	$\overline{84}.29450$
12	$.20877 \times 10^{-8}$	$\overline{9}.31966$	62	$.31776 \times 10^{-85}$	$\overline{86}.50210$
13	$.16059 \times 10^{-9}$	$\overline{10}.20572$	63	$.50439 \times 10^{-87}$	$\overline{88}.70276$
14	$.11471 \times 10^{-10}$	$\overline{11}.05959$	64	$.78810 \times 10^{-89}$	$\overline{90}.89658$
15	$.76472 \times 10^{-12}$	$\overline{13}.88350$	65	$.12125 \times 10^{-90}$	$\overline{91}.08367$
16	$.47795 \times 10^{-13}$	$\overline{14}.67938$	66	$.18371 \times 10^{-92}$	$\overline{93}.26413$
17	$.28115 \times 10^{-14}$	$\overline{15}.44893$	67	$.27419 \times 10^{-94}$	$\overline{95}.43805$
18	$.15619 \times 10^{-15}$	$\overline{16}.19366$	68	$.40322 \times 10^{-96}$	$\overline{97}.60554$
19	$.82206 \times 10^{-17}$	$\overline{18}.91491$	69	$.58438 \times 10^{-98}$	$\overline{99}.76669$
20	$.41103 \times 10^{-18}$	$\overline{19}.61388$	70	$.83482 \times 10^{-100}$	$\overline{101}.92159$
21	$.19573 \times 10^{-19}$	$\overline{20}.29166$	71	$.11758 \times 10^{-101}$	$\overline{102}.07034$
22	$.88968 \times 10^{-21}$	$\overline{22}.94923$	72	$.16331 \times 10^{-103}$	$\overline{104}.21300$
23	$.38682 \times 10^{-22}$	$\overline{23}.58751$	73	$.22371 \times 10^{-105}$	$\overline{106}.34968$
24	$.16117 \times 10^{-23}$	$\overline{24}.20729$	74	$.30231 \times 10^{-107}$	$\overline{108}.48045$
25	$.64470 \times 10^{-25}$	$\overline{26}.80935$	75	$.40308 \times 10^{-109}$	$\overline{110}.60539$
26	$.24796 \times 10^{-26}$	$\overline{27}.39438$	76	$.53036 \times 10^{-111}$	$\overline{112}.72457$
27	$.91837 \times 10^{-28}$	$\overline{29}.96302$	77	$.68879 \times 10^{-113}$	$\overline{114}.83808$
28	$.32799 \times 10^{-29}$	$\overline{30}.51586$	78	$.88306 \times 10^{-115}$	$\overline{116}.94599$
29	$.11310 \times 10^{-30}$	$\overline{31}.05346$	79	$.11178 \times 10^{-116}$	$\overline{117}.04836$
30	$.37700 \times 10^{-32}$	$\overline{33}.57634$	80	$.13972 \times 10^{-118}$	$\overline{119}.14527$
31	$.12161 \times 10^{-33}$	$\overline{34}.08498$	81	$.17250 \times 10^{-120}$	$\overline{121}.23679$
32	$.38004 \times 10^{-35}$	$\overline{36}.57983$	82	$.21036 \times 10^{-122}$	$\overline{123}.32297$
33	$.11516 \times 10^{-36}$	$\overline{37}.06131$	83	$.25345 \times 10^{-124}$	$\overline{125}.40390$
34	$.33872 \times 10^{-38}$	$\overline{39}.52984$	84	$.30173 \times 10^{-126}$	$\overline{127}.47962$
35	$.96776 \times 10^{-40}$	$\overline{41}.98577$	85	$.35497 \times 10^{-128}$	$\overline{129}.55020$
36	$.26882 \times 10^{-41}$	$\overline{42}.42946$	86	$.41276 \times 10^{-130}$	$\overline{131}.61570$
37	$.72655 \times 10^{-43}$	$\overline{44}.86126$	87	$.47444 \times 10^{-132}$	$\overline{133}.67618$
38	$.19120 \times 10^{-44}$	$\overline{45}.28148$	88	$.53913 \times 10^{-134}$	$\overline{135}.73170$
39	$.49025 \times 10^{-46}$	$\overline{47}.69041$	89	$.60577 \times 10^{-136}$	$\overline{137}.78231$
40	$.12256 \times 10^{-47}$	$\overline{48}.08835$	90	$.67308 \times 10^{-138}$	$\overline{139}.82806$
41	$.29893 \times 10^{-49}$	$\overline{50}.47557$	91	$.73964 \times 10^{-140}$	$\overline{141}.86902$
42	$.71174 \times 10^{-51}$	$\overline{52}.85232$	92	$.80396 \times 10^{-142}$	$\overline{143}.90524$
43	$.16552 \times 10^{-52}$	$\overline{53}.21885$	93	$.86447 \times 10^{-144}$	$\overline{145}.93675$
44	$.37618 \times 10^{-54}$	$\overline{55}.57540$	94	$.91965 \times 10^{-146}$	$\overline{147}.96362$
45	$.83597 \times 10^{-56}$	$\overline{57}.92219$	95	$.96806 \times 10^{-148}$	$\overline{149}.98590$
46	$.18173 \times 10^{-57}$	$\overline{58}.25943$	96	$.10084 \times 10^{-149}$	$\overline{150}.00363$
47	$.38666 \times 10^{-59}$	$\overline{60}.58733$	97	$.10396 \times 10^{-151}$	$\overline{152}.01686$
48	$.80555 \times 10^{-61}$	$\overline{62}.90609$	98	$.10608 \times 10^{-153}$	$\overline{154}.02563$
49	$.16440 \times 10^{-62}$	$\overline{63}.21590$	99	$.10715 \times 10^{-155}$	$\overline{156}.03000$
50	$.32879 \times 10^{-64}$	$\overline{65}.51693$	100	$.10715 \times 10^{-157}$	$\overline{158}.03000$

* For example $\log \dfrac{1}{4!} = \overline{2}.61979 = .61979 - 2 = 8.61979 - 10.$

POSITIONAL NOTATION

In our ordinary system of writing numbers, the value of any digit depends on its position in the number. The value of a digit in any position is ten times the value of the same digit one position to the right, or one-tenth the value of the same digit one position to the left. Thus, for example,

$$173.246 = 1 \times 10^2 + 7 \times 10^1 + 3 + 2 \times \frac{1}{10} + 4 \times \frac{1}{10^2} + 6 \times \frac{1}{10^3}.$$

There is no reason that a number other than 10 cannot be used as the *base*, or *radix*, of the number system. In fact, bases of 2, 8, and 16 are commonly used in working with digital computers. When the base used is not clear from the context, it is usually indicated as a parenthesized subscript or merely as a subscript. Thus

$$743_{(8)} = 7 \times 8^2 + 4 \times 8 + 3 = 7 \times 64 + 4 \times 8 + 3 = 448 + 32 + 3 = 483_{(10)}$$

$$1011.101_{(2)} = 1 \times 2^3 + 0 \times 2^2 + 1 \times 2 + 1 + 1 \times \tfrac{1}{2} + 0 \times \tfrac{1}{4} + 1 \times \tfrac{1}{8} = 11.625_{(10)}$$

CHANGE OF BASE

In this section, it is assumed that all calculations will be performed in base 10, since this is the only base in which most people can easily compute. However, there is no logical reason that some other base could not be used for the computations.

To convert a number from another base into base 10:

Simply write down the digits of the number, with each one multiplied by its appropriate positional value. Then perform the indicated computations in base 10, and write down the answer.

For examples, see the two examples in the previous section.

To convert a number from base 10 into another base:

The part of the number to the left of the point and the part to the right must be operated on separately. For the integer part (the part to the left of the point):

a. Divide the number by the new base, getting an integer quotient and remainder.

b. Write down the remainder as the last digit of the number in the new base.

c. Using the quotient from the last division in place of the original number, repeat the above two steps until the quotient becomes zero.

For the fractional part (the part to the right of the point):

a. Multiply the number by the new base.

b. Write down the integral part of the product as the first digit of the fractional part in the new base.

c. Using the fractional part of the last product in place of the original number, repeat the above two steps until the product becomes an integer, or until the desired number of places have been computed.

51

Examples:

These examples show a convenient method of arranging the computations.

1. Convert $103.118_{(10)}$ to base 8.

```
8  |103|  7                              .118
8   |12|  4                                8
     1              147.074324...         .944
                                           8
```

The calculation of the fractional part could be carried out as far as desired. It is a non-terminating fraction which will eventually repeat itself.

```
                                          7.552
                                            8
                                          4.416
                                            8
                                          3.328
                                            8
                                          2.624
                                            8
103.118_{(10)} = 147.074324..._{(8)}      4.992
```

The calculations may be further shortened by not writing down the multiplier and divisor at each step of the algorithm, as shown in the next example.

2. Convert $275.824_{(10)}$ to base 5.

```
5  |275|  0                               .824
    |55|  0                               4.120
    |11|  1                               0.600
     2                                    3.000

275.824_{(10)} = 2100.403_{(5)}
```

To convert from one base to another (neither of which is 10):

The easiest procedure is usually to convert first to base 10, and then to the desired base. However, there are two exceptions to this:

1. If computational facility is possessed in either of the bases, it may be used instead of base 10, and the appropriate one of the above methods applied.
2. If the two bases are different powers of the same number, the conversion may be done digit-by-digit to the base which is the common root of both bases, and then digit-by-digit back to the other base.

Example: Convert $127.653_{(8)}$ to base 16. (For base 16, the letters A–F are used for the digits $10_{(10)}-15_{(10)}$.)

The first step is to convert the number to base 2, simply by converting each digit to its binary equivalent:

$$127.653_{(8)} = 001\ 010\ 111 \cdot 110\ 101\ 011_{(2)}$$

Now by simply regrouping the binary number into groups of four binary digits, starting at the point, we convert to base 16:

$$127.653_{(8)} = 101\ 0111 \cdot 1101\ 0101\ 1_{(2)} = 57.D58_{(16)}$$

$10^{\pm n}$ IN OCTAL SCALE

10^n	n	10^{-n}
1	0	1.000 000 000 000 000
12	1	0.063 146 314 631 463
144	2	0.005 075 341 217 270
1 750	3	0.000 406 111 564 571
23 420	4	0.000 032 155 613 531
303 240	5	0.000 002 476 132 611
3 641 100	6	0.000 000 206 157 364
46 113 200	7	0.000 000 015 327 745
575 360 400	8	0.000 000 001 257 144
7 346 545 000	9	0.000 000 000 104 560

10^n	n	10^{-n}
112 402 762 000	10	0.000 000 000 006 676
1 351 035 564 000	11	0.000 000 000 000 538
16 432 451 210 000	12	0.000 000 000 000 043
221 441 634 520 000	13	0.000 000 000 000 003
2 657 142 036 440 000	14	0.000 000 000 000 000
34 327 724 461 500 000	15	0.000 000 000 000 000
434 157 115 760 200 000	16	0.000 000 000 000 000
5 432 127 413 542 400 000	17	0.000 000 000 000 000
67 405 553 164 731 000 000	18	0.000 000 000 000 000

2^n IN DECIMAL SCALE

n	2^n	n	2^n	n	2^n
0.001	1.00069 33874 62581	0.01	1.00695 55500 56719	0.1	1.07177 34625 36293
0.002	1.00138 72557 11335	0.02	1.01395 94797 90029	0.2	1.14869 83549 97035
0.003	1.00208 16050 79633	0.03	1.02101 21257 07193	0.3	1.23114 44133 44916
0.004	1.00277 64359 01078	0.04	1.02811 38266 56067	0.4	1.31950 79107 72894
0.005	1.00347 17485 09503	0.05	1.03526 49238 41377	0.5	1.41421 35623 73095
0.006	1.00416 75432 38973	0.06	1.04246 57608 41121	0.6	1.51571 65665 10398
0.007	1.00486 38204 23785	0.07	1.04971 66836 23067	0.7	1.62450 47927 12471
0.008	1.00556 05803 98468	0.08	1.05701 80405 61380	0.8	1.74110 11265 92248
0.009	1.00625 78234 97782	0.09	1.06437 01824 53360	0.9	1.86606 59830 73615

$n \log_{10} 2$, $n \log_2 10$ IN DECIMAL SCALE

n	$n \log_{10} 2$	$n \log_2 10$	n	$n \log_{10} 2$	$n \log_2 10$
1	0.30102 99957	3.32192 80949	6	1.80617 99740	19.93156 85693
2	0.60205 99913	6.64385 61898	7	2.10720 99696	23.25349 66642
3	0.90308 99870	9.96578 42847	8	2.40823 99653	26.57542 47591
4	1.20411 99827	13.28771 23795	9	2.70926 99610	29.89735 28540
5	1.50514 99783	16.60964 04744	10	3.01029 99566	33.21928 09489

ADDITION AND MULTIPLICATION TABLES

Binary Scale

Addition

$$0 + 0 = 0$$
$$0 + 1 = 1 + 0 = 1$$
$$1 + 1 = 10$$

Multiplication

$$0 \times 0 = 0$$
$$0 \times 1 = 1 \times 0 = 0$$
$$1 \times 1 = 1$$

Octal Scale

Addition

0	01	02	03	04	05	06	07
1	02	03	04	05	06	07	10
2	03	04	05	06	07	10	11
3	04	05	06	07	10	11	12
4	05	06	07	10	11	12	13
5	06	07	10	11	12	13	14
6	07	10	11	12	13	14	15
7	10	11	12	13	14	15	16

Multiplication

1	02	03	04	05	06	07
2	04	06	10	12	14	16
3	06	11	14	17	22	25
4	10	14	20	24	30	34
5	12	17	24	31	36	43
6	14	22	30	36	44	52
7	16	25	34	43	52	61

MATHEMATICAL CONSTANTS IN OCTAL SCALE

$\pi = (3.11037\ 552421)_{(8)}$

$\pi^{-1} = (0.24276\ 301556)_{(8)}$

$\sqrt{\pi} = (1.61337\ 611067)_{(8)}$

$\log_e \pi = (1.11206\ 404435)_{(8)}$

$\log_2 \pi = (1.51544\ 163223)_{(8)}$

$\sqrt{10} = (3.12305\ 407267)_{(8)}$

$e = (2.55760\ 521305)_{(8)}$

$e^{-1} = (0.27426\ 530661)_{(8)}$

$\sqrt{e} = (1.51411\ 230704)_{(8)}$

$\log_{10} e = (0.33626\ 754251)_{(8)}$

$\log_2 e = (1.34252\ 166245)_{(8)}$

$\log_2 10 = (3.24464\ 741136)_{(8)}$

$\gamma = (0.44742\ 147707)_{(8)}$

$\log_e \gamma = -(0.43127\ 233602)_{(8)}$

$\log_2 \gamma = -(0.62573\ 030645)_{(8)}$

$\sqrt{2} = (1.32404\ 746320)_{(8)}$

$\log_e 2 = (0.54271\ 027760)_{(8)}$

$\log_e 10 = (2.23273\ 067355)_{(8)}$

OCTAL-DECIMAL INTEGER CONVERSION TABLE

	0	1	2	3	4	5	6	7
0000	0000	0001	0002	0003	0004	0005	0006	0007
0010	0008	0009	0010	0011	0012	0013	0014	0015
0020	0016	0017	0018	0019	0020	0021	0022	0023
0030	0024	0025	0026	0027	0028	0029	0030	0031
0040	0032	0033	0034	0035	0036	0037	0038	0039
0050	0040	0041	0042	0043	0044	0045	0046	0047
0060	0048	0049	0050	0051	0052	0053	0054	0055
0070	0056	0057	0058	0059	0060	0061	0062	0063
0100	0064	0065	0066	0067	0068	0069	0070	0071
0110	0072	0073	0074	0075	0076	0077	0078	0079
0120	0080	0081	0082	0083	0084	0085	0086	0087
0130	0088	0089	0090	0091	0092	0093	0094	0095
0140	0096	0097	0098	0099	0100	0101	0102	0103
0150	0104	0105	0106	0107	0108	0109	0110	0111
0160	0112	0113	0114	0115	0116	0117	0118	0119
0170	0120	0121	0122	0123	0124	0125	0126	0127
0200	0128	0129	0130	0131	0132	0133	0134	0135
0210	0136	0137	0138	0139	0140	0141	0142	0143
0220	0144	0145	0146	0147	0148	0149	0150	0151
0230	0152	0153	0154	0155	0156	0157	0158	0159
0240	0160	0161	0162	0163	0164	0165	0166	0167
0250	0168	0169	0170	0171	0172	0173	0174	0175
0260	0176	0177	0178	0179	0180	0181	0182	0183
0270	0184	0185	0186	0187	0188	0189	0190	0191
0300	0192	0193	0194	0195	0196	0197	0198	0199
0310	0200	0201	0202	0203	0204	0205	0206	0207
0320	0208	0209	0210	0211	0212	0213	0214	0215
0330	0216	0217	0218	0219	0220	0221	0222	0223
0340	0224	0225	0226	0227	0228	0229	0230	0231
0350	0232	0233	0234	0235	0236	0237	0238	0239
0360	0240	0241	0242	0243	0244	0245	0246	0247
0370	0248	0249	0250	0251	0252	0253	0254	0255

	0	1	2	3	4	5	6	7
0400	0256	0257	0258	0259	0260	0261	0262	0263
0410	0264	0265	0266	0267	0268	0269	0270	0271
0420	0272	0273	0274	0275	0276	0277	0278	0279
0430	0280	0281	0282	0283	0284	0285	0286	0287
0440	0288	0289	0290	0291	0292	0293	0294	0295
0450	0296	0297	0298	0299	0300	0301	0302	0303
0460	0304	0305	0306	0307	0308	0309	0310	0311
0470	0312	0313	0314	0315	0316	0317	0318	0319
0500	0320	0321	0322	0323	0324	0325	0326	0327
0510	0328	0329	0330	0331	0332	0333	0334	0335
0520	0336	0337	0338	0339	0340	0341	0342	0343
0530	0344	0345	0346	0347	0348	0349	0350	0351
0540	0352	0353	0354	0355	0356	0357	0358	0359
0550	0360	0361	0362	0363	0364	0365	0366	0367
0560	0368	0369	0370	0371	0372	0373	0374	0375
0570	0376	0377	0378	0379	0380	0381	0382	0383
0600	0384	0385	0386	0387	0388	0389	0390	0391
0610	0392	0393	0394	0395	0396	0397	0398	0399
0620	0400	0401	0402	0403	0404	0405	0406	0407
0630	0408	0409	0410	0411	0412	0413	0414	0415
0640	0416	0417	0418	0419	0420	0421	0422	0423
0650	0424	0425	0426	0427	0428	0429	0430	0431
0660	0432	0433	0434	0435	0436	0437	0438	0439
0670	0440	0441	0442	0443	0444	0445	0446	0447
0700	0448	0449	0450	0451	0452	0453	0454	0455
0710	0456	0457	0458	0459	0460	0461	0462	0463
0720	0464	0465	0466	0467	0468	0469	0470	0471
0730	0472	0473	0474	0475	0476	0477	0478	0479
0740	0480	0481	0482	0483	0484	0485	0486	0487
0750	0488	0489	0490	0491	0492	0493	0494	0495
0760	0496	0497	0498	0499	0500	0501	0502	0503
0770	0504	0505	0506	0507	0508	0509	0510	0511

0000	0000
to	to
0777	0511
(Octal)	(Decimal)

Octal	Decimal
10000-	4096
20000-	8192
30000-	12288
40000-	16384
50000-	20480
60000-	24576
70000-	28672

	0	1	2	3	4	5	6	7
1000	0512	0513	0514	0515	0516	0517	0518	0519
1010	0520	0521	0522	0523	0524	0525	0526	0527
1020	0528	0529	0530	0531	0532	0533	0534	0535
1030	0536	0537	0538	0539	0540	0541	0542	0543
1040	0544	0545	0546	0547	0548	0549	0550	0551
1050	0552	0553	0554	0555	0556	0557	0558	0559
1060	0560	0561	0562	0563	0564	0565	0566	0567
1070	0568	0569	0570	0571	0572	0573	0574	0575
1100	0576	0577	0578	0579	0580	0581	0582	0583
1110	0584	0585	0586	0587	0588	0589	0590	0591
1120	0592	0593	0594	0595	0596	0597	0598	0599
1130	0600	0601	0602	0603	0604	0605	0606	0607
1140	0608	0609	0610	0611	0612	0613	0614	0615
1150	0616	0617	0618	0619	0620	0621	0622	0623
1160	0624	0625	0626	0627	0628	0629	0630	0631
1170	0632	0633	0634	0635	0636	0637	0638	0639
1200	0640	0641	0642	0643	0644	0645	0646	0647
1210	0648	0649	0650	0651	0652	0653	0654	0655
1220	0656	0657	0658	0659	0660	0661	0662	0663
1230	0664	0665	0666	0667	0668	0669	0670	0671
1240	0672	0673	0674	0675	0676	0677	0678	0679
1250	0680	0681	0682	0683	0684	0685	0686	0687
1260	0688	0689	0690	0691	0692	0693	0694	0695
1270	0696	0697	0698	0699	0700	0701	0702	0703
1300	0704	0705	0706	0707	0708	0709	0710	0711
1310	0712	0713	0714	0715	0716	0717	0718	0719
1320	0720	0721	0722	0723	0724	0725	0726	0727
1330	0728	0729	0730	0731	0732	0733	0734	0735
1340	0736	0737	0738	0739	0740	0741	0742	0743
1350	0744	0745	0746	0747	0748	0749	0750	0751
1360	0752	0753	0754	0755	0756	0757	0758	0759
1370	0760	0761	0762	0763	0764	0765	0766	0767

	0	1	2	3	4	5	6	7
1400	0768	0769	0770	0771	0772	0773	0774	0775
1410	0776	0777	0778	0779	0780	0781	0782	0783
1420	0784	0785	0786	0787	0788	0789	0790	0791
1430	0792	0793	0794	0795	0796	0797	0798	0799
1440	0800	0801	0802	0803	0804	0805	0806	0807
1450	0808	0809	0810	0811	0812	0813	0814	0815
1460	0816	0817	0818	0819	0820	0821	0822	0823
1470	0824	0825	0826	0827	0828	0829	0830	0831
1500	0832	0833	0834	0835	0836	0837	0838	0839
1510	0840	0841	0842	0843	0844	0845	0846	0847
1520	0848	0849	0850	0851	0852	0853	0854	0855
1530	0856	0857	0858	0859	0860	0861	0862	0863
1540	0864	0865	0866	0867	0868	0869	0870	0871
1550	0872	0873	0874	0875	0876	0877	0878	0879
1560	0880	0881	0882	0883	0884	0885	0886	0887
1570	0888	0889	0890	0891	0892	0893	0894	0895
1600	0896	0897	0898	0899	0900	0901	0902	0903
1610	0904	0905	0906	0907	0908	0909	0910	0911
1620	0912	0913	0914	0915	0916	0917	0918	0919
1630	0920	0921	0922	0923	0924	0925	0926	0927
1640	0928	0929	0930	0931	0932	0933	0934	0935
1650	0936	0937	0938	0939	0940	0941	0942	0943
1660	0944	0945	0946	0947	0948	0949	0950	0951
1670	0952	0953	0954	0955	0956	0957	0958	0959
1700	0960	0961	0962	0963	0964	0965	0966	0967
1710	0968	0969	0970	0971	0972	0973	0974	0975
1720	0976	0977	0978	0979	0980	0981	0982	0983
1730	0984	0985	0986	0987	0988	0989	0990	0991
1740	0992	0993	0994	0995	0996	0997	0998	0999
1750	1000	1001	1002	1003	1004	1005	1006	1007
1760	1008	1009	1010	1011	1012	1013	1014	1015
1770	1016	1017	1018	1019	1020	1021	1022	1023

1000	0512
to	to
1777	1023
(Octal)	(Decimal)

OCTAL-DECIMAL INTEGER CONVERSION TABLE (Continued)

	0	1	2	3	4	5	6	7		0	1	2	3	4	5	6	7
2000	1024	1025	1026	1027	1028	1029	1030	1031	2400	1280	1281	1282	1283	1284	1285	1286	1287
2010	1032	1033	1034	1035	1036	1037	1038	1039	2410	1288	1289	1290	1291	1292	1293	1294	1295
2020	1040	1041	1042	1043	1044	1045	1046	1047	2420	1296	1297	1298	1299	1300	1301	1302	1303
2030	1048	1049	1050	1051	1052	1053	1054	1055	2430	1304	1305	1306	1307	1308	1309	1310	1311
2040	1056	1057	1058	1059	1060	1061	1062	1063	2440	1312	1313	1314	1315	1316	1317	1318	1319
2050	1064	1065	1066	1067	1068	1069	1070	1071	2450	1320	1321	1322	1323	1324	1325	1326	1327
2060	1072	1073	1074	1075	1076	1077	1078	1079	2460	1328	1329	1330	1331	1332	1333	1334	1335
2070	1080	1081	1082	1083	1084	1085	1086	1087	2470	1336	1337	1338	1339	1340	1341	1342	1343
2100	1088	1089	1090	1091	1092	1093	1094	1095	2500	1344	1345	1346	1347	1348	1349	1350	1351
2110	1096	1097	1098	1099	1100	1101	1102	1103	2510	1352	1353	1354	1355	1356	1357	1358	1359
2120	1104	1105	1106	1107	1108	1109	1110	1111	2520	1360	1361	1362	1363	1364	1365	1366	1367
2130	1112	1113	1114	1115	1116	1117	1118	1119	2530	1368	1369	1370	1371	1372	1373	1374	1375
2140	1120	1121	1122	1123	1124	1125	1126	1127	2540	1376	1377	1378	1379	1380	1381	1382	1383
2150	1128	1129	1130	1131	1132	1133	1134	1135	2550	1384	1385	1386	1387	1388	1389	1390	1391
2160	1136	1137	1138	1139	1140	1141	1142	1143	2560	1392	1393	1394	1395	1396	1397	1398	1399
2170	1144	1145	1146	1147	1148	1149	1150	1151	2570	1400	1401	1402	1403	1404	1405	1406	1407
2200	1152	1153	1154	1155	1156	1157	1158	1159	2600	1408	1409	1410	1411	1412	1413	1414	1415
2210	1160	1161	1162	1163	1164	1165	1166	1167	2610	1416	1417	1418	1419	1420	1421	1422	1423
2220	1168	1169	1170	1171	1172	1173	1174	1175	2620	1424	1425	1426	1427	1428	1429	1430	1431
2230	1176	1177	1178	1179	1180	1181	1182	1183	2630	1432	1433	1434	1435	1436	1437	1438	1439
2240	1184	1185	1186	1187	1188	1189	1190	1191	2640	1440	1441	1442	1443	1444	1445	1446	1447
2250	1192	1193	1194	1195	1196	1197	1198	1199	2650	1448	1449	1450	1451	1452	1453	1454	1455
2260	1200	1201	1202	1203	1204	1205	1206	1207	2660	1456	1457	1458	1459	1460	1461	1462	1463
2270	1208	1209	1210	1211	1212	1213	1214	1215	2670	1464	1465	1466	1467	1468	1469	1470	1471
2300	1216	1217	1218	1219	1220	1221	1222	1223	2700	1472	1473	1474	1475	1476	1477	1478	1479
2310	1224	1225	1226	1227	1228	1229	1230	1231	2710	1480	1481	1482	1483	1484	1485	1486	1487
2320	1232	1233	1234	1235	1236	1237	1238	1239	2720	1488	1489	1490	1491	1492	1493	1494	1495
2330	1240	1241	1242	1243	1244	1245	1246	1247	2730	1496	1497	1498	1499	1500	1501	1502	1503
2340	1248	1249	1250	1251	1252	1253	1254	1255	2740	1504	1505	1506	1507	1508	1509	1510	1511
2350	1256	1257	1258	1259	1260	1261	1262	1263	2750	1512	1513	1514	1515	1516	1517	1518	1519
2360	1264	1265	1266	1267	1268	1269	1270	1271	2760	1520	1521	1522	1523	1524	1525	1526	1527
2370	1272	1273	1274	1275	1276	1277	1278	1279	2770	1528	1529	1530	1531	1532	1533	1534	1535

Left-margin legend:

```
2000     1024
to       to
2777     1535
(Octal)  (Decimal)

Octal    Decimal
10000-   4096
20000-   8192
30000- 12288
40000- 16384
50000- 20480
60000- 24576
70000- 28672
```

	0	1	2	3	4	5	6	7		0	1	2	3	4	5	6	7
3000	1536	1537	1538	1539	1540	1541	1542	1543	3400	1792	1793	1794	1795	1796	1797	1798	1799
3010	1544	1545	1546	1547	1548	1549	1550	1551	3410	1800	1801	1802	1803	1804	1805	1806	1807
3020	1552	1553	1554	1555	1556	1557	1558	1559	3420	1808	1809	1810	1811	1812	1813	1814	1815
3030	1560	1561	1562	1563	1564	1565	1566	1567	3430	1816	1817	1818	1819	1820	1821	1822	1823
3040	1568	1569	1570	1571	1572	1573	1574	1575	3440	1824	1825	1826	1827	1828	1829	1830	1831
3050	1576	1577	1578	1579	1580	1581	1582	1583	3450	1832	1833	1834	1835	1836	1837	1838	1839
3060	1584	1585	1586	1587	1588	1589	1590	1591	3460	1840	1841	1842	1843	1844	1845	1846	1847
3070	1592	1593	1594	1595	1596	1597	1598	1599	3470	1848	1849	1850	1851	1852	1853	1854	1855
3100	1600	1601	1602	1603	1604	1605	1606	1607	3500	1856	1857	1858	1859	1860	1861	1862	1863
3110	1608	1609	1610	1611	1612	1613	1614	1615	3510	1864	1865	1866	1867	1868	1869	1870	1871
3120	1616	1617	1618	1619	1620	1621	1622	1623	3520	1872	1873	1874	1875	1876	1877	1878	1879
3130	1624	1625	1626	1627	1628	1629	1630	1631	3530	1880	1881	1882	1883	1884	1885	1886	1887
3140	1632	1633	1634	1635	1636	1637	1638	1639	3540	1888	1889	1890	1891	1892	1893	1894	1895
3150	1640	1641	1642	1643	1644	1645	1646	1647	3550	1896	1897	1898	1899	1900	1901	1902	1903
3160	1648	1649	1650	1651	1652	1653	1654	1655	3560	1904	1905	1906	1907	1908	1909	1910	1911
3170	1656	1657	1658	1659	1660	1661	1662	1663	3570	1912	1913	1914	1915	1916	1917	1918	1919
3200	1664	1665	1666	1667	1668	1669	1670	1671	3600	1920	1921	1922	1923	1924	1925	1926	1927
3210	1672	1673	1674	1675	1676	1677	1678	1679	3610	1928	1929	1930	1931	1932	1933	1934	1935
3220	1680	1681	1682	1683	1684	1685	1686	1687	3620	1936	1937	1938	1939	1940	1941	1942	1943
3230	1688	1689	1690	1691	1692	1693	1694	1695	3630	1944	1945	1946	1947	1948	1949	1950	1951
3240	1696	1697	1698	1699	1700	1701	1702	1703	3640	1952	1953	1954	1955	1956	1957	1958	1959
3250	1704	1705	1706	1707	1708	1709	1710	1711	3650	1960	1961	1962	1963	1964	1965	1966	1967
3260	1712	1713	1714	1715	1716	1717	1718	1719	3660	1968	1969	1970	1971	1972	1973	1974	1975
3270	1720	1721	1722	1723	1724	1725	1726	1727	3670	1976	1977	1978	1979	1980	1981	1982	1983
3300	1728	1729	1730	1731	1732	1733	1734	1735	3700	1984	1985	1986	1987	1988	1989	1990	1991
3310	1736	1737	1738	1739	1740	1741	1742	1743	3710	1992	1993	1994	1995	1996	1997	1998	1999
3320	1744	1745	1746	1747	1748	1749	1750	1751	3720	2000	2001	2002	2003	2004	2005	2006	2007
3330	1752	1753	1754	1755	1756	1757	1758	1759	3730	2008	2009	2010	2011	2012	2013	2014	2015
3340	1760	1761	1762	1763	1764	1765	1766	1767	3740	2016	2017	2018	2019	2020	2021	2022	2023
3350	1768	1769	1770	1771	1772	1773	1774	1775	3750	2024	2025	2026	2027	2028	2029	2030	2031
3360	1776	1777	1778	1779	1780	1781	1782	1783	3760	2032	2033	2034	2035	2036	2037	2038	2039
3370	1784	1785	1786	1787	1788	1789	1790	1791	3770	2040	2041	2042	2043	2044	2045	2046	2047

Left-margin legend:

```
3000     1536
to       to
3777     2047
(Octal)  (Decimal)
```

Numerical Tables

OCTAL-DECIMAL INTEGER CONVERSION TABLE (Continued)

	0	1	2	3	4	5	6	7
4000	2048	2049	2050	2051	2052	2053	2054	2055
4010	2056	2057	2058	2059	2060	2061	2062	2063
4020	2064	2065	2066	2067	2068	2069	2070	2071
4030	2072	2073	2074	2075	2076	2077	2078	2079
4040	2080	2081	2082	2083	2084	2085	2086	2087
4050	2088	2089	2090	2091	2092	2093	2094	2095
4060	2096	2097	2098	2099	2100	2101	2102	2103
4070	2104	2105	2106	2107	2108	2109	2110	2111
4100	2112	2113	2114	2115	2116	2117	2118	2119
4110	2120	2121	2122	2123	2124	2125	2126	2127
4120	2128	2129	2130	2131	2132	2133	2134	2135
4130	2136	2137	2138	2139	2140	2141	2142	2143
4140	2144	2145	2146	2147	2148	2149	2150	2151
4150	2152	2153	2154	2155	2156	2157	2158	2159
4160	2160	2161	2162	2163	2164	2165	2166	2167
4170	2168	2169	2170	2171	2172	2173	2174	2175
4200	2176	2177	2178	2179	2180	2181	2182	2183
4210	2184	2185	2186	2187	2188	2189	2190	2191
4220	2192	2193	2194	2195	2196	2197	2198	2199
4230	2200	2201	2202	2203	2204	2205	2206	2207
4240	2208	2209	2210	2211	2212	2213	2214	2215
4250	2216	2217	2218	2219	2220	2221	2222	2223
4260	2224	2225	2226	2227	2228	2229	2230	2231
4270	2232	2233	2234	2235	2236	2237	2238	2239
4300	2240	2241	2242	2243	2244	2245	2246	2247
4310	2248	2249	2250	2251	2252	2253	2254	2255
4320	2256	2257	2258	2259	2260	2261	2262	2263
4330	2264	2265	2266	2267	2268	2269	2270	2271
4340	2272	2273	2274	2275	2276	2277	2278	2279
4350	2280	2281	2282	2283	2284	2285	2286	2287
4360	2288	2289	2290	2291	2292	2293	2294	2295
4370	2296	2297	2298	2299	2300	2301	2302	2303

	0	1	2	3	4	5	6	7
4400	2304	2305	2306	2307	2308	2309	2310	2311
4410	2312	2313	2314	2315	2316	2317	2318	2319
4420	2320	2321	2322	2323	2324	2325	2326	2327
4430	2328	2329	2330	2331	2332	2333	2334	2335
4440	2336	2337	2338	2339	2340	2341	2342	2343
4450	2344	2345	2346	2347	2348	2349	2350	2351
4460	2352	2353	2354	2355	2356	2357	2358	2359
4470	2360	2361	2362	2363	2364	2365	2366	2367
4500	2368	2369	2370	2371	2372	2373	2374	2375
4510	2376	2377	2378	2379	2380	2381	2382	2383
4520	2384	2385	2386	2387	2388	2389	2390	2391
4530	2392	2393	2394	2395	2396	2397	2398	2399
4540	2400	2401	2402	2403	2404	2405	2406	2407
4550	2408	2409	2410	2411	2412	2413	2414	2415
4560	2416	2417	2418	2419	2420	2421	2422	2423
4570	2424	2425	2426	2427	2428	2429	2430	2431
4600	2432	2433	2434	2435	2436	2437	2438	2439
4610	2440	2441	2442	2443	2444	2445	2446	2447
4620	2448	2449	2450	2451	2452	2453	2454	2455
4630	2456	2457	2458	2459	2460	2461	2462	2463
4640	2464	2465	2466	2467	2468	2469	2470	2471
4650	2472	2473	2474	2475	2476	2477	2478	2479
4660	2480	2481	2482	2483	2484	2485	2486	2487
4670	2488	2489	2490	2491	2492	2493	2494	2495
4700	2496	2497	2498	2499	2500	2501	2502	2503
4710	2504	2505	2506	2507	2508	2509	2510	2511
4720	2512	2513	2514	2515	2516	2517	2518	2519
4730	2520	2521	2522	2523	2524	2525	2526	2527
4740	2528	2529	2530	2531	2532	2533	2534	2535
4750	2536	2537	2538	2539	2540	2541	2542	2543
4760	2544	2545	2546	2547	2548	2549	2550	2551
4770	2552	2553	2554	2555	2556	2557	2558	2559

4000	2048
to	to
4777	2559
(Octal)	(Decimal)

Octal	Decimal
10000-	4096
20000-	8192
30000-	12288
40000-	16384
50000-	20480
60000-	24576
70000-	28672

	0	1	2	3	4	5	6	7
5000	2560	2561	2562	2563	2564	2565	2566	2567
5010	2568	2569	2570	2571	2572	2573	2574	2575
5020	2576	2577	2578	2579	2580	2581	2582	2583
5030	2584	2585	2586	2587	2588	2589	2590	2591
5040	2592	2593	2594	2595	2596	2597	2598	2599
5050	2600	2601	2602	2603	2604	2605	2606	2607
5060	2608	2609	2610	2611	2612	2613	2614	2615
5070	2616	2617	2618	2619	2620	2621	2622	2623
5100	2624	2625	2626	2627	2628	2629	2630	2631
5110	2632	2633	2634	2635	2636	2637	2638	2639
5120	2640	2641	2642	2643	2644	2645	2646	2647
5130	2648	2649	2650	2651	2652	2653	2654	2655
5140	2656	2657	2658	2659	2660	2661	2662	2663
5150	2664	2665	2666	2667	2668	2669	2670	2671
5160	2672	2673	2674	2675	2676	2677	2678	2679
5170	2680	2681	2682	2683	2684	2685	2686	2687
5200	2688	2689	2690	2691	2692	2693	2694	2695
5210	2696	2697	2698	2699	2700	2701	2702	2703
5220	2704	2705	2706	2707	2708	2709	2710	2711
5230	2712	2713	2714	2715	2716	2717	2718	2719
5240	2720	2721	2722	2723	2724	2725	2726	2727
5250	2728	2729	2730	2731	2732	2733	2734	2735
5260	2736	2737	2738	2739	2740	2741	2742	2743
5270	2744	2745	2746	2747	2748	2749	2750	2751
5300	2752	2753	2754	2755	2756	2757	2758	2759
5310	2760	2761	2762	2763	2764	2765	2766	2767
5320	2768	2769	2770	2771	2772	2773	2774	2775
5330	2776	2777	2778	2779	2780	2781	2782	2783
5340	2784	2785	2786	2787	2788	2789	2790	2791
5350	2792	2793	2794	2795	2796	2797	2798	2799
5360	2800	2801	2802	2803	2804	2805	2806	2807
5370	2808	2809	2810	2811	2812	2813	2814	2815

	0	1	2	3	4	5	6	7
5400	2816	2817	2818	2819	2820	2821	2822	2823
5410	2824	2825	2826	2827	2828	2829	2830	2831
5420	2832	2833	2834	2835	2836	2837	2838	2839
5430	2840	2841	2842	2843	2844	2845	2846	2847
5440	2848	2849	2850	2851	2852	2853	2854	2855
5450	2856	2857	2858	2859	2860	2861	2862	2863
5460	2864	2865	2866	2867	2868	2869	2870	2871
5470	2872	2873	2874	2875	2876	2877	2878	2879
5500	2880	2881	2882	2883	2884	2885	2886	2887
5510	2888	2889	2890	2891	2892	2893	2894	2895
5520	2896	2897	2898	2899	2900	2901	2902	2903
5530	2904	2905	2906	2907	2908	2909	2910	2911
5540	2912	2913	2914	2915	2916	2917	2918	2919
5550	2920	2921	2922	2923	2924	2925	2926	2927
5560	2928	2929	2930	2931	2932	2933	2934	2935
5570	2936	2937	2938	2939	2940	2941	2942	2943
5600	2944	2945	2946	2947	2948	2949	2950	2951
5610	2952	2953	2954	2955	2956	2957	2958	2959
5620	2960	2961	2962	2963	2964	2965	2966	2967
5630	2968	2969	2970	2971	2972	2973	2974	2975
5640	2976	2977	2978	2979	2980	2981	2982	2983
5650	2984	2985	2986	2987	2988	2989	2990	2991
5660	2992	2993	2994	2995	2996	2997	2998	2999
5670	3000	3001	3002	3003	3004	3005	3006	3007
5700	3008	3009	3010	3011	3012	3013	3014	3015
5710	3016	3017	3018	3019	3020	3021	3022	3023
5720	3024	3025	3026	3027	3028	3029	3030	3031
5730	3032	3033	3034	3035	3036	3037	3038	3039
5740	3040	3041	3042	3043	3044	3045	3046	3047
5750	3048	3049	3050	3051	3052	3053	3054	3055
5760	3056	3057	3058	3059	3060	3061	3062	3063
5770	3064	3065	3066	3067	3068	3069	3070	3071

5000	2560
to	to
5777	3071
(Octal)	(Decimal)

OCTAL-DECIMAL INTEGER CONVERSION TABLE (Continued)

	0	1	2	3	4	5	6	7
6000	3072	3073	3074	3075	3076	3077	3078	3079
6010	3080	3081	3082	3083	3084	3085	3086	3087
6020	3088	3089	3090	3091	3092	3093	3094	3095
6030	3096	3097	3098	3099	3100	3101	3102	3103
6040	3104	3105	3106	3107	3108	3109	3110	3111
6050	3112	3113	3114	3115	3116	3117	3118	3119
6060	3120	3121	3122	3123	3124	3125	3126	3127
6070	3128	3129	3130	3131	3132	3133	3134	3135
6100	3136	3137	3138	3139	3140	3141	3142	3143
6110	3144	3145	3146	3147	3148	3149	3150	3151
6120	3152	3153	3154	3155	3156	3157	3158	3159
6130	3160	3161	3162	3163	3164	3165	3166	3167
6140	3168	3169	3170	3171	3172	3173	3174	3175
6150	3176	3177	3178	3179	3180	3181	3182	3183
6160	3184	3185	3186	3187	3188	3189	3190	3191
6170	3192	3193	3194	3195	3196	3197	3198	3199
6200	3200	3201	3202	3203	3204	3205	3206	3207
6210	3208	3209	3210	3211	3212	3213	3214	3215
6220	3216	3217	3218	3219	3220	3221	3222	3223
6230	3224	3225	3226	3227	3228	3229	3230	3231
6240	3232	3233	3234	3235	3236	3237	3238	3239
6250	3240	3241	3442	3243	3244	3245	3246	3247
6260	3248	3249	3250	3251	3252	3253	3254	3255
6270	3256	3257	3258	3259	3260	3261	3262	3263
6300	3264	3265	3266	3267	3268	3269	3270	3871
6310	3272	3273	3274	3275	3276	3277	3278	3279
6320	3280	3281	3282	3283	3284	3285	3286	3287
6330	3288	3289	3290	3291	3292	3293	3294	3295
6340	3296	3297	3298	3299	3300	3301	3302	3003
6350	3304	3305	3306	3307	3308	3309	3310	3311
6360	3312	3313	3314	3315	3316	3317	3318	3319
6370	3320	3321	3322	3323	3324	3325	3326	3327

	0	1	2	3	4	5	6	7
6400	3328	3329	3330	3331	3332	3333	3334	3335
6410	3336	3337	3338	3339	3340	3341	3342	3343
6420	3344	3345	3346	3347	3348	3349	3350	3351
6430	3352	3353	3354	3355	3356	3357	3358	3359
6440	3360	3361	3362	3363	3364	3365	3366	3367
6450	3368	3369	3370	3371	3372	3373	3374	3375
6460	3376	3377	3378	3379	3380	3381	3382	3383
6470	3384	3385	3386	3387	3388	3389	3390	3391
6500	3392	3393	3394	3395	3396	3397	3398	3399
6510	3400	3401	3402	3403	3404	3405	3406	3407
6520	3408	3409	3410	3411	3412	3413	3414	3415
6530	3416	3417	3418	3419	3420	3421	3422	3423
6540	3424	3425	3426	3427	3428	3429	3430	3431
6550	3432	3433	3434	3435	3436	3437	3438	3439
6560	3440	3441	3442	3443	3444	3445	3446	3447
6570	3448	3449	3450	3451	3452	3453	3454	3455
6600	3456	3457	3458	3459	3460	3461	3462	3463
6610	3464	3465	3466	3467	3468	3469	3470	3471
6620	3472	3473	3474	3475	3476	3477	3478	3479
6630	3480	3481	3482	3483	3484	3485	3486	3487
6640	3488	3489	3490	3491	3492	3493	3494	3495
6650	3496	3497	3498	3499	3500	3501	3502	3503
6660	3504	3505	3506	3507	3508	3509	3510	3511
6670	3512	3513	3514	3515	3516	3517	3518	3519
6700	3520	3521	3522	3523	3524	3525	3526	3527
6710	3528	3529	3530	3531	3532	3533	3534	3535
6720	3536	3537	3538	3539	3540	3541	3542	3543
6730	3544	3545	3546	3547	3548	3549	3550	3551
6740	3552	3553	3554	3555	3556	3557	3558	3559
6750	3560	3561	3562	3563	3564	3655	3566	3567
6760	3568	3569	3570	3571	3572	3573	3574	3575
6770	3576	3577	3578	3579	3580	3581	3582	3583

6000 to 6777 (Octal) | 3072 to 3583 (Decimal)

Octal	Decimal
10000-	4096
20000-	8192
30000-	12288
40000-	16384
50000-	20480
60000-	24576
70000-	28672

	0	1	2	3	4	5	6	7
7000	3584	3585	3586	3587	3588	3589	3590	3591
7010	3592	3593	3594	3595	3596	3597	3598	3599
7020	3600	3601	3602	3603	3604	3605	3606	3607
7030	3608	3609	3610	3611	3612	3613	3614	3615
7040	3616	3617	3618	3619	3620	3621	3622	3623
7050	3624	3625	3626	3627	3628	3629	3630	3631
7060	3632	3633	3634	3635	3636	3637	3638	3639
7070	3640	3641	3642	3643	3644	3645	3646	3647
7100	3648	3649	3650	3651	3652	3653	3654	3655
7110	3656	3657	3658	3659	3660	3661	3662	3663
7120	3664	3665	3666	3667	3668	3669	3670	3671
7130	3672	3673	3674	3675	3676	3677	3678	3679
7140	3680	3681	3682	3683	3684	3685	3686	3687
7150	3688	3689	3690	3691	3692	3693	3694	3695
7160	3696	3697	3698	3699	3700	3701	3702	3703
7170	3704	3705	3706	3707	3708	3709	3710	3711
7200	3712	3713	3714	3715	3716	3717	3718	3719
7210	3720	3721	3722	3723	3724	3725	3726	3727
7220	3728	3729	3730	3731	3732	3733	3734	3735
7230	3736	3737	3738	3739	3740	3741	3742	3743
7240	3744	3745	3746	3747	3748	3749	3750	3751
7250	3752	3753	3754	3755	3756	3757	3758	3759
7260	3760	3761	3762	3763	3764	3765	3766	3767
7270	3768	3769	3770	3771	3772	3773	3774	3775
7300	3776	3777	3778	3779	3780	3781	3782	3783
7310	3784	3785	3786	3787	3788	3789	3790	3791
7320	3792	3893	3794	3795	3796	3797	3798	3799
7330	3800	3801	3802	3803	3804	3805	3806	3807
7340	3808	3809	3810	3811	3812	3813	3814	3815
7350	3816	3817	3818	3819	3820	3821	3822	3823
7360	3824	3825	3826	3827	3828	3829	3830	3831
7370	3832	3833	3834	3835	3836	3837	3838	3839

	0	1	2	3	4	5	6	7
7400	3840	3841	3482	3843	3844	3845	3846	3847
7410	3848	3849	3850	3851	3852	3853	3854	3855
7420	3856	3857	3858	3859	3860	3861	3862	3863
7430	3864	3865	3866	3867	3868	3869	3870	3871
7440	3872	3873	3874	3875	3876	3877	3878	3879
7450	3880	3881	3882	3883	3884	3885	3886	3887
7460	3888	3889	3890	3891	3892	3893	3894	3895
7470	3896	3897	3898	3899	3900	3901	3902	3903
7500	3904	3905	3906	3907	3908	3909	3910	3911
7510	3912	3913	3914	3915	3916	3917	3918	3919
7520	3920	3921	3922	3923	3924	3925	3926	3927
7530	3928	3929	3930	3931	3932	3933	3934	3935
7540	3936	3937	3938	3939	3940	3941	3942	3943
7550	3944	3945	3946	3947	3948	3949	3950	3951
7560	3952	3953	3954	3955	3956	3957	3958	3959
7570	3960	3961	3962	3963	3964	3965	3966	3967
7600	3968	3969	3970	3971	3972	3973	3974	3975
7610	3976	3977	3978	3979	3980	3981	3982	3983
7620	3984	3985	3986	3987	3988	3989	3990	3991
7630	3992	3993	3994	3995	3996	3997	3998	3999
7640	4000	4001	4002	4003	4004	4005	4006	4007
7650	4008	4009	4010	4011	4012	4013	4014	4015
7660	4016	4017	4018	4019	4020	4021	4022,	4023
7670	4024	4025	4026	4027	4028	4029	4030	4031
7700	4032	4033	4034	4035	4036	4037	4038	4039
7710	4040	4041	4042	4043	4044	4045	4046	4047
7720	4048	4049	4050	4051	4052	4053	4054	4055
7730	4056	4057	4058	4059	4060	4061	4062	4063
7740	4064	4065	4066	4067	4068	4069	4070	4071
7750	4072	4073	4074	4075	4076	4077	4078	4079
7760	4080	4081	4082	4083	4084	4085	4086	4087
7770	4088	4089	4090	4091	4092	4093	4094	4095

7000 to 7777 (Octal) | 3584 to 4095 (Decimal)

OCTAL-DECIMAL FRACTION CONVERSION TABLE

This table covers the entries from $(.000)_8$ to $(.377)_8$. For entries from $(.400)_8$ to $(.777)_8$, cognizance should be made of the fact that $(.400)_8$ is $(.500)_{10}$. Hence if $(.637)_8$ is desired, find $(.237)_8$ in table, namely, $(.310456)_{10}$ and add $(.50000)_{10}$ for $(.400)_8$. Thus

$(.637)_8$ = $(.237)_8$ + $(.400)_8$
= $(.310456)_{10}$ + $(.50000)_{10}$
= $(.810456)_{10}$.

OCTAL	DEC.	OCTAL	DEC.	OCTAL	DEC.	OCTAL	DEC.
.000	.000000	.100	.125000	.200	.250000	.300	.375000
.001	.001953	.101	.126953	.201	.251953	.301	.376953
.002	.003906	.102	.128906	.202	.253906	.302	.378906
.003	.005859	.103	.130859	.203	.255859	.303	.380859
.004	.007812	.104	.132812	.204	.257812	.304	.382812
.005	.009765	.105	.134765	.205	.259765	.305	.384765
.006	.011718	.106	.136718	.206	.261718	.306	.386718
.007	.013671	.107	.138671	.207	.263671	.307	.388671
.010	.015625	.110	.140625	.210	.265625	.310	.390625
.011	.017578	.111	.142578	.211	.267578	.311	.392578
.012	.019531	.112	.144531	.212	.269531	.312	.394531
.013	.021484	.113	.146484	.213	.271484	.313	.396484
.014	.023437	.114	.148437	.214	.273437	.314	.398437
.015	.025390	.115	.150390	.215	.275390	.315	.400490
.016	.027343	.116	.152343	.216	.277343	.316	.402343
.017	.029296	.117	.154296	.217	.279296	.317	.404296
.020	.031250	.120	.156250	.220	.281250	.320	.406250
.021	.033203	.121	.158203	.221	.283203	.321	.408203
.022	.035156	.122	.160156	.222	.285156	.322	.410156
.023	.037109	.123	.162109	.223	.287109	.323	.412109
.024	.039062	.124	.164062	.224	.289062	.324	.414062
.025	.041015	.125	.166015	.225	.291015	.325	.416015
.026	.042968	.126	.167968	.226	.292968	.326	.417968
.027	.044921	.127	.169921	.227	.294921	.327	.419921
.030	.046875	.130	.171875	.230	.294875	.330	.421875
.031	.048828	.131	.173828	.231	.298828	.331	.423828
.032	.050781	.132	.175781	.232	.300781	.332	.425781
.033	.052734	.133	.177734	.233	.302734	.333	.427734
.034	.054687	.134	.179687	.234	.304687	.334	.429687
.035	.056640	.135	.181640	.235	.306640	.335	.431640
.036	.058593	.136	.183593	.236	.308593	.336	.433593
.037	.060546	.137	.185546	.237	.310546	.337	.435546
.040	.062500	.140	.187500	.240	.312500	.340	.437500
.041	.064453	.141	.189453	.241	.314453	.341	.439453
.042	.066406	.142	.191406	.242	.316406	.342	.441406
.043	.068359	.143	.193359	.243	.318359	.343	.443359
.044	.070312	.144	.195312	.244	.320312	.344	.445312
.045	.072265	.145	.197265	.245	.322265	.345	.447265
.046	.074218	.146	.199218	.246	.324218	.346	.449218
.047	.076171	.147	.201171	.247	.326171	.347	.451171
.050	.078125	.150	.203125	.250	.328125	.350	.453125
.051	.080078	.151	.205078	.251	.330078	.351	.455078
.052	.082031	.152	.207031	.252	.332031	.352	.457031
.053	.083984	.153	.208984	.253	.333984	.353	.458984
.054	.085937	.154	.210937	.254	.335937	.354	.460937
.055	.087890	.155	.212890	.255	.337890	.355	.462890
.056	.089843	.156	.214843	.256	.339843	.356	.464843
.057	.091796	.157	.216796	.257	.341796	.357	.466796
.060	.093750	.160	.218750	.260	.343750	.360	.468750
.061	.095703	.161	.220703	.261	.345703	.361	.470703
.062	.097656	.162	.222656	.262	.347656	.362	.472656
.063	.099609	.163	.224609	.263	.349609	.363	.474609
.064	.101562	.164	.226562	.264	.351562	.364	.476562
.065	.103515	.165	.228515	.265	.353515	.365	.478515
.066	.105468	.166	.230468	.266	.355468	.366	.480468
.067	.107421	.167	.232421	.267	.357421	.367	.482421
.070	.109375	.170	.234375	.270	.359375	.370	.484375
.071	.111328	.171	.236328	.271	.361328	.371	.486328
.072	.113281	.172	.238281	.272	.363281	.372	.488281
.073	.115234	.173	.240234	.273	.365234	.373	.490234
.074	.117187	.174	.242187	.274	.367187	.374	.492187
.075	.119140	.175	.244140	.275	.369140	.375	.494140
.076	.121093	.176	.246093	.276	.371093	.376	.496093
.077	.123046	.177	.248046	.277	.373046	.377	.498046

OCTAL-DECIMAL FRACTION CONVERSION TABLE (Continued)

OCTAL	DEC.	OCTAL	DEC.	OCTAL	DEC.	OCTAL	DEC.
.000000	.000000	.000100	.000244	.000200	.000488	.000300	.000732
.000001	.000004	.000101	.000247	.000201	.000492	.000301	.000736
.000002	.000007	.000102	.000251	.000202	.000495	.000302	.000740
.000003	.000011	.000103	.000255	.000203	.000499	.000303	.000743
.000004	.000015	.000104	.000259	.000204	.000503	.000304	.000747
.000005	.000019	.000105	.000263	.000205	.000507	.000305	.000751
.000006	.000022	.000106	.000267	.000206	.000511	.000306	.000755
.000007	.000026	.000107	.000270	.000207	.000514	.000307	.000759
.000010	.000030	.000110	.000274	.000210	.000518	.000310	.000762
.000011	.000034	.000111	.000278	.000211	.000522	.000311	.000766
.000012	.000038	.000112	.000282	.000212	.000526	.000312	.000770
.000013	.000041	.000113	.000286	.000213	.000530	.000313	.000774
.000014	.000045	.000114	.000289	.000214	.000534	.000314	.000778
.000015	.000049	.000115	.000293	.000215	.000537	.000315	.000782
.000016	.000053	.000116	.000297	.000216	.000541	.000316	.000785
.000017	.000057	.000117	.000301	.000217	.000545	.000317	.000789
.000020	.000061	.000120	.000305	.000220	.000549	.000320	.000793
.000021	.000064	.000121	.000308	.000221	.000553	.000321	.000797
.000022	.000068	.000122	.000312	.000222	.000556	.000322	.000801
.000023	.000072	.000123	.000316	.000223	.000560	.000323	.000805
.000024	.000076	.000124	.000320	.000224	.000564	.000324	.000808
.000025	.000080	.000125	.000324	.000225	.000568	.000325	.000812
.000026	.000083	.000126	.000328	.000226	.000572	.000326	.000816
.000027	.000087	.000127	.000331	.000227	.000576	.000327	.000820
.000030	.000091	.000130	.000335	.000230	.000579	.000330	.000823
.000031	.000095	.000131	.000339	.000231	.000583	.000331	.000827
.000032	.000099	.000132	.000343	.000232	.000587	.000332	.000831
.000033	.000102	.000133	.000347	.000233	.000591	.000333	.000835
.000034	.000106	.000134	.000350	.000234	.000595	.000334	.000839
.000035	.000110	.000135	.000354	.C00235	.000598	.000335	.000843
.000036	.000114	.000136	.000358	.000236	.000602	.000336	.000846
.000037	.000118	.000137	.000362	.000237	.000606	.000337	.000850
.000040	.000122	.000140	.000366	.000240	.000610	.000340	.000854
.000041	.000125	.000141	.000370	.000241	.000614	.000341	.000858
.000042	.000129	.000142	.000373	.000242	.000617	.000342	.000862
.000043	.000133	.000143	.000377	.000243	.000621	.000343	.000865
.000044	.000137	.000144	.000381	.000244	.000625	.000344	.000869
.000045	.000141	.000145	.000385	.000245	.000629	.000345	.000873
.000046	.000144	.000146	.000389	.000246	.000633	.000346	.000877
.000047	.000148	.000147	.000392	.000247	.000637	.000347	.000881
.000050	.000152	.000150	.000396	.000250	.000640	.000350	.000885
.000051	.000156	.000151	.000400	.000251	.000644	.000351	.000888
.000052	.000160	.000152	.000404	.000252	.000648	.000352	.000892
.000053	.000164	.000153	.000408	.000253	.000652	.000353	.000896
.000054	.000167	.000154	.000411	.000254	.000656	.000354	.000900
.000055	.000171	.000155	.000415	.000255	.000659	.000355	.000904
.000056	.000175	.000156	.000419	.000256	.000663	.000356	.000907
.000057	.000179	.000157	.000423	.000257	.000667	.000357	.000911
.000060	.000183	.000160	.000427	.000260	.000671	.000360	.000915
.000061	.000186	.000161	.000431	.000261	.000675	.000361	.000919
.000062	.000190	.000162	.000434	.000262	.000679	.000362	.000923
.000063	.000194	.000163	.000438	.000263	.000682	.000363	.000926
.000064	.000198	.000164	.000442	.000264	.000686	.000364	.000930
.000065	.000202	.000165	.000446	.000265	.000690	.000365	.000934
.000066	.000205	.000166	.000450	.000266	.000694	.000366	.000938
.000067	.000209	.000167	.000453	.000267	.000698	.000367	.000942
.000070	.000213	.000170	.000457	.000270	.000701	.000370	.000946
.000071	.000217	.000171	.000461	.000271	.000705	.000371	.000949
.000072	.000221	.000172	.000465	.000272	.000709	.000372	.000953
.000073	.000225	.000173	.000469	.000273	.000713	.000373	.000957
.000074	.000228	.000174	.000473	.000274	.000717	.000374	.000961
.000075	.000232	.000175	.000476	.000275	.000720	.000375	.000965
.000076	.000326	.000176	.000480	.000276	.000724	.000376	.000968
.000077	.000240	.000177	.000484	.000277	.000728	.000377	.000972

OCTAL-DECIMAL FRACTION CONVERSION TABLE (Continued)

OCTAL	DEC.	OCTAL	DEC.	OCTAL	DEC.	OCTAL	DEC.
.000400	.000976	.000500	.001220	.000600	.001464	.000700	.001708
.000401	.000980	.000501	.001224	.000601	.001468	.000701	.001712
.000402	.000984	.000502	.001228	.000602	.001472	.000702	.001716
.000403	.000988	.000503	.001232	.000603	.001476	.000703	.001720
.000404	.000991	.000504	.001235	.000604	.001480	.000704	.001724
.000405	.000995	.000505	.001239	.000605	.001483	.000705	.001728
.000406	.000999	.000506	.001243	.000606	.001487	.000706	.001731
.000407	.001003	.000507	.001247	.000607	.001491	.000707	.001735
.000410	.001007	.000510	.001251	.000610	.001495	.000710	.001739
.000411	.001010	.000511	.001255	.000611	.001499	.000711	.001743
.000412	.001014	.000512	.001258	.000612	.001502	.000712	.001747
.000413	.001018	.000513	.001262	.000613	.001506	.000713	.001750
.000414	.001022	.000514	.001266	.000614	.001510	.000714	.001754
.000415	.001026	.000515	.001270	.000615	.001514	.000715	.001758
.000416	.001029	.000516	.001274	.000616	.001518	.000716	.001762
.000417	.001033	.000517	.001277	.000617	.001522	.000717	.001766
.000420	.001037	.000520	.001281	.000620	.001525	.000720	.001770
.000421	.001041	.000521	.001285	.000621	.001529	.000721	.001773
.000422	.001045	.000522	.001289	.000622	.001533	.000722	.001777
.000423	.001049	.000523	.001293	.000623	.001537	.000723	.001781
.000424	.001052	.000524	.001296	.000624	.001541	.000724	.001785
.000425	.001056	.000525	.001300	.000625	.001544	.000725	.001789
.000426	.001060	.000526	.001304	.000626	.001548	.000726	.001792
.000427	.001064	.000527	.001308	.000627	.001552	.000727	.001796
.000430	.001068	.000530	.001312	.000630	.001556	.000730	.001800
.000431	.001071	.000531	.001316	.000631	.001560	.000731	.001804
.000432	.001075	.000532	.001319	.000632	.001564	.000732	.001808
.000433	.001079	.000533	.001323	.000633	.001567	.000733	.001811
.000434	.001083	.000534	.001327	.000634	.001571	.000734	.001815
.000435	.001087	.000535	.001331	.000635	.001575	.000735	.001819
.000436	.001091	.000536	.001335	.000636	.001579	.000736	.001823
.000437	.001094	.000537	.001338	.000637	.001583	.000737	.001827
.000440	.001098	.000540	.001342	.000640	.001586	.000740	.001831
.000441	.001102	.000541	.001346	.000641	.001590	.000741	.001834
.000442	.001106	.000542	.001350	.000642	.001594	.000742	.001838
.000443	.001110	.000543	.001354	.000643	.001598	.000743	.001842
.000444	.001113	.000544	.001358	.000644	.001602	.000744	.001846
.000445	.001117	.000545	.001361	.000645	.001605	.000745	.001850
.000446	.001121	.000546	.001365	.000646	.001609	.000746	.001853
.000447	.001125	.000547	.001369	.000647	.001613	.000747	.001857
.000450	.001129	.000550	.001373	.000650	.001617	.000750	.001861
.000451	.001132	.000551	.001377	.000651	.001621	.000751	.001865
.000452	.001136	.000552	.001380	.000652	.001625	.000752	.001869
.000453	.001140	.000553	.001384	.000653	.001628	.000753	.001873
.000454	.001144	.000554	.001388	.000654	.001632	.000754	.001876
.000455	.001148	.000555	.001392	.000655	.001636	.000755	.001880
.000456	.001152	.000556	.001396	.000656	.001640	.000756	.001884
.000457	.001155	.000557	.001399	.000657	.001644	.000757	.001888
.000460	.001159	.000560	.001403	.000660	.001647	.000760	.001892
.000461	.001163	.000561	.001407	.000661	.001651	.000761	.001895
.000462	.001167	.000562	.001411	.000662	.001655	.000762	.001899
.000463	.001171	.000563	.001415	.000663	.001659	.000763	.001903
.000464	.001174	.000564	.001419	.000664	.001663	.000764	.001907
.000465	.001178	.000565	.001422	.000665	.001667	.000765	.001911
.000466	.001182	.000566	.001426	.000666	.001670	.000766	.001914
.000467	.001186	.000567	.001430	.000667	.001674	.000767	.001918
.000470	.001190	.000570	.001434	.000670	.001678	.000770	.001922
.000471	.001194	.000571	.001438	.000671	.001682	.000771	.001926
.000472	.001197	.000572	.001441	.000672	.001686	.000772	.001930
.000473	.001201	.000573	.001445	.000673	.001689	.000773	.001934
.000474	.001205	.000574	.001449	.000674	.001693	.000774	.001937
.000475	.001209	.000575	.001453	.000675	.001697	.000775	.001941
.000476	.001213	.000576	.001457	.000676	.001701	.000776	.001945
.000477	.001216	.000577	.001461	.000677	.001705	.000777	.001949

I. HEXADECIMAL AND DECIMAL DIRECT CONVERSION TABLE

The following tables aid in converting hexadecimal (base 16) numbers to decimal, and the reverse. Note that the base 16 digits for the decimal values 10–15 are represented by the letters A–F, respectively.

This table provides direct conversion of decimal and hexadecimal numbers in these ranges:

HEXADECIMAL	DECIMAL
1000	4096
2000	8192
3000	12288
4000	16384
5000	20480
6000	24576
7000	28672
8000	32768
9000	36864
A000	40960
B000	45056
C000	49152
D000	53248
E000	57344
F000	61440

HEXADECIMAL	DECIMAL
000 to FFF	0000 to 4095

For numbers outside the range of the table, add the following values to the table figures:

	0	1	2	3	4	5	6	7	8	9	A	B	C	D	E	F
00_	0000	0001	0002	0003	0004	0005	0006	0007	0008	0009	0010	0011	0012	0013	0014	0015
01_	0016	0017	0018	0019	0020	0021	0022	0023	0024	0025	0026	0027	0028	0029	0030	0031
02_	0032	0033	0034	0035	0036	0037	0038	0039	0040	0041	0042	0043	0044	0045	0046	0047
03_	0048	0049	0050	0051	0052	0053	0054	0055	0056	0057	0058	0059	0060	0061	0062	0063
04_	0064	0065	0066	0067	0068	0069	0070	0071	0072	0073	0074	0075	0076	0077	0078	0079
05_	0080	0081	0082	0083	0084	0085	0086	0087	0088	0089	0090	0091	0092	0093	0094	0095
06_	0096	0097	0098	0099	0100	0101	0102	0103	0104	0105	0106	0107	0108	0109	0110	0111
07_	0112	0113	0114	0115	0116	0117	0118	0119	0120	0121	0122	0123	0124	0125	0126	0127
08_	0128	0129	0130	0131	0132	0133	0134	0135	0136	0137	0138	0139	0140	0141	0142	0143
09_	0144	0145	0146	0147	0148	0149	0150	0151	0152	0153	0154	0155	0156	0157	0158	0159
0A_	0160	0161	0162	0163	0164	0165	0166	0167	0168	0169	0170	0171	0172	0173	0174	0175
0B_	0176	0177	0178	0179	0180	0181	0182	0183	0184	0185	0186	0187	0188	0189	0190	0191
0C_	0192	0193	0194	0195	0196	0197	0198	0199	0200	0201	0202	0203	0204	0205	0206	0207
0D_	0208	0209	0210	0211	0212	0213	0214	0215	0216	0217	0218	0219	0220	0221	0222	0223
0E_	0224	0225	0226	0227	0228	0229	0230	0231	0232	0233	0234	0235	0236	0237	0238	0239
0F_	0240	0241	0242	0243	0244	0245	0246	0247	0248	0249	0250	0251	0252	0253	0254	0255
10_	0256	0257	0258	0259	0260	0261	0262	0263	0264	0265	0266	0267	0268	0269	0270	0271
11_	0272	0273	0274	0275	0276	0277	0278	0279	0280	0281	0282	0283	0284	0285	0286	0287
12_	0288	0289	0290	0291	0292	0293	0294	0295	0296	0297	0298	0299	0300	0301	0302	0303
13_	0304	0305	0306	0307	0308	0309	0310	0311	0312	0313	0314	0315	0316	0317	0318	0319
14_	0320	0321	0322	0323	0324	0325	0326	0327	0328	0329	0330	0331	0332	0333	0334	0335
15_	0336	0337	0338	0339	0340	0341	0342	0343	0344	0345	0346	0347	0348	0349	0350	0351
16_	0352	0353	0354	0355	0356	0357	0358	0359	0360	0361	0362	0363	0364	0365	0366	0367
17_	0368	0369	0370	0371	0372	0373	0374	0375	0376	0377	0378	0379	0380	0381	0382	0383
18_	0384	0385	0386	0387	0388	0389	0390	0391	0392	0393	0394	0395	0396	0397	0398	0399
19_	0400	0401	0402	0403	0404	0405	0406	0407	0408	0409	0410	0411	0412	0413	0414	0415
1A_	0416	0417	0418	0419	0420	0421	0422	0423	0424	0425	0426	0427	0428	0429	0430	0431
1B_	0432	0433	0434	0435	0436	0437	0438	0439	0440	0441	0442	0443	0444	0445	0446	0447
1C_	0448	0449	0450	0451	0452	0453	0454	0455	0456	0457	0458	0459	0460	0461	0462	0463
1D_	0464	0465	0466	0467	0468	0469	0470	0471	0472	0473	0474	0475	0476	0477	0478	0479
1E_	0480	0481	0482	0483	0484	0485	0486	0487	0488	0489	0490	0491	0492	0493	0494	0495
1F_	0496	0497	0498	0499	0500	0501	0502	0503	0504	0505	0506	0507	0508	0509	0510	0511

DIRECT CONVERSION TABLE (Continued)

	0	1	2	3	4	5	6	7	8	9	A	B	C	D	E	F
20__	0512	0513	0514	0515	0516	0517	0518	0519	0520	0521	0522	0523	0524	0525	0526	0527
21__	0528	0529	0530	0531	0532	0533	0534	0535	0536	0537	0538	0539	0540	0541	0542	0543
22__	0544	0545	0546	0547	0548	0549	0550	0551	0552	0553	0554	0555	0556	0557	0558	0559
23__	0560	0561	0562	0563	0564	0565	0566	0567	0568	0569	0570	0571	0572	0573	0574	0575
24__	0576	0577	0578	0579	0580	0581	0582	0583	0584	0585	0586	0587	0588	0589	0590	0591,
25__	0592	0593	0594	0595	0596	0597	0598	0599	0600	0601	0602	0603	0604	0605	0606	0607
26__	0608	0609	0610	0611	0612	0613	0614	0615	0616	0617	0618	0619	0620	0621	0622	0623
27__	0624	0625	0626	0627	0628	0629	0630	0631	0632	0633	0634	0635	0636	0637	0638	0639
28__	0640	0641	0642	0643	0644	0645	0646	0647	0648	0649	0650	0651	0652	0653	0654	0655
29__	0656	0657	0658	0659	0660	0661	0662	0663	0664	0665	0666	0667	0668	0669	0670	0671
2A__	0672	0673	0674	0675	0676	0677	0678	0679	0680	0681	0682	0683	0684	0685	0686	0687
2B__	0688	0689	0690	0691	0692	0693	0694	0695	0696	0697	0698	0699	0700	0701	0702	0703
2C__	0704	0705	0706	0707	0708	0709	0710	0711	0712	0713	0714	0715	0716	0717	0718	0719
2D__	0720	0721	0722	0723	0724	0725	0726	0727	0728	0729	0730	0731	0732	0733	0734	0735
2E__	0736	0737	0738	0739	0740	0741	0742	0743	0744	0745	0746	0747	0748	0749	0750	0751
2F__	0752	0753	0754	0755	0756	0757	0758	0759	0760	0761	0762	0763	0764	0765	0766	0767
30__	0768	0769	0770	0771	0772	0773	0774	0775	0776	0777	0778	0779	0780	0781	0782	0783
31__	0784	0785	0786	0787	0788	0789	0790	0791	0792	0793	0794	0795	0796	0797	0798	0799
32__	0800	0801	0802	0803	0804	0805	0806	0807	0808	0809	0810	0811	0812	0813	0814	0815
33__	0816	0817	0818	0819	0820	0821	0822	0823	0824	0825	0826	0827	0828	0829	0830	0831
34__	0832	0833	0834	0835	0836	0837	0838	0839	0840	0841	0842	0843	0844	0845	0846	0847
35__	0848	0849	0850	0851	0852	0853	0854	0855	0856	0857	0858	0859	0860	0861	0862	0863
36__	0864	0865	0866	0867	0868	0869	0870	0871	0872	0873	0874	0875	0876	0877	0878	0879
37__	0880	0881	0882	0883	0884	0885	0886	0887	0888	0889	0890	0891	0892	0893	0894	0895
38__	0896	0897	0898	0899	0900	0901	0902	0903	0904	0905	0906	0907	0908	0909	0910	0911
39__	0912	0913	0914	0915	0916	0917	0918	0919	0920	0921	0922	0923	0924	0925	0926	0927
3A__	0928	0929	0930	0931	0932	0933	0934	0935	0936	0937	0938	0939	0940	0941	0942	0943
3B__	0944	0945	0946	0947	0948	0949	0950	0951	0952	0953	0954	0955	0956	0957	0958	0959
3C__	0960	0961	0962	0963	0964	0965	0966	0967	0968	0969	0970	0971	0972	0973	0974	0975
3D__	0976	0977	0978	0979	0980	0981	0982	0983	0984	0985	0986	0987	0988	0989	0990	0991
3E__	0992	0993	0994	0995	0996	0997	0998	0999	1000	1001	1002	1003	1004	1005	1006	1007
3F__	1008	1009	1010	1011	1012	1013	1014	1015	1016	1017	1018	1019	1020	1021	1022	1023
40__	1024	1025	1026	1027	1028	1029	1030	1031	1032	1033	1034	1035	1036	1037	1038	1039
41__	1040	1041	1042	1043	1044	1045	1046	1047	1048	1049	1050	1051	1052	1053	1054	1055
42__	1056	1057	1058	1059	1060	1061	1062	1063	1064	1065	1066	1067	1068	1069	1070	1071
43__	1072	1073	1074	1075	1076	1077	1078	1079	1080	1081	1082	1083	1084	1085	1086	1087
44__	1088	1089	1090	1091	1092	1093	1094	1095	1096	1097	1098	1099	1100	1101	1102	1103
45__	1104	1105	1106	1107	1108	1109	1110	1111	1112	1113	1114	1115	1116	1117	1118	1119
46__	1120	1121	1122	1123	1124	1125	1126	1127	1128	1129	1130	1131	1132	1133	1134	1135
47__	1136	1137	1138	1139	1140	1141	1142	1143	1144	1145	1146	1147	1148	1149	1150	1151
48__	1152	1153	1154	1155	1156	1157	1158	1159	1160	1161	1162	1163	1164	1165	1166	1167
49__	1168	1169	1170	1171	1172	1173	1174	1175	1176	1177	1178	1179	1180	1181	1182	1183
4A__	1184	1185	1186	1187	1188	1189	1190	1191	1192	1193	1194	1195	1196	1197	1198	1199
4B__	1200	1201	1202	1203	1204	1205	1206	1207	1208	1209	1210	1211	1212	1213	1214	1215
4C__	1216	1217	1218	1219	1220	1221	1222	1223	1224	1225	1226	1227	1228	1229	1230	1231
4D__	1232	1233	1234	1235	1236	1237	1238	1239	1240	1241	1242	1243	1244	1245	1246	1247
4E__	1248	1249	1250	1251	1252	1253	1254	1255	1256	1257	1258	1259	1260	1261	1262	1263
4F__	1264	1265	1266	1267	1268	1269	1270	1271	1272	1273	1274	1275	1276	1277	1278	1279
50__	1280	1281	1282	1283	1284	1285	1286	1287	1288	1289	1290	1291	1292	1293	1294	1295
51__	1296	1297	1298	1299	1300	1301	1302	1303	1304	1305	1306	1307	1308	1309	1310	1311
52__	1312	1313	1314	1315	1316	1317	1318	1319	1320	1321	1322	1323	1324	1325	1326	1327
53__	1328	1329	1330	1331	1332	1333	1334	1335	1336	1337	1338	1339	1340	1341	1342	1343
54__	1344	1345	1346	1347	1348	1349	1350	1351	1352	1353	1354	1355	1356	1357	1358	1359
55__	1360	1361	1362	1363	1364	1365	1366	1367	1368	1369	1370	1371	1372	1373	1374	1375
56__	1376	1377	1378	1379	1380	1381	1382	1383	1384	1385	1386	1387	1388	1389	1390	1391
57__	1392	1393	1394	1395	1396	1397	1398	1399	1400	1401	1402	1403	1404	1405	1406	1407
58__	1408	1409	1410	1411	1412	1413	1414	1415	1416	1417	1418	1419	1420	1421	1422	1423
59__	1424	1425	1426	1427	1428	1429	1430	1431	1432	1433	1434	1435	1436	1437	1438	1439
5A__	1440	1441	1442	1443	1444	1445	1446	1447	1448	1449	1450	1451	1452	1453	1454	1455
5B__	1456	1457	1458	1459	1460	1461	1462	1463	1464	1465	1466	1467	1468	1469	1470	1471
5C__	1472	1473	1474	1475	1476	1477	1478	1479	1480	1481	1482	1483	1484	1485	1486	1487
5D__	1488	1489	1490	1491	1492	1493	1494	1495	1496	1497	1498	1499	1500	1501	1502	1503
5E__	1504	1505	1506	1507	1508	1509	1510	1511	1512	1513	1514	1515	1516	1517	1518	1519
5F__	1520	1521	1522	1523	1524	1525	1526	1527	1528	1529	1530	1531	1532	1533	1534	1535

DIRECT CONVERSION TABLE (Continued)

	0	1	2	3	4	5	6	7	8	9	A	B	C	D	E	F
60__	1536	1537	1538	1539	1540	1541	1542	1543	1544	1545	1546	1547	1548	1549	1550	1551
61__	1552	1553	1554	1555	1556	1557	1558	1559	1560	1561	1562	1563	1564	1565	1566	1567
62__	1568	1569	1570	1571	1572	1573	1574	1575	1576	1577	1578	1579	1580	1581	1582	1583
63__	1584	1585	1586	1587	1588	1589	1590	1591	1592	1593	1594	1595	1596	1597	1598	1599
64__	1600	1601	1602	1603	1604	1605	1606	1607	1608	1609	1610	1611	1612	1613	1614	1615
65__	1616	1617	1618	1619	1620	1621	1622	1623	1624	1625	1626	1627	1628	1629	1630	1631
66__	1632	1633	1634	1635	1636	1637	1638	1639	1640	1641	1642	1643	1644	1645	1646	1647
67__	1648	1649	1650	1651	1652	1653	1654	1655	1656	1657	1658	1659	1660	1661	1662	1663
68__	1664	1665	1666	1667	1668	1669	1670	1671	1672	1673	1674	1675	1676	1677	1678	1679
69__	1680	1681	1682	1683	1684	1685	1686	1687	1688	1689	1690	1691	1692	1693	1694	1695
6A__	1696	1697	1698	1699	1700	1701	1702	1703	1704	1705	1706	1707	1708	1709	1710	1711
6B__	1712	1713	1714	1715	1716	1717	1718	1719	1720	1721	1722	1723	1724	1725	1726	1727
6C__	1728	1729	1730	1731	1732	1733	1734	1735	1736	1737	1738	1739	1740	1741	1742	1743
6D__	1744	1745	1746	1747	1748	1749	1750	1751	1752	1753	1754	1755	1756	1757	1758	1759
6E__	1760	1761	1762	1763	1764	1765	1766	1767	1768	1769	1770	1771	1772	1773	1774	1775
6F__	1776	1777	1778	1779	1780	1781	1782	1783	1784	1785	1786	1787	1788	1789	1790	1791
70__	1792	1793	1794	1795	1796	1797	1798	1799	1800	1801	1802	1803	1804	1805	1806	1807
71__	1808	1809	1810	1811	1812	1813	1814	1815	1816	1817	1818	1819	1820	1821	1822	1823
72__	1824	1825	1826	1827	1828	1829	1830	1831	1832	1833	1834	1835	1836	1837	1838	1839
73__	1840	1841	1842	1843	1844	1845	1846	1847	1848	1849	1850	1851	1852	1853	1854	1855
74__	1856	1857	1858	1859	1860	1861	1862	1863	1864	1865	1866	1867	1868	1869	1870	1871
75__	1872	1873	1874	1875	1876	1877	1878	1879	1880	1881	1882	1883	1884	1885	1886	1887
76__	1888	1889	1890	1891	1892	1893	1894	1895	1896	1897	1898	1899	1900	1901	1902	1903
77__	1904	1905	1906	1907	1908	1909	1910	1911	1912	1913	1914	1915	1916	1917	1918	1919
78__	1920	1921	1922	1923	1924	1925	1926	1927	1928	1929	1930	1931	1932	1933	1934	1935
79__	1936	1937	1938	1939	1940	1941	1942	1943	1944	1945	1946	1947	1948	1949	1950	1951
7A__	1952	1953	1954	1955	1956	1957	1958	1959	1960	1961	1962	1963	1964	1965	1966	1967
7B__	1968	1969	1970	1971	1972	1973	1974	1975	1976	1977	1978	1979	1980	1981	1982	1983
7C__	1984	1985	1986	1987	1988	1989	1990	1991	1992	1993	1994	1995	1996	1997	1998	1999
7D__	2000	2001	2002	2003	2004	2005	2006	2007	2008	2009	2010	2011	2012	2013	2014	2015
7E__	2016	2017	2018	2019	2020	2021	2022	2023	2024	2025	2026	2027	2028	2029	2030	2031
7F__	2032	2033	2034	2035	2036	2037	2038	2039	2040	2041	2042	2043	2044	2045	2046	2047
80__	2048	2049	2050	2051	2052	2053	2054	2055	2056	2057	2058	2059	2060	2061	2062	2063
81__	2064	2065	2066	2067	2068	2069	2070	2071	2072	2073	2074	2075	2076	2077	2078	2079
82__	2080	2081	2082	2083	2084	2085	2086	2087	2088	2089	2090	2091	2092	2093	2094	2095
83__	2096	2097	2098	2099	2100	2101	2102	2103	2104	2105	2106	2107	2108	2109	2110	2111
84__	2112	2113	2114	2115	2116	2117	2118	2119	2120	2121	2122	2123	2124	2125	2126	2127
85__	2128	2129	2130	2131	2132	2133	2134	2135	2136	2137	2138	2139	2140	2141	2142	2143
86__	2144	2145	2146	2147	2148	2149	2150	2151	2152	2153	2154	2155	2156	2157	2158	2159
87__	2160	2161	2162	2163	2164	2165	2166	2167	2168	2169	2170	2171	2172	2173	2174	2175
88__	2176	2177	2178	2179	2180	2181	2182	2183	2184	2185	2186	2187	2188	2189	2190	2191
89__	2192	2193	2194	2195	2196	2197	2198	2199	2200	2201	2202	2203	2204	2205	2206	2207
8A__	2208	2209	2210	2211	2212	2213	2214	2215	2216	2217	2218	2219	2220	2221	2222	2223
8B__	2224	2225	2226	2227	2228	2229	2230	2231	2232	2233	2234	2235	2236	2237	2238	2239
8C__	2240	2241	2242	2243	2244	2245	2246	2247	2248	2249	2250	2251	2252	2253	2254	2255
8D__	2256	2257	2258	2259	2260	2261	2262	2263	2264	2265	2266	2267	2268	2269	2270	2271
8E__	2272	2273	2274	2275	2276	2277	2278	2279	2280	2281	2282	2283	2284	2285	2286	2287
8F__	2288	2289	2290	2291	2292	2293	2294	2295	2296	2297	2298	2299	2300	2301	2302	2303
90__	2304	2305	2306	2307	2308	2309	2310	2311	2312	2313	2314	2315	2316	2317	2318	2319
91__	2320	2321	2322	2323	2324	2325	2326	2327	2328	2329	2330	2331	2332	2333	2334	2335
92__	2336	2337	2338	2339	2340	2341	2342	2343	2344	2345	2346	2347	2348	2349	2350	2351
93__	2352	2353	2354	2355	2356	2357	2358	2359	2360	2361	2362	2363	2364	2365	2366	2367
94__	2368	2369	2370	2371	2372	2373	2374	2375	2376	2377	2378	2379	2380	2381	2382	2383
95__	2384	2385	2386	2387	2388	2389	2390	2391	2392	2393	2394	2395	2396	2397	2398	2399
96__	2400	2401	2402	2403	2404	2405	2406	2407	2408	2409	2410	2411	2412	2413	2414	2415
97__	2416	2417	2418	2419	2420	2421	2422	2423	2424	2425	2426	2427	2428	2429	2430	2431
98__	2432	2433	2434	2435	2436	2437	2438	2439	2440	2441	2442	2443	2444	2445	2446	2447
99__	2448	2449	2450	2451	2452	2453	2454	2455	2456	2457	2458	2459	2460	2461	2462	2463
9A__	2464	2465	2466	2467	2468	2469	2470	2471	2472	2473	2474	2475	2476	2477	2478	2479
9B__	2480	2481	2482	2483	2484	2485	2486	2487	2488	2489	2490	2491	2492	2493	2494	2495
9C__	2496	2497	2498	2499	2500	2501	2502	2503	2504	2505	2506	2507	2508	2509	2510	2511
9D__	2512	2513	2514	2515	2516	2517	2518	2519	2520	2521	2522	2523	2524	2525	2526	2527
9E__	2528	2529	2530	2531	2532	2533	2534	2535	2536	2537	2538	2539	2540	2541	2542	2543
9F__	2544	2545	2546	2547	2548	2549	2550	2551	2552	2553	2554	2555	2556	2557	2558	2559

DIRECT CONVERSION TABLE (Continued)

	0	1	2	3	4	5	6	7	8	9	A	B	C	D	E	F
A0__	2560	2561	2562	2563	2564	2565	2566	2567	2568	2569	2570	2571	2572	2573	2574	2575
A1__	2576	2577	2578	2579	2580	2581	2582	2583	2584	2585	2586	2587	2588	2589	2590	2591
A2__	2592	2593	2594	2595	2596	2597	2598	2599	2600	2601	2602	2603	2604	2605	2606	2607
A3__	2608	2609	2610	2611	2612	2613	2614	2615	2616	2617	2618	2619	2620	2621	2622	2623
A4__	2624	2625	2626	2627	2628	2629	2630	2631	2632	2633	2634	2635	2636	2637	2638	2639
A5__	2640	2641	2642	2643	2644	2645	2646	2647	2648	2649	2650	2651	2652	2653	2654	2655
A6__	2656	2657	2658	2659	2660	2661	2662	2663	2664	2665	2666	2667	2668	2669	2670	2671
A7__	2672	2673	2674	2675	2676	2677	2678	2679	2680	2681	2682	2683	2684	2685	2686	2687
A8__	2688	2689	2690	2691	2692	2693	2694	2695	2696	2697	2698	2699	2700	2701	2702	2703
A9__	2704	2705	2706	2707	2708	2709	2710	2711	2712	2713	2714	2715	2716	2717	2718	2719
AA__	2720	2721	2722	2723	2724	2725	2726	2727	2728	2729	2730	2731	2732	3733	2734	2735
AB__	2736	2737	2738	2739	2740	2741	2742	2743	2744	2745	2746	2747	2748	2749	2750	2751
AC__	2752	2753	2754	2755	2756	2757	2758	2759	2760	2761	2762	2763	2764	2765	2766	2767
AD__	2768	2769	2770	2771	2772	2773	2774	2775	2776	2777	2778	2779	2780	2781	2782	2783
AE__	2784	2785	2786	2787	2788	2789	2790	2791	2792	2793	2794	2795	2796	2797	2798	2799
AF__	2800	2801	2802	2803	2804	2805	2806	2807	2808	2809	2810	2811	2812	2813	2814	2815
B0__	2816	2817	2818	2819	2820	2821	2822	2823	2824	2825	2826	2827	2828	2829	2830	2831
B1__	2832	2833	2834	2835	2836	2837	2838	2839	2840	2841	2842	2843	2844	2845	2846	2847
B2__	2848	2849	2850	2851	2852	2853	2854	2855	2856	2857	2858	2859	2860	2861	2862	2863
B3__	2864	2865	2866	2867	2868	2869	2870	2871	2872	2873	2874	2875	2876	2877	2878	2879
B4__	2880	2881	2882	2883	2884	2885	2886	2887	2888	2889	2890	2891	2892	2893	2894	2895
B5__	2896	2897	2898	2899	2900	2901	2902	2903	2904	2905	2906	2907	2908	2909	2910	2911
B6__	2912	2913	2914	2915	2916	2917	2918	2919	2920	2921	2922	2923	2924	2925	2926	2927
B7__	2928	2929	2930	2931	2932	2933	2934	2935	2936	2937	2938	2939	2940	2941	2942	2943
B8__	2944	2945	2946	2947	2948	2949	2950	2951	2952	2953	2954	2955	2956	2957	2958	2959
B9__	2960	2961	2962	2963	2964	2965	2966	2967	2968	2969	2970	2971	2972	2973	2974	2975
BA__	2976	2977	2978	2979	2980	2981	2982	2983	2984	2985	2986	2987	2988	2989	2990	2991
BB__	2992	2993	2994	2995	2996	2997	2998	2999	3000	3001	3002	3003	3004	3005	3006	3007
BC__	3008	3009	3010	3011	3012	3013	3014	3015	3016	3017	3018	3019	3020	3021	3022	3023
BD__	3024	3025	3026	3027	3028	3029	3030	3031	3032	3033	3034	3035	3036	3037	3038	3039
BE__	3040	3041	3042	3043	3044	3045	3046	3047	3048	3049	3050	3051	3052	3053	3054	3055
BF__	3056	3057	3058	3059	3060	3061	3062	3063	3064	3065	3066	3067	3068	3069	3070	3071
C0__	3072	3073	3074	3075	3076	3077	3078	3079	3080	3081	3082	3083	3084	3085	3086	3087
C1__	3088	3089	3090	3091	3092	3093	3094	3095	3096	3097	3098	3099	3100	3101	3102	3103
C2__	3104	3105	3106	3107	3108	3109	3110	3111	3112	3113	3114	3115	3116	3117	3118	3119
C3__	3120	3121	3122	3123	3124	3125	3126	3127	3128	3129	3130	3131	3132	3133	3134	3135
C4__	3136	3137	3138	3139	3140	3141	3142	3143	3144	3145	3146	3147	3148	3149	3150	3151
C5__	3152	3153	3154	3155	3156	3157	3158	3159	3160	3161	3162	3613	3164	3165	3166	3167
C6__	3168	3169	3170	3171	3172	3173	3174	3175	3176	3177	3178	3179	3180	3181	3182	3183
C7__	3184	3185	3186	3187	3188	3189	3190	3191	3192	3193	3194	3195	3196	3197	3198	3199
C8__	3200	3201	3202	3203	3204	3205	3206	3207	3208	3209	3210	3211	3212	3213	3214	3215
C9__	3216	3217	3218	3219	3220	3221	3222	3223	3224	3225	3226	3227	3228	3229	3230	3231
CA__	3232	3233	3234	3235	3236	3237	3238	3239	3240	3241	3242	3243	3244	3245	3246	3247
CB__	3248	3249	3250	3251	3252	3253	3254	3255	3256	3257	3258	3259	3260	3261	3262	3263
CC__	3264	3265	3266	3267	3268	3269	3270	3271	3272	3273	3274	3275	3276	3277	3278	3279
CD__	3280	3281	3282	3283	3284	3285	3286	3287	3288	3289	3290	3291	3292	3293	3294	3295
CE__	3296	3297	3298	3299	3300	3301	3302	3303	3304	3305	3306	3307	3308	3309	3310	3311
CF__	3312	3313	3314	3315	3316	3317	3318	3319	3320	3321	3322	3323	3324	3325	3326	3327
D0__	3328	3329	3330	3331	3332	3333	3334	3335	3336	3337	3338	3339	3340	3341	3342	3343
D1__	3344	3345	3346	3347	3348	3349	3350	3351	3352	3353	3354	3355	3356	3357	3358	3359
D2__	3360	3361	3362	3363	3364	3365	3366	3367	3368	3369	3370	3371	3372	3373	3374	3375
D3__	3376	3377	3378	3379	3380	3381	3382	3383	3384	3385	3386	3387	3388	3389	3390	3391
D4__	3392	3393	3394	3395	3396	3397	3398	3399	3400	3401	3402	3403	3404	3405	3406	3407
D5__	3408	3409	3410	3411	3412	3413	3414	3415	3416	3417	3418	3419	3420	3421	3422	3423
D6__	3424	3425	3426	3427	3428	3429	3430	3431	3432	3433	3434	3435	3436	3437	3438	3439
D7__	3440	3441	3442	3443	3444	3445	3446	3447	3448	3449	3450	3451	3452	3453	3454	3455
D8__	3456	3457	3458	3459	3460	3461	3462	3463	3464	3465	3466	3467	3468	3469	3470	3471
D9__	3472	3473	3474	3475	3476	3477	3478	3479	3480	3481	3482	3483	3484	3485	3486	3487
DA__	3488	3489	3490	3491	3492	3493	3494	3495	3496	3497	3498	3499	3500	3501	3502	3503
DB__	3504	3505	3506	3507	3508	3509	3510	3511	3512	3513	3514	3515	3516	3517	3518	3519
DC__	3520	3521	3522	3523	3524	3525	3526	3527	3528	3529	3530	3531	3532	3533	3534	3535
DD__	3536	3537	3538	3539	3540	3541	3542	3543	3544	3545	3546	3547	3548	3549	3550	3551
DE__	3552	3553	3554	3555	3556	3557	3558	3559	3560	3561	3562	3563	3564	3565	3566	3567
DF__	3568	3569	3570	3571	3572	3573	3574	3575	3576	3577	3578	3579	3580	3581	3582	3583

DIRECT CONVERSION TABLE (Continued)

	0	1	2	3	4	5	6	7	8	9	A	B	C	D	E	F
E0_	3584	3585	3586	3587	3588	3589	3590	3591	3592	3593	3594	3595	3596	3597	3598	3599
E1_	3600	3601	3602	3603	3604	3605	3606	3607	3608	3609	3610	3611	3612	3613	3614	3615
E2_	3616	3617	3618	3619	3620	3621	3622	3623	3624	3625	3626	3627	3628	3629	3630	3631
E3_	3632	3633	3634	3635	3636	3637	3638	3639	3640	3641	3642	3643	3644	3645	3646	3647
E4_	3648	3649	3650	3651	3652	3653	3654	3655	3656	3657	3658	3659	3660	3661	3662	3663
E5_	3664	3665	3666	3667	3668	3669	3670	3671	3672	3673	3674	3675	3676	3677	3678	3679
E6_	3680	3681	3682	3683	3684	3685	3686	3687	3688	3689	3690	3691	3692	3693	3694	3695
E7_	3696	3697	3698	3699	3700	3701	3702	3703	3704	3705	3706	3707	3708	3709	3710	3711
E8_	3712	3713	3714	3715	3716	3717	3718	3719	3720	3721	3722	3723	3724	3725	3726	3727
E9_	3728	3729	3730	3731	3732	3733	3734	3735	3736	3737	3738	3739	3740	3741	3742	3743
EA_	3744	3745	3746	3747	3748	3749	3750	3751	3752	3753	3754	3755	3756	3757	3758	3759
EB_	3760	3761	3762	3763	3764	3765	3766	3767	3768	3769	3770	3771	3772	3773	3774	3775
EC_	3776	3777	3778	3779	3780	3781	3782	3783	3784	3785	3786	3787	3788	3789	3790	3791
ED_	3792	3793	3794	3795	3796	3797	3798	3799	3800	3801	3802	3803	3804	3805	3806	3807
EE_	3808	3809	3810	3811	3812	3813	3814	3815	3816	3817	3818	3819	3820	3821	3822	3823
EF_	3824	3825	3826	3827	3828	3829	3830	3831	3832	3833	3834	3835	3836	3837	3838	3839
F0_	3840	3841	3842	3843	3844	3845	3846	3847	3848	3849	3850	3851	3852	3853	3854	3855
F1_	3856	3857	3858	3859	3860	3861	3862	3863	3864	3865	3866	3867	3868	3869	3870	3871
F2_	3872	3873	3874	3875	3876	3877	3878	3879	3880	3881	3882	3883	3884	3885	3886	3887
F3_	3888	3889	3890	3891	3892	3893	3894	3895	3896	3897	3898	3899	3900	3901	3902	3903
F4_	3904	3905	3906	3907	3908	3909	3910	3911	3912	3913	3914	3915	3916	3917	3918	3919
F5_	3920	3921	3922	3923	3924	3925	3926	3927	3928	3929	3930	3931	3932	3933	3934	3935
F6_	3936	3937	3938	3939	3940	3941	3942	3943	3944	3945	3946	3947	3948	3949	3950	3951
F7_	3952	3953	3954	3955	3956	3957	3958	3959	3960	3961	3962	3963	3964	3965	3966	3967
F8_	3968	3969	3970	3971	3972	3973	3974	3975	3976	3977	3978	3979	3980	3981	3982	3983
F9_	3984	3985	3986	3987	3988	3989	3990	3991	3992	3993	3994	3995	3996	3997	3998	3999
FA_	4000	4001	4002	4003	4004	4005	4006	4007	4008	4009	4010	4011	4012	4013	4014	4015
FB_	4016	4017	4018	4019	4020	4021	4022	4023	4024	4025	4026	4027	4028	4029	4030	4031
FC_	4032	4033	4034	4035	4036	4037	4038	4039	4040	4041	4042	4043	4044	4045	4046	4047
FD_	4048	4049	4050	4051	4052	4053	4054	4055	4056	4057	4058	4059	4060	4061	4062	4063
FE_	4064	4065	4066	4067	4068	4069	4070	4071	4072	4073	4074	4075	4076	4077	4078	4079
FF_	4080	4081	4082	4083	4084	4085	4086	4087	4088	4089	4090	4091	4092	4093	4094	4095

II. HEXADECIMAL AND DECIMAL INTEGER CONVERSION TABLE

| | 8 | | 7 | | 6 | | 5 | | 4 | | 3 | | 2 | | 1 |
Hex	Decimal	Hex	Decimal	Hex	Decimal	Hex	Decimal	Hex	Decimal	Hex	Decimal	Hex	Decimal	Hex	Decimal
0	0	0	0	0	0	0	0	0	0	0	0	0	0	0	0
1	268,435,456	1	16,777,216	1	1,048,576	1	65,536	1	4,096	1	256	1	16	1	1
2	536,870,912	2	33,554,432	2	2,097,152	2	131,072	2	8,192	2	512	2	32	2	2
3	805,306,368	3	50,331,648	3	3,145,728	3	196,608	3	12,288	3	768	3	48	3	3
4	1,073,741,824	4	67,108,864	4	4,194,304	4	262,144	4	16,384	4	1,024	4	64	4	4
5	1,342,177,280	5	83,886,080	5	5,242,880	5	327,680	5	20,480	5	1,280	5	80	5	5
6	1,610,612,736	6	100,663,296	6	6,291,456	6	393,216	6	24,576	6	1,536	6	96	6	6
7	1,879,048,192	7	117,440,512	7	7,340,032	7	458,752	7	28,672	7	1,792	7	112	7	7
8	2,147,483,648	8	134,217,728	8	8,388,608	8	524,288	8	32,768	8	2,048	8	128	8	8
9	2,415,919,104	9	150,994,944	9	9,437,184	9	589,824	9	36,864	9	2,304	9	144	9	9
A	2,684,354,560	A	167,772,160	A	10,485,760	A	655,360	A	40,960	A	2,560	A	160	A	10
B	2,952,790,016	B	184,549,376	B	11,534,336	B	720,896	B	45,056	B	2,816	B	176	B	11
C	3,221,225,472	C	201,326,592	C	12,582,912	C	786,432	C	49,152	C	3,072	C	192	C	12
D	3,489,660,928	D	218,103,808	D	13,631,488	D	851,968	D	53,248	D	3,328	D	208	D	13
E	3,758,096,384	E	234,881,024	E	14,680,064	E	917,504	E	57,344	E	3,584	E	224	E	14
F	4,026,531,840	F	251,658,240	F	15,728,640	F	983,040	F	61,440	F	3,840	F	240	F	15
	8		7		6		5		4		3		2		1

INTEGER CONVERSION TABLE (Continued)

TO CONVERT HEXADECIMAL TO DECIMAL

1. Locate the column of decimal numbers corresponding to the left-most digit or letter of the hexadecimal; select from this column and record the number that corresponds to the position of the hexadecimal digit or letter.
2. Repeat step 1 for the next (second from the left) position.
3. Repeat step 1 for the units (third from the left) position.
4. Add the numbers selected from the table to form the decimal number.

To convert integer numbers greater than the capacity of table, use the techniques below:

HEXADECIMAL TO DECIMAL

Successive cumulative multiplication from left to right, adding units position.

Example: $D34_{16} = 3380_{10}$

$$
\begin{array}{rr}
D = & 13 \\
& \times 16 \\
\hline
& 208 \\
3 = & +3 \\
\hline
& 211 \\
& \times 16 \\
\hline
& 3376 \\
4 = & +4 \\
\hline
& 3380
\end{array}
$$

TO CONVERT DECIMAL TO HEXADECIMAL

1. (a) Select from the table the highest decimal number that is equal to or less than the number to be converted.
   (b) Record the hexadecimal of the column containing the selected number.
   (c) Subtract the selected decimal from the number to be converted.
2. Using the remainder from step 1(c) repeat all of step 1 to develop the second position of the hexadecimal (and a remainder).
3. Using the remainder from step 2 repeat all of step 1 to develop the units position of the hexadecimal.
4. Combine terms to form the hexadecimal number.

DECIMAL TO HEXADECIMAL

Divide and collect the remainder in reverse order.

Example: $3380_{10} = X_{16}$

$$
\begin{array}{ll}
16 \underline{\smash{|3380}} & \text{remainder} \\
16 \underline{\smash{|211}} & 4 \\
16 \underline{\smash{|13}} & 3 \\
\quad\quad D &
\end{array}
$$

$3380_{10} = D34_{16}$

EXAMPLE

Conversion of
Hexadecimal
Value   D34

1. D		3328
2. 3		48
3. 4		4
4. Decimal		3380

EXAMPLE

Conversion of
Decimal
Value   3380

1. D		−3328
		52
2. 3		−48
		4
3. 4		−4
4. Hexa-decimal		D34

INTEGER CONVERSION TABLE (Continued)

POWERS OF 16 TABLE

Example: $268,435,456_{10} = (2.68435456 \times 10^8)_{10} = 1000\ 0000_{16} = (10^7)_{16}$

16^n	n
1	0
16	1
256	2
4 096	3
65 536	4
1 048 576	5
16 777 216	6
268 435 456	7
4 294 967 296	8
68 719 476 736	9
1 099 511 627 776	10 = A
17 592 186 044 416	11 = B
281 474 976 710 656	12 = C
4 503 599 627 370 496	13 = D
72 057 594 037 927 936	14 = E
1 152 921 504 606 846 976	15 = F

Decimal Values

III. HEXADECIMAL AND DECIMAL FRACTION CONVERSION TABLE

	1		2			3				4			
Hex	Decimal	Hex	Decimal		Hex	Decimal			Hex	Decimal Equivalent			
.0	.0000	.00	.0000	0000	.000	.0000	0000	0000	.0000	.0000	0000	0000	0000
.1	.0625	.01	.0039	0625	.001	.0002	4414	0625	.0001	.0000	1525	8789	0625
.2	.1250	.02	.0078	1250	.002	.0004	8828	1250	.0002	.0000	3051	7578	1250
.3	.1875	.03	.0117	1875	.003	.0007	3242	1875	.0003	.0000	4577	6367	1875
.4	.2500	.04	.0156	2500	.004	.0009	7656	2500	.0004	.0000	6103	5156	2500
.5	.3125	.05	.0195	3125	.005	.0012	2070	3125	.0005	.0000	7629	3945	3125
.6	.3750	.06	.0234	3750	.006	.0014	6484	3750	.0006	.0000	9155	2734	3750
.7	.4375	.07	.0273	4375	.007	.0017	0898	4375	.0007	.0001	0681	1523	4375
.8	.5000	.08	.0312	5000	.008	.0019	5312	5000	.0008	.0001	2207	0312	5000
.9	.5625	.09	.0351	5625	.009	.0021	9726	5625	.0009	.0001	3732	9101	5625
.A	.6250	.0A	.0390	6250	.00A	.0024	4140	6250	.000A	.0001	5258	7890	6250
.B	.6875	.0B	.0429	6875	.00B	.0026	8554	6875	.000B	.0001	6784	6679	6875
.C	.7500	.0C	.0468	7500	.00C	.0029	2968	7500	.000C	.0001	8310	5468	7500
.D	.8125	.0D	.0507	8125	.00D	.0031	7382	8125	.000D	.0001	9836	4257	8125
.E	.8750	.0E	.0546	8750	.00E	.0034	1796	8750	.000E	.0002	1362	3046	8750
.F	.9375	.0F	.0585	9375	.00F	.0036	6210	9375	.000F	.0002	2888	1835	9375
	1		2			3				4			

TO CONVERT .ABC HEXADECIMAL TO DECIMAL

Find .A   in position 1   .6250
Find .0B in position 2   .0429 6875
Find .00C in position 3   .0029 2968 7500
.ABC Hex is equal to   .6708 9843 7500

FRACTION CONVERSION TABLE (Continued)

TO CONVERT .13 DECIMAL TO HEXADECIMAL

1. Find .1250 next lowest to   .1300
              subtract   − .1250   = .2 Hex
2. Find .0039 0625 next lowest to   .0050 0000
                                     − .0039 0625   = .01
3. Find .0009 7656 2500   .0010 9375 0000
                                     − .0009 7656 2500   = .004
4. Find .0001 0681 1523 4375   .0001 1718 7500 0000
                                     − .0001 0681 1523 4375 = .0007
                                       .0000 1037 5976 5625 = .2147 Hex

5. 13 Decimal is approximately equal to ⎯⎯⎯⎯⎯⎯⎯⎯⎯⎯⎯⎯⎯⎯⎯↑

To convert fractions beyond the capacity of table, use techniques below:

HEXADECIMAL FRACTION TO DECIMAL

Convert the hexadecimal fraction to its decimal equivalent using the same technique as for integer numbers.
Divide the results by 16^n (n is the number of fraction
positions).

Example: $.8A7_{16} = .540771_{10}$

$$8A7_{16} = 2215_{10}$$

$$16^3 = 4096 \qquad 4096 \overline{\smash{\big)}\ 2215.000000} \quad .540771$$

DECIMAL FRACTION TO HEXADECIMAL

Collect integer parts of product in the order of calculation.

Example: $.5408_{10} = .8A7_{16}$

```
             .5408
           × 16
  8 ←  [ 8 ] .6528
           × 16
  A ← [ 10 ] .4448
           × 16
  7 ←  [ 7 ] .1168
```

HEXADECIMAL ADDITION AND SUBTRACTION TABLE

Example: 6 + 2 = 8,   8 − 2 = 6,   and   8 − 6 = 2

	1	2	3	4	5	6	7	8	9	A	B	C	D	E	F
1	02	03	04	05	06	07	08	09	0A	0B	0C	0D	0E	0F	10
2	03	04	05	06	07	08	09	0A	0B	0C	0D	0E	0F	10	11
3	04	05	06	07	08	09	0A	0B	0C	0D	0E	0F	10	11	12
4	05	06	07	08	09	0A	0B	0C	0D	0E	0F	10	11	12	13
5	06	07	08	09	0A	0B	0C	0D	0E	0F	10	11	12	13	14
6	07	08	09	0A	0B	0C	0D	0E	0F	10	11	12	13	14	15
7	08	09	0A	0B	0C	0D	0E	0F	10	11	12	13	14	15	16
8	09	0A	0B	0C	0D	0E	0F	10	11	12	13	14	15	16	17
9	0A	0B	0C	0D	0E	0F	10	11	12	13	14	15	16	17	18
A	0B	0C	0D	0E	0F	10	11	12	13	14	15	16	17	18	19
B	0C	0D	0E	0F	10	11	12	13	14	15	16	17	18	19	1A
C	0D	0E	0F	10	11	12	13	14	15	16	17	18	19	1A	1B
D	0E	0F	10	11	12	13	14	15	16	17	18	19	1A	1B	1C
E	0F	10	11	12	13	14	15	16	17	18	19	1A	1B	1C	1D
F	10	11	12	13	14	15	16	17	18	19	1A	1B	1C	1D	1E

HEXADECIMAL MULTIPLICATION TABLE

Example: 2 × 4 = 08,   F × 2 = 1E

	1	2	3	4	5	6	7	8	9	A	B	C	D	E	F
1	01	02	03	04	05	06	07	08	09	0A	0B	0C	0D	0E	0F
2	02	04	06	08	0A	0C	0E	10	12	14	16	18	1A	1C	1E
3	03	06	09	0C	0F	12	15	18	1B	1E	21	24	27	2A	2D
4	04	08	0C	10	14	18	1C	20	24	28	2C	30	34	38	3C
5	05	0A	0F	14	19	1E	23	28	2D	32	37	3C	41	46	4B
6	06	0C	12	18	1E	24	2A	30	36	3C	42	48	4E	54	5A
7	07	0E	15	1C	23	2A	31	38	3F	46	4D	54	5B	62	69
08	08	10	18	20	28	30	38	40	48	50	58	60	68	70	78
9	09	12	1B	24	2D	36	3F	48	51	5A	63	6C	75	7E	87
A	0A	14	1E	28	32	3C	46	50	5A	64	6E	78	82	8C	96
B	0B	16	21	2C	37	42	4D	58	63	6E	79	84	8F	9A	A5
C	0C	18	24	30	3C	48	54	60	6C	78	84	90	9C	A8	B4
D	0D	1A	27	34	41	4E	5B	68	75	82	8F	9C	A9	B6	C3
E	0E	1C	2A	38	46	54	62	70	7E	8C	9A	A8	B6	C4	D2
F	0F	1E	2D	3C	4B	5A	69	78	87	96	A5	B4	C3	D2	E1

SQUARES, SQUARE ROOT, CUBES AND CUBE ROOT

The squares and cubes from 1 to 1000 are given exactly. The roots are given to seven significant figures. Since the square roots of $10n$ are given, values of the square roots from 1 to 10 000 may be found directly. For the square roots of numbers below and above this range, use may be made of the following relations: $\sqrt{100n} = 10\sqrt{n}$; $\sqrt{1000n} = 10\sqrt{10n}$; $\sqrt{\frac{1}{10}n} = \frac{1}{10}\sqrt{10n}$; $\sqrt{\frac{1}{100}n} = \frac{1}{10}\sqrt{n}$; $\sqrt{\frac{1}{1000}n} = \frac{1}{100}\sqrt{10n}$. For example, the square root of 0.268 may be found by using the form $\sqrt{0.268} = \frac{1}{100}\sqrt{10 \times 268}$. The tabular value for the square root of $10n$ for 268 is 51.76872. Hence, the desired root is 0.5176872.

Values of cube roots for all numbers from 1 to 100 000 will be found directly in the table. Cube roots for numbers above or below this range will be found from the following relations: $\sqrt[3]{1000n} = 10\sqrt[3]{n}$; $\sqrt[3]{10\,000n} = 10\sqrt[3]{10n}$; $\sqrt[3]{100\,000n} = 10\sqrt[3]{100n}$; $\sqrt[3]{\frac{1}{10}n} = \frac{1}{10}\sqrt[3]{100n}$; $\sqrt[3]{\frac{1}{100}n} = \frac{1}{10}\sqrt[3]{10n}$; $\sqrt[3]{\frac{1}{1000}n} = \frac{1}{10}\sqrt[3]{n}$. For example, the cube root of 731 000 may be found by using the form, $\sqrt[3]{731\,000} = 10\sqrt[3]{731}$. The tabular value of the root for 731 is 9.008 223. The desired root is, therefore, 90.08223.

For fourth and fifth roots, see the table following this one. For higher integral powers of numbers, see table "Powers of Numbers."

We note on page 37, that

$$\sum_{k=1}^{n} k^p = 1^p + 2^p + 3^p + \cdots + n^p \text{ is a function of } n \text{ which can be conveniently generated}$$

by use of the *following proposition*

If
$$\sum_{k=1}^{n} k^p = a_1 n^{p+1} + a_2 n^p + a_3 n^{p-1} + \cdots + a_{p+1}n$$

then

$$\sum_{k=1}^{n} k^{p+1} = \frac{p+1}{p+2}a_1 n^{p+2} + \frac{p+1}{p+1}a_2 n^{p+1} + \frac{p+1}{p}a_3 n^p$$
$$+ \cdots + \frac{p+1}{2}a_{p+1}n^2 + \left[1 - (p+1)\sum_{k=1}^{p+1}\frac{a_k}{(p+3-k)}\right]n$$

Example Since $\displaystyle\sum_{k=1}^{n} k = \frac{1}{2}n^2 + \frac{1}{2}n$, then

$$\sum_{k=1}^{n} k^2 = \frac{1}{3}n^3 + \frac{1}{2}n^2 + \frac{1}{6}n \text{ and from this result}$$

$$\sum_{k=1}^{n} k^3 = \frac{1}{4}n^4 + \frac{1}{2}n^3 + \frac{1}{4}n^2 \quad \text{etc.}$$

This proposition is extracted from a paper written by Michael A. Budin and Arnold J. Cantor entitled "Simplified Computation of Sums of Powers of Integers."

SQUARES, SQUARE ROOT, CUBES AND CUBE ROOT

n	n^2	$\sqrt{n}$	$\sqrt{10n}$	n^3	$\sqrt[3]{n}$	$\sqrt[3]{10n}$	$\sqrt[3]{100n}$
1	1	1.000 000	3.162 278	1	1.000 000	2.154 435	4.641 589
2	4	1.414 214	4.472 136	8	1.259 921	2.714 418	5.848 035
3	9	1.732 051	5.477 226	27	1.442 250	3.107 233	6.694 330
4	16	2.000 000	6.324 555	64	1.587 401	3.419 952	7.368 063
5	25	2.236 068	7.071 068	125	1.709 976	3.684 031	7.937 005
6	36	2.449 490	7.745 967	216	1.817 121	3.914 868	8.434 327
7	49	2.645 751	8.366 600	343	1.912 931	4.121 285	8.879 040
8	64	2.828 427	8.944 272	512	2.000 000	4.308 869	9.283 178
9	81	3.000 000	9.486 833	729	2.080 084	4.481 405	9.654 894
10	100	3.162 278	10.00000	1 000	2.154 435	4.641 589	10.00000
11	121	3.316 625	10.48809	1 331	2.223 980	4.791 420	10.32280
12	144	3.464 102	10.95445	1 728	2.289 428	4.932 424	10.62659
13	169	3.605 551	11.40175	2 197	2.351 335	5.065 797	10.91393
14	196	3.741 657	11.83216	2 744	2.410 142	5.192 494	11.18689
15	225	3.872 983	12.24745	3 375	2.466 212	5.313 293	11.44714
16	256	4.000 000	12.64911	4 096	2.519 842	5.428 835	11.69607
17	289	4.123 106	13.03840	4 913	2.571 282	5.539 658	11.93483
18	324	4.242 641	13.41641	5 832	2.620 741	5.646 216	12.16440
19	361	4.358 899	13.78405	6 859	2.668 402	5.748 897	12.38562
20	400	4.472 136	14.14214	8 000	2.714 418	5.848 035	12.59921
21	441	4.582 576	14.49138	9 261	2.758 924	5.943 922	12.80579
22	484	4.690 416	14.83240	10 648	2.802 039	6.036 811	13.00591
23	529	4.795 832	15.16575	12 167	2.843 867	6.126 926	13.20006
24	576	4.898 979	15.49193	13 824	2.884 499	6.214 465	13.38866
25	625	5.000 000	15.81139	15 625	2.924 018	6.299 605	13.57209
26	676	5.099 020	16.12452	17 576	2.962 496	6.382 504	13.75069
27	729	5.196 152	16.43168	19 683	3.000 000	6.463 304	13.92477
28	784	5.291 503	16.73320	21 952	3.036 589	6.542 133	14.09460
29	841	5.385 165	17.02939	24 389	3.072 317	6.619 106	14.26043
30	900	5.477 226	17.32051	27 000	3.107 233	6.694 330	14.42250
31	961	5.567 764	17.60682	29 791	3.141 381	6.767 899	14.58100
32	1 024	5.656 854	17.88854	32 768	3.174 802	6.839 904	14.73613
33	1 089	5.744 563	18.16590	35 937	3.207 534	6.910 423	14.88806
34	1 156	5.830 952	18.43909	39 304	3.239 612	6.979 532	15.03695
35	1 225	5.916 080	18.70829	42 875	3.271 066	7.047 299	15.18294
36	1 296	6.000 000	18.97367	46 656	3.301 927	7.113 787	15.32619
37	1 369	6.082 763	19.23538	50 653	3.332 222	7.179 054	15.46680
38	1 444	6.164 414	19.49359	54 872	3.361 975	7.243 156	15.60491
39	1 521	6.244 998	19.74842	59 319	3.391 211	7.306 144	15.74061
40	1 600	6.324 555	20.00000	64 000	3.419 952	7.368 063	15.87401
41	1 681	6.403 124	20.24846	68 921	3.448 217	7.428 959	16.00521
42	1 764	6.480 741	20.49390	74 088	3.476 027	7.488 872	16.13429
43	1 849	6.557 439	20.73644	79 507	3.503 398	7.547 842	16.26133
44	1 936	6.633 250	20.97618	85 184	3.530 348	7.605 905	16.38643
45	2 025	6.708 204	21.21320	91 125	3.556 893	7.663 094	16.50964
46	2 116	6.782 330	21.44761	97 336	3.583 048	7.719 443	16.63103
47	2 209	6.855 655	21.67948	103 823	3.608 826	7.774 980	16.75069
48	2 304	6.928 203	21.90890	110 592	3.634 241	7.829 735	16.86865
49	2 401	7.000 000	22.13594	117 649	3.659 306	7.883 735	16.98499
50	2 500	7.071 068	22.36068	125 000	3.684 031	7.937 005	17.09976

SQUARES, SQUARE ROOT, CUBES AND CUBE ROOT (Continued)

n	n^2	$\sqrt{n}$	$\sqrt{10n}$	n^3	$\sqrt[3]{n}$	$\sqrt[3]{10n}$	$\sqrt[3]{100n}$
50	2 500	7.071 068	22.36068	125 000	3.684 031	7.937 005	17.09976
51	2 601	7.141 428	22.58318	132 651	3.708 430	7.989 570	17.21301
52	2 704	7.211 103	22.80351	140 608	3.732 511	8.041 452	17.32478
53	2 809	7.280 110	23.02173	148 877	3.756 286	8.092 672	17.43513
54	2 916	7.348 469	23.23790	157 464	3.779 763	8.143 253	17.54411
55	3 025	7.416 198	23.45208	166 375	3.802 952	8.193 213	17.65174
56	3 136	7.483 315	23.66432	175 616	3.825 862	8.242 571	17.75808
57	3 249	7.549 834	23.87467	185 193	3.848 501	8.291 344	17.86316
58	3 364	7.615 773	24.08319	195 112	3.870 877	8.339 551	17.96702
59	3 481	7.681 146	24.28992	205 379	3.892 996	8.387 207	18.06969
60	3 600	7.745 967	24.49490	216 000	3.914 868	8.434 327	18.17121
61	3 721	7.810 250	24.69818	226 981	3.936 497	8.480 926	18.27160
62	3 844	7.874 008	24.89980	238 328	3.957 892	8.527 019	18.37091
63	3 969	7.937 254	25.09980	250 047	3.979 057	8.572 619	18.46915
64	4 096	8.000 000	25.29822	262 144	4.000 000	8.617 739	18.56636
65	4 225	8.062 258	25.49510	274 625	4.020 726	8.662 391	18.66256
66	4 356	8.124 038	25.69047	287 496	4.041 240	8.706 588	18.75777
67	4 489	8.185 353	25.88436	300 763	4.061 548	8.750 340	18.85204
68	4 624	8.246 211	26.07681	314 432	4.081 655	8.793 659	18.94536
69	4 761	8.306 624	26.26785	328 509	4.101 566	8.836 556	19.03778
70	4 900	8.366 600	26.45751	343 000	4.121 285	8.879 040	19.12931
71	5 041	8.426 150	26.64583	357 911	4.140 818	8.921 121	19.21997
72	5 184	8.485 281	26.83282	373 248	4.160 168	8.962 809	19.30979
73	5 329	8.544 004	27.01851	389 017	4.179 339	9.004 113	19.39877
74	5 476	8.602 325	27.20294	405 224	4.198 336	9.045 042	19.48695
75	5 625	8.660 254	27.38613	421 875	4.217 163	9.085 603	19.57434
76	5 776	8.717 798	27.56810	438 976	4.235 824	9.125 805	19.66095
77	5 929	8.774 964	27.74887	456 533	4.254 321	9.165 656	19.74681
78	6 084	8.831 761	27.92848	474 552	4.272 659	9.205 164	19.83192
79	6 241	8.888 194	28.10694	493 039	4.290 840	9.244 335	19.91632
80	6 400	8.944 272	28.28427	512 000	4.308 869	9.283 178	20.00000
81	6 561	9.000 000	28.46050	531 441	4.326 749	9.321 698	20.08299
82	6 724	9.055 385	28.63564	551 368	4.344 481	9.359 902	20.16530
83	6 889	9.110 434	28.80972	571 787	4.362 071	9.397 796	20.24694
84	7 056	9.165 151	28.98275	592 704	4.379 519	9.435 388	20.32793
85	7 225	9.219 544	29.15476	614 125	4.396 830	9.472 682	20.40828
86	7 396	9.273 618	29.32576	636 056	4.414 005	9.509 685	20.48800
87	7 569	9.327 379	29.49576	658 503	4.431 048	9.546 403	20.56710
88	7 744	9.380 832	29.66479	681 472	4.447 960	9.582 840	20.64560
89	7 921	9.433 981	29.83287	704 969	4.464 745	9.619 002	20.72351
90	8 100	9.486 833	30.00000	729 000	4.481 405	9.654 894	20.80084
91	8 281	9.539 392	30.16621	753 571	4.497 941	9.690 521	20.87759
92	8 464	9.591 663	30.33150	778 688	4.514 357	9.725 888	20.95379
93	8 649	9.643 651	30.49590	804 357	4.530 655	9.761 000	21.02944
94	8 836	9.695 360	30.65942	830 584	4.546 836	9.795 861	21.10454
95	9 025	9.746 794	30.82207	857 375	4.562 903	9.830 476	21.17912
96	9 216	9.797 959	30.98387	884 736	4.578 857	9.864 848	21.25317
97	9 409	9.848 858	31.14482	912 673	4.594 701	9.898 983	21.32671
98	9 604	9.899 495	31.30495	941 192	4.610 436	9.932 884	21.39975
99	9 801	9.949 874	31.46427	970 299	4.626 065	9.966 555	21.47229
100	10 000	10.00000	31.62278	1 000 000	4.641 589	10.00000	21.54435

SQUARES, SQUARE ROOT, CUBES AND CUBE ROOT (Continued)

n	n^2	$\sqrt{n}$	$\sqrt{10n}$	n^3	$\sqrt[3]{n}$	$\sqrt[3]{10n}$	$\sqrt[3]{100n}$
100	10 000	10.00000	31.62278	1 000 000	4.641 589	10.00000	21.54435
101	10 201	10.04988	31.78050	1 030 301	4.657 010	10.03322	21.61592
102	10 404	10.09950	31.93744	1 061 208	4.672 329	10.06623	21.68703
103	10 609	10.14889	32.09361	1 092 727	4.687 548	10.09902	21.75767
104	10 816	10.19804	32.24903	1 124 864	4.702 669	10.13159	21.82786
105	11 025	10.24695	32.40370	1 157 625	4.717 694	10.16396	21.89760
106	11 236	10.29563	32.55764	1 191 016	4.732 623	10.19613	21.96689
107	11 449	10.34408	32.71085	1 225 043	4.747 459	10.22809	22.03575
108	11 664	10.39230	32.86335	1 259 712	4.762 203	10.25986	22.10419
109	11 881	10.44031	33.01515	1 295 029	4.776 856	10.29142	22.17220
110	12 100	10.48809	33.16625	1 331 000	4.791 420	10.32280	22.23980
111	12 321	10.53565	33.31666	1 367 631	4.805 896	10.35399	22.30699
112	12 544	10.58301	33.46640	1 404 928	4.820 285	10.38499	22.37378
113	12 769	10.63015	33.61547	1 442 897	4.834 588	10.41580	22.44017
114	12 996	10.67708	33.76389	1 481 544	4.848 808	10.44644	22.50617
115	13 225	10.72381	33.91165	1 520 875	4.862 944	10.47690	22.57179
116	13 456	10.77033	34.05877	1 560 896	4.876 999	10.50718	22.63702
117	13 689	10.81665	34.20526	1 601 613	4.890 973	10.53728	22.70189
118	13 924	10.86278	34.35113	1 643 032	4.904 868	10.56722	22.76638
119	14 161	10.90871	34.49638	1 685 159	4.918 685	10.59699	22.83051
120	14 400	10.95445	34.64102	1 728 000	4.932 424	10.62659	22.89428
121	14 641	11.00000	34.78505	1 771 561	4.946 087	10.65602	22.95770
122	14 884	11.04536	34.92850	1 815 848	4.959 676	10.68530	23.02078
123	15 129	11.09054	35.07136	1 860 867	4.973 190	10.71441	23.08350
124	15 376	11.13553	35.21363	1 906 624	4.986 631	10.74337	23.14589
125	15 625	11.18034	35.35534	1 953 125	5.000 000	10.77217	23.20794
126	15 876	11.22497	35.49648	2 000 376	5.013 298	10.80082	23.26967
127	16 129	11.26943	35.63706	2 048 383	5.026 526	10.82932	23.33107
128	16 384	11.31371	35.77709	2 097 152	5.039 684	10.85767	23.39214
129	16 641	11.35782	35.91657	2 146 689	5.052 774	10.88587	23.45290
130	16 900	11.40175	36.05551	2 197 000	5.065 797	10.91393	23.51335
131	17 161	11.44552	36.19392	2 248 091	5.078 753	10.94184	23.57348
132	17 424	11.48913	36.33180	2 299 968	5.091 643	10.96961	23.63332
133	17 689	11.53256	36.46917	2 352 637	5.104 469	10.99724	23.69285
134	17 956	11.57584	36.60601	2 406 104	5.117 230	11.02474	23.75208
135	18 225	11.61895	36.74235	2 460 375	5.129 928	11.05209	23.81102
136	18 496	11.66190	36.87818	2 515 456	5.142 563	11.07932	23.86966
137	18 769	11.70470	37.01351	2 571 353	5.155 137	11.10641	23.92803
138	19 044	11.74734	37.14835	2 628 072	5.167 649	11.13336	23.98610
139	19 321	11.78983	37.28270	2 685 619	5.180 101	11.16019	24.04390
140	19 600	11.83216	37.41657	2 744 000	5.192 494	11.18689	24.10142
141	19 881	11.87434	37.54997	2 803 221	5.204 828	11.21346	24.15867
142	20 164	11.91638	37.68289	2 863 288	5.217 103	11.23991	24.21565
143	20 449	11.95826	37.81534	2 924 207	5.229 322	11.26623	24.27236
144	20 736	12.00000	37.94733	2 985 984	5.241 483	11.29243	24.32881
145	21 025	12.04159	38.07887	3 048 625	5.253 588	11.31851	24.38499
146	21 316	12.08305	38.20995	3 112 136	5.265 637	11.34447	24.44092
147	21 609	12.12436	38.34058	3 176 523	5.277 632	11.37031	24.49660
148	21 904	12.16553	38.47077	3 241 792	5.289 572	11.39604	24.55202
149	22 201	12.20656	38.60052	3 307 949	5.301 459	11.42165	24.60719
150	22.500	12.24745	38.72983	3 375 000	5.313 293	11.44714	24.66212

SQUARES, SQUARE ROOT, CUBES AND CUBE ROOT (Continued)

n	n^2	$\sqrt{n}$	$\sqrt{10n}$	n^3	$\sqrt[3]{n}$	$\sqrt[3]{10n}$	$\sqrt[3]{100n}$
150	22 500	12.24745	38.72983	3 375 000	5.313 293	11.44714	24.66212
151	22 801	12.28821	38.85872	3 442 951	5.325 074	11.47252	24.71680
152	23 104	12.32883	38.98718	3 511 808	5.336 803	11.49779	24.77125
153	23 409	12.36932	39.11521	3 581 577	5.348 481	11.52295	24.82545
154	23 716	12.40967	39.24283	3 652 264	5.360 108	11.54800	24.87942
155	24 025	12.44990	39.37004	3 723 875	5.371 685	11.57295	24.93315
156	24 336	12.49000	39.49684	3 796 416	5.383 213	11.59778	24.98666
157	24 649	12.52996	39.62323	3 869 893	5.394 691	11.62251	25.03994
158	24 964	12.56981	39.74921	3 944 312	5.406 120	11.64713	25.09299
159	25 281	12.60952	39.87480	4 019 679	5.417 502	11.67165	25.14581
160	25 600	12.64911	40.00000	4 096 000	5.428 835	11.69607	25.19842
161	25 921	12.68858	40.12481	4 173 281	5.440 122	11.72039	25.25081
162	26 244	12.72792	40.24922	4 251 528	5.451 362	11.74460	25.30298
163	26 569	12.76715	40.37326	4 330 747	5.462 556	11.76872	25.35494
164	26 896	12.80625	40.49691	4 410 944	5.473 704	11.79274	25.40668
165	27 225	12.84523	40.62019	4 492 125	5.484 807	11.81666	25.45822
166	27 556	12.88410	40.74310	4 574 296	5.495 865	11.84048	25.50954
167	27 889	12.92285	40.86563	4 657 463	5.506 878	11.86421	25.56067
168	28 224	12.96148	40.98780	4 741 632	5.517 848	11.88784	25.61158
169	28 561	13.00000	41.10961	4 826 809	5.528 775	11.91138	25.66230
170	28 900	13.03840	41.23106	4 913 000	5.539 658	11.93483	25.71282
171	29 241	13.07670	41.35215	5 000 211	5.550 499	11.95819	25.76313
172	29 584	13.11488	41.47288	5 088 448	5.561 298	11.98145	25.81326
173	29 929	13.15295	41.59327	5 177 717	5.572 055	12.00463	25.86319
174	30 276	13.19091	41.71331	5 268 024	5.582 770	12.02771	25.91292
175	30 625	13.22876	41.83300	5 359 375	5.593 445	12.05071	25.96247
176	30 976	13.26650	41.95235	5 451 776	5.604 079	12.07362	26.01183
177	31 329	13.30413	42.07137	5 545 233	5.614 672	12.09645	26.06100
178	31 684	13.34166	42.19005	5 639 752	5.625 226	12.11918	26.10999
179	32 041	13.37909	42.30839	5 735 339	5.635 741	12.14184	26.15879
180	32 400	13.41641	42.42641	5 832 000	5.646 216	12.16440	26.20741
181	32 761	13.45362	42.54409	5 929 741	5.656 653	12.18689	26.25586
182	33 124	13.49074	42.66146	6 028 568	5.667 051	12.20929	26.30412
183	33 489	13.52775	42.77850	6 128 487	5.677 411	12.23161	26.35221
184	33 856	13.56466	42.89522	6 229 504	5.687 734	12.25385	26.40012
185	34 225	13.60147	43.01163	6 331 625	5.698 019	12.27601	26.44786
186	34 596	13.63818	43.12772	6 434 856	5.708 267	12.29809	26.49543
187	34 969	13.67479	43.24350	6 539 203	5.718 479	12.32009	26.54283
188	35 344	13.71131	43.35897	6 644 672	5.728 654	12.34201	26.59006
189	35 721	13.74773	43.47413	6 751 269	5.738 794	12.36386	26.63712
190	36 100	13.78405	43.58899	6 859 000	5.748 897	12.38562	26.68402
191	36 481	13.82027	43.70355	6 967 871	5.758 965	12.40731	26.73075
192	36 864	13.85641	43.81780	7 077 888	5.768 998	12.42893	26.77732
193	37 249	13.89244	43.93177	7 189 057	5.778 997	12.45047	26.82373
194	37 636	13.92839	44.04543	7 301 384	5.788 960	12.47194	26.86997
195	38 025	13.96424	44.15880	7 414 875	5.798 890	12.49333	26.91606
196	38 416	14.00000	44.27189	7 529 536	5.808 786	12.51465	26.96199
197	38 809	14.03567	44.38468	7 645 373	5.818 648	12.53590	27.00777
198	39 204	14.07125	44.49719	7 762 392	5.828 477	12.55707	27.05339
199	39 601	14.10674	44.60942	7 880 599	5.838 272	12.57818	27.09886
200	40 000	14.14214	44.72136	8 000 000	5.848 035	12.59921	27.14418

SQUARES, SQUARE ROOT, CUBES AND CUBE ROOT (Continued)

n	n^2	$\sqrt{n}$	$\sqrt{10n}$	n^3	$\sqrt[3]{n}$	$\sqrt[3]{10n}$	$\sqrt[3]{100n}$
200	40 000	14.14214	44.72136	8 000 000	5.848 035	12.59921	27.14418
201	40 401	14.17745	44.83302	8 120 601	5.857 766	12.62017	27.18934
202	40 804	14.21267	44.94441	8 242 408	5.867 464	12.64107	27.23436
203	41 209	14.24781	45.05552	8 365 427	5.877 131	12.66189	27.27922
204	41 616	14.28286	45.16636	8 489 664	5.886 765	12.68265	27.32394
205	42 025	14.31782	45.27693	8 615 125	5.896 369	12.70334	27.36852
206	42 436	14.35270	45.38722	8 741 816	5.905 941	12.72396	27.41295
207	42 849	14.38749	45.49725	8 869 743	5.915 482	12.74452	27.45723
208	43 264	14.42221	45.60702	8 998 912	5.924 992	12.76501	27.50138
209	43 681	14.45683	45.71652	9 129 329	5.934 472	12.78543	27.54538
210	44 100	14.49138	45.82576	9 261 000	5.943 922	12.80579	27.58924
211	44 521	14.52584	45.93474	9 393 931	5.953 342	12.82609	27.63296
212	44 944	14.56022	46.04346	9 528 128	5.962 732	12.84632	27.67655
213	45 369	14.59452	46.15192	9 663 597	5.972 093	12.86648	27.72000
214	45 796	14.62874	46.26013	9 800 344	5.981 424	12.88659	27.76331
215	46 225	14.66288	46.36809	9 938 375	5.990 726	12.90663	27.80649
216	46 656	14.69694	46.47580	10 077 696	6.000 000	12.92661	27.84953
217	47 089	14.73092	46.58326	10 218 313	6.009 245	12.94653	27.89244
218	47 524	14.76482	46.69047	10 360 232	6.018 462	12.96638	27.93522
219	47 961	14.79865	46.79744	10 503 459	6.027 650	12.98618	27.97787
220	48 400	14.83240	46.90416	10 648 000	6.036 811	13.00591	28.02039
221	48 841	14.86607	47.01064	10 793 861	6.045 944	13.02559	28.06278
222	49 284	14.89966	47.11688	10 941 048	6.055 049	13.04521	28.10505
223	49 729	14.93318	47.22288	11 089 567	6.064 127	13.06477	28.14718
224	50 176	14.96663	47.32864	11 239 424	6.073 178	13.08427	28.18919
225	50 625	15.00000	47.43416	11 390 625	6.082 202	13.10371	28.23108
226	51 076	15.03330	47.53946	11 543 176	6.091 199	13.12309	28.27284
227	51 529	15.06652	47.64452	11 697 083	6.100 170	13.14242	28.31448
228	51 984	15.09967	47.74935	11 852 352	6.109 115	13.16169	28.35600
229	52 441	15.13275	47.85394	12 008 989	6.118 033	13.18090	28.39739
230	52 900	15.16575	47.95832	12 167 000	6.126 926	13.20006	28.43867
231	53 361	15.19868	48.06246	12 326 391	6.135 792	13.21916	28.47983
232	53 824	15.23155	48.16638	12 487 168	6.144 634	13.23821	28.52086
233	54 289	15.26434	48.27007	12 649 337	6.153 449	13.25721	28.56178
234	54 756	15.29706	48.37355	12 812 904	6.162 240	13.27614	28.60259
235	55 225	15.32971	48.47680	12 977 875	6.171 006	13.29503	28.64327
236	55 696	15.36229	48.57983	13 144 256	6.179 747	13.31386	28.68384
237	56 169	15.39480	48.68265	13 312 053	6.188 463	13.33264	28.72430
238	56 644	15.42725	48.78524	13 481 272	6.197 154	13.35136	28.76464
239	57 121	15.45962	48.88763	13 651 919	6.205 822	13.37004	28.80487
240	57 600	15.49193	48.98979	13 824 000	6.214 465	13.38866	28.84499
241	58 081	15.52417	49.09175	13 997 521	6.223 084	13.40723	28.88500
242	58 564	15.55635	49.19350	14 172 488	6.231 680	13.42575	28.92489
243	59 049	15.58846	49.29503	14 348 907	6.240 251	13.44421	28.96468
244	59 536	15.62050	49.39636	14 526 784	6.248 800	13.46263	29.00436
245	60 025	15.65248	49.49747	14 706 125	6.257 325	13.48100	29.04393
246	60 516	15.68439	49.59839	14 886 936	6.265 827	13.49931	29.08339
247	61 009	15.71623	49.69909	15 069 223	6.274 305	13.51758	29.12275
248	61 504	15.74802	49.79960	15 252 992	6.282 761	13.53580	29.16199
249	62 001	15.77973	49.89990	15 438 249	6.291 195	13.55397	29.20114
250	62 500	15.81139	50.00000	15 625 000	6.299 605	13.57209	29.24018

SQUARES, SQUARE ROOT, CUBES AND CUBE ROOT (Continued)

n	n^2	$\sqrt{n}$	$\sqrt{10n}$	n^3	$\sqrt[3]{n}$	$\sqrt[3]{10n}$	$\sqrt[3]{100n}$
250	62 500	15.81139	50.00000	15 625 000	6.299 605	13.57209	29.24018
251	63 001	15.84298	50.09990	15 813 251	6.307 994	13.59016	29.27911
252	63 504	15.87451	50.19960	16 003 008	6.316 360	13.60818	29.31794
253	64 009	15.90597	50.29911	16 194 277	6.324 704	13.62616	29.35667
254	64 516	15.93738	50.39841	16 387 064	6.333 026	13.64409	29.39530
255	65 025	15.96872	50.49752	16 581 375	6.341 326	13.66197	29.43383
256	65 536	16.00000	50.59644	16 777 216	6.349 604	13.67981	29.47225
257	66 049	16.03122	50.69517	16 974 593	6.357 861	13.69760	29.51058
258	66 564	16.06238	50.79370	17 173 512	6.366 097	13.71534	29.54880
259	67 081	16.09348	50.89204	17 373 979	6.374 311	13.73304	29.58693
260	67 600	16.12452	50.99020	17 576 000	6.382 504	13.75069	29.62496
261	68 121	16.15549	51.08816	17 779 581	6.390 677	13.76830	29.66289
262	68 644	16.18641	51.18594	17 984 728	6.398 828	13.78586	29.70073
263	69 169	16.21727	51.28353	18 191 447	6.406 959	13.80337	29.73847
264	69 696	16.24808	51.38093	18 399 744	6.415 069	13.82085	29.77611
265	70 225	16.27882	51.47815	18 609 625	6.423 158	13.83828	29.81366
266	70 756	16.30951	51.57519	18 821 096	6.431 228	13.85566	29.85111
267	71 289	16.34013	51.67204	19 034 163	6.439 277	13.87300	29.88847
268	71 824	16.37071	51.76872	19 248 832	6.447 306	13.89030	29.92574
269	72 361	16.40122	51.86521	19 465 109	6.455 315	13.90755	29.96292
270	72 900	16.43168	51.96152	19 683 000	6.463 304	13.92477	30.00000
271	73 441	16.46208	52.05766	19 902 511	6.471 274	13.94194	30.03699
272	73 984	16.49242	52.15362	20 123 648	6.479 224	13.95906	30.07389
273	74 529	16.52271	52.24940	20 346 417	6.487 154	13.97615	30.11070
274	75 076	16.55295	52.34501	20 570 824	6.495 065	13.99319	30.14742
275	75 625	16.58312	52.44044	20 796 875	6.502 957	14.01020	30.18405
276	76 176	16.61325	52.53570	21 024 576	6.510 830	14.02716	30.22060
277	76 729	16.64332	52.63079	21 253 933	6.518 684	14.04408	30.25705
278	77 284	16.67333	52.72571	21 484 952	6.526 519	14.06096	30.29342
279	77 841	16.70329	52.82045	21 717 639	6.534 335	14.07780	30.32970
280	78 400	16.73320	52.91503	21 952 000	6.542 133	14.09460	30.36589
281	78 961	16.76305	53.00943	22 188 041	6.549 912	14.11136	30.40200
282	79 524	16.79286	53.10367	22 425 768	6.557 672	14.12808	30.43802
283	80 089	16.82260	53.19774	22 665 187	6.565 414	14.14476	30.47395
284	80 656	16.85230	53.29165	22 906 304	6.573 138	14.16140	30.50981
285	81 225	16.88194	53.38539	23 149 125	6.580 844	14.17800	30.54557
286	81 796	16.91153	53.47897	23 393 656	6.588 532	14.19456	30.58126
287	82 369	16.94107	53.57238	23 639 903	6.596 202	14.21109	30.61686
288	82 944	16.97056	53.66563	23 887 872	6.603 854	14.22757	30.65238
289	83 521	17.00000	53.75872	24 137 569	6.611 489	14.24402	30.68781
290	84 100	17.02939	53.85165	24 389 000	6.619 106	14.26043	30.72317
291	84 681	17.05872	53.94442	24 642 171	6.626 705	14.27680	30.75844
292	85 264	17.08801	54.03702	24 897 088	6.634 287	14.29314	30.79363
293	85 849	17.11724	54.12947	25 153 757	6.641 852	14.30944	30.82875
294	86 436	17.14643	54.22177	25 412 184	6.649 400	14.32570	30.86378
295	87 025	17.17556	54.31390	25 672 375	6.656 930	14.34192	30.89873
296	87 616	17.20465	54.40588	25 934 336	6.664 444	14.35811	30.93361
297	88 209	17.23369	54.49771	26 198 073	6.671 940	14.37426	30.96840
298	88 804	17.26268	54.58938	26 463 592	6.679 420	14.39037	31.00312
299	89 401	17.29162	54.68089	26 730 899	6.686 883	14.40645	31.03776
300	90 000	17.32051	54.77226	27 000 000	6.694 330	14.42250	31.07233

SQUARES, SQUARE ROOT, CUBES AND CUBE ROOT (Continued)

n	n^2	$\sqrt{n}$	$\sqrt{10n}$	n^3	$\sqrt[3]{n}$	$\sqrt[3]{10n}$	$\sqrt[3]{100n}$
300	90 000	17 32051	54.77226	27 000 000	6.694 330	14.42250	31.07233
301	90 601	17.34935	54.86347	27 270 901	6.701 759	14.43850	31.10681
302	91 204	17.37815	54.95453	27 543 608	6.709 173	14.45447	31.14122
303	91 809	17.40690	55.04544	27 818 127	6.716 570	14.47041	31.17556
304	92 416	17.43560	55.13620	28 094 464	6.723 951	14.48631	31.20982
305	93 025	17.46425	55.22681	28 372 625	6.731 315	14.50218	31.24400
306	93 636	17.49286	55.31727	28 652 616	6.738 664	14.51801	31.27811
307	94 249	17.52142	55.40758	28 934 443	6.745 997	14.53381	31.31214
308	94 864	17.54993	55.49775	29 218 112	6.753 313	14.54957	31.34610
309	95 481	17.57840	55.58777	29 503 629	6.760 614	14.56530	31.37999
310	96 100	17.60682	55.67764	29 791 000	6.767 899	14.58100	31.41381
311	96 721	17.63519	55.76737	30 080 231	6.775 169	14.59666	31.44755
312	97 344	17.66352	55.85696	30 371 328	6.782 423	14.61229	31.48122
313	97 969	17.69181	55.94640	30 664 297	6.789 661	14.62788	31.51482
314	98 596	17.72005	56.03570	30 959 144	6.796 884	14.64344	31.54834
315	99 225	17.74824	56.12486	31 255 875	6.804 092	14.65897	31.58180
316	99 856	17.77639	56.21388	31 554 496	6.811 285	14.67447	31.61518
317	100 489	17.80449	56.30275	31 855 013	6.818 462	14.68993	31.64850
318	101 124	17.83255	56.39149	32 157 432	6.825 624	14.70536	31.68174
319	101 761	17.86057	56.48008	32 461 759	6.832 771	14.72076	31.71492
320	102 400	17.88854	56.56854	32 768 000	6.839 904	14.73613	31.74802
321	103 041	17.91647	56.65686	33 076 161	6.847 021	14.75146	31.78106
322	103 684	17.94436	56.74504	33 386 248	6.854 124	14.76676	31.81403
323	104 329	17.97220	56.83309	33 698 267	6.861 212	14.78203	31.84693
324	104 976	18.00000	56.92100	34 012 224	6.868 285	14.79727	31.87976
325	105 625	18.02776	57.00877	34 328 125	6.875 344	14.81248	31.91252
326	106 276	18.05547	57.09641	34 645 976	6.882 389	14.82766	31.94522
327	106 929	18.08314	57.18391	34 965 783	6.889 419	14.84280	31.97785
328	107 584	18.11077	57.27128	35 287 552	6.896 434	14.85792	32.01041
329	108 241	18.13836	57.35852	35 611 289	6.903 436	14.87300	32.04291
330	108 900	18.16590	57.44563	35 937 000	6.910 423	14.88806	32.07534
331	109 561	18.19341	57.53260	36 264 691	6.917 396	14.90308	32.10771
332	110 224	18.22087	57.61944	36 594 368	6.924 356	14.91807	32.14001
333	110 889	18.24829	57.70615	36 926 037	6.931 301	14.93303	32.17225
334	111 556	18.27567	57.79273	37 259 704	6.938 232	14.94797	32.20442
335	112 225	18.30301	57.87918	37 595 375	6.945 150	14.96287	32.23653
336	112 896	18.33030	57.96551	37 933 056	6.952 053	14.97774	32.26857
337	113 569	18.35756	58.05170	38 272 753	6.958 943	14.99259	32.30055
338	114 244	18.38478	58.13777	38 614 472	6.965 820	15.00740	32.33247
339	114 921	18.41195	58.22371	38 958 219	6.972 683	15.02219	32.36433
340	115 600	18.43909	58.30952	39 304 000	6.979 532	15.03695	32.39612
341	116 281	18.46619	58.39521	39 651 821	6.986 368	15.05167	32.42785
342	116 964	18.49324	58.48077	40 001 688	6.993 191	15.06637	32.45952
343	117 649	18.52026	58.56620	40 353 607	7.000 000	15.08104	32.49112
344	118 336	18.54724	58.65151	40 707 584	7.006 796	15.09568	32.52267
345	119 025	18.57418	58.73670	41 063 625	7.013 579	15.11030	32.55415
346	119 716	18.60108	58.82176	41 421 736	7.020 349	15.12488	32.58557
347	120 409	18.62794	58.90671	41 781 923	7.027 106	15.13944	32.61694
348	121 104	18.65476	58.99152	42 144 192	7.033 850	15.15397	32.64824
349	121 801	18.68154	59.07622	42 508 549	7.040 581	15.16847	32.67948
350	122 500	18.70829	59.16080	42 875 000	7.047 299	15.18294	32.71066

SQUARES, SQUARE ROOT, CUBES AND CUBE ROOT (Continued)

n	n^2	$\sqrt{n}$	$\sqrt{10n}$	n^3	$\sqrt[3]{n}$	$\sqrt[3]{10n}$	$\sqrt[3]{100n}$
350	122 500	18.70829	59.16080	42 875 000	7.047 299	15.18294	32.71066
351	123 201	18.73499	59.24525	43 243 551	7.054 004	15.19739	32.74179
352	123 904	18.76166	59.32959	43 614 208	7.060 697	15.21181	32.77285
353	124 609	18.78829	59.41380	43 986 977	7.067 377	15.22620	32.80386
354	125 316	18.81489	59.49790	44 361 864	7.074 044	15.24057	32.83480
355	126 025	18.84144	59.58188	44 738 875	7.080 699	15.25490	32.86569
356	126 736	18.86796	59.66574	45 118 016	7.087 341	15.26921	32.89652
357	127 449	18.89444	59.74948	45 499 293	7.093 971	15.28350	32.92730
358	128 164	18.92089	59.83310	45 882 712	7.100 588	15.29775	32.95801
359	128 881	18.94730	59.91661	46 268 279	7.107 194	15.31198	32.98867
360	129 600	18.97367	60.00000	46 656 000	7.113 787	15.32619	33.01927
361	130 321	19.00000	60.08328	47 045 881	7.120 367	15.34037	33.04982
362	131 044	19.02630	60.16644	47 437 928	7.126 936	15.35452	33.08031
363	131 769	19.05256	60.24948	47 832 147	7.133 492	15.36864	33.11074
364	132 496	19.07878	60.33241	48 228 544	7.140 037	15.38274	33.14112
365	133 225	19.10497	60.41523	48 627 125	7.146 569	15.39682	33.17144
366	133 956	19.13113	60.49793	49 027 896	7.153 090	15.41087	33.20170
367	134 689	19.15724	60.58052	49 430 863	7.159 599	15.42489	33.23191
368	135 424	19.18333	60.66300	49 836 032	7.166 096	15.43889	33.26207
369	136 161	19.20937	60.74537	50 243 409	7.172 581	15.45286	33.29217
370	136 900	19.23538	60.82763	50 653 000	7.179 054	15.46680	33.32222
371	137 641	19.26136	60.90977	51 064 811	7.185 516	15.48073	33.35221
372	138 384	19.28730	60.99180	51 478 848	7.191 966	15.49462	33.38215
373	139 129	19.31321	61.07373	51 895 117	7.198 405	15.50849	33.41204
374	139 876	19.33908	61.15554	52 313 624	7.204 832	15.52234	33.44187
375	140 625	19.36492	61.23724	52 734 375	7.211 248	15.53616	33.47165
376	141 376	19.39072	61.31884	53 157 376	7.217 652	15.54996	33.50137
377	142 129	19.41649	61.40033	53 582 633	7.224 045	15.56373	33.53105
378	142 884	19.44222	61.48170	54 010 152	7.230 427	15.57748	33.56067
379	143 641	19.46792	61.56298	54 439 939	7.236 797	15.59121	33.59024
380	144 400	19.49359	61.64414	54 872 000	7.243 156	15.60491	33.61975
381	145 161	19.51922	61.72520	55 306 341	7.249 505	15.61858	33.64922
382	145 924	19.54482	61.80615	55 742 968	7.255 842	15.63224	33.67863
383	146 689	19.57039	61.88699	56 181 887	7.262 167	15.64587	33.70800
384	147 456	19.59592	61.96773	56 623 104	7.268 482	15.65947	33.73731
385	148 225	19.62142	62.04837	57 066 625	7.274 786	15.67305	33.76657
386	148 996	19.64688	62.12890	57 512 456	7.281 079	15.68661	33.79578
387	149 769	19.67232	62.20932	57 960 603	7.287 362	15.70014	33.82494
388	150 544	19.69772	62.28965	58 411 072	7.293 633	15.71366	33.85405
389	151 321	19.72308	62.36986	58 863 869	7.299 894	15.72714	33.88310
390	152 100	19.74842	62.44998	59 319 000	7.306 144	15.74061	33.91211
391	152 881	19.77372	62.52999	59 776 471	7.312 383	15.75405	33.94107
392	153 664	19.79899	62.60990	60 236 288	7.318 611	15.76747	33.96999
393	154 449	19.82423	62.68971	60 698 457	7.324 829	15.78087	33.99885
394	155 236	19.84943	62.76942	61 162 984	7.331 037	15.79424	34.02766
395	156 025	19.87461	62.84903	61 629 875	7.337 234	15.80759	34.05642
396	156 816	19.89975	62.92853	62 099 136	7.343 420	15.82092	34.08514
397	157 609	19.92486	63.00794	62 570 773	7.349 597	15.83423	34.11381
398	158 404	19.94994	63.08724	63 044 792	7.355 762	15.84751	34.14242
399	159 201	19.97498	63.16645	63 521 199	7.361 918	15.86077	34.17100
400	160 000	20.00000	63.24555	64 000 000	7.368 063	15.87401	34.19952

SQUARES, SQUARE ROOT, CUBES AND CUBE ROOT (Continued)

n	n^2	$\sqrt{n}$	$\sqrt{10n}$	n^3	$\sqrt[3]{n}$	$\sqrt[3]{10n}$	$\sqrt[3]{100n}$
400	160 000	20.00000	63.24555	64 000 000	7.368 063	15.87401	34.19952
401	160 801	20.02498	63.32456	64 481 201	7.374 198	15.88723	34.22799
402	161 604	20.04994	63.40347	64 964 808	7.380 323	15.90042	34.25642
403	162 409	20.07486	63.48228	65 450 827	7.386 437	15.91360	34.28480
404	163 216	20.09975	63.56099	65 939 264	7.392 542	15.92675	34.31314
405	164 025	20.12461	63.63961	66 430 125	7.398 636	15.93988	34.34143
406	164 836	20.14944	63.71813	66 923 416	7.404 721	15.95299	34.36967
407	165 649	20.17424	63.79655	67 419 143	7.410 795	15.96607	34.39786
408	166 464	20.19901	63.87488	67 917 312	7.416 860	15.97914	34.42601
409	167 281	20.22375	63.95311	68 417 929	7.422 914	15.99218	34.45412
410	168 100	20.24846	64.03124	68 921 000	7.428 959	16.00521	34.48217
411	168 921	20.27313	64.10928	69 426 531	7.434 994	16.01821	34.51018
412	169 744	20.29778	64.18723	69 934 528	7.441 019	16.03119	34.53815
413	170 569	20.32240	64.26508	70 444 997	7.447 034	16.04415	34.56607
414	171 396	20.34699	64.34283	70 957 944	7.453 040	16.05709	34.59395
415	172 225	20.37155	64.42049	71 473 375	7.459 036	16.07001	34.62178
416	173 056	20.39608	64.49806	71 991 296	7.465 022	16.08290	34.64956
417	173 889	20.42058	64.57554	72 511 713	7.470 999	16.09578	34.67731
418	174 724	20.44505	64.65292	73 034 632	7.476 966	16.10864	34.70500
419	175 561	20.46949	64.73021	73 560 059	7.482 924	16.12147	34.73266
420	176 400	20.49390	64.80741	74 088 000	7.488 872	16.13429	34.76027
421	177 241	20.51828	64.88451	74 618 461	7.494 811	16.14708	34.78783
422	178 084	20.54264	64.96153	75 151 448	7.500 741	16.15986	34.81535
423	178 929	20.56696	65.03845	75 686 967	7.506 661	16.17261	34.84283
424	179 776	20.59126	65.11528	76 225 024	7.512 572	16.18534	34.87027
425	180 625	20.61553	65.19202	76 765 625	7.518 473	16.19806	34.89766
426	181 476	20.63977	65.26868	77 308 776	7.524 365	16.21075	34.92501
427	182 329	20.66398	65.34524	77 854 483	7.530 248	16.22343	34.95232
428	183 184	20.68816	65.42171	78 402 752	7.536 122	16.23608	34.97958
429	184 041	20.71232	65.49809	78 953 589	7.541 987	16.24872	35.00680
430	184 900	20.73644	65.57439	79 507 000	7.547 842	16.26133	35.03398
431	185 761	20.76054	65.65059	80 062 991	7.553 689	16.27393	35.06112
432	186 624	20.78461	65.72671	80 621 568	7.559 526	16.28651	35.08821
433	187 489	20.80865	65.80274	81 182 737	7.565 355	16.29906	35.11527
434	188 356	20.83267	65.87868	81 746 504	7.571 174	16.31160	35.14228
435	189 225	20.85665	65.95453	82 312 875	7.576 985	16.32412	35.16925
436	190 096	20.88061	66.03030	82 881 856	7.582 787	16.33662	35.19618
437	190 969	20.90454	66.10598	83 453 453	7.588 579	16.34910	35.22307
438	191 844	20.92845	66.18157	84 027 672	7.594 363	16.36156	35.24991
439	192 721	20.95233	66.25708	84 604 519	7.600 139	16.37400	35.27672
440	193 600	20.97618	66.33250	85 184 000	7.605 905	16.38643	35.30348
441	194 481	21.00000	66.40783	85 766 121	7.611 663	16.39883	35.33021
442	195 364	21.02380	66.48308	86 350 888	7.617 412	16.41122	35.35689
443	196 249	21.04757	66.55825	86 938 307	7.623 152	16.42358	35.38354
444	197 136	21.07131	66.63332	87 528 384	7.628 884	16.43593	35.41014
445	198 025	21.09502	66.70832	88 121 125	7.634 607	16.44826	35.43671
446	198 916	21.11871	66.78323	88 716 536	7.640 321	16.46057	35.46323
447	199 809	21.14237	66.85806	89 314 623	7.646 027	16.47287	35.48971
448	200 704	21.16601	66.93280	89 915 392	7.651 725	16.48514	35.51616
449	201 601	21.18962	67.00746	90 518 849	7.657 414	16.49740	35.54257
450	202 500	21.21320	67.08204	91 125 000	7.663 094	16.50964	35.56893

SQUARES, SQUARE ROOT, CUBES AND CUBE ROOT (Continued)

n	n^2	$\sqrt{n}$	$\sqrt{10n}$	n^3	$\sqrt[3]{n}$	$\sqrt[3]{10n}$	$\sqrt[3]{100n}$
450	202 500	21.21320	67.08204	91 125 000	7.663 094	16.50964	35.56893
451	203 401	21.23676	67.15653	91 733 851	7.668 766	16.52186	35.59526
452	204 304	21.26029	67.23095	92 345 408	7.674 430	16.53406	35.62155
453	205 209	21.28380	67.30527	92 959 677	7.680 086	16.54624	35.64780
454	206 116	21.30728	67.37952	93 576 664	7.685 733	16.55841	35.67401
455	207 025	21.33073	67.45369	94 196 375	7.691 372	16.57056	35.70018
456	207 936	21.35416	67.52777	94 818 816	7.697 002	16.58269	35.72632
457	208 849	21.37756	67.60178	95 443 993	7.702 625	16.59480	35.75242
458	209 764	21.40093	67.67570	96 071 912	7.708 239	16.60690	35.77848
459	210 681	21.42429	67.74954	96 702 579	7.713 845	16.61897	35.80450
460	211 600	21.44761	67.82330	97 336 000	7.719 443	16.63103	35.83048
461	212 521	21.47091	67.89698	97 972 181	7.725 032	16.64308	35.85642
462	213 444	21.49419	67.97058	98 611 128	7.730 614	16.65510	35.88233
463	214 369	21.51743	68.04410	99 252 847	7.736 188	16.66711	35.90820
464	215 296	21.54066	68.11755	99 897 344	7.741 753	16.67910	35.93404
465	216 225	21.56386	68.19091	100 544 625	7.747 311	16.69108	35.95983
466	217 156	21.58703	68.26419	101 194 696	7.752 861	16.70303	35.98559
467	218 089	21.61018	68.33740	101 847 563	7.758 402	16.71497	36.01131
468	219 024	21.63331	68.41053	102 503 232	7.763 936	16.72689	36.03700
469	219 961	21.65641	68.48357	103 161 709	7.769 462	16.73880	36.06265
470	220 900	21.67948	68.55655	103 823 000	7.774 980	16.75069	36.08826
471	221 841	21.70253	68.62944	104 487 111	7.780 490	16.76256	36.11384
472	222 784	21.72556	68.70226	105 154 048	7.785 993	16.77441	36.13938
473	223 729	21.74856	68.77500	105 823 817	7.791 488	16.78625	36.16488
474	224 676	21.77154	68.84766	106 496 424	7.796 975	16.79807	36.19035
475	225 625	21.79449	68.92024	107 171 875	7.802 454	16.80988	36.21578
476	226 576	21.81742	68.99275	107 850 176	7.807 925	16.82167	36.24118
477	227 529	21.84033	69.06519	108 531 333	7.813 389	16.83344	36.26654
478	228 484	21.86321	69 13754	109 215 352	7.818 846	16.84519	36.29187
479	229 441	21.88607	69.20983	109 902 239	7.824 294	16.85693	36.31716
480	230 400	21.90890	69 28203	110 592 000	7.829 735	16.86865	36.34241
481	231 361	21.93171	69.35416	111 284 641	7.835 169	16.88036	36.36763
482	232 324	21.95450	69.42622	111 980 168	7.840 595	16.89205	36.39282
483	233 289	21.97726	69 49820	112 678 587	7.846 013	16.90372	36.41797
484	234 256	22.00000	69.57011	113 379 904	7.851 424	16.91538	36.44308
485	235 225	22.02272	69.64194	114 084 125	7.856 828	16.92702	36.46817
486	236 196	22.04541	69.71370	114 791 256	7.862 224	16.93865	36.49321
487	237 169	22.06808	69.78539	115 501 303	7.867 613	16.95026	36.51822
488	238 144	22.09072	69.85700	116 214 272	7.872 994	16.96185	36.54320
489	239 121	22.11334	69.92853	116 930 169	7.878 368	16.97343	36.56815
490	240 100	22.13594	70.00000	117 649 000	7.883 735	16.98499	36.59306
491	241 081	22.15852	70:07139	118 370 771	7.889 095	16.99654	36.61793
492	242 064	22.18107	70.14271	119 095 488	7.894 447	17.00807	36.64278
493	243 049	22.20360	70.21396	119 823 157	7.899 792	17.01959	36.66758
494	244 036	22.22611	70.28513	120 553 784	7.905 129	17.03108	36.69236
495	245 025	22.24860	70.35624	121 287 375	7.910 460	17.04257	36.71710
496	246 016	22.27106	70.42727	122 023 936	7.915 783	17.05404	36.74181
497	247 009	22.29350	70.49823	122 763 473	7.921 099	17.06549	36.76649
498	248 004	22.31591	70.56912	123 505 992	7.926 408	17.07693	36.79113
499	249 001	22.33831	70.63993	124 251 499	7.931 710	17.08835	36.81574
500	250 000	22.36068	70.71068	125 000 000	7.937 005	17.09976	36.84031

SQUARES, SQUARE ROOT, CUBES AND CUBE ROOT (Continued)

n	n^2	$\sqrt{n}$	$\sqrt{10n}$	n^3	$\sqrt[3]{n}$	$\sqrt[3]{10n}$	$\sqrt[3]{100n}$
500	250 000	22.36068	70.71068	125 000 000	7.937 005	17.09976	36.84031
501	251 001	22.38303	70.78135	125 751 501	7.942 293	17.11115	36.86486
502	252 004	22.40536	70.85196	126 506 008	7.947 574	17.12253	36.88937
503	253 009	22.42766	70.92249	127 263 527	7.952 848	17.13389	36.91385
504	254 016	22.44994	70.99296	128 024 064	7.958 114	17.14524	36.93830
505	255 025	22.47221	71.06335	128 787 625	7.963 374	17.15657	36.96271
506	256 036	22.49444	71.13368	129 554 216	7.968 627	17.16789	36.98709
507	257 049	22.51666	71.20393	130 323 843	7.973 873	17.17919	37.01144
508	258 064	22.53886	71.27412	131 096 512	7.979 112	17.19048	37.03576
509	259 081	22.56103	71.34424	131 872 229	7.984 344	17.20175	37.06004
510	260 100	22.58318	71.41428	132 651 000	7.989 570	17.21301	37.08430
511	261 121	22.60531	71.48426	133 432 831	7.994 788	17.22425	37.10852
512	262 144	22.62742	71.55418	134 217 728	8.000 000	17.23548	37.13271
513	263 169	22.64950	71.62402	135 005 697	8.005 205	17.24669	37.15687
514	264 196	22.67157	71.69379	135 796 744	8.010 403	17.25789	37.18100
515	265 225	22.69361	71.76350	136 590 875	8.015 595	17.26908	37.20509
516	266 256	22.71563	71.83314	137 388 096	8.020 779	17.28025	37.22916
517	267 289	22.73763	71.90271	138 188 413	8.025 957	17.29140	37.25319
518	268 324	22.75961	71.97222	138 991 832	8.031 129	17.30254	37.27720
519	269 361	22.78157	72.04165	139 798 359	8.036 293	17.31367	37.30117
520	270 400	22.80351	72.11103	140 608 000	8.041 452	17.32478	37.32511
521	271 441	22.82542	72.18033	141 420 761	8.046 603	17.33588	37.34902
522	272 484	22.84732	72.24957	142 236 648	8.051 748	17.34696	37.37290
523	273 529	22.86919	72.31874	143 055 667	8.056 886	17.35804	37.39675
524	274 576	22.89105	72.38784	143 877 824	8.062 018	17.36909	37.42057
525	275 625	22.91288	72.45688	144 703 125	8.067 143	17.38013	37.44436
526	276 676	22.93469	72.52586	145 531 576	8.072 262	17.39116	37.46812
527	277 729	22.95648	72.59477	146 363 183	8.077 374	17.40218	37.49185
528	278 784	22.97825	72.66361	147 197 952	8.082 480	17.41318	37.51555
529	279 841	23.00000	72.73239	148 035 889	8.087 579	17.42416	37.53922
530	280 900	23.02173	72.80110	148 877 000	8.092 672	17.43513	37.56286
531	281 961	23.04344	72.86975	149 721 291	8.097 759	17.44609	37.58647
532	283 024	23.06513	72.93833	150 568 768	8.102 839	17.45704	37.61005
533	284 089	23.08679	73.00685	151 419 437	8.107 913	17.46797	37.63360
534	285 156	23.10844	73.07530	152 273 304	8.112 980	17.47889	37.65712
535	286 225	23.13007	73.14369	153 130 375	8.118 041	17.48979	37.68061
536	287 296	23.15167	73.21202	153 990 656	8.123 096	17.50068	37.70407
537	288 369	23.17326	73.28028	154 854 153	8.128 145	17.51156	37.72751
538	289 444	23.19483	73.34848	155 720 872	8.133 187	17.52242	37.75091
539	290 521	23.21637	73.41662	156 590 819	8.138 223	17.53327	37.77429
540	291 600	23.23790	73.48469	157 464 000	8.143 253	17.54411	37.79763
541	292 681	23.25941	73.55270	158 340 421	8.148 276	17.55493	37.82095
542	293 764	23.28089	73.62065	159 220 088	8.153 294	17.56574	37.84424
543	294 849	23.30236	73.68853	160 103 007	8.158 305	17.57654	37.86750
544	295 936	23.32381	73.75636	160 989 184	8.163 310	17.58732	37.89073
545	297 025	23.34524	73.82412	161 878 625	8.168 309	17.59809	37.91393
546	298 116	23.36664	73.89181	162 771 336	8.173 302	17.60885	37.93711
547	299 209	23.38803	73.95945	163 667 323	8.178 289	17.61959	37.96025
548	300 304	23.40940	74.02702	164 566 592	8.183 269	17.63032	37.98337
549	301 401	23.43075	74.09453	165 469 149	8.188 244	17.64104	38.00646
550	302 500	23.45208	74.16198	166 375 000	8.193 213	17.65174	38.02952

SQUARES, SQUARE ROOT, CUBES AND CUBE ROOT (Continued)

n	n^2	$\sqrt{n}$	$\sqrt{10n}$	n^3	$\sqrt[3]{n}$	$\sqrt[3]{10n}$	$\sqrt[3]{100n}$
550	302 500	23.45208	74.16198	166 375 000	8.193 213	17.65174	38.02952
551	303 601	23.47339	74.22937	167 284 151	8.198 175	17.66243	38.05256
552	304 704	23.49468	74.29670	168 196 608	8.203 132	17.67311	38.07557
553	305 809	23.51595	74.36397	169 112 377	8.208 082	17.68378	38.09854
554	306 916	23.53720	74.43118	170 031 464	8.213 027	17.69443	38.12149
555	308 025	23.55844	74.49832	170 953 875	8.217 966	17.70507	38.14442
556	309 136	23.57965	74.56541	171 879 616	8.222 899	17.71570	38.16731
557	310 249	23.60085	74.63243	172 808 693	8.227 825	17.72631	38.19018
558	311 364	23.62202	74.69940	173 741 112	8.232 746	17.73691	38.21302
559	312 481	23.64318	74.76630	174 676 879	8.237 661	17.74750	38.23584
560	313 600	23.66432	74.83315	175 616 000	8.242 571	17.75808	38.25862
561	314 721	23.68544	74.89993	176 558 481	8.247 474	17.76864	38.28138
562	315 844	23.70654	74.96666	177 504 328	8.252 372	17.77920	38.30412
563	316 969	23.72762	75.03333	178 453 547	8.257 263	17.78973	38.32682
564	318 096	23.74868	75.09993	179 406 144	8.262 149	17.80026	38.34950
565	319 225	23.76973	75.16648	180 362 125	8.267 029	17.81077	38.37215
566	320 356	23.79075	75.23297	181 321 496	8.271 904	17.82128	38.39478
567	321 489	23.81176	75.29940	182 284 263	8.276 773	17.83177	38.41737
568	322 624	23.83275	75.36577	183 250 432	8.281 635	17.84224	38.43995
569	323 761	23.85372	75.43209	184 220 009	8.286 493	17.85271	38.46249
570	324 900	23.87467	75.49834	185 193 000	8.291 344	17.86316	38.48501
571	326 041	23.89561	75.56454	186 169 411	8.296 190	17.87360	38.50750
572	327 184	23.91652	75.63068	187 149 248	8.301 031	17.88403	38.52997
573	328 329	23.93742	75.69676	188 132 517	8.305 865	17.89444	38.55241
574	329 476	23.95830	75.76279	189 119 224	8.310 694	17.90485	38.57482
575	330 625	23.97916	75.82875	190 109 375	8.315 517	17.91524	38.59721
576	331 776	24.00000	75.89466	191 102 976	8.320 335	17.92562	38.61958
577	332 929	24.02082	75.96052	192 100 033	8.325 148	17.93599	38.64191
578	334 084	24.04163	76.02631	193 100 552	8.329 954	17.94634	38.66422
579	335 241	24.06242	76.09205	194 104 539	8.334 755	17.95669	38.68651
580	336 400	24.08319	76.15773	195 112 000	8.339 551	17.96702	38.70877
581	337 561	24.10394	76.22336	196 122 941	8.344 341	17.97734	38.73100
582	338 724	24.12468	76.28892	197 137 368	8.349 126	17.98765	38.75321
583	339 889	24.14539	76.35344	198 155 287	8.353 905	17.99794	38.77539
584	341 056	24.16609	76.41989	199 176 704	8.358 678	18.00823	38.79755
585	342 225	24.18677	76.48529	200 201 625	8.363 447	18.01850	38.81968
586	343 396	24.20744	76.55064	201 230 056	8.368 209	18.02876	38.84179
587	344 569	24.22808	76.61593	202 262 003	8.372 967	18.03901	38.86387
588	345 744	24.24871	76.68116	203 297 472	8.377 719	18.04925	38.88593
589	346 921	24.26932	76.74634	204 336 469	8.382 465	18.05947	38.90796
590	348 100	24.28992	76.81146	205 379 000	8.387 207	18.06969	38.92996
591	349 281	24.31049	76.87652	206 425 071	8.391 942	18.07989	38.95195
592	350 464	24.33105	76.94154	207 474 688	8.396 673	18.09008	38.97390
593	351 649	24.35159	77.00649	208 527 857	8.401 398	18.10026	38.99584
594	352 836	24.37212	77.07140	209 584 584	8.406 118	18.11043	39.01774
595	354 025	24.39262	77.13624	210 644 875	8.410 833	18.12059	39.03963
596	355 216	24.41311	77.20104	211 708 736	8.415 542	18.13074	39.06149
597	356 409	24.43358	77.26578	212 776 173	8.420 246	18.14087	39.08332
598	357 604	24.45404	77.33046	213 847 192	8.424 945	18.15099	39.10513
599	358 801	24.47448	77.39509	214 921 799	8.429 638	18.16111	39.12692
600	360 000	24.49490	77.45967	216 000 000	8.434 327	18.17121	39.14868

SQUARES, SQUARE ROOT, CUBES AND CUBE ROOT (Continued)

n	n^2	$\sqrt{n}$	$\sqrt{10n}$	n^3	$\sqrt[3]{n}$	$\sqrt[3]{10n}$	$\sqrt[3]{100n}$
600	360 000	24.49490	77.45967	216 000 000	8.434 327	18.17121	**39.14868**
601	361 201	24.51530	77.52419	217 081 801	8.439 010	18.18130	**39.17041**
602	362 404	24.53569	77.58866	218 167 208	8.443 688	18.19137	**39.19213**
603	363 609	24.55606	77.65307	219 256 227	8.448 361	18.20144	39.21382
604	364 816	24.57641	77.71744	220 348 864	8.453 028	18.21150	39.23548
605	366 025	24.59675	77.78175	221 445 125	8.457 691	18.22154	39.25712
606	367 236	24.61707	77.84600	222 545 016	8.462 348	18.23158	39.27874
607	368 449	24.63737	77.91020	223 648 543	8.467 000	18.24160	39.30033
608	369 664	24.65766	77.97435	224 755 712	8.471 647	18.25161	39.32190
609	370 881	24.67793	78.03845	225 866 529	8.476 289	18.26161	39.34345
610	372 100	24.69818	78.10250	226 981 000	8.480 926	18.27160	39.36497
611	373 321	24.71841	78.16649	228 099 131	8.485 558	18.28158	39.38647
612	374 544	24.73863	78.23043	229 220 928	8.490 185	18.29155	39.40795
613	375 769	24.75884	78.29432	230 346 397	8.494 807	18.30151	39.42940
614	376 996	24.77902	78.35815	231 475 544	8.499 423	18.31145	39.45083
615	378 225	24.79919	78.42194	232 608 375	8.504 035	18.32139	39.47223
616	379 456	24.81935	78.48567	233 744 896	8.508 642	18.33131	39.49362
617	380 689	24.83948	78.54935	234 885 113	8.513 243	18.34123	39.51498
618	381 924	24.85961	78.61298	236 029 032	8.517 840	18.35113	39.53631
619	383 161	24.87971	78.67655	237 176 659	8.522 432	18.36102	39.55763
620	384 400	24.89980	78.74008	238 328 000	8.527 019	18.37091	39.57892
621	385 641	24.91987	78.80355	239 483 061	8.531 601	18.38078	39.60018
622	386 884	24.93993	78.86698	240 641 848	8.536 178	18.39064	39.62143
623	388 129	24.95997	78.93035	241 804 367	8.540 750	18.40049	39.64265
624	389 376	24.97999	78.99367	242 970 624	8.545 317	18.41033	39.66385
625	390 625	25.00000	79.05694	244 140 625	8.549 880	18.42016	39.68503
626	391 876	25.01999	79.12016	245 314 376	8.554 437	18.42998	39.70618
627	393 129	25.03997	79.18333	246 491 883	8.558 990	18.43978	39.72731
628	394 384	25.05993	79.24645	247 673 152	8.563 538	18.44958	39.74842
629	395 641	25.07987	79.30952	248 858 189	8.568 081	18.45937	39.76951
630	396 900	25.09980	79.37254	250 047 000	8.572 619	18.46915	39.79057
631	398 161	25.11971	79.43551	251 239 591	8.577 152	18.47891	39.81161
632	399 424	25.13961	79.49843	252 435 968	8.581 681	18.48867	39.83263
633	400 689	25.15949	79.56130	253 636 137	8.586 205	18.49842	39.85363
634	401 956	25.17936	79.62412	254 840 104	8.590 724	18.50815	39.87461
635	403 225	25.19921	79.68689	256 047 875	8.595 238	18.51788	39.89556
636	404 496	25.21904	79.74961	257 259 456	8.599 748	18.52759	39.91649
637	405 769	25.23886	79.81228	258 474 853	8.604 252	18.53730	39.93740
638	407 044	25.25866	79.87490	259 694 072	8.608 753	18.54700	39.95829
639	408 321	25.27845	79.93748	260 917 119	8.613 248	18.55668	39.97916
640	409 600	25.29822	80.00000	262 144 000	8.617 739	18.56636	40.00000
641	410 881	25.31798	80.06248	263 374 721	8.622 225	18.57602	40.02082
642	412 164	25.33772	80.12490	264 609 288	8.626 706	18.58568	40.04162
643	413 449	25.35744	80.18728	265 847 707	8.631 183	18.59532	40.06240
644	414 736	25 37716	80.24961	267 089 984	8.635 655	18.60495	40.08316
645	416 025	25.39685	80.31189	268 336 125	8.640 123	18.61458	40.10390
646	417 316	25.41653	80.37413	269 586 136	8.644 585	18.62419	40.12461
647	418 609	25.43619	80.43631	270 840 023	8.649 044	18.63380	40.14530
648	419 904	25.45584	80.49845	272 097 792	8.653 497	18.64340	40.16598
649	421 201	25.47548	80.56054	273 359 449	8.657 947	18.65298	40.18663
650	422 500	25.49510	80.62258	274 625 000	8.662 391	18.66256	40.20726

SQUARES, SQUARE ROOT, CUBES AND CUBE ROOT (Continued)

n	n^2	$\sqrt{n}$	$\sqrt{10n}$	n^3	$\sqrt[3]{n}$	$\sqrt[3]{10n}$	$\sqrt[3]{100n}$
650	422 500	25.49510	80.62258	274 625 000	8.662 391	18.66256	40.20726
651	423 801	25.51470	80.68457	275 894 451	8.666 831	18.67212	40.22787
652	425 104	25.53429	80.74652	277 167 808	8.671 266	18.68168	40.24845
653	426 409	25.55386	80.80842	278 445 077	8.675 697	18.69122	40.26902
654	427 716	25.57342	80.87027	279 726 264	8.680 124	18.70076	40.28957
655	429 025	25.59297	80.93207	281 011 375	8.684 546	18.71029	40.31009
656	430 336	25.61250	80.99383	282 300 416	8.688 963	18.71980	40.33059
657	431 649	25.63201	81.05554	283 593 393	8.693 376	18.72931	40.35108
658	432 964	25.65151	81.11720	284 890 312	8.697 784	18.73881	40.37154
659	434 281	25.67100	81.17881	286 191 179	8.702 188	18.74830	40.39198
660	435 600	25.69047	81.24038	287 496 000	8.706 588	18.75777	40.41240
661	436 921	25.70992	81.30191	288 804 781	8.710 983	18.76724	40.43280
662	438 244	25.72936	81.36338	290 117 528	8.715 373	18.77670	40.45318
663	439 569	25.74879	81.42481	291 434 247	8.719 760	18.78615	40.47354
664	440 896	25.76820	81.48620	292 754 944	8.724 141	18.79559	40.49388
665	442 225	25.78759	81.54753	294 079 625	8.728 519	18.80502	40.51420
666	443 556	25.80698	81.60882	295 408 296	8.732 892	18.81444	40.53449
667	444 889	25.82634	81.67007	296 740 963	8.737 260	18.82386	40.55477
668	446 224	25.84570	81.73127	298 077 632	8.741 625	18.83326	40.57503
669	447 561	25.86503	81.79242	299 418 309	8.745 985	18.84265	40.59526
670	448 900	25.88436	81.85353	300 763 000	8.750 340	18.85204	40.61548
671	450 241	25.90367	81.91459	302 111 711	8.754 691	18.86141	40.63568
672	451 584	25.92296	81.97561	303 464 448	8.759 038	18.87078	40.65585
673	452 929	25.94224	82.03658	304 821 217	8.763 381	18.88013	40.67601
674	454 276	25.96151	82.09750	306 182 024	8.767 719	18.88948	40.69615
675	455 625	25.98076	82.15838	307 546 875	8.772 053	18.89882	40.71626
676	456 976	26.00000	82.21922	308 915 776	8.776 383	18.90814	40.73636
677	458 329	26.01922	82.28001	310 288 733	8.780 708	18.91746	40.75644
678	459 684	26.03843	82.34076	311 665 752	8.785 030	18.92677	40.77650
679	461 041	26.05763	82.40146	313 046 839	8.789 347	18.93607	40.79653
680	462 400	26.07681	82.46211	314 432 000	8.793 659	18.94536	40.81655
681	463 761	26.09598	82.52272	315 821 241	8.797 968	18.95465	40.83655
682	465 124	26.11513	82.58329	317 214 568	8.802 272	18.96392	40.85653
683	466 489	26.13427	82.64381	318 611 987	8.806 572	18.97318	40.87649
684	467 856	26.15339	82.70429	320 013 504	8.810 868	18.98244	40.89643
685	469 225	26.17250	82.76473	321 419 125	8.815 160	18.99169	40.91635
686	470 596	26.19160	82.82512	322 828 856	8.819 447	19.00092	40.93625
687	471 969	26.21068	82.88546	324 242 703	8.823 731	19.01015	40.95613
688	473 344	26.22975	82.94577	325 660 672	8.828 010	19.01937	40.97599
689	474 721	26.24881	83.00602	327 082 769	8.832 285	19.02858	40.99584
690	476 100	26.26785	83.06624	328 509 000	8.836 556	19.03778	41.01566
691	477 481	26.28688	83.12641	329 939 371	8.840 823	19.04698	41.03546
692	478 864	26.30589	83.18654	331 373 888	8.845 085	19.05616	41.05525
693	480 249	26.32489	83.24662	332 812 557	8.849 344	19.06533	41.07502
694	481 636	26.34388	83.30666	334 255 384	8.853 599	19.07450	41.09476
695	483 025	26.36285	83.36666	335 702 375	8.857 849	19.08366	41.11449
696	484 416	26.38181	83.42661	337 153 536	8.862 095	19.09281	41.13420
697	485 809	26.40076	83.48653	338 608 873	8.866 338	19.10195	41.15389
698	487 204	26.41969	83.54639	340 068 392	8.870 576	19.11108	41.17357
699	488 601	26.43861	83.60622	341 532 099	8.874 810	19.12020	41.19322
700	490 000	26.45751	83.66600	343 000 000	8.879 040	19.12931	41.21285

SQUARES, SQUARE ROOT, CUBES AND CUBE ROOT (Continued)

n	n^2	$\sqrt{n}$	$\sqrt{10n}$	n^3	$\sqrt[3]{n}$	$\sqrt[3]{10n}$	$\sqrt[3]{100n}$
700	490 000	26.45751	83.66600	343 000 000	8.879 040	19.12931	41.21285
701	491 401	26.47640	83.72574	344 472 101	8.883 266	19.13842	41.23247
702	492 804	26.49528	83.78544	345 948 408	8.887 488	19.14751	41.25207
703	494 209	26.51415	83.84510	347 428 927	8.891 706	19.15660	41.27164
704	495 616	26.53300	83.90471	348 913 664	8.895 920	19.16568	41.29120
705	497 025	26.55184	83.96428	350 402 625	8.900 130	19.17475	41.31075
706	498 436	26.57066	84.02381	351 895 816	8.904 337	19.18381	41.33027
707	499 849	26.58947	84.08329	353 393 243	8.908 539	19.19286	41.34977
708	501 264	26.60827	84.14274	354 894 912	8.912 737	19.20191	41.36926
709	502 681	26.62705	84.20214	356 400 829	8.916 931	19.21095	41.38873
710	504 100	26.64583	84.26150	357 911 000	8.921 121	19.21997	41.40818
711	505 521	26.66458	84.32082	359 425 431	8.925 308	19.22899	41.42761
712	506 944	26.68333	84.38009	360 944 128	8.929 490	19.23800	41.44702
713	508 369	26.70206	84.43933	362 467 097	8.933 669	19.24701	41.46642
714	509 796	26.72078	84.49852	363 994 344	8.937 843	19.25600	41.48579
715	511 225	26.73948	84.55767	365 525 875	8.942 014	19.26499	41.50515
716	512 656	26.75818	84.61678	367 061 696	8.946 181	19.27396	41.52449
717	514 089	26.77686	84.67585	368 601 813	8.950 344	19.28293	41.54382
718	515 524	26.79552	84.73488	370 146 232	8.954 503	19.29189	41.56312
719	516 961	26.81418	84.79387	371 694 959	8.958 658	19.30084	41.58241
720	518 400	26.83282	84.85281	373 248 000	8.962 809	19.30979	41.60168
721	519 841	26.85144	84.91172	374 805 361	8.966 957	19.31872	41.62093
722	521 284	26.87006	84.97058	376 367 048	8.971 101	19.32765	41.64016
723	522 729	26.88866	85.02941	377 933 067	8.975 241	19.33657	41.65938
724	524 176	26.90725	85.08819	379 503 424	8.979 377	19.34548	41.67857
725	525 625	26.92582	85.14693	381 078 125	8.983 509	19.35438	41.69775
726	527 076	26.94439	85.20563	382 657 176	8.987 637	19.36328	41.71692
727	528 529	26.96294	85.26429	384 240 583	8.991 762	19.37216	41.73606
728	529 984	26.98148	85.32292	385 828 352	8.995 883	19.38104	41.75519
729	531 441	27.00000	85.38150	387 420 489	9.000 000	19.38991	41.77430
730	532 900	27.01851	85.44004	389 017 000	9.004 113	19.39877	41.79339
731	534 361	27.03701	85.49854	390 617 891	9.008 223	19.40763	41.81247
732	535 824	27.05550	85.55700	392 223 168	9.012 329	19.41647	41.83152
733	537 289	27.07397	85.61542	393 832 837	9.016 431	19.42531	41.85056
734	538 756	27.09243	85.67380	395 446 904	9.020 529	19.43414	41.86959
735	540 225	27.11088	85.73214	397 065 375	9.024 624	19.44296	41.88859
736	541 696	27.12932	85.79044	398 688 256	9.028 715	19.45178	41.90758
737	543 169	27.14774	85.84870	400 315 553	9.032 802	19.46058	41.92655
738	544 644	27.16616	85.90693	401 947 272	9.036 886	19.46938	41.94551
739	546 121	27.18455	85.96511	403 583 419	9.040 966	19.47817	41.96444
740	547 600	27.20294	86.02325	405 224 000	9.045 042	19.48695	41.98336
741	549 081	27.22132	86.08136	406 869 021	9.049 114	19.49573	42.00227
742	550 564	27.23968	86.13942	408 518 488	9.053 183	19.50449	42.02115
743	552 049	27.25803	86.19745	410 172 407	9.057 248	19.51325	42.04002
744	553 536	27.27636	86.25543	411 830 784	9.061 310	19.52200	42.05887
745	555 025	27.29469	86.31338	413 493 625	9.065 368	19.53074	42.07771
746	556 516	27.31300	86.37129	415 160 936	9.069 422	19.53948	42.09653
747	558 009	27.33130	86.42916	416 832 723	9.073 473	19.54820	42.11533
748	559 504	27.34959	86.48699	418 508 992	9.077 520	19.55692	42.13411
749	561 001	27.36786	86.54479	420 189 749	9.081 563	19.56563	42.15288
750	562 500	27.38613	86.60254	421 875 000	9.085 603	19.57434	42.17163

SQUARES, SQUARE ROOT, CUBES AND CUBE ROOT (Continued)

n	n^2	$\sqrt{n}$	$\sqrt{10n}$	n^3	$\sqrt[3]{n}$	$\sqrt[3]{10n}$	$\sqrt[3]{100n}$
750	562 500	27.38613	86.60254	421 875 000	9.085 603	19.57434	42.17163
751	564 001	27.40438	86.66026	423 564 751	9.089 639	19.58303	42.19037
752	565 504	27.42262	86.71793	425 259 008	9.093 672	19.59172	42.20909
753	567 009	27.44085	86.77557	426 957 777	9.097 701	19.60040	42.22779
754	568 516	27.45906	86.83317	428 661 064	9.101 727	19.60908	42.24647
755	570 025	27.47726	86.89074	430 368 875	9.105 748	19.61774	42.26514
756	571 536	27.49545	86.94826	432 081 216	9.109 767	19.62640	42.28379
757	573 049	27.51363	87.00575	433 798 093	9.113 782	19.63505	42.30243
758	574 564	27.53180	87.06320	435 519 512	9.117 793	19.64369	42.32105
759	576 081	27.54995	87.12061	437 245 479	9.121 801	19.65232	42.33965
760	577 600	27.56810	87.17798	438 976 000	9.125 805	19.66095	42.35824
761	579 121	27.58623	87.23531	440 711 081	9.129 806	19.66957	42.37681
762	580 644	27.60435	87.29261	442 450 728	9.133 803	19.67818	42.39536
763	582 169	27.62245	87.34987	444 194 947	9.137 797	19.68679	42.41390
764	583 696	27.64055	87.40709	445 943 744	9.141 787	19.69538	42.43242
765	585 225	27.65863	87.46428	447 697 125	9.145 774	19.70397	42.45092
766	586 756	27.67671	87.52143	449 455 096	9.149 758	19.71256	42.46941
767	588 289	27.69476	87.57854	451 217 663	9.153 738	19.72113	42.48789
768	589 824	27.71281	87.63561	452 984 832	9.157 714	19.72970	42.50634
769	591 361	27.73085	87.69265	454 756 609	9.161 687	19.73826	42.52478
770	592 900	27.74887	87.74964	456 533 000	9.165 656	19.74681	42.54321
771	594 441	27.76689	87.80661	458 314 011	9.169 623	19.75535	42.56162
772	595 984	27.78489	87.86353	460 099 648	9.173 585	19.76389	42.58001
773	597 529	27.80288	87.92042	461 889 917	9.177 544	19.77242	42.59839
774	599 076	27.82086	87.97727	463 684 824	9.181 500	19.78094	42.61675
775	600 625	27.83882	88.03408	465 484 375	9.185 453	19.78946	42.63509
776	602 176	27.85678	88.09086	467 288 576	9.189 402	19.79797	42.65342
777	603 729	27.87472	88.14760	469 097 433	9.193 347	19.80647	42.67174
778	605 284	27.89265	88.20431	470 910 952	9.197 290	19.81496	42.69004
779	606 841	27.91057	88.26098	472 729 139	9.201 229	19.82345	42.70832
780	608 400	27.92848	88.31761	474 552 000	9.205 164	19.83192	42.72659
781	609 961	27.94638	88.37420	476 379 541	9.209 096	19.84040	42.74484
782	611 524	27.96426	88.43076	478 211 768	9.213 025	19.84886	42.76307
783	613 089	27.98214	88.48729	480 048 687	9.216 950	19.85732	42.78129
784	614 656	28.00000	88.54377	481 890 304	9.220 873	19.86577	42.79950
785	616 225	28.01785	88.60023	483 736 625	9.224 791	19.87421	42.81769
786	617 796	28.03569	88.65664	485 587 656	9.228 707	19.88265	42.83586
787	619 369	28.05352	88.71302	487 443 403	9.232 619	19.89107	42.85402
788	620 944	28.07134	88.76936	489 303 872	9.236 528	19.89950	42.87216
789	622 521	28.08914	88.82567	491 169 069	9.240 433	19.90791	42.89029
790	624 100	28.10694	88.88194	493 039 000	9.244 335	19.91632	42.90840
791	625 681	28.12472	88.93818	494 913 671	9.248 234	19.92472	42.92650
792	627 264	28.14249	88.99438	496 793 088	9.252 130	19.93311	42.94458
793	628 849	28.16026	89.05055	498 677 257	9.256 022	19.94150	42.96265
794	630 436	28.17801	89.10668	500 566 184	9.259 911	19.94987	42.98070
795	632 025	28.19574	89.16277	502 459 875	9.263 797	19.95825	42.99874
796	633 616	28.21347	89.21883	504 358 336	9.267 680	19.96661	43.01676
797	635 209	28.23119	89.27486	506 261 573	9.271 559	19.97497	43.03477
798	636 804	28.24889	89.33085	508 169 592	9.275 435	19.98332	43.05276
799	638 401	28.26659	89.38680	510 082 399	9.279 308	19.99166	43.07073
800	640 000	28.28427	89.44272	512 000 000	9.283 178	20.00000	43.08869

SQUARES, SQUARE ROOT, CUBES AND CUBE ROOT (Continued)

n	n²	√n	√10n	n³	∛n	∛10n	∛100n
800	640 000	28.28427	89.44272	512 000 000	9.283 178	20.00000	43.08869
801	641 601	28.30194	89.49860	513 922 401	9.287 044	20.00833	43.10664
802	643 204	28.31960	89.55445	515 849 608	9.290 907	20.01665	43.12457
803	644 809	28.33725	89.61027	517 781 627	9.294 767	20.02497	43.14249
804	646 416	28.35489	89.66605	519 718 464	9.298 624	20.03328	43.16039
805	648 025	28.37252	89.72179	521 660 125	9.302 477	20.04158	43.17828
806	649 636	28.39014	89.77750	523 606 616	9.306 328	20.04988	43.19615
807	651 249	28.40775	89.83318	525 557 943	9.310 175	20.05816	43.21400
808	652 864	28.42534	89.88882	527 514 112	9.314 019	20.06645	43.23185
809	654 481	28.44293	89.94443	529 475 129	9.317 860	20.07472	43.24967
810	656 100	28.46050	90.00000	531 441 000	9.321 698	20.08299	43.26749
811	657 721	28.47806	90.05554	533 411 731	9.325 532	20.09125	43.28529
812	659 344	28.49561	90.11104	535 387 328	9.329 363	20.09950	43.30307
813	660 969	28.51315	90.16651	537 367 797	9.333 192	20.10775	43.32084
814	662 596	28.53069	90.22195	539 353 144	9.337 017	20.11599	43.33859
815	664 225	28.54820	90.27735	541 343 375	9.340 839	20.12423	43.35633
816	665 856	28.56571	90.33272	543 338 496	9.344 657	20.13245	43.37406
817	667 489	28.58321	90.38805	545 338 513	9.348 473	20.14067	43.39177
818	669 124	28.60070	90.44335	547 343 432	9.352 286	20.14889	43.40947
819	670 761	28.61818	90.49862	549 353 259	9.356 095	20.15710	43.42715
820	672 400	28.63564	90.55385	551 368 000	9.359 902	20.16530	43.44481
821	674 041	28.65310	90.60905	553 387 661	9.363 705	20.17349	43.46247
822	675 684	28.67054	90.66422	555 412 248	9.367 505	20.18168	43.48011
823	677 329	28.68798	90.71935	557 441 767	9.371 302	20.18986	43.49773
824	678 976	28.70540	90.77445	559 476 224	9.375 096	20.19803	43.51534
825	680 625	28.72281	90.82951	561 515 625	9.378 887	20.20620	43.53294
826	682 276	28.74022	90.88454	563 559 976	9.382 675	20.21436	43.55052
827	683 929	28.75761	90.93954	565 609 283	9.386 460	20.22252	43.56809
828	685 584	28.77499	90.99451	567 663 552	9.390 242	20.23066	43.58564
829	687 241	28.79236	91.04944	569 722 789	9.394 021	20.23880	43.60318
830	688 900	28.80972	91.10434	571 787 000	9.397 796	20.24694	43.62071
831	690 561	28.82707	91.15920	573 856 191	9.401 569	20.25507	43.63822
832	692 224	28.84441	91.21403	575 930 368	9.405 339	20.26319	43.65572
833	693 889	28.86174	91.26883	578 009 537	9.409 105	20.27130	43.67320
834	695 556	28.87906	91.32360	580 093 704	9.412 869	20.27941	43.69067
835	697 225	28.89637	91.37833	582 182 875	9.416 630	20.28751	43.70812
836	698 896	28.91366	91.43304	584 277 056	9.420 387	20.29561	43.72556
837	700 569	28.93095	91.48770	586 376 253	9.424 142	20.30370	43.74299
838	702 244	28.94823	91.54234	588 480 472	9.427 894	20.31178	43.76041
839	703 921	28.96550	91.59694	590 589 719	9.431 642	20.31986	43.77781
840	705 600	28.98275	91.65151	592 704 000	9.435 388	20.32793	43.79519
841	707 281	29.00000	91.70605	594 823 321	9.439 131	20.33599	43.81256
842	708 964	29.01724	91.76056	596 947 688	9.442 870	20.34405	43.82992
843	710 649	29.03446	91.81503	599 077 107	9.446 607	20.35210	43.84727
844	712 336	29.05168	91.86947	601 211 584	9.450 341	20.36014	43.86460
845	714 025	29.06888	91.92388	603 351 125	9.454 072	20.36818	43.88191
846	715 716	29.08608	91.97826	605 495 736	9.457 800	20.37621	43.89922
847	717 409	29.10326	92.03260	607 645 423	9.461 525	20.38424	43.91651
848	719 104	29.12044	92.08692	609 800 192	9.465 247	20.39226	43.93378
849	720 801	29.13760	92.14120	611 960 049	9.468 966	20.40027	43.95105
850	722 500	29.15476	92.19544	614 125 000	9.472 682	20.40828	43.96830

SQUARES, SQUARE ROOT, CUBES AND CUBE ROOT (Continued)

n	n^2	$\sqrt{n}$	$\sqrt{10n}$	n^3	$\sqrt[3]{n}$	$\sqrt[3]{10n}$	$\sqrt[3]{100n}$
850	722 500	29.15476	92.19544	614 125 000	9.472 682	20.40828	43.96830
851	724 201	29.17190	92.24966	616 295 051	9.476 396	20.41628	43.98553
852	725 904	29.18904	92.30385	618 470 208	9.480 106	20.42427	44.00275
853	727 609	29.20616	92.35800	620 650 477	9.483 814	20.43226	44.01996
854	729 316	29.22328	92.41212	622 835 864	9.487 518	20.44024	44.03716
855	731 025	29.24038	92.46621	625 026 375	9.491 220	20.44821	44.05434
856	732 736	29.25748	92.52027	627 222 016	9.494 919	20.45618	44.07151
857	734 449	29.27456	92.57429	629 422 793	9.498 615	20.46415	44.08866
858	736 164	29.29164	92.62829	631 628 712	9.502 308	20.47210	44.10581
859	737 881	29.30870	92.68225	633 839 779	9.505 998	20.48005	44.12293
860	739 600	29.32576	92.73618	636 056 000	9.509 685	20.48800	44.14005
861	741 321	29.34280	92.79009	638 277 381	9.513 370	20.49593	44.15715
862	743 044	29.35984	92.84396	640 503 928	9.517 052	20.50387	44.17424
863	744 769	29.37686	92.89779	642 735 647	9.520 730	20.51179	44.19132
864	746 496	29.39388	92.95160	644 972 544	9.524 406	20.51971	44.20838
865	748 225	29.41088	93.00538	647 214 625	9.528 079	20.52762	44.22543
866	749 956	29.42788	93.05912	649 461 896	9.531 750	20.53553	44.24246
867	751 689	29.44486	93.11283	651 714 363	9.535 417	20.54343	44.25949
868	753 424	29.46184	93.16652	653 972 032	9.539 082	20.55133	44.27650
869	755 161	29.47881	93.22017	656 234 909	9.542 744	20.55922	44.29349
870	756 900	29.49576	93.27379	658 503 000	9.546 403	20.56710	44.31048
871	758 641	29.51271	93.32738	660 776 311	9.550 059	20.57498	44.32745
872	760 384	29.52965	93.38094	663 054 848	9.553 712	20.58285	44.34440
873	762 129	29.54657	93.43447	665 338 617	9.557 363	20.59071	44.36135
874	763 876	29.56349	93.48797	667 627 624	9.561 011	20.59857	44.37828
875	765 625	29.58040	93.54143	669 921 875	9.564 656	20.60643	44.39520
876	767 376	29.59730	93.59487	672 221 376	9.568 298	20.61427	44.41211
877	769 129	29.61419	93.64828	674 526 133	9.571 938	20.62211	44.42900
878	770 884	29.63106	93.70165	676 836 152	9.575 574	20.62995	44.44588
879	772 641	29.64793	93.75500	679 151 439	9.579 208	20.63778	44.46275
880	774 400	29.66479	93.80832	681 472 000	9.582 840	20.64560	44.47960
881	776 161	29.68164	93.86160	683 797 841	9.586 468	20.65342	44.49644
882	777 924	29.69848	93.91486	686 128 968	9.590 094	20.66123	44.51327
883	779 689	29.71532	93.96808	688 465 387	9.593 717	20.66904	44.53009
884	781 456	29.73214	94.02127	690 807 104	9.597 337	20.67684	44.54689
885	783 225	29.74895	94.07444	693 154 125	9.600 955	20.68463	44.56368
886	784 996	29.76575	94.12757	695 506 456	9.604 570	20.69242	44.58046
887	786 769	29.78255	94.18068	697 864 103	9.608 182	20.70020	44.59723
888	788 544	29.79933	94.23375	700 227 072	9.611 791	20.70798	44.61398
889	790 321	29.81610	94.28680	702 595 369	9.615 398	20.71575	44.63072
890	792 100	29.83287	94.33981	704 969 000	9.619 002	20.72351	44.64745
891	793 881	29.84962	94.39280	707 347 971	9.622 603	20.73127	44.66417
892	795 664	29.86637	94.44575	709 732 288	9.626 202	20.73902	44.68087
893	797 449	29.88311	94.49868	712 121 957	9.629 797	20.74677	44.69756
894	799 236	29.89983	94.55157	714 516 984	9.633 391	20.75451	44.71424
895	801 025	29.91655	94.60444	716 917 375	9.636 981	20.76225	44.73090
896	802 816	29.93326	94.65728	719 323 136	9.640 569	20.76998	44.74756
897	804 609	29.94996	94.71008	721 734 273	9.644 154	20.77770	44.76420
898	806 404	29.96665	94.76286	724 150 792	9.647 737	20.78542	44.78083
899	808 201	29.98333	94.81561	726 572 699	9.651 317	20.79313	44.79744
900	810 000	30.00000	94.86833	729 000 000	9.654 894	20.80084	44.81405

SQUARES, SQUARE ROOT, CUBES AND CUBE ROOT (Continued)

n	n^2	$\sqrt{n}$	$\sqrt{10n}$	n^3	$\sqrt[3]{n}$	$\sqrt[3]{10n}$	$\sqrt[3]{100n}$
900	810 000	30.00000	94.86833	729 000 000	9.654 894	20.80084	44.81405
901	811 801	30.01666	94.92102	731 432 701	9.658 468	20.80854	44.83064
902	813 604	30.03331	94.97368	733 870 808	9.662 040	20.81623	44.84722
903	815 409	30.04996	95.02631	736 314 327	9.665 610	20.82392	44.86379
904	817 216	30.06659	95.07891	738 763 264	9.669 176	20.83161	44.88034
905	819 025	30.08322	95.13149	741 217 625	9.672 740	20.83929	44.89688
906	820 836	30.09983	95.18403	743 677 416	9.676 302	20.84696	44.91341
907	822 649	30.11644	95.23655	746 142 643	9.679 860	20.85463	44.92993
908	824 464	30.13304	95.28903	748 613 312	9.683 417	20.86229	44.94644
909	826 281	30.14963	95.34149	751 089 429	9.686 970	20.86994	44.96293
910	828 100	30.16621	95.39392	753 571 000	9.690 521	20.87759	44.97941
911	829 921	30.18278	95.44632	756 058 031	9.694 069	20.88524	44.99588
912	831 744	30.19934	95.49869	758 550 528	9.697 615	20.89288	45.01234
913	833 569	30.21589	95.55103	761 048 497	9.701 158	20.90051	45.02879
914	835 396	30.23243	95.60335	763 551 944	9.704 699	20.90814	45.04522
915	837 225	30.24897	95.65563	766 060 875	9.708 237	20.91576	45.06164
916	839 056	30.26549	95.70789	768 575 296	9.711 772	20.92338	45.07805
917	840 889	30.28201	95.76012	771 095 213	9.715 305	20.93099	45.09445
918	842 724	30.29851	95.81232	773 620 632	9.718 835	20.93860	45.11084
919	844 561	30.31501	95.86449	776 151 559	9.722 363	20.94620	45.12721
920	846 400	30.33150	95.91663	778 688 000	9.725 888	20.95379	45.14357
921	848 241	30.34798	95.96874	781 229 961	9.729 411	20.96138	45.15992
922	850 084	30.36445	96.02083	783 777 448	9.732 931	20.96896	45.17626
923	851 929	30.38092	96.07289	786 330 467	9.736 448	20.97654	45.19259
924	853 776	30.39737	96.12492	788 889 024	9.739 963	20.98411	45.20891
925	855 625	30.41381	96.17692	791 453 125	9.743 476	20.99168	45.22521
926	857 476	30.43025	96.22889	794 022 776	9.746 986	20.99924	45.24150
927	859 329	30.44667	96.28084	796 597 983	9.750 493	21.00680	45.25778
928	861 184	30.46309	96.33276	799 178 752	9.753 998	21.01435	45.27405
929	863 041	30.47950	96.38465	801 765 089	9.757 500	21.02190	45.29030
930	864 900	30.49590	96.43651	804 357 000	9.761 000	21.02944	45.30655
931	866 761	30.51229	96.48834	806 954 491	9.764 497	21.03697	45.32278
932	868 624	30.52868	96.54015	809 557 568	9.767 992	21.04450	45.33900
933	870 489	30.54505	96.59193	812 166 237	9.771 485	21.05203	45.35521
934	872 356	30.56141	96.64368	814 780 504	9.774 974	21.05954	45.37141
935	874 225	30.57777	96.69540	817 400 375	9.778 462	21.06706	45.38760
936	876 096	30.59412	96.74709	820 025 856	9.781 946	21.07456	45.40377
937	877 969	30.61046	96.79876	822 656 953	9.785 429	21.08207	45.41994
938	879 844	30.62679	96.85040	825 293 672	9.788 909	21.08956	45.43609
939	881 721	30.64311	96.90201	827 936 019	9.792 386	21.09706	45.45223
940	883 600	30.65942	96.95360	830 584 000	9.795 861	21.10454	45.46836
941	885 481	30.67572	97.00515	833 237 621	9.799 334	21.11202	45.48448
942	887 364	30.69202	97.05668	835 896 888	9.802 804	21.11950	45.50058
943	889 249	30.70831	97.10819	838 561 807	9.806 271	21.12697	45.51668
944	891 136	30.72458	97.15966	841 232 384	9.809 736	21.13444	45.53276
945	893 025	30.74085	97.21111	843 908 625	9.813 199	21.14190	45.54883
946	894 916	30.75711	97.26253	846 590 536	9.816 659	21.14935	45.56490
947	896 809	30.77337	97.31393	849 278 123	9.820 117	21.15680	45.58095
948	898 704	30.78961	97.36529	851 971 392	9.823 572	21.16424	45.59698
949	900 601	30.80584	97.41663	854 670 349	9.827 025	21.17168	45.61301
950	902 500	30.82207	97.46794	857 375 000	9.830 476	21.17912	45.62903

SQUARES, SQUARE ROOT, CUBES AND CUBE ROOT (Continued)

n	n^2	$\sqrt{n}$	$\sqrt{10n}$	n^3	$\sqrt[3]{n}$	$\sqrt[3]{10n}$	$\sqrt[3]{100n}$
950	902 500	30.82207	97.46794	857 375 000	9.830 476	21.17912	45.62903
951	904 401	30.83829	97.51923	860 085 351	9.833 924	21.18655	45.64503
952	906 304	30.85450	97.57049	862 801 408	9.837 369	21.19397	45.66102
953	908 209	30.87070	97.62172	865 523 177	9.840 813	21.20139	45.67701
954	910 116	30.88689	97.67292	868 250 664	9.844 254	21.20880	45.69298
955	912 025	30.90307	97.72410	870 983 875	9.847 692	21.21621	45.70894
956	913 936	30.91925	97.77525	873 722 816	9.851 128	21.22361	45.72489
957	915 849	30.93542	97.82638	876 467 493	9.854 562	21.23101	45.74082
958	917 764	30.95158	97.87747	879 217 912	9.857 993	21.23840	45.75675
959	919 681	30.96773	97.92855	881 974 079	9.861 422	21.24579	45.77267
960	921 600	30.98387	97.97959	884 736 000	9.864 848	21.25317	45.78857
961	923 521	31.00000	98.03061	887 503 681	9.868 272	21.26055	45.80446
962	925 444	31.01612	98.08160	890 277 128	9.871 694	21.26792	45.82035
963	927 369	31.03224	98.13256	893 056 347	9.875 113	21.27529	45.83622
964	929 296	31.04835	98.18350	895 841 344	9.878 530	21.28265	45.85208
965	931 225	31.06445	98.23441	898 632 125	9.881 945	21.29001	45.86793
966	933 156	31.08054	98.28530	901 428 696	9.885 357	21.29736	45.88376
967	935 089	31.09662	98.33616	904 231 063	9.888 767	21.30470	45.89959
968	937 024	31.11270	98.38699	907 039 232	9.892 175	21.31204	45.91541
969	938 961	31.12876	98.43780	909 853 209	9.895 580	21.31938	45.93121
970	940 900	31.14482	98.48858	912 673 000	9.898 983	21.32671	45.94701
971	942 841	31.16087	98.53933	915 498 611	9.902 384	21.33404	45.96279
972	944 784	31.17691	98.59006	918 330 048	9.905 782	21.34136	45.97857
973	946 729	31.19295	98.64076	921 167 317	9.909 178	21.34868	45.99433
974	948 676	31.20897	98.69144	924 010 424	9.912 571	21.35599	46.01008
975	950 625	31.22499	98.74209	926 859 375	9.915 962	21.36329	46.02582
976	952 576	31.24100	98.79271	929 714 176	9.919 351	21.37059	46.04155
977	954 529	31.25700	98.84331	932 574 833	9.922 738	21.37789	46.05727
978	956 484	31.27299	98.89388	935 441 352	9.926 122	21.38518	46.07298
979	958 441	31.28898	98.94443	938 313 739	9.929 504	21.39247	46.08868
980	960 400	31.30495	98.99495	941 192 000	9.932 884	21.39975	46.10436
981	962 361	31.32092	99.04544	944 076 141	9.936 261	21.40703	46.12004
982	964 324	31.33688	99.09591	946 966 168	9.939 636	21.41430	46.13571
983	966 289	31.35283	99.14636	949 862 087	9.943 009	21.42156	46.15136
984	968 256	31.36877	99.19677	952 763 904	9.946 380	21.42883	46.16700
985	970 225	31.38471	99.24717	955 671 625	9.949 748	21.43608	46.18264
986	972 196	31.40064	99.29753	958 585 256	9.953 114	21.44333	46.19826
987	974 169	31.41656	99.34787	961 504 803	9.956 478	21.45058	46.21387
988	976 144	31.43247	99.39819	964 430 272	9.959 839	21.45782	46.22948
989	978 121	31.44837	99.44848	967 361 669	9.963 198	21.46506	46.24507
990	980 100	31.46427	99.49874	970 299 000	9.966 555	21.47229	46.26065
991	982 081	31.48015	99.54898	973 242 271	9.969 910	21.47952	46.27622
992	984 064	31.49603	99.59920	976 191 488	9.973 262	21.48674	46.29178
993	986 049	31.51190	99.64939	979 146 657	9.976 612	21.49396	46.30733
994	988 036	31.52777	99.69955	982 107 784	9.979 960	21.50117	46.32287
995	990 025	31.54362	99.74969	985 074 875	9.983 305	21.50838	46.33840
996	992 016	31.55947	99.79980	988 047 936	9.986 649	21.51558	46.35392
997	994 009	31.57531	99.84989	991 026 973	9.989 990	21.52278	46.36943
998	996 004	31.59114	99.89995	994 011 992	9.993 329	21.52997	46.38492
999	998 001	31.60696	99.94999	997 002 999	9.996 666	21.53716	46.40041
1000	1 000 000	31.62278	100.00000	1 000 000.000	10.000 000	21.54435	46.41589

FOURTH AND FIFTH ROOTS

n	$\sqrt[4]{n}$	$\sqrt[5]{n}$	n	$\sqrt[4]{n}$	$\sqrt[5]{n}$
1	1.0000 00	1.0000 00	51	2.6723 45	2.1954 02
2	1.1892 07	1.1486 98	52	2.6853 50	2.2039 45
3	1.3160 74	1.2457 31	53	2.6981 68	2.2123 57
4	1.4142 14	1.3195 08	54	2.7108 06	2.2206 43
5	1.4953 49	1.3797 30	55	2.7232 70	2.2288 07
6	1.5650 85	1.4309 69	56	2.7355 65	2.2368 54
7	1.6265 77	1.4757 73	57	2.7476 96	2.2447 86
8	1.6817 93	1.5157 17	58	2.7596 69	2.2526 08
9	1.7320 51	1.5518 46	59	2.7714 88	2.2603 22
10	1.7782 79	1.5848 93	60	2.7831 58	2.2679 33
11	1.8211 60	1.6153 94	61	2.7946 82	2.2754 43
12	1.8612 10	1.6437 52	62	2.8060 66	2.2828 55
13	1.8988 29	1.6702 78	63	2.8173 13	2.2901 72
14	1.9343 36	1.6952 18	64	2.8284 27	2.2973 97
15	1.9679 90	1.7187 72	65	2.8394 12	2.3045 32
16	2.0000 00	1.7411 01	66	2.8502 70	2.3115 79
17	2.0305 43	1.7623 40	67	2.8610 06	2.3185 42
18	2.0597 67	1.7826 02	68	2.8716 22	2.3254 22
19	2.0877 98	1.8019 83	69	2.8821 21	2.3322 22
20	2.1147 43	1.8205 64	70	2.8925 08	2.3389 43
21	2.1406 95	1.8384 16	71	2.9027 83	2.3455 88
22	2.1657 37	1.8556 01	72	2.9129 51	2.3521 58
23	2.1899 39	1.8721 71	73	2.9230 13	2.3586 56
24	2.2133 64	1.8881 75	74	2.9329 72	2.3650 83
25	2.2360 68	1.9036 54	75	2.9428 31	2.3714 41
26	2.2581 01	1.9186 45	76	2.9525 92	2.3777 31
27	2.2795 07	1.9331 82	77	2.9622 57	2.3839 56
28	2.3003 27	1.9472 94	78	2.9718 28	2.3901 16
29	2.3205 96	1.9610 09	79	2.9813 08	2.3962 13
30	2.3403 47	1.9743 50	80	2.9906 98	2.4022 49
31	2.3596 11	1.9873 41	81	3.0000 00	2.4082 25
32	2.3784 14	2.0000 00	82	3.0092 17	2.4141 42
33	2.3967 82	2.0123 47	83	3.0183 49	2.4200 01
34	2.4147 36	2.0243 97	84	3.0274 00	2.4258 05
35	2.4322 99	2.0361 68	85	3.0363 70	2.4315 53
36	2.4494 90	2.0476 73	86	3.0452 62	2.4372 48
37	2.4663 26	2.0589 24	87	3.0540 76	2.4428 90
38	2.4828 24	2.0699 35	88	3.0628 14	2.4484 80
39	2.4989 99	2.0807 17	89	3.0714 79	2.4540 19
40	2.5148 67	2.0912 79	90	3.0800 70	2.4595 09
41	2.5304 40	2.1016 32	91	3.0885 91	2.4649 51
42	2.5457 30	2.1117 86	92	3.0970 41	2.4703 45
43	2.5607 50	2.1217 47	93	3.1054 23	2.4756 92
44	2.5755 10	2.1315 26	94	3.1137 37	2.4809 93
45	2.5900 20	2.1411 27	95	3.1219 86	2.4862 50
46	2.6042 91	2.1505 60	96	3.1301 69	2.4914 62
47	2.6183 30	2.1598 30	97	3.1382 89	2.4966 31
48	2.6321 48	2.1689 44	98	3.1463 46	2.5017 58
49	2.6457 51	2.1779 06	99	3.1543 42	2.5068 42
50	2.6591 48	2.1867 24	100	3.1622 78	2.5118 86

FOURTH AND FIFTH ROOTS (Continued)

n	$\sqrt[4]{n}$	$\sqrt[5]{n}$	n	$\sqrt[4]{n}$	$\sqrt[5]{n}$
101	3.1701 54	2.5168 90	151	3.5054 54	2.7276 92
102	3.1779 72	2.5218 55	152	3.5112 43	2.7312 96
103	3.1857 33	2.5267 80	153	3.5170 04	2.7348 80
104	3.1934 37	2.5316 68	154	3.5227 37	2.7384 46
105	3.2010 86	2.5365 17	155	3.5284 42	2.7419 93
106	3.2086 80	2.5413 31	156	3.5341 19	2.7455 22
107	3.2162 21	2.5461 08	157	3.5397 69	2.7490 33
108	3.2237 10	2.5508 49	158	3.5453 92	2.7525 26
109	3.2311 46	2.5555 55	159	3.5509 89	2.7560 01
110	3.2385 32	2.5602 27	160	3.5565 59	2.7594 59
111	3.2458 67	2.5648 65	161	3.5621 03	2.7629 00
112	3.2531 53	2.5694 70	162	3.5676 21	2.7663 24
113	3.2603 90	2.5740 42	163	3.5731 14	2.7697 31
114	3.2675 80	2.5785 82	164	3.5785 82	2.7731 21
115	3.2747 22	2.5830 90	165	3.5840 25	2.7764 94
116	3.2818 18	2.5875 67	166	3.5894 43	2.7798 52
117	3.2888 68	2.5920 13	167	3.5948 36	2.7831 93
118	3.2958 73	2.5964 29	168	3.6002 06	2.7865 18
119	3.3028 34	2.6008 15	169	3.6055 51	2.7898 27
120	3.3097 51	2.6051 71	170	3.6108 73	2.7931 21
121	3.3166 25	2.6094 99	171	3.6161 72	2.7964 00
122	3.3234 56	2.6137 98	172	3.6214 47	2.7996 63
123	3.3302 46	2.6180 69	173	3.6266 99	2.8029 10
124	3.3369 94	2.6223 12	174	3.6319 29	2.8061 43
125	3.3437 02	2.6265 28	175	3.6371 36	2.8093 61
126	3.3503 69	2.6307 17	176	3.6423 21	2.8125 65
127	3.3569 97	2.6348 79	177	3.6474 83	2.8157 54
128	3.3635 86	2.6390 16	178	3.6526 24	2.8189 28
129	3.3701 36	2.6431 26	179	3.6577 44	2.8220 88
130	3.3766 48	2.6472 12	180	3.6628 42	2.8252 35
131	3.3831 23	2.6512 72	181	3.6679 18	2.8283 67
132	3.3895 61	2.6553 07	182	3.6729 74	2.8314 85
133	3.3959 63	2.6593 18	183	3.6780 09	2.8345 90
134	3.4023 28	2.6633 05	184	3.6830 23	2.8376 81
135	3.4086 58	2.6672 69	185	3.6880 17	2.8407 59
136	3.4149 53	2.6712 08	186	3.6929 91	2.8438 23
137	3.4212 13	2.6751 25	187	3.6979 45	2.8468 74
138	3.4274 39	2.6790 19	188	3.7028 79	2.8499 13
139	3.4336 32	2.6828 91	189	3.7077 93	2.8529 38
140	3.4397 91	2.6867 40	190	3.7126 88	2.8559 51
141	3.4459 17	2.6905 67	191	3.7175 63	2.8589 51
142	3.4520 10	2.6943 73	192	3.7224 19	2.8619 38
143	3.4580 72	2.6981 57	193	3.7272 57	2.8649 13
144	3.4641 02	2.7019 20	194	3.7320 76	2.8678 76
145	3.4701 00	2.7056 62	195	3.7368 76	2.8708 26
146	3.4760 68	2.7093 84	196	3.7416 57	2.8737 65
147	3.4820 05	2.7130 85	197	3.7464 21	2.8766 91
148	3.4879 11	2.7167 67	198	3.7511 66	2.8796 06
149	3.4937 88	2.7204 28	199	3.7558 93	2.8825 09
150	3.4996 36	2.7240 70	200	3.7606 03	2.8854 00

FOURTH AND FIFTH ROOTS (Continued)

n	$\sqrt[4]{n}$	$\sqrt[5]{n}$	n	$\sqrt[4]{n}$	$\sqrt[5]{n}$
201	3.7652 95	2.8882 79	251	3.9803 24	3.0194 98
202	3.7699 70	2.8911 48	252	3.9842 83	3.0219 00
203	3.7746 27	2.8940 05	253	3.9882 29	3.0242 95
204	3.7792 67	2.8968 50	254	3.9921 65	3.0266 82
205	3.7838 90	2.8996 85	255	3.9960 88	3.0290 61
206	3.7884 96	2.9025 08	256	4.0000 00	3.0314 33
207	3.7930 85	2.9053 21	257	4.0039 01	3.0337 98
208	3.7976 58	2.9081 22	258	4.0077 90	3.0361 55
209	3.8022 14	2.9109 13	259	4.0116 68	3.0385 05
210	3.8067 54	2.9136 93	260	4.0155 34	3.0408 48
211	3.8112 78	2.9164 63	261	4.0193 90	3.0431 83
212	3.8157 86	2.9192 22	262	4.0232 34	3.0455 12
213	3.8202 77	2.9219 71	263	4.0270 68	3.0478 33
214	3.8247 53	2.9247 10	264	4.0308 90	3.0501 47
215	3.8292 14	2.9274 38	265	4.0347 02	3.0524 54
216	3.8336 59	2.9301 56	266	4.0385 03	3.0547 55
217	3.8380 88	2.9328 64	267	4.0422 93	3.0570 48
218	3.8425 02	2.9355 62	268	4.0460 73	3.0593 34
219	3.8469 01	2.9382 51	269	4.0498 42	3.0616 14
220	3.8512 85	2.9409 29	270	4.0536 00	3.0638 87
221	3.8556 54	2.9435 98	271	4.0573 49	3.0661 53
222	3.8600 08	2.9462 57	272	4.0610 86	3.0684 13
223	3.8643 48	2.9489 06	273	4.0648 14	3.0706 66
224	3.8686 73	2.9515 46	274	4.0685 31	3.0729 12
225	3.8729 83	2.9541 77	275	4.0722 38	3.0751 52
226	3.8772 80	2.9567 98	276	4.0759 35	3.0773 85
227	3.8815 61	2.9594 10	277	4.0796 22	3.0796 12
228	3.8858 29	2.9620 13	278	4.0832 99	3.0818 32
229	3.8900 83	2.9646 07	279	4.0869 66	3.0840 46
230	3.8943 23	2.9671 91	280	4.0906 23	3.0862 54
231	3.8985 49	2.9697 67	281	4.0942 71	3.0884 55
232	3.9027 61	2.9723 34	282	4.0979 09	3.0906 50
233	3.9069 60	2.9748 92	283	4.1015 37	3.0928 39
234	3.9111 45	2.9774 41	284	4.1051 55	3.0950 21
235	3.9153 17	2.9799 82	285	4.1087 64	3.0971 98
236	3.9194 76	2.9825 13	286	4.1123 64	3.0993 68
237	3.9236 21	2.9850 37	287	4.1159 54	3.1015 33
238	3.9277 54	2.9875 51	288	4.1195 34	3.1036 91
239	3.9318 73	2.9900 58	289	4.1231 06	3.1058 44
240	3.9359 79	2.9925 56	290	4.1266 68	3.1079 90
241	3.9400 73	2.9950 45	291	4.1302 21	3.1101 30
242	3.9441 54	2.9975 27	292	4.1337 64	3.1122 65
243	3.9482 22	3.0000 00	293	4.1372 99	3.1143 94
244	3.9522 78	3.0024 65	294	4.1408 25	3.1165 17
245	3.9563 21	3.0049 22	295	4.1443 41	3.1186 34
246	3.9603 52	3.0073 71	296	4.1478 49	3.1207 45
247	3.9643 71	3.0098 12	297	4.1513 48	3.1228 51
248	3.9683 77	3.0122 45	298	4.1548 38	3.1249 51
249	3.9723 71	3.0146 71	299	4.1583 19	3.1270 46
250	3.9763 54	3.0170 88	300	4.1617 91	3.1291 35

FOURTH AND FIFTH ROOTS (Continued)

n	$\sqrt[4]{n}$	$\sqrt[5]{n}$	n	$\sqrt[4]{n}$	$\sqrt[5]{n}$
301	4.1652 55	3.1312 18	351	4.3283 94	3.2289 51
302	4.1687 10	3.1332 96	352	4.3314 74	3.2307 89
303	4.1721 57	3.1353 68	353	4.3345 47	3.2326 22
304	4.1755 95	3.1374 35	354	4.3376 13	3.2344 52
305	4.1790 25	3.1394 96	355	4.3406 73	3.2362 77
306	4.1824 46	3.1415 52	356	4.3437 27	3.2380 98
307	4.1858 59	3.1436 03	357	4.3467 74	3.2399 15
308	4.1892 64	3.1456 48	358	4.3498 15	3.2417 28
309	4.1926 60	3.1476 88	359	4.3528 49	3.2435 37
310	4.1960 48	3.1497 23	360	4.3558 77	3.2453 42
311	4.1994 28	3.1517 52	361	4.3588 99	3.2471 43
312	4.2027 99	3.1537 77	362	4.3619 14	3.2489 40
313	4.2061 63	3.1557 96	363	4.3649 24	3.2507 33
314	4.2095 18	3.1578 10	364	4.3679 27	3.2525 22
315	4.2128 66	3.1598 18	365	4.3709 24	3.2543 07
316	4.2162 06	3.1618 22	366	4.3739 14	3.2560 89
317	4.2195 37	3.1638 21	367	4.3768 99	3.2578 66
318	4.2228 61	3.1658 14	368	4.3798 77	3.2596 39
319	4.2261 77	3.1678 03	369	4.3828 50	3.2614 09
320	4.2294 85	3.1697 86	370	4.3858 16	3.2631 75
321	4.2327 85	3.1717 65	371	4.3887 77	3.2649 37
322	4.2360 78	3.1737 39	372	4.3917 31	3.2666 95
323	4.2393 63	3.1757 08	373	4.3946 80	3.2684 49
324	4.2426 41	3.1776 72	374	4.3976 22	3.2702 00
325	4.2459 11	3.1796 31	375	4.4005 59	3.2719 47
326	4.2491 73	3.1815 85	376	4.4034 89	3.2736 90
327	4.2524 28	3.1835 34	377	4.4064 14	3.2754 30
328	4.2556 75	3.1854 79	378	4.4093 34	3.2771 65
329	4.2589 15	3.1874 19	379	4.4122 47	3.2788 98
330	4.2621 48	3.1893 54	380	4.4151 54	3.2806 26
331	4.2653 73	3.1912 85	381	4.4180 56	3.2823 51
332	4.2685 91	3.1932 11	382	4.4209 52	3.2840 72
333	4.2718 01	3.1951 32	383	4.4238 43	3.2857 90
334	4.2750 05	3.1970 49	384	4.4267 28	3.2875 04
335	4.2782 01	3.1989 61	385	4.4296 07	3.2892 14
336	4.2813 90	3.2008 69	386	4.4324 80	3.2909 21
337	4.2845 72	3.2027 72	387	4.4353 48	3.2926 24
338	4.2877 47	3.2046 70	388	4.4382 11	3.2943 24
339	4.2909 15	3.2065 64	389	4.4410 68	3.2960 21
340	4.2940 76	3.2084 54	390	4.4439 19	3.2977 13
341	4.2972 30	3.2103 39	391	4.4467 65	3.2994 03
342	4.3003 77	3.2122 20	392	4.4496 06	3.3010 89
343	4.3035 17	3.2140 96	393	4.4524 41	3.3027 71
344	4.3066 50	3.2159 68	394	4.4552 70	3.3044 50
345	4.3097 77	3.2178 35	395	4.4580 95	3.3061 26
346	4.3128 96	3.2196 99	396	4.4609 13	3.3077 98
347	4.3160 09	3.2215 58	397	4.4637 27	3.3094 67
348	4.3191 15	3.2234 12	398	4.4665 35	3.3111 33
349	4.3222 15	3.2252 63	399	4.4693 38	3.3127 95
350	4.3253 08	3.2271 09	400	4.4721 36	3.3144 54

FOURTH AND FIFTH ROOTS (Continued)

n	$\sqrt[4]{n}$	$\sqrt[5]{n}$	n	$\sqrt[4]{n}$	$\sqrt[5]{n}$
401	4.4749 28	3.3161 10	451	4.6083 36	3.3949 65
402	4.4777 16	3.3177 62	452	4.6108 88	3.3964 69
403	4.4804 98	3.3194 11	453	4.6134 37	3.3979 71
404	4.4832 75	3.3210 57	454	4.6159 80	3.3994 70
405	4.4860 46	3.3226 99	455	4.6185 20	3.4009 66
406	4.4888 13	3.3243 38	456	4.6210 56	3.4024 60
407	4.4915 74	3.3259 74	457	4.6235 87	3.4039 51
408	4.4943 31	3.3276 07	458	4.6261 14	3.4054 39
409	4.4970 82	3.3292 37	459	4.6286 38	3.4069 25
410	4.4998 29	3.3308 63	460	4.6311 57	3.4084 08
411	4.5025 70	3.3324 86	461	4.6336 71	3.4098 89
412	4.5053 06	3.3341 06	462	4.6361 82	3.4113 67
413	4.5080 37	3.3357 23	463	4.6386 89	3.4128 42
414	4.5107 64	3.3373 37	464	4.6411 92	3.4143 15
415	4.5134 85	3.3389 48	465	4.6436 90	3.4157 85
416	4.5162 02	3.3405 55	466	4.6461 85	3.4172 53
417	4.5189 13	3.3421 60	467	4.6486 75	3.4187 19
418	4.5216 20	3.3437 61	468	4.6511 62	3.4201 82
419	4.5243 22	3.3453 60	469	4.6536 45	3.4216 42
420	4.5270 19	3.3469 55	470	4.6561 23	3.4231 00
421	4.5297 11	3.3485 47	471	4.6585 98	3.4245 55
422	4.5323 99	3.3501 36	472	4.6610 69	3.4260 08
423	4.5350 81	3.3517 23	473	4.6635 35	3.4274 59
424	4.5377 59	3.3533 06	474	4.6659 98	3.4289 07
425	4.5404 33	3.3548 86	475	4.6684 57	3.4303 52
426	4.5431 01	3.3564 63	476	4.6709 13	3.4317 95
427	4.5457 65	3.3580 38	477	4.6733 64	3.4332 36
428	4.5484 24	3.3596 09	478	4.6758 11	3.4346 74
429	4.5510 78	3.3611 78	479	4.6782 55	3.4361 10
430	4.5537 28	3.3627 43	480	4.6806 95	3.4375 44
431	4.5563 74	3.3643 06	481	4.6831 31	3.4389 75
432	4.5590 14	3.3658 65	482	4.6855 63	3.4404 04
433	4.5616 50	3.3674 22	483	4.6879 91	3.4418 30
434	4.5642 82	3.3689 76	484	4.6904 16	3.4432 54
435	4.5669 09	3.3705 27	485	4.6928 37	3.4446 76
436	4.5695 31	3.3720 76	486	4.6952 54	3.4460 95
437	4.5721 49	3.3736 21	487	4.6976 67	3.4475 12
438	4.5747 62	3.3751 64	488	4.7000 77	3.4489 27
439	4.5773 71	3.3767 03	489	4.7024 83	3.4503 39
440	4.5799 76	3.3782 40	490	4.7048 85	3.4517 49
441	4.5825 76	3.3797 74	491	4.7072 84	3.4531 57
442	4.5851 71	3.3813 06	492	4.7096 79	3.4545 62
443	4.5877 63	3.3828 34	493	4.7120 70	3.4559 65
444	4.5903 49	3.3843 60	494	4.7144 58	3.4573 66
445	4.5929 32	3.3858 83	495	4.7168 42	3.4587 65
446	4.5955 10	3.3874 04	496	4.7192 22	3.4601 61
447	4.5980 84	3.3889 21	497	4.7215 99	3.4615 55
448	4.6006 53	3.3904 36	498	4.7239 72	3.4629 47
449	4.6032 18	3.3919 49	499	4.7263 42	3.4643 37
450	4.6057 79	3.3934 58	500	4.7287 08	3.4657 24

FOURTH AND FIFTH ROOTS (Continued)

n	$\sqrt[4]{n}$	$\sqrt[5]{n}$	n	$\sqrt[4]{n}$	$\sqrt[5]{n}$
501	4.7310 71	3.4671 09	551	4.8449 34	3.5337 05
502	4.7334 30	3.4684 92	552	4.8471 31	3.5349 87
503	4.7357 85	3.4698 73	553	4.8493 25	3.5362 67
504	4.7381 37	3.4712 52	554	4.8515 16	3.5375 45
505	4.7404 86	3.4726 28	555	4.8537 04	3.5388 21
506	4.7428 31	3.4740 02	556	4.8558 88	3.5400 95
507	4.7451 72	3.4753 74	557	4.8580 70	3.5413 68
508	4.7475 10	3.4767 44	558	4.8602 49	3.5426 39
509	4.7498 45	3.4781 12	559	4.8624 25	3.5439 07
510	4.7521 76	3.4794 78	560	4.8645 99	3.5451 74
511	4.7545 04	3.4808 41	561	4.8667 69	3.5464 40
512	4.7568 28	3.4822 02	562	4.8689 36	3.5477 03
513	4.7591 49	3.4835 61	563	4.8711 01	3.5489 65
514	4.7614 67	3.4849 18	564	4.8732 62	3.5502 25
515	4.7637 81	3.4862 73	565	4.8754 21	3.5514 83
516	4.7660 92	3.4876 26	566	4.8775 77	3.5527 39
517	4.7684 00	3.4889 77	567	4.8797 30	3.5539 93
518	4.7707 04	3.4903 26	568	4.8818 80	3.5552 46
519	4.7730 04	3.4916 72	569	4.8840 27	3.5564 97
520	4.7753 02	3.4930 17	570	4.8861 72	3.5577 46
521	4.7775 96	3.4943 59	571	4.8883 13	3.5589 94
522	4.7798 87	3.4957 00	572	4.8904 52	3.5602 39
523	4.7821 75	3.4970 38	573	4.8925 88	3.5614 83
524	4.7844 59	3.4983 74	574	4.8947 21	3.5627 26
525	4.7867 40	3.4997 08	575	4.8968 52	3.5639 66
526	4.7890 18	3.5010 41	576	4.8989 79	3.5652 05
527	4.7912 92	3.5023 71	577	4.9011 04	3.5664 42
528	4.7935 63	3.5036 99	578	4.9032 27	3.5676 77
529	4.7958 32	3.5050 25	579	4.9053 46	3.5689 11
530	4.7980 96	3.5063 49	580	4.9074 63	3.5701 43
531	4.8003 58	3.5076 71	581	4.9095 77	3.5713 73
532	4.8026 16	3.5089 92	582	4.9116 88	3.5726 02
533	4.8048 72	3.5103 10	583	4.9137 96	3.5738 29
534	4.8071 24	3.5116 26	584	4.9159 02	3.5750 54
535	4.8093 73	3.5129 40	585	4.9180 05	3.5762 77
536	4.8116 19	3.5142 52	586	4.9201 05	3.5774 99
537	4.8138 61	3.5155 63	587	4.9222 03	3.5787 19
538	4.8161 01	3.5168 71	588	4.9242 98	3.5799 38
539	4.8183 37	3.5181 78	589	4.9263 90	3.5811 55
540	4.8205 71	3.5194 82	590	4.9284 80	3.5823 70
541	4.8228 01	3.5207 85	591	4.9305 67	3.5835 83
542	4.8250 28	3.5220 85	592	4.9326 51	3.5847 95
543	4.8272 52	3.5233 84	593	4.9347 33	3.5860 05
544	4.8294 73	3.5246 81	594	4.9368 12	3.5872 14
545	4.8316 91	3.5259 76	595	4.9388 89	3.5884 21
546	4.8339 06	3.5272 69	596	4.9409 63	3.5896 26
547	4.8361 17	3.5285 60	597	4.9430 34	3.5908 30
548	4.8383 26	3.5298 49	598	4.9451 02	3.5920 32
549	4.8405 32	3.5311 36	599	4.9471 69	3.5932 33
550	4.8427 35	3.5324 22	600	4.9492 32	3.5944 32

FOURTH AND FIFTH ROOTS (Continued)

n	$\sqrt[4]{n}$	$\sqrt[5]{n}$	n	$\sqrt[4]{n}$	$\sqrt[5]{n}$
601	4.9512 93	3.5956 29	651	5.0512 08	3.6535 60
602	4.9533 51	3.5968 25	652	5.0531 47	3.6546 81
603	4.9554 07	3.5980 19	653	5.0550 83	3.6558 02
604	4.9574 60	3.5992 12	654	5.0570 17	3.6569 21
605	4.9595 11	3.6004 03	655	5.0589 49	3.6580 38
606	4.9615 59	3.6015 92	656	5.0608 79	3.6591 55
607	4.9636 05	3.6027 80	657	5.0628 07	3.6602 70
608	4.9656 48	3.6039 66	658	5.0647 32	3.6613 83
609	4.9676 88	3.6051 51	659	5.0666 55	3.6624 95
610	4.9697 26	3.6063 34	660	5.0685 76	3.6636 06
611	4.9717 62	3.6075 16	661	5.0704 95	3.6647 16
612	4.9737 95	3.6086 96	662	5.0724 12	3.6658 24
613	4.9758 25	3.6098 74	663	5.0743 26	3.6669 31
614	4.9778 53	3.6110 51	664	5.0762 39	3.6680 36
615	4.9798 79	3.6122 27	665	5.0781 49	3.6691 40
616	4.9819 02	3.6134 01	666	5.0800 57	3.6702 43
617	4.9839 23	3.6145 73	667	5.0819 63	3.6713 45
618	4.9859 41	3.6157 44	668	5.0838 66	3.6724 45
619	4.9879 57	3.6169 14	669	5.0857 68	3.6735 44
620	4.9899 70	3.6180 81	670	5.0876 67	3.6746 41
621	4.9919 81	3.6192 48	671	5.0895 65	3.6757 38
622	4.9939 89	3.6204 13	672	5.0914 60	3.6768 33
623	4.9959 95	3.6215 76	673	5.0933 53	3.6779 26
624	4.9979 99	3.6227 38	674	5.0952 44	3.6790 19
625	5.0000 00	3.6238 98	675	5.0971 33	3.6801 10
626	5.0019 99	3.6250 57	676	5.0990 20	3.6811 99
627	5.0039 95	3.6262 15	677	5.1009 04	3.6822 88
628	5.0059 89	3.6273 71	678	5.1027 87	3.6833 75
629	5.0079 81	3.6285 25	679	5.1046 67	3.6844 61
630	5.0099 70	3.6296 78	680	5.1065 46	3.6855 46
631	5.0119 57	3.6308 30	681	5.1084 22	3.6866 29
632	5.0139 42	3.6319 80	682	5.1102 96	3.6877 11
633	5.0159 24	3.6331 28	683	5.1121 69	3.6887 92
634	5.0179 04	3.6342 76	684	5.1140 39	3.6898 71
635	5.0198 81	3.6354 21	685	5.1159 07	3.6909 50
636	5.0218 56	3.6365 66	686	5.1177 73	3.6920 27
637	5.0238 29	3.6377 08	687	5.1196 37	3.6931 02
638	5.0258 00	3.6388 50	688	5.1214 99	3.6941 77
639	5.0277 68	3.6399 90	689	5.1233 59	3.6952 50
640	5.0297 34	3.6411 28	690	5.1252 17	3.6963 22
641	5.0316 97	3.6422 66	691	5.1270 73	3.6973 93
642	5.0336 59	3.6434 01	692	5.1289 27	3.6984 62
643	5.0356 18	3.6445 36	693	5.1307 79	3.6995 31
644	5.0375 74	3.6456 68	694	5.1326 29	3.7005 98
645	5.0395 29	3.6468 00	695	5.1344 77	3.7016 64
646	5.0414 81	3.6479 30	696	5.1363 23	3.7027 28
647	5.0434 31	3.6490 59	697	5.1381 67	3.7037 92
648	5.0453 78	3.6501 86	698	5.1400 09	3.7048 54
649	5.0473 24	3.6513 12	699	5.1418 49	3.7059 15
650	5.0492 67	3.6524 36	700	5.1436 87	3.7069 75

FOURTH AND FIFTH ROOTS (Continued)

n	$\sqrt[4]{n}$	$\sqrt[5]{n}$	n	$\sqrt[4]{n}$	$\sqrt[5]{n}$
701	5.1455 23	3.7080 33	751	5.2349 19	3.7594 82
702	5.1473 57	3.7090 90	752	5.2366 61	3.7604 82
703	5.1491 89	3.7101 47	753	5.2384 01	3.7614 82
704	5.1510 19	3.7112 01	754	5.2401 39	3.7624 81
705	5.1528 47	3.7122 55	755	5.2418 76	3.7634 78
706	5.1546 74	3.7133 08	756	5.2436 11	3.7644 74
707	5.1564 98	3.7143 59	757	5.2453 44	3.7654 70
708	5.1583 20	3.7154 09	758	5.2470 75	3.7664 64
709	5.1601 41	3.7164 58	759	5.2488 05	3.7674 57
710	5.1619 59	3.7175 06	760	5.2505 33	3.7684 50
711	5.1637 76	3.7185 53	761	5.2522 59	3.7694 41
712	5.1655 91	3.7195 98	762	5.2539 84	3.7704 31
713	5.1674 04	3.7206 42	763	5.2557 07	3.7714 20
714	5.1692 14	3.7216 85	764	5.2574 28	3.7724 08
715	5.1710 23	3.7227 27	765	5.2591 48	3.7733 95
716	5.1728 31	3.7237 68	766	5.2608 65	3.7743 81
717	5.1746 36	3.7248 07	767	5.2625 82	3.7753 66
718	5.1764 39	3.7258 46	768	5.2642 96	3.7763 50
719	5.1782 41	3.7268 83	769	5.2660 09	3.7773 33
720	5.1800 40	3.7279 19	770	5.2677 20	3.7783 15
721	5.1818 38	3.7289 54	771	5.2694 29	3.7792 96
722	5.1836 34	3.7299 88	772	5.2711 37	3.7802 76
723	5.1854 28	3.7310 21	773	5.2728 43	3.7812 54
724	5.1872 20	3.7320 52	774	5.2745 48	3.7822 32
725	5.1890 10	3.7330 83	775	5.2762 51	3.7832 09
726	5.1907 98	3.7341 12	776	5.2779 52	3.7841 85
727	5.1925 85	3.7351 40	777	5.2796 51	3.7851 60
728	5.1943 70	3.7361 67	778	5.2813 49	3.7861 33
729	5.1961 52	3.7371 93	779	5.2830 46	..7871 06
730	5.1979 33	3.7382 18	780	5.2847 40	3.7880 78
731	5.1997 13	3.7392 41	781	5.2864 33	3.7890 49
732	5.2014 90	3.7402 64	782	5.2881 25	3.7900 19
733	5.2032 66	3.7412 85	783	5.2898 14	3.7909 87
734	5.2050 39	3.7423 05	784	5.2915 03	3.7919 55
735	5.2068 11	3.7433 24	785	5.2931 89	3.7929 22
736	5.2085 81	3.7443 42	786	5.2948 74	3.7938 88
737	5.2103 50	3.7453 59	787	5.2965 57	3.7948 53
738	5.2121 16	3.7463 75	788	5.2982 39	3.7958 17
739	5.2138 81	3.7473 90	789	5.2999 19	3.7967 80
740	5.2156 44	3.7484 04	790	5.3015 98	3.7977 42
741	5.2174 05	3.7494 16	791	5.3032 75	3.7987 03
742	5.2191 64	3.7504 28	792	5.3049 50	3.7996 63
743	5.2209 22	3.7514 38	793	5.3066 24	3.8006 22
744	5.2226 78	3.7524 47	794	5.3082 96	3.8015 80
745	5.2244 32	3.7534 55	795	5.3099 67	3.8025 37
746	5.2261 84	3.7544 62	796	5.3116 36	3.8034 93
747	5.2279 35	3.7554 68	797	5.3133 03	3.8044 48
748	5.2296 83	3.7564 73	798	5.3149 69	3.8054 02
749	5.2314 30	3.7574 77	799	5.3166 33	3.8063 56
750	5.2331 76	3.7584 80	800	5.3182 96	3.8073 08

FOURTH AND FIFTH ROOTS (Continued)

n	$\sqrt[4]{n}$	$\sqrt[5]{n}$	n	$\sqrt[4]{n}$	$\sqrt[5]{n}$
801	5.3199 57	3.8082 59	851	5.4011 02	3.8546 59
802	5.3216 17	3.8092 10	852	5.4026 88	3.8555 64
803	5.3232 75	3.8101 59	853	5.4042 73	3.8564 69
804	5.3249 31	3.8111 08	854	5.4058 56	3.8573 72
805	5.3265 86	3.8120 55	855	5.4074 38	3.8582 75
806	5.3282 40	3.8130 02	856	5.4090 18	3.8591 77
807	5.3298 92	3.8139 47	857	5.4105 97	3.8600 79
808	5.3315 42	3.8148 92	858	5.4121 75	3.8609 79
809	5.3331 91	3.8158 36	859	5.4137 51	3.8618 79
810	5.3348 38	3.8167 79	860	5.4153 26	3.8627 77
811	5.3364 84	3.8177 21	861	5.4169 00	3.8636 75
812	5.3381 28	3.8186 62	862	5.4184 72	3.8645 72
813	5.3397 71	3.8196 02	863	5.4200 43	3.8654 69
814	5.3414 12	3.8205 41	864	5.4216 12	3.8663 64
815	5.3430 52	3.8214 79	865	5.4231 80	3.8672 59
816	5.3446 90	3.8224 17	866	5.4247 47	3.8681 52
817	5.3463 27	3.8233 53	867	5.4263 12	3.8690 45
818	5.3479 62	3.8242 89	868	5.4278 76	3.8699 37
819	5.3495 96	3.8252 23	869	5.4294 39	3.8708 29
820	5.3512 28	3.8261 57	870	5.4310 00	3.8717 19
821	5.3528 59	3.8270 90	871	5.4325 60	3.8726 09
822	5.3544 88	3.8280 21	872	5.4341 19	3.8734 98
823	5.3561 16	3.8289 52	873	5.4356 76	3.8743 86
824	5.3577 42	3.8298 82	874	5.4372 32	3.8752 73
825	5.3593 67	3.8308 12	875	5.4387 87	3.8761 59
826	5.3609 90	3.8317 40	876	5.4403 40	3.8770 45
827	5.3626 12	3.8326 67	877	5.4418 92	3.8779 30
828	5.3642 32	3.8335 94	878	5.4434 42	3.8788 14
829	5.3658 51	3.8345 19	879	5.4449 92	3.8796 97
830	5.3674 69	3.8354 44	880	5.4465 40	3.8805 79
831	5.3690 85	3.8363 68	881	5.4480 86	3.8814 61
832	5.3706 99	3.8372 90	882	5.4496 32	3.8823 41
833	5.3723 12	3.8382 12	883	5.4511 76	3.8832 21
834	5.3739 24	3.8391 33	884	5.4527 18	3.8841 00
835	5.3755 34	3.8400 54	885	5.4542 60	3.8849 79
836	5.3771 43	3.8409 73	886	5.4558 00	3.8858 56
837	5.3787 50	3.8418 91	887	5.4573 39	3.8867 33
838	5.3803 56	3.8428 09	888	5.4588 76	3.8876 09
839	5.3819 60	3.8437 26	889	5.4604 12	3.8884 84
840	5.3835 63	3.8446 42	890	5.4619 47	3.8893 59
841	5.3851 65	3.8455 57	891	5.4634 81	3.8902 32
842	5.3867 65	3.8464 71	892	5.4650 13	3.8911 05
843	5.3883 64	3.8473 84	893	5.4665 44	3.8919 77
844	5.3899 61	3.8482 96	894	5.4680 74	3.8928 49
845	5.3915 57	3.8492 08	895	5.4696 02	3.8937 19
846	5.3931 51	3.8501 18	896	5.4711 30	3.8945 89
847	5.3947 44	3.8510 28	897	5.4726 56	3.8954 58
848	5.3963 36	3.8519 37	898	5.4741 80	3.8963 26
849	5.3979 26	3.8528 45	899	5.4757 03	3.8971 93
850	5.3995 15	3.8537 52	900	5.4772 26	3.8980 60

FOURTH AND FIFTH ROOTS (Continued)

n	$\sqrt[4]{n}$	$\sqrt[5]{n}$	n	$\sqrt[4]{n}$	$\sqrt[5]{n}$
901	5.4787 46	3.8989 26	951	5.5532 23	3.9412 69
902	5.4802 66	3.8997 91	952	5.5546 82	3.9420 98
903	5.4817 84	3.9006 55	953	5.5561 41	3.9429 26
904	5.4833 01	3.9015 19	954	5.5575 98	3.9437 53
905	5.4848 17	3.9023 81	955	5.5590 53	3.9445 79
906	5.4863 32	3.9032 43	956	5.5605 08	3.9454 05
907	5.4878 45	3.9041 05	957	5.5619 62	3.9462 30
908	5.4893 57	3.9049 65	958	5.5634 14	3.9470 54
909	5.4908 68	3.9058 25	959	5.5648 65	3.9478 78
910	5.4923 77	3.9066 84	960	5.5663 15	3.9487 01
911	5.4938 85	3.9075 42	961	5.5677 64	3.9495 23
912	5.4953 92	3.9084 00	962	5.5692 12	3.9503 45
913	5.4968 98	3.9092 56	963	5.5706 59	3.9511 66
914	5.4984 03	3.9101 12	964	5.5721 05	3.9519 86
915	5.4999 06	3.9109 68	965	5.5735 49	3.9528 06
916	5.5014 08	3.9118 22	966	5.5749 92	3.9536 25
917	5.5029 09	3.9126 76	967	5.5764 35	3.9544 43
918	5.5044 09	3.9135 29	968	5.5778 76	3.9552 60
919	5.5059 07	3.9143 81	969	5.5793 16	3.9560 77
920	5.5074 04	3.9152 33	970	5.5807 55	3.9568 93
921	5.5089 00	3.9160 83	971	5.5821 92	3.9577 09
922	5.5103 95	3.9169 33	972	5.5836 29	3.9585 24
923	5.5118 89	3.9177 83	973	5.5850 65	3.9593 38
924	5.5133 81	3.9186 31	974	5.5864 99	3.9601 51
925	5.5148 72	3.9194 79	975	5.5879 33	3.9609 64
926	5.5163 62	3.9203 26	976	5.5893 65	3.9617 76
927	5.5178 51	3.9211 72	977	5.5907 96	3.9625 88
928	5.5193 38	3.9220 18	978	5.5922 26	3.9633 99
929	5.5208 24	3.9228 63	979	5.5936 55	3.9642 09
930	5.5223 09	3.9237 07	980	5.5950 83	3.9650 18
931	5.5237 93	3.9245 51	981	5.5965 10	3.9658 27
932	5.5252 76	3.9253 93	982	5.5979 35	3.9666 36
933	5.5267 58	3.9262 35	983	5.5993 60	3.9674 43
934	5.5282 38	3.9270 77	984	5.6007 83	3.9682 50
935	5.5297 17	3.9279 17	985	5.6022 06	3.9690 56
936	5.5311 95	3.9287 57	986	5.6036 27	3.9698 62
937	5.5326 72	3.9295 96	987	5.6050 47	3.9706 67
938	5.5341 47	3.9304 35	988	5.6064 67	3.9714 71
939	5.5356 22	3.9312 72	989	5.6078 85	3.9722 75
940	5.5370 95	3.9321 09	990	5.6093 02	3.9730 78
941	5.5385 67	3.9329 45	991	5.6107 18	3.9738 80
942	5.5400 38	3.9337 81	992	5.6121 33	3.9746 82
943	5.5415 07	3.9346 16	993	5.6135 46	3.9754 83
944	5.5429 76	3.9354 50	994	5.6149 59	3.9762 83
945	5.5444 43	3.9362 83	995	5.6163 71	3.9770 83
946	5.5459 10	3.9371 16	996	5.6177 81	3.9778 82
947	5.5473 75	3.9379 48	997	5.6191 91	3.9786 80
948	5.5488 38	3.9387 79	998	5.6205 99	3.9794 78
949	5.5503 01	3.9396 10	999	5.6220 07	3.9802 75
950	5.5517 63	3.9404 40	1000	5.6234 13	3.9810 72

FACTORS AND EXPANSIONS

$(a \pm b)^2 = a^2 \pm 2ab + b^2.$

$(a \pm b)^3 = a^3 \pm 3a^2b + 3ab^2 \pm b^3.$

$(a \pm b)^4 = a^4 \pm 4a^3b + 6a^2b^2 \pm 4ab^3 + b^4.$

$a^2 - b^2 = (a - b)(a + b).$

$a^2 + b^2 = (a + b\sqrt{-1})(a - b\sqrt{-1}).$

$a^3 - b^3 = (a - b)(a^2 + ab + b^2).$

$a^3 + b^3 = (a + b)(a^2 - ab + b^2).$

$a^4 + b^4 = (a^2 + ab\sqrt{2} + b^2)(a^2 - ab\sqrt{2} + b^2).$

$a^n - b^n = (a - b)(a^{n-1} + a^{n-2}b + \ldots + b^{n-1}).$

$a^n - b^n = (a + b)(a^{n-1} - a^{n-2}b + \ldots - b^{n-1}),$
$$\text{for even values of } n.$$

$a^n + b^n = (a + b)(a^{n-1} - a^{n-2}b + \ldots + b^{n-1}),$
$$\text{for odd values of } n.$$

$a^4 + a^2b^2 + b^4 = (a^2 + ab + b^2)(a^2 - ab + b^2).$

$(a + b + c)^2 = a^2 + b^2 + c^2 + 2ab + 2ac + 2bc.$

$(a + b + c)^3 = a^3 + b^3 + c^3 + 3a^2(b + c) + 3b^2(a + c) +$
$$3c^2(a + b) + 6abc.$$

$(a + b + c + d + \ldots)^2 = a^2 + b^2 + c^2 + d^2 + \ldots +$
$2a(b + c + d + \ldots) + 2b(c + d + \ldots) + 2c(d + \ldots) + \ldots$

See also under Series.

POWERS AND ROOTS

$a^x \times a^y = a^{(x+y)}.$ $\qquad a^0 = 1 \text{ [if } a \neq 0]$ $\qquad (ab)^x = a^xb^x.$

$\dfrac{a^x}{a^y} = a^{(x-y)}.$ $\qquad a^{-x} = \dfrac{1}{a^x}.$ $\qquad \left(\dfrac{a}{b}\right)^x = \dfrac{a^x}{b^x}.$

$(a^x)^y = a^{xy}.$ $\qquad a^{\frac{1}{x}} = \sqrt[x]{a}.$ $\qquad \sqrt[x]{ab} = \sqrt[x]{a}\,\sqrt[x]{b}.$

$\sqrt[x]{\sqrt[y]{a}} = \sqrt[xy]{a}.$ $\qquad a^{\frac{x}{y}} = \sqrt[y]{a^x}.$ $\qquad \sqrt[x]{\dfrac{a}{b}} = \dfrac{\sqrt[x]{a}}{\sqrt[x]{b}}$

PROPORTION

If $\dfrac{a}{b} = \dfrac{c}{d}$, then $\dfrac{a+b}{b} = \dfrac{c+d}{d}$,

$\dfrac{a-b}{b} = \dfrac{c-d}{d}$, $\qquad \dfrac{a-b}{a+b} = \dfrac{c-d}{c+d}.$

*ARITHMETIC PROGRESSION

An arithmetic progression is a sequence of numbers such that each number differs from the previous number by a constant amount, called the *common difference*.

If a_1 is the first term; a_n the nth term; d the common difference; n the number of terms; and s_n the sum of n terms—

$$a_n = a_1 + (n - 1)d, \quad s_n = \frac{n}{2}[a_1 + a_n].$$

$$s_n = \frac{n}{2}[2a_1 + (n - 1)d].$$

The arithmetic mean between a and b is given by $\frac{a + b}{2}$.

*GEOMETRIC PROGRESSION

A geometric progression is a sequence of numbers such that each number bears a constant ratio, called the *common ratio*, to the previous number.

If a_1 is the first term; a_n the nth term; r the common ratio; n the number of terms; and s_n the sum of n terms

$$a_n = a_1 r^{n-1}; \quad s_n = a_1 \frac{1 - r^n}{1 - r}$$

$$= a_1 \frac{r^n - 1}{r - 1}, \quad r \neq 1.$$

$$= \frac{a_1 - r a_n}{1 - r}$$

$$= \frac{r a_n - a_1}{r - 1}$$

If $|r| < 1$, then the sum of an infinite geometrical progression converges to the limiting value

$$\frac{a_1}{1 - r}, \quad \left[s_\infty = \lim_{n \to \infty} \frac{a_1(1 - r^n)}{1 - r} = \frac{a_1}{1 - r} \right]$$

The geometric mean between a and b is given by $\sqrt{ab}$.

*It is customary to represent a_n by l in a finite progression and refer to it as the last term.

HARMONIC PROGRESSION

A sequence of numbers whose reciprocals form an arithmetic progression is called an harmonic progression. Thus

$$\frac{1}{a_1}, \quad \frac{1}{a_1 + d}, \quad \frac{1}{a_1 + 2d}, \dots, \frac{1}{a_1 + (n - 1)d}, \dots,$$

where

$$\frac{1}{a_n} = \frac{1}{a_1 + (n - 1)d}$$

forms an harmonic progression. The harmonic mean between a and b is given by $\frac{2ab}{a + b}$.

If A, G, H respectively represent the arithmetic mean, geometric mean, and harmonic mean between a and b, then $G^2 = AH$.

FACTORIALS

$\underline{|n} = n! = e^{-n}n^n \sqrt{2\pi n}$,   approximately, known as Stirling's formula

$\log_e n! = n \log_e n - n$, approximately

PERMUTATIONS

If $M = {_nP_r} = P_{n:r}$ denotes the number of permutations of n distinct things taken r at a time,—

$$M = n(n - 1)(n - 2)\cdots(n - r + 1) = \frac{n!}{(n - r)!}$$

COMBINATIONS

If $M = {_nC_r} = C_{n:r} = \binom{n}{r}$ denotes the number of combinations of n distinct things taken r at a time,—

$$M = \frac{n(n - 1)(n - 2)\cdots(n - r + 1)}{r!} = \frac{n!}{r!(n - r)!}$$

By definition $\binom{n}{0} = 1$

QUADRATIC EQUATIONS

Any quadratic equation may be reduced to the form,—

$$ax^2 + bx + c = 0.$$

Then

$$x = \frac{-b \pm \sqrt{b^2 - 4ac}}{2a}$$

If a, b, and c are real then:

If $b^2 - 4ac$ is positive, the roots are real and unequal;

If $b^2 - 4ac$ is zero, the roots are real and equal;

If $b^2 - 4ac$ is negative, the roots are imaginary and unequal.

CUBIC EQUATIONS

A cubic equation, $y^3 + py^2 + qy + r = 0$ may be reduced to the form,—

$$x^3 + ax + b = 0$$

by substituting for y the value, $x - \dfrac{p}{3}$. Here

$$a = \tfrac{1}{3}(3q - p^2) \text{ and } b = \tfrac{1}{27}(2p^3 - 9pq + 27r).$$

For solution let,—

$$A = \sqrt[3]{-\frac{b}{2} + \sqrt{\frac{b^2}{4} + \frac{a^3}{27}}}, \qquad B = \sqrt[3]{-\frac{b}{2} - \sqrt{\frac{b^2}{4} + \frac{a^3}{27}}},$$

then the values of x will be given by,

$$x = A + B, \quad -\frac{A + B}{2} + \frac{A - B}{2}\sqrt{-3}, \quad -\frac{A + B}{2} - \frac{A - B}{2}\sqrt{-3}.$$

If p, q, r are real, then:

If $\dfrac{b^2}{4} + \dfrac{a^3}{27} > 0$,   there will be one real root and two conjugate imaginary roots;

If $\dfrac{b^2}{4} + \dfrac{a^3}{27} = 0$,   there will be three real roots of which at least two are equal;

If $\dfrac{b^2}{4} + \dfrac{a^3}{27} < 0$,   there will be three real and unequal roots.

Trignometric Solution of the Cubic Equation

The form $x^3 + ax + b = 0$ with $ab \neq 0$ can always be solved by transforming it to the trignometric identity

$$4 \cos^3 \theta - 3 \cos \theta - \cos (3\theta) \equiv 0.$$

Let $x = m \cos \theta$, then

$$x^3 + ax + b \equiv m^3 \cos^3 \theta + am \cos \theta + b \equiv 4 \cos^3 \theta - 3 \cos \theta - \cos (3\theta) \equiv 0.$$

Hence

$$\frac{4}{m^3} = -\frac{3}{am} = \frac{-\cos(3\theta)}{b},$$

from which follows that

$$m = 2 \sqrt{-\frac{a}{3}}, \quad \cos (3\theta) = \frac{3b}{am}.$$

Any solution θ_1 which satisfies $\cos (3\theta) = \dfrac{3b}{am}$, will also have the solutions

$$\theta_1 + \frac{2\pi}{3} \quad \text{and} \quad \theta_1 + \frac{4\pi}{3}.$$

The roots of the cubic $x^3 + ax + b = 0$ are

$$2 \sqrt{-\frac{a}{3}} \cos \theta_1, \quad 2 \sqrt{-\frac{a}{3}} \cos \left(\theta_1 + \frac{2\pi}{3}\right), \quad 2 \sqrt{-\frac{a}{3}} \cos \left(\theta_1 + \frac{4\pi}{3}\right).$$

Example where hyperbolic functions are necessary for solution with latter procedure

The roots of the equation $x^3 - x + 2 = 0$ may be found as follows:

Here

$$a = -1, \quad b = 2, \quad m = 2\sqrt{\tfrac{1}{3}} = 1.155$$

$$\cos (3\theta) = \frac{6}{-1.155} = -5.196$$

$$\cos (3\theta) = -\cos (3\theta - \pi) = -\cosh [i(3\theta - \pi)] = -5.196.$$

Using hyperbolic function tables for cosh $[i(3\theta - \pi)] = 5.196$, it is found that

$$i(3\theta - \pi) = 2.332.$$

Thus

$$3\theta - \pi = -i(2.332).$$

$$3\theta = \pi - i(2.332)$$

$$\theta_1 = \frac{\pi}{3} - i(0.777)$$

$$\theta_1 + \frac{2\pi}{3} = \pi - i(0.777)$$

$$\theta_1 + \frac{4\pi}{3} = \frac{5\pi}{3} - i(0.777)$$

$$\cos \theta_1 = \cos \left[\frac{\pi}{3} - i(0.777) \right]$$

$$= \left(\cos \frac{\pi}{3} \right) [\cos i(0.777)] + \left(\sin \frac{\pi}{3} \right) [\sin i(0.777)]$$

$$= \left(\cos \frac{\pi}{3} \right) (\cosh 0.777) + i \left(\sin \frac{\pi}{3} \right) (\sinh 0.777)$$

$$= (0.5)(1.317) + i(0.866)(0.858) = 0.659 + i(0.743).$$

Note that

$$\cos \mu = \cosh (i\mu) \quad \text{and} \quad \sin \mu = -i \sinh (i\mu).$$

Similarly

$$\cos \left(\theta_1 + \frac{2\pi}{3} \right) = \cos [\pi - i(0.777)]$$

$$= (\cos \pi)(\cosh 0.777) + i(\sin \pi)(\sinh 0.777)$$

$$= -1.317,$$

and

$$\cos \left(\theta_1 + \frac{4\pi}{3} \right) = \cos \left[\frac{5\pi}{3} - i(0.777) \right]$$

$$= \left(\cos \frac{5\pi}{3} \right) (\cosh 0.777) + i \left(\sin \frac{5\pi}{3} \right) (\sinh 0.777)$$

$$= (0.5)(1.317) - i(0.866)(0.858) = 0.659 - i(0.743).$$

The required roots are

$$1.155[0.659 + i(0.743)] = 0.760 + i(0.858)$$

$$(1.155)(-1.317) = -1.520$$

$$(1.155)[0.659 - i(0.743)] = 0.760 - i(0.858).$$

QUARTIC OR BIQUADRATIC EQUATION

A quartic equation,

$$x^4 + ax^3 + bx^2 + cx + d = 0,$$

has the *resolvent cubic equation*

$$y^3 - by^2 + (ac - 4d)y - a^2d + 4bd - c^2 = 0.$$

Let y be any root of this equation, and

$$R = \sqrt{\frac{a^2}{4} - b + y}.$$

If $R \neq 0$, then let

$$D = \sqrt{\frac{3a^2}{4} - R^2 - 2b + \frac{4ab - 8c - a^3}{4R}}$$

and

$$E = \sqrt{\frac{3a^2}{4} - R^2 - 2b - \frac{4ab - 8c - a^3}{4R}}.$$

If $R = 0$, then let

$$D = \sqrt{\frac{3a^2}{4} - 2b + 2\sqrt{y^2 - 4d}}$$

and

$$E = \sqrt{\frac{3a^2}{4} - 2b - 2\sqrt{y^2 - 4d}}.$$

Then the four roots of the original equation are given by

$$x = -\frac{a}{4} + \frac{R}{2} \pm \frac{D}{2}$$

and

$$x = -\frac{a}{4} - \frac{R}{2} \pm \frac{E}{2}.$$

PARTIAL FRACTIONS

This section applies only to rational algebraic fractions with numerator of lower degree than the denominator. Improper fractions can be reduced to proper fractions by long division.

Every fraction may be expressed as the sum of component fractions whose denominators are factors of the denominator of the original fraction.

Let $N(x)$ = numerator, a polynomial of the form

$$N(x) = n_0 + n_1 x + n_2 x^2 + \cdots + n_i x^i$$

I. *Non-repeated Linear Factors*

$$\frac{N(x)}{(x - a)G(x)} = \frac{A}{x - a} + \frac{F(x)}{G(x)}$$

$$A = \left[\frac{N(x)}{G(x)}\right]_{x=a}$$

$F(x)$ determined by methods discussed in the following sections.

Example:

$$\frac{x^2 + 3}{x(x - 2)(x^2 + 2x + 4)} = \frac{A}{x} + \frac{B}{x - 2} + \frac{F(x)}{x^2 + 2x + 4}$$

$$A = \left[\frac{x^2 + 3}{(x - 2)(x^2 + 2x + 4)}\right]_{x=0} = -\frac{3}{8}$$

$$B = \left[\frac{x^2 + 3}{x(x^2 + 2x + 4)}\right]_{x=2} = \frac{4 + 3}{2(4 + 4 + 4)} = \frac{7}{24}$$

II. *Repeated Linear Factors*

$$\frac{N(x)}{x^m G(x)} = \frac{A_0}{x^m} + \frac{A_1}{x^{m-1}} + \cdots + \frac{A_{m-1}}{x} + \frac{F(x)}{G(x)}$$

$$F(x) = f_0 + f_1 x + f_2 x^2 + \cdots, \quad G(x) = g_0 + g_1 x + g_2 x^2 + \cdots$$

$$A_0 = \frac{n_0}{g_0}, \quad A_1 = \frac{n_1 - A_0 g_1}{g_0}, \quad A_2 = \frac{n_2 - A_0 g_2 - A_1 g_1}{g_0}$$

General term:

$$A_k = \frac{1}{g_0}\left[n_k - \sum_{i=0}^{k-1} A_i g_{k-i}\right]$$

$$*m = 1 \begin{cases} f_0 = n_1 - A_0 g_1 \\ f_1 = n_2 - A_0 g_2 \\ f_j = n_{j+1} - A_0 g_{j+1} \end{cases}$$

$$m = 2 \begin{cases} f_0 = n_2 - A_0 g_2 - A_1 g_1 \\ f_1 = n_3 - A_0 g_3 - A_1 g_2 \\ f_j = n_{j+2} - [A_0 g_{j+2} + A_1 g_{j+1}] \end{cases}$$

$$m = 3 \begin{cases} f_0 = n_3 - A_0 g_3 - A_1 g_2 - A_2 g_1 \\ f_1 = n_3 - A_0 g_4 - A_1 g_3 - A_2 g_2 \\ f_j = n_{j+3} - [A_0 g_{j+3} + A_1 g_{j+2} + A_2 g_{j+1}] \end{cases}$$

$$\text{any } m: \ f_j = n_{m+j} - \sum_{i=0}^{m-1} A_i g_{m+j-i}$$

Example:

$$\frac{x^2 + 1}{x^3(x^2 - 3x + 6)} = \frac{A_0}{x^3} + \frac{A_1}{x^2} + \frac{A_2}{x} + \frac{f_1 x + f_0}{x^2 - 3x + 6}$$

$$A_0 = \frac{1}{6}, \quad A_1 = \frac{0 - (\frac{1}{6})(-3)}{6} = \frac{1}{12},$$

$$A_2 = \frac{1 - (\frac{1}{6})(1) - (\frac{1}{12})(-3)}{6} = \frac{13}{72},$$

$$m = 3 \begin{cases} f_0 = 0 - \frac{1}{6}(0) + \frac{1}{12}(1) - \frac{13}{72}(-3) = \frac{11}{24} \\ f_1 = 0 - \frac{1}{6}(0) - \frac{1}{12}(0) - \frac{13}{72}(1) = -\frac{13}{72} \end{cases}$$

*Note: If $G(x)$ contains linear factors, $F(x)$ may be determined by previous section I.

III. *Repeated Linear Factors*

$$\frac{N(x)}{(x - a)^m G(x)} = \frac{A_0}{(x - a)^m} + \frac{A_1}{(x - a)^{m-1}} + \cdots + \frac{A_{m-1}}{(x - a)} + \frac{F(x)}{G(x)}$$

Change to form $\dfrac{N'(y)}{y^m G'(y)}$ by substitution of $x = y + a$. Resolve into partial fractions in terms of y as described in Section II. Then express in terms of x by substitution $y = x - a$.

Example:

$$\frac{x - 3}{(x - 2)^2(x^2 + x + 1)}.$$

Let $x - 2 = y$, $x = y + 2$

$$\frac{(y + 2) - 3}{y^2[(y + 2)^2 + (y + 2) + 1]} = \frac{y - 1}{y^2(y^2 + 5y + 7)} = \frac{A_0}{y^2} + \frac{A_1}{y} + \frac{f_1 y + f_0}{y^2 + 5y + 7}$$

$$A_0 = -\frac{1}{7}, \quad A_1 = \frac{1 - (-\frac{1}{7})(5)}{7} = \frac{12}{49},$$

$$m = 2 \begin{cases} f_0 = 0 - (-\frac{1}{7})(1) - (\frac{12}{49})(5) = -\frac{53}{49} \\ f_1 = 0 - (-\frac{1}{7})(0) - (\frac{12}{49})(1) = -\frac{12}{49} \end{cases}$$

$$\therefore \frac{y - 1}{y^2(y^2 + 5y + 7)} = \frac{-\frac{1}{7}}{y^2} + \frac{\frac{12}{49}}{y} + \frac{-\frac{12}{49}y - \frac{53}{49}}{y^2 + 5y + 7}$$

Let $y = x - 2$, then

$$\frac{x - 3}{(x - 2)^2(x^2 + x + 1)} = \frac{-\frac{1}{7}}{(x - 2)^2} + \frac{\frac{12}{35}}{(x - 2)} + \frac{-\frac{12}{49}(x - 2) - \frac{53}{49}}{x^2 + x + 1}$$

$$= -\frac{1}{7(x - 2)^2} + \frac{12}{35(x - 2)} + \frac{-12x - 29}{49(x^2 + x + 1)}$$

IV. *Repeated Linear Factors*

Alternative method of determining coefficients:

$$\frac{N(x)}{(x - a)^m G(x)} = \frac{A_0}{(x - a)^m} + \cdots + \frac{A_k}{(x - a)^{m-k}} + \cdots + \frac{A_{m-1}}{x - a} + \frac{F(x)}{G(x)}$$

$$A_k = \frac{1}{k!} \left\{ D_x^k \left[\frac{N(x)}{G(x)} \right] \right\}_{x = a}$$

where D_x^k is the differentiating operator, and the derivative of zero order is defined as:

$$D_x^0 u = u.$$

V. *Factors of Higher Degree*

Factors of higher degree have the corresponding numerators indicated.

$$\frac{N(x)}{(x^2 + h_1 x + h_0) G(x)} = \frac{a_1 x + a_0}{x^2 + h_1 x + h_0} + \frac{F(x)}{G(x)}$$

$$\frac{N(x)}{(x^2 + h_1 x + h_0)^2 G(x)} = \frac{a_1 x + a_0}{(x^2 + h_1 x + h_0)^2} + \frac{b_1 x + b_0}{(x^2 + h_1 x + h_0)} + \frac{F(x)}{G(x)}$$

$$\frac{N(x)}{(x^3 + h_2 x^2 + h_1 x + h_0) G(x)} = \frac{a_2 x^2 + a_1 x + a_0}{x^3 + h_2 x^2 + h_1 x + h_0} + \frac{F(x)}{G(x)}$$

etc.

Problems of this type are determined first by solving for the coefficients due to linear factors as shown above, and then determining the remaining coefficients by the general methods given below.

VI. *General Methods for Evaluating Coefficients*

1.
$$\frac{N(x)}{D(x)} = \frac{N(x)}{G(x) H(x) L(x)} = \frac{A(x)}{G(x)} + \frac{B(x)}{H(x)} + \frac{C(x)}{L(x)} + \cdots$$

Multiply both sides of equation by $D(x)$ to clear fractions. Then collect terms, equate like powers of x, and solve the resulting simultaneous equations for the unknown coefficients.

2. Clear fractions as above. Then let x assume certain convenient values ($x = 1, 0, -1, \ldots$). Solve the resulting equations for the unknown coefficients.

3.
$$\frac{N(x)}{G(x) H(x)} = \frac{A(x)}{G(x)} + \frac{B(x)}{H(x)}$$

Then

$$\frac{N(x)}{G(x) H(x)} - \frac{A(x)}{G(x)} = \frac{B(x)}{H(x)}$$

If $A(x)$ can be determined, such as by Method I, then $B(x)$ can be found as above.

BASIC CONCEPTS IN ALGEBRA

Dr. W. E. Deskins

I. ALGEBRA OF SETS

1. Intuitively a set is a collection of objects called the elements of the set. Set and set membership are generally accepted as basic, undefined terms used to define and construct mathematical systems.

    The notation $a \in A$ indicates that a is an element of the set A. The notation $a \notin A$ means that a is not a member of A.

    A set is sometimes specified by listing its elements within a set of braces: $\{a\}$ is the set containing only the element a.

2. Set A is a subset of set B provided $a \in A$ implies $a \in B$. This is denoted by $A \subseteq B$. Every set has as a subset the empty or null set, denoted by ϕ, which has no elements.

3. Set A equals set B, written $A = B$, if and only if $A \subseteq B$ and $B \subseteq A$. A is a proper subset of B, sometimes indicated by $A \subset B$, if and only if $A \subseteq B$ and $A \neq B$; then B has at least one element which does not belong to A.

4. The Cartesian product of sets A and B, denoted by $A \times B$, is the set of all ordered pairs (a, b) where $a \in A$ and $b \in B$. A subset R of $A \times A$ is a binary relation on A, and this is an equivalence relation on A provided (i) $(a, a) \in R$ for every $a \in A$, (ii) $(a, b) \in R$ implies $(b, a) \in R$, and (iii) $(a, b) \in R$ and $(b, c) \in R$ imply $(a, c) \in R$. Ordinary equality of numbers, equality of sets, and congruence of plane figures are examples of equivalence relations.

5. A subset F of $A \times B$ is a *function* from A to B provided each element of A appears exactly once as the first element of a pair in F. A function F from A to B is *onto* provided each element of B appears at least once as the second element of a pair in F. It is *one-to-one* provided each element of B appears at most once as the second element of a pair in F. A function from $A \times A$ to A is a *binary operation* on A. Addition and multiplication of ordinary numbers are examples of binary operations.

6. If consideration is restricted to elements and subsets of a particular set I, then I is the universal set.

7. Common binary operations on subsets of I are: $A \cup B$, the union or join of sets A and B, is the set of all elements of I which belong to either A or B or both A and B.

    $A \cap B$, the intersection or meet of sets A and B, is the set of all elements of I which belong to both A and B.

    $A \setminus B$, the difference of sets A and B, is the set of elements of I which belong to A but not B.

    The difference $I \setminus A$ is denoted by A' and called the complement of A (relative to I). Except in dealing with the concept of complementation the use of a universal set is not essential to the above ideas.

8. Some theorems basic to the Algebra of Sets:

    Let A, B, and C be arbitrary subsets of a universal set I.

    (a) (Commutativity) $\quad A \cup B = B \cup A$ and $A \cap B = B \cap A$.

    (b) (Associativity) $\quad (A \cup B) \cup C = A \cup (B \cup C)$ and
    $(A \cap B) \cap C = A \cap (B \cap C)$.

(c) (Distributivity) $A \cap (B \cup C) = (A \cap B) \cup (A \cap C)$ and
                                    $A \cup (B \cap C) = (A \cup B) \cap (A \cup C)$.

(d) (Idempotency) $A \cup A = A \cap A = A$.

(e) Properties of I and ϕ: $A \cap I = A \cup \phi = A$,
                                 $A \cup I = I$, and
                                 $A \cap \phi = \phi$.

(f) $(A \cap B) \cup (A \backslash B) = A$.

(g) $(A \backslash B) \cup B = A \cup B$.

(h) $A \subseteq A \cup B$.

(i) $A \cap B \subseteq A$.

(j) $A \cup B = A$ if and only if $B \subseteq A$.

(k) $A \cap B = A$ if and only if $A \subseteq B$.

(m) $A \backslash B = A \backslash (A \cap B)$.

(n) (DeMorgan's Theorem) $(A \backslash B) \cap (A \backslash C) = A \backslash (B \cup C)$ and
                                       $(A \backslash B) \cup (A \backslash C) = A \backslash (B \cap C)$.

(o) $(A \cup B)' = A' \cap B'$ and $(A \cap B)' = A' \cup B'$.

(p) $A \cup A' = I$ and $A \cap A' = \phi$.

9. A mathematical system S is a set $S = \{E, O, A\}$ where E is a nonempty set of elements, O is a set of relations and operations on E, and A is a set of axioms, postulates, or assumptions concerning the elements of E and O.

10. The Algebra of Sets provides an example of a mathematical system called a Boolean Algebra (or Boolean Ring) which is defined as:

     Set E of elements $a, b, c, \ldots$;

     Set O of 2 binary operations $\oplus$ and $\otimes$; (Here $a \oplus b$ denotes the image of (a, b) under the binary operation.)

     Set A of axioms for all a, b, c of E:

A_1.   The binary operations are commutative; i.e.,

$$a \oplus b = b \oplus a \quad \text{and} \quad a \otimes b = b \otimes a.$$

A_2.   Each binary operation is distributive over the other; i.e.,

$$a \oplus (b \otimes c) = (a \oplus b) \otimes (a \oplus c) \quad \text{and} \quad a \otimes (b \oplus c) = (a \otimes b) + (a \otimes c).$$

A_3.   There exist elements e and z in E such that for each $a \in E$, $a \oplus z = a$ and $a \otimes e = a$.

A_4.   For each $a \in E$ there exists an element $a' \in E$ such that $a \otimes a' = e$ and $a \oplus a' = z$.

     In the algebra of subsets of a (universal) set I, ϕ plays the role of z, I that of e, $\cup$ that of $\oplus$, and $\cap$ that of $\otimes$.

11. A Boolean Algebra has the Principle of Duality: If the interchanges of $\begin{Bmatrix} \oplus \text{ and } \otimes \\ e \text{ and } z \end{Bmatrix}$ are made in a correct statement, then the result is also a correct statement.

12. In addition to the Algrebra of Sets which is a Boolean Algebra, other representations of Boolean Algebra that are interesting of themselves and valuable for their applications are:

     (a) The Algebra of Symbolic Logic

     (b) The Algebra of Switching Currents

Algebra of Sets	*Binary Operator*	*Symbolic Logic*	*Binary Operator*	*Switching Circuits*	*Binary Operator*
Union of 2 sets	$\cup$	Disjunction of 2 propositions	$\vee$	2 switches in $\parallel$	$+$
Intersection of 2 sets	$\cap$	Conjunction of 2 propositions	$\wedge$	2 switches in series	$\times$
Complement of a set A		Negation of a proposition T, F	$\sim$	on-off, or 1, 0	1 or $^-$

Both in symbolic logic and in switching circuits, we can consider "0" and "1" as the elements, in the former representing "False" and "True"; in the latter, "Off" and "On", satisfying the following "rules":

$$\left. \begin{array}{l} 0 + 0 = 0 \\ 1 + 1 = 1 \end{array} \right\} \text{ i.e. } a + a = a$$

$$\left. \begin{array}{l} 0 \times 0 = 0 \\ 1 \times 1 = 1 \end{array} \right\} \text{ i.e. } a \times a = a$$

$$0' = 1$$
$$1' = 0$$

$$\left. \begin{array}{l} 0 + 0' = 0 + 1 = 1 \\ 1 + 1' = 1 + 0 = 1 \end{array} \right\} \text{ i.e. } a + a' = 1$$

$$\left. \begin{array}{l} 0 \times 0' = 0 \times 1 = 0 \\ 1 \times 1' = 1 \times 0 = 0 \end{array} \right\} a \times a' = 0$$

In switching circuits:

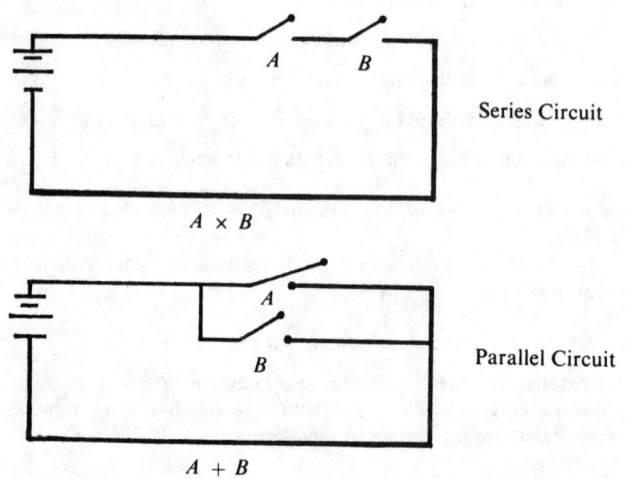

Series Circuit

$A \times B$

Parallel Circuit

$A + B$

here, "0" represents an open circuit: and "1"

$A = 0$

a closed circuit:

$A = 1$

In the Algebra of Symbolic Logic, we use *Truth Tables* to define the operations $\wedge$, $\vee$, $\sim$ as follows:

Other Operators Used

p	q	$p \wedge q$	$p \vee q$	$\sim p$	$p \rightarrow q$	$p \leftrightarrow q$
T	T	T	T	F	T	T
T	F	F	T	F	F	F
F	T	F	T	T	T	F
F	F	F	F	T	T	T

13. Two sets A and B are equivalent (have same cardinal) if and only if there exists a one-to-one correspondence between the elements of the two sets. This is an equivalence relation on the collection of subsets of set I.

A set is infinite if and only if it is equivalent to a proper subset of itself.

A set is called countably (denumerably) infinite if it is equivalent to the set of all positive integers. The set of all rational numbers is countably infinite but the set of all real numbers is noncountably infinite. The cardinal of the set of all rational numbers is denoted by (aleph null); the cardinal of the set of reals is denoted by (aleph), or C.

II. ABSTRACT ALGEBRAIC SYSTEMS

1. *Semigroup.* A semigroup is a system $\{S, 0, A\}$; S is a nonempty set $\{a, b, c, \ldots\}$, θ consists of one binary operation on S, denoted by $*$, and A consists of the axiom

A_1.   Associativity: $a*(b*c) = (a*b)*c$ for all a, b, $c \in S$.

Basic Theorem. (*Generalized Associativity*). If $a_1, a_2, \ldots, a_n$ are elements of S then all associations of the n elements yield the same "product". (For example,

$$a*((b*c)*d) = a*(b*(c*d)) = (a*b)*(c*d), \text{etc.})$$

2. *Group.* A group is a system $\{G, 0, A\}$; G is a nonempty set $\{a, b, c, \ldots\}$, θ consists of one binary operation denoted by $\circ$, and A consists of the axioms:

A_1.   Associativity: $a \circ (b \circ c) = (a \circ b) \circ c$ for all a, b, $c \in G$.

A_2.   Identity Element: G contains an element e having the property, $a \circ e = e \circ a = a$ for every $a \in G$.

A_3.   Inverse Element: For each $a \in G$ there is an element $a' \in G$ with the property, $a \circ a' = a' \circ a = e$.

If the following additional axiom belongs to A,

A_4.   Commutativity: $a \circ b = b \circ a$ for all $a, b \in G$. Then the group is called Abelian (after Niels Henrik Abel). Some basic theorems:

(a) The element e (Axiom A_2) is unique. Then e is *the* identity element of G.

(b) The element a' (Axiom A_3) is unique for each $a \in G$.   Then a' is *the* inverse of a in G.

(c) The equation $a \circ x = b$ has a unique solution in G, viz., $x = a' \circ b$.

(d) $(a')' = a$ and $(a \circ b)' = b' \circ a'$.

(e) $a \circ b = a \circ c$ if and only if $b = c$.

If a nonempty subset H of G satisfies the two conditions:

H_1. $a \circ b \in H$ whenever $a, b \in H$.   (Closure)

H_2. $a \in H$ if and only if $a' \in H$.

then H is a *subgroup* of G.

(Lagrange).   If G is a finite set then the number of elements in H divides the number of elements in G.

Example of group. Let G be the set of all one-to-one functions from a nonempty S onto itself. For any $f, g \in G$, define the function $f \circ g$ as the function which maps s onto $f(g(s))$, for each $s \in S$. Relative to this binary operation G is a group, the *symmetric group* of all permutations on S.

Each group is essentially a subgroup of the symmetric group of some set S.

3. *Ring.* A ring is a system $\{R, \theta, A\}$; R is a nonempty set $\{a, b, c, \ldots\}$, θ consists of two binary operations denoted by $+$ and $\times$, and A consists of the axioms:

A_0. Relative to addition (i.e., $+$) R is an Abelian group in which the identity element is denoted by z and the inverse of a is denoted by $-a$.

M_0. Relative to multiplication (i.e., $\times$) R is a semigroup.

D_1. Left distributive: $a \times (b + c) = (a \times b) + (a \times c)$, all $a, b, c \in R$.

D_2. Right distributive: $(b + c)a = (b \times a) + (c \times a)$, all $a, b, c \in R$.

EXAMPLE 1. The set of all integers (whole numbers) and ordinary addition and multiplication.

EXAMPLE 2. The set of all real functions continuous on the interval $0 \leq y \leq 1$, with addition and multiplication defined by $(f + g)(y) = f(y) + g(y)$, sum of real numbers, and $(f \times g)(y) = f(y) \times g(y)$, product of real numbers.

Special types of rings have been studied extensively.

3.1 *Integral Domain.* An integral domain is a ring R in which multiplication ($\times$) satisfies the additional assumptions:

M_1. Commutativity: $a \times b = b \times a$ for all a and b in R.

M_2. Multiplicative identity: R contains an element $e \neq z$ with the property $a \times e = e \times a = a$ for all a in R.

M_3. Cancellation: $a \times b = a \times c$ if and only if $b = c$.

An element u of integral domain R is a *unit* provided R contains v such that $u \times v = e$.

An element p of integral domain R is a *prime* (irreducible element) provided $p = a \times b$ implies that exactly one of the elements a or b is a unit.

The elements of integral domain R which differ from z and are neither units nor primes are *composites*.

In some integral domains (such as the ring of integers) each composite can be factored uniquely (up to unit factors) as the product of a finite set of primes. However in the integral domain of all entire functions this is not true.

3.2 *Field.* A field is an integral domain in which every element except z is a unit. In other words, the non-z elements form an Abelian group relative to multiplication ($\times$).

EXAMPLE 1. The rational field consisting of ordinary fractions, addition, and multiplication.

EXAMPLE 2. The set of all real numbers $a + b\sqrt{2}$, a and b rational. Then

$$(a + b\sqrt{2}) + (c + d\sqrt{2}) = (a + c) + (b + d)\sqrt{2} \text{ and}$$
$$(a + b\sqrt{2}) \times (c + d\sqrt{2}) = (ac + 2bd) + (ad + bc)\sqrt{2}.$$

Besides these well-known examples there exist finite fields (sometimes called Galois fields).

EXAMPLE 3. Let p be a prime integer. Denote by $GF(p)$ the p integers $0, 1, \ldots,$ $p - 1$. Define addition($\oplus$) of two of these elements a and b as the remainder of $a + b$ (ordinary addition) after division by p. (Thus $1 \oplus (p - 1) = 0$.)

Define $a \otimes b$, the product, to be the remainder of ab (ordinary multiplication) after division by p. (Thus, when $p = 3$, $2 \otimes 2 = 1$.) The resulting system $\{GF(p), \oplus, \otimes\}$ is the (modular) field of integers modulo p.

3.3 *Skew Field or Division Ring.* A skew field is a ring in which the non-z elements form a group relative to multiplication ($\times$).

The classical example of a skew field is the ring of real *quaternions*, first described by W. R. Hamilton. A quaternion is expressible in the form $ae + bi + cj + dk$ where $a, b, c,$ and d are real numbers and $e, i, j,$ and k are elements which commute with all real numbers and multiply as follows:

$$e \times e = e, \quad e \times i = i \times e = i, \quad e \times j = j \times e = j, \quad e \times k = k \times e = k;$$
$$i \times i = -e, \quad i \times j = k, \quad j \times i = -k, \quad i \times k = -j, \quad k \times i = j,$$
$$j \times j = -e, \quad j \times k = i, \quad k \times j = -i, \quad k \times k = -e.$$

These elements distribute over addition. e is generally identified with and written as the real number 1.

3.4 *Matric Ring.* The matric ring $M_n(R)$ over the ring R, where n is a positive integer, consists of all doubly-ordered sets of n^2 elements of R, written as an array

$$\begin{pmatrix} a_{1,1} & a_{1,2} \cdots a_{1,n} \\ a_{2,1} & a_{2,2} \cdots a_{2,n} \\ \vdots & \\ a_{n,1} & \cdots \quad\quad a_{n,n} \end{pmatrix} = (a_{i,j})$$

with addition and multiplication defined as follows:

$$(a_{i,j}) + (b_{i,j}) = (a_{i,j} + b_{i,j})$$
$$(a_{i,j}) \times (b_{i,j}) = (c_{i,j})$$

where

$$c_{i,j} = \sum_{k=1}^{n} a_{i,k} b_{k,j}, \quad i = 1, \ldots, n \quad \text{and} \quad j = 1, \ldots, n.$$

If $n > 1$, then multiplication is noncommutative in general; i.e., $(a_{i,j}) \times (b_{i,j})$ can differ from $(b_{i,j}) \times (a_{i,j})$. Moreover, the product of two nonzero matrices can be the zero matrix (which consists of only the element z in all n^2 positions).

A similar useful method for forming a new ring from a known ring utilizes sequences.

3.5 *Power Series and Polynomial Ring.* Let R be a ring in which multiplication ($\times$) is commutative. The set $PS(R)$ of all sequences $(a_0, a_1, \ldots)$ with $a_i \in R$ is the power series ring of R, with addition and multiplication defined as

$$(a_0, a_1, \ldots) \oplus (b_0, b_1, \ldots) = (a_0 + b_0, \ a_1 + b_1, \ldots) \text{ and}$$
$$(a_0, a_1, \ldots) \oplus (b_0, b_1, \ldots) = (c_0, c_1, \ldots)$$

where

$$c_0 = a_0 \times b_0, \quad c_1 = a_0 \times b_1 + a_1 \times b_0, \ldots, \text{ and,}$$

generally,

$$c_n = a_0 \times b_n + a_1 \times b_{n-1} + \cdots + a_n \times b_0.$$

The subset $P(R)$ of $PS(R)$ consisting of those sequences $(a_0, a_1, \ldots)$ in which at most only finitely many of the a_i differ from z, form a ring relative to the addition and multiplication just defined. This ring $\{P(R),\oplus,\otimes\}$, is the polynomial ring of R.

Some theorems for rings, fields, etc.

(a) In a ring R, if $a = b$ and $c = d$, then $a + c = b + d$ and $a \times c = b \times d$.

(b) In a ring R, $-(-a) = a$; $(-a) \times b = a \times (-b) = -(a \times b)$; and $(-a) \times (-b) = a \times b$, for all $a,b \in R$.

(c) In a ring R, $a \times z = z \times a = z$, for all $a \in R$.

(d) In a ring R the equation $a + x = b$ has a unique solution, viz., $x = -a + b$.

(f) In a field, skew field, or integral domain, $a \times b = z$ if and only if a and/or b equals z.

(g) A finite integral domain is a field.

(h) The polynomial ring of an integral domain is also an integral domain.

(i) The power series ring of an integral domain is also an integral domain.

(j) A ring is a field provided it is both an integral domain and a skew field.

(k) If R is a (skew) field, then the equation $a \times y = b$, $a \neq z$, has a unique solution $y = a' \times b$.

(l) The polynomial ring and the power series ring of a field are unique factorization domains.

4. *Vector Space.*   A vector space $V(F)$ over a field F consists of a nonempty set V (the vectors), a binary operation $(\oplus)$ on V, a function (called *scalar multiplication*) from the product set $F \times V$ onto V with the image of (a,v) denoted by $a \circ v$, and the following axioms:

A_0.   Relative to addition $(\oplus)$ V is an Abelian group in which the identity element (vector) is denoted by z and the inverse of v is denoted by $-v$.

M_1. $a \circ (b \circ v) = (ab) \circ v$ for all $a,b \in F$ and $v \in F$. (Here ab denotes the product of a and b in F.)

M_2. $1 \circ v = v$ for all $v \in V$. (Here 1 denotes the multiplicative indentity element of F.)

D_1. $a \circ (\mu \oplus v) = (a \circ \mu) \oplus (a \circ v)$ for all $a \in F$, $\mu, v \in V$.

D_2. $(a + b) \circ v \doteq (a \circ v) \oplus (b \circ v)$ for all $a,b \in F$, $v \in V$. (Here + denotes addition in the field F.)

The elements of F are referred to as *scalars*.

EXAMPLE 1.   The polynomial ring $P(F)$ of a field F is a vector space over F. In this example scalar multiplication is a special case of the multiplication defined for $P(F)$.

EXAMPLE 2.   Denote by $C_n(F)$ the set of all n-tuples, $(a_1,a_2,\ldots,a_n)$,n a positive integer, with all $a_i \in F$. Define

$$(a_1,\ldots,a_n) \oplus (b_1,\ldots,b_n) = (a_1 + b_1,\ldots,a_n + b_n) \quad \text{and}$$
$$c \circ (a_1,\ldots,a_n) = (c \times a_1,\ldots,c \times a_n),$$

where + and × denote the addition and multiplication, respectively, of the field F.   Relative to $\oplus$ and $\circ$, $C_n(F)$ is a vector space, called the *n-dimensional coordinate space* over F.

A vector space $V(F)$ is *n-dimensional* over F provided V contains n elements v_1, v_2, $\ldots$, v_n such that each element $v \in V$ is uniquely expressible in the form

$$v = a_1 \circ v_1 \oplus a_2 \circ v_2 \oplus \cdots \oplus a_n \circ v_n$$

for some $a_1,a_2,\ldots,a_n \in F$.

Two vector spaces $V(F)$ and $W(F)$ over the field of scalars F are *isomorphic* provided there is a one-to-one correspondence between the elements of V and the elements of W which is preserved under the arithmetic of the two spaces.

Basic Theorem.   An n-dimensional vector space $V(F)$ is isomorphic with the coordinate space $C_n(F)$ (of Example 2, above).

MATRICES AND DETERMINANTS

Dr. R. E. Bargmann

1. GENERAL DEFINITIONS

1.1. A matrix is an array of numbers, consisting of m rows and n columns. It is usually denoted by a bold-face capital letter, e.g.,

$$\mathbf{A} \qquad \Sigma \qquad \mathbf{M}$$

1.2. The (i, j) element of a matrix is the element occurring in row i and column j. It is usually denoted by a lower-case letter with subscripts, e.g.,

$$a_{ij} \qquad \sigma_{ij} \qquad m_{ij}$$

Exceptions to this convention will be stated where required.

1.3. A matrix is called rectangular if m (number of rows) $\neq n$ (number of columns).

1.4. A matrix is called square if $m = n$.

1.5a. In the transpose of a matrix $\mathbf{A}$, denoted by $\mathbf{A}'$, the element in the j'th row and i'th column of $\mathbf{A}$ is equal to the element in the i'th row and j'th column of $\mathbf{A}'$. Formally $(\mathbf{A}')_{ij} = (\mathbf{A})_{ji}$ where the symbol $(\mathbf{A}')_{ij}$ denotes the (i, j) element of $\mathbf{A}'$.

1.5b. The Hermitian conjugate of a matrix $\mathbf{A}$, denoted by $\mathbf{A}^H$ or $\mathbf{A}^\dagger$ is obtained by transposing $\mathbf{A}$ and replacing each element by its conjugate complex. Hence if

$$a_{kl} = u_{kl} + iv_{kl}$$

then

$$(\mathbf{A}^H)_{kl} = u_{lk} - iv_{lk}$$

where typical elements have been denoted by (k, l) to avoid confusion with $i = \sqrt{-1}$.

1.6a. A square matrix is called symmetric if $\mathbf{A} = \mathbf{A}'$.

1.6b. A square matrix is called Hermitian if $\mathbf{A} = \mathbf{A}^H$.

1.7. A matrix with m rows and 1 column is called a column vector and is usually denoted by bold faced, lower-case letters, e.g.,

$$\beta \qquad \mathbf{x} \qquad \mathbf{a}$$

1.8. A matrix with one row and n columns is called a row vector and is usually denoted by a primed, bold faced, lower-case letter, e.g.,

$$\mathbf{a}' \qquad \mathbf{c}' \qquad \mu'$$

1.9. A matrix with one row and one column is called a scalar, and is usually denoted by a lower-case letter, occasionally italicized.

1.10. The diagonal extending from upper left (NW) to lower right (SE) is called the principal diagonal of a square matrix.

1.11a. A matrix with all elements above the principal diagonal equal to zero is called a lower triangular matrix.

Example

$$\mathbf{T} = \begin{bmatrix} t_{11} & 0 & 0 \\ t_{21} & t_{22} & 0 \\ t_{31} & t_{32} & t_{33} \end{bmatrix} \text{ is lower triangular}$$

117

1.11b. The transpose of a lower triangular matrix is called an upper triangular matrix.

1.12. A square matrix with all off-diagonal elements equal to zero is called a diagonal matrix, denoted by the letter **D** with subscript indicating the typical element in the principal diagonal.

Example

$$\mathbf{D}_a = \begin{bmatrix} a_1 & 0 & 0 \\ 0 & a_2 & 0 \\ 0 & 0 & a_3 \end{bmatrix} \text{ is diagonal}$$

2. ADDITION, SUBTRACTION, AND MULTIPLICATION

2.1. Two matrices **A** and **B** can be added (subtracted) if the number of rows (columns) in **A** equals the number of rows (columns) in **B**.

$$\mathbf{A} \pm \mathbf{B} = \mathbf{C}$$

implies

$$a_{ij} \pm b_{ij} = c_{ij} \qquad i = 1, 2, \ldots m$$
$$j = 1, 2, \ldots n$$

2.2. Multiplication of a matrix or vector by a scalar implies multiplication of each element by the scalar. If

$$\mathbf{B} = \gamma \mathbf{A}$$

then

$$b_{ij} = \gamma a_{ij}$$

for all elements.

2.3a. Two matrices, **A** and **B**, can be multiplied if the number of columns in **A** equals the number of rows in **B**.

2.3b. Let **A** be of order $(m \times n)$ (have m rows and n columns) and **B** of order $(n \times p)$. Then the product of two matrices $\mathbf{C} = \mathbf{AB}$, is a matrix of order $(m \times p)$ with elements

$$c_{ij} = \sum_{k=1}^{n} a_{ik} b_{kj}$$

This states that c_{ij} is the scalar product of the i'th row vector of **A** and the j'th column vector of **B**.

Example

$$\begin{bmatrix} 3 & 4 & 2 \\ 2 & 3 & -1 \end{bmatrix} \begin{bmatrix} 1 & -2 & -4 \\ 0 & -1 & 2 \\ 6 & -3 & 9 \end{bmatrix} = \begin{bmatrix} 15 & -16 & 14 \\ -4 & -4 & -11 \end{bmatrix}$$

e.g.,

$$c_{23} = [2 \quad 3 \quad -1] \begin{bmatrix} -4 \\ 2 \\ 9 \end{bmatrix}$$

$$= 2 \times (-4) + 3 \times 2 + (-1) \times 9 = -11$$

2.3c. In general, matrix multiplication is not commutative

$$AB \neq BA$$

2.3d. Matrix multiplication is associative

$$A(BC) = (AB)C$$

2.3e. The distributive law for multiplication and addition holds as in the case of scalars,

$$(A + B)C = AC + BC$$
$$C(A + B) = CA + CB$$

2.4. In some applications, the term-by-term product of two matrices **A** and **B** of identical order is defined as

$$C = A * B$$

where

$$c_{ij} = a_{ij}b_{ij}$$

2.5. $(ABC)' = C'B'A'$

2.6. $(ABC)^H = C^H B^H A^H$

2.7. If both **A** and **B** are symmetric, then $(AB)' = BA$. Note that the product of two symmetric matrices is generally not symmetric.

3. RECOGNITION RULES AND SPECIAL FORMS

3.1. A column (row) vector with all elements equal to zero is called a null vector, and usually denoted by the symbol **0**.

3.2. A null matrix has all elements equal to zero.

3.3a. A diagonal matrix with all elements equal to one in the principal diagonal is called the identity matrix **I**.

3.3b. γI, i.e., a diagonal matrix with all diagonal elements equal to a constant γ, is called a scalar matrix.

3.4. A matrix which has only one element equal to one and all others equal to zero is called an elementary matrix $(EL)_{ij}$.

Example

$$(EL)_{23} = \begin{bmatrix} 0 & 0 & 0 & 0 & 0 \\ 0 & 0 & 1 & 0 & 0 \\ 0 & 0 & 0 & 0 & 0 \\ 0 & 0 & 0 & 0 & 0 \end{bmatrix}$$

The order of the matrix is usually implicit.

3.5a. The symbol **j** is reserved for a column vector with all elements equal to 1.

3.5b. The symbol **j'** is reserved for a row vector with all elements equal to 1.

3.6. An expression ending with a column vector is a column vector.

Example

$$ABx = y$$

(It is assumed that rule 2.3a is satisfied, else matrix multiplication would not be defined.)

3.7. An expression beginning with a row vector is a row vector.

Example

$$y'(A + BC) = d'$$

3.8. An expression beginning with a row vector and ending with a column vector, is a scalar.

Example

$$\mathbf{a'Bc} = \gamma$$

3.9a. If $\mathbf{Q}$ is a square matrix, the scalar $\mathbf{x'Qx}$ is called a quadratic form. If $\mathbf{Q}$ is non-symmetric, one can always find a symmetric matrix $\mathbf{Q^*}$ such that

$$\mathbf{x'Qx} = \mathbf{x'Q^*x}$$

where

$$(\mathbf{Q^*})_{ij} = \tfrac{1}{2}(q_{ij} + q_{ji})$$

3.9b. If $\mathbf{Q}$ is a square matrix the scalar $\mathbf{x^H Qx}$ is called a Hermitian form.

3.10. A scalar $\mathbf{x'Qy}$ is called a bilinear form.

3.11. The scalar $\mathbf{x'x} = \Sigma x_i^2$, i.e., the sum of squares of all elements of $\mathbf{x}$.

3.12. The scalar $\mathbf{x'y} = \Sigma x_i y_i$, i.e., the sum of products of elements in $\mathbf{x}$ by those in $\mathbf{y}$. $\mathbf{x}$ and $\mathbf{y}$ have the same number of elements.

3.13. The scalar $\mathbf{x'D_w x} = \Sigma w_i x_i^2$ is called a weighted sum of squares.

3.14. The scalar $\mathbf{x'D_w y} = \Sigma w_i x_i y_i$ is called a weighted sum of products.

3.15a. The vector $\mathbf{Aj}$ is a column vector whose elements are the row sums of $\mathbf{A}$.

3.15b. The vector $\mathbf{j'A}$ is a row vector whose elements are the column sums of $\mathbf{A}$.

3.15c. The scalar $\mathbf{j'Aj}$ is the sum of all elements in $\mathbf{A}$. Schematically

$\mathbf{A}$	$\mathbf{Aj}$
$\mathbf{j'A}$	$\mathbf{j'Aj}$

3.16a. If $\mathbf{B} = \mathbf{D_w A}$; then $b_{ij} = w_i a_{ij}$.

3.16b. If $\mathbf{B} = \mathbf{AD_w}$; then $b_{ij} = a_{ij} w_j$.

3.17. Interchanging summation and matrix notation:

If

$$\mathbf{ABCD} = \mathbf{E}$$

then

$$e_{ij} = \sum_k \sum_l \sum_m a_{ik} b_{kl} c_{lm} d_{mj}$$

The second subscript of an element must coincide with the first of the next one. Reordering and transposing may be required.

Example

If

$$e_{ij} = \sum_k \sum_l \sum_m a_{kl} b_{ki} c_{jm} d_{ml}$$

$$= \sum_k \sum_l \sum_m b_{ki} a_{kl} d_{ml} c_{jm}$$

Then

$$\mathbf{E} = \mathbf{B'AD'C'}$$

3.18a. $\mathbf{A'A}$ is a symmetric matrix whose (i, j) element is the scalar product of the i'th column vector and the j'th column vector of $\mathbf{A'}$.

3.18b. $\mathbf{AA'}$ is a symmetric matrix whose (i, j) element is the scalar product of the i'th row vector and the j'th row vector of $\mathbf{A}$.

4. DETERMINANTS

4.1a. A determinant $|A|$ or $\det(A)$ is a scalar function of a square matrix defined in such a way that

$$|A|\,|B| = |AB|$$

and

$$\begin{vmatrix} a_{11} & a_{12} \\ a_{21} & a_{22} \end{vmatrix} = a_{11}a_{22} - a_{12}a_{21}$$

4.1b. $|A| = |A'|$

4.2.
$$\begin{vmatrix} a_{11} & a_{12} & a_{13} \\ a_{21} & a_{22} & a_{23} \\ a_{31} & a_{32} & a_{33} \end{vmatrix} = \begin{matrix} a_{11}a_{22}a_{33} + a_{12}a_{23}a_{31} + a_{13}a_{21}a_{32} \\ - a_{13}a_{22}a_{31} - a_{11}a_{23}a_{32} - a_{12}a_{21}a_{33} \end{matrix}$$

4.3.
$$\begin{vmatrix} a_{11} & a_{12} & \cdots & a_{1n} \\ a_{21} & a_{22} & \cdots & a_{2n} \\ & & \cdots & \\ a_{n1} & a_{n2} & \cdots & a_{nm} \end{vmatrix} = \sum (-1)^{\delta} a_{1i_1} a_{2i_2} \cdots a_{ni_n}$$

where the sum is over all permutations

$$i_1 \neq i_2 \neq \cdots i_n$$

and δ denotes the number of exchanges necessary to bring the sequence $(i_1, i_2, \ldots i_n)$ back into the natural order $(1, 2, \ldots n)$.

4.4. If two rows (columns) in a matrix are exchanged, the determinant will change its sign.

4.5. A determinant does not change its value if a linear combination of other rows (columns) is added to any given row (column).

Example

$$\begin{vmatrix} a_{11} & a_{12} & a_{13} & a_{14} \\ b_{21} & b_{22} & b_{23} & b_{24} \\ a_{31} & a_{32} & a_{33} & a_{34} \\ a_{41} & a_{42} & a_{43} & a_{44} \end{vmatrix} = \begin{vmatrix} a_{11} & a_{12} & a_{13} & a_{14} \\ a_{21} & a_{22} & a_{23} & a_{24} \\ a_{31} & a_{32} & a_{33} & a_{34} \\ a_{41} & a_{42} & a_{43} & a_{44} \end{vmatrix}$$

where

$$b_{2i} = a_{2i} + \gamma_1 a_{1i} + \gamma_3 a_{3i} + \gamma_4 a_{4i}$$
$$i = 1, 2, 3, 4$$

$\gamma_1, \gamma_3, \gamma_4$ arbitrary.

4.6. If the i'th row (column) equals (a constant times) the j'th row (column) of a matrix, its determinant is equal to zero, $(i \neq j)$.

4.7. If, in a matrix A, each element of a row (column) is multiplied by a constant γ, the determinant is multiplied by γ.

4.8. $|\gamma A| = \gamma^n |A|$ assuming that A is of order $(n \times n)$.

4.9. The cofactor of a square matrix A, $\text{cof}_{ij}(A)$ is the determinant of a matrix obtained by striking the i'th row and j'th column of A and choosing positive (negative) sign if $i + j$ is even (odd).

Example

$$\text{cof}_{23} \begin{bmatrix} 2 & 4 & 3 \\ 6 & 1 & 5 \\ -2 & 1 & 3 \end{bmatrix} = - \begin{vmatrix} 2 & 4 \\ -2 & 1 \end{vmatrix}$$

$$= -(2 + 8) = -10$$

4.10. (Laplace Development)

$$|\mathbf{A}| = a_{i1}\text{cof}_{i1}(\mathbf{A}) + a_{i2}\text{cof}_{i2}(\mathbf{A}) + \cdots + a_{in}\text{cof}_{in}(\mathbf{A})$$

$$= a_{1j}\text{cof}_{1j}(\mathbf{A}) + a_{2j}\text{cof}_{2j}(\mathbf{A}) + \cdots + a_{nj}\text{cof}_{nj}(\mathbf{A})$$

for any row i or any column j.

4.11. Numerical Evaluation of the determinant of a symmetric matrix.

Note: If $\mathbf{A}$ is non-symmetric, form $\mathbf{A'A}$ or $\mathbf{AA'}$ by rule 3.18, obtain its determinant, and take the square root.

("Forward Doolittle Scheme", "left side")

Let

$$p_{11} = a_{11}, \quad p_{12} = a_{12} = a_{21}, \ldots p_{1n} = a_{1n}$$

$$
\begin{array}{ccccc}
p_{11} & p_{12} & p_{13} & \cdots & p_{1n} \\
\hline
1 & u_{12} & u_{13} & \cdots & u_{1n} \\
\hline
 & a_{22} & a_{23} & \cdots & a_{2n} \\[4pt]
 & p_{22} & p_{23} & \cdots & p_{2n} \\
\hline
 & 1 & u_{23} & \cdots & u_{2n} \\
\hline
 & & a_{33} & \cdots & a_{3n} \\[4pt]
 & & p_{33} & \cdots & p_{3n} \\
\hline
 & & 1 & \cdots & u_{3n} \\
\hline
 & & \cdot & \cdots & \cdot \\[4pt]
 & & & & a_{nn} \\[4pt]
 & & & & p_{nn} \\[4pt]
 & & & & 1
\end{array}
$$

$$u_{1i} = p_{1i}/p_{11} \qquad\qquad\qquad\qquad\qquad i = 1, 2, \ldots n$$

$$p_{2i} = a_{2i} - u_{12}p_{1i} \qquad\qquad\qquad\qquad i = 2, 3, \ldots n$$

$$u_{2i} = p_{2i}/p_{22}$$

$$p_{3i} = a_{3i} - u_{13}p_{1i} - u_{23}p_{2i} \qquad\qquad\quad i = 3, 4, \ldots n$$

$$u_{3i} = p_{3i}/p_{33}$$

$$p_{ki} = a_{ki} - u_{1k}p_{1i} - u_{2k}p_{2i} - \cdots - u_{k-1,k}p_{k-1,i} \quad i = k, k+1, \ldots n$$

$$\qquad\qquad\qquad\qquad\qquad\qquad\qquad\qquad\qquad k = 2, 3, \ldots n$$

$$u_{ki} = p_{ki}/p_{kk}$$

If, at some stage, $p_{kk} = 0$, reordering of rows and columns may be required. If the matrix is positive-definite (see 8.16) (always true for $\mathbf{AA'}$ or $\mathbf{A'A}$, see rule 10.24), none of the

p_{kk} will be zero. The p_{ii} are called pivots. Then

$$|A| = \prod_{i=1}^{n} p_{ii}$$

Further, if A is partitioned

$$A = \begin{bmatrix} A_{11} & A_{12} \\ A'_{12} & A_{22} \end{bmatrix}$$

where A_{11} is of order $(k \times k)$, then

$$|A_{11}| = \prod_{i=1}^{k} p_{ii}$$

(Numerical Examples: see 6.14.)

5. SINGULARITY AND RANK

5.1. A matrix A is called singular if there exists a vector $x \neq 0$ such that $Ax = 0$ or $A'x = 0$. Note $x \neq 0$ if a single element of x is unequal 0. If a matrix is not singular, it is called non-singular.

5.2. If a matrix A_1 can be formed by selection of r rows and columns of A such that $A_1x \neq 0$ or $A'_1x \neq 0$ for every $x \neq 0$, and if addition of an $(r + 1)st$ row and column would produce a singular matrix, r is called the rank of A.

Example

$$A = \begin{bmatrix} 2 & 4 & 6 \\ 1 & 3 & 7 \\ 3 & 7 & 13 \\ 1 & 1 & -1 \end{bmatrix}$$

Note that

$$[1, \quad 1, \quad -1] \begin{bmatrix} 2 & 4 & 6 \\ 1 & 3 & 7 \\ 3 & 7 & 13 \end{bmatrix} = [0 \quad 0 \quad 0]$$

and

$$[1, \quad -1, \quad -1] \begin{bmatrix} 2 & 4 & 6 \\ 1 & 3 & 7 \\ 1 & 1 & -1 \end{bmatrix} = [0 \quad 0 \quad 0]$$

but

$$\begin{bmatrix} 2 & 4 \\ 1 & 3 \end{bmatrix} \begin{bmatrix} x_1 \\ x_2 \end{bmatrix} \neq \begin{bmatrix} 0 \\ 0 \end{bmatrix}$$

or

$$[x_1 \quad x_2] \begin{bmatrix} 2 & 4 \\ 1 & 3 \end{bmatrix} \neq [0, \quad 0]$$

for any arbitrary

$$[x_1, \quad x_2] \neq [0, \quad 0].$$

Hence the matrix has rank 2.

5.3. If A has rank r and if A_1 is a non-singular submatrix consisting of r rows and columns of A, then A_1 is called a basis of A.

5.4a. The determinant of a square singular matrix is 0.

5.4b. The determinant of a non-singular matrix is $\neq 0$.

5.5. rank $(AB) \leq$ min [rank (A), rank (B)].

5.6. rank $(AA') =$ rank $(A'A) =$ rank (A).

5.7. $|A'A| = |AA'| = |A|^2$ if A is square.

5.8. $|A'A| = |AA'| \geq 0$ for every A with real elements.

6. INVERSION

(Regular Case, non-singular matrices)

6.1. If A is square and non-singular ($|A| \neq 0$) there exists a unique matrix A^{-1} such that $AA^{-1} = A^{-1}A = I$.

6.2. $(ABC)^{-1} = C^{-1}B^{-1}A^{-1}$ (provided that all inverses exist).

6.3. $(A^{-1})' = (A')^{-1}$

6.4. $Ax = b$ is a system of linear equations. If A is square and non-singular, there exists a unique solution

$$x = A^{-1}b$$

6.5. $(\gamma A)^{-1} = (1/\gamma)A^{-1}$

6.6. $|A^{-1}| = 1/|A|$

6.7. $D_w^{-1} = D_{1/w}$ where D is a diagonal matrix.

6.8. If

$$A = B + uv'$$

then

$$A^{-1} = B^{-1} - \lambda yz'$$

where

$$y = B^{-1}u, \quad z' = v'B^{-1},$$

and

$$\lambda = 1/(1 + z'u)$$

Example 6.8.1

$$A = \begin{bmatrix} 4 & 2 & 4 & 5 \\ 3 & 9 & 12 & 15 \\ 2 & 4 & 11 & 10 \\ 1 & 2 & 4 & 10 \end{bmatrix}$$

This matrix can be written as

$$\begin{bmatrix} 3 & 0 & 0 & 0 \\ 0 & 3 & 0 & 0 \\ 0 & 0 & 3 & 0 \\ 0 & 0 & 0 & 5 \end{bmatrix} + \begin{bmatrix} 1 \\ 3 \\ 2 \\ 1 \end{bmatrix} \begin{bmatrix} 1 & 2 & 4 & 5 \end{bmatrix} = B + uv'$$

$$\mathbf{B}^{-1} = \begin{bmatrix} 1/3 & 0 & 0 & 0 \\ 0 & 1/3 & 0 & 0 \\ 0 & 0 & 1/3 & 0 \\ 0 & 0 & 0 & 1/5 \end{bmatrix}$$

$$\mathbf{y} = \mathbf{B}^{-1}\mathbf{u} = \begin{bmatrix} 1/3 \\ 1 \\ 2/3 \\ 1/5 \end{bmatrix}$$

$$\mathbf{z}' = \mathbf{v}'\mathbf{B}^{-1} = [1/3 \quad 2/3 \quad 4/3 \quad 1]$$

$$\mathbf{z}'\mathbf{u} = 1/3 \times 1 + 2/3 \times 3 + 4/3 \times 2 + 1 \times 1 = 6$$

$$\lambda = 1/7$$

$$\mathbf{A}^{-1} = \begin{bmatrix} 1/3 & 0 & 0 & 0 \\ 0 & 1/3 & 0 & 0 \\ 0 & 0 & 1/3 & 0 \\ 0 & 0 & 0 & 1/5 \end{bmatrix} - (1/7)\begin{bmatrix} 1/3 \\ 1 \\ 2/3 \\ 1/5 \end{bmatrix}[1/3 \quad 2/3 \quad 4/3 \quad 1]$$

$$= (1/315)\begin{bmatrix} 100 & -10 & -20 & -15 \\ -15 & 75 & -60 & -45 \\ -10 & -20 & 65 & -30 \\ -3 & -6 & -12 & 54 \end{bmatrix}$$

(This rule is especially useful if all off-diagonal elements are equal, then $\mathbf{u} = k\mathbf{j}$ and $\mathbf{v}' = \mathbf{j}'$ and $\mathbf{B}$ is diagonal.)

6.9. Let $\mathbf{B}$ (elements b_{ij}) have a known inverse, $\mathbf{B}^{-1}$ (elements b^{ij}). Let $\mathbf{A} = \mathbf{B}$ except for one element $a_{rs} = b_{rs} + k$. Then the elements of $\mathbf{A}^{-1}$ are

$$a^{ij} = b^{ij} - \frac{kb^{ir}b^{sj}}{1 + kb^{sr}}.$$

6.10. (Partitioning)

Let

$$\mathbf{A} = \begin{matrix} (p) \\ (q) \end{matrix} \begin{matrix} (p) & (q) \\ \begin{bmatrix} \mathbf{B} & \mathbf{C} \\ \mathbf{D} & \mathbf{E} \end{bmatrix} \end{matrix}$$

(letters in parentheses denote order of the submatrices)

Let $\mathbf{B}^{-1}$ and $\mathbf{E}^{-1}$ exist. Then

$$\mathbf{A}^{-1} = \begin{bmatrix} \mathbf{X} & \mathbf{Y} \\ \mathbf{Z} & \mathbf{U} \end{bmatrix}$$

where

$$\mathbf{X} = (\mathbf{B} - \mathbf{C}\mathbf{E}^{-1}\mathbf{D})^{-1}$$
$$\mathbf{U} = (\mathbf{E} - \mathbf{D}\mathbf{B}^{-1}\mathbf{C})^{-1}$$
$$\mathbf{Y} = -\mathbf{B}^{-1}\mathbf{C}\mathbf{U}$$
$$\mathbf{Z} = -\mathbf{E}^{-1}\mathbf{D}\mathbf{X}$$

6.11. (Partitioning of Determinants)

Let

$$|\mathbf{A}| = \begin{vmatrix} \mathbf{B} & \mathbf{C} \\ \mathbf{D} & \mathbf{E} \end{vmatrix} \qquad \text{(same structure as in 6.10)}$$

Then

$$|\mathbf{A}| = |\mathbf{E}| \, |(\mathbf{B} - \mathbf{C}\mathbf{E}^{-1}\mathbf{D})| = |\mathbf{B}| \, |(\mathbf{E} - \mathbf{D}\mathbf{B}^{-1}\mathbf{C})|$$

6.12. Let

$$\mathbf{A} = \mathbf{B} + \mathbf{U}\mathbf{V}$$

where $\mathbf{B}(n \times n)$ has an inverse

$\mathbf{U}$ is of order $(n \times k)$, with k usually very small

$\mathbf{V}$ is of order $(k \times n)$

(the special case for $k = 1$ is treated in 6.8).

Then
$$\mathbf{A}^{-1} = \mathbf{B}^{-1} - \mathbf{Y}\Lambda\mathbf{Z}$$

where

$$\mathbf{Y} = \mathbf{B}^{-1}\mathbf{U}(n \times k)$$
$$\mathbf{Z} = \mathbf{V}\mathbf{B}^{-1}(k \times n)$$

and

$$\Lambda(k \times k) = [\mathbf{I} + \mathbf{Z}\mathbf{U}]^{-1}$$

6.13. Let a_{ij} denote the elements of $\mathbf{A}$ and a^{ij} those of $\mathbf{A}^{-1}$. Then

$$a^{ij} = \mathrm{cof}_{ji}(\mathbf{A})/|\mathbf{A}|$$

where cof is the determinant defined in 4.9.

6.14. "Doolittle" Method of inverting symmetric matrices (see also 4.11). Let

$$p_{11} = a_{11}, \quad p_{12} = a_{12} = a_{21}, \dots p_{1n} = a_{1n} = a_{n1}$$

Forward Solution

p_{11}	p_{12}	p_{13}	$\cdots$	p_{1n}	1				
1	u_{12}	u_{13}	$\cdots$	u_{1n}	u_{11}				
	a_{22}	a_{23}	$\cdots$	a_{2n}	0	1			
	p_{22}	p_{23}	$\cdots$	p_{2n}	p_{21}	$p_{2\mathrm{II}}$			
	1	u_{23}	$\cdots$	u_{2n}	u_{21}	$u_{2\mathrm{II}}$			
		a_{33}	$\cdots$	a_{3n}	0	0	1		
		p_{33}	$\cdots$	p_{3n}	p_{31}	$p_{3\mathrm{II}}$	$p_{3\mathrm{III}}$		
		1	$\cdots$	u_{3n}	u_{31}	$u_{3\mathrm{II}}$	$u_{3\mathrm{III}}$		
		$\cdot$	$\cdots$	$\cdot$	$\cdot$	$\cdots$	$\cdot$		
				a_{nn}	0	0	0	$\cdots$	1
				p_{nn}	p_{n1}	$p_{n\mathrm{II}}$	$p_{n\mathrm{III}}$	$\cdots$	p_{nN}
				1	u_{n1}	$u_{n\mathrm{II}}$	$u_{n\mathrm{III}}$	$\cdots$	u_{nN}

$$u_{1i} = p_{1i}/p_{11} \qquad\qquad i = 1, 2, \ldots n, \text{I}$$
$$p_{2i} = a_{2i} - u_{12}p_{1i} \qquad\qquad i = 2, 3, \ldots n, \text{I}, \text{II}$$
$$u_{2i} = p_{2i}/p_{22}$$
$$p_{3i} = a_{3i} - u_{13}p_{1i} - u_{23}p_{2i} \qquad i = 3, 4, \ldots n, \text{I}, \text{II}, \text{III}$$
$$u_{3i} = p_{3i}/p_{33}$$
$$p_{ki} = a_{ki} - u_{1k}p_{1i} - u_{2k}p_{2i} - \cdots - u_{k-1,k}p_{k-1,i} \quad i = k, k+1, \ldots n, \text{I}, \text{II}, \ldots \text{K}$$
$$k = 2, 3, \ldots n$$
$$u_{ki} = p_{ki}/p_{kk}$$

Backward Solution

(*j* refers to Arabic, *J* refers to Roman numerals)

The elements of $\mathbf{A}^{-1}$ are a^{ij}

$$a^{nj} = u_{nJ} \qquad\qquad \begin{array}{l} j = 1, 2, \ldots n; \\ J = \text{I}, \text{II}, \ldots N \end{array}$$

$$a^{n-1,j} = u_{n-1,J} - u_{n-1,n}a^{nj} \qquad\qquad \begin{array}{l} j = 1, 2, \ldots (n-1); \\ J = \text{I}, \text{II}, \ldots (N-1) \end{array}$$

$$a^{n-2,j} = u_{n-2,J} - u_{n-2,n}a^{nj} - u_{n-2,n-1}a^{n-1,j} \qquad \begin{array}{l} j = 1, 2, \ldots (n-2); \\ J = \text{I}, \text{II}, \ldots (N-2) \end{array}$$

$$a^{n-k,j} = u_{n-k,J} - u_{n-k,n}a^{nj} - u_{n-k,n-1}a^{n-1,j} - \cdots - u_{n-k,n-k+1}a^{n-k+1,j} \qquad \begin{array}{l} j = 1, 2, \ldots (n-k); \\ J = \text{I}, \text{II}, \ldots (N-k); \\ k = 1, 2, \ldots (n-1), \end{array}$$

and $a^{ji} = a^{ij}$.

Numerical Example 6.14.1.

Invert the Matrix

$$\begin{bmatrix} 25 & 30 & -10 \\ 30 & 40 & -6 \\ -10 & -6 & 17 \end{bmatrix}$$

a_1	25	30	-10	1	
u_1	1	1.2	-0.4	0.04	
	a_2	40	-6	0	1
	p_2	4	6	-1.2	1
	u_2	1	1.5	-0.3	0.25
		a_3	17	0	0	1
		p_3	4	2.2	-1.5	1
		u_3	1	0.55	-0.375	0.25

1.61	-1.125	0.55
-1.125	0.8125	-0.375
0.55	-0.375	0.25

Enter row a_1.
Elements in u_1 = Elements in a_1 divided by $a_{11}(=25)$.
Enter row a_2.

$$p_{22} = 40 - 1.2 \times 30 = 4$$
$$p_{23} = -6 - 1.2 \times (-10) = 6$$
$$p_{21} = 0 - 1.2 \times 1 = -1.2$$
$$p_{211} = 1$$

Elements in u_2 = Elements in p_2 divided by $p_{22}(=4)$.
Enter row a_3.

$$p_{33} = 17 - (-0.4) \times (-10) - 1.5 \times 6 = 4$$
$$p_{31} = 0 - (-0.4) \times 1 - 1.5 \times (-1.2) = 2.2$$
$$p_{311} = 0 - 1.5 \times 1 = -1.5$$
$$p_{3111} = 1$$

Elements in u_3 = Elements in p_3 divided by $p_{33}(=4)$.
Copy the right-hand side of the last (third) u – row as the last column below the double line.

$$a^{21} = -0.3 - 1.5 \times 0.55 = -1.125$$
$$a^{22} = 0.25 - 1.5 \times (-0.375) = 0.8125$$
$$a^{23} = 0 - 1.5 \times 0.25 = -0.375 \quad \text{(check against } a^{32}\text{)}.$$

These are entered in the next to last (second) column below.

$$a^{11} = 0.04 - (-0.4) \times 0.55 - 1.2 \times (-1.125) = 1.61$$
$$a^{12} = 0 - (-0.4) \times (-0.375) - 1.2 \times 0.8125 = -1.125 \quad \text{(check against } a^{21}\text{)}$$
$$a^{13} = 0 - (-0.4) \times (0.25) - 1.2 \times (-0.375) = 0.55 \quad \text{(check against } a^{31}\text{)}.$$

6.15. A matrix is called orthogonal if $\mathbf{A}' = \mathbf{A}^{-1}$ (or $\mathbf{A}\mathbf{A}' = \mathbf{I}$).

7. TRACES

7.1. If $\mathbf{A}$ is a square matrix then the trace of $\mathbf{A}$ is $tr\,\mathbf{A} = \sum_i a_{ii}$, i.e., the sum of the diagonal elements.

7.2. If $\mathbf{A}$ is of order $(m \times k)$ and $\mathbf{B}$ of order $(k \times m)$ then $tr(\mathbf{AB}) = tr(\mathbf{BA})$.

7.3. If $\mathbf{A}$ is of order $(m \times k)$, $\mathbf{B}$ of order $(k \times r)$ and $\mathbf{C}$ of order $(r \times m)$, then

$$tr(\mathbf{ABC}) = tr(\mathbf{BCA}) = tr(\mathbf{CAB}).$$

7.3a. If $\mathbf{b}$ is a column vector and $\mathbf{c}'$ a row vector, then

$$tr(\mathbf{Abc}') = tr(\mathbf{bc}'\mathbf{A}) = \mathbf{c}'\mathbf{Ab}$$

since the trace of a scalar is the scalar.

7.4. $tr(\mathbf{A} + \gamma\mathbf{B}) = tr\mathbf{A} + \gamma tr\mathbf{B}$; where γ is a scalar.

7.5. $tr(\mathbf{EL})_{ij}\mathbf{A} = tr\mathbf{A}(\mathbf{EL})_{ij} = a_{ji}$; where $(\mathbf{EL})_{ij}$ is an elementary matrix as defined in 3.4.

7.6. $tr(\mathbf{EL})_{ij}\mathbf{A}(\mathbf{EL})_{rs}\mathbf{B} = a_{jr}b_{si}$

(These rules are useful in matrix differentiation)

7.7. The trace of the second order of a square matrix $\mathbf{A}$ is the sum of the determinants of all $\binom{n}{2}$ matrices of order (2×2) which can be formed by intersecting rows i and j with columns i and j.

$$tr_2 \mathbf{A} = \begin{vmatrix} a_{11} & a_{12} \\ a_{21} & a_{22} \end{vmatrix} + \begin{vmatrix} a_{11} & a_{13} \\ a_{31} & a_{33} \end{vmatrix}$$

$$+ \cdots + \begin{vmatrix} a_{11} & a_{1n} \\ a_{n1} & a_{nn} \end{vmatrix} + \begin{vmatrix} a_{22} & a_{23} \\ a_{32} & a_{33} \end{vmatrix}$$

$$+ \cdots + \begin{vmatrix} a_{22} & a_{2n} \\ a_{n2} & a_{nn} \end{vmatrix} + \cdots + \begin{vmatrix} a_{n-1,n-1} & a_{n-1,n} \\ a_{n,n-1} & a_{nn} \end{vmatrix}.$$

7.8. The trace of the k'th order of a square matrix is the sum of the determinants of all $\binom{n}{k}$ matrices of order $(k \times k)$ which can be formed by intersecting any k rows of $\mathbf{A}$ with the same k columns.

$$tr_k \mathbf{A} = \sum \begin{vmatrix} a_{i_1 i_1} & a_{i_1 i_2} & \cdots & a_{i_1 i_k} \\ a_{i_2 i_1} & a_{i_2 i_2} & \cdots & a_{i_2 ik} \\ \cdot & \cdot & \cdots & \cdot \\ a_{i_k i_1} & a_{i_k i_2} & \cdots & a_{i_k i_k} \end{vmatrix}$$

where the sum extends over all combinations of n elements taken k at a time in order

$$i_1 < i_2 < \cdots < i_k.$$

7.9. Rules 7.2 and 7.3 (cyclic exchange) are valid for trace of k'th order.

7.10. $tr_n \mathbf{A} = |\mathbf{A}|$ if $\mathbf{A}$ is of order $(n \times n)$.

8. CHARACTERISTIC ROOTS AND VECTORS

8.1. If $\mathbf{A}$ is a square matrix of order $(n \times n)$, then $|\mathbf{A} - \lambda \mathbf{I}| = 0$ is called the characteristic equation of the matrix $\mathbf{A}$. It is a polynomial of the n'th degree in λ.

8.2. The n roots of the characteristic equation (not necessarily distinct) are called the characteristic roots of $\mathbf{A}$

$$ch(\mathbf{A}) = \lambda_1, \lambda_2, \ldots \lambda_n$$

8.3. The characteristic equation of $\mathbf{A}$ can be obtained by the relation

$$\lambda^n - (tr\mathbf{A})\lambda^{n-1} + (tr_2\mathbf{A})\lambda^{n-2} - (tr_3\mathbf{A})\lambda^{n-3} \cdots - (-1)^n(tr_{n-1}\mathbf{A})\lambda + (-1)^n |\mathbf{A}| = 0$$

where tr_k is defined in 7.8.

Example 8.3.1

$$\mathbf{A} = \begin{bmatrix} 25 & 30 & -10 \\ 30 & 40 & -6 \\ -10 & -6 & 17 \end{bmatrix}$$

$tr\mathbf{A} = 25 + 40 + 17 = 82$

$tr_2\mathbf{A} = (25 \times 40 - 30 \times 30) + (25 \times 17 - 10 \times 10) + (40 \times 17 - 6 \times 6) = 1069$

$tr_3\mathbf{A} = |\mathbf{A}| = 25 \times 4 \times 4 = 400$

    (cf. 6.14 and procedure stated in 4.11)

Hence

$$\lambda^3 - 82\lambda^2 + 1069\lambda - 400 = 0$$

The solutions (by Newton iteration) are

$$\lambda_1 = 65.86108$$
$$\lambda_2 = 15.75339$$
$$\lambda_3 = 0.38553$$

These are the characteristic roots of A.

8.4. $ch(A + \gamma I) = \gamma + ch(A)$

8.5. $ch(AB) = ch(BA)$

    (except that AB or BA may have additional roots equal to zero).

8.6. $ch(A^{-1}) = 1/ch(A)$

8.7. If $\lambda_1, \lambda_2, \ldots \lambda_n$ are the roots of A then

$$\sum_i \lambda_i = tr A$$

$$\sum_{i<j} \lambda_i \lambda_j = tr_2 A$$

$$\sum_{i<j<k} \lambda_i \lambda_j \lambda_k = tr_3 A$$

$$\prod_i \lambda_i = |A|$$

8.8. If x' denotes the radius vector (running coordinates $[x, y, z]$) and if a matrix Q is positive-definite, then

$$(x' - x_0') Q^{-1} (x - x_0) = 1$$

is the equation of an ellipsoid with center at $[x_0, y_0, z_0] = x_0'$ and semi-axes equal to the square roots of the characteristic roots of Q.

8.9. The characteristic roots of a triangular (or diagonal) matrix are the diagonal elements of the matrix.

8.10. If A is a real matrix with positive roots, then

$$ch_{\min}(AA') \leq [ch_{\min}(A)]^2 \leq [ch_{\max}(A)]^2 \leq ch_{\max}(AA')$$

where $ch_{\min}$ denotes the smallest and $ch_{\max}$ the largest root.

8.11. The ratio of two quadratic forms (B non-singular)

$$u = \frac{x'Ax}{x'Bx}$$

attains stationary values at the roots of $B^{-1}A$. In particular

$$u_{\max} = ch_{\max}(B^{-1}A) \qquad \text{and} \qquad u_{\min} = ch_{\min}(B^{-1}A)$$

8.12. The equation system

$$Ax = \lambda x$$

permits non-zero solutions only if λ is one of the characteristic roots of A. Such a solution x is called a characteristic vector.

8.13. If x is a solution to 8.12, so is γx for an arbitrary scalar γ.

8.14. A solution x which has unit length ($x'x = 1$) is called the eigenvector associated with the characteristic root λ of A. The vector is frequently denoted by e.

8.15. A real symmetric matrix has real roots.

8.16. A matrix A is called positive-definite (abbreviated p.d.) if the quadratic form $x'Ax > 0$ for every $x \neq 0$.

8.17. A matrix $\mathbf{A}$ is called positive-semidefinite (abbreviated p.s.d.) if the quadratic form $\mathbf{x}'\mathbf{A}\mathbf{x} > 0$ and/or $\mathbf{x}'\mathbf{A}\mathbf{x} = 0$ for some $\mathbf{x} \neq \mathbf{0}$.

8.18. A positive-definite real symmetric matrix has only positive characteristic roots.

8.19. If a real symmetric matrix is positive-semidefinite, it has no negative roots. The number of non-zero roots equals the rank of the matrix.

8.20. If all roots of a real symmetric matrix are distinct, the associated eigenvectors are distinct.

8.21. The matrix of eigenvectors

$$\mathbf{E} = [\mathbf{e}_1, \mathbf{e}_2, \ldots \mathbf{e}_n]$$

of a real symmetric matrix is (or can be chosen to be) orthogonal.

8.22. $\mathbf{A}\mathbf{E} = \mathbf{E}\mathbf{D}_\lambda$.

8.23. For a real symmetric matrix, $\mathbf{A} = \mathbf{E}\mathbf{D}_\lambda\mathbf{E}'$ (decomposition into matrices of unit rank)

$$\mathbf{E}'\mathbf{A}\mathbf{E} = \mathbf{D}_\lambda$$

where $\mathbf{D}_\lambda$ denotes the diagonal matrix of characteristic roots ordered in the same way as the eigenvector columns in $\mathbf{E}$.

8.24. If $f(\lambda)$ is a polynomial in λ, then

$$f(\mathbf{A}) = \mathbf{E}\mathbf{D}_{f(\lambda)}\mathbf{E}^{-1}$$

where λ are the characteristic roots of $\mathbf{A}$ and $\mathbf{E}$ is the matrix of associated eigenvectors. If $\mathbf{A}$ is symmetric, $\mathbf{E}^{-1} = \mathbf{E}'$.

Example 8.24.1

Consider the matrix in 8.3 (and 6.14).

$$\mathbf{A} = \begin{bmatrix} 25 & 30 & -10 \\ 30 & 40 & -6 \\ -10 & -6 & 17 \end{bmatrix}$$

The characteristic roots were found in Example 8.3.1,

$$\lambda_1 = 65.86108 \qquad \lambda_2 = 15.75339 \qquad \lambda_3 = 0.38553.$$

To find some $\mathbf{x}$ such that $\mathbf{A}\mathbf{x} = \lambda_1\mathbf{x}$, we arbitrarily set the first element of $\mathbf{x}$ equal to 1. Using only the first two rows of $\mathbf{A}$ we solve the equation system

$$25 + 30x_2 - 10x_3 = 65.86108$$
$$30 + 40x_2 - 6x_3 = 65.86108x_2$$

which yields $x_2 = 1.24294$ and $x_3 = -0.35729$. Substitution of these values into the third equation

$$-10 - 6x_2 + 17x_3 = 65.86108x_3$$

yields zero to five decimal places, indicating the accuracy of the first characteristic root. To reduce to unit length the characteristic vector

$$[1 \qquad 1.24294 \qquad -0.35729]$$

we divide each element by

$$\sqrt{1 + 1.24294^2 + 0.35729^2}$$

and thus obtain the first eigenvector

$$[0.61170 \qquad 0.76030 \qquad -0.21855]$$

This, written as a column vector, is e_1. Repeating the same process for the second and third eigenvectors we obtain

$$e_2 = \begin{bmatrix} -0.08659 \\ 0.33896 \\ 0.93681 \end{bmatrix} \qquad e_3 = \begin{bmatrix} 0.78634 \\ -0.55412 \\ 0.27318 \end{bmatrix}$$

The three vectors can be placed into the eigenvector matrix **E**, which is easily seen to be orthogonal.

9. CONDITIONAL INVERSES

9.1. Any matrix **A** (singular or non-singular, rectangular or square) has some conditional or generalized inverse $A^{(-1)}$ defined by the relation

$$AA^{(-1)}A = A.$$

9.2. If (and only if) **A** is square and non-singular, $A^{(-1)}$ is unique and equals A^{-1}. Otherwise there will be infinitely many matrices $A^{(-1)}$ which satisfy the defining relation 9.1.

9.3a. If **A** is rectangular $(n \times m)$ of rank m, with $m < n$, then $A^{(-1)}$ is of order $(m \times n)$ and $A^{(-1)}A = I(m \times m)$. Then $A^{(-1)}$ is called an inverse from the left. $AA^{(-1)} \neq I$ in this case.

9.3b. If **A** is rectangular $(n \times m)$ of rank n, with $m > n$, then $A^{(-1)}$ is of order $(m \times n)$ and $AA^{(-1)} = I(n \times n)$. Then $A^{(-1)}$ is called an inverse to the right. In this case,

$$A^{(-1)}A \neq I.$$

9.3c. For a square, singular matrix, $AA^{(-1)} \neq I$ and $A^{(-1)}A \neq I$.

Example 9.3.1

$$A = \begin{bmatrix} 3 \\ 2 \\ 1 \end{bmatrix}$$

The row vector $[1/3 \quad 0 \quad 0]$ is an inverse from the left. The row vector

$$[x \quad y \quad (1 - 3x - 2y)]$$

is a conditional inverse of the above matrix **A** for any values of x and y. It is called the generalized inverse of **A**.

Example 9.3.2

$$A = \begin{bmatrix} 1 & 2 & 3 \\ 2 & 5 & 6 \\ 3 & 7 & 9 \end{bmatrix}$$

A conditional inverse is

$$A^{(-1)} = \begin{bmatrix} 5 & -2 & 0 \\ -2 & 1 & 0 \\ 0 & 0 & 0 \end{bmatrix}$$

Here it was obtained by inversion of the basis (the 2×2 matrix in the upper left-hand corner) and replacement of the other elements by zeros.

9.4. A square matrix A is called idempotent if $AA = A^2 = A$.

9.5. $AA^{(-1)}$ and $A^{(-1)}A$ are idempotent.

9.6. All characteristic roots of idempotent matrices are either zero or one.

9.7. A system of linear equations (m equations in n unknowns)

$$Ax = b$$

is called consistent if there exists some solution x which satisfies the equation system.

Example 9.7.1

The system

$$x + y = 2$$
$$2x + 2y = 4 \qquad \text{is consistent.}$$

Example 9.7.2

The system

$$x + y = 2$$
$$2x + 2y = 5 \qquad \text{is inconsistent,}$$

for no pair of values (x, y) will satisfy this system.

9.8. If, in a system of equations (rectangular or square)

$$Ax = b$$

$AA^{(-1)}b = b$ for some conditional inverse $A^{(-1)}$, then $AA^{(-1)}b = b$ for every conditional inverse of A, and $Ax = b$ is consistent. Conversely, if $AA^{(-1)}b \neq b$ for some conditional inverse $A^{(-1)}$ then $AA^{(-1)}b \neq b$ for every conditional inverse of A, and $Ax = b$ is inconsistent.

9.9. If $Ax = b$ is consistent, then $x = A^{(-1)}b$ is a solution (generally a different one for each $A^{(-1)}$).

9.10. Let y ($p \times 1$) be a set of linear functions of the solutions x ($n \times 1$) of a consistent system of equations $Ax = b$, given by the relation $y = Cx$. Then $y = Cx$ is called unique if the same values of y will result regardless which solution x is used.

Example 9.10.1

$$3x + 4y + 5z = 22$$
$$x + y + z = 6$$

is a consistent system. One solution would be

$$x = 3 \quad y = 2 \quad z = 1$$

Another solution is

$$x = 2 \quad y = 4 \quad z = 0$$

The linear function

$$[7 \quad 9 \quad 11] \begin{bmatrix} x \\ y \\ z \end{bmatrix} = u$$

($7x + 9y + 11z = u$) will have the same value (50) regardless which of the two (or any other) solutions is substituted. Thus u is unique.

9.11. Let $\mathbf{Ax} = \mathbf{b}$ be a consistent system of equations. For $\mathbf{Cx} = \mathbf{y}$ to be a unique linear combination of the solution $\mathbf{x}$, it is necessary and sufficient that $\mathbf{CA}^{(-1)}\mathbf{A} = \mathbf{C}$. If this relation holds for some $\mathbf{A}^{(-1)}$ it will hold for every conditional inverse of $\mathbf{A}$. If it is violated for some $\mathbf{A}^{(-1)}$ it will be violated for every $\mathbf{A}^{(-1)}$, and $\mathbf{y}$ will be non-unique.

9.12. Let $\mathbf{A}$ be of rank r and select r rows and r columns which form a basis of $\mathbf{A}$. Then a conditional inverse of $\mathbf{A}$ can be obtained as follows: Invert the $(r \times r)$ matrix, place the inverse (without transposing) into the r rows corresponding to the column numbers and the r columns corresponding to the row numbers of the basis, and place zero into all remaining elements. Thus, if $\mathbf{A}$ is of order (5×4) and rank 3, and if rows $1, 2, 4$ and columns $2, 3, 4$ are selected as a basis, $\mathbf{A}^{(-1)}$, of order (4×5) will contain the inverse elements of the basis in rows $2, 3, 4$ and columns $1, 2, 4$, and zeros elsewhere. (See example 9.3.2)

9.13. If $\mathbf{A}$ is a square, singular matrix of order $(n \times n)$ and rank r, let $\mathbf{M}$ be a matrix of order $[n \times (n - r)]$ and $\mathbf{K}$ another matrix of order $[(n - r) \times n]$ chosen in such a way that $\mathbf{A} + \mathbf{MK}$ is non-singular. Then $(\mathbf{A} + \mathbf{MK})^{-1}$ is a conditional inverse of $\mathbf{A}$.

Example 9.13.1

$$\mathbf{A} = \begin{bmatrix} 3 & -1 & -1 & -1 \\ -1 & 3 & -1 & -1 \\ -1 & -1 & 3 & -1 \\ -1 & -1 & -1 & 3 \end{bmatrix}$$

is of order (4×4) and rank 3. Take $\mathbf{M} = \mathbf{j}$ (column vector of ones) and $\mathbf{K} = \mathbf{j}'$ (row vector of ones). Then $\mathbf{A} + \mathbf{MK} = \mathbf{A} + \mathbf{jj}' = 4\mathbf{I}$. Hence $(1/4)\,\mathbf{I}$ is a conditional inverse of $\mathbf{A}$.

9.14. The "Doolittle" method (see 6.14) can be employed to obtain a conditional inverse of a symmetric matrix. If, at any stage, the leading element of the p-row is zero, that cycle is disregarded.

Example 9.14.1

Invert, conditionally, the matrix

$$\mathbf{A} = \begin{bmatrix} 4 & 2 & -2 & 4 \\ 2 & 17 & 11 & 6 \\ -2 & 11 & 10 & 1 \\ 4 & 6 & 1 & 30 \end{bmatrix}$$

4	2	-2	4	1			
1	.5	-.5	1	.25			
	17	11	6	0	1		
	16	12	4	-.5	1		
	1	.75	.25	-.03125	.0625		
		10	1	0	0	1	
		0					
			30	0	0	0	1
			25	-.875	-.25	0	1
			1	-.035	-.01	0	.04

$$\begin{bmatrix} .29625 & -.0225 & 0 & -.035 \\ -.0225 & .065 & 0 & -.01 \\ 0 & 0 & 0 & 0 \\ -.035 & -.01 & 0 & .04 \end{bmatrix} = \mathbf{A}^{(-1)}$$

10. MATRIX DIFFERENTIATION

10.1a. If the elements of a matrix $\mathbf{Y}$ ($m \times n$) are functions of a scalar, x, the expression

$$\partial \mathbf{Y}/\partial x$$

denotes a matrix of order ($m \times n$) with elements $\partial y_{ij}/\partial x$.

10.1b. If the elements of a column (row) vector $\mathbf{y}$ ($\mathbf{y}'$) are functions of a scalar, x, the expression

$$\partial \mathbf{y}/\partial x \quad (\partial \mathbf{y}'/\partial x)$$

denotes a column (row) vector with elements $\partial y_i/\partial x$.

10.2a. If y is a scalar function of $m \times n$ variables, x_{ij}, arranged into a matrix $\mathbf{X}$, the expression

$$\partial y/\partial \mathbf{X}$$

denotes a matrix with elements $\partial y/\partial x_{ij}$.

(Note: Partial differentiation is performed with respect to the element in row i and column j of $\mathbf{X}$. If the same x-variable occurs in another place as, e.g., in a symmetric matrix, differentiation with respect to the distinct (repeated) variable is performed in two stages.)

Example 10.2.1

If $y = \mathbf{j}'\mathbf{X}\mathbf{j}$ (sum of all elements of a square matrix), $\partial y/\partial \mathbf{X}$ is a matrix of ones. If $\mathbf{X}$ is symmetric, one can introduce a new notation $x_{ij} = x_{ji} = z_{ij}$. Then

$$\begin{aligned} \partial y/\partial z_{ij} &= (\partial y/\partial x_{ij})(\partial x_{ij}/\partial z_{ij}) \\ &\quad + (\partial y/\partial x_{ji})(\partial x_{ji}/\partial z_{ij}) \\ &= 1 + 1 = 2 \quad (\text{if } i \neq j) \\ &= 1 \quad\quad\quad (\text{if } i = j). \end{aligned}$$

10.2b. If y is a scalar function of n variables, x_i, arranged into a column (row) vector $\mathbf{x}$ ($\mathbf{x}'$), the expression

$$\partial y/\partial \mathbf{x} \quad (\partial y/\partial \mathbf{x}')$$

denotes a column (row) vector with elements $\partial y/\partial x_i$.

10.3. If $\mathbf{y}$ is a column vector with m elements, each a function of n variables, x_i, arranged into a row vector $\mathbf{x}'$, the expression $\partial \mathbf{y}/\partial \mathbf{x}'$ denotes a matrix with m rows and n columns, with elements $\partial y_i/\partial x_j$.

10.4. $\partial \mathbf{Y}/\partial y_{ij} = (\mathbf{EL})_{ij}$ (see definition of $(\mathbf{EL})$ in 3.4).

10.5. $\partial \mathbf{UV}/\partial x = (\partial \mathbf{U}/\partial x)\mathbf{V} + \mathbf{U}(\partial \mathbf{V}/\partial x)$.

10.6. $\partial \mathbf{AY}/\partial x = \mathbf{A}(\partial \mathbf{Y}/\partial x)$ (if elements of $\mathbf{A}$ are not functions of x).

10.7. $\partial \mathbf{Y}'/\partial y_{ij} = (\mathbf{EL})_{ji}$

10.8. $\partial \mathbf{A}'\mathbf{YA}/\partial x = \mathbf{A}'(\partial \mathbf{Y}/\partial x)\mathbf{A}$

10.9. $\partial \mathbf{Y}'\mathbf{AY}/\partial x = (\partial \mathbf{Y}'/\partial x)\mathbf{AY} + \mathbf{Y}'\mathbf{A}(\partial \mathbf{Y}/\partial x)$

10.10. $\partial \mathbf{a}'\mathbf{x}/\partial \mathbf{x} = \mathbf{a}$

10.11. $\partial \mathbf{x}'\mathbf{x}/\partial \mathbf{x} = 2\mathbf{x}$

10.12. $\partial x' A x / \partial x = Ax + A'x$

10.13. (Chain Rule No. 1) $\partial y / \partial x' = (\partial y / \partial z')(\partial z / \partial x')$

10.14. $\partial Ax / \partial x' = A$

10.15. $\partial tr X / \partial X = I$

10.16. $\partial tr A X / \partial X = \partial tr X A / \partial X = A'$

10.17. $\partial tr A X B / \partial X = A'B'$

10.18. $\partial tr X' A X / \partial X = AX + A'X$

10.19. $\partial \log |X| / \partial X = (X')^{-1}$ (log to base e).

10.20. $\partial Y^{-1} / \partial x = -Y^{-1}(\partial Y / \partial x) Y^{-1}$.

10.21. (Chain Rule No. 2)

$$\partial y / \partial x = tr(\partial y / \partial Z)(\partial Z' / \partial x)$$

where y and x are scalars. The scalar y is a function of $m \times n$ variables z_{ij}, and each of the z_{ij} is a function of x.

Example 10.21.1

Obtain $\log |R - FF'| / \partial F$, where R is symmetric.

By Chain Rule No. 2:

$\partial \log |R - FF'| / \partial f_{ij}$

$= tr[\partial \log |R - FF'| / \partial (R - FF')] [\partial (R - FF') / \partial f_{ij}]$ (since R and FF' are symmetric)

$= tr(R - FF')^{-1} [\partial (R - FF') / \partial f_{ij}]$ (by 10.19)

$= tr(R - FF')^{-1} [-(\partial F / \partial f_{ij}) F' - F(\partial F' / \partial f_{ij})]$ (by 10.5)

$= tr(R - FF')^{-1} [-(EL)_{ij} F' - F(EL)_{ji}]$ (by 10.4 and 10.7)

$= -tr(R - FF')^{-1}(EL)_{ij} F' - tr(R - FF')^{-1} F(EL)_{ji}$

$= -tr(EL)_{ij} F'(R - FF')^{-1} - tr(EL)_{ji}(R - FF')^{-1} F$ (by 7.3)

$= -[F'(R - FF')^{-1}]_{ji} - [(R - FF')^{-1} F]_{ij}$,

where $[\ ]_{ij}$ denotes the (i, j) element of the matrix in brackets (by 7.5),

$= -[(R - FF')^{-1} F]_{ij} - [(R - FF')^{-1} F]_{ij}$ (since $R - FF'$ is symmetric)

$= -2[(R - FF')^{-1} F]_{ij}$.

Hence, by definition 10.2a

$$\partial \log |R - FF'| / \partial F = -2(R - FF')^{-1} F.$$

10.22. $|\partial y / \partial x'| = J(y; x)$ is called the Jacobian or Functional Determinant used in variable transformation of multiple integrals. Formally, if y is a column vector with m elements, each a function of m variables x_i arranged into a row vector x',

$$dx_1 dx_2 \ldots dx_m = |\partial y / \partial x'|^{-1} dy_1 dy_2 \ldots dy_m.$$

10.23. For a scalar y (a function of m variables x_i) to attain a stationary value, it is necessary that

$$\partial y / \partial x = 0.$$

10.24. For a stationary value to be a minimum (maximum) it is necessary that

$$\partial (\partial y / \partial x) / \partial x'   (-\partial (\partial y / \partial x) / \partial x')$$

be a positive-definite matrix for the value of x satisfying 10.23.

Example 10.24.1

Find the values of β which minimize $u = x'x$ (the sum of squares of x_i) where $x = y - A\beta$ (with y and A known and fixed).

$$\partial u/\partial \beta' = (\partial u/\partial \mathbf{x}')(\partial \mathbf{x}/\partial \beta') \quad \text{(by Chain Rule No. 1)}$$
$$= -2\mathbf{x}'\mathbf{A} \quad \text{(by 10.11 and 10.14)}$$

Hence

$$\partial u/\partial \beta = -2\mathbf{A}'\mathbf{x}$$
$$= -2\mathbf{A}'(\mathbf{y} - \mathbf{A}\beta).$$

Hence, for a stationary value, by 10.23, it is necessary that

$$\mathbf{A}'\mathbf{A}\hat{\beta} = \mathbf{A}'\mathbf{y}$$

where $\hat{\beta}$ denotes the values which make u stationary. Now,

$$\partial(\partial u/\partial \beta)/\partial \beta' = 2\partial(\mathbf{A}'\mathbf{A}\beta)/\partial \beta' = 2\mathbf{A}'\mathbf{A}.$$

If $\mathbf{A}$ has real elements, and if $\mathbf{A}'\mathbf{A}$ is non-singular, then it is positive-definite (since, given an arbitrary real $\mathbf{x} \neq \mathbf{0}$, $\mathbf{x}'\mathbf{A}'\mathbf{A}\mathbf{x} = \mathbf{z}'\mathbf{z}$, with $\mathbf{z} = \mathbf{A}\mathbf{x}$; thus this is a sum of squares). Hence $\hat{\beta}$ minimizes u.

10.25. (Generalized Newton Iteration)

Let $\mathbf{x}_0'$ be an initial estimate (m elements) of the roots of the m equations

$$\mathbf{f}(\mathbf{x}') = \mathbf{0}$$

where the m elements of the column vector $\mathbf{f}$ are each functions of $x_1, x_2, \ldots x_m$. Then an improved root is

$$\mathbf{x}_1 = \mathbf{x}_0 - \mathbf{Q}_0^{-1}\mathbf{f}(\mathbf{x}_0'),$$

where $\mathbf{Q}_0$ is the matrix of derivatives $\partial \mathbf{f}/\partial \mathbf{x}'$ evaluated at $\mathbf{x} = \mathbf{x}_0$. The usual procedure consists of evaluating $\mathbf{f}(\mathbf{x}_0')$, then solving $\mathbf{Q}_0\mathbf{u} = \mathbf{f}(\mathbf{x}_0')$ for $\mathbf{u}$. Then $\mathbf{x}_1 = \mathbf{x}_0 - \mathbf{u}$.

Example 10.25.1

Solve

$$f_1(x, y) = x^3 - x^2 y + y^2 - 3.526 = 0$$
$$f_2(x, y) = x^3 + y^3 - 14.911 = 0$$

$$\mathbf{Q} = \begin{bmatrix} 3x^2 - 2xy & 2y - x^2 \\ 3x^2 & 3y^2 \end{bmatrix}$$

Take $x_0 = 1$, $y_0 = 2$

$$f_1(x_0, y_0) = -0.526$$
$$f_2(x_0, y_0) = -5.911$$

$$\mathbf{Q}_0 = \begin{bmatrix} -1 & 3 \\ 3 & 12 \end{bmatrix}$$

$$-u + 3v = -0.526$$
$$3u + 12v = -5.911$$

$$\text{yields } u = -0.55, \quad v = -0.36.$$

Then,

$$x_1 = x_0 - u = 1.55$$
$$y_1 = y_0 - v = 2.36$$
$$f_1(x_1, y_1) = 0.0976$$
$$f_2(x_1, y_1) = 1.9572$$

$$\mathbf{Q}_1 = \begin{bmatrix} -0.1085 & 2.3175 \\ 7.2075 & 16.7088 \end{bmatrix}$$

$$-0.1085u + 2.3175v = 0.0976$$
$$7.2075u + 16.7088v = 1.9572$$

yields $u = 0.157$, $v = 0.049$.

Then

$$x_2 = x_1 - u = 1.393$$
$$y_2 = y_1 - v = 2.311$$
$$f_1(x_2, y_2) = 0.03337$$
$$f_2(x_2, y_2) = 0.13443$$

$$\mathbf{Q}_2 = \begin{bmatrix} -0.61710 & 2.68155 \\ 5.82135 & 16.02216 \end{bmatrix}$$

$$-0.61710u + 2.68155v = 0.03337$$
$$5.82135u + 16.02216v = 0.13443$$

yields $u = -0.0068$, $v = 0.0109$.

Then,

$$x_3 = x_2 - u = 1.3998$$
$$y_3 = y_2 - v = 2.3001$$

(The exact roots are $x = 1.4$ and $y = 2.3$).

11. STATISTICAL MATRIX FORMS

11.1. Let E denote the expectation operator, and let $\mathbf{y}$ be a set of p random variables. Then

$$E(\mathbf{y}) = \mu$$

states that $E(y_i) = \mu_i$ $(i = 1, 2, \ldots p)$.

11.2. Let var denote variance. Then

$$\text{var}(\mathbf{y}) = \Sigma$$

denotes a $p \times p$ symmetric matrix whose elements are $\text{cov}(y_i, y_j)$, and whose diagonal elements are $\text{var}(y_i)$, where cov denotes covariance.

11.3. $E(\mathbf{AY} + \mathbf{b}) = \mathbf{A}E(\mathbf{y}) + \mathbf{b} = \mathbf{A}\mu + \mathbf{b}$

11.4. $\text{var}(\mathbf{Ay} + \mathbf{b}) = \mathbf{A}\,\text{var}(\mathbf{y})\,\mathbf{A}' = \mathbf{A}\Sigma\mathbf{A}'$

11.5. $\text{cov}(\mathbf{y}, \mathbf{z}')$ denotes a matrix with elements $\text{cov}(y_i, z_j)$.
    $\text{cov}(\mathbf{z}, \mathbf{y}') = [\text{cov}(\mathbf{y}, \mathbf{z}')]'$.

11.6. $\text{cov}(\mathbf{Ay} + \mathbf{b}, \mathbf{z}'\mathbf{C} + \mathbf{d}') = \mathbf{A}\,\text{cov}(\mathbf{y}, \mathbf{z}')\,\mathbf{C}$

11.7. $\text{var}(\mathbf{y}) = E(\mathbf{yy}') - E(\mathbf{y})E(\mathbf{y}')$

11.8. $\text{cov}(\mathbf{y}, \mathbf{z}') = E(\mathbf{yz}') - E(\mathbf{y})E(\mathbf{z}')$

11.9. (Expected "sum of squares")

$$E(\mathbf{y}'\mathbf{Qy}) = tr[\mathbf{Q}\,\text{var}(\mathbf{y})] + E(\mathbf{y}')\mathbf{Q}E(\mathbf{y}).$$

11.10. If a matrix $\mathbf{Q}$ is symmetric and positive-definite, one can find a lower triangular matrix $\mathbf{T}$ (with positive diagonal terms, for uniqueness) such that $\mathbf{TT}' = \mathbf{Q}$. The matrices $\mathbf{T}$ and $\mathbf{T}^{-1}$ can be obtained from the Doolittle pattern (6.14) (Gauss elimination or square-root method) as follows: In each cycle, divide the p-row (left and right hand side) by $\sqrt{p_{ii}}$ (instead of p_{ii} for the u-row). Thus obtain rows designated as t-rows. The left-hand side (Arabic subscripts) is $\mathbf{T}'$, and the right-hand side (Roman subscripts) is $\mathbf{T}^{-1}$

11.11. If a coordinate system $\mathbf{x}$ is oblique, and if the cosines between reference vectors (scalar products of basis vectors of unit length) are stated in a symmetric matrix $\mathbf{Q}$, then $\mathbf{T}^{-1}\mathbf{x} = \mathbf{y}$ is an orthogonal system, where $\mathbf{T}$ is obtained from $\mathbf{Q}$ by 11.10.

11.12. The likelihood function of a sample of size n from a multivariate normal distribution (p responses), with common variance-covariance matrix $\Sigma(p \times p)$, and with means or main effects replaced by maximum-likelihood or least-squares estimates, can be written as

$$\log L = -\frac{np}{2} \log 2\pi - \frac{n}{2} \log |\Sigma| - \frac{n}{2} tr \Sigma^{-1}\mathbf{S}$$

where $\Sigma(p \times p)$ is the common variance-covariance matrix, and $\mathbf{S}$ is its maximum-likelihood estimate (matrix of sums of squares and products due to error, divided by sample size n).

11.13. If Σ has a structure under a model or null hypothesis, and if elements of Σ are to be estimated, by maximum-likelihood, two cases can be distinguished: (11.14) Σ^{-1} has the same structure (intraclass correlation, mixed model, compound symmetry, factor analysis). (11.15) Σ^{-1} has a different structure (autocorrelation, Simplex structure).

11.14. If the structure of Σ and Σ^{-1} is identical, and if u and v are elements (or functions of elements) of Σ^{-1} then estimates of Σ can be obtained from the relations (usually requiring Newton iteration, see 10.25):

$$\partial \log L/\partial u = \frac{n}{2} tr \mathbf{A}(\Sigma - \mathbf{S})$$

where $\mathbf{A} = \partial\Sigma^{-1}/\partial u$, is frequently an elementary matrix (see 3.4 and, especially, the rules 7.5 and 7.6).

$$\partial^2 \log L/\partial u \partial v = \frac{n}{2} tr(\partial\mathbf{A}/\partial v)(\Sigma - \mathbf{S}) + \frac{n}{2} tr \mathbf{A}\Sigma^{-1}\mathbf{B}\Sigma^{-1}$$

where $\mathbf{B} = \partial\Sigma^{-1}/\partial v$. These rules are useful to obtain Newton iterations and asymptotic variance-covariance matrices of the estimates.

11.15. If the structures of Σ and Σ^{-1} are different, then an estimate of Σ can be obtained from the relations

$$\partial \log L/\partial x = -\frac{n}{2} tr \mathbf{A}(\Sigma^{-1} - \mathbf{Q}),$$

where

$$\mathbf{Q} = \Sigma^{-1}\mathbf{S}\Sigma^{-1}$$

and

$$\mathbf{A} = \partial\Sigma/\partial x \quad \text{(see comments in 11.14).}$$

$$\partial^2 \log L/\partial x \partial y = -\frac{n}{2} tr(\partial\mathbf{A}/\partial y)(\Sigma^{-1} - \mathbf{Q}) + \frac{n}{2} tr \mathbf{A}\Sigma^{-1}\mathbf{B}(\Sigma^{-1} - \mathbf{Q}) - \frac{n}{2} tr \mathbf{A}\mathbf{Q}\mathbf{B}\Sigma^{-1},$$

where

$$\mathbf{B} = \partial\Sigma/\partial y$$

x and y are elements (or functions of elements) of Σ. The comments of 11.14 apply, but the iterative procedure is considerably more complex.

Suggestions for further reading:

A. S. Householder, *The Theory of Matrices in Numerical Analysis*, Blaisdell, 1964.

S. R. Searle, *Matrix Algebra for the Biological Sciences*, Wiley, 1966.

P. H. Schonemann, Matrix differentiation of traces and determinants, *Psychometrika*, 1966.

TOTIENT FUNCTION $\phi(n)$

Introductory facts

$\phi(n)$ is the number of integers not exceeding and relatively prime to n.

σ_k is the sum of the k'th powers of divisors of n.

σ_0 is usually denoted by $d(n)$ and specifies the number of divisors of n.

For example if $n = 10$, then the divisors are 1, 2, 5, 10 and the sum of the first powers is 18, i.e. $\sigma_0 = d(10) = 4$; $\sigma_1 = 18$; $\phi(10) = 4$.

n	$\phi(n)$	σ_0	σ_1	n	$\phi(n)$	σ_0	σ_1	n	$\phi(n)$	σ_0	σ_1	n	$\phi(n)$	σ_0	σ_1
1	1	1	1	41	40	2	42	81	54	5	121	121	110	3	133
2	1	2	3	42	12	8	96	82	40	4	126	122	60	4	186
3	2	2	4	43	42	2	44	83	82	2	84	123	80	4	168
4	2	3	7	44	20	6	84	84	24	12	224	124	60	6	224
5	4	2	6	45	24	6	78	85	64	4	108	125	100	4	156
6	2	4	12	46	22	4	72	86	42	4	132	126	36	12	312
7	6	2	8	47	46	2	48	87	56	4	120	127	126	2	128
8	4	4	15	48	16	10	124	88	40	8	180	128	64	8	255
9	6	3	13	49	42	3	57	89	88	2	90	129	84	4	176
10	4	4	18	50	20	6	93	90	24	12	234	130	48	8	252
11	10	2	12	51	32	4	72	91	72	4	112	131	130	2	132
12	4	6	28	52	24	6	98	92	44	6	168	132	40	12	336
13	12	2	14	53	52	2	54	93	60	4	128	133	108	4	160
14	6	4	24	54	18	8	120	94	46	4	144	134	66	4	204
15	8	4	24	55	40	4	72	95	72	4	120	135	72	8	240
16	8	5	31	56	24	8	120	96	32	12	252	136	64	8	270
17	16	2	18	57	36	4	80	97	96	2	98	137	136	2	138
18	6	6	39	58	28	4	90	98	42	6	171	138	44	8	288
19	18	2	20	59	58	2	60	99	60	6	156	139	138	2	140
20	8	6	42	60	16	12	168	100	40	9	217	140	48	12	336
21	12	4	32	61	60	2	62	101	100	2	102	141	92	4	192
22	10	4	36	62	30	4	96	102	32	8	216	142	70	4	216
23	22	2	24	63	36	6	104	103	102	2	104	143	120	4	168
24	8	8	60	64	32	7	127	104	48	8	210	144	48	15	403
25	20	3	31	65	48	4	84	105	48	8	192	145	112	4	180
26	12	4	42	66	20	8	144	106	52	4	162	146	72	4	222
27	18	4	40	67	66	2	68	107	106	2	108	147	84	6	228
28	12	6	56	68	32	6	126	108	36	12	280	148	72	6	266
29	28	2	30	69	44	4	96	109	108	2	110	149	148	2	150
30	8	8	72	70	24	8	144	110	40	8	216	150	40	12	372
31	30	2	32	71	70	2	72	111	72	4	152	151	150	2	152
32	16	6	63	72	24	12	195	112	48	10	248	152	72	8	300
33	20	4	48	73	72	2	74	113	112	2	114	153	96	6	234
34	16	4	54	74	36	4	114	114	36	8	240	154	60	8	288
35	24	4	48	75	40	6	124	115	88	4	144	155	120	4	192
36	12	9	91	76	36	6	140	116	56	6	210	156	48	12	392
37	36	2	38	77	60	4	96	117	72	6	182	157	156	2	158
38	18	4	60	78	24	8	168	118	58	4	180	158	78	4	240
39	24	4	56	79	78	2	80	119	96	4	144	159	104	4	216
40	16	8	90	80	32	10	186	120	32	16	360	160	64	12	378

TOTIENT FUNCTION $\phi(n)$ (Continued)

n	$\phi(n)$	σ_0	σ_1	n	$\phi(n)$	σ_0	σ_1	n	$\phi(n)$	σ_0	σ_1	n	$\phi(n)$	σ_0	σ_1
161	132	4	192	211	210	2	212	261	168	6	390	311	310	2	312
162	54	10	363	212	104	6	378	262	130	4	396	312	96	16	840
163	162	2	164	213	140	4	288	263	262	2	264	313	312	2	314
164	80	6	294	214	106	4	324	264	80	16	720	314	156	4	474
165	80	8	288	215	168	4	264	265	208	4	324	315	144	12	624
166	82	4	252	216	72	16	600	266	108	8	480	316	156	6	560
167	166	2	168	217	180	4	256	267	176	4	360	317	316	2	318
168	48	16	480	218	108	4	330	268	132	6	476	318	104	8	648
169	156	3	183	219	144	4	296	269	268	2	270	319	280	4	360
170	64	8	324	220	80	12	504	270	72	16	720	320	128	14	762
171	108	6	260	221	192	4	252	271	270	2	272	321	212	4	432
172	84	6	308	222	72	8	456	272	128	10	558	322	132	8	576
173	172	2	174	223	222	2	224	273	144	8	448	323	288	4	360
174	56	8	360	224	96	12	504	274	136	4	414	324	108	15	847
175	120	6	248	225	120	9	403	275	200	6	372	325	240	6	434
176	80	10	372	226	112	4	342	276	88	12	672	326	162	4	492
177	116	4	240	227	226	2	228	277	276	2	278	327	216	4	440
178	88	4	270	228	72	12	560	278	138	4	420	328	160	8	630
179	178	2	180	229	228	2	230	279	180	6	416	329	276	4	384
180	48	18	546	230	88	8	432	280	96	16	720	330	80	16	864
181	180	2	182	231	120	8	384	281	280	2	282	331	330	2	332
182	72	8	336	232	112	8	450	282	92	8	576	332	164	6	588
183	120	4	248	233	232	2	234	283	282	2	284	333	216	6	494
184	88	8	360	234	72	12	546	284	140	6	504	334	166	4	504
185	144	4	228	235	184	4	288	285	144	8	480	335	264	4	408
186	60	8	384	236	116	6	420	286	120	8	504	336	96	20	992
187	160	4	216	237	156	4	320	287	240	4	336	337	336	2	338
188	92	6	336	238	96	8	432	288	96	18	819	338	156	6	549
189	108	8	320	239	238	2	240	289	272	3	307	339	224	4	456
190	72	8	360	240	64	20	744	290	112	8	540	340	128	12	756
191	190	2	192	241	240	2	242	291	192	4	392	341	300	4	384
192	64	14	508	242	110	6	399	292	144	6	518	342	108	12	780
193	192	2	194	243	162	6	364	293	292	2	294	343	294	4	400
194	96	4	294	244	120	6	434	294	84	12	684	344	168	8	660
195	96	8	336	245	168	6	342	295	232	4	360	345	176	8	576
196	84	9	399	246	80	8	504	296	144	8	570	346	172	4	522
197	196	2	198	247	216	4	280	297	180	8	480	347	346	2	348
198	60	12	468	248	120	8	480	298	148	4	450	348	112	12	840
199	198	2	200	249	164	4	336	299	264	4	336	349	348	2	350
200	80	12	465	250	100	8	468	300	80	18	868	350	120	12	744
201	132	4	272	251	250	2	252	301	252	4	352	351	216	8	560
202	100	4	306	252	72	18	728	302	150	4	456	352	160	12	756
203	168	4	240	253	220	4	288	303	200	4	408	353	352	2	354
204	64	12	504	254	126	4	384	304	144	10	620	354	116	8	720
205	160	4	252	255	128	8	432	305	240	4	372	355	280	4	432
206	102	4	312	256	128	9	511	306	96	12	702	356	176	6	630
207	132	6	312	257	256	2	258	307	306	2	308	357	192	8	576
208	96	10	434	258	84	8	528	308	120	12	672	358	178	4	540
209	180	4	240	259	216	4	304	309	204	4	416	359	358	2	360
210	48	16	576	260	96	12	588	310	120	8	576	360	96	24	1170

TOTIENT FUNCTION $\phi(n)$ (Continued)

n	$\phi(n)$	σ_0	σ_1	n	$\phi(n)$	σ_0	σ_1	n	$\phi(n)$	σ_0	σ_1	n	$\phi(n)$	σ_0	σ_1
361	342	3	381	411	272	4	552	461	460	2	462	511	432	4	592
362	180	4	546	412	204	6	728	462	120	16	1152	512	256	10	1023
363	220	6	532	413	348	4	480	463	462	2	464	513	324	8	800
364	144	12	784	414	132	12	936	464	224	10	930	514	256	4	774
365	288	4	444	415	328	4	504	465	240	8	768	515	408	4	624
366	120	8	744	416	192	12	882	466	232	4	702	516	168	12	1232
367	366	2	368	417	276	4	560	467	466	2	468	517	460	4	576
368	176	10	744	418	180	8	720	468	144	18	1274	518	216	8	912
369	240	6	546	419	418	2	420	469	396	4	544	519	344	4	696
370	144	8	684	420	96	24	1344	470	184	8	864	520	192	16	1260
371	312	4	432	421	420	2	422	471	312	4	632	521	520	2	522
372	120	12	896	422	210	4	636	472	232	8	900	522	168	12	1170
373	372	2	374	423	276	6	624	473	420	4	528	523	522	2	524
374	160	8	648	424	208	8	810	474	156	8	960	524	260	6	924
375	200	8	624	425	320	6	558	475	360	6	620	525	240	12	992
376	184	8	720	426	140	8	864	476	192	12	1008	526	262	4	792
377	336	4	420	427	360	4	496	477	312	6	702	527	480	4	576
378	108	16	960	428	212	6	756	478	238	4	720	528	160	20	1488
379	378	2	380	429	240	8	672	479	478	2	480	529	506	3	553
380	144	12	840	430	168	8	792	480	128	24	1512	530	208	8	972
381	252	4	512	431	430	2	432	481	432	4	532	531	348	6	780
382	190	4	576	432	144	20	1240	482	240	4	726	532	216	12	1120
383	382	2	384	433	432	2	434	483	264	8	768	533	480	4	588
384	128	16	1020	434	180	8	768	484	220	9	931	534	176	8	1080
385	240	8	576	435	224	8	720	485	384	4	588	535	424	4	648
386	192	4	582	436	216	6	770	486	162	12	1092	536	264	8	1020
387	252	6	572	437	396	4	480	487	486	2	488	537	356	4	720
388	192	6	686	438	144	8	888	488	240	8	930	538	268	4	810
389	388	2	390	439	438	2	440	489	324	4	656	539	420	6	684
390	96	16	1008	440	160	16	1080	490	168	12	1026	540	144	24	1680
391	352	4	432	441	252	9	741	491	490	2	492	541	540	2	542
392	168	12	855	442	192	8	756	492	160	12	1176	542	270	4	816
393	260	4	528	443	442	2	444	493	448	4	540	543	360	4	728
394	196	4	594	444	144	12	1064	494	216	8	840	544	256	12	1134
395	312	4	480	445	352	4	540	495	240	12	936	545	432	4	660
396	120	18	1092	446	222	4	672	496	240	10	992	546	144	16	1344
397	396	2	398	447	296	4	600	497	420	4	576	547	546	2	548
398	198	4	600	448	192	14	1016	498	164	8	1008	548	272	6	966
399	216	8	640	449	448	2	450	499	498	2	500	549	360	6	806
400	160	15	961	450	120	18	1209	500	200	12	1092	550	200	12	1116
401	400	2	402	451	400	4	504	501	332	4	672	551	504	4	600
402	132	8	816	452	224	6	798	502	250	4	756	552	176	16	1440
403	360	4	448	453	300	4	608	503	502	2	504	553	468	4	640
404	200	6	714	454	226	4	684	504	144	24	1560	554	276	4	834
405	216	10	726	455	288	8	672	505	400	4	612	555	288	8	912
406	168	8	720	456	144	16	1200	506	220	8	864	556	276	6	980
407	360	4	456	457	456	2	458	507	312	6	732	557	556	2	558
408	128	16	1080	458	228	4	690	508	252	6	896	558	180	12	1248
409	408	2	410	459	288	8	720	509	508	2	510	559	504	4	616
410	160	8	756	460	176	12	1008	510	128	16	1296	560	192	20	1488

TOTIENT FUNCTION $\phi(n)$ (Continued)

n	$\phi(n)$	σ_0	σ_1	n	$\phi(n)$	σ_0	σ_1	n	$\phi(n)$	σ_0	σ_1	n	$\phi(n)$	σ_0	σ_1
561	320	8	864	611	552	4	672	661	660	2	662	711	468	6	1040
562	280	4	846	612	192	18	1638	662	330	4	996	712	352	8	1350
563	562	2	564	613	612	2	614	663	384	8	1008	713	660	4	768
564	184	12	1344	614	306	4	924	664	328	8	1260	714	192	16	1728
565	448	4	684	615	320	8	1008	665	432	8	960	715	480	8	1008
566	282	4	852	616	240	16	1440	666	216	12	1482	716	356	6	1260
567	324	10	968	617	616	2	618	667	616	4	720	717	476	4	960
568	280	8	1080	618	204	8	1248	668	332	6	1176	718	358	4	1080
569	568	2	570	619	618	2	620	669	444	4	896	719	718	2	720
570	144	16	1440	620	240	12	1344	670	264	8	1224	720	192	30	2418
571	570	2	572	621	396	8	960	671	600	4	744	721	612	4	832
572	240	12	1176	622	310	4	936	672	192	24	2016	722	342	6	1143
573	380	4	768	623	528	4	720	673	672	2	674	723	480	4	968
574	240	8	1008	624	192	20	1736	674	336	4	1014	724	360	6	1274
575	440	6	744	625	500	5	781	675	360	12	1240	725	560	6	930
576	192	21	1651	626	312	4	942	676	312	9	1281	726	220	12	1596
577	576	2	578	627	360	8	960	677	676	2	678	727	726	2	728
578	272	6	921	628	312	6	1106	678	224	8	1368	728	288	16	1680
579	384	4	776	629	576	4	684	679	576	4	784	729	486	7	1093
580	224	12	1260	630	144	24	1872	680	256	16	1620	730	288	8	1332
581	492	4	672	631	630	2	632	681	452	4	912	731	672	4	792
582	192	8	1176	632	312	8	1200	682	300	8	1152	732	240	12	1736
583	520	4	648	633	420	4	848	683	682	2	684	733	732	2	734
584	288	8	1110	634	316	4	954	684	216	18	1820	734	366	4	1104
585	288	12	1092	635	504	4	768	685	544	4	828	735	336	12	1368
586	292	4	882	636	208	12	1512	686	294	8	1200	736	352	12	1512
587	586	2	588	637	504	6	798	687	456	4	920	737	660	4	816
588	168	18	1596	638	280	8	1080	688	336	10	1364	738	240	12	1638
589	540	4	640	639	420	6	936	689	624	4	756	739	738	2	740
590	232	8	1080	640	256	16	1530	690	176	16	1728	740	288	12	1596
591	392	4	792	641	640	2	642	691	690	2	692	741	432	8	1120
592	288	10	1178	642	212	8	1296	692	344	6	1218	742	312	8	1296
593	592	2	594	643	642	2	644	693	360	12	1248	743	742	2	744
594	180	16	1440	644	264	12	1344	694	346	4	1044	744	240	16	1920
595	384	8	864	645	336	8	1056	695	552	4	840	745	592	4	900
596	296	6	1050	646	288	8	1080	696	224	16	1800	746	372	4	1122
597	396	4	800	647	646	2	648	697	640	4	756	747	492	6	1092
598	264	8	1008	648	216	20	1815	698	348	4	1050	748	320	12	1512
599	598	2	600	649	580	4	720	699	464	4	936	749	636	4	864
600	160	24	1860	650	240	12	1302	700	240	18	1736	750	200	16	1872
601	600	2	602	651	360	8	1024	701	700	2	702	751	750	2	752
602	252	8	1056	652	324	6	1148	702	216	16	1680	752	368	10	1488
603	396	6	884	653	652	2	654	703	648	4	760	753	500	4	1008
604	300	6	1064	654	216	8	1320	704	320	14	1524	754	336	8	1260
605	440	6	798	655	520	4	792	705	368	8	1152	755	600	4	912
606	200	8	1224	656	320	10	1302	706	352	4	1062	756	216	24	2240
607	606	2	608	657	432	6	962	707	600	4	816	757	756	2	758
608	288	12	1260	658	276	8	1152	708	232	12	1680	758	378	4	1140
609	336	8	960	659	658	2	660	709	708	2	710	759	440	8	1152
610	240	8	1116	660	160	24	2016	710	280	8	1296	760	288	16	1800

TOTIENT FUNCTION $\phi(n)$ (Continued)

n	$\phi(n)$	σ_0	σ_1	n	$\phi(n)$	σ_0	σ_1	n	$\phi(n)$	σ_0	σ_1	n	$\phi(n)$	σ_0	σ_1
761	760	2	762	811	810	2	812	861	480	8	1344	911	910	2	912
762	252	8	1536	812	336	12	1680	862	430	4	1296	912	288	20	2480
763	648	4	880	813	540	4	1088	863	862	2	864	913	820	4	1008
764	380	6	1344	814	360	8	1368	864	288	24	2520	914	456	4	1374
765	384	12	1404	815	648	4	984	865	688	4	1044	915	480	8	1488
766	382	4	1152	816	256	20	2232	866	432	4	1302	916	456	6	1610
767	696	4	840	817	756	4	880	867	544	6	1228	917	780	4	1056
768	256	18	2044	818	408	4	1230	868	360	12	1792	918	288	16	2160
769	768	2	770	819	432	12	1456	869	780	4	960	919	918	2	920
770	240	16	1728	820	320	12	1764	870	224	16	2160	920	352	16	2160
771	512	4	1032	821	820	2	822	871	792	4	952	921	612	4	1232
772	384	6	1358	822	272	8	1656	872	432	8	1650	922	460	4	1386
773	772	2	774	823	822	2	824	873	576	6	1274	923	840	4	1008
774	252	12	1716	824	408	8	1560	874	396	8	1440	924	240	24	2688
775	600	6	992	825	400	12	1488	875	600	8	1248	925	720	6	1178
776	384	8	1470	826	348	8	1440	876	288	12	2072	926	462	4	1392
777	432	8	1216	827	826	2	828	877	876	2	878	927	612	6	1352
778	388	4	1170	828	264	18	2184	878	438	4	1320	928	448	12	1890
779	720	4	840	829	828	2	830	879	584	4	1176	929	928	2	930
780	192	24	2352	830	328	8	1512	880	320	20	2232	930	240	16	2304
781	700	4	864	831	552	4	1112	881	880	2	882	931	756	6	1140
782	352	8	1296	832	384	14	1778	882	252	18	2223	932	464	6	1638
783	504	8	1200	833	672	6	1026	883	882	2	884	933	620	4	1248
784	336	15	1767	834	276	8	1680	884	384	12	1764	924	466	4	1404
785	624	4	948	835	664	4	1008	885	464	8	1440	935	640	8	1296
786	260	8	1584	836	360	12	1680	886	442	4	1332	936	288	24	2730
787	786	2	788	837	540	8	1280	887	886	2	888	937	936	2	938
788	392	6	1386	838	418	4	1260	888	288	16	2280	938	396	8	1632
789	524	4	1056	839	838	2	840	889	756	4	1024	939	624	4	1256
790	312	8	1440	840	192	32	2880	890	352	8	1620	940	368	12	2016
791	672	4	912	841	812	3	871	891	540	10	1452	941	940	2	942
792	240	24	2340	842	420	4	1266	892	444	6	1568	942	312	8	1896
793	720	4	868	843	560	4	1128	893	828	4	960	943	880	4	1008
794	396	4	1194	844	420	6	1484	894	296	8	1800	944	464	10	1860
795	416	8	1296	845	624	6	1098	895	712	4	1080	945	432	16	1920
796	396	6	1400	846	276	12	1872	896	384	16	2040	946	420	8	1584
797	796	2	798	847	660	6	1064	897	528	8	1344	947	946	2	948
798	216	16	1920	848	416	10	1674	898	448	4	1350	948	312	12	2240
799	736	4	864	849	564	4	1136	899	840	4	960	949	864	4	1036
800	320	18	1953	850	320	12	1674	900	240	27	2821	950	360	12	1860
801	528	6	1170	851	792	4	912	901	832	4	972	951	632	4	1272
802	400	4	1206	852	280	12	2016	902	400	8	1512	952	384	16	2160
803	720	4	888	853	852	2	854	903	504	8	1408	953	952	2	954
804	264	12	1904	854	360	8	1488	904	448	8	1710	954	312	12	2106
805	528	8	1152	855	432	12	1560	905	720	4	1092	955	760	4	1152
806	360	8	1344	856	424	8	1620	906	300	8	1824	956	476	6	1680
807	536	4	1080	857	856	2	858	907	906	2	908	957	560	8	1440
808	400	8	1530	858	240	16	2016	908	452	6	1596	958	478	4	1440
809	808	2	810	859	858	2	860	909	600	6	1326	959	816	4	1104
810	216	20	2178	860	336	12	1848	910	288	16	2016	960	256	28	3048

TOTIENT FUNCTION $\phi(n)$ (Continued)

n	$\phi(n)$	σ_0	σ_1	n	$\phi(n)$	σ_0	σ_1	n	$\phi(n)$	σ_0	σ_1	n	$\phi(n)$	σ_0	σ_1
961	930	3	993	971	970	2	972	981	648	6	1430	991	990	2	992
962	432	8	1596	972	324	18	2548	982	490	4	1476	992	480	12	2016
963	636	6	1404	973	828	4	1120	983	982	2	984	993	660	4	1328
964	480	6	1694	974	486	4	1464	984	320	16	2520	994	420	8	1728
965	768	4	1164	975	480	12	1736	985	784	4	1188	995	792	4	1200
966	264	16	2304	976	480	10	1922	986	448	8	1620	996	328	12	2352
967	966	2	968	977	976	2	978	987	552	8	1536	997	996	2	998
968	440	12	1995	978	324	8	1968	988	432	12	1960	998	498	4	1500
969	576	8	1440	979	880	4	1080	989	924	4	1056	999	648	8	1520
970	384	8	1764	980	336	18	2394	990	240	24	2808	1000	400	16	2340

TABLES OF INDICES AND POWER RESIDUES

H. C. Williams, Ph.D.

1. Introduction

Let a and b be any two positive integers. If the largest integer that divides both a and b is unity, a and b are said to be *relatively prime*. If m is any positive integer, the *totient of m*, denoted by $\phi(m)$, is defined to be the number of positive integers less than m and relatively prime to m. If one writes

$$m = p_1^{\alpha_1} p_2^{\alpha_2} \ldots p_n^{\alpha_n},$$

where $p_1, p_2, \ldots, p_n$ are distinct primes, it can be shown that
$$\phi(m) = p_1^{\alpha_1-1} p_2^{\alpha_2-1} \ldots p_n^{\alpha_n-1}(p_1-1)(p_2-1) \ldots (p_n-1).$$

Two integers a and b are said to be *congruent modulo* an integer m if m is an integer divisor of $a-b$. This relation between a and b is denoted by

$$a \equiv b \pmod{m}.$$

If a is congruent to b modulo m and $0 \le b < m$, b is called the residue of a modulo m. a and b are said to be distinct modulo m if m is not an integer divisor of $a-b$. A well-known result is the

Theorem. If a and m ($\geqslant 0$) are relatively prime integers, then

$$a^{\phi(m)} \equiv 1 \pmod{m}.$$

Corollary. If p is a prime which is not a divisor of an integer a, then

$$a^{p-1} \equiv 1 \pmod{p}.$$

If a and m (>0) are relatively prime integers, and μ is the least positive integer for which

$$a^\mu \equiv 1 \pmod{m},$$

μ is called the *exponent* to which a belongs modulo m. If the exponent to which a belongs modulo m is $\phi(m)$, a is defined to be a *primitive root* modulo m (or a primitive root of m).
Theorem. The only integers which possess primitive roots are 2, 4, p^n, $2p^n$, where p is an odd prime.

If m does have a primitive root, it has $\phi(\phi(m))$ distinct primitive roots modulo m.

Let p be any prime, and let g be any primitive root of p. To each integer a relatively prime to p there corresponds a unique integer i such that

$$a \equiv g^i \pmod{p} \qquad (0 < i < p-1).$$

i is called the *index* to base g of a modulo p. This is written

$$i = \text{ind}_g a.$$

For example, consider the prime 11 which has a primitive root $g = 2$. Construct the table below, where

$$r_i \equiv g^i \pmod{p} \qquad (0 < r_i < p).$$

i	0	1	2	3	4	5	6	7	8	9	10
r_i	1	2	4	8	5	10	9	7	3	6	1

Note that the bottom row runs through all possible residues modulo 11, except zero. The index, then, of any number in this row is the corresponding entry in the top row. That is, $\text{ind}_2 1 = 0$, $\text{ind}_2 2 = 1$, $\text{ind}_2 3 = 8$, $\text{ind}_2 4 = 2$, $\text{ind}_2 5 = 4$, $\text{ind}_2 6 = 9$, etc. Indices possess the following important properties (analogous to those of logarithms).

TABLES OF INDICES AND POWER RESIDUES (Continued)

(1) $\text{ind}_g 1 = 0$

(2) $\text{ind}_g(-1) = (p-1)/2$

(3) $\text{ind}_g(ab) \equiv \text{ind}_g a + \text{ind}_g b \pmod{p-1}$

(4) $\text{ind}_g a^n \equiv n \, \text{ind}_g a \pmod{p-1}$

(5) $\text{ind}_g a \equiv \text{ind}_g g' \cdot \text{ind}_{g'} a \pmod{p-1}$,

where g' is any other primitive root of p.

The *power residue* of an integer b to base g is simply the integer r such that

$$r \equiv g^b \pmod{p} \qquad (0 < r < p).$$

Since the power residue of $\text{ind}_g a$ is congruent to a modulo p, it is clear that the concept of indices and power residues is analogous to that of logarithms and antilogarithms.

2. Use of the tables

In the tables that follow, the indices and power residues are given for all primes less than 100. (A table of indices and power residues for all primes and prime powers less than 2000 is given in [1].) In the tables which follow, the base g for the indices and power residues is chosen as the smallest primitive root of p.

To determine the index or power residue of an integer a modulo p, look at the appropriate table for prime p and select the entry in the column under j and in the row under i, where

$$a \equiv 10i + j \pmod{p} \qquad (0 \le i, j \le 9).$$

For example, the index modulo 97 of 134 ($\equiv 37 \pmod{97}$) is the entry under the number 7 and across from the number 3. This is found to be 91.

Indices and power residues can be used to simplify number-theoretic calculations. The following two examples illustrate the use of indices and power residues.

Example. Find an integer congruent to

$$(134)^{92} (54)^{67} \quad \text{modulo (97)}.$$

Let

$$a \equiv (134)^{92} (54)^{67} \pmod{97};$$

then

$$\text{ind}_g a \equiv 92 \, \text{ind}_g 37 + 67 \, \text{ind}_g 54 \pmod{96}$$

$$\equiv 92 \, (91) + 67 \, (52) \pmod{96}$$

$$\equiv 48 \pmod{96}.$$

Hence

$$a \equiv g^{48} \equiv 96 \pmod{97}.$$

This is obtained by looking in the body of the table of indices under $p = 97$ and locating the index 48, and then reading the appropriate quadratic residue from the first column and top row.

Example. Find an integer x such that

$$44x^{21} \equiv 53 \pmod{73}.$$

If we take indices of both sides, we get

$$\text{ind}_g 44 + 21 \, \text{ind}_g x \equiv \text{ind}_g 53 \pmod{72}$$

$$71 + 21 \, \text{ind}_g x \equiv 53 \pmod{72}$$

$$21 \, \text{ind}_g x \equiv 54 \pmod{72}$$

$$7 \, \text{ind}_g x \equiv 18 \pmod{24}$$

TABLES OF INDICES AND POWER RESIDUES (Continued)

Multiplying by 7, we get

$$\text{ind}_g x \equiv 7(18) \equiv 6 \quad (\text{mod } 24).$$

Hence

$$x \equiv g^6, g^{30}, g^{54} \quad (\text{mod } 73)$$

and

$$x \equiv 3, 24, 46 \quad (\text{mod } 73).$$

Reference

1. *A Table of Indices and Power Residues*, University of Oklahoma Mathematical Tables Project, W. W. Norton and Co., New York, N.Y., 1962.

INDICES FOR PRIMES 3 to 97

Prime 3
g = 2

Indices

	0	1	2	3	4	5	6	7	8	9
0		0	1							

Prime 5
g = 2

Indices

	0	1	2	3	4	5	6	7	8	9
0		0	1	3	2					

Prime 7
g = 3

Indices

	0	1	2	3	4	5	6	7	8	9
0		0	2	1	4	5	3			

Prime 11
g = 2

Indices

	0	1	2	3	4	5	6	7	8	9
0		0	1	8	2	4	9	7	3	6
1	5									

Prime 13
g = 2

Indices

	0	1	2	3	4	5	6	7	8	9
0		0	1	4	2	9	5	11	3	8
1	10	7	6							

Prime 17
g = 3

Indices

	0	1	2	3	4	5	6	7	8	9
0		0	14	1	12	5	15	11	10	2
1	3	7	13	4	9	6	8			

Prime 19
g = 2

Indices

	0	1	2	3	4	5	6	7	8	9
0		0	1	13	2	16	14	6	3	8
1	17	12	15	5	7	11	4	10	9	

Prime 23
g = 5

Indices

	0	1	2	3	4	5	6	7	8	9
0		0	2	16	4	1	18	19	6	10
1	3	9	20	14	21	17	8	7	12	15
2	5	13	11							

Prime 29
g = 2

Indices

	0	1	2	3	4	5	6	7	8	9
0		0	1	5	2	22	6	12	3	10
1	23	25	7	18	13	27	4	21	11	9
2	24	17	26	20	8	16	19	15	14	

Prime 31
g = 3

Indices

	0	1	2	3	4	5	6	7	8	9
0		0	24	1	18	20	25	28	12	2
1	14	23	19	11	22	21	6	7	26	4
2	8	29	17	27	13	10	5	3	16	9
3	14									

Prime 37
g = 2

Indices

	0	1	2	3	4	5	6	7	8	9
0		0	1	26	2	23	27	32	3	16
1	24	30	28	11	33	13	4	7	17	35
2	25	22	31	15	29	10	12	6	34	21
3	14	9	5	20	8	19	18			

Prime 41
g = 6

Indices

	0	1	2	3	4	5	6	7	8	9
0		0	26	15	12	22	1	39	38	30
1	8	3	27	31	25	37	24	33	16	9
2	34	14	29	36	13	4	17	5	11	7
3	23	28	10	18	19	21	2	32	35	6
4	20									

Prime 43
g = 3

Indices

	0	1	2	3	4	5	6	7	8	9
0		0	27	1	12	25	28	35	39	2
1	10	30	13	32	20	26	24	38	29	19
2	37	36	15	16	40	8	17	3	5	41
3	11	34	9	31	23	18	14	7	4	33
4	22	6	21							

Prime 47
g = 5

Indices

	0	1	2	3	4	5	6	7	8	9
0		0	18	20	36	1	38	32	8	40
1	19	7	10	11	4	21	26	16	12	45
2	37	6	25	5	28	2	29	14	22	35
3	39	3	44	27	34	33	30	42	17	31
4	9	15	24	13	43	41	23			

Prime 53
g = 2

Indices

	0	1	2	3	4	5	6	7	8	9
0		0	1	17	2	47	18	14	3	34
1	48	6	19	24	15	12	4	10	35	37
2	49	31	7	39	20	42	25	51	16	46
3	13	33	5	23	11	9	36	30	38	41
4	50	45	32	22	8	29	40	44	21	28
5	43	27	26							

Prime 59
g = 2

Indices

	0	1	2	3	4	5	6	7	8	9
0		0	1	50	2	6	51	18	3	42
1	7	25	52	45	19	56	4	40	43	38
2	8	10	26	15	53	12	46	34	20	28
3	57	49	5	17	41	24	44	55	39	37
4	9	14	11	33	27	48	16	23	54	36
5	13	32	47	22	35	31	21	30	29	

Prime 61
g = 2

Indices

	0	1	2	3	4	5	6	7	8	9
0		0	1	6	2	22	7	49	3	12
1	23	15	8	40	50	28	4	47	13	26
2	24	55	16	57	9	44	41	18	51	35
3	29	59	5	21	48	11	14	39	27	46
4	25	54	56	43	17	34	58	20	10	38
5	45	53	42	33	19	37	52	32	36	31
6	30									

INDICES FOR PRIMES 3 to 97 (Continued)

Prime 67
$g = 2$

Indices

	0	1	2	3	4	5	6	7	8	9
0		0	1	39	2	15	40	23	3	12
1	16	59	41	19	24	54	4	64	13	10
2	17	62	60	28	42	30	20	51	25	44
3	55	47	5	32	65	38	14	22	11	58
4	18	53	63	9	61	27	29	50	43	46
5	31	37	21	57	52	8	26	49	45	36
6	56	7	48	35	6	34	33			

Prime 71
$g = 7$

Indices

	0	1	2	3	4	5	6	7	8	9
0		0	6	26	12	28	32	1	18	52
1	34	31	38	39	7	54	24	49	58	16
2	40	27	37	15	44	56	45	8	13	68
3	60	11	30	57	55	29	64	20	22	65
4	46	25	33	48	43	10	21	9	50	2
5	62	5	51	23	14	59	19	42	4	3
6	66	69	17	53	36	67	63	47	61	41
7	35									

Prime 73
$g = 5$

Indices

	0	1	2	3	4	5	6	7	8	9
0		0	8	6	16	1	14	33	24	12
1	9	55	22	59	41	7	32	21	20	62
2	17	39	63	46	30	2	67	18	49	35
3	15	11	40	61	29	34	28	64	70	65
4	25	4	47	51	71	13	54	31	38	66
5	10	27	3	53	26	56	57	68	43	5
6	23	58	19	45	48	60	69	50	37	52
7	42	44	36							

Prime 79
$g = 3$

Indices

	0	1	2	3	4	5	6	7	8	9
0		0	4	1	8	62	5	43	12	2
1	66	68	9	34	57	63	16	21	6	32
2	70	54	72	26	13	46	38	3	61	11
3	67	56	20	69	25	37	10	19	36	35
4	74	75	58	49	76	64	30	59	17	28
5	50	22	42	77	7	52	65	33	15	31
6	71	45	60	55	24	18	73	48	29	27
7	41	51	14	44	23	47	40	43	39	

Prime 83
$g = 2$

Indices

	0	1	2	3	4	5	6	7
0		0	1	72	2	27	73	8
1	28	24	74	77	9	17	4	56
2	29	80	25	60	75	54	78	52
3	18	38	5	14	57	35	64	20
4	30	40	81	71	26	7	61	23
5	55	46	79	59	53	51	11	37
6	19	66	39	70	6	22	15	45
7	36	33	65	69	21	44	49	32
8	31	42	41					

Prime 89
$g = 3$

Indices

	0	1	2	3	4	5	6	7
0		0	16	1	32	70	17	81
1	86	84	33	23	9	71	64	6
2	14	82	12	57	49	52	39	3
3	87	31	80	85	22	63	34	11
4	30	21	10	29	28	72	73	54
5	68	7	55	78	19	66	41	36
6	15	69	47	83	8	5	13	56
7	79	62	50	20	27	53	67	77
8	46	4	37	61	26	76	45	60

Prime 97
$g = 5$

Indices

	0	1	2	3	4	5	6	7
0		0	34	70	68	1	8	31
1	35	86	42	25	65	71	40	89
2	69	5	24	77	76	2	59	18
3	9	46	74	60	27	32	16	91
4	7	85	39	4	58	45	15	84
5	36	63	93	10	52	87	37	55
6	43	64	80	75	12	26	94	57
7	66	11	50	28	29	72	53	21
8	41	88	23	17	73	90	38	83

PRIMITIVE ROOTS FOR PRIMES 3 to 5003

In this table

 g denotes the least primitive root of p

 G denotes the least negative primitive root of p

 ϵ denotes whether 10, -10 both or neither are primitive roots of p

Introductory Facts

As noted in the preceding Totient and Indices Tables, the number of integers not exceeding and relatively prime to a fixed integer n is represented by $\phi(n)$. These integers form a group; the group is cyclic if and only if $n = 2, 4$, or n is of the form p^k or $2p^k$ where p is an odd prime. We refer to g as a primitive root of n if it generates that group i.e. if $g, g^2, \ldots,$ $g^{\phi(n)}$ are distinct modulo n. There are $\phi(\phi(n))$ primitive roots of n. If g is a primitive root of p and $g^{p-1} \not\equiv 1 \pmod{p^2}$, then g is a primitive root of p^k for all k. If $g^{p-1} \equiv 1 \pmod{p^2}$ then $g + p$ is a primitive root of p^k for all k.

If g is a primitive root of p^k then either g or $g + p^k$, whichever is odd, is a primitive root of $2p^k$.

If g is a primitive root of n, then g^k is a primitive root of n if and only if k and $\phi(n)$ are relatively prime, and each primitive root of n is of this form, i.e. $(k, \phi(n)) = 1$.

p	$p-1$	g	$-G$	ϵ	p	$p-1$	g	$-G$	ϵ
3	2	2	1	-10	167	$2\cdot83$	5	2	10
5	2^2	2	2	—	173	$2^2\cdot43$	2	2	—
7	$2\cdot3$	3	2	10	179	$2\cdot89$	2	3	10
11	$2\cdot5$	2	3	—	181	$2^2\cdot3^2\cdot5$	2	2	±10
13	$2^2\cdot3$	2	2	—	191	$2\cdot5\cdot19$	19	2	-10
17	2^4	3	3	±10	193	$2^6\cdot3$	5	5	±10
19	$2\cdot3^2$	2	4	10	197	$2^2\cdot7^2$	2	2	—
23	$2\cdot11$	5	2	10	199	$2\cdot3^2\cdot11$	3	2	-10
29	$2^2\cdot7$	2	2	±10	211	$2\cdot3\cdot5\cdot7$	2	4	—
31	$2\cdot3\cdot5$	3	7	-10	223	$2\cdot3\cdot37$	3	9	10
37	$2^2\cdot3^2$	2	2	—	227	$2\cdot113$	2	3	-10
41	$2^3\cdot5$	6	6	—	229	$2^2\cdot3\cdot19$	6	6	±10
43	$2\cdot3\cdot7$	3	9	-10	233	$2^3\cdot29$	3	3	±10
47	$2\cdot23$	5	2	10	239	$2\cdot7\cdot17$	7	2	—
53	$2^2\cdot13$	2	2	—	241	$2^4\cdot3\cdot5$	7	7	—
59	$2\cdot29$	2	3	10	251	$2\cdot5^3$	6	3	—
61	$2^2\cdot3\cdot5$	2	2	±10	257	2^8	3	3	±10
67	$2\cdot3\cdot11$	2	4	-10	263	$2\cdot131$	5	2	10
71	$2\cdot5\cdot7$	7	2	-10	269	$2^2\cdot67$	2	2	±10
73	$2^3\cdot3^2$	5	5	—	271	$2\cdot3^3\cdot5$	6	2	—
79	$2\cdot3\cdot13$	3	2	—	277	$2^2\cdot3\cdot23$	5	5	—
83	$2\cdot41$	2	3	-10	281	$2^3\cdot5\cdot7$	3	3	—
89	$2^3\cdot11$	3	3	—	283	$2\cdot3\cdot47$	3	6	-10
97	$2^5\cdot3$	5	5	±10	293	$2^2\cdot73$	2	2	—
101	$2^2\cdot5^2$	2	2	—	307	$2\cdot3^2\cdot17$	5	7	-10
103	$2\cdot3\cdot17$	5	2	—	311	$2\cdot5\cdot31$	17	2	-10
107	$2\cdot53$	2	3	-10	313	$2^3\cdot3\cdot13$	10	10	±10
109	$2^2\cdot3^3$	6	6	±10	317	$2^2\cdot79$	2	2	—
113	$2^4\cdot7$	3	3	±10	331	$2\cdot3\cdot5\cdot11$	3	5	—
127	$2\cdot3^2\cdot7$	3	9	—	337	$2^4\cdot3\cdot7$	10	10	±10
131	$2\cdot5\cdot13$	2	3	10	347	$2\cdot173$	2	3	-10
137	$2^3\cdot17$	3	3	—	349	$2^2\cdot3\cdot29$	2	2	—
139	$2\cdot3\cdot23$	2	4	—	353	$2^5\cdot11$	3	3	—
149	$2^2\cdot37$	2	2	±10	359	$2\cdot179$	7	2	-10
151	$2\cdot3\cdot5^2$	6	5	-10	367	$2\cdot3\cdot61$	6	2	10
157	$2^2\cdot3\cdot13$	5	5	—	373	$2^2\cdot3\cdot31$	2	2	—
163	$2\cdot3^4$	2	4	-10	379	$2\cdot3^3\cdot7$	2	4	10

PRIMITIVE ROOTS FOR PRIMES 3 to 5003 (Continued)

p	$p-1$	g	$-G$	ϵ	p	$p-1$	g	$-G$	ϵ
383	$2 \cdot 191$	5	2	10	769	$2^8 \cdot 3$	11	11	—
389	$2^2 \cdot 97$	2	2	± 10	773	$2^2 \cdot 193$	2	2	—
397	$2^2 \cdot 3^2 \cdot 11$	5	5	—	787	$2 \cdot 3 \cdot 131$	2	4	-10
401	$2^4 \cdot 5^2$	3	3	—	797	$2^2 \cdot 199$	2	2	—
409	$2^3 \cdot 3 \cdot 17$	21	21	—	809	$2^3 \cdot 101$	3	3	—
419	$2 \cdot 11 \cdot 19$	2	3	10	811	$2 \cdot 3^4 \cdot 5$	3	5	10
421	$2^2 \cdot 3 \cdot 5 \cdot 7$	2	2	—	821	$2^2 \cdot 5 \cdot 41$	2	2	± 10
431	$2 \cdot 5 \cdot 43$	7	5	-10	823	$2 \cdot 3 \cdot 137$	3	2	10
433	$2^4 \cdot 3^3$	5	5	± 10	827	$2 \cdot 7 \cdot 59$	2	3	-10
439	$2 \cdot 3 \cdot 73$	15	5	-10	829	$2^2 \cdot 3^2 \cdot 23$	2	2	—
443	$2 \cdot 13 \cdot 17$	2	3	-10	839	$2 \cdot 419$	11	2	-10
449	$2^6 \cdot 7$	3	3	—	853	$2^2 \cdot 3 \cdot 71$	2	2	—
457	$2^3 \cdot 3 \cdot 19$	13	13	—	857	$2^3 \cdot 107$	3	3	± 10
461	$2^2 \cdot 5 \cdot 23$	2	2	± 10	859	$2 \cdot 3 \cdot 11 \cdot 13$	2	4	—
463	$2 \cdot 3 \cdot 7 \cdot 11$	3	2	—	863	$2 \cdot 431$	5	2	10
467	$2 \cdot 233$	2	3	-10	877	$2^2 \cdot 3 \cdot 73$	2	2	—
479	$2 \cdot 239$	13	2	-10	881	$2^4 \cdot 5 \cdot 11$	3	3	—
487	$2 \cdot 3^5$	3	2	10	883	$2 \cdot 3^2 \cdot 7^2$	2	4	-10
491	$2 \cdot 5 \cdot 7^2$	2	4	10	887	$2 \cdot 443$	5	2	10
499	$2 \cdot 3 \cdot 83$	7	5	10	907	$2 \cdot 3 \cdot 151$	2	4	—
503	$2 \cdot 251$	5	2	10	911	$2 \cdot 5 \cdot 7 \cdot 13$	17	3	-10
509	$2^2 \cdot 127$	2	2	± 10	919	$2 \cdot 3^3 \cdot 17$	7	5	-10
521	$2^3 \cdot 5 \cdot 13$	3	3	—	929	$2^5 \cdot 29$	3	3	—
523	$2 \cdot 3^2 \cdot 29$	2	4	-10	937	$2^3 \cdot 3^2 \cdot 13$	5	5	± 10
541	$2^2 \cdot 3^3 \cdot 5$	2	2	± 10	941	$2^2 \cdot 5 \cdot 47$	2	2	± 10
547	$2 \cdot 3 \cdot 7 \cdot 13$	2	4	—	947	$2 \cdot 11 \cdot 43$	2	3	-10
557	$2^2 \cdot 139$	2	2	—	953	$2^3 \cdot 7 \cdot 17$	3	3	± 10
563	$2 \cdot 281$	2	3	-10	967	$2 \cdot 3 \cdot 7 \cdot 23$	5	2	—
569	$2^3 \cdot 71$	3	3	—	971	$2 \cdot 5 \cdot 97$	6	3	10
571	$2 \cdot 3 \cdot 5 \cdot 19$	3	5	10	977	$2^4 \cdot 61$	3	3	± 10
577	$2^6 \cdot 3^2$	5	5	± 10	983	$2 \cdot 491$	5	2	10
587	$2 \cdot 293$	2	3	-10	991	$2 \cdot 3^2 \cdot 5 \cdot 11$	6	2	-10
593	$2^4 \cdot 37$	3	3	± 10	997	$2^2 \cdot 3 \cdot 83$	7	7	—
599	$2 \cdot 13 \cdot 23$	7	2	-10	1009	$2^4 \cdot 3^2 \cdot 7$	11	11	—
601	$2^3 \cdot 3 \cdot 5^2$	7	7	—	1013	$2^2 \cdot 11 \cdot 23$	3	3	—
607	$2 \cdot 3 \cdot 101$	3	2	—	1019	$2 \cdot 509$	2	3	10
613	$2^2 \cdot 3^2 \cdot 17$	2	2	—	1021	$2^2 \cdot 3 \cdot 5 \cdot 17$	10	10	± 10
617	$2^3 \cdot 7 \cdot 11$	3	3	—	1031	$2 \cdot 5 \cdot 103$	14	2	—
619	$2 \cdot 3 \cdot 103$	2	4	10	1033	$2^3 \cdot 3 \cdot 43$	5	5	± 10
631	$2 \cdot 3^2 \cdot 5 \cdot 7$	3	9	-10	1039	$2 \cdot 3 \cdot 173$	3	2	-10
641	$2^7 \cdot 5$	3	3	—	1049	$2^3 \cdot 131$	3	3	—
643	$2 \cdot 3 \cdot 107$	11	7	—	1051	$2 \cdot 3 \cdot 5^2 \cdot 7$	7	5	10
647	$2 \cdot 17 \cdot 19$	5	2	10	1061	$2^2 \cdot 5 \cdot 53$	2	2	—
653	$2^2 \cdot 163$	2	2	—	1063	$2 \cdot 3^2 \cdot 59$	3	2	10
659	$2 \cdot 7 \cdot 47$	2	3	10	1069	$2^2 \cdot 3 \cdot 89$	6	6	± 10
661	$2^2 \cdot 3 \cdot 5 \cdot 11$	2	2	—	1087	$2 \cdot 3 \cdot 181$	3	2	10
673	$2^5 \cdot 3 \cdot 7$	5	5	—	1091	$2 \cdot 5 \cdot 109$	2	4	10
677	$2^2 \cdot 13^2$	2	2	—	1093	$2^2 \cdot 3 \cdot 7 \cdot 13$	5	5	—
683	$2 \cdot 11 \cdot 31$	5	10	-10	1097	$2^3 \cdot 137$	3	3	± 10
691	$2 \cdot 3 \cdot 5 \cdot 23$	3	6	—	1103	$2 \cdot 19 \cdot 29$	5	3	10
701	$2^2 \cdot 5^2 \cdot 7$	2	2	± 10	1109	$2^2 \cdot 277$	2	2	± 10
709	$2^2 \cdot 3 \cdot 59$	2	2	± 10	1117	$2^2 \cdot 3^2 \cdot 31$	2	2	—
719	$2 \cdot 359$	11	2	-10	1123	$2 \cdot 3 \cdot 11 \cdot 17$	2	4	-10
727	$2 \cdot 3 \cdot 11^2$	5	7	10	1129	$2^3 \cdot 3 \cdot 47$	11	11	—
733	$2^2 \cdot 3 \cdot 61$	6	6	—	1151	$2 \cdot 5^2 \cdot 23$	17	2	-10
739	$2 \cdot 3^2 \cdot 41$	3	6	—	1153	$2^7 \cdot 3^2$	5	5	± 10
743	$2 \cdot 7 \cdot 53$	5	2	10	1163	$2 \cdot 7 \cdot 83$	5	3	-10
751	$2 \cdot 3 \cdot 5^3$	3	2	—	1171	$2 \cdot 3^2 \cdot 5 \cdot 13$	2	4	10
757	$2^2 \cdot 3^3 \cdot 7$	2	2	—	1181	$2^2 \cdot 5 \cdot 59$	7	7	± 10
761	$2^3 \cdot 5 \cdot 19$	6	6	—	1187	$2 \cdot 593$	2	3	-10

p	$p-1$	g	$-G$	ϵ	p	$p-1$	g	$-G$	ϵ
1193	$2^3 \cdot 149$	3	3	± 10	1619	$2 \cdot 809$	2	3	10
1201	$2^4 \cdot 3 \cdot 5^2$	11	11	—	1621	$2^2 \cdot 3^4 \cdot 5$	2	2	± 10
1213	$2^2 \cdot 3 \cdot 101$	2	2	—	1627	$2 \cdot 3 \cdot 271$	3	6	—
1217	$2^6 \cdot 19$	3	3	± 10	1637	$2^2 \cdot 409$	2	2	—
1223	$2 \cdot 13 \cdot 47$	5	2	10	1657	$2^3 \cdot 3^2 \cdot 23$	11	11	—
1229	$2^2 \cdot 307$	2	2	± 10	1663	$2 \cdot 3 \cdot 277$	3	2	10
1231	$2 \cdot 3 \cdot 5 \cdot 41$	3	2	—	1667	$2 \cdot 7^2 \cdot 17$	2	3	-10
1237	$2^2 \cdot 3 \cdot 103$	2	2	—	1669	$2^2 \cdot 3 \cdot 139$	2	2	—
1249	$2^5 \cdot 3 \cdot 13$	7	7	—	1693	$2^2 \cdot 3^2 \cdot 47$	2	2	—
1259	$2 \cdot 17 \cdot 37$	2	3	10	1697	$2^5 \cdot 53$	3	3	± 10
1277	$2^2 \cdot 11 \cdot 29$	2	2	—	1699	$2 \cdot 3 \cdot 283$	3	6	—
1279	$2 \cdot 3^2 \cdot 71$	3	2	-10	1709	$2^2 \cdot 7 \cdot 61$	3	3	± 10
1283	$2 \cdot 641$	2	3	-10	1721	$2^3 \cdot 5 \cdot 43$	3	3	—
1289	$2^3 \cdot 7 \cdot 23$	6	6	—	1723	$2 \cdot 3 \cdot 7 \cdot 41$	3	6	—
1291	$2 \cdot 3 \cdot 5 \cdot 43$	2	4	10	1733	$2^2 \cdot 433$	2	2	—
1297	$2^4 \cdot 3^4$	10	10	± 10	1741	$2^2 \cdot 3 \cdot 5 \cdot 29$	2	2	± 10
1301	$2^2 \cdot 5^2 \cdot 13$	2	2	± 10	1747	$2 \cdot 3^2 \cdot 97$	2	4	—
1303	$2 \cdot 3 \cdot 7 \cdot 31$	6	2	10	1753	$2^3 \cdot 3 \cdot 73$	7	7	—
1307	$2 \cdot 653$	2	3	-10	1759	$2 \cdot 3 \cdot 293$	6	2	-10
1319	$2 \cdot 659$	13	2	-10	1777	$2^4 \cdot 3 \cdot 37$	5	5	± 10
1321	$2^3 \cdot 3 \cdot 5 \cdot 11$	13	13	—	1783	$2 \cdot 3^4 \cdot 11$	10	2	10
1327	$2 \cdot 3 \cdot 13 \cdot 17$	3	9	10	1787	$2 \cdot 19 \cdot 47$	2	3	-10
1361	$2^4 \cdot 5 \cdot 17$	3	3	—	1789	$2^2 \cdot 3 \cdot 149$	6	6	± 10
1367	$2 \cdot 683$	5	2	10	1801	$2^3 \cdot 3^2 \cdot 5^2$	11	11	—
1373	$2^2 \cdot 7^3$	2	2	—	1811	$2 \cdot 5 \cdot 181$	6	3	10
1381	$2^2 \cdot 3 \cdot 5 \cdot 23$	2	2	± 10	1823	$2 \cdot 911$	5	2	10
1399	$2 \cdot 3 \cdot 233$	13	5	-10	1831	$2 \cdot 3 \cdot 5 \cdot 61$	3	9	—
1409	$2^7 \cdot 11$	3	3	—	1847	$2 \cdot 13 \cdot 71$	5	2	10
1423	$2 \cdot 3^2 \cdot 79$	3	9	—	1861	$2^2 \cdot 3 \cdot 5 \cdot 31$	2	2	± 10
1427	$2 \cdot 23 \cdot 31$	2	3	-10	1867	$2 \cdot 3 \cdot 311$	2	4	-10
1429	$2^2 \cdot 3 \cdot 7 \cdot 17$	6	6	± 10	1871	$2 \cdot 5 \cdot 11 \cdot 17$	14	2	-10
1433	$2^3 \cdot 179$	3	3	± 10	1873	$2^4 \cdot 3^2 \cdot 13$	10	10	± 10
1439	$2 \cdot 719$	7	2	-10	1877	$2^2 \cdot 7 \cdot 67$	2	2	—
1447	$2 \cdot 3 \cdot 241$	3	2	10	1879	$2 \cdot 3 \cdot 313$	6	2	—
1451	$2 \cdot 5^2 \cdot 29$	2	3	—	1889	$2^5 \cdot 59$	3	3	—
1453	$2^2 \cdot 3 \cdot 11^2$	2	2	—	1901	$2^2 \cdot 5^2 \cdot 19$	2	2	—
1459	$2 \cdot 3^6$	3	6	—	1907	$2 \cdot 953$	2	3	-10
1471	$2 \cdot 3 \cdot 5 \cdot 7^2$	6	5	-10	1913	$2^3 \cdot 239$	3	3	± 10
1481	$2^3 \cdot 5 \cdot 37$	3	3	—	1931	$2 \cdot 5 \cdot 193$	2	3	—
1483	$2 \cdot 3 \cdot 13 \cdot 19$	2	4	—	1933	$2^2 \cdot 3 \cdot 7 \cdot 23$	5	5	—
1487	$2 \cdot 743$	5	2	10	1949	$2^2 \cdot 487$	2	2	± 10
1489	$2^4 \cdot 3 \cdot 31$	14	14	—	1951	$2 \cdot 3 \cdot 5^2 \cdot 13$	3	2	—
1493	$2^2 \cdot 373$	2	2	—	1973	$2^2 \cdot 17 \cdot 29$	2	2	—
1499	$2 \cdot 7 \cdot 107$	2	3	—	1979	$2 \cdot 23 \cdot 43$	2	3	10
1511	$2 \cdot 5 \cdot 151$	11	2	-10	1987	$2 \cdot 3 \cdot 331$	2	4	—
1523	$2 \cdot 761$	2	3	-10	1993	$2^3 \cdot 3 \cdot 83$	5	5	—
1531	$2 \cdot 3^2 \cdot 5 \cdot 17$	2	4	10	1997	$2^2 \cdot 499$	2	2	—
1543	$2 \cdot 3 \cdot 257$	5	2	10	1999	$2 \cdot 3^3 \cdot 37$	3	5	-10
1549	$2^2 \cdot 3^2 \cdot 43$	2	2	± 10	2003	$2 \cdot 7 \cdot 11 \cdot 13$	5	3	-10
1553	$2^4 \cdot 97$	3	3	± 10	2011	$2 \cdot 3 \cdot 5 \cdot 67$	3	5	—
1559	$2 \cdot 19 \cdot 41$	19	2	-10	2017	$2^5 \cdot 3^2 \cdot 7$	5	5	± 10
1567	$2 \cdot 3^3 \cdot 29$	3	2	10	2027	$2 \cdot 1013$	2	3	-10
1571	$2 \cdot 5 \cdot 157$	2	3	10	2029	$2^2 \cdot 3 \cdot 13^2$	2	2	± 10
1579	$2 \cdot 3 \cdot 263$	3	5	10	2039	$2 \cdot 1019$	7	2	-10
1583	$2 \cdot 7 \cdot 113$	5	2	10	2053	$2^2 \cdot 3^3 \cdot 19$	2	2	—
1597	$2^2 \cdot 3 \cdot 7 \cdot 19$	11	11	—	2063	$2 \cdot 1031$	5	2	10
1601	$2^6 \cdot 5^2$	3	3	—	2069	$2^3 \cdot 11 \cdot 47$	2	2	± 10
1607	$2 \cdot 11 \cdot 73$	5	2	10	2081	$2^5 \cdot 5 \cdot 13$	3	3	—
1609	$2^3 \cdot 3 \cdot 67$	7	7	—	2083	$2 \cdot 3 \cdot 347$	2	4	-10
1613	$2^2 \cdot 13 \cdot 31$	3	3	—	2087	$2 \cdot 7 \cdot 149$	5	2	—

PRIMITIVE ROOTS FOR PRIMES 3 to 5003 (Continued)

p	$p-1$	g	$-G$	ϵ	p	$p-1$	g	$-G$	ϵ
2089	$2^3 \cdot 3^2 \cdot 29$	7	7	—	2579	$2 \cdot 1289$	2	3	10
2099	$2 \cdot 1049$	2	3	10	2591	$2 \cdot 5 \cdot 7 \cdot 37$	7	2	—
2111	$2 \cdot 5 \cdot 211$	7	2	-10	2593	$2^5 \cdot 3^4$	7	7	± 10
2113	$2^6 \cdot 3 \cdot 11$	5	5	± 10	2609	$2^4 \cdot 163$	3	3	—
2129	$2^4 \cdot 7 \cdot 19$	3	3	—	2617	$2^3 \cdot 3 \cdot 109$	5	5	± 10
2131	$2 \cdot 3 \cdot 5 \cdot 71$	2	4	—	2621	$2^2 \cdot 5 \cdot 131$	2	2	± 10
2137	$2^3 \cdot 3 \cdot 89$	10	10	± 10	2633	$2^3 \cdot 7 \cdot 47$	3	3	± 10
2141	$2^2 \cdot 5 \cdot 107$	2	2	± 10	2647	$2 \cdot 3^3 \cdot 7^2$	3	2	—
2143	$2 \cdot 3^2 \cdot 7 \cdot 17$	3	9	10	2657	$2^5 \cdot 83$	3	3	± 10
2153	$2^3 \cdot 269$	3	3	± 10	2659	$2 \cdot 3 \cdot 443$	2	4	—
2161	$2^4 \cdot 3^3 \cdot 5$	23	23	—	2663	$2 \cdot 11^3$	5	2	10
2179	$2 \cdot 3^2 \cdot 11^2$	7	5	10	2671	$2 \cdot 3 \cdot 5 \cdot 89$	7	5	-10
2203	$2 \cdot 3 \cdot 367$	5	7	-10	2677	$2^2 \cdot 3 \cdot 223$	2	2	—
2207	$2 \cdot 1103$	5	2	10	2683	$2 \cdot 3^2 \cdot 149$	2	4	—
2213	$2^2 \cdot 7 \cdot 79$	2	2	—	2687	$2 \cdot 17 \cdot 79$	5	3	10
2221	$2^2 \cdot 3 \cdot 5 \cdot 37$	2	2	± 10	2689	$2^7 \cdot 3 \cdot 7$	19	19	—
2237	$2^2 \cdot 13 \cdot 43$	2	2	—	2693	$2^2 \cdot 673$	2	2	—
2239	$2 \cdot 3 \cdot 373$	3	2	-10	2699	$2 \cdot 19 \cdot 71$	2	3	10
2243	$2 \cdot 19 \cdot 59$	2	3	-10	2707	$2 \cdot 3 \cdot 11 \cdot 41$	2	4	-10
2251	$2 \cdot 3^2 \cdot 5^3$	7	5	10	2711	$2 \cdot 5 \cdot 271$	7	2	-10
2267	$2 \cdot 11 \cdot 103$	2	3	-10	2713	$2^3 \cdot 3 \cdot 113$	5	5	± 10
2269	$2^2 \cdot 3^4 \cdot 7$	2	2	± 10	2719	$2 \cdot 3^2 \cdot 151$	3	2	-10
2273	$2^5 \cdot 71$	3	3	± 10	2729	$2^3 \cdot 11 \cdot 31$	3	3	—
2281	$2^3 \cdot 3 \cdot 5 \cdot 19$	7	7	—	2731	$2 \cdot 3 \cdot 5 \cdot 7 \cdot 13$	3	5	10
2287	$2 \cdot 3^2 \cdot 127$	19	7	—	2741	$2^2 \cdot 5 \cdot 137$	2	2	± 10
2293	$2^2 \cdot 3 \cdot 191$	2	2	—	2749	$2^2 \cdot 3 \cdot 229$	6	6	—
2297	$2^3 \cdot 7 \cdot 41$	5	5	± 10	2753	$2^6 \cdot 43$	3	3	± 10
2309	$2^2 \cdot 577$	2	2	± 10	2767	$2 \cdot 3 \cdot 461$	3	9	10
2311	$2 \cdot 3 \cdot 5 \cdot 7 \cdot 11$	3	2	—	2777	$2^3 \cdot 347$	3	3	± 10
2333	$2^2 \cdot 11 \cdot 53$	2	2	—	2789	$2^2 \cdot 17 \cdot 41$	2	2	± 10
2339	$2 \cdot 7 \cdot 167$	2	3	10	2791	$2 \cdot 3^2 \cdot 5 \cdot 31$	6	7	—
2341	$2^2 \cdot 3^2 \cdot 5 \cdot 13$	7	7	± 10	2797	$2^2 \cdot 3 \cdot 233$	2	2	—
2347	$2 \cdot 3 \cdot 17 \cdot 23$	3	6	-10	2801	$2^4 \cdot 5^2 \cdot 7$	3	3	—
2351	$2 \cdot 5^2 \cdot 47$	13	3	-10	2803	$2 \cdot 3 \cdot 467$	2	4	-10
2357	$2^2 \cdot 19 \cdot 31$	2	2	—	2819	$2 \cdot 1409$	2	3	10
2371	$2 \cdot 3 \cdot 5 \cdot 79$	2	4	10	2833	$2^4 \cdot 3 \cdot 59$	5	5	± 10
2377	$2^3 \cdot 3^3 \cdot 11$	5	5	—	2837	$2^2 \cdot 709$	2	2	—
2381	$2^2 \cdot 5 \cdot 7 \cdot 17$	3	3	—	2843	$2 \cdot 7^2 \cdot 29$	2	4	-10
2383	$2 \cdot 3 \cdot 397$	5	13	10	2851	$2 \cdot 3 \cdot 5^2 \cdot 19$	2	4	10
2389	$2^2 \cdot 3 \cdot 199$	2	2	± 10	2857	$2^3 \cdot 3 \cdot 7 \cdot 17$	11	11	—
2393	$2^3 \cdot 13 \cdot 23$	3	3	—	2861	$2^2 \cdot 5 \cdot 11 \cdot 13$	2	2	± 10
2399	$2 \cdot 11 \cdot 109$	11	2	-10	2879	$2 \cdot 1439$	7	2	-10
2411	$2 \cdot 5 \cdot 241$	6	3	10	2887	$2 \cdot 3 \cdot 13 \cdot 37$	5	2	10
2417	$2^4 \cdot 151$	3	3	± 10	2897	$2^4 \cdot 181$	3	3	± 10
2423	$2 \cdot 7 \cdot 173$	5	2	10	2903	$2 \cdot 1451$	5	2	10
2437	$2^2 \cdot 3 \cdot 7 \cdot 29$	2	2	—	2909	$2^2 \cdot 727$	2	2	± 10
2441	$2^3 \cdot 5 \cdot 61$	6	6	—	2917	$2^2 \cdot 3^6$	5	5	—
2447	$2 \cdot 1223$	5	2	10	2927	$2 \cdot 7 \cdot 11 \cdot 19$	5	2	10
2459	$2 \cdot 1229$	2	3	10	2939	$2 \cdot 13 \cdot 113$	2	3	10
2467	$2 \cdot 3^2 \cdot 137$	2	4	—	2953	$2^3 \cdot 3^2 \cdot 41$	13	13	—
2473	$2^3 \cdot 3 \cdot 103$	5	5	± 10	2957	$2^2 \cdot 739$	2	2	—
2477	$2^2 \cdot 619$	2	2	—	2963	$2 \cdot 1481$	2	2	-10
2503	$2 \cdot 3^2 \cdot 139$	3	2	—	2969	$2^3 \cdot 7 \cdot 53$	3	3	—
2521	$2^3 \cdot 3^2 \cdot 5 \cdot 7$	17	17	—	2971	$2 \cdot 3^3 \cdot 5 \cdot 11$	10	5	10
2531	$2 \cdot 5 \cdot 11 \cdot 23$	2	3	—	2999	$2 \cdot 1499$	17	2	-10
2539	$2 \cdot 3^3 \cdot 47$	2	4	10	3001	$2^3 \cdot 3 \cdot 5^3$	14	14	—
2543	$2 \cdot 31 \cdot 41$	5	2	10	3011	$2 \cdot 5 \cdot 7 \cdot 43$	2	3	10
2549	$2^2 \cdot 7^2 \cdot 13$	2	2	± 10	3019	$2 \cdot 3 \cdot 503$	2	4	10
2551	$2 \cdot 3 \cdot 5^2 \cdot 17$	6	2	—	3023	$2 \cdot 1511$	5	2	10
2557	$2^2 \cdot 3^2 \cdot 71$	2	2	—	3037	$2^2 \cdot 3 \cdot 11 \cdot 23$	2	2	—

PRIMITIVE ROOTS FOR PRIMES 3 to 5003 (Continued)

p	$p-1$	g	$-G$	ϵ	p	$p-1$	g	$-G$	ϵ
3041	$2^5 \cdot 5 \cdot 19$	3	3	—	3541	$2^2 \cdot 3 \cdot 5 \cdot 59$	7	7	—
3049	$2^3 \cdot 3 \cdot 127$	11	11	—	3547	$2 \cdot 3^2 \cdot 197$	2	4	-10
3061	$2^2 \cdot 3^2 \cdot 5 \cdot 17$	6	6	—	3557	$2^2 \cdot 7 \cdot 127$	2	2	—
3067	$2 \cdot 3 \cdot 7 \cdot 73$	2	4	-10	3559	$2 \cdot 3 \cdot 593$	3	2	-10
3079	$2 \cdot 3^4 \cdot 19$	6	2	-10	3571	$2 \cdot 3 \cdot 5 \cdot 7 \cdot 17$	2	4	10
3083	$2 \cdot 23 \cdot 67$	2	3	-10	3581	$2^2 \cdot 5 \cdot 179$	2	2	± 10
3089	$2^4 \cdot 193$	3	3	—	3583	$2 \cdot 3^2 \cdot 199$	3	2	—
3109	$2^2 \cdot 3 \cdot 7 \cdot 37$	6	6	—	3593	$2^3 \cdot 449$	3	3	± 10
3119	$2 \cdot 1559$	7	2	-10	3607	$2 \cdot 3 \cdot 601$	5	11	10
3121	$2^4 \cdot 3 \cdot 5 \cdot 13$	7	7	—	3613	$2^2 \cdot 3 \cdot 7 \cdot 43$	2	2	—
3137	$2^6 \cdot 7^2$	3	3	± 10	3617	$2^5 \cdot 113$	3	3	± 10
3163	$2 \cdot 3 \cdot 17 \cdot 31$	3	6	-10	3623	$2 \cdot 1811$	5	2	10
3167	$2 \cdot 1583$	5	2	10	3631	$2 \cdot 3 \cdot 5 \cdot 11^2$	15	10	-10
3169	$2^5 \cdot 3^2 \cdot 11$	7	7	—	3637	$2^2 \cdot 3^2 \cdot 101$	2	2	—
3181	$2^2 \cdot 3 \cdot 5 \cdot 53$	7	7	—	3643	$2 \cdot 3 \cdot 607$	2	4	-10
3187	$2 \cdot 3^3 \cdot 59$	2	4	—	3659	$2 \cdot 31 \cdot 59$	2	3	10
3191	$2 \cdot 5 \cdot 11 \cdot 29$	11	5	—	3671	$2 \cdot 5 \cdot 367$	13	2	—
3203	$2 \cdot 1601$	2	3	-10	3673	$2^3 \cdot 3^3 \cdot 17$	5	5	± 10
3209	$2^3 \cdot 401$	3	3	—	3677	$2^2 \cdot 919$	2	2	—
3217	$2^4 \cdot 3 \cdot 67$	5	5	—	3691	$2 \cdot 3^2 \cdot 5 \cdot 41$	2	4	—
3221	$2^2 \cdot 5 \cdot 7 \cdot 23$	10	10	± 10	3697	$2 \cdot 43^2$	5	5	—
3229	$2^2 \cdot 3 \cdot 269$	6	6	—	3701	$2^2 \cdot 5^2 \cdot 37$	2	2	± 10
3251	$2 \cdot 5^3 \cdot 13$	6	3	10	3709	$2^2 \cdot 3^2 \cdot 103$	2	2	± 10
3253	$2^2 \cdot 3 \cdot 271$	2	2	—	3719	$2 \cdot 11 \cdot 13^2$	7	2	-10
3257	$2^3 \cdot 11 \cdot 37$	3	3	± 10	3727	$2 \cdot 3^4 \cdot 23$	3	2	10
3259	$2 \cdot 3^2 \cdot 181$	3	5	10	3733	$2^2 \cdot 3 \cdot 311$	2	2	—
3271	$2 \cdot 3 \cdot 5 \cdot 109$	3	5	-10	3739	$2 \cdot 3 \cdot 7 \cdot 89$	7	5	—
3299	$2 \cdot 17 \cdot 97$	2	3	10	3761	$2^4 \cdot 5 \cdot 47$	3	3	—
3301	$2^2 \cdot 3 \cdot 5^2 \cdot 11$	6	6	± 10	3767	$2 \cdot 7 \cdot 269$	5	2	10
3307	$2 \cdot 3 \cdot 19 \cdot 29$	2	4	-10	3769	$2^3 \cdot 3 \cdot 157$	7	7	—
3313	$2^4 \cdot 3^2 \cdot 23$	10	10	± 10	3779	$2 \cdot 1889$	2	3	10
3319	$2 \cdot 3 \cdot 7 \cdot 79$	6	2	—	3793	$2^4 \cdot 3 \cdot 79$	5	5	—
3323	$2 \cdot 11 \cdot 151$	2	3	-10	3797	$2^2 \cdot 13 \cdot 73$	2	2	—
3329	$2^8 \cdot 13$	3	3	—	3803	$2 \cdot 1901$	2	3	-10
3331	$2 \cdot 3^2 \cdot 5 \cdot 37$	3	5	10	3821	$2^2 \cdot 5 \cdot 191$	3	3	± 10
3343	$2 \cdot 3 \cdot 557$	5	11	10	3823	$2 \cdot 3 \cdot 7^2 \cdot 13$	3	9	—
3347	$2 \cdot 7 \cdot 239$	2	3	-10	3833	$2^3 \cdot 479$	3	3	± 10
3359	$2 \cdot 23 \cdot 73$	11	2	-10	3847	$2 \cdot 3 \cdot 641$	5	2	10
3361	$2^5 \cdot 3 \cdot 5 \cdot 7$	22	22	—	3851	$2 \cdot 5^2 \cdot 7 \cdot 11$	2	4	—
3371	$2 \cdot 5 \cdot 337$	2	3	10	3853	$2^2 \cdot 3^2 \cdot 107$	2	2	—
3373	$2^2 \cdot 3 \cdot 281$	5	5	—	3863	$2 \cdot 1931$	5	2	10
3389	$2^2 \cdot 7 \cdot 11^2$	3	3	± 10	3877	$2^2 \cdot 3 \cdot 17 \cdot 19$	2	2	—
3391	$2 \cdot 3 \cdot 5 \cdot 113$	3	5	-10	3881	$2^3 \cdot 5 \cdot 97$	13	13	—
3407	$2 \cdot 13 \cdot 131$	5	2	10	3889	$2^4 \cdot 3^5$	11	11	—
3413	$2^2 \cdot 853$	2	2	—	3907	$2 \cdot 3^2 \cdot 7 \cdot 31$	2	4	-10
3433	$2^3 \cdot 3 \cdot 11 \cdot 13$	5	5	± 10	3911	$2 \cdot 5 \cdot 17 \cdot 23$	13	2	-10
3449	$2^3 \cdot 431$	3	3	—	3917	$2^2 \cdot 11 \cdot 89$	2	2	—
3457	$2^7 \cdot 3^3$	7	7	—	3919	$2 \cdot 3 \cdot 653$	3	2	—
3461	$2^2 \cdot 5 \cdot 173$	2	2	± 10	3923	$2 \cdot 37 \cdot 53$	2	3	-10
3463	$2 \cdot 3 \cdot 577$	3	9	10	3929	$2^3 \cdot 491$	3	3	—
3467	$2 \cdot 1733$	2	3	-10	3931	$2 \cdot 3 \cdot 5 \cdot 131$	2	4	—
3469	$2^2 \cdot 3 \cdot 17^2$	2	2	± 10	3943	$2 \cdot 3^3 \cdot 73$	3	9	10
3491	$2 \cdot 5 \cdot 349$	2	3	—	3947	$2 \cdot 1973$	2	3	-10
3499	$2 \cdot 3 \cdot 11 \cdot 53$	2	4	—	3967	$2 \cdot 3 \cdot 661$	6	2	10
3511	$2 \cdot 3^3 \cdot 5 \cdot 13$	7	2	-10	3989	$2^2 \cdot 997$	2	2	± 10
3517	$2^2 \cdot 3 \cdot 293$	2	2	—	4001	$2^5 \cdot 5^3$	3	3	—
3527	$2 \cdot 41 \cdot 43$	5	2	10	4003	$2 \cdot 3 \cdot 23 \cdot 29$	2	4	—
3529	$2^3 \cdot 3^2 \cdot 7^2$	17	17	—	4007	$2 \cdot 2003$	5	2	10
3533	$2^2 \cdot 883$	2	2	—	4013	$2^2 \cdot 17 \cdot 59$	2	2	—
3539	$2 \cdot 29 \cdot 61$	2	3	10	4019	$2 \cdot 7^2 \cdot 41$	2	4	10

PRIMITIVE ROOTS FOR PRIMES 3 to 5003 (Continued)

p	$p-1$	g	$-G$	ϵ	p	$p-1$	g	$-G$	ϵ
4021	$2^2 \cdot 3 \cdot 5 \cdot 67$	2	2	—	4519	$2 \cdot 3^2 \cdot 251$	3	9	—
4027	$2 \cdot 3 \cdot 11 \cdot 61$	3	6	-10	4523	$2 \cdot 7 \cdot 17 \cdot 19$	5	3	-10
4049	$2^4 \cdot 11 \cdot 23$	3	3	—	4547	$2 \cdot 2273$	2	3	-10
4051	$2 \cdot 3^4 \cdot 5^2$	10	5	10	4549	$2^2 \cdot 3 \cdot 379$	6	6	—
4057	$2^3 \cdot 3 \cdot 13^2$	5	5	± 10	4561	$2^4 \cdot 3 \cdot 5 \cdot 19$	11	11	—
4073	$2^3 \cdot 509$	3	3	± 10	4567	$2 \cdot 3 \cdot 761$	3	7	10
4079	$2 \cdot 2039$	11	2	-10	4583	$2 \cdot 29 \cdot 79$	5	2	10
4091	$2 \cdot 5 \cdot 409$	2	3	10	4591	$2 \cdot 3^3 \cdot 5 \cdot 17$	11	2	-10
4093	$2^2 \cdot 3 \cdot 11 \cdot 31$	2	2	—	4597	$2^2 \cdot 3 \cdot 383$	5	5	—
4099	$2 \cdot 3 \cdot 683$	2	4	10	4603	$2 \cdot 3 \cdot 13 \cdot 59$	2	4	-10
4111	$2 \cdot 3 \cdot 5 \cdot 137$	12	2	-10	4621	$2^2 \cdot 3 \cdot 5 \cdot 7 \cdot 11$	2	2	—
4127	$2 \cdot 2063$	5	2	10	4637	$2^2 \cdot 19 \cdot 61$	2	2	—
4129	$2^5 \cdot 3 \cdot 43$	13	13	—	4639	$2 \cdot 3 \cdot 773$	3	2	-10
4133	$2^2 \cdot 1033$	2	2	—	4643	$2 \cdot 11 \cdot 211$	5	3	-10
4139	$2 \cdot 2069$	2	3	10	4649	$2^3 \cdot 7 \cdot 83$	3	3	—
4153	$2^3 \cdot 3 \cdot 173$	5	5	± 10	4651	$2 \cdot 3 \cdot 5^2 \cdot 31$	3	5	10
4157	$2^2 \cdot 1039$	2	2	—	4657	$2^4 \cdot 3 \cdot 97$	15	15	—
4159	$2 \cdot 3^3 \cdot 7 \cdot 11$	3	2	—	4663	$2 \cdot 3^2 \cdot 7 \cdot 37$	3	9	—
4177	$2^4 \cdot 3^2 \cdot 29$	5	5	± 10	4673	$2^6 \cdot 73$	3	3	± 10
4201	$2^3 \cdot 3 \cdot 5^2 \cdot 7$	11	11	—	4679	$2 \cdot 2339$	11	2	-10
4211	$2 \cdot 5 \cdot 421$	6	3	10	4691	$2 \cdot 5 \cdot 7 \cdot 67$	2	3	10
4217	$2^3 \cdot 17 \cdot 31$	3	3	± 10	4703	$2 \cdot 2351$	5	2	10
4219	$2 \cdot 3 \cdot 19 \cdot 37$	2	4	10	4721	$2^4 \cdot 5 \cdot 59$	6	6	—
4229	$2^2 \cdot 7 \cdot 151$	2	2	± 10	4723	$2 \cdot 3 \cdot 787$	2	4	-10
4231	$2 \cdot 3^2 \cdot 5 \cdot 47$	3	2	-10	4729	$2^3 \cdot 3 \cdot 197$	17	17	—
4241	$2^4 \cdot 5 \cdot 53$	3	3	—	4733	$2^2 \cdot 7 \cdot 13^2$	5	5	—
4243	$2 \cdot 3 \cdot 7 \cdot 101$	2	4	-10	4751	$2 \cdot 5^3 \cdot 19$	19	3	-10
4253	$2^2 \cdot 1063$	2	2	—	4759	$2 \cdot 3 \cdot 13 \cdot 61$	3	5	-10
4259	$2 \cdot 2129$	2	3	10	4783	$2 \cdot 3 \cdot 797$	6	2	10
4261	$2^2 \cdot 3 \cdot 5 \cdot 71$	2	2	± 10	4787	$2 \cdot 2393$	2	3	-10
4271	$2 \cdot 5 \cdot 7 \cdot 61$	7	3	-10	4789	$2^2 \cdot 3^2 \cdot 7 \cdot 19$	2	2	—
4273	$2^4 \cdot 3 \cdot 89$	5	5	—	4793	$2^3 \cdot 599$	3	3	± 10
4283	$2 \cdot 2141$	2	3	-10	4799	$2 \cdot 2399$	7	2	-10
4289	$2^6 \cdot 67$	3	3	—	4801	$2^6 \cdot 3 \cdot 5^2$	7	7	—
4297	$2^3 \cdot 3 \cdot 179$	5	5	—	4813	$2^2 \cdot 3 \cdot 401$	2	2	—
4327	$2 \cdot 3 \cdot 7 \cdot 103$	3	2	10	4817	$2^4 \cdot 7 \cdot 43$	3	3	± 10
4337	$2^4 \cdot 271$	3	3	± 10	4831	$2 \cdot 3 \cdot 5 \cdot 7 \cdot 23$	3	2	—
4339	$2 \cdot 3^2 \cdot 241$	10	5	10	4861	$2^2 \cdot 3^5 \cdot 5$	11	11	—
4349	$2^2 \cdot 1087$	2	2	± 10	4871	$2 \cdot 5 \cdot 487$	11	3	-10
4357	$2^2 \cdot 3^2 \cdot 11^2$	2	2	—	4877	$2^2 \cdot 23 \cdot 53$	2	2	—
4363	$2 \cdot 3 \cdot 727$	2	4	-10	4889	$2^3 \cdot 13 \cdot 47$	3	3	—
4373	$2^2 \cdot 1093$	2	2	—	4903	$2 \cdot 3 \cdot 19 \cdot 43$	3	2	—
4391	$2 \cdot 5 \cdot 439$	14	2	-10	4909	$2^2 \cdot 3 \cdot 409$	6	6	—
4397	$2^2 \cdot 7 \cdot 157$	2	2	—	4919	$2 \cdot 2459$	13	2	-10
4409	$2^3 \cdot 19 \cdot 29$	3	3	—	4931	$2 \cdot 5 \cdot 17 \cdot 29$	6	3	10
4421	$2^2 \cdot 5 \cdot 13 \cdot 17$	3	3	± 10	4933	$2^2 \cdot 3^2 \cdot 137$	2	2	—
4423	$2 \cdot 3 \cdot 11 \cdot 67$	3	7	10	4937	$2^3 \cdot 617$	3	3	± 10
4441	$2^3 \cdot 3 \cdot 5 \cdot 37$	21	21	—	4943	$2 \cdot 7 \cdot 353$	7	2	10
4447	$2 \cdot 3^2 \cdot 13 \cdot 19$	3	2	10	4951	$2 \cdot 3^2 \cdot 5^2 \cdot 11$	6	2	-10
4451	$2 \cdot 5^2 \cdot 89$	2	3	10	4957	$2^2 \cdot 3 \cdot 7 \cdot 59$	2	2	—
4457	$2^3 \cdot 557$	3	3	± 10	4967	$2 \cdot 13 \cdot 191$	5	2	10
4463	$2 \cdot 23 \cdot 97$	5	2	10	4969	$2^3 \cdot 3^3 \cdot 23$	11	11	—
4481	$2^7 \cdot 5 \cdot 7$	3	3	—	4973	$2^2 \cdot 11 \cdot 113$	2	2	—
4483	$2 \cdot 3^3 \cdot 83$	2	4	—	4987	$2 \cdot 3^2 \cdot 277$	2	4	-10
4493	$2^2 \cdot 1123$	2	2	—	4993	$2^7 \cdot 3 \cdot 13$	5	5	—
4507	$2 \cdot 3 \cdot 751$	2	4	—	4999	$2 \cdot 3 \cdot 7^2 \cdot 17$	3	9	—
4513	$2^5 \cdot 3 \cdot 47$	7	7	—	5003	$2 \cdot 41 \cdot 61$	2	3	-10
4517	$2^2 \cdot 1129$	2	2	—					

From Applied Mathematics Series—55, Primitive Roots, Factorization of $p-1$, pages 864, 866, 867. By permission of United States Department of Commerce, National Bureau of Standards, Washington, D.C.

DIOPHANTINE EQUATIONS

H. C. Williams

Let $f(x_1, x_2, \ldots, x_n)$ be a given polynomial in the n variables $x_1, x_2, \ldots, x_n$ with integral coefficients. The equation

$$(*) \qquad f(x_1, x_2, \ldots, x_n) = 0$$

is said to be a *Diophantine equation* when it is to be solved with integral (or rational) values for the unknowns $x_1, x_2, \ldots, x_n$.

The general or complete integral (rational) solution of (*) is that solution which contains all integral (rational) solutions of (*). For the equations that follow, we shall only be concerned with integral solutions. When it is possible, the general solution of these equations will be presented; however, many of these equations have not yet been completely solved. In the course of discussing such equations, some partial results will be given.

Much more information about Diophantine equations can be found in the following works: (1) Z. I. Borevich and I. R. Shafarevich, *Number Theory*, Academic Press, New York and London (1966); (2) R. D. Carmichael, *The Theory of Numbers and Diophantine Analysis*, Dover, New York, N.Y., 1959; (3) B. N. Delone and D. K. Faddeev, *The Theory of Irrationalities of the Third Degree*, Vol. 10, Translations of Mathematical Monographs, American Mathematical Society, Providence, R.I., 1964; (4) L. E. Dickson, *History of the Theory of Numbers*, Vol. II, Chelsea, New York, N.Y., 1952; (5) L. E. Dickson, *Introduction to the Theory of Numbers*, Dover, New York, N.Y., 1957; (6) L. J. Mordell, *Diophantine Equations*, Academic Press, London and New York, 1969. The book by Mordell is especially valuable for modern developments in the theory of Diophantine Equations.

Some Selected Equations

The symbols m,n, will be used exclusively to denote integer parameters.

The linear Diophantine equation

$$ax + by = c$$

and the equation

$$ax^2 - by^2 = c$$

will be dealt with in the following section on continued fractions.

Diophantine Equations of Degree Two

1. All solutions with even y of the Pythagorean Diophantine equation

$$(1) \qquad x^2 + y^2 = z^2$$

are given by

$$x = r(m^2 - n^2), \quad y = 2rmn, \quad z = r(m^2 + n^2),$$

where r,m,n, are integer parameters.

DIOPHANTINE EQUATIONS

2. All solutions of

(2) $x^2 + y^2 = z^2 + w^2$

are given by

$2x = mn + pq, \; 2z = mp + nq,$
$2y = mp - nq, \; 2w = mn - pq,$

where m,q, are both even; n,p, are both even; or all four are odd.

3. The general integer solution of the equation

(3) $x_1^2 + x_2^2 + \ldots + x_n^2 = x^2, \; (x_1, x_2, \ldots, x_n) = 1, \; x > 0$, is given by
$dx_i = 2q_i q_n \; (i = 1, 2, \ldots, n-1),$
$dx_n = q_n^2 - q_1^2 - \ldots - q_{n-1}^2,$
$dx = q_n^2 + q_1^2 + \ldots + q_{n-1}^2,$

where the q's are arbitrary integers with $(q_1, q_2, \ldots, q_n) = 1$ and $d > 0$ is chosen so that $(x_1, x_2, \ldots, x_n) = 1$.

4. If $e \neq 0$ and $d = b^2 - 4ac$ is not the square of an integer, and if (u,v,w) is a given solution (u, v, w not all zero) of

(4) $ax^2 + bxy + cy^2 = ez^2,$

then all of its integer solutions are

$x = kr, \; y = ks, \; z = kt,$
$r = -(au+bv)m^2 - 2cvmn + cun^2,$
$s = avm^2 - 2aumn - (bu+cv)n^2, \; t = wT, \; T = am^2 + bmn + cn^2$

where m and n are relatively prime and k is an irreducible fraction whose denominator is gD, where g divides w, and D divides both T and the expression $2aum + 2cvn + b(un+vm)$ and hence also $(b^2 - 4ac)eg^2$.

5. If a,b,c, are square free, $(a,b) = (b,c) = (a,c) = 1$, and a,b,c, do not have the same sign, then the equation

(5) $ax^2 + by^2 + cz^2 = 0$

has non-trivial solutions if and only if $-bc, -ca, -ab$, are quadratic residues of a,b,c, respectively, and if

$$ax^2 + by^2 + cz^2 \equiv 0 \pmod 8$$

is solvable. In fact, if (5) is put in its canonical form, i.e., $a > 0, \; b > 0, \; c < 0$, there exists a non-trivial solution with

$$|x| < \sqrt{b|c|}, \; |y| \leqslant \sqrt{|c|a}, \; |z| \leqslant \sqrt{ab},$$

DIOPHANTINE EQUATIONS

and $(x,y) = (z,y) = (z,x) = 1$.

If a,b,c, are coprime in pairs and abc $\neq$ 0, and if u,v,w, is a solution of (5) such that $(u,v) = (u,w) = 1$, we may assume that au is even and determine integers r,s,t, such that aur + bvs + cwt = 1 (r even). Express abc as a product $k\ell$ of two integers in all ways. Select integers d,m,n, subject to the following conditions:

$$(n,m) = (n,\ell) = (m,k) = 1,$$

and

d is even; or d,m,n, all odd, $k \equiv \ell \pmod 2$.

Put

$$t_1 = d\ell m^2, t_2 = dkn^2, t_3 = dmn, h = ar^2 + bs^2 + ct^2, U = 2r-hu,$$
$$V = 2s-hv, W = 2t-hw, 2u_1 = vW-wV, 2v_1 = wU-uW, 2w_1 = uV-vU.$$

Then

$$x = (ut_1 + Ut_2 - 2bcu_1 t_3)/2,$$
$$y = (vt_1 + Vt_2 - 2cav_1 t_3)/2,$$
$$z = (wt_1 + Wt_2 - 2baw_1 t_3)/2,$$

satisfy (5), and all integer solutions of (5) are so obtained.

Equations of Degree Three

Apart from the trivial solutions x=y=0, u=-w, x=z, y=w, the general solution of

$$(6) \quad x^3 + y^3 = z^3 + w^3$$

is given by

$$x = r(HQ-M^2), y = r(GQ+M^2),$$
$$z = r(Q^2-MH), w = r(Q^2+MG),$$

where

$M = m^2+3n^2$,
$Q = q^2+3p^2$,
$H = 3mp + 3np - mq + 3nq$,
$G = 3mp - 3np + mq + 3nq$, and r,m,n,p,q, are integer parameters.

7. The complete solution of

$$(7) \quad z^2 = x^3 + y^3$$

such that y is odd and prime to x is given by

DIOPHANTINE EQUATIONS

$x = -4p^3 q + 4q^3, y = p^4 + 8pq^3,$
$x = -p^4 + 6p^2 q^2 + 3q^4, y = p^4 + 6p^2 q^2 - 3q^4,$
$x = p^4 + 6p^2 q^2 - 3q^4, y = -p^4 + 6p^2 q^2 + 3q^4,$
$x = 2p^4 - 4p^3 q - 4pq^3 + 2q^4, y = p^4 + 4p^3 q - 6p^2 q^2 + 4pq^3 + q^4,$
$x = 4p^3 q + 24p^2 q^2 + 48pq^3 + 36q^4, y = p^4 + 8p^3 q + 24p^2 q^2 + 24pq^3,$

where p and q are selected so that y is odd and prime to x.

8. The equation

$$(8) \qquad x^3 + y^3 = Az^3$$

has no non-trivial integer solutions if

$$A = p, 2p, 9p, p^2, 9p^2, 4p^2, pq, p_1 p_2^2,$$

or if

$$A = q, 4q, 9q, 2q^2, q^2, 9q^2, q_1 q_2^2, p^2 q^2,$$

where p and q are primes with $p \equiv 5 \pmod{18}$ and $q \equiv 11 \pmod{18}$. When (8) does have non-trivial solutions, it can be shown that all of these solutions can be derived by applying certain operations to a finite number of basic solutions. A table of these basic solutions for all $A \leqslant 500$ is given in Selmer [5,6].

9. The equation

$$(9) \qquad ax^3 + by^3 = c$$

with $a > b > 1$, $c = 1$ or 3, $(ab,c) = 1$, $b = 1$ if $c = 3$, has at most one integer solution (x,y), and for this solution $c^{-1} (x a^{1/3} + y b^{1/3})^3$ is either the fundamental unit or its square in the cubic field $Q(d^{1/3})$ defined by $Q(a^{1/3} b^{2/3})$. The only exception is the equation $2x^3 + y^3 = 3$, which has the two solutions $(1,1)$ and $(4,-5)$.

10. The equation

$$(10) \qquad x^3 + dy^3 = 1 \quad (d > 1, d \neq 19, 20, 28)$$

has at most one solution with $xy \neq 0$. This is given by the fundamental unit in the cubic field $Q(d^{1/3})$ when it is a binomial unit, i.e., when the unit has the form $x + y d^{1/3}$. If $d = 19$, the only solution of (10) is $(-8, 3)$; if $d = 20$, the only solution of (10) is $(-19, 7)$; and if $d = 28$, the only solution of (10) is $(-3, 1)$. A table of fundamental units of pure cubic fields $K(d^{1/3})$, $d \leqslant 1000$, is given in [2].

11. If the equation

$$(11) \qquad y^2 = ax^3 + by^2 + cx + d, a \neq 0,$$

has a solution (x,y), then max $(|x|,|y|) < \exp[(AH)^A]$ where $A = 10^6$ and $H = \max(|a|,|b|,|c|,|d|)$ (see Baker [1]).

DIOPHANTINE EQUATIONS

12. The special case of (11)

$$(12) \qquad y^2 - k = x^3$$

is discussed extensively in Mordell's book. A table of all solutions of (12) for $0 < k \leqslant 100$, as well as all (see Coghlan & Stevens [3]) solutions for $0 < -k < 100$, can be found in Hemer.[4]

Equations of Degree Four

13. The equation

$$(13) \qquad x^4 + y^4 = z^4 + w^4$$

has an infinitude of solutions given by

$$x = m^7 + m^5 n^2 - 2m^3 n^4 + 3m^2 n^5 + mn^6,$$
$$y = m^6 n - 3m^5 n^2 - 2m^4 n^3 + m^2 n^5 + n^7,$$
$$z = m^7 + m^5 n^2 - 2m^3 n^4 - 3m^2 n^5 + mn^6,$$
$$w = m^6 n + 3m^5 n^2 - 2m^4 n^3 + m^2 n^5 + n^7.$$

14. The equation

$$(14) \qquad x^4 + y^4 + z^4 = w^4$$

has no solution for $w < 220{,}000$.

15. The equation

$$(15) \qquad x^4 + y^4 + z^4 = 2w^4$$

has an infinitude of solutions given by

$$x = m^2 - n^2, \quad y = 2mn + n^2,$$
$$z = m^2 + 2mn, \quad w = m^2 + mn + n^2.$$

16. If the equation

$$(16) \qquad x^4 + ay^4 + bz^4 = w^2$$

has a solution x,t,u,v, then a second solution is given by

$$x = s^4 - at^4 - bu^4, \quad y = 2stv,$$
$$z = 2suv, \quad w = v^4 + 4as^4 t^4 + 4bs^4 u^4.$$

17. The special case

$$(17) \qquad x^4 + y^4 + z^4 = w^2$$

DIOPHANTINE EQUATIONS

of (16) has an infinitude of solutions given by

$$x = 2mn(m^2 - n^2), \ y = 2mn(m^2 + n^2),$$
$$z = m^4 - n^4, \ w = m^8 + 14m^4 n^4 + n^8.$$

18. If the equation

(18) $$ax^4 + bx^2 y^2 + cy^4 = ez^2$$

has a solution (r,s,t) , it has a second solution given by

$$x = r(4ces^4 t^2 - q^2), \ y = s(4aer^4 t^2 - q^2),$$
$$z = t[4dr^4 s^4 q^2 - (e^2 t^4 - dr^4 s^4)^2],$$

where

$$q = ar^4 - cs^4, \ d = b^2 - 4ac.$$

19. The equations

(19) $$x^4 \pm y^4 = z^2$$

have no solutions such that $xyz \neq 0$.

20. The equation

(20) $$ax^4 - by^4 = c$$

has at most one solution in positive integers when $c = 1,2,4,8$.

21. The equations

(21) $$x^4 - dy^4 = \pm 1$$

have at most one solution in positive integers. This will be given by $x=a$, $y=b$, if the fundamental unit of the ring of integers in $Q[(-4d)^{1/4}]$ takes the form $a^2 + ab(-4d)^{1/4} + b^2(-d)^{1/2}$.

Let $\epsilon = a + bd^{1/2}$ be the fundamental unit in the ring $Z[d^{1/2}]$ formed by adjoining $d^{1/2}$ to the rational integers. If $a^2 - db^2 = -1$, the equation $x^4 - dy^4 = 1$ has no solution unless $d=5$. If $d=5$ the equation has the solution $(3,2)$. If $a^2 - db^2 = 1$ and (r,s) is a solution of $x^4 - dy^4 = 1$ $(d \neq 7140)$, than $a=r^2$ and $b=s^2$. If $d = 7140$, the equation has the solution $(239, 26)$.

Equations of Degree Greater than Four

22. The equations

(22) $$y^2 = x^r \pm 1 \ (r > 3)$$

have no solutions for which $xy \neq 0$.

DIOPHANTINE EQUATIONS

23. The equations

$$(23) \qquad y^3 = x^r \pm 1 \ (r > 2)$$

have no non-trivial solutions.

24. The equation

$$(24) \qquad 1 + x^2 = 2y^n \ (n > 2, \ n \neq 4)$$

has no solution (r,s) for which $|rs| \neq 1$. When n=4 , the only solutions of (24) in positive integers are (1,1) and (239, 13).

25. The equations

$$(25) \qquad ax^n - by^n = \pm 1,$$

where $a > 0, b > 0$, and $n \geqslant 5$, have at most two solutions in positive integers.

26. The equations

$$(26) \qquad x^n - dy^n = \pm 1,$$

where $d > 0$ and $n \geqslant 5$, has at most one solution in positive integers x,y, except possibly when d=2 or when n=5 or 6 and $d = 2^n \pm 1$. If $d > 1250 \cdot 20^{1/6}$, the equation $x^5 + dy^5 = 1$ has at most one solution in non-zero integers.

27. If

$$f(x) = a_0 x^n + a_1 x^{n-1} + \ldots + a_n,$$

has at least three simple zeros, then all integer solutions of

$$(27) \qquad y^2 = f(x)$$

satisfy the inequality

$$\max \ (|x|, |y|) < \exp \exp \exp \ (n^{10 n^3} A^{n^2}),$$

where

$$A = \max|a_i| \ (i = 0, 1, \ldots, n).$$

28. The equation

$$(28) \qquad x^n + y^n = z^n \ (n > 2)$$

has no solution x,y,z, where $xyz \neq 0$, if n is a prime $< 25,000$ and n divides z; or if n is a prime $< 253,747,888$ and (n,z) = 1.

DIOPHANTINE EQUATIONS

REFERENCES

1. A. Baker, *The Diophantine Equation* $y^2 = ax^3 + bx^2 + cx + d$, *J. Lond. Math. Soc.*, Vol. 43 (1968), pp. 1-9.

2. B. D. Beach, H. C. Williams, C. R. Zarnke, *Some Computer Results on Units in Quadratic and Cubic Fields,* Proc. 25th Summer Meeting Can. Math. Congress, 1971, pp. 609-648.

3. F. B. Coghlan and N. M. Stevens, *The Diophantine Equation* $x^3 - y^2 = k$, Computers in Number Theory, Academic Press, London and New York, 1971, pp. 199-205.

4. O. Hemer, *Notes on the Diophantine Equation* $y^2 - k = x^3$, *Arkiv för Math.*, 3, 67, 1954.

5. E. S. Selmer, *The Diophantine Equation* $ax^3 + by^3 + cz^3 = 0$, *Acta Math.*, 85, 203, 1951.

6. *The Diophantine Equation* $ax^3 + by^3 + cz^3 = 0$, Completion of the tables, *Acta Math.*, 91, 191, 1954.

CONTINUED FRACTIONS

H. C. Williams

Many problems in Number Theory can be solved by making use of the theory of continued fractions. In this section, some of the more important results concerning simple continued fractions are presented. Much more information concerning this subject can be found in (1) G. Chyrstal, *Algebra*, Vol. II, Dover, New York, New York, 1961; (2) O. Perron, *Die Lehre von den Kettenbrüchen*, Chelsea, New York, New York.

1. Finite Simple Continued Fractions

Let a and b, where $b > 0$, be two relatively prime integers. Then we write

$$a = q_0 b + r_0 \ (0 < r_0 < b), \ b = q_1 r_0 + r_1 \ (0 < r_1 < r_0, q_1 > 0),$$
$$r_0 = q_2 r_1 + r_2 \ (0 < r_2 < r_1, q_2 > 0), \ldots,$$
$$r_{k-2} = q_k r_{k-1} + r_k \ (0 < r_k < r_{k-1}, q_k < 0), \ldots$$

until for some n, $r_n = 0$ and $r_{n-2} = q_n r_{n-1}$.
Then, the expression

(1.1)
$$\frac{a}{b} = q_0 + \cfrac{1}{q_1 + \cfrac{1}{q_2 + \cfrac{1}{q_3 + \cfrac{1}{\ddots + \cfrac{1}{q_{n-1} + \cfrac{1}{q_n}}}}}}$$

is the simple continued fraction expansion of a/b. The integers q_i (i = 0, 1, ..., n), which, with the possible exception of q_0, are positive, are called *partial quotients*. The continued fraction in (1.1) is often denoted by

$$q_0 + \frac{1}{q_1 +} \frac{1}{q_2 +} \frac{1}{q_3 +} \cdots \frac{1}{q_{n-1} +} \frac{1}{q_n}$$

or, more conveniently, by

$$< q_0, q_1, q_2, \ldots, q_n >.$$

The *convergents* C_i (i = 0, 1, 2, ..., n) of $< q_0, q_1, q_2, \ldots, q_n >$ are defined by the formula

(1.2)
$$C_i = q_0 + \cfrac{1}{q_1 + \cfrac{1}{q_2 + \cfrac{1}{\ddots + \cfrac{1}{q_i}}}}$$

$$= < q_0, q_1, q_2, \ldots, q_i >.$$

CONTINUED FRACTIONS

If we define A_n and B_n by using the recursive formulas

$$A_n = q_n A_{n-1} + A_{n-2}, B_n = q_n B_{n-1} + B_{n-2},$$

where $A_{-2} = B_{-1} = 0, B_{-2} = A_{-1} = 1$,

then $C_i = A_i / B_i$.

Theorem. If A_i and B_i are defined as above,

$$A_i B_{i-1} - B_i A_{i-1} = (-1)^{i-1}.$$

2. The Linear Diophantine Equation

The solution of the Diophantine equation

(2.1) $ax + by = c \quad (a, b > 0)$

can be obtained by use of simple continued fractions. It is assumed that a and b are relatively prime. If a and b were not relatively prime, a, b, c, in (2.1) could be replaced by a', b', c', where $a' = a/(a,b)$, $b' = b/(a,b)$, $c' = c/(a,b)$, and (a,b) is the greatest common divisor of a and b.

Expand a/b into the simple continued fraction $< q_0, q_1, q_2, \ldots, q_n >$. Then $a/b = C_n = A_n / B_n$; hence,

$$a = A_n, b = B_n$$

and

$$a B_{n-1} - b A_{n-1} = (-1)^{n-1}.$$

Thus, a solution of (2.1) is given by

$$x = (-1)^{n-1} B_{n-1} c, y = (-1)^n A_{n-1} c.$$

All solutions of (2.1) are given by

$$x = (-1)^{n-1} B_{n-1} c + tb, y = (-1)^n A_{n-1} c - ta,$$

where t is an integer parameter.

Example. Find all integer solutions of

$$241x + 37y = 6.$$

We have

$$241 = 6(37) + 19, 37 = 1(19) + 18, 19 = 1(18) + 1, 18 = 18(1) + 0.$$

CONTINUED FRACTIONS

Hence,

$$\frac{241}{37} = <6, 1, 1, 18>.$$

We form the table

i	0	1	2	3
q_i	6	1	1	18
A_i	6	7	13	241
B_i	1	1	2	37

All solutions of the equation are of the form

$$x = 6(2) + 37t = 12 + 37t, \quad y = 6(-13) - 241t = -78 - 241t.$$

3. Infinite Simple Continued Fractions

An infinite sequence $q_0, q_1, q_2, \ldots$ of integers, all positive except perhaps for q_0, determines an *infinite simple continued fraction* $<q_0, q_1, q_2, \ldots>$. The convergents C_i ($i = 0, 1, 2, \ldots$) of this type of continued fraction are defined in the same way as those of a finite continued fraction. The *value* of $<q_0, q_1, q_2, \ldots>$ is defined to be

$$\lim_{n \to \infty} C_n.$$

It can be shown that this limit always exists and is irrational.

Let $\theta_0 = \theta$ be any given irrational, and denote by $[a]$ the greatest integer less than or equal to a. Define the infinite sequence of integers $q_0, q_1, q_2, \ldots$, by using the recursive relations

$$q_i = [\theta_i]$$
$$\theta_{i+1} = 1/(\theta_i - q_i) \quad (i = 0, 1, 2, \ldots).$$

The value of $<q_0, q_1, q_2, \ldots>$ is θ, and this simple infinite continued fraction expression for θ is unique.

A result which is often of great importance in approximation theory is given in the following

Theorem. Let θ be an irrational number. If there is a rational number a/b with $b \geqslant 1$ such that

$$\left| \theta - \frac{a}{b} \right| < \frac{1}{2b^2},$$

then a/b is one of the convergents of the simple infinite continued fraction expansion of θ.

CONTINUED FRACTIONS

4. Periodic Continued Fractions

If, for an infinite simple continued fraction $< q_0, q_1, q_2, \ldots >$, there is an integer n such that $q_j = q_{n+j}$ for all j greater than k, say, the continued fraction $< q_0, q_1, q_2, \ldots >$ is said to be *periodic*. Such a continued fraction can be written in the form

$$< r_0, r_1, \ldots, r_k, s_0, s_1, s_2, \ldots, s_{n-1}, s_0, s_1, \ldots, s_{n-1}, \ldots >$$

or

$$< r_0, r_1, \ldots, r_k; \overline{s_0, s_1, s_2, \ldots, s_{n-1}} >,$$

where the periodic part of the expansion, called a *period*, has a bar drawn over it. The *length* of a period of $< q_0, q_1, q_2, \ldots >$ is the number of partial quotients which make up this period. The period of $< q_0, q_1, q_2, \ldots >$ which contains the least number of partial quotients is called the *primitive period*; its length will be denoted by p.

Theorem. The value of any periodic simple continued fraction is a quadratic irrational. Conversely, the simple infinite continued fraction expansion of any quadratic irrational is periodic.

The periodic continued fraction expansion for any quadratic irrational θ can be determined by using the following algorithm. Let $\theta = (P + \sqrt{D})/Q$, where P, Q, D, are integers and D is positive and not a perfect square. It can be assumed that Q is a divisor of $D - P^2$; for, if this is not the case, replace P by $|Q|P$, Q by $|Q|Q$ and D by $Q^2 D$. Put $P_0 = P$, $Q_0 = Q$, $q_0 = [(P + \sqrt{D})/Q]$ and define

$$P_n = q_{n-1} Q_{n-1} - P_{n-1}, \quad Q_n = (D - P_n^2)/Q_{n-1}, \quad q_n = [(P_n + \sqrt{D})/Q_n]$$

for $n = 1, 2, \ldots$. Eventually, for some integers k and p, it will be found that

$$P_{k+1} = P_{p+k+1} \text{ and } Q_{k+1} = Q_{p+k+1}.$$

Then

$$\theta = < q_0, q_1, q_2, \ldots, q_k; \overline{q_{k+1}, q_{k+2}, \ldots, q_{p+k}} >.$$

For implementing this algorithm on a computer, it is often more convenient to use a modified form of it. We put $Q_{-1} = (D - P^2)/Q$ and use the formulas

$$P_n = [\sqrt{D}] - R_{n-1}$$
$$Q_n = Q_{n-2} + q_{n-1} (P_{n-1} - P_n)$$
$$q_n = [(P_n + [\sqrt{D}])/Q_n]$$
$$R_n = \text{remainder on dividing } P_n + [\sqrt{D}] \text{ by } Q_n.$$

If $\theta = \sqrt{D}/Q$, where Q is a divisor of D and $Q < \sqrt{D}$, there is a simple method for terminating the algorithm. In this case, there must exist an integer i such that $Q_i = Q_{i+1}$ or an integer j such that $P_j = P_{j+1}$.

CONTINUED FRACTIONS

If $Q_i = Q_{i+1}$, where i is minimal, then p = 2i + 1 and

$$\theta = < q_0 ; \overline{q_1, q_2, \ldots, q_{i-1}, q_i, q_i, q_{i-1}, q_{i-2}, \ldots, q_1, 2q_0} >.$$

If $P_j = P_{j+1}$, where j is minimal, then p = 2j and

$$\theta = < q_0 ; \overline{q_1, q_2, \ldots, q_{j-1}, q_j, q_{j-1}, q_{j-2}, \ldots, q_1, 2q_0} >.$$

Tables of the continued fraction expansion of $\sqrt{D}$ for D = 1, 2, ..., 10,000 can be found in Kortum and McNiel[1] and Patz.[2]

5. The Diophantine Equation $ax^2 - by^2 = c$

Let a < b and, a,b > 0. By the method of Section 4, develop $\sqrt{b/a} = \sqrt{ab}/a$ into a periodic continued fraction with smallest period length p. It can be shown that

$$aA_{n-1}^2 - bB_{n-1}^2 = (-1)^n Q_n,$$

where A_{n-1} and B_{n-1} are calculated by using the formulas in Section 1. Also, $Q_{n+pt} = Q_n$ for any positive integral values of n and t; hence, it is clear that, if

$$c = (-1)^n Q_n \text{ for some n} < 2p,$$

(5.1) $ax^2 - by^2 = c \ (a < b)$

has an infinitude of solutions.

It is possible in several important cases of (5.1) to be more precise than in the above result. For example, if the equation

(5.2) $x^2 - Dy^2 = L \ (|L| < \sqrt{D})$

has a solution in relatively prime integers u, v, then u/v must appear as a convergent in the continued fraction expansion of $\sqrt{D}$, that is, L must equal $(-1)^n Q_n$ for some n < 2p. In order to solve the equation (5.2) when $|L| > \sqrt{D}$, the algorithm of Lagrange can be used (see Chrystal's Algebra).

The best known special cases of (5.1) are the equations

(5.3) $x^2 - Dy^2 = 1$

and

(5.4) $x^2 - Dy^2 = -1.$

A solution (u, v) of (5.3) or (5.4) is called *positive* if both u and v are positive. The *fundamental* solution (u, v) of (5.3) is that solution which is positive and such that, if (x, y) is any other positive solution of (5.3), then x > u and y > v. There is a similar definition for the fundamental solution of (5.4).

Theorem. If p is the length of the primitive period for the continued fraction expansion

CONTINUED FRACTIONS

of $\sqrt{D}$, the fundamental solution (u, v) of (5.3) is given by

$$u = A_{p-1}, v = B_{p-1} \text{ (p even)}$$

or

$$u = A_{2p-1}, v = B_{2p-1} \text{ (p odd).}$$

There is a solution of (5.4) if and only if p is odd; in this case, the fundamental solution (u, v) is given by

$$u = A_{p-1}, v = B_{p-1}.$$

Since

$$A_{kp-1} + B_{kp-1}\sqrt{D} = (A_{p-1} + \sqrt{D}B_{p-1})^k,$$

it is easy to show that if (u, v) is the fundamental solution of (5.3), all positive solutions of (5.3) are given by (x_n, y_n), where x_n, y_n, are determined by using the formula

$$x_n + y_n\sqrt{D} = (u + v\sqrt{D})^n \ (u = 1, 2, 3, \dots)$$

Also, all positive solutions of (5.4) are given by (x_n, y_n), where

$$x_n + y_n\sqrt{D} = (u + v\sqrt{D})^n \ (n = 1, 3, 5, \dots)$$

and (u, v) is the fundamental solution of (5.4).

In calculating a solution of (5.3) or (5.4), the formulae below are often useful. If $p = 2k$,

$$A_{p-1} = A_k B_{k-1} + A_{k-1} B_{k-2}, B_{p-1} = B_{k-1} (B_k + B_{k-2}).$$

If $p = 2k + 1$,

$$A_{p-1} = A_k B_k + A_{k-1} B_{k-1}, B_{p-1} = B_k^2 + B_{k-1}^2.$$

Example. Find the fundamental solutions of $x^2 - 61y^2 = -1$ and $x^2 - 61y^2 = 1$.

We expand $\sqrt{61}$ into a continued fraction and form the following table

i	0	1	2	3	4	5	6
P_i	0	7	5	7	5	4	6
Q_i	1	12	3	4	9	5	5
q_i	7	1	4	3	1	2	
A_i	7	8	39	125	164	453	
B_i	1	1	5	16	21	58	

CONTINUED FRACTIONS

Since $Q_5 = Q_6$, $p = 11$ and

$$A_{10} = A_5 B_5 + A_4 B_4 = 453 \cdot 58 + 164 \cdot 21 = 29718$$

$$B_{10} = B_5^2 + B_4^2 = 58^2 + 21^2 = 3805.$$

Also,

$$A_{21} + \sqrt{61} B_{21} = (29718 + 3805 \sqrt{61})^2 ;$$

hence,

$$A_{21} = 1766319049 , B_{21} = 226,153,980.$$

The fundamental solution of $x^2 - 61y^2 = -1$ is $(29,718, 3805)$, and the fundamental solution of $x^2 - 61y^2 = +1$ is $(1,766,319,049, 226,153,980)$.

REFERENCES

1. Kortum, R. and McNiel, G., *A Table of Periodic Continued Fractions*, Lockheed Aircraft Corporation, Sunnyvale, California, 1961.
2. Patz, W., *Tafel der Regelmässigen Kettenbrüche*, Akademie-Verlag, Berlin, 1955.

PRIMES

The following table contains all primes from 1 to 100,000. Taken from the Handbook of Mathematical Functions, Applied Mathematics Series 55, Permission received from National Bureau of Standards, Washington, D. C.

	0	1	2	3	4	5	6	7	8	9	10	11	12	13	14	15	16	17	18	19	20	21	22	23	24
1	2	547	1229	1993	2749	3581	4421	5281	6143	7001	7927	8837	9739	10663	11677	12569	13513	14533	15413	16411	17393	18329	19427	20359	21391
2	3	557	1231	1997	2753	3583	4423	5297	6151	7013	7933	8839	9743	10667	11681	12577	13523	14537	15427	16417	17401	18341	19429	20369	21397
3	5	563	1237	1999	2767	3593	4441	5303	6163	7019	7937	8849	9749	10687	11689	12583	13537	14543	15439	16421	17417	18353	19433	20389	21401
4	7	569	1249	2003	2777	3607	4447	5309	6173	7027	7949	8861	9767	10691	11699	12589	13553	14549	15443	16427	17419	18367	19441	20393	21407
5	11	571	1259	2011	2789	3613	4451	5323	6197	7039	7951	8863	9769	10709	11701	12601	13567	14551	15451	16433	17431	18371	19447	20399	21419
6	13	577	1277	2017	2791	3617	4457	5333	6199	7043	7963	8867	9781	10711	11717	12611	13577	14557	15461	16447	17443	18379	19457	20407	21433
7	17	587	1279	2027	2797	3623	4463	5347	6203	7057	7993	8887	9787	10723	11719	12613	13591	14561	15467	16451	17449	18397	19463	20411	21467
8	19	593	1283	2029	2801	3631	4481	5351	6211	7069	8009	8893	9791	10729	11731	12619	13597	14563	15473	16453	17467	18401	19469	20431	21481
9	23	599	1289	2039	2803	3637	4483	5381	6217	7079	8011	8923	9803	10733	11743	12637	13613	14591	15493	16477	17471	18413	19471	20441	21487
10	29	601	1291	2053	2819	3643	4493	5387	6221	7103	8017	8929	9811	10739	11777	12641	13619	14593	15497	16481	17477	18427	19477	20443	21491
11	31	607	1297	2063	2833	3659	4507	5393	6229	7109	8039	8933	9817	10753	11779	12647	13627	14621	15511	16487	17483	18433	19483	20477	21493
12	37	613	1301	2069	2837	3671	4513	5399	6247	7121	8053	8941	9829	10771	11783	12653	13633	14627	15527	16493	17489	18439	19489	20479	21499
13	41	617	1303	2081	2843	3673	4517	5407	6257	7127	8059	8951	9833	10781	11789	12659	13649	14629	15541	16519	17491	18443	19501	20483	21503
14	43	619	1307	2083	2851	3677	4519	5413	6263	7129	8069	8963	9839	10789	11801	12671	13669	14633	15551	16529	17497	18451	19507	20507	21517
15	47	631	1319	2087	2857	3691	4523	5417	6269	7151	8081	8969	9851	10799	11807	12689	13679	14639	15559	16547	17509	18457	19531	20509	21521
16	53	641	1321	2089	2861	3697	4547	5419	6271	7159	8087	8971	9857	10831	11813	12697	13681	14653	15569	16553	17519	18461	19541	20521	21523
17	59	643	1327	2099	2879	3701	4549	5431	6277	7177	8089	8999	9859	10837	11821	12703	13687	14657	15581	16561	17539	18481	19553	20533	21529
18	61	647	1361	2111	2887	3709	4561	5437	6287	7187	8093	9001	9871	10847	11827	12713	13691	14669	15583	16567	17551	18493	19559	20543	21557
19	67	653	1367	2113	2897	3719	4567	5441	6299	7193	8101	9007	9883	10853	11831	12721	13693	14683	15601	16573	17569	18503	19571	20549	21559
20	71	659	1373	2129	2903	3727	4583	5443	6301	7207	8111	9011	9887	10859	11833	12739	13697	14699	15607	16603	17573	18517	19577	20551	21563
21	73	661	1381	2131	2909	3733	4591	5449	6311	7211	8117	9013	9901	10861	11839	12743	13709	14713	15619	16607	17579	18521	19583	20563	21569
22	79	673	1399	2137	2917	3739	4597	5471	6317	7213	8123	9029	9907	10867	11863	12757	13711	14717	15629	16619	17581	18523	19597	20593	21577
23	83	677	1409	2141	2927	3761	4603	5477	6323	7219	8147	9041	9923	10883	11867	12763	13721	14723	15641	16631	17597	18539	19603	20599	21587
24	89	683	1423	2143	2939	3767	4621	5479	6329	7229	8161	9043	9929	10889	11887	12781	13723	14731	15643	16633	17599	18541	19609	20611	21589
25	97	691	1427	2153	2953	3769	4637	5483	6337	7237	8167	9049	9931	10891	11897	12791	13729	14737	15647	16649	17609	18553	19661	20627	21599
26	101	701	1429	2161	2957	3779	4639	5501	6343	7243	8171	9059	9941	10903	11903	12799	13751	14741	15649	16651	17623	18583	19681	20639	21601
27	103	709	1433	2179	2963	3793	4643	5503	6353	7247	8179	9067	9949	10909	11909	12809	13757	14747	15661	16657	17627	18587	19687	20641	21611
28	107	719	1439	2203	2969	3797	4649	5507	6359	7253	8191	9091	9967	10937	11923	12821	13759	14753	15667	16661	17657	18593	19697	20663	21613
29	109	727	1447	2207	2971	3803	4651	5519	6361	7283	8209	9103	9973	10939	11927	12823	13763	14759	15671	16673	17659	18617	19699	20681	21617
30	113	733	1451	2213	2999	3821	4657	5521	6367	7297	8219	9109	10007	10949	11933	12829	13781	14767	15679	16691	17669	18637	19709	20693	21647
31	127	739	1453	2221	3001	3823	4663	5527	6373	7307	8221	9127	10009	10957	11939	12841	13789	14771	15683	16693	17681	18661	19717	20707	21649
32	131	743	1459	2237	3011	3833	4673	5531	6379	7309	8231	9133	10037	10973	11941	12853	13799	14779	15727	16699	17683	18671	19727	20717	21661
33	137	751	1471	2239	3019	3847	4679	5557	6389	7321	8233	9137	10039	10979	11953	12889	13807	14783	15731	16703	17707	18679	19739	20719	21673
34	139	757	1481	2243	3023	3851	4691	5563	6397	7331	8237	9151	10061	10987	11959	12893	13829	14797	15733	16729	17713	18691	19751	20731	21683
35	149	761	1483	2251	3037	3853	4703	5569	6421	7333	8243	9157	10067	10993	11969	12899	13831	14813	15737	16741	17729	18701	19753	20743	21701
36	151	769	1487	2267	3041	3863	4721	5573	6427	7349	8263	9161	10069	11003	11971	12907	13841	14821	15739	16747	17737	18713	19759	20747	21713
37	157	773	1489	2269	3049	3877	4723	5581	6449	7351	8269	9173	10079	11027	11981	12911	13859	14827	15749	16759	17747	18719	19763	20749	21727
38	163	787	1493	2273	3061	3881	4729	5591	6451	7369	8273	9181	10091	11047	11987	12917	13873	14831	15761	16763	17749	18731	19777	20753	21737
39	167	797	1499	2281	3067	3889	4733	5623	6469	7393	8287	9187	10093	11057	12007	12919	13877	14843	15767	16787	17761	18743	19793	20759	21739
40	173	809	1511	2287	3079	3907	4751	5639	6473	7411	8291	9199	10099	11059	12011	12923	13879	14851	15773	16811	17783	18749	19801	20771	21751
41	179	811	1523	2293	3083	3911	4759	5641	6481	7417	8293	9203	10103	11069	12037	12941	13883	14867	15787	16823	17789	18757	19813	20773	21757
42	181	821	1531	2297	3089	3917	4783	5647	6491	7433	8297	9209	10111	11071	12041	12953	13901	14869	15791	16829	17791	18773	19819	20789	21767
43	191	823	1543	2309	3109	3919	4787	5651	6521	7451	8311	9221	10133	11083	12043	12959	13903	14879	15797	16831	17807	18787	19841	20807	21773
44	193	827	1549	2311	3119	3923	4789	5653	6529	7457	8317	9227	10139	11087	12049	12967	13907	14887	15803	16843	17827	18793	19843	20809	21787
45	197	829	1553	2333	3121	3929	4793	5657	6547	7459	8329	9239	10141	11093	12071	12973	13913	14891	15809	16871	17837	18797	19853	20849	21799
46	199	839	1559	2339	3137	3931	4799	5659	6551	7477	8353	9241	10151	11113	12073	12979	13921	14897	15817	16879	17839	18803	19861	20857	21803
47	211	853	1567	2341	3163	3943	4801	5669	6553	7481	8363	9257	10159	11117	12097	12983	13931	14923	15823	16883	17851	18839	19867	20873	21817
48	223	857	1571	2347	3167	3947	4813	5683	6563	7487	8369	9277	10163	11119	12101	13001	13933	14929	15859	16889	17863	18859	19889	20879	21821
49	227	859	1579	2351	3169	3967	4817	5689	6569	7489	8377	9281	10169	11131	12107	13003	13963	14939	15877	16901	17881	18869	19891	20887	21839
50	229	863	1583	2357	3181	3989	4831	5693	6571	7499	8387	9283	10177	11149	12109	13007	13967	14947	15881	16903	17891	18899	19913	20897	21841

PRIMES (continued)

n	0	1	2	3	4	5	6	7	8	9	10	11	12	13	14	15	16	17	18	19	20	21	22	23	24
51	233	877	1597	2371	3187	4001	4861	5701	6577	7507	8389	9293	10181	11159	12113	13009	13997	14951	15887	16921	17903	18911	19913	20899	21851
52	239	881	1601	2377	3191	4003	4871	5711	6581	7517	8419	9311	10193	11161	12119	13033	13999	14957	15889	16927	17909	18913	19919	20903	21859
53	241	883	1607	2381	3203	4007	4877	5717	6599	7523	8423	9319	10211	11171	12143	13037	14009	14969	15901	16931	17911	18917	19927	20921	21863
54	251	887	1609	2383	3209	4013	4889	5737	6607	7529	8429	9323	10223	11173	12149	13043	14011	14983	15907	16937	17921	18919	19937	20929	21871
55	257	907	1613	2389	3217	4019	4903	5741	6619	7537	8431	9337	10243	11177	12157	13049	14029	15013	15913	16943	17923	18947	19949	20939	21881
56	263	911	1619	2393	3221	4021	4909	5743	6637	7541	8443	9341	10247	11197	12161	13063	14033	15017	15919	16963	17929	18959	19961	20947	21893
57	269	919	1621	2399	3229	4027	4919	5749	6653	7547	8447	9343	10253	11213	12163	13093	14051	15031	15923	16979	17939	18973	19963	20959	21911
58	271	929	1627	2411	3251	4049	4931	5779	6659	7549	8461	9349	10259	11239	12197	13099	14057	15053	15937	16981	17957	18979	19973	20963	21929
59	277	937	1637	2417	3253	4051	4933	5783	6661	7559	8467	9371	10267	11243	12203	13103	14071	15061	15959	16987	17959	19001	19979	20981	21937
60	281	941	1657	2423	3257	4057	4937	5791	6673	7561	8501	9377	10271	11251	12211	13109	14081	15073	15971	16993	17971	19009	19991	20983	21943
61	283	947	1663	2437	3259	4073	4943	5801	6679	7573	8513	9391	10273	11257	12227	13121	14083	15077	15973	17011	17977	19013	19993	21001	21961
62	293	953	1667	2441	3271	4079	4951	5807	6689	7577	8521	9397	10289	11261	12239	13127	14087	15083	15991	17021	17981	19031	19997	21011	21977
63	307	967	1669	2447	3299	4091	4957	5813	6691	7583	8527	9403	10301	11273	12241	13147	14107	15091	16001	17027	17987	19037	20011	21013	21991
64	311	971	1693	2459	3301	4093	4967	5821	6701	7589	8537	9413	10303	11279	12251	13151	14143	15101	16007	17029	17989	19051	20021	21017	21997
65	313	977	1697	2467	3307	4099	4969	5827	6703	7591	8539	9419	10313	11287	12253	13159	14149	15107	16033	17033	18013	19069	20023	21019	22003
66	317	983	1699	2473	3313	4111	4973	5839	6709	7603	8543	9421	10321	11299	12263	13163	14153	15121	16057	17041	18041	19073	20029	21023	22013
67	331	991	1709	2477	3319	4127	4987	5843	6719	7607	8563	9431	10331	11311	12269	13171	14159	15131	16061	17047	18043	19079	20047	21031	22027
68	337	997	1721	2503	3323	4129	4993	5849	6733	7621	8573	9433	10333	11317	12277	13177	14173	15137	16063	17053	18047	19081	20051	21059	22031
69	347	1009	1723	2521	3329	4133	4999	5851	6737	7639	8581	9437	10337	11321	12281	13183	14177	15139	16067	17077	18049	19087	20063	21061	22037
70	349	1013	1733	2531	3331	4139	5003	5857	6761	7643	8597	9439	10343	11329	12289	13187	14197	15149	16069	17093	18059	19121	20071	21067	22039
71	353	1019	1741	2539	3343	4153	5009	5861	6763	7649	8599	9461	10357	11351	12301	13217	14207	15161	16073	17099	18061	19139	20089	21089	22051
72	359	1021	1747	2543	3347	4157	5011	5867	6779	7669	8609	9463	10369	11353	12323	13219	14221	15173	16087	17107	18077	19141	20101	21101	22063
73	367	1031	1753	2549	3359	4159	5021	5869	6781	7673	8623	9467	10391	11369	12329	13229	14243	15187	16091	17117	18089	19157	20107	21107	22067
74	373	1033	1759	2551	3361	4177	5023	5879	6791	7681	8627	9473	10399	11383	12343	13241	14249	15193	16097	17123	18097	19163	20113	21121	22073
75	379	1039	1777	2557	3371	4201	5039	5881	6793	7687	8629	9479	10427	11393	12347	13249	14251	15199	16103	17137	18119	19181	20117	21139	22079
76	383	1049	1783	2579	3373	4211	5051	5897	6803	7691	8641	9491	10429	11399	12373	13259	14281	15217	16111	17159	18121	19183	20123	21143	22091
77	389	1051	1787	2591	3389	4217	5059	5903	6823	7699	8647	9497	10433	11411	12377	13267	14293	15227	16127	17167	18127	19207	20129	21149	22093
78	397	1061	1789	2593	3391	4219	5077	5923	6827	7703	8663	9511	10453	11423	12379	13291	14303	15233	16139	17183	18131	19211	20143	21157	22109
79	401	1063	1801	2609	3407	4229	5081	5927	6829	7717	8669	9521	10457	11437	12391	13297	14321	15241	16141	17189	18133	19213	20147	21163	22111
80	409	1069	1811	2617	3413	4231	5087	5939	6833	7723	8677	9533	10459	11443	12401	13309	14323	15259	16183	17191	18143	19219	20149	21169	22123
81	419	1087	1823	2621	3433	4241	5099	5953	6841	7727	8681	9539	10463	11447	12409	13313	14327	15263	16187	17203	18149	19231	20161	21179	22129
82	421	1091	1831	2633	3449	4243	5101	5981	6857	7741	8689	9547	10477	11467	12413	13327	14341	15269	16189	17207	18169	19237	20173	21187	22133
83	431	1093	1847	2647	3457	4253	5107	5987	6863	7753	8693	9551	10487	11471	12421	13331	14347	15271	16193	17209	18181	19249	20177	21191	22147
84	433	1097	1861	2657	3461	4259	5113	6007	6869	7757	8699	9587	10499	11483	12433	13337	14369	15277	16217	17231	18191	19259	20183	21193	22153
85	439	1103	1867	2659	3463	4261	5119	6011	6871	7759	8707	9601	10501	11489	12437	13339	14387	15287	16223	17239	18199	19267	20201	21211	22157
86	443	1109	1871	2663	3467	4271	5147	6029	6883	7789	8713	9613	10513	11491	12451	13367	14389	15289	16229	17257	18211	19273	20219	21221	22159
87	449	1117	1873	2671	3469	4273	5153	6037	6899	7793	8719	9619	10529	11497	12457	13381	14401	15299	16231	17291	18217	19289	20231	21227	22171
88	457	1123	1877	2677	3491	4283	5167	6043	6907	7817	8731	9623	10531	11503	12473	13397	14407	15307	16249	17293	18223	19301	20233	21247	22189
89	461	1129	1879	2683	3499	4289	5171	6047	6911	7823	8737	9629	10559	11519	12479	13399	14411	15313	16253	17299	18229	19309	20249	21269	22193
90	463	1151	1889	2687	3511	4297	5179	6053	6917	7829	8741	9631	10567	11527	12487	13411	14419	15319	16267	17317	18233	19319	20261	21277	22229
91	467	1153	1901	2689	3517	4327	5189	6067	6947	7841	8747	9643	10589	11549	12491	13417	14423	15329	16273	17321	18251	19333	20269	21283	22247
92	479	1163	1907	2693	3527	4337	5197	6073	6949	7853	8753	9649	10597	11551	12497	13421	14431	15331	16301	17327	18253	19373	20287	21313	22259
93	487	1171	1913	2699	3529	4339	5209	6079	6959	7867	8761	9661	10601	11579	12503	13441	14437	15349	16319	17333	18257	19379	20297	21317	22271
94	491	1181	1931	2707	3533	4349	5227	6089	6961	7873	8779	9677	10607	11587	12511	13451	14447	15359	16333	17341	18269	19381	20323	21319	22273
95	499	1187	1933	2711	3539	4357	5231	6091	6967	7877	8783	9679	10613	11593	12517	13457	14449	15361	16339	17351	18287	19387	20327	21323	22277
96	503	1193	1949	2713	3541	4363	5233	6101	6971	7879	8803	9689	10627	11597	12527	13463	14461	15373	16349	17359	18289	19391	20333	21341	22279
97	509	1201	1951	2719	3547	4373	5237	6113	6977	7883	8807	9697	10631	11617	12539	13469	14479	15377	16361	17377	18301	19403	20341	21347	22283
98	521	1213	1973	2729	3557	4391	5261	6121	6983	7901	8819	9719	10639	11621	12541	13477	14489	15383	16363	17383	18307	19417	20347	21377	22291
99	523	1217	1979	2731	3559	4397	5273	6131	6991	7907	8821	9721	10651	11633	12547	13487	14503	15391	16369	17387	18311	19421	20353	21379	22303
100	541	1223	1987	2741	3571	4409	5279	6133	6997	7919	8831	9733	10657	11657	12553	13499	14519	15401	16381	17389	18313	19423	20357	21383	22307

Combinatorial Analysis

PRIMES (continued)

#	25	26	27	28	29	30	31	32	33	34	35	36	37	38	39	40	41	42	43	44	45	46	47	48	49
1	22343	23327	24317	25409	26407	27457	28513	29453	30577	31607	32687	33617	34651	35771	36787	37831	38923	39979	41113	42089	43063	44203	45317	46451	47533
2	22349	23333	24329	25411	26417	27479	28517	29473	30593	31627	32693	33619	34667	35797	36791	37847	38933	39983	41117	42101	43067	44207	45319	46457	47543
3	22367	23339	24337	25423	26423	27481	28537	29483	30631	31643	32707	33623	34673	35801	36793	37853	38953	39989	41131	42131	43093	44221	45329	46471	47563
4	22369	23357	24359	25439	26431	27487	28541	29501	30637	31649	32713	33629	34679	35803	36809	37861	38959	40009	41141	42139	43103	44249	45337	46477	47569
5	22381	23369	24371	25447	26437	27509	28547	29527	30643	31657	32717	33637	34687	35809	36821	37871	38971	40013	41143	42157	43117	44257	45341	46489	47581
6	22391	23371	24373	25453	26449	27527	28549	29531	30649	31663	32719	33641	34693	35831	36833	37879	38977	40031	41149	42169	43133	44263	45343	46499	47591
7	22397	23399	24379	25457	26459	27529	28559	29537	30661	31667	32749	33647	34703	35837	36847	37889	38993	40037	41161	42179	43151	44267	45361	46507	47599
8	22409	23417	24391	25463	26479	27539	28571	29567	30671	31687	32771	33679	34721	35839	36857	37897	39019	40039	41177	42187	43159	44269	45377	46511	47609
9	22433	23431	24407	25469	26489	27541	28573	29569	30677	31699	32779	33703	34729	35851	36871	37907	39023	40063	41179	42193	43177	44273	45389	46523	47623
10	22441	23447	24413	25471	26497	27551	28579	29573	30689	31721	32783	33713	34739	35863	36877	37951	39041	40087	41183	42197	43189	44279	45403	46549	47629
11	22447	23459	24419	25523	26501	27581	28591	29581	30697	31723	32789	33721	34747	35869	36887	37957	39043	40093	41189	42209	43201	44281	45413	46559	47639
12	22453	23473	24421	25537	26513	27583	28597	29587	30703	31727	32797	33739	34757	35879	36899	37963	39047	40099	41201	42221	43207	44293	45427	46567	47653
13	22469	23497	24439	25541	26539	27611	28603	29599	30707	31729	32801	33749	34759	35897	36901	37967	39079	40111	41203	42223	43223	44351	45433	46573	47657
14	22481	23509	24443	25561	26557	27617	28607	29611	30713	31741	32803	33751	34763	35899	36913	37987	39089	40123	41213	42227	43237	44357	45439	46589	47659
15	22483	23531	24469	25577	26561	27631	28619	29629	30727	31751	32831	33757	34781	35911	36919	37991	39097	40127	41221	42239	43261	44371	45481	46591	47681
16	22501	23537	24473	25579	26573	27647	28621	29633	30757	31769	32833	33767	34807	35923	36923	37993	39103	40129	41227	42257	43271	44381	45491	46601	47699
17	22511	23539	24481	25583	26591	27653	28627	29641	30763	31771	32839	33769	34819	35933	36929	37997	39107	40151	41231	42281	43283	44383	45497	46619	47701
18	22531	23549	24499	25589	26597	27673	28631	29663	30773	31793	32843	33773	34841	35951	36931	38011	39113	40153	41233	42283	43291	44389	45503	46633	47711
19	22541	23557	24509	25601	26627	27689	28643	29669	30781	31799	32869	33791	34843	35963	36943	38039	39119	40163	41243	42293	43313	44417	45523	46639	47713
20	22543	23561	24517	25603	26633	27691	28649	29671	30803	31817	32887	33797	34847	35969	36947	38047	39133	40169	41257	42299	43319	44449	45533	46643	47717
21	22549	23563	24527	25609	26641	27697	28657	29683	30809	31847	32909	33809	34849	35977	36973	38053	39139	40177	41263	42307	43321	44453	45541	46649	47737
22	22567	23567	24547	25621	26647	27701	28661	29717	30817	31849	32911	33811	34871	35983	36979	38069	39157	40189	41269	42323	43331	44483	45553	46663	47741
23	22571	23581	24551	25633	26669	27733	28663	29723	30829	31859	32917	33827	34877	35993	36997	38083	39161	40193	41281	42331	43391	44491	45557	46679	47743
24	22573	23593	24571	25639	26681	27737	28669	29741	30839	31873	32933	33829	34883	35999	37003	38113	39163	40213	41299	42337	43397	44497	45569	46681	47777
25	22613	23599	24593	25643	26683	27739	28687	29753	30841	31883	32939	33851	34897	36007	37013	38119	39181	40231	41333	42349	43399	44501	45587	46687	47779
26	22619	23603	24611	25657	26687	27743	28697	29759	30851	31891	32941	33857	34913	36011	37019	38149	39191	40237	41341	42359	43403	44507	45589	46691	47791
27	22621	23609	24623	25667	26693	27749	28703	29761	30853	31907	32957	33863	34919	36013	37021	38153	39199	40241	41351	42373	43411	44519	45599	46703	47797
28	22637	23623	24631	25673	26699	27751	28711	29789	30859	31957	32969	33871	34939	36017	37039	38167	39209	40253	41357	42379	43427	44531	45613	46723	47807
29	22639	23629	24659	25679	26701	27763	28723	29803	30869	31963	32971	33889	34949	36037	37049	38177	39217	40277	41381	42391	43441	44533	45631	46727	47809
30	22643	23633	24671	25693	26711	27767	28729	29819	30871	31973	32983	33893	34961	36061	37057	38183	39227	40283	41387	42397	43451	44537	45641	46747	47819
31	22651	23663	24677	25703	26713	27773	28751	29833	30881	31981	32987	33911	34963	36067	37061	38189	39229	40289	41389	42403	43457	44543	45659	46751	47837
32	22669	23669	24683	25717	26717	27779	28753	29837	30893	31991	32993	33923	34981	36073	37087	38197	39233	40343	41399	42409	43481	44549	45673	46757	47843
33	22679	23671	24691	25733	26723	27791	28759	29851	30911	32003	32999	33931	35023	36083	37097	38201	39239	40351	41411	42433	43487	44563	45677	46769	47857
34	22691	23677	24697	25741	26729	27793	28771	29863	30931	32009	33013	33937	35027	36097	37117	38219	39241	40357	41413	42437	43499	44579	45691	46771	47869
35	22697	23687	24709	25747	26731	27799	28789	29867	30937	32027	33023	33941	35051	36107	37123	38231	39251	40361	41443	42443	43517	44587	45697	46807	47881
36	22699	23689	24733	25759	26737	27803	28793	29873	30941	32029	33029	33961	35053	36109	37139	38237	39293	40387	41453	42451	43541	44617	45707	46811	47903
37	22709	23719	24749	25763	26759	27809	28807	29879	30949	32051	33037	33967	35059	36131	37159	38239	39301	40423	41467	42457	43543	44621	45737	46817	47911
38	22717	23741	24763	25771	26777	27817	28813	29881	30971	32057	33049	33997	35069	36137	37171	38261	39313	40427	41479	42461	43573	44623	45751	46819	47917
39	22721	23743	24767	25793	26783	27823	28817	29917	30977	32059	33053	34019	35081	36151	37181	38273	39317	40429	41491	42463	43577	44633	45757	46829	47933
40	22727	23747	24781	25799	26801	27827	28837	29921	30983	32063	33071	34031	35083	36161	37189	38281	39323	40433	41507	42467	43579	44641	45763	46831	47939
41	22739	23753	24793	25801	26813	27847	28843	29927	31013	32069	33073	34033	35089	36187	37199	38287	39341	40459	41513	42473	43591	44647	45767	46853	47947
42	22741	23761	24799	25819	26821	27851	28859	29947	31019	32077	33083	34039	35099	36191	37201	38299	39343	40471	41519	42487	43597	44651	45779	46861	47951
43	22751	23767	24809	25841	26833	27883	28867	29959	31033	32083	33091	34057	35107	36209	37217	38303	39359	40483	41521	42491	43607	44657	45817	46867	47963
44	22769	23773	24821	25847	26839	27893	28871	29983	31039	32089	33107	34061	35117	36217	37223	38317	39367	40487	41539	42499	43609	44683	45821	46877	47969
45	22777	23789	24841	25849	26849	27901	28879	29989	31051	32099	33113	34123	35129	36229	37243	38321	39371	40493	41543	42509	43613	44687	45823	46889	47977
46	22783	23801	24847	25867	26861	27917	28901	30011	31063	32117	33119	34127	35141	36241	37253	38327	39373	40499	41549	42533	43627	44699	45827	46901	47981
47	22787	23813	24851	25873	26863	27919	28909	30013	31069	32119	33149	34129	35149	36251	37273	38329	39383	40507	41579	42557	43633	44701	45833	46919	48017
48	22807	23819	24859	25889	26879	27941	28921	30029	31079	32141	33151	34141	35153	36263	37277	38333	39397	40519	41593	42569	43649	44711	45841	46933	48023
49	22811	23827	24877	25903	26881	27943	28927	30047	31081	32143	33161	34147	35159	36269	37307	38351	39409	40529	41597	42577	43651	44729	45853	46957	48029
50	22817	23831	24889	25913	26891	27947	28933	30059	31091	32159	33179	34157	35171	36277	37309	38371	39419	40531	41603	42589	43661	44741	45863	46993	48049

PRIMES (continued)

PRIMES (continued)

	25	26	27	28	29	30	31	32	33	34	35	36	37	38	39	40	41	42	43	44	45	46	47	48	49
51	22853	23831	24889	25919	26893	27953	28949	30071	31121	32173	33119	34159	35171	36293	37313	38377	39439	40543	41609	42569	43669	44753	45863	46997	48073
52	22859	23833	24907	25931	26903	27961	28961	30089	31123	32183	33149	34171	35201	36299	37321	38393	39443	40559	41611	42571	43691	44771	45869	47017	48079
53	22861	23857	24917	25933	26921	27967	28979	30091	31139	32189	33161	34183	35221	36307	37337	38431	39451	40577	41617	42577	43711	44777	45887	47041	48091
54	22871	23869	24919	25939	26927	27983	29009	30097	31147	32191	33179	34211	35227	36313	37339	38447	39461	40583	41621	42589	43717	44789	45893	47051	48109
55	22877	23873	24923	25943	26947	27997	29017	30103	31151	32203	33181	34213	35251	36319	37357	38449	39499	40591	41627	42611	43721	44797	45943	47057	48119
56	22901	23879	24943	25951	26951	28001	29021	30109	31153	32213	33191	34217	35257	36341	37361	38453	39503	40597	41641	42641	43753	44809	45949	47059	48121
57	22907	23887	24953	25969	26953	28019	29023	30113	31159	32233	33199	34231	35267	36343	37363	38459	39509	40609	41647	42643	43759	44819	45953	47087	48131
58	22921	23893	24967	25981	26959	28027	29027	30119	31177	32237	33203	34253	35279	36353	37369	38461	39511	40627	41651	42649	43777	44839	45959	47093	48157
59	22937	23899	24971	25997	26981	28031	29033	30133	31181	32251	33211	34259	35281	36373	37379	38501	39521	40637	41659	42667	43781	44843	45971	47111	48163
60	22943	23909	24977	25999	26987	28051	29059	30137	31183	32257	33223	34261	35291	36383	37397	38543	39541	40639	41669	42677	43783	44851	45979	47119	48179
61	22961	23911	24979	26003	26993	28057	29063	30139	31189	32261	33227	34267	35311	36389	37409	38557	39551	40693	41681	42683	43787	44867	45989	47123	48187
62	22963	23917	24989	26017	27011	28069	29077	30161	31193	32297	33247	34273	35317	36433	37423	38561	39563	40697	41687	42689	43789	44879	46021	47129	48193
63	22973	23929	25013	26021	27017	28081	29101	30169	31219	32299	33287	34283	35323	36451	37441	38567	39569	40699	41719	42697	43793	44887	46027	47137	48197
64	22993	23957	25031	26029	27031	28087	29123	30181	31223	32303	33289	34297	35327	36457	37447	38569	39581	40709	41729	42701	43801	44893	46049	47143	48221
65	23003	23971	25033	26041	27043	28097	29129	30187	31231	32309	33301	34301	35339	36467	37463	38593	39607	40739	41737	42703	43853	44909	46051	47147	48239
66	23011	23977	25037	26053	27059	28099	29131	30197	31237	32321	33311	34303	35353	36469	37483	38603	39619	40751	41759	42709	43867	44917	46061	47149	48247
67	23017	23981	25057	26083	27061	28109	29137	30203	31247	32323	33317	34313	35363	36473	37489	38609	39623	40759	41761	42719	43889	44927	46073	47161	48259
68	23021	23993	25073	26099	27067	28111	29147	30211	31249	32327	33329	34319	35381	36479	37493	38611	39631	40763	41771	42727	43891	44939	46091	47189	48271
69	23027	24001	25087	26107	27073	28123	29153	30223	31253	32341	33337	34327	35393	36493	37501	38629	39659	40771	41777	42737	43913	44953	46093	47207	48281
70	23029	24007	25097	26111	27077	28151	29167	30241	31259	32353	33343	34337	35401	36497	37507	38639	39667	40787	41801	42743	43933	44959	46099	47221	48299
71	23039	24019	25111	26113	27091	28163	29173	30253	31267	32359	33347	34351	35407	36523	37511	38651	39671	40801	41809	42751	43943	44963	46103	47237	48311
72	23041	24023	25117	26119	27103	28181	29179	30259	31271	32363	33349	34361	35419	36527	37517	38653	39679	40813	41813	42767	43951	44971	46133	47251	48313
73	23053	24029	25121	26141	27107	28183	29191	30269	31277	32369	33353	34367	35423	36529	37529	38669	39703	40819	41843	42773	43961	44983	46141	47269	48337
74	23057	24043	25127	26153	27109	28201	29201	30271	31307	32371	33359	34369	35437	36541	37537	38671	39709	40823	41849	42787	43963	44987	46147	47279	48341
75	23059	24049	25147	26161	27127	28211	29207	30293	31319	32377	33377	34381	35447	36551	37547	38677	39719	40829	41851	42793	43969	45007	46153	47287	48353
76	23063	24061	25153	26171	27143	28219	29209	30307	31321	32381	33391	34403	35449	36559	37549	38699	39727	40841	41863	42797	43973	45013	46171	47293	48371
77	23071	24071	25163	26177	27179	28229	29221	30313	31327	32401	33403	34421	35461	36563	37561	38707	39733	40847	41879	42821	43987	45053	46181	47297	48383
78	23081	24077	25169	26183	27191	28277	29231	30319	31333	32411	33409	34429	35491	36571	37567	38711	39749	40849	41887	42829	43997	45061	46187	47303	48397
79	23087	24083	25171	26189	27197	28279	29243	30323	31337	32413	33413	34439	35507	36583	37571	38713	39761	40853	41893	42839	44017	45077	46199	47309	48407
80	23099	24091	25183	26203	27211	28283	29251	30341	31357	32423	33427	34457	35509	36587	37573	38723	39769	40867	41897	42841	44021	45083	46217	47317	48409
81	23117	24097	25189	26209	27239	28289	29269	30347	31379	32429	33457	34469	35521	36599	37579	38729	39779	40879	41903	42853	44027	45119	46219	47339	48437
82	23131	24103	25219	26227	27241	28297	29287	30367	31387	32441	33461	34471	35527	36607	37589	38737	39791	40883	41911	42859	44029	45121	46229	47351	48449
83	23143	24107	25229	26237	27253	28307	29297	30389	31391	32443	33469	34483	35531	36629	37591	38747	39799	40897	41927	42863	44041	45127	46237	47353	48463
84	23159	24109	25237	26249	27259	28309	29303	30391	31393	32467	33479	34487	35533	36637	37607	38749	39821	40903	41941	42899	44053	45131	46261	47363	48473
85	23167	24113	25243	26251	27271	28319	29311	30403	31397	32479	33487	34499	35537	36643	37619	38767	39827	40927	41947	42901	44059	45137	46271	47381	48479
86	23173	24121	25247	26261	27277	28349	29327	30427	31469	32491	33493	34501	35543	36653	37633	38783	39829	40933	41953	42923	44071	45139	46273	47387	48481
87	23189	24133	25253	26263	27281	28351	29333	30431	31477	32497	33503	34511	35569	36671	37643	38791	39839	40939	41957	42929	44087	45161	46279	47389	48487
88	23197	24137	25261	26267	27283	28387	29339	30449	31481	32503	33521	34513	35573	36677	37649	38803	39841	40949	41959	42937	44089	45179	46301	47407	48491
89	23201	24151	25301	26293	27299	28393	29347	30467	31489	32507	33529	34519	35591	36683	37657	38821	39847	40961	41969	42943	44101	45181	46307	47417	48497
90	23203	24169	25303	26297	27329	28403	29363	30469	31511	32531	33533	34537	35593	36691	37663	38833	39857	40973	41981	42953	44111	45191	46309	47419	48523
91	23209	24179	25307	26309	27337	28409	29383	30491	31513	32537	33547	34543	35597	36697	37691	38839	39863	40993	41983	42961	44119	45197	46327	47431	48527
92	23251	24181	25321	26317	27361	28411	29387	30497	31517	32561	33563	34549	35603	36709	37693	38851	39869	41011	41999	42967	44123	45233	46337	47441	48533
93	23269	24197	25339	26321	27367	28429	29389	30509	31531	32563	33569	34583	35617	36713	37699	38861	39877	41017	42013	42979	44129	45247	46349	47459	48539
94	23279	24203	25343	26339	27397	28433	29399	30517	31541	32569	33577	34589	35671	36721	37717	38867	39883	41023	42017	43003	44131	45259	46351	47491	48541
95	23291	24223	25349	26347	27407	28439	29401	30523	31543	32573	33581	34591	35677	36739	37747	38873	39887	41039	42019	43013	44159	45263	46381	47497	48563
96	23293	24229	25357	26357	27409	28447	29411	30529	31547	32579	33587	34603	35729	36749	37781	38891	39901	41047	42023	43019	44171	45281	46399	47501	48571
97	23297	24239	25367	26371	27427	28463	29423	30539	31567	32587	33589	34607	35731	36761	37783	38903	39929	41051	42043	43037	44179	45289	46411	47507	48589
98	23311	24247	25373	26387	27431	28477	29429	30553	31573	32603	33599	34613	35747	36767	37799	38917	39937	41057	42061	43049	44189	45293	46439	47513	48593
99	23321	24251	25391	26393	27437	28493	29437	30557	31583	32609	33601	34631	35753	36779	37811	38921	39953	41077	42071	43051	44201	45307	46441	47521	48611
100	23327	24281	25409	26399	27449	28499	29443	30559	31601	32611	33613	34649	35759	36781	37813	38933	39971	41081	42073	43063	44203	45317	46447	47527	48619

PRIMES (continued)

PRIMES (continued)

#	50	51	52	53	54	55	56	57	58	59	60	61	62	63	64	65	66	67	68	69	70	71	72	73	74
1	48619	49667	50767	51817	52937	54001	55109	56197	57193	58243	59359	60509	61637	62791	63823	65071	66107	67247	68389	69497	70663	71719	72859	73999	75083
2	48623	49669	50773	51827	52951	54011	55117	56207	57203	58271	59369	60521	61643	62801	63839	65089	66109	67261	68399	69499	70667	71741	72869	74017	75109
3	48647	49681	50777	51829	52957	54013	55127	56209	57221	58309	59377	60527	61651	62819	63841	65099	66137	67271	68437	69539	70687	71761	72871	74021	75133
4	48649	49697	50789	51839	52963	54037	55147	56237	57223	58313	59387	60539	61657	62827	63853	65101	66161	67273	68447	69557	70709	71777	72883	74027	75149
5	48661	49711	50821	51853	52967	54049	55163	56239	57241	58321	59393	60589	61667	62851	63857	65111	66169	67289	68449	69593	70717	71789	72889	74047	75161
6	48673	49727	50833	51859	52973	54059	55171	56249	57251	58337	59399	60601	61673	62861	63863	65119	66173	67307	68473	69623	70729	71807	72893	74051	75167
7	48677	49739	50839	51869	52981	54083	55201	56263	57259	58363	59407	60607	61681	62869	63901	65123	66179	67339	68477	69653	70753	71809	72901	74071	75169
8	48679	49741	50849	51871	52999	54091	55207	56267	57269	58367	59417	60611	61687	62873	63907	65129	66191	67343	68483	69661	70769	71821	72907	74077	75181
9	48731	49747	50857	51893	53003	54101	55213	56269	57271	58369	59419	60617	61703	62897	63913	65141	66221	67349	68489	69677	70783	71837	72911	74093	75193
10	48733	49757	50867	51899	53017	54121	55217	56299	57283	58379	59441	60623	61717	62903	63929	65147	66239	67369	68491	69691	70793	71843	72923	74099	75209
11	48751	49783	50873	51907	53047	54133	55219	56311	57287	58391	59443	60631	61723	62921	63949	65167	66271	67391	68501	69697	70823	71849	72931	74101	75211
12	48757	49787	50891	51913	53051	54139	55229	56333	57301	58393	59447	60637	61729	62927	63977	65171	66293	67399	68507	69709	70841	71861	72937	74131	75217
13	48761	49789	50893	51929	53069	54151	55243	56359	57329	58403	59453	60647	61751	62929	63997	65173	66301	67409	68521	69737	70843	71867	72949	74143	75223
14	48767	49801	50909	51941	53077	54163	55249	56369	57331	58411	59467	60649	61757	62939	64007	65179	66337	67411	68531	69739	70849	71879	72953	74149	75227
15	48779	49807	50923	51949	53087	54167	55259	56377	57347	58417	59471	60659	61781	62969	64013	65183	66343	67421	68539	69761	70853	71881	72959	74159	75239
16	48781	49811	50929	51971	53089	54181	55291	56383	57349	58427	59473	60661	61813	62971	64019	65203	66359	67427	68543	69763	70867	71887	72973	74161	75253
17	48787	49823	50951	51973	53093	54193	55313	56393	57367	58439	59497	60679	61819	62981	64033	65213	66361	67429	68567	69767	70877	71899	72977	74167	75269
18	48799	49831	50957	51977	53101	54217	55331	56401	57373	58441	59509	60689	61837	62983	64037	65239	66373	67433	68581	69779	70879	71909	72997	74177	75277
19	48809	49843	50969	51991	53113	54251	55333	56417	57383	58451	59513	60703	61843	62987	64063	65257	66377	67447	68597	69809	70891	71917	73009	74189	75289
20	48817	49853	50971	52009	53117	54269	55337	56431	57389	58453	59539	60719	61861	62989	64067	65267	66383	67453	68611	69821	70901	71933	73013	74197	75307
21	48821	49871	50989	52021	53129	54277	55339	56437	57397	58477	59557	60727	61871	63029	64081	65269	66403	67477	68633	69827	70913	71941	73019	74201	75323
22	48823	49877	51001	52027	53147	54287	55343	56443	57413	58481	59561	60733	61879	63031	64091	65287	66413	67481	68639	69829	70919	71947	73037	74203	75329
23	48847	49891	51013	52051	53149	54293	55351	56453	57427	58511	59567	60737	61909	63059	64109	65293	66431	67489	68659	69833	70921	71963	73039	74209	75337
24	48857	49919	51031	52057	53161	54311	55373	56467	57457	58537	59581	60757	61927	63067	64123	65309	66449	67493	68669	69847	70937	71971	73043	74219	75347
25	48859	49921	51043	52067	53171	54319	55381	56473	57467	58543	59611	60761	61933	63073	64151	65323	66457	67499	68683	69857	70949	71983	73061	74231	75353
26	48869	49927	51047	52069	53173	54323	55399	56477	57487	58549	59617	60763	61949	63079	64153	65327	66463	67511	68687	69859	70951	71987	73063	74257	75367
27	48871	49937	51059	52081	53189	54331	55411	56479	57493	58567	59621	60773	61961	63097	64157	65353	66467	67523	68699	69877	70957	71993	73079	74279	75377
28	48883	49939	51061	52103	53197	54347	55439	56489	57503	58573	59627	60779	61967	63103	64171	65357	66491	67531	68711	69899	70969	71999	73091	74287	75389
29	48889	49943	51071	52121	53201	54361	55441	56501	57527	58579	59629	60793	61979	63113	64187	65371	66499	67537	68713	69911	70979	72019	73121	74293	75391
30	48907	49957	51109	52127	53231	54367	55457	56503	57529	58601	59651	60811	61981	63127	64189	65381	66509	67547	68729	69929	70981	72031	73127	74297	75401
31	48947	49991	51131	52147	53239	54377	55469	56509	57557	58603	59659	60821	61987	63131	64217	65393	66523	67559	68737	69931	70991	72043	73133	74311	75403
32	48953	49993	51133	52153	53267	54401	55487	56519	57571	58613	59663	60859	61991	63149	64223	65407	66529	67567	68743	69941	70997	72047	73141	74317	75431
33	48973	49999	51137	52163	53269	54403	55501	56527	57587	58631	59669	60869	62003	63179	64231	65413	66533	67577	68749	69959	71011	72053	73181	74323	75437
34	48989	50021	51151	52177	53279	54409	55511	56531	57593	58657	59671	60887	62011	63197	64237	65419	66541	67579	68767	69991	71023	72073	73189	74353	75479
35	48991	50023	51157	52181	53281	54413	55529	56533	57601	58661	59693	60889	62017	63199	64271	65423	66553	67589	68771	69997	71039	72077	73237	74357	75503
36	49003	50033	51169	52183	53299	54419	55541	56543	57637	58679	59699	60899	62039	63211	64279	65437	66569	67601	68777	70001	71059	72089	73243	74363	75511
37	49009	50047	51193	52189	53309	54421	55547	56569	57641	58687	59707	60901	62047	63241	64283	65447	66571	67607	68791	70003	71069	72091	73259	74377	75521
38	49019	50051	51197	52201	53323	54437	55579	56591	57649	58693	59723	60913	62053	63247	64301	65449	66587	67619	68813	70009	71081	72101	73277	74381	75527
39	49031	50053	51199	52223	53327	54443	55589	56597	57653	58699	59729	60917	62057	63277	64303	65479	66593	67631	68819	70019	71089	72103	73291	74383	75533
40	49033	50069	51203	52237	53353	54449	55603	56599	57667	58711	59743	60919	62071	63281	64319	65497	66601	67651	68821	70039	71119	72109	73303	74411	75539
41	49037	50077	51217	52249	53359	54469	55609	56611	57679	58727	59747	60923	62081	63299	64327	65519	66617	67679	68863	70051	71129	72139	73309	74413	75541
42	49043	50087	51229	52253	53377	54493	55619	56629	57689	58733	59753	60937	62099	63311	64333	65521	66629	67699	68879	70061	71143	72161	73327	74419	75553
43	49057	50093	51239	52259	53381	54497	55621	56633	57697	58741	59771	60943	62119	63313	64373	65537	66643	67709	68881	70067	71147	72167	73331	74441	75557
44	49069	50101	51241	52267	53401	54499	55631	56659	57709	58757	59779	60953	62129	63317	64381	65539	66653	67723	68891	70079	71153	72169	73351	74449	75571
45	49081	50111	51257	52289	53407	54503	55633	56663	57713	58763	59791	60961	62131	63331	64399	65543	66683	67733	68897	70099	71161	72173	73361	74453	75577
46	49103	50119	51263	52291	53411	54517	55639	56671	57719	58771	59797	61001	62137	63337	64403	65551	66697	67741	68899	70111	71167	72211	73363	74471	75583
47	49109	50123	51283	52301	53419	54521	55661	56681	57727	58787	59809	61007	62141	63347	64433	65557	66701	67751	68903	70117	71171	72221	73379	74489	75589
48	49117	50129	51287	52313	53437	54539	55663	56687	57731	58789	59833	61027	62143	63353	64439	65563	66713	67757	68909	70123	71191	72223	73387	74507	75611
49	49121	50131	51307	52321	53441	54541	55667	56701	57737	58831	59863	61031	62171	63361	64451	65579	66721	67759	68917	70139	71209	72227	73417	74509	75617
50	49123	50147	51329	52361	53453	54547	55673	56711	57751	58889	59879	61043	62189	63367	64453	65581	66733	67763	68927	70141	71233	72229	73421	74521	75619

PRIMES (continued)

	50	51	52	53	54	55	56	57	58	59	60	61	62	63	64	65	66	67	68	69	70	71	72	73	74
51	49139	50153	51341	52363	53453	54547	55681	56713	57751	58897	59921	61057	62191	63377	64483	65587	66733	67777	68927	70141	71233	72251	73421	74527	75629
52	49157	50159	51343	52369	53479	54559	55691	56731	57773	58901	59929	61091	62201	63389	64489	65599	66739	67783	68947	70157	71237	72253	73433	74531	75641
53	49169	50177	51347	52379	53503	54563	55697	56737	57781	58907	59951	61099	62207	63391	64499	65609	66749	67789	68963	70163	71249	72269	73453	74551	75653
54	49171	50207	51349	52387	53507	54577	55711	56747	57787	58909	59957	61121	62213	63397	64513	65617	66751	67801	68993	70177	71257	72271	73459	74561	75659
55	49177	50221	51361	52391	53527	54581	55717	56767	57791	58913	59971	61129	62219	63409	64553	65629	66763	67807	69001	70181	71261	72277	73471	74567	75679
56	49193	50227	51383	52433	53549	54583	55721	56773	57793	58921	59981	61141	62233	63419	64567	65633	66791	67819	69011	70183	71263	72287	73477	74573	75683
57	49199	50231	51407	52453	53551	54601	55733	56779	57803	58937	59999	61151	62273	63421	64577	65647	66797	67829	69019	70199	71287	72307	73483	74587	75689
58	49201	50261	51413	52457	53569	54617	55763	56783	57809	58943	60013	61153	62297	63439	64579	65651	66809	67843	69029	70201	71293	72313	73517	74597	75703
59	49207	50263	51419	52489	53591	54623	55787	56807	57829	58963	60017	61169	62299	63443	64591	65657	66821	67853	69031	70207	71317	72337	73523	74609	75707
60	49211	50273	51421	52501	53593	54629	55793	56809	57839	58967	60029	61211	62303	63463	64601	65677	66841	67867	69061	70223	71327	72341	73529	74611	75709
61	49223	50287	51427	52511	53597	54631	55799	56813	57847	58979	60037	61223	62311	63467	64609	65687	66851	67883	69067	70229	71329	72353	73547	74623	75721
62	49253	50291	51431	52517	53609	54647	55807	56821	57853	58991	60041	61231	62323	63473	64613	65699	66853	67891	69073	70237	71333	72367	73553	74653	75731
63	49261	50311	51437	52529	53611	54667	55813	56827	57859	58997	60077	61253	62327	63487	64621	65701	66863	67901	69109	70241	71339	72379	73561	74687	75743
64	49277	50321	51439	52541	53617	54673	55817	56843	57881	59009	60083	61261	62347	63499	64627	65707	66877	67927	69119	70249	71341	72383	73571	74699	75767
65	49279	50329	51449	52543	53623	54679	55819	56857	57899	59011	60089	61283	62351	63521	64633	65713	66883	67931	69127	70271	71347	72421	73583	74707	75773
66	49297	50333	51461	52553	53629	54709	55823	56873	57901	59021	60091	61291	62383	63527	64661	65717	66889	67933	69143	70289	71353	72431	73589	74713	75781
67	49307	50341	51473	52561	53639	54713	55829	56891	57917	59023	60101	61297	62401	63533	64663	65719	66919	67939	69149	70297	71359	72461	73597	74717	75787
68	49331	50359	51479	52567	53653	54721	55837	56893	57923	59029	60103	61331	62417	63541	64667	65729	66923	67943	69151	70309	71363	72467	73607	74719	75793
69	49333	50363	51481	52571	53657	54727	55843	56897	57943	59051	60107	61333	62423	63559	64679	65731	66931	67957	69163	70313	71387	72469	73609	74729	75797
70	49339	50377	51487	52579	53681	54751	55849	56909	57947	59053	60127	61339	62459	63577	64693	65761	66943	67961	69191	70321	71389	72481	73613	74731	75821
71	49363	50383	51503	52583	53693	54767	55871	56911	57973	59063	60133	61357	62467	63587	64709	65777	66947	67979	69193	70327	71399	72493	73637	74747	75833
72	49367	50387	51511	52609	53699	54773	55889	56921	57977	59069	60139	61363	62473	63589	64717	65789	66949	67987	69197	70351	71411	72497	73643	74759	75853
73	49369	50411	51517	52627	53717	54779	55897	56923	57991	59077	60149	61379	62477	63599	64747	65809	66959	67993	69203	70373	71413	72503	73651	74761	75869
74	49391	50417	51521	52631	53719	54787	55901	56929	58013	59083	60161	61381	62483	63601	64763	65827	66973	68023	69221	70379	71419	72533	73673	74771	75883
75	49393	50423	51539	52639	53731	54799	55903	56941	58027	59093	60167	61403	62497	63607	64781	65831	66977	68041	69233	70381	71429	72547	73679	74779	75913
76	49409	50441	51551	52667	53759	54829	55921	56951	58031	59107	60209	61409	62501	63611	64783	65837	67003	68053	69239	70393	71437	72551	73681	74797	75931
77	49411	50459	51563	52673	53773	54833	55927	56957	58043	59113	60217	61417	62507	63617	64793	65839	67021	68059	69247	70423	71443	72559	73693	74821	75937
78	49417	50461	51577	52691	53777	54851	55931	56963	58049	59119	60223	61441	62533	63629	64811	65843	67033	68071	69257	70429	71453	72577	73699	74827	75941
79	49429	50497	51581	52697	53783	54869	55933	56983	58057	59123	60251	61463	62539	63647	64817	65851	67043	68087	69259	70439	71471	72613	73709	74831	75967
80	49433	50503	51593	52709	53791	54877	55949	56989	58061	59141	60257	61469	62549	63649	64849	65867	67049	68099	69263	70451	71473	72617	73721	74843	75979
81	49451	50513	51599	52711	53813	54881	55967	56993	58067	59149	60259	61471	62563	63659	64853	65881	67057	68111	69313	70457	71479	72623	73727	74857	75983
82	49459	50527	51607	52721	53819	54907	55987	57017	58073	59159	60271	61483	62581	63667	64871	65899	67061	68113	69317	70459	71483	72643	73751	74861	75989
83	49463	50539	51613	52727	53831	54917	55997	57037	58099	59167	60289	61487	62591	63671	64877	65921	67073	68141	69337	70481	71503	72647	73757	74869	75991
84	49477	50543	51631	52733	53849	54919	56003	57041	58109	59183	60293	61493	62597	63689	64879	65927	67079	68147	69341	70487	71527	72649	73771	74873	75997
85	49481	50549	51637	52747	53857	54941	56009	57047	58111	59197	60317	61511	62603	63691	64891	65929	67103	68161	69371	70489	71537	72661	73783	74887	76001
86	49499	50551	51647	52757	53861	54949	56039	57059	58129	59207	60331	61519	62617	63697	64901	65951	67121	68171	69379	70501	71549	72671	73819	74891	76003
87	49523	50581	51659	52769	53881	54959	56041	57073	58147	59209	60337	61543	62627	63703	64919	65957	67129	68207	69383	70507	71551	72673	73823	74897	76031
88	49529	50587	51673	52783	53887	54973	56053	57077	58151	59219	60343	61547	62633	63709	64921	65963	67139	68209	69389	70529	71563	72679	73847	74903	76039
89	49531	50591	51679	52807	53891	54979	56081	57089	58153	59221	60353	61553	62639	63719	64927	65981	67147	68213	69401	70537	71569	72689	73849	74923	76079
90	49537	50593	51683	52813	53897	54983	56087	57097	58169	59233	60373	61559	62653	63727	64937	65983	67157	68219	69403	70549	71593	72701	73859	74929	76081
91	49547	50599	51691	52817	53899	55001	56093	57107	58171	59239	60383	61561	62659	63737	64951	65993	67169	68227	69427	70571	71597	72707	73867	74933	76091
92	49549	50627	51713	52837	53917	55009	56099	57119	58189	59243	60397	61583	62683	63743	64969	66029	67181	68239	69431	70573	71633	72719	73877	74941	76099
93	49559	50647	51719	52859	53923	55021	56101	57131	58193	59263	60413	61603	62687	63761	64997	66037	67187	68261	69439	70583	71647	72727	73883	74959	76103
94	49597	50651	51721	52861	53927	55049	56113	57139	58199	59273	60427	61609	62701	63773	65003	66041	67189	68279	69457	70589	71663	72733	73897	75011	76123
95	49603	50671	51749	52879	53939	55051	56123	57143	58207	59281	60443	61613	62723	63781	65011	66047	67211	68281	69463	70607	71671	72739	73907	75013	76129
96	49613	50683	51767	52883	53951	55057	56131	57149	58211	59333	60449	61627	62731	63793	65027	66067	67217	68311	69467	70619	71693	72763	73939	75017	76147
97	49627	50707	51769	52889	53959	55061	56149	57163	58217	59341	60457	61631	62743	63799	65029	66071	67219	68329	69473	70621	71699	72767	73943	75029	76157
98	49633	50723	51787	52901	53987	55073	56167	57173	58229	59351	60493	61637	62753	63803	65033	66083	67231	68351	69481	70627	71707	72797	73951	75037	76159
99	49639	50741	51797	52903	53993	55087	56171	57179	58231	59357	60497	61643	62761	63809	65053	66089	67247	68371	69491	70639	71711	72817	73961	75041	76163
100	49663	50753	51803	52919	54001	55103	56179	57191	58237	59359	60509	61651	62773	63823	65063	66103	67261	68389	69493	70657	71713	72823	73973	75079	76207

Combinatorial Analysis

PRIMES (continued)

	75	76	77	78	79	80	81	82	83	84	85	86	87	88	89	90	91	92	93	94	95
1	76213	77359	78487	79627	80737	81817	82903	84131	85243	86381	87557	88807	89867	90989	92177	93187	94151	95443	96587	97829	98953
2	76231	77369	78497	79631	80747	81839	82913	84139	85247	86389	87559	88811	89891	90997	92189	93199	94153	95461	96589	97841	98963
3	76243	77377	78509	79633	80749	81847	82939	84143	85259	86399	87583	88813	89897	91009	92203	93229	94169	95467	96601	97843	98981
4	76249	77383	78511	79657	80761	81853	82963	84163	85297	86413	87587	88817	89899	91019	92219	93239	94201	95471	96643	97847	98993
5	76253	77417	78517	79669	80777	81869	82981	84179	85303	86423	87589	88819	89909	91033	92221	93241	94207	95479	96661	97849	98999
6	76259	77419	78539	79687	80779	81883	82997	84181	85313	86441	87613	88843	89917	91079	92227	93251	94219	95483	96667	97859	99013
7	76261	77431	78541	79691	80783	81899	83003	84191	85331	86453	87623	88853	89923	91081	92233	93253	94229	95507	96671	97861	99017
8	76283	77447	78553	79693	80789	81901	83009	84199	85333	86461	87629	88861	89939	91097	92237	93257	94253	95527	96697	97871	99023
9	76289	77471	78569	79697	80803	81919	83023	84211	85361	86467	87631	88867	89959	91099	92243	93263	94261	95531	96703	97879	99041
10	76303	77477	78571	79699	80809	81929	83047	84221	85363	86477	87641	88873	89963	91121	92251	93281	94273	95539	96731	97883	99053
11	76333	77479	78577	79757	80819	81931	83059	84223	85369	86491	87643	88883	89977	91127	92269	93283	94291	95549	96737	97919	99079
12	76343	77489	78583	79769	80831	81937	83063	84229	85381	86501	87649	88897	89983	91129	92297	93287	94307	95561	96739	97927	99083
13	76367	77491	78593	79777	80833	81943	83071	84239	85411	86509	87671	88903	89989	91139	92311	93307	94309	95569	96749	97931	99089
14	76369	77509	78607	79801	80849	81953	83077	84247	85427	86531	87679	88919	90001	91141	92317	93319	94321	95581	96757	97943	99103
15	76379	77513	78623	79811	80863	81967	83089	84263	85429	86533	87683	88937	90007	91151	92333	93323	94327	95597	96763	97961	99109
16	76387	77521	78643	79813	80897	81971	83093	84299	85439	86539	87697	88951	90011	91153	92347	93329	94331	95603	96769	97967	99119
17	76403	77527	78649	79817	80909	81973	83101	84307	85447	86561	87701	88969	90017	91159	92353	93337	94343	95617	96779	97973	99131
18	76421	77543	78653	79823	80911	81989	83117	84317	85451	86573	87719	88993	90019	91163	92357	93371	94349	95621	96787	97987	99133
19	76423	77549	78691	79829	80917	82007	83137	84319	85453	86579	87721	88997	90031	91183	92363	93377	94351	95629	96797	98009	99137
20	76441	77551	78697	79841	80923	82009	83177	84347	85469	86587	87739	89003	90053	91193	92369	93383	94379	95633	96799	98011	99139
21	76463	77557	78707	79843	80929	82013	83203	84349	85487	86599	87743	89009	90059	91199	92377	93407	94397	95651	96821	98017	99149
22	76471	77563	78713	79847	80933	82021	83207	84377	85513	86627	87751	89017	90067	91229	92381	93419	94421	95701	96823	98041	99173
23	76481	77569	78721	79861	80953	82031	83219	84389	85517	86629	87767	89021	90071	91237	92383	93427	94427	95707	96827	98047	99181
24	76487	77573	78737	79867	80963	82037	83221	84391	85523	86677	87793	89041	90073	91243	92387	93463	94433	95713	96847	98057	99191
25	76493	77587	78779	79873	80989	82039	83227	84401	85531	86689	87797	89051	90089	91249	92399	93479	94439	95717	96851	98081	99223
26	76507	77591	78781	79889	81001	82051	83231	84407	85549	86693	87803	89057	90107	91253	92401	93481	94441	95723	96857	98101	99233
27	76511	77611	78787	79901	81013	82067	83233	84421	85571	86711	87811	89069	90121	91283	92413	93487	94447	95731	96893	98123	99241
28	76519	77617	78791	79903	81017	82073	83243	84431	85577	86719	87833	89071	90127	91291	92419	93491	94463	95737	96907	98129	99251
29	76537	77621	78797	79907	81019	82129	83257	84437	85597	86729	87853	89083	90149	91297	92431	93493	94477	95747	96911	98143	99257
30	76541	77641	78803	79939	81023	82139	83267	84443	85601	86743	87869	89087	90163	91303	92459	93497	94483	95773	96931	98179	99259
31	76543	77647	78809	79943	81031	82141	83269	84449	85607	86753	87877	89101	90173	91309	92461	93503	94513	95783	96953	98207	99277
32	76561	77659	78823	79967	81041	82153	83273	84457	85619	86767	87881	89107	90187	91331	92467	93523	94529	95789	96959	98213	99289
33	76579	77681	78839	79973	81043	82163	83299	84463	85621	86771	87887	89113	90191	91367	92479	93529	94531	95791	96973	98221	99317
34	76597	77687	78853	79979	81047	82171	83311	84467	85627	86783	87911	89119	90197	91369	92489	93553	94543	95801	96979	98227	99347
35	76603	77689	78857	79987	81049	82183	83339	84481	85639	86813	87917	89123	90199	91373	92503	93557	94547	95803	96989	98251	99349
36	76607	77699	78877	79997	81071	82189	83341	84499	85643	86837	87931	89137	90203	91381	92507	93559	94559	95813	96997	98257	99367
37	76631	77711	78887	79999	81077	82193	83357	84503	85661	86843	87943	89153	90217	91387	92551	93563	94561	95819	97001	98269	99371
38	76649	77713	78889	80021	81083	82207	83383	84509	85667	86851	87959	89189	90227	91393	92557	93581	94573	95857	97003	98297	99377
39	76651	77719	78893	80039	81097	82217	83389	84521	85669	86857	87961	89203	90239	91397	92567	93601	94583	95869	97007	98299	99391
40	76667	77723	78901	80051	81101	82219	83399	84523	85691	86861	87973	89209	90247	91411	92569	93607	94597	95873	97021	98317	99397
41	76673	77731	78919	80071	81119	82223	83407	84533	85703	86869	87977	89227	90263	91423	92581	93629	94603	95881	97039	98321	99401
42	76679	77743	78929	80077	81131	82231	83417	84551	85711	86923	87991	89231	90271	91433	92593	93637	94613	95891	97073	98323	99409
43	76697	77747	78941	80107	81157	82237	83423	84559	85717	86927	88001	89237	90281	91453	92623	93683	94621	95911	97081	98327	99431
44	76717	77761	78977	80111	81163	82241	83431	84589	85733	86929	88003	89261	90289	91457	92627	93701	94649	95917	97103	98347	99439
45	76733	77773	78979	80141	81173	82261	83437	84629	85751	86939	88007	89269	90313	91459	92639	93703	94651	95923	97117	98369	99469
46	76753	77783	78989	80147	81181	82267	83443	84631	85781	86951	88019	89273	90353	91463	92641	93719	94687	95929	97127	98377	99487
47	76757	77797	79031	80149	81197	82279	83449	84649	85793	86959	88037	89293	90359	91493	92647	93739	94693	95947	97151	98387	99497
48	76771	77801	79039	80153	81199	82301	83459	84653	85817	86969	88069	89303	90371	91499	92657	93761	94709	95957	97157	98389	99523
49	76777	77813	79043	80167	81203	82307	83471	84659	85819	86981	88079	89317	90373	91513	92669	93763	94723	95959	97159	98407	99527
50	76781	77839	79063	80173	81223	82339	83477	84673	85829	86993	88093	89329	90379	91529	92671	93787	94727	95971	97169	98411	99529

PRIMES (continued)

PRIMES (continued)

	75	76	77	78	79	80	81	82	83	84	85	86	87	88	89	90	91	92	93	94	95
51	76801	77849	79087	80177	81233	82349	83477	84673	85831	87013	88093	89329	90379	91541	92681	93809	94907	95989	97171	98519	99551
52	76819	77863	79103	80191	81239	82351	83497	84691	85837	87037	88117	89363	90397	91571	92683	93811	94933	96001	97177	98533	99559
53	76829	77867	79111	80207	81281	82361	83537	84697	85843	87041	88129	89371	90401	91573	92693	93827	94949	96013	97187	98543	99563
54	76831	77893	79133	80209	81283	82373	83557	84701	85847	87049	88169	89381	90403	91577	92699	93851	94951	96017	97213	98561	99571
55	76837	77899	79139	80221	81293	82387	83561	84713	85853	87071	88177	89387	90407	91583	92707	93871	94961	96043	97231	98563	99577
56	76847	77929	79147	80231	81299	82393	83563	84719	85889	87083	88211	89393	90437	91591	92717	93887	94993	96053	97241	98573	99581
57	76871	77933	79151	80233	81307	82421	83579	84731	85903	87103	88223	89399	90439	91621	92723	93889	94999	96059	97259	98597	99607
58	76873	77951	79153	80239	81331	82457	83591	84737	85909	87107	88237	89413	90469	91631	92737	93893	95003	96079	97283	98621	99611
59	76883	77969	79159	80251	81343	82463	83597	84751	85931	87119	88241	89417	90473	91639	92753	93901	95009	96097	97301	98627	99623
60	76907	77977	79181	80263	81349	82469	83609	84761	85933	87121	88259	89431	90481	91673	92761	93911	95021	96137	97303	98639	99643
61	76913	77983	79187	80273	81353	82471	83617	84787	85991	87133	88261	89443	90499	91691	92767	93913	95027	96149	97327	98641	99661
62	76919	77999	79193	80279	81359	82483	83621	84793	85999	87143	88289	89449	90511	91703	92779	93923	95063	96157	97367	98663	99667
63	76943	78007	79201	80287	81371	82487	83639	84809	86011	87151	88301	89459	90523	91711	92789	93937	95071	96167	97369	98669	99679
64	76949	78017	79229	80309	81373	82493	83641	84811	86017	87179	88321	89477	90527	91733	92791	93941	95083	96179	97373	98711	99689
65	76961	78031	79231	80317	81401	82499	83653	84827	86027	87181	88327	89491	90529	91753	92801	93949	95087	96181	97379	98713	99707
66	76963	78041	79241	80329	81409	82507	83663	84857	86029	87187	88337	89501	90533	91757	92809	93967	95089	96199	97381	98717	99709
67	76991	78049	79259	80341	81421	82529	83689	84859	86069	87211	88339	89513	90547	91771	92821	93971	95093	96211	97387	98729	99713
68	77003	78059	79273	80347	81439	82531	83701	84869	86077	87221	88379	89519	90583	91781	92831	93979	95101	96221	97397	98737	99719
69	77017	78079	79279	80363	81457	82549	83717	84871	86083	87223	88397	89521	90599	91801	92849	93983	95107	96223	97423	98773	99721
70	77023	78101	79283	80369	81463	82559	83719	84913	86111	87251	88411	89527	90617	91807	92857	93997	95111	96233	97429	98779	99733
71	77029	78121	79301	80387	81509	82561	83737	84919	86113	87253	88423	89533	90619	91811	92861	94007	95131	96259	97441	98801	99761
72	77041	78137	79309	80407	81517	82567	83761	84947	86117	87257	88427	89561	90631	91813	92863	94009	95143	96263	97453	98807	99767
73	77047	78139	79319	80429	81527	82571	83773	84961	86131	87277	88463	89563	90641	91823	92867	94033	95153	96281	97459	98809	99787
74	77069	78157	79333	80447	81547	82591	83777	84967	86143	87281	88469	89567	90647	91837	92893	94049	95177	96289	97463	98837	99793
75	77081	78163	79337	80449	81551	82601	83791	84977	86161	87293	88471	89591	90659	91841	92899	94057	95189	96293	97499	98849	99809
76	77093	78167	79349	80471	81559	82609	83813	84991	86171	87299	88493	89597	90677	91867	92921	94063	95191	96323	97501	98867	99817
77	77101	78173	79357	80473	81569	82613	83833	85009	86179	87313	88499	89599	90679	91873	92927	94079	95203	96329	97511	98869	99823
78	77137	78179	79367	80489	81611	82619	83843	85021	86183	87317	88513	89603	90697	91909	92941	94099	95213	96331	97523	98873	99829
79	77141	78191	79379	80491	81619	82633	83857	85027	86197	87323	88523	89611	90703	91921	92951	94109	95219	96337	97549	98887	99833
80	77153	78193	79393	80513	81629	82651	83869	85037	86201	87337	88547	89627	90709	91939	92957	94111	95231	96353	97553	98893	99839
81	77167	78203	79397	80527	81637	82657	83873	85049	86209	87359	88589	89633	90731	91943	92959	94117	95233	96377	97561	98897	99859
82	77171	78229	79399	80537	81647	82699	83891	85061	86239	87383	88591	89653	90749	91951	92987	94121	95239	96401	97571	98899	99871
83	77191	78233	79411	80557	81649	82721	83903	85081	86243	87403	88607	89657	90787	91957	92993	94151	95257	96419	97577	98909	99877
84	77201	78241	79423	80567	81667	82723	83911	85087	86249	87407	88609	89659	90793	91961	93001	94153	95261	96431	97579	98911	99881
85	77213	78259	79427	80599	81677	82727	83921	85091	86257	87421	88643	89669	90803	91967	93047	94169	95267	96443	97583	98927	99901
86	77237	78277	79451	80603	81701	82729	83933	85093	86263	87427	88651	89671	90821	91969	93053	94201	95273	96451	97607	98929	99907
87	77239	78283	79481	80611	81703	82757	83939	85103	86269	87443	88657	89681	90823	91997	93059	94207	95279	96457	97609	98939	99923
88	77243	78301	79493	80621	81727	82759	83969	85109	86287	87473	88661	89689	90833	92003	93077	94219	95287	96461	97613	98947	99929
89	77249	78307	79531	80627	81737	82763	83983	85121	86291	87481	88663	89753	90841	92009	93083	94229	95311	96469	97649		99961
90	77261	78311	79549	80629	81749	82781	83987	85133	86293	87491	88667	89759	90847	92033	93089	94253	95317	96479	97651		99971
91	77263	78317	79537	80651	81761	82787	84011	85147	86297	87481	88681	89767	90863	92041	93097	94261	95327	96487	97673		99989
92	77267	78341	79549	80657	81769	82793	84017	85159	86311	87491	88721	89779	90887	92051	93103	94273	95339	96493	97687		99991
93	77269	78347	79559	80669	81773	82799	84047	85193	86323	87509	88729	89783	90901	92077	93113	94291	95369	96497	97711		
94	77279	78367	79561	80671	81799	82811	84053	85199	86341	87511	88741	89797	90907	92083	93131	94307	95383	96517	97729		
95	77291	78401	79579	80677		82813	84059	85201	86351	87517	88747	89809	90911	92107	93133	94309	95393	96527	97771		
96	77317	78427	79589	80681		82837	84061	85213	86357	87523	88771	89819	90917	92111	93139	94321	95401	96553	97777		
97	77323	78437	79601	80683		82847	84067	85223	86369	87539	88789	89821	90931	92119	93151	94327	95413	96557	97787		
98	77339	78439	79609	80687		82883	84089	85229	86371	87541	88793	89833	90947	92143	93169	94331	95419	96581	97789		
99	77347	78467	79613	80701		82889	84121	85237		87547	88799	89839	90971	92153	93179	94343	95429		97813		
100	77351	78479	79621	80713		82891	84127			87553	88801	89849	90977	92173		94349	95441				

USE OF LOGARITHMS

LAWS OF EXPONENTS

For a any real number and m a positive integer, the exponential a^m is defined as

$$\underbrace{a \cdot a \cdot a \cdot \cdots \cdot a}_{m \text{ terms}}$$

Using this definition, it is easy to show that the following three *laws of exponents* hold:

I. $a^m \cdot a^n = a^{m+n}$

II. $\dfrac{a^m}{a^n} = \begin{cases} a^{m-n} & \text{if } m > n \\ 1 & \text{if } m = n \\ \dfrac{1}{a^{n-m}} & \text{if } m < n \end{cases}$

III. $(a^m)^n = a^{mn}$

The n-th root function is defined as the inverse of the n-th power function; that is, if

$$b^n = a, \quad \text{then} \quad b = \sqrt[n]{a}.$$

If n is odd, there will be a unique real number satisfying the above definition for $\sqrt[n]{a}$, for any real value of a. If n is even, for positive values of a there will be two real values for $\sqrt[n]{a}$, one positive and one negative. By convention, the symbol $\sqrt[n]{a}$ is understood to mean the positive value. If n is even and a is negative, there are no real values for $\sqrt[n]{a}$.

If we now attempt to extend the definition of the exponential a^t to all rational values of the exponent t, in such a way that the three laws of exponents continue to hold, it is easily shown that the required definitions are:

$$a^0 = 1$$
$$a^{p/q} = \sqrt[q]{a^p}$$
$$a^{-t} = \frac{1}{a^t}$$

In order to avoid difficulties with imaginary numbers and division by zero, a must now be restricted to be positive, if p is odd, and q is even.

With this extended definition, it is possible to restate the second law of exponents in a simpler form:

II′. $\dfrac{a^m}{a^n} = a^{m-n}$

It is shown in advanced calculus that this definition may be further extended so that the exponent may be any real number, and the laws of exponents continue to hold. When the quantity a^x thus defined is viewed as a function of the exponent x, with the base a held constant, it is a continuous function. Also, if $a > 1$, the exponential function is monotone increasing, and if $0 < a < 1$, it is monotone decreasing.

180

LOGARITHMS

Any monotone function has a single-valued inverse function, which is also monotone. Furthermore, if the original function is continuous, so is the inverse. Therefore, the inverse function to the exponential function a^x exists for all positive values of a, except $a = 1$. This function is given the name *logarithm to the base a*, abbreviated $\log_a$. That is, if

$$x = a^y, \quad \text{then} \quad y = \log_a x.$$

This function is defined and continuous for all positive values of x. It is monotone increasing if $a > 1$, and monotone decreasing if $0 < a < 1$.

If the laws of exponents are rewritten in terms of logarithms, they become the *laws of logarithms*:

I. $\log_a(xy) = \log_a x + \log_a y$

II. $\log_a \left(\dfrac{x}{y} \right) = \log_a x - \log_a y$

III. $\log_a(x^n) = n \log_a x$

Logarithms derive their main usefulness in computation from the above laws, since they allow multiplication, division, and exponentiation to be replaced by the simpler operations of addition, subtraction, and multiplication, respectively. See the examples which follow.

Further recourse to the definition of logarithm leads to the following formula for change of base

$$\log_a x = \log_b x / \log_b a = (\log_b x) \cdot (\log_a b)$$

Two numbers are commonly used as bases for logarithms. Logarithms to the base 10 are most convenient for use in computation. These logarithms are called common or Briggsian logarithms.

The other usual base for logarithms is an irrational number denoted by e, whose value is approximately $2.71828\ldots$. These logarithms are called natural, Naperian, or hyperbolic logarithms, and occur in many formulas of higher mathematics. The abbreviation ln is frequently used for the natural logarithm function.

Other bases for logarithms, such as 2 and 3, occur in certain applications. These applications are rather specialized and separate tables for these bases are not given. Instead, the formulas for change of base are applied to common or natural logarithms.

If the formulas for change of base are applied to the two usual bases, the following formulas result:

$$\log_{10} x = \log_e x / \log_e 10 = (\log_{10} e)(\log_e x) = M \log_e x$$
$$= 0.43429\ 44819 \log_e x$$
$$\log_e x = \log_{10} x / \log_{10} e = (\log_e 10)(\log_{10} x) = \frac{1}{M} \log_{10} x$$
$$= 2.30258\ 50930 \log_{10} x$$

The following remarks apply to common logarithms.

Since most numbers are irrational powers of ten, a common logarithm, in general, consists of an integer, which is called the characteristic, and an endless decimal, the mantissa.

It is to be observed that the common logarithms of all numbers expressed by the same figures in the same order with the decimal point in different positions have different characteristics but the same mantissa. To illustrate:—if the decimal point stand after the first figure of a number, counting from the left, the characteristic is 0; if after two figures, it is 1; if after three figures, it is 2; and so forth. If the decimal point stands before the first significant figure the characteristic is –1, usually written $\bar{1}$; if there is one zero between the decimal point and the first significant figure it is $\bar{2}$, and so on. For example: log 256 = 2.40824, log 2.56 = 0.40824, log 0.256 = $\bar{1}$.40824, log 0.00256 = $\bar{3}$.40824. The two latter are often written log 0.256 = 9.40824 – 10, log 0.00256 = 7.40824 – 10.

Notice that, although the common logarithm of a number less than one is a negative number, it is customarily written as a negative characteristic and a *positive* mantissa, since the mantissas are usually given in tables as positive numbers. This is the reason that the negative sign is written above the characteristic, since it does not apply to the mantissa. Thus log 0.00256 = $\bar{3}$.40824 = 7.40824 – 10 = –2.59176.

A method of determining characteristics of logarithms is to write the number with one figure to the left of the decimal point multiplied by the appropriate power of 10. The characteristic is then the exponent used. For example:

$$256\ 000\ 000 = 2.56 \times 10^8 \qquad \log = 8.40824$$
$$0.000\ 000\ 256 = 2.56 \times 10^{-7} \qquad \log = \bar{7}.40824 \text{ or } 3.40824 - 10$$

Inasmuch as the characteristic may be determined by inspection, the mantissas only are given in tables of common logarithms.

USE OF LOGARITHM TABLES

To find the common logarithm of a number:

The description and examples 1–8 refer specifically to the table entitled "Five-Place Mantissas for Common Logarithms." This table is also referred to as a five-place table for common logarithms.

In the five-place table, the first two digits of each mantissa are given only once for each line. The remaining three digits are given in the correct place in the table. When the leading two digits are not given on a line, they should be taken from the last line above it on which they do appear. When a mantissa is marked with an asterisk, it indicates that the value for the leading digits is to be taken from the *next* line instead of the present line.

For a number of more than four figures, interpolation must be used. There are several precautions that must be observed when interpolating:

1. Linear interpolation, as described below, may only be used to add one extra digit to the argument (i.e., in the present case, for a four-digit argument).

2. Even though the mantissas given in the table are accurate to five decimal places, interpolated values are accurate only to the same number of places as in the argument, i.e., four places.

If the above precautions cannot be observed, then higher order interpolation should be used. Where applicable, linear interpolation is carried out as follows:

Take the tabular value of the mantissa for the first four figures; find the difference between the mantissa and the next greater tabular mantissa and multiply the difference so found by the remaining figures of the number as a decimal and add the product to the mantissa of the first four figures. For example, to find log 46.762:

$$\log 46.76 = 1.66987$$

Tabular difference between this mantissa and that for 4677 is .00010

$$\log 46.762 = 1.66987 + .2 \times (.00010)$$
$$= 1.66987 + .00002$$
$$= 1.66989$$

The last digit is not accurate, so must be rounded out. Thus

$$\log 46.762 = 1.66989$$

The accuracy will not ordinarily be affected by more than 1 in the last place if the mantissas are rounded to five decimal places before interpolation, and this makes the computation somewhat easier.

In both the four and five-place logarithmic tables, a column of proportional parts is given at the end of each line. If we use the four-place table the number in the column under the fourth digit of the argument is the amount that must be added to any mantissa in that line to interpolate for the fourth digit. This number is to be added to the last place of the mantissa. These numbers are averages for the entire line, so may be off by 1 in the last place.

For example, to find log 33.74

$$\log 33.7 = 1.5276$$
$$\text{proportional part for } 4 = \qquad 5$$
$$\therefore \log 33.74 = 1.5281$$

To *find the number corresponding to a given logarithm*:

(*Note*: This number is called the antilogarithm, and is denoted by $\log^{-1}$. Since the logarithm function is the inverse of the exponential function, $\log_a^{-1} x = a^x$. Therefore, any procedure or table which calculates antilogarithms may also be used to calculate exponentials, and vice-versa. In particular, tables of e^x may be used to compute antilogarithms to the base e.)

The procedure given below refers to a five-place logarithm table. As before, any significant deviation for other tables will be noted.

If the mantissa is found exactly in the table, join the figure at the top which is directly above the given mantissa to the three figures on the line at the left and place the decimal point according to the characteristic of the logarithm. For example,

$$\log^{-1} 3.39967 = \text{antilog } 3.39967 = 2510.$$

If the mantissa is not found exactly in the table it is necessary to interpolate. For example, to find antilog 3.40028, we find in the table

$$\text{antilog } 3.40019 = 2513.$$
$$\text{antilog } 3.40037 = 2514.$$
$$\text{tabular difference} \qquad 18$$

The required difference is 9, so we must add $\frac{9}{18} = .5$.

$$\therefore \text{antilog } 3.40028 = 2513.5$$

The same precautions must be observed for interpolation in finding antilogarithms as in finding logarithms.

A four-place antilogarithm table is also provided. When using this table, the mantissa of the logarithm is looked up on the margins of the table, and the significant digits of the antilogarithm are read from the body of the table. Lookup and interpolation are done in the same manner as when looking up logarithms in a table of logarithms.

Tables of natural logarithms are used in the same way as tables of common logarithms, except that they contain both the characteristics and the mantissas of the logarithms.

Examples of the use of logarithms in computation follow. Almost all computation with logarithms is done with common logarithms, since the computation of the characteristic is simpler, and since only the significant digits of the argument need be given in the table, without regard for the decimal point location. These examples all use the table of five-place common logarithms.

1. $52600 \times 0.00381 \times 2.74 = 549.11$

log 52600	= 4.72099
log 0.00381	= $\overline{3}$.58092
log 2.74	= 0.43775
adding	= 2.73966
antilog	= 549.11

The sum is the logarithm of the product, the mantissa of which is 73966. On looking up this mantissa in the logarithm tables we see that it corresponds to the digits 54911. The characteristic is 2, hence there are three figures before the decimal point. The number corresponding to the logarithm, called the antilogarithm, is 549.11.

2. $0.00123 \div 52.7 = 0.000\ 023\ 34$

log 0.00123	= $\overline{3}$.08991
log 52.7	= 1.72181
subtracting	= $\overline{5}$.36810
antilog	= 0.000 023 34

The characteristic $\overline{5}(5. - 10)$ shows four zeros after the decimal point before the first significant figure.

3. $\dfrac{273 \times 780}{292 \times 760} \times 15 \times 0.09 = 1.2954$

log 273	= 2.43616	log 292	= 2.46538
log 780	= 2.89209	log 760	= 2.88081
log 15	= 1.17609	log denominator	= 5.34619
log 0.09	= $\overline{2}$.95424		
log numerator	= 5.45858		

log numerator	= 5.45858
log denominator	= 5.34619
subtracting	= 0.11239
antilog	= 1.2954

As division may be accomplished by multiplying by the reciprocal of a number, the above may be considerably simplified. The logarithm of the reciprocal of a number, called the cologarithm, is readily obtained from the table by subtracting the logarithm of the number from zero. This may be readily read off from the table of mantissas. Change the sign of the characteristic algebraically adding to it −1, then mentally subtract each figure of the mantissa from 9 proceeding from left to right, the last figure being subtracted from 10. The example then is:

$$
\begin{aligned}
\log 273 \quad &= 2.43616 \\
\log 780 \quad &= 2.89209 \\
\log \ 15 \quad &= 1.17609 \\
\log \ \ 0.09 \quad &= \overline{2}.95424 \\
\text{colog } 292 \quad &= \overline{3}.53462 \\
\text{colog } 760 \quad &= \underline{\overline{3}.11919} \\
&\quad \ \ 0.11239
\end{aligned}
$$

4. $(0.00098)^4 = 9.224 \times 10^{-13}$ An alternative method:

$\log 0.00098$	$= \overline{4}.99123$		$\log 0.00098 =$	$6.99123 - 10$	
	$\underline{\quad 4 \quad}$			$\underline{\qquad 4 \qquad}$	
	3.96492	(a)		$27.96492 - 40$	
$\overline{4} \times 4$	$= \overline{16}.$	(b)	or	$7.96492 - 20$	
$\log (0.00098)^4$	$= \overline{13}.96492$	(c)	or	$\overline{13}.96492$	
antilog	$= 9.224 \times 10^{-13}$		antilog	$= 9.224 \times 10^{-13}$	

In the above it will be noted that the mantissa is always positive, hence the multiplication of the mantissa shown at (a), while (b) shows the multiplication of the characteristic. (c) is the algebraic sum.

5. $\sqrt[5]{492} = 3.4546$
   $\log 492 = 2.69197$

Dividing the logarithm by 5 gives as the logarithm of the root 0.53839, the antilogarithm of which is 3.4546, both characteristic and mantissa being positive. When the characteristic is negative and not evenly divisible by the root to be taken, a modification of the logarithm is necessary, as the following example shows:

6. $\sqrt[3]{0.000372} = 0.07192$
   $\log 3.72 \times 10^{-4} = \ \ \overline{4}.57054$ (a)
                $= 26.57054 - 30$ (b)

Dividing (b) by 3 gives 8.85685 − 10, which may be written $\overline{2}.85685$, and is the logarithm of the root sought, which is 0.07192.

7. $(0.000\ 372)^{1.2} = 0.000\ 076\ 674$
   $\log 0.000\ 372 \ = \overline{4}.57054$
              or $6.57054 - 10$
                     $\underline{\quad 1.2 \quad}$
              $7.88465 - 12$
   antilog $= 0.000\ 076\ 674$

8. $(0.000372)^{-1.32} = 33642$
   colog $0.000372 \ = 3.42946$
                    $\underline{\quad 1.32 \quad}$
                 4.52689
   antilog $= 33642$

*FOUR-PLACE MANTISSAS FOR COMMON LOGARITHMS OF DECIMAL FRACTIONS

N	0	1	2	3	4	5	6	7	8	9
.10	−1.000	−.9957	−.9914	−.9872	−.9830	−.9788	−.9747	−.9706	−.9666	−.9626
.11	−.9586	−.9547	−.9508	−.9469	−.9431	−.9393	−.9355	−.9318	−.9281	−.9245
.12	−.9208	−.9172	−.9136	−.9101	−.9066	−.9031	−.8996	−.8962	−.8928	−.8894
.13	−.8861	−.8827	−.8794	−.8761	−.8729	−.8697	−.8665	−.8633	−.8601	−.8570
.14	−.8539	−.8508	−.8477	−.8447	−.8416	−.8386	−.8356	−.8327	−.8297	−.8268
.15	−.8239	−.8210	−.8182	−.8153	−.8125	−.8097	−.8069	−.8041	−.8013	−.7986
.16	−.7959	−.7932	−.7905	−.7878	−.7852	−.7825	−.7799	−.7773	−.7747	−.7721
.17	−.7696	−.7670	−.7645	−.7620	−.7595	−.7570	−.7545	−.7520	−.7496	−.7471
.18	−.7447	−.7423	−.7399	−.7375	−.7352	−.7328	−.7305	−.7282	−.7258	−.7235
.19	−.7212	−.7190	−.7167	−.7144	−.7122	−.7100	−.7077	−.7055	−.7033	−.7011
.20	−.6990	−.6968	−.6946	−.6925	−.6904	−.6882	−.6861	−.6840	−.6819	−.6799
.21	−.6778	−.6757	−.6737	−.6716	−.6696	−.6676	−.6655	−.6635	−.6615	−.6596
.22	−.6576	−.6556	−.6536	−.6517	−.6498	−.6478	−.6459	−.6440	−.6421	−.6402
.23	−.6383	−.6364	−.6345	−.6326	−.6308	−.6289	−.6271	−.6253	−.6234	−.6216
.24	−.6198	−.6180	−.6162	−.6144	−.6126	−.6108	−.6091	−.6073	−.6055	−.6038
.25	−.6021	−.6003	−.5986	−.5969	−.5952	−.5935	−.5918	−.5901	−.5884	−.5867
.26	−.5850	−.5834	−.5817	−.5800	−.5784	−.5768	−.5751	−.5735	−.5719	−.5702
.27	−.5686	−.5670	−.5654	−.5638	−.5622	−.5607	−.5591	−.5575	−.5560	−.5544
.28	−.5528	−.5513	−.5498	−.5482	−.5467	−.5452	−.5436	−.5421	−.5406	−.5391
.29	−.5376	−.5361	−.5346	−.5331	−.5317	−.5302	−.5287	−.5272	−.5258	−.5243
.30	−.5229	−.5214	−.5200	−.5186	−.5171	−.5157	−.5143	−.5129	−.5114	−.5100
.31	−.5086	−.5072	−.5058	−.5045	−.5031	−.5017	−.5003	−.4989	−.4976	−.4962
.32	−.4949	−.4935	−.4921	−.4908	−.4895	−.4881	−.4868	−.4855	−.4841	−.4828
.33	−.4815	−.4802	−.4789	−.4776	−.4763	−.4750	−.4737	−.4724	−.4711	−.4698
.34	−.4685	−.4672	−.4660	−.4647	−.4634	−.4622	−.4609	−.4597	−.4584	−.4572
.35	−.4559	−.4547	−.4535	−.4522	−.4510	−.4498	−.4486	−.4473	−.4461	−.4449
.36	−.4437	−.4425	−.4413	−.4401	−.4389	−.4377	−.4365	−.4353	−.4342	−.4330
.37	−.4318	−.4306	−.4295	−.4283	−.4271	−.4260	−.4248	−.4237	−.4225	−.4214
.38	−.4202	−.4191	−.4179	−.4168	−.4157	−.4145	−.4134	−.4123	−.4112	−.4101
.39	−.4089	−.4078	−.4067	−.4056	−.4045	−.4034	−.4023	−.4012	−.4001	−.3990
.40	−.3979	−.3969	−.3958	−.3947	−.3936	−.3925	−.3915	−.3904	−.3893	−.3883
.41	−.3872	−.3862	−.3851	−.3840	−.3830	−.3820	−.3809	−.3799	−.3788	−.3778
.42	−.3768	−.3757	−.3747	−.3737	−.3726	−.3716	−.3706	−.3696	−.3686	−.3675
.43	−.3665	−.3655	−.3645	−.3635	−.3625	−.3615	−.3605	−.3595	−.3585	−.3575
.44	−.3565	−.3556	−.3546	−.3536	−.3526	−.3516	−.3507	−.3497	−.3487	−.3478
.45	−.3468	−.3458	−.3449	−.3439	−.3429	−.3420	−.3410	−.3401	−.3391	−.3382
.46	−.3372	−.3363	−.3354	−.3344	−.3335	−.3325	−.3316	−.3307	−.3298	−.3288
.47	−.3279	−.3270	−.3261	−.3251	−.3242	−.3233	−.3224	−.3215	−.3206	−.3197
.48	−.3188	−.3179	−.3170	−.3161	−.3152	−.3143	−.3134	−.3125	−.3116	−.3107
.49	−.3098	−.3089	−.3080	−.3072	−.3063	−.3054	−.3045	−.3036	−.3028	−.3019
.50	−.3010	−.3002	−.2993	−.2984	−.2976	−.2967	−.2958	−.2950	−.2941	−.2933
.51	−.2924	−.2916	−.2907	−.2899	−.2890	−.2882	−.2874	−.2865	−.2857	−.2848
.52	−.2840	−.2832	−.2823	−.2815	−.2807	−.2798	−.2790	−.2782	−.2774	−.2765
.53	−.2757	−.2749	−.2741	−.2733	−.2725	−.2716	−.2708	−.2700	−.2692	−.2684
.54	−.2676	−.2668	−.2660	−.2652	−.2644	−.2636	−.2628	−.2620	−.2612	−.2604

* This table gives the logarithms of the decimal fractions which are negative numbers.

For example log 0.61 = −0.2147 = 9.7853 − 10. It should be noted that the entries as given can be used conveniently to find cologarithms of positive numbers. Every positive number $N = P \cdot (10)^k$, where $0 < P \leq 1$. Since colog $N = -$ log N, it follows that colog $N = -$ log $P - k$.

For example colog 0.61 = − log 0.61 = 0.2147; colog 61 = 0.2147 − 2; and colog 0.00061 = 3.2147.

*FOUR-PLACE MANTISSAS FOR COMMON LOGARITHMS OF DECIMAL FRACTIONS (Continued)

N	0	1	2	3	4	5	6	7	8	9
.55	−.2596	−.2588	−.2581	−.2573	−.2565	−.2557	−.2549	−.2541	−.2534	−.2526
.56	−.2518	−.2510	−.2503	−.2495	−.2487	−.2480	−.2472	−.2464	−.2457	−.2449
.57	−.2441	−.2434	−.2426	−.2418	−.2411	−.2403	−.2396	−.2388	−.2381	−.2373
.58	−.2366	−.2358	−.2351	−.2343	−.2336	−.2328	−.2321	−.2314	−.2306	−.2299
.59	−.2291	−.2284	−.2277	−.2269	−.2262	−.2255	−.2248	−.2240	−.2233	−.2226
.60	−.2218	−.2211	−.2204	−.2197	−.2190	−.2182	−.2175	−.2168	−.2161	−.2154
.61	−.2147	−.2140	−.2132	−.2125	−.2118	−.2111	−.2104	−.2097	−.2090	−.2083
.62	−.2076	−.2069	−.2062	−.2055	−.2048	−.2041	−.2034	−.2027	−.2020	−.2013
.63	−.2007	−.2000	−.1993	−.1986	−.1979	−.1972	−.1965	−.1959	−.1952	−.1945
.64	−.1938	−.1931	−.1925	−.1918	−.1911	−.1904	−.1898	−.1891	−.1884	−.1878
.65	−.1871	−.1864	−.1858	−.1851	−.1844	−.1838	−.1831	−.1824	−.1818	−.1811
.66	−.1805	−.1798	−.1791	−.1785	−.1778	−.1772	−.1765	−.1759	−.1752	−.1746
.67	−.1739	−.1733	−.1726	−.1720	−.1713	−.1707	−.1701	−.1694	−.1688	−.1681
.68	−.1675	−.1669	−.1662	−.1656	−.1649	−.1643	−.1637	−.1630	−.1624	−.1618
.69	−.1612	−.1605	−.1599	−.1593	−.1586	−.1580	−.1574	−.1568	−.1561	−.1555
.70	−.1549	−.1543	−.1537	−.1530	−.1524	−.1518	−.1512	−.1506	−.1500	−.1494
.71	−.1487	−.1481	−.1475	−.1469	−.1463	−.1457	−.1451	−.1445	−.1439	−.1433
.72	−.1427	−.1421	−.1415	−.1409	−.1403	−.1397	−.1391	−.1385	−.1379	−.1373
.73	−.1367	−.1361	−.1355	−.1349	−.1343	−.1337	−.1331	−.1325	−.1319	−.1314
.74	−.1308	−.1302	−.1296	−.1290	−.1284	−.1278	−.1273	−.1267	−.1261	−.1255
.75	−.1249	−.1244	−.1238	−.1232	−.1226	−.1221	−.1215	−.1209	−.1203	−.1198
.76	−.1192	−.1186	−.1180	−.1175	−.1169	−.1163	−.1158	−.1152	−.1146	−.1141
.77	−.1135	−.1129	−.1124	−.1118	−.1113	−.1107	−.1101	−.1096	−.1090	−.1085
.78	−.1079	−.1073	−.1068	−.1062	−.1057	−.1051	−.1046	−.1040	−.1035	−.1029
.79	−.1024	−.1018	−.1013	−.1007	−.1002	−.0996	−.0991	−.0985	−.0980	−.0975
.80	−.0969	−.0964	−.0958	−.0953	−.0947	−.0942	−.0937	−.0931	−.0926	−.0921
.81	−.0915	−.0910	−.0904	−.0899	−.0894	−.0888	−.0883	−.0878	−.0872	−.0867
.82	−.0862	−.0857	−.0851	−.0846	−.0841	−.0835	−.0830	−.0825	−.0820	−.0814
.83	−.0809	−.0804	−.0799	−.0794	−.0788	−.0783	−.0778	−.0773	−.0768	−.0762
.84	−.0757	−.0752	−.0747	−.0742	−.0737	−.0731	−.0726	−.0721	−.0716	−.0711
.85	−.0706	−.0701	−.0696	−.0691	−.0685	−.0680	−.0675	−.0670	−.0665	−.0660
.86	−.0655	−.0650	−.0645	−.0640	−.0635	−.0630	−.0625	−.0620	−.0615	−.0610
.87	−.0605	−.0600	−.0595	−.0590	−.0585	−.0580	−.0575	−.0570	−.0565	−.0560
.88	−.0555	−.0550	−.0545	−.0540	−.0535	−.0531	−.0526	−.0521	−.0516	−.0511
.89	−.0506	−.0501	−.0496	−.0491	−.0487	−.0482	−.0477	−.0472	−.0467	−.0462
.90	−.0458	−.0453	−.0448	−.0443	−.0438	−.0434	−.0429	−.0424	−.0419	−.0414
.91	−.0410	−.0405	−.0400	−.0395	−.0391	−.0386	−.0381	−.0376	−.0372	−.0367
.92	−.0362	−.0357	−.0353	−.0348	−.0343	−.0339	−.0334	−.0329	−.0325	−.0320
.93	−.0315	−.0311	−.0306	−.0301	−.0297	−.0292	−.0287	−.0283	−.0278	−.0273
.94	−.0269	−.0264	−.0259	−.0255	−.0250	−.0246	−.0241	−.0237	−.0232	−.0227
.95	−.0223	−.0218	−.0214	−.0209	−.0205	−.0200	−.0195	−.0191	−.0186	−.0182
.96	−.0177	−.0173	−.0168	−.0164	−.0159	−.0155	−.0150	−.0146	−.0141	−.0137
.97	−.0132	−.0128	−.0123	−.0119	−.0114	−.0110	−.0106	−.0101	−.0097	−.0092
.98	−.0088	−.0083	−.0079	−.0074	−.0070	−.0066	−.0061	−.0057	−.0052	−.0048
.99	−.0044	−.0039	−.0035	−.0031	−.0026	−.0022	−.0017	−.0013	−.0009	−.0004

* See footnote page 186.

FOUR-PLACE MANTISSAS FOR COMMON LOGARITHMS

N	0	1	2	3	4	5	6	7	8	9	Proportional Parts 1	2	3	4	5	6	7	8	9
10	0000	0043	0086	0128	0170	0212	0253	0294	0334	0374	*4	8	12	17	21	25	29	33	37
11	0414	0453	0492	0531	0569	0607	0645	0682	0719	0755	4	8	11	15	19	23	26	30	34
12	0792	0828	0864	0899	0934	0969	1004	1038	1072	1106	3	7	10	14	17	21	24	28	31
13	1139	1173	1206	1239	1271	1303	1335	1367	1399	1430	3	6	10	13	16	19	23	26	29
14	1461	1492	1523	1553	1584	1614	1644	1673	1703	1732	3	6	9	12	15	18	21	24	27
15	1761	1790	1818	1847	1875	1903	1931	1959	1987	2014	*3	6	8	11	14	17	20	22	25
16	2041	2068	2095	2122	2148	2175	2201	2227	2253	2279	3	5	8	11	13	16	18	21	24
17	2304	2330	2355	2380	2405	2430	2455	2480	2504	2529	2	5	7	10	12	15	17	20	22
18	2553	2577	2601	2625	2648	2672	2695	2718	2742	2765	2	5	7	9	12	14	16	19	21
19	2788	2810	2833	2856	2878	2900	2923	2945	2967	2989	2	4	7	9	11	13	16	18	20
20	3010	3032	3054	3075	3096	3118	3139	3160	3181	3201	2	4	6	8	11	13	15	17	19
21	3222	3243	3263	3284	3304	3324	3345	3365	3385	3404	2	4	6	8	10	12	14	16	18
22	3424	3444	3464	3483	3502	3522	3541	3560	3579	3598	2	4	6	8	10	12	14	15	17
23	3617	3636	3655	3674	3692	3711	3729	3747	3766	3784	2	4	6	7	9	11	13	15	17
24	3802	3820	3838	3856	3874	3892	3909	3927	3945	3962	2	4	5	7	9	11	12	14	16
25	3979	3997	4014	4031	4048	4065	4082	4099	4116	4133	2	3	5	7	9	10	12	14	15
26	4150	4166	4183	4200	4216	4232	4249	4265	4281	4298	2	3	5	7	8	10	11	13	15
27	4314	4330	4346	4362	4378	4393	4409	4425	4440	4456	2	3	5	6	8	9	11	13	14
28	4472	4487	4502	4518	4533	4548	4564	4579	4594	4609	2	3	5	6	8	9	11	12	14
29	4624	4639	4654	4669	4683	4698	4713	4728	4742	4757	1	3	4	6	7	9	10	12	13
30	4771	4786	4800	4814	4829	4843	4857	4871	4886	4900	1	3	4	6	7	9	10	11	13
31	4914	4928	4942	4955	4969	4983	4997	5011	5024	5038	1	3	4	6	7	8	10	11	12
32	5051	5065	5079	5092	5105	5119	5132	5145	5159	5172	1	3	4	5	7	8	9	11	12
33	5185	5198	5211	5224	5237	5250	5263	5276	5289	5302	1	3	4	5	6	8	9	10	12
34	5315	5328	5340	5353	5366	5378	5391	5403	5416	5428	1	3	4	5	6	8	9	10	11
35	5441	5453	5465	5478	5490	5502	5514	5527	5539	5551	1	2	4	5	6	7	9	10	11
36	5563	5575	5587	5599	5611	5623	5635	5647	5658	5670	1	2	4	5	6	7	8	10	11
37	5682	5694	5705	5717	5729	5740	5752	5763	5775	5786	1	2	3	5	6	7	8	9	10
38	5798	5809	5821	5832	5843	5855	5866	5877	5888	5899	1	2	3	5	6	7	8	9	10
39	5911	5922	5933	5944	5955	5966	5977	5988	5999	6010	1	2	3	4	5	7	8	9	10
40	6021	6031	6042	6053	6064	6075	6085	6096	6107	6117	1	2	3	4	5	6	8	9	10
41	6128	6138	6149	6160	6170	6180	6191	6201	6212	6222	1	2	3	4	5	6	7	8	9
42	6232	6243	6253	6263	6274	6284	6294	6304	6314	6325	1	2	3	4	5	6	7	8	9
43	6335	6345	6355	6365	6375	6385	6395	6405	6415	6425	1	2	3	4	5	6	7	8	9
44	6435	6444	6454	6464	6474	6484	6493	6503	6513	6522	1	2	3	4	5	6	7	8	9
45	6532	6542	6551	6561	6571	6580	6590	6599	6609	6618	1	2	3	4	5	6	7	8	9
46	6628	6637	6646	6656	6665	6675	6684	6693	6702	6712	1	2	3	4	5	6	7	7	8
47	6721	6730	6739	6749	6758	6767	6776	6785	6794	6803	1	2	3	4	5	5	6	7	8
48	6812	6821	6830	6839	6848	6857	6866	6875	6884	6893	1	2	3	4	4	5	6	7	8
49	6902	6911	6920	6928	6937	6946	6955	6964	6972	6981	1	2	3	4	4	5	6	7	8
50	6990	6998	7007	7016	7024	7033	7042	7050	7059	7067	1	2	3	3	4	5	6	7	8
51	7076	7084	7093	7101	7110	7118	7126	7135	7143	7152	1	2	3	3	4	5	6	7	8
52	7160	7168	7177	7185	7193	7202	7210	7218	7226	7235	1	2	2	3	4	5	6	7	7
53	7243	7251	7259	7267	7275	7284	7292	7300	7308	7316	1	2	2	3	4	5	6	6	7
54	7324	7332	7340	7348	7356	7364	7372	7380	7388	7396	1	2	2	3	4	5	6	6	7
N	0	1	2	3	4	5	6	7	8	9	1	2	3	4	5	6	7	8	9

*The use of proportional parts for log 1.01 to log 1.59 is less accurate than usual.

FOUR-PLACE MANTISSAS FOR COMMON LOGARITHMS (Continued)

N	0	1	2	3	4	5	6	7	8	9	Proportional Parts								
											1	2	3	4	5	6	7	8	9
55	7404	7412	7419	7427	7435	7443	7451	7459	7466	7474	1	2	2	3	4	5	5	6	7
56	7482	7490	7497	7505	7513	7520	7528	7536	7543	7551	1	2	2	3	4	5	5	6	7
57	7559	7566	7574	7582	7589	7597	7604	7612	7619	7627	1	2	2	3	4	5	5	6	7
58	7634	7642	7649	7657	7664	7672	7679	7686	7694	7701	1	1	2	3	4	4	5	6	7
59	7709	7716	7723	7731	7738	7745	7752	7760	7767	7774	1	1	2	3	4	4	5	6	7
60	7782	7789	7796	7803	7810	7818	7825	7832	7839	7846	1	1	2	3	4	4	5	6	6
61	7853	7860	7868	7875	7882	7889	7896	7903	7910	7917	1	1	2	3	4	4	5	6	6
62	7924	7931	7938	7945	7952	7959	7966	7973	7980	7987	1	1	2	3	3	4	5	6	6
63	7993	8000	8007	8014	8021	8028	8035	8041	8048	8055	1	1	2	3	3	4	5	5	6
64	8062	8069	8075	8082	8089	8096	8102	8109	8116	8122	1	1	2	3	3	4	5	5	6
65	8129	8136	8142	8149	8156	8162	8169	8176	8182	8189	1	1	2	3	3	4	5	5	6
66	8195	8202	8209	8215	8222	8228	8235	8241	8248	8254	1	1	2	3	3	4	5	5	6
67	8261	8267	8274	8280	8287	8293	8299	8306	8312	8319	1	1	2	3	3	4	5	5	6
68	8325	8331	8338	8344	8351	8357	8363	8370	8376	8382	1	1	2	3	3	4	4	5	6
69	8388	8395	8401	8407	8414	8420	8426	8432	8439	8445	1	1	2	2	3	4	4	5	6
70	8451	8457	8463	8470	8476	8482	8488	8494	8500	8506	1	1	2	2	3	4	4	5	6
71	8513	8519	8525	8531	8537	8543	8549	8555	8561	8567	1	1	2	2	3	4	4	5	5
72	8573	8579	8585	8591	8597	8603	8609	8615	8621	8627	1	1	2	2	3	4	4	5	5
73	8633	8639	8645	8651	8657	8663	8669	8675	8681	8686	1	1	2	2	3	4	4	5	5
74	8692	8698	8704	8710	8716	8722	8727	8733	8739	8745	1	1	2	2	3	4	4	5	5
75	8751	8756	8762	8768	8774	8779	8785	8791	8797	8802	1	1	2	2	3	3	4	5	5
76	8808	8814	8820	8825	8831	8837	8842	8848	8854	8859	1	1	2	2	3	3	4	5	5
77	8865	8871	8876	8882	8887	8893	8899	8904	8910	8915	1	1	2	2	3	3	4	4	5
78	8921	8927	8932	8938	8943	8949	8954	8960	8965	8971	1	1	2	2	3	3	4	4	5
79	8976	8982	8987	8993	8998	9004	9009	9015	9020	9025	1	1	2	2	3	3	4	4	5
80	9031	9036	9042	9047	9053	9058	9063	9069	9074	9079	1	1	2	2	3	3	4	4	5
81	9085	9090	9096	9101	9106	9112	9117	9122	9128	9133	1	1	2	2	3	3	4	4	5
82	9138	9143	9149	9154	9159	9165	9170	9175	9180	9186	1	1	2	2	3	3	4	4	5
83	9191	9196	9201	9206	9212	9217	9222	9227	9232	9238	1	1	2	2	3	3	4	4	5
84	9243	9248	9253	9258	9263	9269	9274	9279	9284	9289	1	1	2	2	3	3	4	4	5
85	9294	9299	9304	9309	9315	9320	9325	9330	9335	9340	1	1	2	2	3	3	4	4	5
86	9345	9350	9355	9360	9365	9370	9375	9380	9385	9390	1	1	2	2	3	3	4	4	5
87	9395	9400	9405	9410	9415	9420	9425	9430	9435	9440	0	1	1	2	2	3	3	4	4
88	9445	9450	9455	9460	9465	9469	9474	9479	9484	9489	0	1	1	2	2	3	3	4	4
89	9494	9499	9504	9509	9513	9518	9523	9528	9533	9538	0	1	1	2	2	3	3	4	4
90	9542	9547	9552	9557	9562	9566	9571	9576	9581	9586	0	1	1	2	2	3	3	4	4
91	9590	9595	9600	9605	9609	9614	9619	9624	9628	9633	0	1	1	2	2	3	3	4	4
92	9638	9643	9647	9652	9657	9661	9666	9671	9675	9680	0	1	1	2	2	3	3	4	4
93	9685	9689	9694	9699	9703	9708	9713	9717	9722	9727	0	1	1	2	2	3	3	4	4
94	9731	9736	9741	9745	9750	9754	9759	9763	9768	9773	0	1	1	2	2	3	3	4	4
95	9777	9782	9786	9791	9795	9800	9805	9809	9814	9818	0	1	1	2	2	3	3	4	4
96	9823	9827	9832	9836	9841	9845	9850	9854	9859	9863	0	1	1	2	2	3	3	4	4
97	9868	9872	9877	9881	9886	9890	9894	9899	9903	9908	0	1	1	2	2	3	3	4	4
98	9912	9917	9921	9926	9930	9934	9939	9943	9948	9952	0	1	1	2	2	3	3	4	4
99	9956	9961	9965	9969	9974	9978	9983	9987	9991	9996	0	1	1	2	2	3	3	3	4
N	0	1	2	3	4	5	6	7	8	9	1	2	3	4	5	6	7	8	9

ANTILOGARITHMS

	0	1	2	3	4	5	6	7	8	9	Proportional Parts 1	2	3	4	5	6	7	8	9
.00	1000	1002	1005	1007	1009	1012	1014	1016	1019	1021	0	0	1	1	1	1	2	2	2
.01	1023	1026	1028	1030	1033	1035	1038	1040	1042	1045	0	0	1	1	1	1	2	2	2
.02	1047	1050	1052	1054	1057	1059	1062	1064	1067	1069	0	0	1	1	1	1	2	2	2
.03	1072	1074	1076	1079	1081	1084	1086	1089	1091	1094	0	0	1	1	1	1	2	2	2
.04	1096	1099	1102	1104	1107	1109	1112	1114	1117	1119	0	1	1	1	1	2	2	2	2
.05	1122	1125	1127	1130	1132	1135	1138	1140	1143	1146	0	1	1	1	1	2	2	2	2
.06	1148	1151	1153	1156	1159	1161	1164	1167	1169	1172	0	1	1	1	1	2	2	2	2
.07	1175	1178	1180	1183	1186	1189	1191	1194	1197	1199	0	1	1	1	1	2	2	2	2
.08	1202	1205	1208	1211	1213	1216	1219	1222	1225	1227	0	1	1	1	1	2	2	2	3
.09	1230	1233	1236	1239	1242	1245	1247	1250	1253	1256	0	1	1	1	1	2	2	2	3
.10	1259	1262	1265	1268	1271	1274	1276	1279	1282	1285	0	1	1	1	1	2	2	2	3
.11	1288	1291	1294	1297	1300	1303	1306	1309	1312	1315	0	1	1	1	2	2	2	2	3
.12	1318	1321	1324	1327	1330	1334	1337	1340	1343	1346	0	1	1	1	2	2	2	3	3
.13	1349	1352	1355	1358	1361	1365	1368	1371	1374	1377	0	1	1	1	2	2	2	3	3
.14	1380	1384	1387	1390	1393	1396	1400	1403	1406	1409	0	1	1	1	2	2	2	3	3
.15	1413	1416	1419	1422	1426	1429	1432	1435	1439	1442	0	1	1	1	2	2	2	3	3
.16	1445	1449	1452	1455	1459	1462	1466	1469	1472	1476	0	1	1	1	2	2	2	3	3
.17	1479	1483	1486	1489	1493	1496	1500	1503	1507	1510	0	1	1	1	2	2	2	3	3
.18	1514	1517	1521	1524	1528	1531	1535	1538	1542	1545	0	1	1	1	2	2	2	3	3
.19	1549	1552	1556	1560	1563	1567	1570	1574	1578	1581	0	1	1	1	2	2	3	3	3
.20	1585	1589	1592	1596	1600	1603	1607	1611	1614	1618	0	1	1	1	2	2	3	3	3
.21	1622	1626	1629	1633	1637	1641	1644	1648	1652	1656	0	1	1	2	2	2	3	3	3
.22	1660	1663	1667	1671	1675	1679	1683	1687	1690	1694	0	1	1	2	2	2	3	3	3
.23	1698	1702	1706	1710	1714	1718	1722	1726	1730	1734	0	1	1	2	2	2	3	3	4
.24	1738	1742	1746	1750	1754	1758	1762	1766	1770	1774	0	1	1	2	2	2	3	3	4
.25	1778	1782	1786	1791	1795	1799	1803	1807	1811	1816	0	1	1	2	2	2	3	3	4
.26	1820	1824	1828	1832	1837	1841	1845	1849	1854	1858	0	1	1	2	2	3	3	3	4
.27	1862	1866	1871	1875	1879	1884	1888	1892	1897	1901	0	1	1	2	2	3	3	3	4
.28	1905	1910	1914	1919	1923	1928	1932	1936	1941	1945	0	1	1	2	2	3	3	4	4
.29	1950	1954	1959	1963	1968	1972	1977	1982	1986	1991	0	1	1	2	2	3	3	4	4
.30	1995	2000	2004	2009	2014	2018	2023	2028	2032	2037	0	1	1	2	2	3	3	4	4
.31	2042	2046	2051	2056	2061	2065	2070	2075	2080	2084	0	1	1	2	2	3	3	4	4
.32	2089	2094	2099	2104	2109	2113	2118	2123	2128	2133	0	1	1	2	2	3	3	4	4
.33	2138	2143	2148	2153	2158	2163	2168	2173	2178	2183	0	1	1	2	2	3	3	4	4
.34	2188	2193	2198	2203	2208	2213	2218	2223	2228	2234	1	1	2	2	3	3	4	4	5
.35	2239	2244	2249	2254	2259	2265	2270	2275	2280	2286	1	1	2	2	3	3	4	4	5
.36	2291	2296	2301	2307	2312	2317	2323	2328	2333	2339	1	1	2	2	3	3	4	4	5
.37	2344	2350	2355	2360	2366	2371	2377	2382	2388	2393	1	1	2	2	3	3	4	4	5
.38	2399	2404	2410	2415	2421	2427	2432	2438	2443	2449	1	1	2	2	3	3	4	4	5
.39	2455	2460	2466	2472	2477	2483	2489	2495	2500	2506	1	1	2	2	3	3	4	5	5
.40	2512	2518	2523	2529	2535	2541	2547	2553	2559	2564	1	1	2	2	3	4	4	5	5
.41	2570	2576	2582	2588	2594	2600	2606	2612	2618	2624	1	1	2	2	3	4	4	5	5
.42	2630	2636	2642	2649	2655	2661	2667	2673	2679	2685	1	1	2	2	3	4	4	5	6
.43	2692	2698	2704	2710	2716	2723	2729	2735	2742	2748	1	1	2	3	3	4	4	5	6
.44	2754	2761	2767	2773	2780	2786	2793	2799	2805	2812	1	1	2	3	3	4	4	5	6
.45	2818	2825	2831	2838	2844	2851	2858	2864	2871	2877	1	1	2	3	3	4	5	5	6
.46	2884	2891	2897	2904	2911	2917	2924	2931	2938	2944	1	1	2	3	3	4	5	5	6
.47	2951	2958	2965	2972	2979	2985	2992	2999	3006	3013	1	1	2	3	3	4	5	5	6
.48	3020	3027	3034	3041	3048	3055	3062	3069	3076	3083	1	1	2	3	4	4	5	6	6
.49	3090	3097	3105	3112	3119	3126	3133	3141	3148	3155	1	1	2	3	4	4	5	6	6
	0	1	2	3	4	5	6	7	8	9	1	2	3	4	5	6	7	8	9

ANTILOGARITHMS (Continued)

	0	1	2	3	4	5	6	7	8	9	Proportional Parts								
											1	2	3	4	5	6	7	8	9
.50	3162	3170	3177	3184	3192	3199	3206	3214	3221	3228	1	1	2	3	4	4	5	6	7
.51	3236	3243	3251	3258	3266	3273	3281	3289	3296	3304	1	2	2	3	4	5	5	6	7
.52	3311	3319	3327	3334	3342	3350	3357	3365	3373	3381	1	2	2	3	4	5	5	6	7
.53	3388	3396	3404	3412	3420	3428	3436	3443	3451	3459	1	2	2	3	4	5	6	6	7
.54	3467	3475	3483	3491	3499	3508	3516	3524	3532	3540	1	2	2	3	4	5	6	6	7
.55	3548	3556	3565	3573	3581	3589	3597	3606	3614	3622	1	2	2	3	4	5	6	7	7
.56	3631	3639	3648	3656	3664	3673	3681	3690	3698	3707	1	2	3	3	4	5	6	7	8
.57	3715	3724	3733	3741	3750	3758	3767	3776	3784	3793	1	2	3	3	4	5	6	7	8
.58	3802	3811	3819	3828	3837	3846	3855	3864	3873	3882	1	2	3	4	4	5	6	7	8
.59	3890	3899	3908	3917	3926	3936	3945	3954	3963	3972	1	2	3	4	5	5	6	7	8
.60	3981	3990	3999	4009	4018	4027	4036	4046	4055	4064	1	2	3	4	5	6	6	7	8
.61	4074	4083	4093	4102	4111	4121	4130	4140	4150	4159	1	2	3	4	5	6	7	8	9
.62	4169	4178	4188	4198	4207	4217	4227	4236	4246	4256	1	2	3	4	5	6	7	8	9
.63	4266	4276	4285	4295	4305	4315	4325	4335	4345	4355	1	2	3	4	5	6	7	8	9
.64	4365	4375	4385	4395	4406	4416	4426	4436	4446	4457	1	2	3	4	5	6	7	8	9
.65	4467	4477	4487	4498	4508	4519	4529	4539	4550	4560	1	2	3	4	5	6	7	8	9
.66	4571	4581	4592	4603	4613	4624	4634	4645	4656	4667	1	2	3	4	5	6	7	9	10
.67	4677	4688	4699	4710	4721	4732	4742	4753	4764	4775	1	2	3	4	5	7	8	9	10
.68	4786	4797	4808	4819	4831	4842	4853	4864	4875	4887	1	2	3	4	6	7	8	9	10
.69	4898	4909	4920	4932	4943	4955	4966	4977	4989	5000	1	2	3	5	6	7	8	9	10
.70	5012	5023	5035	5047	5058	5070	5082	5093	5105	5117	1	2	4	5	6	7	8	9	11
.71	5129	5140	5152	5164	5176	5188	5200	5212	5224	5236	1	2	4	5	6	7	8	10	11
.72	5248	5260	5272	5284	5297	5309	5321	5333	5346	5358	1	2	4	5	6	7	9	10	11
.73	5370	5383	5395	5408	5420	5433	5445	5458	5470	5483	1	3	4	5	6	8	9	10	11
.74	5495	5508	5521	5534	5546	5559	5572	5585	5598	5610	1	3	4	5	6	8	9	10	12
.75	5623	5636	5649	5662	5675	5689	5702	5715	5728	5741	1	3	4	5	7	8	9	10	12
.76	5754	5768	5781	5794	5808	5821	5834	5848	5861	5875	1	3	4	5	7	8	9	11	12
.77	5888	5902	5916	5929	5943	5957	5970	5984	5998	6012	1	3	4	5	7	8	10	11	12
.78	6026	6039	6053	6067	6081	6095	6109	6124	6138	6152	1	3	4	6	7	8	10	11	13
.79	6166	6180	6194	6209	6223	6237	6252	6266	6281	6295	1	3	4	6	7	9	10	11	13
.80	6310	6324	6339	6353	6368	6383	6397	6412	6427	6442	1	3	4	6	7	9	10	12	13
.81	6457	6471	6486	6501	6516	6531	6546	6561	6577	6592	2	3	5	6	8	9	11	12	14
.82	6607	6622	6637	6653	6668	6683	6699	6714	6730	6745	2	3	5	6	8	9	11	12	14
.83	6761	6776	6792	6808	6823	6839	6855	6871	6887	6902	2	3	5	6	8	9	11	13	14
.84	6918	6934	6950	6966	6982	6998	7015	7031	7047	7063	2	3	5	6	8	10	11	13	15
.85	7079	7096	7112	7129	7145	7161	7178	7194	7211	7228	2	3	5	7	8	10	12	13	15
.86	7244	7261	7278	7295	7311	7328	7345	7362	7379	7396	2	3	5	7	8	10	12	13	15
.87	7413	7430	7447	7464	7482	7499	7516	7534	7551	7568	2	3	5	7	9	10	12	14	16
.88	7586	7603	7621	7638	7656	7674	7691	7709	7727	7745	2	4	5	7	9	11	12	14	16
.89	7762	7780	7798	7816	7834	7852	7870	7889	7907	7925	2	4	5	7	9	11	13	14	16
.90	7943	7962	7980	7998	8017	8035	8054	8072	8091	8110	2	4	6	7	9	11	13	15	17
.91	8128	8147	8166	8185	8204	8222	8241	8260	8279	8299	2	4	6	8	9	11	13	15	17
.92	8318	8337	8356	8375	8395	8414	8433	8453	8472	8492	2	4	6	8	10	12	14	15	17
.93	8511	8531	8551	8570	8590	8610	8630	8650	8670	8690	2	4	6	8	10	12	14	16	18
.94	8710	8730	8750	8770	8790	8810	8831	8851	8872	8892	2	4	6	8	10	12	14	16	18
.95	8913	8933	8954	8974	8995	9016	9036	9057	9078	9099	2	4	6	8	10	12	15	17	19
.96	9120	9141	9162	9183	9204	9226	9247	9268	9290	9311	2	4	6	8	11	13	15	17	19
.97	9333	9354	9376	9397	9419	9441	9462	9484	9506	9528	2	4	7	9	11	13	15	17	20
.98	9550	9572	9594	9616	9638	9661	9683	9705	9727	9750	2	4	7	9	11	13	16	18	20
.99	9772	9795	9817	9840	9863	9886	9908	9931	9954	9977	2	5	7	9	11	14	16	18	20
	0	1	2	3	4	5	6	7	8	9	1	2	3	4	5	6	7	8	9

FIVE-PLACE MANTISSAS FOR COMMON LOGARITHMS

N.	0	1	2	3	4	5	6	7	8	9
100	00 000	043	087	130	173	217	260	303	346	389
101	432	475	518	561	604	647	689	732	775	817
102	860	903	945	988	*030	*072	*115	*157	*199	*242
103	01 284	326	368	410	452	494	536	578	620	662
104	703	745	787	828	870	912	953	995	*036	*078
105	02 119	160	202	243	284	325	366	407	449	490
106	531	572	612	653	694	735	776	816	857	898
107	938	979	*019	*060	*100	*141	*181	*222	*262	*302
108	03 342	383	423	463	503	543	583	623	663	703
109	743	⁻32	822	862	902	941	981	*021	*060	*100
110	04 139	179	218	258	297	336	376	415	454	493
111	532	571	610	650	689	727	766	805	844	883
112	922	961	999	*038	*077	*115	*154	*192	*231	*269
113	05 308	346	385	423	461	500	538	576	614	652
114	690	729	767	805	843	881	918	956	994	*032
115	06 070	108	145	183	221	258	296	333	371	408
116	446	483	521	558	595	633	670	707	744	781
117	819	856	893	930	967	*004	*041	*078	*115	*151
118	07 188	225	262	298	335	372	408	445	482	518
119	555	591	628	664	700	737	773	809	846	882
120	918	954	990	*027	*063	*099	*135	*171	*207	*243
121	08 279	314	350	386	422	458	493	529	565	600
122	636	672	707	743	778	814	849	884	920	955
123	991	*026	*061	*096	*132	*167	*202	*237	*272	*307
124	09 342	377	412	447	482	517	552	587	621	656
125	691	726	760	795	830	864	899	934	968	*003
126	10 037	072	106	140	175	209	243	278	312	346
127	380	415	449	483	517	551	585	619	653	687
128	721	755	789	823	857	890	924	958	992	*025
129	11 059	093	126	160	193	227	261	294	327	361
130	394	428	461	494	528	561	594	628	661	694
131	727	760	793	826	860	893	926	959	992	*024
132	12 057	090	123	156	189	222	254	287	320	352
133	385	418	450	483	516	548	581	613	646	678
134	710	743	775	808	840	872	905	937	969	*001
135	13 033	066	098	130	162	194	226	258	290	322
136	354	386	418	450	481	513	545	577	609	640
137	672	704	735	767	799	830	862	893	925	956
138	988	*019	*051	*082	*114	*145	*176	*208	*239	*270
139	14 301	333	364	395	426	457	489	520	551	582
140	613	644	675	706	737	768	799	829	860	891
141	922	953	983	*014	*045	*076	*106	*137	*168	*198
142	15 229	259	290	320	351	381	412	442	473	503
143	534	564	594	625	655	685	715	746	776	806
144	836	866	897	927	957	987	*017	*047	*077	*107
145	16 137	167	197	227	256	286	316	346	376	406
146	435	465	495	524	554	584	613	643	673	702
147	732	761	791	820	850	879	909	938	967	997
148	17 026	056	085	114	143	173	202	231	260	289
149	319	348	377	406	435	464	493	522	551	580
150	609	638	667	696	725	754	782	811	840	869

Proportional parts

	44	43	42
1	4.4	4.3	4.2
2	8.8	8.6	8.4
3	13.2	12.9	12.6
4	17.6	17.2	16.8
5	22.0	21.5	21.0
6	26.4	25.8	25.2
7	30.8	30.1	29.4
8	35.2	34.4	33.6
9	39.6	38.7	37.8

	41	40	39
1	4.1	4.0	3.9
2	8.2	8.0	7.8
3	12.3	12.0	11.7
4	16.4	16.0	15.6
5	20.5	20.0	19.5
6	24.6	24.0	23.4
7	28.7	28.0	27.3
8	32.8	32.0	31.2
9	36.9	36.0	35.1

	38	37	36
1	3.8	3.7	3.6
2	7.6	7.4	7.2
3	11.4	11.1	10.8
4	15.2	14.8	14.4
5	19.0	18.5	18.0
6	22.8	22.2	21.6
7	26.6	25.9	25.2
8	30.4	29.6	28.8
9	34.2	33.3	32.4

	35	34	33
1	3.5	3.4	3.3
2	7.0	6.8	6.6
3	10.5	10.2	9.9
4	14.0	13.6	13.2
5	17.5	17.0	16.5
6	21.0	20.4	19.8
7	24.5	23.8	23.1
8	28.0	27.2	26.4
9	31.5	30.6	29.7

	32	31	30
1	3.2	3.1	3.0
2	6.4	6.2	6.0
3	9.6	9.3	9.0
4	12.8	12.4	12.0
5	16.0	15.5	15.0
6	19.2	18.6	18.0
7	22.4	21.7	21.0
8	25.6	24.8	24.0
9	28.8	27.9	27.0

N.	0	1	2	3	4	5	6	7	8	9	Proportional parts

FIVE-PLACE MANTISSAS FOR COMMON LOGARITHMS

N.	0	1	2	3	4	5	6	7	8	9
150	17 609	638	667	696	725	754	782	811	840	869
151	898	926	955	984	*013	*041	*070	*099	*127	*156
152	18 184	213	241	270	298	327	355	384	412	441
153	469	498	526	554	583	611	639	667	696	724
154	752	780	808	837	865	893	921	949	977	*005
155	19 033	061	089	117	145	173	201	229	257	285
156	312	340	368	396	424	451	479	507	535	562
157	590	618	645	673	700	728	756	783	811	838
158	866	893	921	948	976	*003	*030	*058	*085	*112
159	20 140	167	194	222	249	276	303	330	358	385
160	412	439	466	493	520	548	575	602	629	656
161	683	710	737	763	790	817	844	871	898	925
162	952	978	*005	*032	*059	*085	*112	*139	*165	*192
163	21 219	245	272	299	325	352	378	405	431	458
164	484	511	537	564	590	617	643	669	696	722
165	748	775	801	827	854	880	906	932	958	985
166	22 011	037	063	089	115	141	167	194	220	246
167	272	298	324	350	376	401	427	453	479	505
168	531	557	583	608	634	660	686	712	737	763
169	789	814	840	866	891	917	943	968	994	*019
170	23 045	070	096	121	147	172	198	223	249	274
171	300	325	350	376	401	426	452	477	502	528
172	553	578	603	629	654	679	704	729	754	779
173	805	830	855	880	905	930	955	980	*005	*030
174	24 055	080	105	130	155	180	204	229	254	279
175	304	329	353	378	403	428	452	477	502	527
176	551	576	601	625	650	674	699	724	748	773
177	797	822	846	871	895	920	944	969	993	*018
178	25 042	066	091	115	139	164	188	212	237	261
179	285	310	334	358	382	406	431	455	479	503
180	527	551	575	600	624	648	672	696	720	744
181	768	792	816	840	864	888	912	935	959	983
182	26 007	031	055	079	102	126	150	174	198	221
183	245	269	293	316	340	364	387	411	435	458
184	482	505	529	553	576	600	623	647	670	694
185	717	741	764	788	811	834	858	881	905	928
186	951	975	998	*021	*045	*068	*091	*114	*138	*161
187	27 184	207	231	254	277	300	323	346	370	393
188	416	439	462	485	508	531	554	577	600	623
189	646	669	692	715	738	761	784	807	830	852
190	875	898	921	944	967	989	*012	*035	*058	*081
191	28 103	126	149	171	194	217	240	262	285	307
192	330	353	375	398	421	443	466	488	511	533
193	556	578	601	623	646	668	691	713	735	758
194	780	803	825	847	870	892	914	937	959	981
195	29 003	026	048	070	092	115	137	159	181	203
196	226	248	270	292	314	336	358	380	403	425
197	447	469	491	513	535	557	579	601	623	645
198	667	688	710	732	754	776	798	820	842	863
199	885	907	929	951	973	994	*016	*038	*060	*081
200	30 103	125	146	168	190	211	233	255	276	298

Proportional parts

	29	28		27	26		25		24	23		22	21
1	2.9	2.8	1	2.7	2.6	1	2.5	1	2.4	2.3	1	2.2	2.1
2	5.8	5.6	2	5.4	5.2	2	5.0	2	4.8	4.6	2	4.4	4.2
3	8.7	8.4	3	8.1	7.8	3	7.5	3	7.2	6.9	3	6.6	6.3
4	11.6	11.2	4	10.8	10.4	4	10.0	4	9.6	9.2	4	8.8	8.4
5	14.5	14.0	5	13.5	13.0	5	12.5	5	12.0	11.5	5	11.0	10.5
6	17.4	16.8	6	16.2	15.6	6	15.0	6	14.4	13.8	6	13.2	12.6
7	20.3	19.6	7	18.9	18.2	7	17.5	7	16.8	16.1	7	15.4	14.7
8	23.2	22.4	8	21.6	20.8	8	20.0	8	19.2	18.4	8	17.6	16.8
9	26.1	25.2	9	24.3	23.4	9	22.5	9	21.6	20.7	9	19.8	18.9

| N. | 0 | 1 | 2 | 3 | 4 | 5 | 6 | 7 | 8 | 9 | Proportional parts |

FIVE-PLACE MANTISSAS FOR COMMON LOGARITHMS

N.	0	1	2	3	4	5	6	7	8	9
200	30 103	125	146	168	190	211	233	255	276	298
201	320	341	363	384	406	428	449	471	492	514
202	535	557	578	600	621	643	664	685	707	728
203	750	771	792	814	835	856	878	899	920	942
204	963	984	*006	*027	*048	*069	*091	*112	*133	*154
205	31 175	197	218	239	260	281	302	323	345	366
206	387	408	429	450	471	492	513	534	555	576
207	597	618	639	660	681	702	723	744	765	785
208	806	827	848	869	890	911	931	952	973	994
209	32 015	035	056	077	098	118	139	160	181	201
210	222	243	263	284	305	325	346	366	387	408
211	428	449	469	490	510	531	552	572	593	613
212	634	654	675	695	715	736	756	777	797	818
213	838	858	879	899	919	940	960	980	*001	*021
214	33 041	062	082	102	122	143	163	183	203	224
215	244	264	284	304	325	345	365	385	405	425
216	445	465	486	506	526	546	566	586	606	626
217	646	666	686	706	726	746	766	786	806	826
218	846	866	885	905	925	945	965	985	*005	*025
219	34 044	064	084	104	124	143	163	183	203	223
220	242	262	282	301	321	341	361	380	400	420
221	439	459	479	498	518	537	557	577	596	616
222	635	655	674	694	713	733	753	772	792	811
223	830	850	869	889	908	928	947	967	986	*005
224	35 025	044	064	083	102	122	141	160	180	199
225	218	238	257	276	295	315	334	353	372	392
226	411	430	449	468	488	507	526	545	564	583
227	603	622	641	660	679	698	717	736	755	774
228	793	813	832	851	870	889	908	927	946	965
229	984	*003	*021	*040	*059	*078	*097	*116	*135	*154
230	36 173	192	211	229	248	267	286	305	324	342
231	361	380	399	418	436	455	474	493	511	530
232	549	568	586	605	624	642	661	680	698	717
233	736	754	773	791	810	829	847	866	884	903
234	922	940	959	977	996	*014	*033	*051	*070	*088
235	37 107	125	144	162	181	199	218	236	254	273
236	291	310	328	346	365	383	401	420	438	457
237	475	493	511	530	548	566	585	603	621	639
238	658	676	694	712	731	749	767	785	803	822
239	840	858	876	894	912	931	949	967	985	*003
240	38 021	039	057	075	093	112	130	148	166	184
241	202	220	238	256	274	292	310	328	346	364
242	382	399	417	435	453	471	489	507	525	543
243	561	578	596	614	632	650	668	686	703	721
244	739	757	775	792	810	828	846	863	881	899
245	917	934	952	970	987	*005	*023	*041	*058	*076
246	39 094	111	129	146	164	182	199	217	235	252
247	270	287	305	322	340	358	375	393	410	428
248	445	463	480	498	515	533	550	568	585	602
249	620	637	655	672	690	707	724	742	759	777
250	794	811	829	846	863	881	898	915	933	950

Proportional parts

	22	21
1	2.2	2.1
2	4.4	4.2
3	6.6	6.3
4	8.8	8.4
5	11.0	10.5
6	13.2	12.6
7	15.4	14.7
8	17.6	16.8
9	19.8	18.9

	20
1	2.0
2	4.0
3	6.0
4	8.0
5	10.0
6	12.0
7	14.0
8	16.0
9	18.0

	19
1	1.9
2	3.8
3	5.7
4	7.6
5	9.5
6	11.4
7	13.3
8	15.2
9	17.1

	18
1	1.8
2	3.6
3	5.4
4	7.2
5	9.0
6	10.8
7	12.6
8	14.4
9	16.2

	17
1	1.7
2	3.4
3	5.1
4	6.8
5	8.5
6	10.2
7	11.9
8	13.6
9	15.3

| N. | 0 | 1 | 2 | 3 | 4 | 5 | 6 | 7 | 8 | 9 | Proportional parts |

FIVE-PLACE MANTISSAS FOR COMMON LOGARITHMS

N.	0	1	2	3	4	5	6	7	8	9	Proportional parts
250	39 794	811	829	846	863	881	898	915	933	950	**18**
251	967	985	*002	*019	*037	*054	*071	*088	*106	*123	1 1.8
252	40 140	157	175	192	209	226	243	261	278	295	2 3.6
253	312	329	346	364	381	398	415	432	449	466	3 5.4
254	483	500	518	535	552	569	586	603	620	637	4 7.2
255	654	671	688	705	722	739	756	773	790	807	5 9.0
256	824	841	858	875	892	909	926	943	960	976	6 10.8
257	993	*010	*027	*044	*061	*078	*095	*111	*128	*145	7 12.6
258	41 162	179	196	212	229	246	263	280	296	313	8 14.4
259	330	347	363	380	397	414	430	447	464	481	9 16.2
260	497	514	531	547	564	581	597	614	631	647	**17**
261	664	681	697	714	731	747	764	780	797	814	1 1.7
262	830	847	863	880	896	913	929	946	963	979	2 3.4
263	996	*012	*029	*045	*062	*078	*095	*111	*127	*144	3 5.1
264	42 160	177	193	210	226	243	259	275	292	308	4 6.8
265	325	341	357	374	390	406	423	439	455	472	5 8.5
266	488	504	521	537	553	570	586	602	619	635	6 10.2
267	651	667	684	700	716	732	749	765	781	797	7 11.9
268	813	830	846	862	878	894	911	927	943	959	8 13.6
269	975	991	*008	*024	*040	*056	*072	*088	*104	*120	9 15.3
270	43 136	152	169	185	201	217	233	249	265	281	**16**
271	297	313	329	345	361	377	393	409	425	441	1 1.6
272	457	473	489	505	521	537	553	569	584	600	2 3.2
273	616	632	648	664	680	696	712	727	743	759	3 4.8
274	775	791	807	823	838	854	870	886	902	917	4 6.4
275	933	949	965	981	996	*012	*028	*044	*059	*075	5 8.0
276	44 091	107	122	138	154	170	185	201	217	232	6 9.6
277	248	264	279	295	311	326	342	358	373	389	7 11.2
278	404	420	436	451	467	483	498	514	529	545	8 12.8
279	560	576	592	607	623	638	654	669	685	700	9 14.4
280	716	731	747	762	778	793	809	824	840	855	**15**
281	871	886	902	917	932	948	963	979	994	*010	1 1.5
282	45 025	040	056	071	086	102	117	133	148	163	2 3.0
283	179	194	209	225	240	255	271	286	301	317	3 4.5
284	332	347	362	378	393	408	423	439	454	469	4 6.0
285	484	500	515	530	545	561	576	591	606	621	5 7.5
286	637	652	667	682	697	712	728	743	758	773	6 9.0
287	788	803	818	834	849	864	879	894	909	924	7 10.5
288	939	954	969	984	*000	*015	*030	*045	*060	*075	8 12.0
289	46 090	105	120	135	150	165	180	195	210	225	9 13.5
290	240	255	270	285	300	315	330	345	359	374	**14**
291	389	404	419	434	449	464	479	494	509	523	1 1.4
292	538	553	568	583	598	613	627	642	657	672	2 2.8
293	687	702	716	731	746	761	776	790	805	820	3 4.2
294	835	850	864	879	894	909	923	938	953	967	4 5.6
295	982	997	*012	*026	*041	*056	*070	*085	*100	*114	5 7.0
296	47 129	144	159	173	188	202	217	232	246	261	6 8.4
297	276	290	305	319	334	349	363	378	392	407	7 9.8
298	422	436	451	465	480	494	509	524	538	553	8 11.2
299	567	582	596	611	625	640	654	669	683	698	9 12.6
300	712	727	741	756	770	784	799	813	828	842	
N.	0	1	2	3	4	5	6	7	8	9	Proportional parts

FIVE-PLACE MANTISSAS FOR COMMON LOGARITHMS

N.	0	1	2	3	4	5	6	7	8	9
300	47 712	727	741	756	770	784	799	813	828	842
301	857	871	885	900	914	929	943	958	972	986
302	48 001	015	029	044	058	073	087	101	116	130
303	144	159	173	187	202	216	230	244	259	273
304	287	302	316	330	344	359	373	387	401	416
305	430	444	458	473	487	501	515	530	544	558
306	572	586	601	615	629	643	657	671	686	700
307	714	728	742	756	770	785	799	813	827	841
308	855	869	883	897	911	926	940	954	968	982
309	996	*010	*024	*038	*052	*066	*080	*094	*108	*122
310	49 136	150	164	178	192	206	220	234	248	262
311	276	290	304	318	332	346	360	374	388	402
312	415	429	443	457	471	485	499	513	527	541
313	554	568	582	596	610	624	638	651	665	679
314	693	707	721	734	748	762	776	790	803	817
315	831	845	859	872	886	900	914	927	941	955
316	969	982	996	*010	*024	*037	*051	*065	*079	*092
317	50 106	120	133	147	161	174	188	202	215	229
318	243	256	270	284	297	311	325	338	352	365
319	379	393	406	420	433	447	461	474	488	501
320	515	529	542	556	569	583	596	610	623	637
321	651	664	678	691	705	718	732	745	759	772
322	786	799	813	826	840	853	866	880	893	907
323	920	934	947	961	974	987	*001	*014	*028	*041
324	51 055	068	081	095	108	121	135	148	162	175
325	188	202	215	228	242	255	268	282	295	308
326	322	335	348	362	375	388	402	415	428	441
327	455	468	481	495	508	521	534	548	561	574
328	587	601	614	627	640	654	667	680	693	706
329	720	733	746	759	772	786	799	812	825	838
330	851	865	878	891	904	917	930	943	957	970
331	983	996	*009	*022	*035	*048	*061	*075	*088	*101
332	52 114	127	140	153	166	179	192	205	218	231
333	244	257	270	284	297	310	323	336	349	362
334	375	388	401	414	427	440	453	466	479	492
335	504	517	530	543	556	569	582	595	608	621
336	634	647	660	673	686	699	711	724	737	750
337	763	776	789	802	815	827	840	853	866	879
338	892	905	917	930	943	956	969	982	994	*007
339	53 020	033	046	058	071	084	097	110	122	135
340	148	161	173	186	199	212	224	237	250	263
341	275	288	301	314	326	339	352	364	377	390
342	403	415	428	441	453	466	479	491	504	517
343	529	542	555	567	580	593	605	618	631	643
344	656	668	681	694	706	719	732	744	757	769
345	782	794	807	820	832	845	857	870	882	895
346	908	920	933	945	958	970	983	995	*008	*020
347	54 033	045	058	070	083	095	108	120	133	145
348	158	170	183	195	208	220	233	245	258	270
349	283	295	307	320	332	345	357	370	382	394
350	407	419	432	444	456	469	481	494	506	518
N.	0	1	2	3	4	5	6	7	8	9

Proportional parts

15		14		13		12	
1	1.5	1	1.4	1	1.3	1	1.2
2	3.0	2	2.8	2	2.6	2	2.4
3	4.5	3	4.2	3	3.9	3	3.6
4	6.0	4	5.6	4	5.2	4	4.8
5	7.5	5	7.0	5	6.5	5	6.0
6	9.0	6	8.4	6	7.8	6	7.2
7	10.5	7	9.8	7	9.1	7	8.4
8	12.0	8	11.2	8	10.4	8	9.6
9	13.5	9	12.6	9	11.7	9	10.8

FIVE-PLACE MANTISSAS FOR COMMON LOGARITHMS

N.	0	1	2	3	4	5	6	7	8	9
350	54 407	419	432	444	456	469	481	494	506	518
351	531	543	555	568	580	593	605	617	630	642
352	654	667	679	691	704	716	728	741	753	765
353	777	790	802	814	827	839	851	864	876	888
354	900	913	925	937	949	962	974	986	998	*011
355	55 023	035	047	060	072	084	096	108	121	133
356	145	157	169	182	194	206	218	230	242	255
357	267	279	291	303	315	328	340	352	364	376
358	388	400	413	425	437	449	461	473	485	497
359	509	522	534	546	558	570	582	594	606	618
360	630	642	654	666	678	691	703	715	727	739
361	751	763	775	787	799	811	823	835	847	859
362	871	883	895	907	919	931	943	955	967	979
363	991	*003	*015	*027	*038	*050	*062	*074	*086	*098
364	56 110	122	134	146	158	170	182	194	205	217
365	229	241	253	265	277	289	301	312	324	336
366	348	360	372	384	396	407	419	431	443	455
367	467	478	490	502	514	526	538	549	561	573
368	585	597	608	620	632	644	656	667	679	691
369	703	714	726	738	750	761	773	785	797	808
370	820	832	844	855	867	879	891	902	914	926
371	937	949	961	972	984	996	*008	*019	*031	*043
372	57 054	066	078	089	101	113	124	136	148	159
373	171	183	194	206	217	229	241	252	264	276
374	287	299	310	322	334	345	357	368	380	392
375	403	415	426	438	449	461	473	484	496	507
376	519	530	542	553	565	576	588	600	611	623
377	634	646	657	669	680	692	703	715	726	738
378	749	761	772	784	795	807	818	830	841	852
379	864	875	887	898	910	921	933	944	955	967
380	978	990	*001	*013	*024	*035	*047	*058	*070	*081
381	58 092	104	115	127	138	149	161	172	184	195
382	206	218	229	240	252	263	274	286	297	309
383	320	331	343	354	365	377	388	399	410	422
384	433	444	456	467	478	490	501	512	524	535
385	546	557	569	580	591	602	614	625	636	647
386	659	670	681	692	704	715	726	737	749	760
387	771	782	794	805	816	827	838	850	861	872
388	883	894	906	917	928	939	950	961	973	984
389	995	*006	*017	*028	*040	*051	*062	*073	*084	*095
390	59 106	118	129	140	151	162	173	184	195	207
391	218	229	240	251	262	273	284	295	306	318
392	329	340	351	362	373	384	395	406	417	428
393	439	450	461	472	483	494	506	517	528	539
394	550	561	572	583	594	605	616	627	638	649
395	660	671	682	693	704	715	726	737	748	759
396	770	780	791	802	813	824	835	846	857	868
397	879	890	901	912	923	934	945	956	966	977
398	988	999	*010	*021	*032	*043	*054	*065	*076	*086
399	60 097	108	119	130	141	152	163	173	184	195
400	206	217	228	239	249	260	271	282	293	304

Proportional parts

	13		12		11		10
1	1.3	1	1.2	1	1.1	1	1.0
2	2.6	2	2.4	2	2.2	2	2.0
3	3.9	3	3.6	3	3.3	3	3.0
4	5.2	4	4.8	4	4.4	4	4.0
5	6.5	5	6.0	5	5.5	5	5.0
6	7.8	6	7.2	6	6.6	6	6.0
7	9.1	7	8.4	7	7.7	7	7.0
8	10.4	8	9.6	8	8.8	8	8.0
9	11.7	9	10.8	9	9.9	9	9.0

FIVE-PLACE MANTISSAS FOR COMMON LOGARITHMS

N.	0	1	2	3	4	5	6	7	8	9
400	60 206	217	228	239	249	260	271	282	293	304
401	314	325	336	347	358	369	379	390	401	412
402	423	433	444	455	466	477	487	498	509	520
403	531	541	552	563	574	584	595	606	617	627
404	638	649	660	670	681	692	703	713	724	735
405	746	756	767	778	788	799	810	821	831	842
406	853	863	874	885	895	906	917	927	938	949
407	959	970	981	991	*002	*013	*023	*034	*045	*055
408	61 066	077	087	098	109	119	130	140	151	162
409	172	183	194	204	215	225	236	247	257	268
410	278	289	300	310	321	331	342	352	363	374
411	384	395	405	416	426	437	448	458	469	479
412	490	500	511	521	532	542	553	563	574	584
413	595	606	616	627	637	648	658	669	679	690
414	700	711	721	731	742	752	763	773	784	794
415	805	815	826	836	847	857	868	878	888	899
416	909	920	930	941	951	962	972	982	993	*003
417	62 014	024	034	045	055	066	076	086	097	107
418	118	128	138	149	159	170	180	190	201	211
419	221	232	242	252	263	273	284	294	304	315
420	325	335	346	356	366	377	387	397	408	418
421	428	439	449	459	469	480	490	500	511	521
422	531	542	552	562	572	583	593	603	613	624
423	634	644	655	665	675	685	696	706	716	726
424	737	747	757	767	778	788	798	808	818	829
425	839	849	859	870	880	890	900	910	921	931
426	941	951	961	972	982	992	*002	*012	*022	*033
427	63 043	053	063	073	083	094	104	114	124	134
428	144	155	165	175	185	195	205	215	225	236
429	246	256	266	276	286	296	306	317	327	337
430	347	357	367	377	387	397	407	417	428	438
431	448	458	468	478	488	498	508	518	528	538
432	548	558	568	579	589	599	609	619	629	639
433	649	659	669	679	689	699	709	719	729	739
434	749	759	769	779	789	799	809	819	829	839
435	849	859	869	879	889	899	909	919	929	939
436	949	959	969	979	988	998	*008	*018	*028	*038
437	64 048	058	068	078	088	098	108	118	128	137
438	147	157	167	177	187	197	207	217	227	237
439	246	256	266	276	286	296	306	316	326	335
440	345	355	365	375	385	395	404	414	424	434
441	444	454	464	473	483	493	503	513	523	532
442	542	552	562	572	582	591	601	611	621	631
443	640	650	660	670	680	689	699	709	719	729
444	738	748	758	768	777	787	797	807	816	826
445	836	846	856	865	875	885	895	904	914	924
446	933	943	953	963	972	982	992	*002	*011	*021
447	65 031	040	050	060	070	079	089	099	108	118
448	128	137	147	157	167	176	186	196	205	215
449	225	234	244	254	263	273	283	292	302	312
450	321	331	341	350	360	369	379	389	398	408

Proportional parts

11		**10**		**9**	
1	1.1	1	1.0	1	0.9
2	2.2	2	2.0	2	1.8
3	3.3	3	3.0	3	2.7
4	4.4	4	4.0	4	3.6
5	5.5	5	5.0	5	4.5
6	6.6	6	6.0	6	5.4
7	7.7	7	7.0	7	6.3
8	8.8	8	8.0	8	7.2
9	9.9	9	9.0	9	8.1

FIVE-PLACE MANTISSAS FOR COMMON LOGARITHMS

N.	0	1	2	3	4	5	6	7	8	9	Proportional parts	
450	65 321	331	341	350	360	369	379	389	398	408		
451	418	427	437	447	456	466	475	485	495	504		
452	514	523	533	543	552	562	571	581	591	600		
453	610	619	629	639	648	658	667	677	686	696		
454	706	715	725	734	744	753	763	772	782	792		
455	801	811	820	830	839	849	858	868	877	887		
456	896	906	916	925	935	944	954	963	973	982		
457	992	*001	*011	*020	*030	*039	*049	*058	*068	*077		**10**
458	66 087	096	106	115	124	134	143	153	162	172	1	1.0
459	181	191	200	210	219	229	238	247	257	266	2	2.0
											3	3.0
460	276	285	295	304	314	323	332	342	351	361	4	4.0
461	370	380	389	398	408	417	427	436	445	455	5	5.0
462	464	474	483	492	502	511	521	530	539	549	6	6.0
463	558	567	577	586	596	605	614	624	633	642	7	7.0
464	652	661	671	680	689	699	708	717	727	736	8	8.0
465	745	755	764	773	783	792	801	811	820	829	9	9.0
466	839	848	857	867	876	885	894	904	913	922		
467	932	941	950	960	969	978	987	997	*006	*015		
468	67 025	034	043	052	062	071	080	089	099	108		
469	117	127	136	145	154	164	173	182	191	201		
470	210	219	228	237	247	256	265	274	284	293		
471	302	311	321	330	339	348	357	367	376	385		
472	394	403	413	422	431	440	449	459	468	477		
473	486	495	504	514	523	532	541	550	560	569		**9**
474	578	587	596	605	614	624	633	642	651	660	1	0.9
475	669	679	688	697	706	715	724	733	742	752	2	1.8
476	761	770	779	788	797	806	815	825	834	843	3	2.7
477	852	861	870	879	888	897	906	916	925	934	4	3.6
478	943	952	961	970	979	988	997	*006	*015	*024	5	4.5
479	68 034	043	052	061	070	079	088	097	106	115	6	5.4
											7	6.3
480	124	133	142	151	160	169	178	187	196	205	8	7.2
481	215	224	233	242	251	260	269	278	287	296	9	8.1
482	305	314	323	332	341	350	359	368	377	386		
483	395	404	413	422	431	440	449	458	467	476		
484	485	494	502	511	520	529	538	547	556	565		
485	574	583	592	601	610	619	628	637	646	655		
486	664	673	681	690	699	708	717	726	735	744		
487	753	762	771	780	789	797	806	815	824	833		
488	842	851	860	869	878	886	895	904	913	922		**8**
489	931	940	949	958	966	975	984	993	*002	*011	1	0.8
											2	1.6
490	69 020	028	037	046	055	064	073	082	090	099	3	2.4
491	108	117	126	135	144	152	161	170	179	188	4	3.2
492	197	205	214	223	232	241	249	258	267	276	5	4.0
493	285	294	302	311	320	329	338	346	355	364	6	4.8
494	373	381	390	399	408	417	425	434	443	452	7	5.6
495	461	469	478	487	496	504	513	522	531	539	8	6.4
496	548	557	566	574	583	592	601	609	618	627	9	7.2
497	636	644	653	662	671	679	688	697	705	714		
498	723	732	740	749	758	767	775	784	793	801		
499	810	819	827	836	845	854	862	871	880	888		
500	897	906	914	923	932	940	949	958	966	975		

N.	0	1	2	3	4	5	6	7	8	9	Proportional parts	

FIVE-PLACE MANTISSAS FOR COMMON LOGARITHMS

N.	0	1	2	3	4	5	6	7	8	9
500	69 897	906	914	923	932	940	949	958	966	975
501	984	992	*001	*010	*018	*027	*036	*044	*053	*062
502	70 070	079	088	096	105	114	122	131	140	148
503	157	165	174	183	191	200	209	217	226	234
504	243	252	260	269	278	286	295	303	312	321
505	329	338	346	355	364	372	381	389	398	406
506	415	424	432	441	449	458	467	475	484	492
507	501	509	518	526	535	544	552	561	569	578
508	586	595	603	612	621	629	638	646	655	663
509	672	680	689	697	706	714	723	731	740	749
510	757	766	774	783	791	800	808	817	825	834
511	842	851	859	868	876	885	893	902	910	919
512	927	935	944	952	961	969	978	986	995	*003
513	71 012	020	029	037	046	054	063	071	079	088
514	096	105	113	122	130	139	147	155	164	172
515	181	189	198	206	214	223	231	240	248	257
516	265	273	282	290	299	307	315	324	332	341
517	349	357	366	374	383	391	399	408	416	425
518	433	441	450	458	466	475	483	492	500	508
519	517	525	533	542	550	559	567	575	584	592
520	600	609	617	625	634	642	650	659	667	675
521	684	692	700	709	717	725	734	742	750	759
522	767	775	784	792	800	809	817	825	834	842
523	850	858	867	875	883	892	900	908	917	925
524	933	941	950	958	966	975	983	991	999	*008
525	72 016	024	032	041	049	057	066	074	082	090
526	099	107	115	123	132	140	148	156	165	173
527	181	189	198	206	214	222	230	239	247	255
528	263	272	280	288	296	304	313	321	329	337
529	346	354	362	370	378	387	395	403	411	419
530	428	436	444	452	460	469	477	485	493	501
531	509	518	526	534	542	550	558	567	575	583
532	591	599	607	616	624	632	640	648	656	665
533	673	681	689	697	705	713	722	730	738	746
534	754	762	770	779	787	795	803	811	819	827
535	835	843	852	860	868	876	884	892	900	908
536	916	925	933	941	949	957	965	973	981	989
537	997	*006	*014	*022	*030	*038	*046	*054	*062	*070
538	73 078	086	094	102	111	119	127	135	143	151
539	159	167	175	183	191	199	207	215	223	231
540	239	247	255	263	272	280	288	296	304	312
541	320	328	336	344	352	360	368	376	384	392
542	400	408	416	424	432	440	448	456	464	472
543	480	488	496	504	512	520	528	536	544	552
544	560	568	576	584	592	600	608	616	624	632
545	640	648	656	664	672	679	687	695	703	711
546	719	727	735	743	751	759	767	775	783	791
547	799	807	815	823	830	838	846	854	862	870
548	878	886	894	902	910	918	926	933	941	949
549	957	965	973	981	989	997	*005	*013	*020	*028
550	74 036	044	052	060	068	076	084	092	099	107
N	0	1	2	3	4	5	6	7	8	9

Proportional parts

	9
1	0.9
2	1.8
3	2.7
4	3.6
5	4.5
6	5.4
7	6.3
8	7.2
9	8.1

	8
1	0.8
2	1.6
3	2.4
4	3.2
5	4.0
6	4.8
7	5.6
8	6.4
9	7.2

	7
1	0.7
2	1.4
3	2.1
4	2.8
5	3.5
6	4.2
7	4.9
8	5.6
9	6.3

Proportional parts

FIVE-PLACE MANTISSAS FOR COMMON LOGARITHMS

N.	0	1	2	3	4	5	6	7	8	9	Proportional parts
550	74 036	044	052	060	068	076	084	092	099	107	
551	115	123	131	139	147	155	162	170	178	186	
552	194	202	210	218	225	233	241	249	257	265	
553	273	280	288	296	304	312	320	327	335	343	
554	351	359	367	374	382	390	398	406	414	421	
555	429	437	445	453	461	468	476	484	492	500	
556	507	515	523	531	539	547	554	562	570	578	
557	586	593	601	609	617	624	632	640	648	656	
558	663	671	679	687	695	702	710	718	726	733	
559	741	749	757	764	772	780	788	796	803	811	
560	819	827	834	842	850	858	865	873	881	889	**8**
561	896	904	912	920	927	935	943	950	958	966	1 0.8
562	974	981	989	997	*005	*012	*020	*028	*035	*043	2 1.6
563	75 051	059	066	074	082	089	097	105	113	120	3 2.4
564	128	136	143	151	159	166	174	182	189	197	4 3.2
565	205	213	220	228	236	243	251	259	266	274	5 4.0
566	282	289	297	305	312	320	328	335	343	351	6 4.8
567	358	366	374	381	389	397	404	412	420	427	7 5.6
568	435	442	450	458	465	473	481	488	496	504	8 6.4
569	511	519	526	534	542	549	557	565	572	580	9 7.2
570	587	595	603	610	618	626	633	641	648	656	
571	664	671	679	686	694	702	709	717	724	732	
572	740	747	755	762	770	778	785	793	800	808	
573	815	823	831	838	846	853	861	868	876	884	
574	891	899	906	914	921	929	937	944	952	959	
575	967	974	982	989	997	*005	*012	*020	*027	*035	
576	76 042	050	057	065	072	080	087	095	103	110	
577	118	125	133	140	148	155	163	170	178	185	
578	193	200	208	215	223	230	238	245	253	260	
579	268	275	283	290	298	305	313	320	328	335	
580	343	350	358	365	373	380	388	395	403	410	**7**
581	418	425	433	440	448	455	462	470	477	485	1 0.7
582	492	500	507	515	522	530	537	545	552	559	2 1.4
583	567	574	582	589	597	604	612	619	626	634	3 2.1
584	641	649	656	664	671	678	686	693	701	708	4 2.8
585	716	723	730	738	745	753	760	768	775	782	5 3.5
586	790	797	805	812	819	827	834	842	849	856	6 4.2
587	864	871	879	886	893	901	908	916	923	930	7 4.9
588	938	945	953	960	967	975	982	989	997	*004	8 5.6
589	77 012	019	026	034	041	048	056	063	070	078	9 6.3
590	085	093	100	107	115	122	129	137	144	151	
591	159	166	173	181	188	195	203	210	217	225	
592	232	240	247	254	262	269	276	283	291	298	
593	305	313	320	327	335	342	349	357	364	371	
594	379	386	393	401	408	415	422	430	437	444	
595	452	459	466	474	481	488	495	503	510	517	
596	525	532	539	546	554	561	568	576	583	590	
597	597	605	612	619	627	634	641	648	656	663	
598	670	677	685	692	699	706	714	721	728	735	
599	743	750	757	764	772	779	786	793	801	808	
600	815	822	830	837	844	851	859	866	873	880	
N.	0	1	2	3	4	5	6	7	8	9	Proportional parts

FIVE-PLACE MANTISSAS FOR COMMON LOGARITHMS

N.	0	1	2	3	4	5	6	7	8	9
600	77 815	822	830	837	844	851	859	866	873	880
601	887	895	902	909	916	924	931	938	945	952
602	960	967	974	981	988	996	*003	*010	*017	*025
603	78 032	039	046	053	061	068	075	082	089	097
604	104	111	118	125	132	140	147	154	161	168
605	176	183	190	197	204	211	219	226	233	240
606	247	254	262	269	276	283	290	297	305	312
607	319	326	333	340	347	355	362	369	376	383
608	390	398	405	412	419	426	433	440	447	455
609	462	469	476	483	490	497	504	512	519	526
610	533	540	547	554	561	569	576	583	590	597
611	604	611	618	625	633	640	647	654	661	668
612	675	682	689	696	704	711	718	725	732	739
613	746	753	760	767	774	781	789	796	803	810
614	817	824	831	838	845	852	859	866	873	880
615	888	895	902	909	916	923	930	937	944	951
616	958	965	972	979	986	993	*000	*007	*014	*021
617	79 029	036	043	050	057	064	071	078	085	092
618	099	106	113	120	127	134	141	148	155	162
619	169	176	183	190	197	204	211	218	225	232
620	239	246	253	260	267	274	281	288	295	302
621	309	316	323	330	337	344	351	358	365	372
622	379	386	393	400	407	414	421	428	435	442
623	449	456	463	470	477	484	491	498	505	511
624	518	525	532	539	546	553	560	567	574	581
625	588	595	602	609	616	623	630	637	644	650
626	657	664	671	678	685	692	699	706	713	720
627	727	734	741	748	754	761	768	775	782	789
628	796	803	810	817	824	831	837	844	851	858
629	865	872	879	886	893	900	906	913	920	927
630	934	941	948	955	962	969	975	982	989	996
631	80 003	010	017	024	030	037	044	051	058	065
632	072	079	085	092	099	106	113	120	127	134
633	140	147	154	161	168	175	182	188	195	202
634	209	216	223	229	236	243	250	257	264	271
635	277	284	291	298	305	312	318	325	332	339
636	346	353	359	366	373	380	387	393	400	407
637	414	421	428	434	441	448	455	462	468	475
638	482	489	496	502	509	516	523	530	536	543
639	550	557	564	570	577	584	591	598	604	611
640	618	625	632	638	645	652	659	665	672	679
641	686	693	699	706	713	720	726	733	740	747
642	754	760	767	774	781	787	794	801	808	814
643	821	828	835	841	848	855	862	868	875	882
644	889	895	902	909	916	922	929	936	943	949
645	956	963	969	976	983	990	996	*003	*010	*017
646	81 023	030	037	043	050	057	064	070	077	084
647	090	097	104	111	117	124	131	137	144	151
648	158	164	171	178	184	191	198	204	211	218
649	224	231	238	245	251	258	265	271	278	285
650	291	298	305	311	318	325	331	338	345	351

Proportional parts

	8		7		6
1	0.8	1	0.7	1	0.6
2	1.6	2	1.4	2	1.2
3	2.4	3	2.1	3	1.8
4	3.2	4	2.8	4	2.4
5	4.0	5	3.5	5	3.0
6	4.8	6	4.2	6	3.6
7	5.6	7	4.9	7	4.2
8	6.4	8	5.6	8	4.8
9	7.2	9	6.3	9	5.4

FIVE-PLACE MANTISSAS FOR COMMON LOGARITHMS

N.	0	1	2	3	4	5	6	7	8	9
650	81 291	298	305	311	318	325	331	338	345	351
651	358	365	371	378	385	391	398	405	411	418
652	425	431	438	445	451	458	465	471	478	485
653	491	498	505	511	518	525	531	538	544	551
654	558	564	571	578	584	591	598	604	611	617
655	624	631	637	644	651	657	664	671	677	684
656	690	697	704	710	717	723	730	737	743	750
657	757	763	770	776	783	790	796	803	809	816
658	823	829	836	842	849	856	862	869	875	882
659	889	895	902	908	915	921	928	935	941	948
660	954	961	968	974	981	987	994	*000	*007	*014
661	82 020	027	033	040	046	053	060	066	073	079
662	086	092	099	105	112	119	125	132	138	145
663	151	158	164	171	178	184	191	197	204	210
664	217	223	230	236	243	249	256	263	269	276
665	282	289	295	302	308	315	321	328	334	341
666	347	354	360	367	373	380	387	393	400	406
667	413	419	426	432	439	445	452	458	465	471
668	478	484	491	497	504	510	517	523	530	536
669	543	549	556	562	569	575	582	588	595	601
670	607	614	620	627	633	640	646	653	659	666
671	672	679	685	692	698	705	711	718	724	730
672	737	743	750	756	763	769	776	782	789	795
673	802	808	814	821	827	834	840	847	853	860
674	866	872	879	885	892	898	905	911	918	924
675	930	937	943	950	956	963	969	975	982	988
676	995	*001	*008	*014	*020	*027	*033	*040	*046	*052
677	83 059	065	072	078	085	091	097	104	110	117
678	123	129	136	142	149	155	161	168	174	181
679	187	193	200	206	213	219	225	232	238	245
680	251	257	264	270	276	283	289	296	302	308
681	315	321	327	334	340	347	353	359	366	372
682	378	385	391	398	404	410	417	423	429	436
683	442	448	455	461	467	474	480	487	493	499
684	506	512	518	525	531	537	544	550	556	563
685	569	575	582	588	594	601	607	613	620	626
686	632	639	645	651	658	664	670	677	683	689
687	696	702	708	715	721	727	734	740	746	753
688	759	765	771	778	784	790	797	803	809	816
689	822	828	835	841	847	853	860	866	872	879
690	885	891	897	904	910	916	923	929	935	942
691	948	954	960	967	973	979	985	992	998	*004
692	84 011	017	023	029	036	042	048	055	061	067
693	073	080	086	092	098	105	111	117	123	130
694	136	142	148	155	161	167	173	180	186	192
695	198	205	211	217	223	230	236	242	248	255
696	261	267	273	280	286	292	298	305	311	317
697	323	330	336	342	348	354	361	367	373	379
698	386	392	398	404	410	417	423	429	435	442
699	448	454	460	466	473	479	485	491	497	504
700	510	516	522	528	535	541	547	553	559	566

N.	0	1	2	3	4	5	6	7	8	9

Proportional parts

	7		6
1	0.7	1	0.6
2	1.4	2	1.2
3	2.1	3	1.8
4	2.8	4	2.4
5	3.5	5	3.0
6	4.2	6	3.6
7	4.9	7	4.2
8	5.6	8	4.8
9	6.3	9	5.4

FIVE-PLACE MANTISSAS FOR COMMON LOGARITHMS

N.	0	1	2	3	4	5	6	7	8	9	Proportional parts	
700	84 510	516	522	528	535	541	547	553	559	566		
701	572	578	584	590	597	603	609	615	621	628		
702	634	640	646	652	658	665	671	677	683	689		
703	696	702	708	714	720	726	733	739	745	751		
704	757	763	770	776	782	788	794	800	807	813		
705	819	825	831	837	844	850	856	862	868	874		
706	880	887	893	899	905	911	917	924	930	936		
707	942	948	954	960	967	973	979	985	991	997		**7**
708	85 003	009	016	022	028	034	040	046	052	058	1	0.7
709	065	071	077	083	089	095	101	107	114	120	2	1.4
											3	2.1
710	126	132	138	144	150	156	163	169	175	181	4	2.8
711	187	193	199	205	211	217	224	230	236	242	5	3.5
712	248	254	260	266	272	278	285	291	297	303	6	4.2
713	309	315	321	327	333	339	345	352	358	364	7	4.9
714	370	376	382	388	394	400	406	412	418	425	8	5.6
715	431	437	443	449	455	461	467	473	479	485	9	6.3
716	491	497	503	509	516	522	528	534	540	546		
717	552	558	564	570	576	582	588	594	600	606		
718	612	618	625	631	637	643	649	655	661	667		
719	673	679	685	691	697	703	709	715	721	727		**6**
											1	0.6
720	733	739	745	751	757	763	769	775	781	788	2	1.2
721	794	800	806	812	818	824	830	836	842	848	3	1.8
722	854	860	866	872	878	884	890	896	902	908	4	2.4
723	914	920	926	932	938	944	950	956	962	968	5	3.0
724	974	980	986	992	998	*004	*010	*016	*022	*028	6	3.6
725	86 034	040	046	052	058	064	070	076	082	088	7	4.2
726	094	100	106	112	118	124	130	136	141	147	8	4.8
727	153	159	165	171	177	183	189	195	201	207	9	5.4
728	213	219	225	231	237	243	249	255	261	267		
729	273	279	285	291	297	303	308	314	320	326		
730	332	338	344	350	356	362	368	374	380	386		**5**
731	392	398	404	410	415	421	427	433	439	445	1	0.5
732	451	457	463	469	475	481	487	493	499	504	2	1.0
733	510	516	522	528	534	540	546	552	558	564	3	1.5
734	570	576	581	587	593	599	605	611	617	623	4	2.0
735	629	635	641	646	652	658	664	670	676	682	5	2.5
736	688	694	700	705	711	717	723	729	735	741	6	3.0
737	747	753	759	764	770	776	782	788	794	800	7	3.5
738	806	812	817	823	829	835	841	847	853	859	8	4.0
739	864	870	876	882	888	894	900	906	911	917	9	4.5
740	923	929	935	941	947	953	958	964	970	976		
741	982	988	994	999	*005	*011	*017	*023	*029	*035		
742	87 040	046	052	058	064	070	075	081	087	093		
743	099	105	111	116	122	128	134	140	146	151		
744	157	163	169	175	181	186	192	198	204	210		
745	216	221	227	233	239	245	251	256	262	268		
746	274	280	286	291	297	303	309	315	320	326		
747	332	338	344	349	355	361	367	373	379	384		
748	390	396	402	408	413	419	425	431	437	442		
749	448	454	460	466	471	477	483	489	495	500		
750	506	512	518	523	529	535	541	547	552	558		
N.	0	1	2	3	4	5	6	7	8	9	Proportional parts	

FIVE-PLACE MANTISSAS FOR COMMON LOGARITHMS

N.	0	1	2	3	4	5	6	7	8	9	Proportional parts	
750	87 506	512	518	523	529	535	541	547	552	558		
751	564	570	576	581	587	593	599	604	610	616		
752	622	628	633	639	645	651	656	662	668	674		
753	679	685	691	697	703	708	714	720	726	731		
754	737	743	749	754	760	766	772	777	783	789		
755	795	800	806	812	818	823	829	835	841	846		
756	852	858	864	869	875	881	887	892	898	904		
757	910	915	921	927	933	938	944	950	955	961		
758	967	973	978	984	990	996	*001	*007	*013	*018		
759	88 024	030	036	041	047	053	058	064	070	076		
760	081	087	093	098	104	110	116	121	127	133		**6**
761	138	144	150	156	161	167	173	178	184	190	1	0.6
762	195	201	207	213	218	224	230	235	241	247	2	1.2
763	252	258	264	270	275	281	287	292	298	304	3	1.8
764	309	315	321	326	332	338	343	349	355	360	4	2.4
765	366	372	377	383	389	395	400	406	412	417	5	3.0
766	423	429	434	440	446	451	457	463	468	474	6	3.6
767	480	485	491	497	502	508	513	519	525	530	7	4.2
768	536	542	547	553	559	564	570	576	581	587	8	4.8
769	593	598	604	610	615	621	627	632	638	643	9	5.4
770	649	655	660	666	672	677	683	689	694	700		
771	705	711	717	722	728	734	739	745	750	756		
772	762	767	773	779	784	790	795	801	807	812		
773	818	824	829	835	840	846	852	857	863	868		
774	874	880	885	891	897	902	908	913	919	925		
775	930	936	941	947	953	958	964	969	975	981		
776	986	992	997	*003	*009	*014	*020	*025	*031	*037		
777	89 042	048	053	059	064	070	076	081	087	092		
778	098	104	109	115	120	126	131	137	143	148		
779	154	159	165	170	176	182	187	193	198	204		
780	209	215	221	226	232	237	243	248	254	260		**5**
781	265	271	276	282	287	293	298	304	310	315	1	0.5
782	321	326	332	337	343	348	354	360	365	371	2	1.0
783	376	382	387	393	398	404	409	415	421	426	3	1.5
784	432	437	443	448	454	459	465	470	476	481	4	2.0
785	487	492	498	504	509	515	520	526	531	537	5	2.5
786	542	548	553	559	564	570	575	581	586	592	6	3.0
787	597	603	609	614	620	625	631	636	642	647	7	3.5
788	653	658	664	669	675	680	686	691	697	702	8	4.0
789	708	713	719	724	730	735	741	746	752	757	9	4.5
790	763	768	774	779	785	790	796	801	807	812		
791	818	823	829	834	840	845	851	856	862	867		
792	873	878	883	889	894	900	905	911	916	922		
793	927	933	938	944	949	955	960	966	971	977		
794	982	988	993	998	*004	*009	*015	*020	*026	*031		
795	90 037	042	048	053	059	064	069	075	080	086		
796	091	097	102	108	113	119	124	129	135	140		
797	146	151	157	162	168	173	179	184	189	195		
798	200	206	211	217	222	227	233	238	244	249		
799	255	260	266	271	276	282	287	293	298	304		
800	309	314	320	325	331	336	342	347	352	358		
N.	0	1	2	3	4	5	6	7	8	9	Proportional parts	

FIVE-PLACE MANTISSAS FOR COMMON LOGARITHMS

N.	0	1	2	3	4	5	6	7	8	9	Proportional parts	
800	90 309	314	320	325	331	336	342	347	352	358		
801	363	369	374	380	385	390	396	401	407	412		
802	417	423	428	434	439	445	450	455	461	466		
803	472	477	482	488	493	499	504	509	515	520		
804	526	531	536	542	547	553	558	563	569	574		
805	580	585	590	596	601	607	612	617	623	628		
806	634	639	644	650	655	660	666	671	677	682		
807	687	693	698	703	709	714	720	725	730	736		
808	741	747	752	757	763	768	773	779	784	789		
809	795	800	806	811	816	822	827	832	838	843		
810	849	854	859	865	870	875	881	886	891	897		**6**
811	902	907	913	918	924	929	934	940	945	950	1	0.6
812	956	961	966	972	977	982	988	993	998	*004	2	1.2
813	91 009	014	020	025	030	036	041	046	052	057	3	1.8
814	062	068	073	078	084	089	094	100	105	110	4	2.4
815	116	121	126	132	137	142	148	153	158	164	5	3.0
816	169	174	180	185	190	196	201	206	212	217	6	3.6
817	222	228	233	238	243	249	254	259	265	270	7	4.2
818	275	281	286	291	297	302	307	312	318	323	8	4.8
819	328	334	339	344	350	355	360	365	371	376	9	5.4
820	381	387	392	397	403	408	413	418	424	429		
821	434	440	445	450	455	461	466	471	477	482		
822	487	492	498	503	508	514	519	524	529	535		
823	540	545	551	556	561	566	572	577	582	587		
824	593	598	603	609	614	619	624	630	635	640		
825	645	651	656	661	666	672	677	682	687	693		
826	698	703	709	714	719	724	730	735	740	745		
827	751	756	761	766	772	777	782	787	793	798		
828	803	808	814	819	824	829	834	840	845	850		
829	855	861	866	871	876	882	887	892	897	903		
830	908	913	918	924	929	934	939	944	950	955		**5**
831	960	965	971	976	981	986	991	997	*002	*007	1	0.5
832	92 012	018	023	028	033	038	044	049	054	059	2	1.0
833	065	070	075	080	085	091	096	101	106	111	3	1.5
834	117	122	127	132	137	143	148	153	158	163	4	2.0
835	169	174	179	184	189	195	200	205	210	215	5	2.5
836	221	226	231	236	241	247	252	257	262	267	6	3.0
837	273	278	283	288	293	298	304	309	314	319	7	3.5
838	324	330	335	340	345	350	355	361	366	371	8	4.0
839	376	381	387	392	397	402	407	412	418	423	9	4.5
840	428	433	438	443	449	454	459	464	469	474		
841	480	485	490	495	500	505	511	516	521	526		
842	531	536	542	547	552	557	562	567	572	578		
843	583	588	593	598	603	609	614	619	624	629		
844	634	639	645	650	655	660	665	670	675	681		
845	686	691	696	701	706	711	716	722	727	732		
846	737	742	747	752	758	763	768	773	778	783		
847	788	793	799	804	809	814	819	824	829	834		
848	840	845	850	855	860	865	870	875	881	886		
849	891	896	901	906	911	916	921	927	932	937		
850	942	947	952	957	962	967	973	978	983	988		

N.	0	1	2	3	4	5	6	7	8	9	Proportional parts

FIVE-PLACE MANTISSAS FOR COMMON LOGARITHMS

N.	0	1	2	3	4	5	6	7	8	9
850	92 942	947	952	957	962	967	973	978	983	988
851	993	998	*003	*008	*013	*018	*024	*029	*034	*039
852	93 044	049	054	059	064	069	075	080	085	090
853	095	100	105	110	115	120	125	131	136	141
854	146	151	156	161	166	171	176	181	186	192
855	197	202	207	212	217	222	227	232	237	242
856	247	252	258	263	268	273	278	283	288	293
857	298	303	308	313	318	323	328	334	339	344
858	349	354	359	364	369	374	379	384	389	394
859	399	404	409	414	420	425	430	435	440	445
860	450	455	460	465	470	475	480	485	490	495
861	500	505	510	515	520	526	531	536	541	546
862	551	556	561	566	571	576	581	586	591	596
863	601	606	611	616	621	626	631	636	641	646
864	651	656	661	666	671	676	682	687	692	697
865	702	707	712	717	722	727	732	737	742	747
866	752	757	762	767	772	777	782	787	792	797
867	802	807	812	817	822	827	832	837	842	847
868	852	857	862	867	872	877	882	887	892	897
869	902	907	912	917	922	927	932	937	942	947
870	952	957	962	967	972	977	982	987	992	997
871	94 002	007	012	017	022	027	032	037	042	047
872	052	057	062	067	072	077	082	086	091	096
873	101	106	111	116	121	126	131	136	141	146
874	151	156	161	166	171	176	181	186	191	196
875	201	206	211	216	221	226	231	236	240	245
876	250	255	260	265	270	275	280	285	290	295
877	300	305	310	315	320	325	330	335	340	345
878	349	354	359	364	369	374	379	384	389	394
879	399	404	409	414	419	424	429	433	438	443
880	448	453	458	463	468	473	478	483	488	493
881	498	503	507	512	517	522	527	532	537	542
882	547	552	557	562	567	571	576	581	586	591
883	596	601	606	611	616	621	626	630	635	640
884	645	650	655	660	665	670	675	680	685	689
885	694	699	704	709	714	719	724	729	734	738
886	743	748	753	758	763	768	773	778	783	787
887	792	797	802	807	812	817	822	827	832	836
888	841	846	851	856	861	866	871	876	880	885
889	890	895	900	905	910	915	919	924	929	934
890	939	944	949	954	959	963	968	973	978	983
891	988	993	998	*002	*007	*012	*017	*022	*027	*032
892	95 036	041	046	051	056	061	066	071	075	080
893	085	090	095	100	105	109	114	119	124	129
894	134	139	143	148	153	158	163	168	173	177
895	182	187	192	197	202	207	211	216	221	226
896	231	236	240	245	250	255	260	265	270	274
897	279	284	289	294	299	303	308	313	318	323
898	328	332	337	342	347	352	357	361	366	371
899	376	381	386	390	395	400	405	410	415	419
900	424	429	434	439	444	448	453	458	463	468

Proportional parts

6

1	0.6
2	1.2
3	1.8
4	2.4
5	3.0
6	3.6
7	4.2
8	4.8
9	5.4

5

1	0.5
2	1.0
3	1.5
4	2.0
5	2.5
6	3.0
7	3.5
8	4.0
9	4.5

4

1	0.4
2	0.8
3	1.2
4	1.6
5	2.0
6	2.4
7	2.8
8	3.2
9	3.6

Logarithm Tables

FIVE-PLACE MANTISSAS FOR COMMON LOGARITHMS

N.	0	1	2	3	4	5	6	7	8	9	Proportional parts	
900	95 424	429	434	439	444	448	453	458	463	468		
901	472	477	482	487	492	497	501	506	511	516		
902	521	525	530	535	540	545	550	554	559	564		
903	569	574	578	583	588	593	598	602	607	612		
904	617	622	626	631	636	641	646	650	655	660		
905	665	670	674	679	684	689	694	698	703	708		
906	713	718	722	727	732	737	742	746	751	756		
907	761	766	770	775	780	785	789	794	799	804		
908	809	813	818	823	828	832	837	842	847	852		
909	856	861	866	871	875	880	885	890	895	899		
910	904	909	914	918	923	928	933	938	942	947		**5**
911	952	957	961	966	971	976	980	985	990	995	1	0.5
912	999	*004	*009	*014	*019	*023	*028	*033	*038	*042	2	1.0
913	96 047	052	057	061	066	071	076	080	085	090	3	1.5
914	095	099	104	109	114	118	123	128	133	137	4	2.0
915	142	147	152	156	161	166	171	175	180	185	5	2.5
916	190	194	199	204	209	213	218	223	227	232	6	3.0
917	237	242	246	251	256	261	265	270	275	280	7	3.5
918	284	289	294	298	303	308	313	317	322	327	8	4.0
919	332	336	341	346	350	355	360	365	369	374	9	4.5
920	379	384	388	393	398	402	407	412	417	421		
921	426	431	435	440	445	450	454	459	464	468		
922	473	478	483	487	492	497	501	506	511	515		
923	520	525	530	534	539	544	548	553	558	562		
924	567	572	577	581	586	591	595	600	605	609		
925	614	619	624	628	633	638	642	647	652	656		
926	661	666	670	675	680	685	689	694	699	703		
927	708	713	717	722	727	731	736	741	745	750		
928	755	759	764	769	774	778	783	788	792	797		
929	802	806	811	816	820	825	830	834	839	844		
930	848	853	858	862	867	872	876	881	886	890		**4**
931	895	900	904	909	914	918	923	928	932	937	1	0.4
932	942	946	951	956	960	965	970	974	979	984	2	0.8
933	988	993	997	*002	*007	*011	*016	*021	*025	*030	3	1.2
934	97 035	039	044	049	053	058	063	067	072	077	4	1.6
935	081	086	090	095	100	104	109	114	118	123	5	2.0
936	128	132	137	142	146	151	155	160	165	169	6	2.4
937	174	179	183	188	192	197	202	206	211	216	7	2.8
938	220	225	230	234	239	243	248	253	257	262	8	3.2
939	267	271	276	280	285	290	294	299	304	308	9	3.6
940	313	317	322	327	331	336	340	345	350	354		
941	359	364	368	373	377	382	387	391	396	400		
942	405	410	414	419	424	428	433	437	442	447		
943	451	456	460	465	470	474	479	483	488	493		
944	497	502	506	511	516	520	525	529	534	539		
945	543	548	552	557	562	566	571	575	580	585		
946	589	594	598	603	607	612	617	621	626	630		
947	635	640	644	649	653	658	663	667	672	676		
948	681	685	690	695	699	704	708	713	717	722		
949	727	731	736	740	745	749	754	759	763	768		
950	772	777	782	786	791	795	800	804	809	813		
N.	0	1	2	3	4	5	6	7	8	9	Proportional parts	

FIVE-PLACE MANTISSAS FOR COMMON LOGARITHMS

N.	0	1	2	3	4	5	6	7	8	9	Proportional parts
950	97 772	777	782	786	791	795	800	804	809	813	
951	818	823	827	832	836	841	845	850	855	859	
952	864	868	873	877	882	886	891	896	900	905	
953	909	914	918	923	928	932	937	941	946	950	
954	955	959	964	968	973	978	982	987	991	996	
955	98 000	005	009	014	019	023	028	032	037	041	
956	046	050	055	059	064	068	073	078	082	087	
957	091	096	100	105	109	114	118	123	127	132	
958	137	141	146	150	155	159	164	168	173	177	
959	182	186	191	195	200	204	209	214	218	223	
960	227	232	236	241	245	250	254	259	263	268	**5**
961	272	277	281	286	290	295	299	304	308	313	1 0.5
962	318	322	327	331	336	340	345	349	354	358	2 1.0
963	363	367	372	376	381	385	390	394	399	403	3 1.5
964	408	412	417	421	426	430	435	439	444	448	4 2.0
965	453	457	462	466	471	475	480	484	489	493	5 2.5
966	498	502	507	511	516	520	525	529	534	538	6 3.0
967	543	547	552	556	561	565	570	574	579	583	7 3.5
968	588	592	597	601	605	610	614	619	623	628	8 4.0
969	632	637	641	646	650	655	659	664	668	673	9 4.5
970	677	682	686	691	695	700	704	709	713	717	
971	722	726	731	735	740	744	749	753	758	762	
972	767	771	776	780	784	789	793	798	802	807	
973	811	816	820	825	829	834	838	843	847	851	
974	856	860	865	869	874	878	883	887	892	896	
975	900	905	909	914	918	923	927	932	936	941	
976	945	949	954	958	963	967	972	976	981	985	
977	989	994	998	*003	*007	*012	*016	*021	*025	*029	
978	99 034	038	043	047	052	056	061	065	069	074	
979	078	083	087	092	096	100	105	109	114	118	
980	123	127	131	136	140	145	149	154	158	162	**4**
981	167	171	176	180	185	189	193	198	202	207	1 0.4
982	211	216	220	224	229	233	238	242	247	251	2 0.8
983	255	260	264	269	273	277	282	286	291	295	3 1.2
984	300	304	308	313	317	322	326	330	335	339	4 1.6
985	344	348	352	357	361	366	370	374	379	383	5 2.0
986	388	392	396	401	405	410	414	419	423	427	6 2.4
987	432	436	441	445	449	454	458	463	467	471	7 2.8
988	476	480	484	489	493	498	502	506	511	515	8 3.2
989	520	524	528	533	537	542	546	550	555	559	9 3.6
990	564	568	572	577	581	585	590	594	599	603	
991	607	612	616	621	625	629	634	638	642	647	
992	651	656	660	664	669	673	677	682	686	691	
993	695	699	704	708	712	717	721	726	730	734	
994	739	743	747	752	756	760	765	769	774	778	
995	782	787	791	795	800	804	808	813	817	822	
996	826	830	835	839	843	848	852	856	861	865	
997	870	874	878	883	887	891	896	900	904	909	
998	913	917	922	926	930	935	939	944	948	952	
999	957	961	965	970	974	978	983	987	991	996	
1000	00 000	004	009	013	017	022	026	030	035	039	
N.	0	1	2	3	4	5	6	7	8	9	Proportional parts

Logarithm Tables

NATURAL OR NAPERIAN LOGARITHMS
0.000–0.499

N	0	1	2	3	4	5	6	7	8	9
0.00	− ∞	−6‡ .90776	−6 .21461	−5 .80914	−5 .52146	−5 .29832	−5 .11600	−4 .96185	−4 .82831	−4 .71053
.01	−4.60517	.50986	.42285	.34281	.26870	.19971	.13517	.07454	.01738	* .96332
.02	−3.91202	.86323	.81671	.77226	.72970	.68888	.64966	.61192	.57555	.54046
.03	.50656	.47377	.44202	.41125	.38139	.35241	.32424	.29684	.27017	.24419
.04	.21888	.19418	.17009	.14656	.12357	.10109	.07911	.05761	.03655	.01593
.05	−2.99573	.97593	.95651	.93746	.91877	.90042	.88240	.86470	.84731	.83022
.06	.81341	.79688	.78062	.76462	.74887	.73337	.71810	.70306	.68825	.67365
.07	.65926	.64508	.63109	.61730	.60369	.59027	.57702	.56395	.55105	.53831
.08	.52573	.51331	.50104	.48891	.47694	.46510	.45341	.44185	.43042	.41912
.09	.40795	.39690	.38597	.37516	.36446	.35388	.34341	.33304	.32279	.31264
0.10	−2.30259	.29263	.28278	.27303	.26336	.25379	.24432	.23493	.22562	.21641
.11	.20727	.19823	.18926	.18037	.17156	.16282	.15417	.14558	.13707	.12863
.12	.12026	.11196	.10373	.09557	.08747	.07944	.07147	.06357	.05573	.04794
.13	.04022	.03256	.02495	.01741	.00992	.00248	* .99510	* .98777	* .98050	* .97328
.14	−1.96611	.95900	.95193	.94491	.93794	.93102	.92415	.91732	.91054	.90381
.15	.89712	.89048	.88387	.87732	.87080	.86433	.85790	.85151	.84516	.83885
.16	.83258	.82635	.82016	.81401	.80789	.80181	.79577	.78976	.78379	.77786
.17	.77196	.76609	.76026	.75446	.74870	.74297	.73727	.73161	.72597	.72037
.18	.71480	.70926	.70375	.69827	.69282	.68740	.68201	.67665	.67131	.66601
.19	.66073	.65548	.65026	.64507	.63990	.63476	.62964	.62455	.61949	.61445
0.20	−1.60944	.60445	.59949	.59455	.58964	.58475	.57988	.57504	.57022	.56542
.21	.56065	.55590	.55117	.54646	.54178	.53712	.53248	.52786	.52326	.51868
.22	.51413	.50959	.50508	.50058	.49611	.49165	.48722	.48281	.47841	.47403
.23	.46968	.46534	.46102	.45672	.45243	.44817	.44392	.43970	.43548	.43129
.24	.42712	.42296	.41882	.41469	.41059	.40650	.40242	.39837	.39433	.39030
.25	.38629	.38230	.37833	.37437	.37042	.36649	.36258	.35868	.35480	.35093
.26	.34707	.34323	.33941	.33560	.33181	.32803	.32426	.32051	.31677	.31304
.27	.30933	.30564	.30195	.29828	.29463	.29098	.28735	.28374	.28013	.27654
.28	.27297	.26940	.26585	.26231	.25878	.25527	.25176	.24827	.24479	.24133
.29	.23787	.23443	.23100	.22758	.22418	.22078	.21740	.21402	.21066	.20731
0.30	−1.20397	.20065	.19733	.19402	.19073	.18744	.18417	.18091	.17766	.17441
.31	.17118	.16796	.16475	.16155	.15836	.15518	.15201	.14885	.14570	.14256
.32	.13943	.13631	.13320	.13010	.12701	.12393	.12086	.11780	.11474	.11170
.33	.10866	.10564	.10262	.09961	.09661	.09362	.09064	.08767	.08471	.08176
.34	.07881	.07587	.07294	.07002	.06711	.06421	.06132	.05843	.05555	.05268
.35	−1.04982	.04697	.04412	.04129	.03846	.03564	.03282	.03002	.02722	.02443
.36	.02165	.01888	.01611	.01335	.01060	.00786	.00512	.00239	* .99967	* .99696
.37	−0.99425	.99155	.98886	.98618	.98350	.98083	.97817	.97551	.97286	.97022
.38	.96758	.96496	.96233	.95972	.95711	.95451	.95192	.94933	.94675	.94418
.39	.94161	.93905	.93649	.93395	.93140	.92887	.92634	.92382	.92130	.91879
0.40	−0.91629	.91379	.91130	.90882	.90634	.90387	.90140	.89894	.89649	.89404
.41	.89160	.88916	.88673	.88431	.88189	.87948	.87707	.87467	.87227	.86988
.42	.86750	.86512	.86275	.86038	.85802	.85567	.85332	.85097	.84863	.84630
.43	.84397	.84165	.83933	.83702	.83471	.83241	.83011	.82782	.82554	.82326
.44	.82098	.81871	.81645	.81419	.81193	.80968	.80744	.80520	.80296	.80073
.45	.79851	.79629	.79407	.79186	.78966	.78746	.78526	.78307	.78089	.77871
.46	.77653	.77436	.77219	.77003	.76787	.76572	.76357	.76143	.75929	.75715
.47	.75502	.75290	.75078	.74866	.74655	.74444	.74234	.74024	.73814	.73605
.48	.73397	.73189	.72981	.72774	.72567	.72361	.72155	.71949	.71744	.71539
.49	.71335	.71131	.70928	.70725	.70522	.70320	.70118	.69917	.69716	.69515

‡ Note that the whole number values are given above the decimal values for the first line. In the second and following lines they are given at the left.

NATURAL OR NAPERIAN LOGARITHMS (Continued)
0.500–0.999

N	0	1	2	3	4	5	6	7	8	9
0.50	−0.69315	.69115	.68916	.68717	.68518	.68320	.68122	.67924	.67727	.67531
.51	.67334	.67139	.66943	.66748	.66553	.66359	.66165	.65971	.65778	.65585
.52	.65393	.65201	.65009	.64817	.64626	.64436	.64245	.64055	.63866	.63677
.53	.63488	.63299	.63111	.62923	.62736	.62549	.62362	.62176	.61990	.61804
.54	.61619	.61434	.61249	.61065	.60881	.60697	.60514	.60331	.60148	.59966
.55	.59784	.59602	.59421	.59240	.59059	.58879	.58699	.58519	.58340	.58161
.56	.57982	.57803	.57625	.57448	.57270	.57093	.56916	.56740	.56563	.56387
.57	.56212	.56037	.55862	.55687	.55513	.55339	.55165	.54991	.54818	.54645
.58	.54473	.54300	.54128	.53957	.53785	.53614	.53444	.53273	.53103	.52933
.59	.52763	.52594	.52425	.52256	.52088	.51919	.51751	.51584	.51416	.51249
0.60	−0.51083	.50916	.50750	.50584	.50418	.50253	.50088	.49923	.49758	.49594
.61	.49430	.49266	.49102	.48939	.48776	.48613	.48451	.48289	.48127	.47965
.62	.47804	.47642	.47482	.47321	.47160	.47000	.46840	.46681	.46522	.46362
.63	.46204	.46045	.45887	.45728	.45571	.45413	.45256	.45099	.44942	.44785
.64	.44629	.44473	.44317	.44161	.44006	.43850	.43696	.43541	.43386	.43232
.65	.43078	.42925	.42771	.42618	.42465	.42312	.42159	.42007	.41855	.41703
.66	.41552	.41400	.41249	.41098	.40947	.40797	.40647	.40497	.40347	.40197
.67	.40048	.39899	.39750	.39601	.39453	.39304	.39156	.39008	.38861	.38713
.68	.38566	.38419	.38273	.38126	.37980	.37834	.37688	.37542	.37397	.37251
.69	.37106	.36962	.36817	.36673	.36528	.36384	.36241	.36097	.35954	.35810
0.70	−0.35667	.35525	.35382	.35240	.35098	.34956	.34814	.34672	.34531	.34390
.71	.34249	.34108	.33968	.33827	.33687	.33547	.33408	.33268	.33129	.32989
.72	.32850	.32712	.32573	.32435	.32296	.32158	.32021	.31883	.31745	.31608
.73	.31471	.31334	.31197	.31061	.30925	.30788	.30653	.30517	.30381	.30246
.74	.30111	.29975	.29841	.29706	.29571	.29437	.29303	.29169	.29035	.28902
.75	.28768	.28635	.28502	.28369	.28236	.28104	.27971	.27839	.27707	.27575
.76	.27444	.27312	.27181	.27050	.26919	.26788	.26657	.26527	.26397	.26266
.77	.26136	.26007	.25877	.25748	.25618	.25489	.25360	.25231	.25103	.24974
.78	.24846	.24718	.24590	.24462	.24335	.24207	.24080	.23953	.23826	.23699
.79	.23572	.23446	.23319	.23193	.23067	.22941	.22816	.22690	.22565	.22439
0.80	−0.22314	.22189	.22065	.21940	.21816	.21691	.21567	.21433	.21319	.21196
.81	.21072	.20949	.20825	.20702	.20579	.20457	.20334	.20212	.20089	.19967
.82	.19845	.19723	.19601	.19480	.19358	.19237	.19116	.18995	.18874	.18754
.83	.18633	.18513	.18392	.18272	.18152	.18032	.17913	.17793	.17674	.17554
.84	.17435	.17316	.17198	.17079	.16960	.16842	.16724	.16605	.16487	.16370
.85	−0.16252	.16134	.16017	.15900	.15782	.15665	.15548	.15432	.15315	.15199
.86	.15082	.14966	.14850	.14734	.14618	.14503	.14387	.14272	.14156	.14041
.87	.13926	.13811	.13697	.13582	.13467	.13353	.13239	.13125	.13011	.12897
.88	.12783	.12670	.12556	.12443	.12330	.12217	.12104	.11991	.11878	.11766
.89	.11653	.11541	.11429	.11317	.11205	.11093	.10981	.10870	.10759	.10647
0.90	−0.10536	.10425	.10314	.10203	.10093	.09982	.09872	.09761	.09651	.09541
.91	.09431	.09321	.09212	.09102	.08992	.08883	.08774	.08665	.08556	.08447
.92	.08338	.08230	.08121	.08013	.07904	.07796	.07688	.07580	.07472	.07365
.93	.07257	.07150	.07042	.06935	.06828	.06721	.06614	.06507	.06401	.06294
.94	.06188	.06081	.05975	.05869	.05763	.05657	.05551	.05446	.05340	.05235
.95	.05129	.05024	.04919	.04814	.04709	.04604	.04500	.04395	.04291	.04186
.96	.04082	.03978	.03874	.03770	.03666	.03563	.03459	.03356	.03252	.03149
.97	.03046	.02943	.02840	.02737	.02634	.02532	.02429	.02327	.02225	.02122
.98	.02020	.01918	.01816	.01715	.01613	.01511	.01410	.01309	.01207	.01106
.99	.01005	.00904	.00803	.00702	.00602	.00501	.00401	.00300	.00200	.00100

NATURAL OR NAPERIAN LOGARITHMS (Continued)

To find the natural logarithm of a number which is $\frac{1}{10}$, $\frac{1}{100}$, $\frac{1}{1000}$, etc. of a number whose logarithm is given, subtract from the given logarithm log, 10, 2 log, 10, 3 log, 10, etc.

To find the natural logarithm of a number which is 10, 100, 1000, etc. times a number whose logarithm is given, add to the given logarithm log, 10, 2 log, 10, 3 log, 10, etc.

log, 10 = 2.30258 50930	6 log, 10 = 13.81551 05580
2 log, 10 = 4.60517 01860	7 log, 10 = 16.11809 56510
3 log, 10 = 6.90775 52790	8 log, 10 = 18.42068 07440
4 log, 10 = 9.21034 03720	9 log, 10 = 20.72326 58369
5 log, 10 = 11.51292 54650	10 log, 10 = 23.02585 09299

See pages 210–211 for logarithms for numbers between 0.000 and 0.999.

1.00–4.99

N	0	1	2	3	4	5	6	7	8	9
1.0	0.00000	.00995	.01980	.02956	.03922	.04879	.05827	.06766	.07696	.08618
.1	.09531	.10436	.11333	.12222	.13103	.13976	.14842	.15700	.16551	.17395
.2	.18232	.19062	.19885	.20701	.21511	.22314	.23111	.23902	.24686	.25464
.3	.26236	.27003	.27763	.28518	.29267	.30010	.30748	.31481	.32208	.32930
.4	.33647	.34359	.35066	.35767	.36464	.37156	.37844	.38526	.39204	.39878
.5	.40547	.41211	.41871	.42527	.43178	.43825	.44469	.45108	.45742	.46373
.6	.47000	.47623	.48243	.48858	.49470	.50078	.50682	.51282	.51879	.52473
.7	.53063	.53649	.54232	.54812	.55389	.55962	.56531	.57098	.57661	.58222
.8	.58779	.59333	.59884	.60432	.60977	.61519	.62058	.62594	.63127	.63658
.9	.64185	.64710	.65233	.65752	.66269	.66783	.67294	.67803	.68310	.68813
2.0	0.69315	.69813	.70310	.70804	.71295	.71784	.72271	.72755	.73237	.73716
.1	.74194	.74669	.75142	.75612	.76081	.76547	.77011	.77473	.77932	.78390
.2	.78846	.79299	.79751	.80200	.80648	.81093	.81536	.81978	.82418	.82855
.3	.83291	.83725	.84157	.84587	.85015	.85442	.85866	.86289	.86710	.87129
.4	.87547	.87963	.88377	.88789	.89200	.89609	.90016	.90422	.90826	.91228
.5	.91629	.92028	.92426	.92822	.93216	.93609	.94001	.94391	.94779	.95166
.6	.95551	.95935	.96317	.96698	.97078	.97456	.97833	.98208	.98582	.98954
.7	.99325	.99695	*.00063	*.00430	*.00796	*.01160	*.01523	*.01885	*.02245	*.02604
.8	1.02962	.03318	.03674	.04028	.04380	.04732	.05082	.05431	.05779	.06126
.9	.06471	.06815	.07158	.07500	.07841	.08181	.08519	.08856	.09192	.09527
3.0	1.09861	.10194	.10526	.10856	.11186	.11514	.11841	.12168	.12493	.12817
.1	.13140	.13462	.13783	.14103	.14422	.14740	.15057	.15373	.15688	.16002
.2	.16315	.16627	.16938	.17248	.17557	.17865	.18173	.18479	.18784	.19089
.3	.19392	.19695	.19996	.20297	.20597	.20896	.21194	.21491	.21788	.22083
.4	.22378	.22671	.22964	.23256	.23547	.23837	.24127	.24415	.24703	.24990
.5	.25276	.25562	.25846	.26130	.26413	.26695	.26976	.27257	.27536	.27815
.6	.28093	.28371	.28647	.28923	.29198	.29473	.29746	.30019	.30291	.30563
.7	.30833	.31103	.31372	.31641	.31909	.32176	.32442	.32708	.32972	.33237
.8	.33500	.33763	.34025	.34286	.34547	.34807	.35067	.35325	.35584	.35841
.9	.36098	.36354	.36609	.36864	.37118	.37372	.37624	.37877	.38128	.38379
4.0	1.38629	.38879	.39128	.39377	.39624	.39872	.40118	.40364	.40610	.40854
.1	.41099	.41342	.41585	.41828	.42070	.42311	.42552	.42792	.43031	.43270
.2	.43508	.43746	.43984	.44220	.44456	.44692	.44927	.45161	.45395	.45629
.3	.45862	.46094	.46326	.46557	.46787	.47018	.47247	.47476	.47705	.47933
.4	.48160	.48387	.48614	.48840	.49065	.49290	.49515	.49739	.49962	.50185
.5	.50408	.50630	.50851	.51072	.51293	.51513	.51732	.51951	.52170	.52388
.6	.52606	.52823	.53039	.53256	.53471	.53687	.53902	.54116	.54330	.54543
.7	.54756	.54969	.55181	.55393	.55604	.55814	.56025	.56235	.56444	.56653
.8	.56862	.57070	.57277	.57485	.57691	.57898	.58104	.58309	.58515	.58719
.9	.58924	.59127	.59331	.59534	.59737	.59939	.60141	.60342	.60543	.60744

NATURAL OR NAPERIAN LOGARITHMS (Continued)
5.00–9.99

N	0	1	2	3	4	5	6	7	8	9
5.0	1.60944	.61144	.61343	.61542	.61741	.61939	.62137	.62334	.62531	.62728
.1	.62924	.63120	.63315	.63511	.63705	.63900	.64094	.64287	.64481	.64673
.2	.64866	.65058	.65250	.65441	.65632	.65823	.66013	.66203	.66393	.66582
.3	.66771	.66959	.67147	.67335	.67523	.67710	.67896	.68083	.68269	.68455
.4	.68640	.68825 ˊ	.69010	.69194	.69378	.69562	.69745	.69928	.70111	.70293
.5	.70475	.70656	.70838	.71019	.71199	.71380	.71560	.71740	.71919	.72098
.6	.72277	.72455	.72633	.72811	.72988	.73166	.73342	.73519	.73695	.73871
.7	.74047	.74222	.74397	.74572	.74746	.74920	.75094	.75267	.75440	.75613
.8	.75786	.75958	.76130	.76302	.76473	.76644	.76815	.76985	.77156	.77326
.9	.77495	.77665	.77834	.78002	.78171	.78339	.78507	.78675	.78842	.79009
6.0	1.79176	.79342	.79509	.79675	.79840	.80006	.80171	.80336	.80500	.80665
.1	.80829	.80993	.81156	.81319	.81482	.81645	.81808	.81970	.82132	.82294
.2	.82455	.82616	.82777	.82938	.83098	.83258	.83418	.83578	.83737	.83896
.3	.84055	.84214	.84372	.84530	.84688	.84845	.85003	.85160	.85317	.85473
.4	.85630	.85786	.85942	.86097	.86253	.86408	.86563	.86718	.86872	.87026
.5	.87180	.87334	.87487	.87641	.87794	.87947	.88099	.88251	.88403	.88555
.6	.88707	.88858	.89010	.89160	.89311	.89462	.89612	.89762	.89912	.90061
.7	.90211	.90360	.90509	.90658	.90806	.90954	.91102	.91250	.91398	.91545
.8	.91692	.91839	.91986	.92132	.92279	.92425	.92571	.92716	.92862	.93007
.9	.93152	.93297	.93442	.93586	.93730	.93874	.94018	.94162	.94305	.94448
7.0	1.94591	.94734	.94876	.95019	.95161	.95303	.95445	.95586	.95727	.95869
.1	.96009	.96150	.96291	.96431	.96571	.96711	.96851	.96991	.97130	.97269
.2	.97408	.97547	.97685	.97824	.97962	.98100	.98238	.98376	.98513	.98650
.3	.98787	.98924	.99061	.99198	.99334	.99470	.99606	.99742	.99877	*.00013
.4	2.00148	00283	.00418	.00553	.00687	.00821	.00956	.01089	.01223	.01357
.5	.01490	.01624	.01757	.01890	.02022	.02155	.02287	.02419	.02551	.02683
.6	.02815	.02946	.03078	.03209	.03340	.03471	.03601	.03732	.03862	.03992
.7	.04122	04252	.04381	.04511	.04640	.04769	.04898	.05027	.05156	.05284
.8	.05412	.05540	.05668	.05796	.05924	.06051	.06179	.06306	.06433	.06560
.9	.06686	.06813	.06939	.07065	.07191	.07317	.07443	.07568	.07694	.07819
8.0	2.07944	.08069	.08194	.08318	.08443	.08567	.08691	.08815	.08939	.09063
.1	.09186	.09310	.09433	.09556	.09679	.09802	.09924	.10047	.10169	.10291
.2	.10413	.10535	.10657	.10779	.10900	.11021	.11142	.11263	.11384	.11505
.3	.11626	.11746	.11866	.11986	.12106	.12226	.12346	.12465	.12585	.12704
.4	.12823	.12942	.13061	.13180	.13298	.13417	.13535	.13653	.13771	.13889
.5	.14007	.14124	.14242	.14359	.14476	.14593	.14710	.14827	.14943	.15060
.6	.15176	.15292	.15409	.15524	.15640	.15756	.15871	.15987	.16102	.16217
.7	.16332	.16447	.16562	.16677	.16791	.16905	.17020	.17134	.17248	.17361
.8	.17475	.17589	.17702	.17816	.17929	.18042	.18155	.18267	.18380	.18493
.9	.18605	.18717	.18830	.18942	.19054	.19165	.19277	.19389	.19500	.19611
9.0	2.19722	.19834	.19944	.20055	.20166	.20276	.20387	.20497	.20607	.20717
.1	.20827	.20937	.21047	.21157	.21266	.21375	.21485	.21594	.21703	.21812
.2	.21920	.22029	.22138	.22246	.22354	.22462	.22570	.22678	.22786	.22894
.3	.23001	.23109	.23216	.23324	.23431	.23538	.23645	.23751	.23858	.23965
.4	.24071	.24177	.24284	.24390	.24496	.24601	.24707	.24813	.24918	.25024
.5	.25129	.25234	.25339	.25444	.25549	.25654	.25759	.25863	.25968	.26072
.6	.26176	.26280	.26384	.26488	.26592	.26696	.26799	.26903	.27006	.27109
.7	.27213	.27316	.27419	.27521	.27624	.27727	.27829	.27932	.28034	.28136
.8	.28238	.28340	.28442	.28544	.28646	.28747	.28849	.28950	.29051	.29152
.9	.29253	.29354	.29455	.29556	.29657	.29757	.29858	.29958	.30058	.30158

NATURAL OR NAPERIAN LOGARITHMS (Continued)

Constants

$\log_e 10 = 2.30258\ 50930$	$6 \log_e 10 = 13.81551\ 05580$
$2 \log_e 10 = 4.60517\ 01860$	$7 \log_e 10 = 16.11809\ 56510$
$3 \log_e 10 = 6.90775\ 52790$	$8 \log_e 10 = 18.42068\ 07440$
$4 \log_e 10 = 9.21034\ 03720$	$9 \log_e 10 = 20.72326\ 58369$
$5 \log_e 10 = 11.51292\ 54650$	$10 \log_e 10 = 23.02585\ 09299$

10.0–49.9

N	0	1	2	3	4	5	6	7	8	9
10.	2.30259	.31254	.32239	.33214	.34181	.35138	.36085	.37024	.37955	.38876
11.	.39790	.40695	.41591	.42480	.43361	.44235	.45101	.45959	.46810	.47654
12.	.48491	.49321	.50144	.50960	.51770	.52573	.53370	.54160	.54945	.55723
13.	.56495	.57261	.58022	.58776	.59525	.60269	.61007	.61740	.62467	.63189
14.	.63906	.64617	.65324	.66026	.66723	.67415	.68102	.68785	.69463	.70136
15.	.70805	.71469	.72130	.72785	.73437	.74084	.74727	.75366	.76001	.76632
16.	.77259	.77882	.78501	.79117	.79728	.80336	.80940	.81541	.82138	.82731
17.	.83321	.83908	.84491	.85071	.85647	.86220	.86790	.87356	.87920	.88480
18.	.89037	.89591	.90142	.90690	.91235	.91777	.92316	.92852	.93386	.93916
19.	.94444	.94969	.95491	.96011	.96527	.97041	.97553	.98062	.98568	.99072
20.	2.99573	*.00072	*.00568	*.01062	*.01553	*.02042	*.02529	*.03013	*.03495	*.03975
21.	3.04452	.04927	.05400	.05871	.06339	.06805	.07269	.07731	.08191	.08649
22.	.09104	.09558	.10009	.10459	.10906	.11352	.11795	.12236	.12676	.13114
23.	.13549	.13983	.14415	.14845	.15274	.15700	.16125	.16548	.16969	.17388
24.	.17805	.18221	.18635	.19048	.19458	.19867	.20275	.20680	.21084	.21487
25.	.21888	.22287	.22684	.23080	.23475	.23868	.24259	.24649	.25037	.25424
26.	.25810	.26194	.26576	.26957	.27336	.27714	.28091	.28466	.28840	.29213
27.	.29584	.29953	.30322	.30689	.31054	.31419	.31782	.32143	.32504	.32863
28.	.33220	.33577	.33932	.34286	.34639	.34990	.35341	.35690	.36038	.36384
29.	.36730	.37074	.37417	.37759	.38099	.38439	.38777	.39115	.39451	.39786
30.	3.40120	.40453	.40784	.41115	.41444	.41773	.42100	.42426	.42751	.43076
31.	.43399	.43721	.44042	.44362	.44681	.44999	.45316	.45632	.45947	.46261
32.	.46574	.46886	.47197	.47507	.47816	.48124	.48431	.48738	.49043	.49347
33.	.49651	.49953	.50255	.50556	.50856	.51155	.51453	.51750	.52046	.52342
34.	.52636	.52930	.53223	.53515	.53806	.54096	.54385	.54674	.54962	.55249
35.	.55535	.55820	.56105	.56388	.56671	.56953	.57235	.57515	.57795	.58074
36.	.58352	.58629	.58906	.59182	.59457	.59731	.60005	.60278	.60550	.60821
37.	.61092	.61362	.61631	.61899	.62167	.62434	.62700	.62966	.63231	.63495
38.	.63759	.64021	.64284	.64545	.64806	.65066	.65325	.65584	.65842	.66099
39.	.66356	.66612	.66868	.67122	.67377	.67630	.67883	.68135	.68387	.68638
40.	3.68888	.69138	.69387	.69635	.69883	.70130	.70377	.70623	.70868	.71113
41.	.71357	.71601	.71844	.72086	.72328	.72569	.72810	.73050	.73290	.73529
42.	.73767	.74005	.74242	.74479	.74715	.74950	.75185	.75420	.75654	.75887
43.	.76120	.76352	.76584	.76815	.77046	.77276	.77506	.77735	.77963	.78191
44.	.78419	.78646	.78872	.79098	.79324	.79549	.79773	.79997	.80221	.80444
45.	.80666	.80888	.81110	.81331	.81551	.81771	.81991	.82210	.82428	.82647
46.	.82864	.83081	.83298	.83514	.83730	.83945	.84160	.84374	.84588	.84802
47.	.85015	.85227	.85439	.85651	.85862	.86073	.86283	.86493	.86703	.86912
48.	.87120	.87328	.87536	.87743	.87950	.88156	.88362	.88568	.88773	.88978
49.	.89182	.89386	.89589	.89792	.89995	.90197	.90399	.90600	.90801	.91002

NATURAL OR NAPERIAN LOGARITHMS (Continued)
50.0–99.9

N	0	1	2	3	4	5	6	7	8	9
50.	3.91202	.91402	.91602	.91801	.91999	.92197	.92395	.92593	.92790	.92986
51.	.93183	.93378	.93574	.93769	.93964	.94158	.94352	.94546	.94739	.94932
52.	.95124	.95316	.95508	.95700	.95891	.96081	.96272	.96462	.96651	.96840
53.	.97029	.97218	.97406	.97594	.97781	.97968	.98155	.98341	.98527	.98713
54.	.98898	.99083	.99268	.99452	.99636	.99820	*.00003	*.00186	*.00369	*.00551
55.	4.00733	.00915	.01096	.01277	.01458	.01638	.01818	.01998	.02177	.02356
56.	.02535	.02714	.02892	.03069	.03247	.03424	.03601	.03777	.03954	.04130
57.	.04305	.04480	.04655	.04830	.05004	.05178	.05352	.05526	.05699	.05872
58.	.06044	.06217	.06389	.06560	.06732	.06903	.07073	.07244	.07414	.07584
59.	.07754	.07923	.08092	.08261	.08429	.08598	.08766	.08933	.09101	.09268
60.	4.09434	.09601	.09767	.09933	.10099	.10264	.10429	.10594	.10759	.10923
61.	.11087	.11251	.11415	.11578	.11741	.11904	.12066	.12228	.12390	.12552
62.	.12713	.12875	.13036	.13196	.13357	.13517	.13677	.13836	.13996	.14155
63.	.14313	.14472	.14630	.14789	.14946	.15104	.15261	.15418	.15575	.15732
64.	.15888	.16044	.16200	.16356	.16511	.16667	.16821	.16976	.17131	.17285
65.	.17439	.17592	.17746	.17899	.18052	.18205	.18358	.18510	.18662	.18814
66.	.18965	.19117	.19268	.19419	.19570	.19720	.19870	.20020	.20170	.20320
67.	.20469	.20618	.20767	.20916	.21065	.21213	.21361	.21509	.21656	.21804
68.	.21951	.22098	.22244	.22391	.22537	.22683	.22829	.22975	.23120	.23266
69.	.23411	.23555	.23700	.23844	.23989	.24133	.24276	.24420	.24563	.24707
70.	4.24850	.24992	.25135	.25277	.25419	.25561	.25703	.25845	.25986	.26127
71.	.26268	.26409	.26549	.26690	.26830	.26970	.27110	.27249	.27388	.27528
72.	.27667	.27805	.27944	.28082	.28221	.28359	.28496	.28634	.28772	.28909
73.	.29046	.29183	.29320	.29456	.29592	.29729	.29865	.30000	.30136	.30271
74.	.30407	.30542	.30676	.30811	.30946	.31080	.31214	.31348	.31482	.31615
75.	.31749	.31882	.32015	.32149	.32281	.32413	:32546	.32678	.32810	.32942
76.	.33073	.33205	.33336	.33467	.33598	.33729	.33860	.33990	.34120	.34251
77.	.34381	.34510	.34640	.34769	.34899	.35028	.35157	.35286	.35414	.35543
78.	.35671	.35800	.35927	.36055	.36182	.36310	.36437	.36564	.36691	.36818
79.	.36945	.37071	.37198	.37324	.37450	.37576	.37701	.37827	.37952	.38078
80.	4.38203	.38328	.38452	.38577	.38701	.38826	.38950	.39074	.39198	.39321
81.	.39445	.39568	.39692	.39815	.39938	.40060	.40183	.40305	.40428	.40550
82.	.40672	.40794	.40916	.41037	.41159	.41280	.41401	.41522	.41643	.41764
83.	.41884	.42004	.42125	.42245	.42365	.42485	.42604	.42724	.42843	.42963
84.	.43082	.43201	.43319	.43438	.43557	.43675	.43793	.43912	.44030	.44147
85.	.44265	.44383	.44500	.44617	.44735	.44852	.44969	.45085	.45202	.45318
86.	.45435	.45551	.45667	.45783	.45899	.46014	.46130	.46245	.46361	.46476
87.	.46591	.46706	.46820	.46935	.47050	.47164	.47278	.47392	.47506	.47620
88.	.47734	.47847	.47961	.48074	.48187	.48300	.48413	.48526	.48639	.48751
89.	.48864	.48976	.49088	.49200	.49312	.49424	.49536	.49647	.49758	.49870
90.	4.49981	.50092	.50203	.50314	.50424	.50535	.50645	.50756	.50866	.50976
91.	.51086	.51196	.51305	.51415	.51525	.51634	.51743	.51852	.51961	.52070
92.	.52179	.52287	.52396	.52504	.52613	.52721	.52829	.52937	.53045	.53152
93.	.53260	.53367	.53475	.53582	.53689	.53796	.53903	.54010	.54116	.54223
94.	.54329	.54436	.54542	.54648	.54754	.54860	.54966	.55071	.55177	.55282
95.	.55388	.55493	.55598	.55703	.55808	.55913	.56017	.56122	.56226	.56331
96.	.56435	.56539	.56643	.56747	.56851	.56954	.57058	.57161	.57265	.57368
97.	.57471	.57574	.57677	.57780	.57883	.57985	.58088	.58190	.58292	.58395
98.	.58497	.58599	.58701	.58802	.58904	.59006	.59107	.59208	.59310	.59411
99.	.59512	.59613	.59714	.59815	.59915	.60016	.60116	.60217	.60317	.60417

NATURAL OR NAPERIAN LOGARITHMS (Continued)
0–499

N	0	1	2	3	4	5	6	7	8	9
0	− ∞	0.00000	0.69315	1.09861	.38629	.60944	.79176	.94591	*.07944	*.19722
1	2.30259	.39790	.48491	.56495	.63906	.70805	.77259	.83321	.89037	.94444
2	.99573	*.04452	*.09104	*.13549	*.17805	*.21888	*.25810	*.29584	*.33220	*.36730
3	3.40120	.43399	.46574	.49651	.52636	.55535	.58352	.61092	,63759	.66356
4	.68888	.71357	.73767	.76120	.78419	.80666	.82864	.85015	:87120	.89182
5	.91202	.93183	.95124	.97029	.98898	*.00733	*02535	*.04305	*.06044	*.07754
6	4.09434	.11087	.12713	.14313	.15888	.17439	.18965	.20469	.21951	.23411
7	.24850	.26268	.27667	.29046	.30407	.31749	.33073	34381	.35671	.36945
8	.38203	.39445	.40672	.41884	.43082	.44265	.45435	.46591	.47734	.48864
9	.49981	.51086	.52179	.53260	.54329	.55388	.56435	.57471	.58497	.59512
10	4.60517	.61512	.62497	.63473	.64439	.65396	.66344	.67283	.68213	.69135
11	.70048	.70953	.71850	.72739	.73620	.74493	.75359	.76217	.77068	.77912
12	.78749	.79579	.80402	.81218	.82028	.82831	.83628	.84419	.85203	.85981
13	.86753	.87520	.88280	.89035	.89784	.90527	.91265	.91998	.92725	.93447
14	.94164	.94876	.95583	.96284	.96981	.97673	.98361	.99043	.99721	*.00395
15	5.01064	.01728	.02388	.03044	.03695	.04343	.04986	.05625	.06260	.06890
16	.07517	.08140	.08760	.09375	.09987	.10595	.11199	.11799	.12396	.12990
17	.13580	.14166	.14749	.15329	.15906	.16479	.17048	.17615	.18178	.18739
18	.19296	.19850	.20401	.20949	.21494	.22036	.22575	.23111	.23644	.24175
19	.24702	.25227	.25750	.26269	.26786	.27300	.27811	.28320	.28827	.29330
20	5.29832	.30330	.30827	.31321	.31812	.32301	.32788	.33272	.33754	.34233
21	.34711	.35186	.35659	.36129	.36598	.37064	.37528	.37990	.38450	.38907
22	.39363	.39816	.40268	.40717	.41165	.41610	.42053	.42495	.42935	.43372
23	.43808	.44242	.44674	.45104	.45532	.45959	.46383	.46806	.47227	.47646
24	.48064	.48480	.48894	.49306	.49717	.50126	.50533	.50939	.51343	.51745
25	.52146	.52545	.52943	.53339	.53733	.54126	.54518	.54908	.55296	.55683
26	.56068	.56452	.56834	.57215	.57595	.57973	.58350	.58725	.59099	.59471
27	.59842	.60212	.60580	.60947	.61313	.61677	.62040	.62402	.62762	.63121
28	.63479	.63835	.64191	.64545	.64897	.65249	.65599	.65948	.66296	.66643
29	.66988	.67332	.67675	.68017	.68358	.68698	.69036	.69373	.69709	.70044
30	5.70378	.70711	.71043	.71373	.71703	.72031	.72359	.72685	.73010	.73334
31	.73657	.73979	.74300	.74620	.74939	.75257	.75574	.75890	.76205	.76519
32	.76832	.77144	.77455	.77765	.78074	.78383	.78690	.78996	.79301	.79606
33	.79909	.80212	.80513	.80814	.81114	.81413	.81711	.82008	.82305	.82600
34	.82895	.83188	.83481	.83773	.84064	.84354	.84644	.84932	.85220	.85507
35	.85793	.86079	.86363	.86647	.86930	.87212	.87493	.87774	.88053	.88332
36	.88610	.88888	.89164	.89440	.89715	.89990	.90263	.90536	.90808	.91080
37	.91350	.91620	.91889	.92158	.92426	.92693	.92959	.93225	.93489	.93754
38	.94017	.94280	.94542	.94803	.95064	.95324	.95584	.95842	.96101	.96358
39	.96615	.96871	.97126	.97381	.97635	.97889	.98141	.98394	.98645	.98896
40	5.99146	.99396	.99645	.99894	*.00141	*.00389	*.00635	*.00881	*.01127	*.01372
41	6.01616	.01859	.02102	.02345	.02587	.02828	.03069	.03309	.03548	.03787
42	.04025	.04263	.04501	.04737	.04973	.05209	.05444	.05678	.05912	.06146
43	.06379	.06611	.06843	.07074	.07304	.07535	.07764	.07993	.08222	.08450
44	.08677	.08904	.09131	.09357	.09582	.09807	.10032	.10256	.10479	.10702
45	.10925	.11147	.11368	.11589	.11810	.12030	.12249	.12468	.12687	.12905
46	.13123	.13340	.13556	.13773	.13988	.14204	.14419	.14633	.14847	.15060
47	.15273	.15486	.15698	.15910	.16121	.16331	.16542	.16752	.16961	.17170
48	.17379	.17587	.17794	.18002	.18208	.18415	.18621	.18826	.19032	.19236
49	.19441	.19644	.19848	.20051	.20254	.20456	.20658	.20859	.21060	.21261

NATURAL OR NAPERIAN LOGARITHMS (Continued)

500–999

N	0	1	2	3	4	5	6	7	8	9
50	6.21461	.21661	.21860	.22059	.22258	.22456	.22654	.22851	.23048	.23245
51	.23441	.23637	.23832	.24028	.24222	.24417	.24611	.24804	.24998	.25190
52	.25383	.25575	.25767	.25958	.26149	.26340	.26530	.26720	.26910	.27099
53	.27288	.27476	.27664	.27852	.28040	.28227	.28413	.28600	.28786	.28972
54	.29157	.29342	.29527	.29711	.29895	.30079	.30262	.30445	.30628	.30810
55	.30992	.31173	.31355	.31536	.31716	.31897	.32077	.32257	.32436	.32615
56	.32794	.32972	.33150	.33328	.33505	.33683	.33859	.34036	.34212	.34388
57	.34564	.34739	.34914	.35089	.35263	.35437	.35611	.35784	.35957	.36130
58	.36303	.36475	.36647	.36819	.36990	.37161	.37332	.37502	.37673	.37843
59	.38012	.38182	.38351	.38519	.38688	.38856	.39024	.39192	.39359	.39526
60	6.39693	.39859	.40026	.40192	.40357	.40523	.40688	.40853	.41017	.41182
61	.41346	.41510	.41673	.41836	.41999	.42162	.42325	.42487	.42649	.42811
62	.42972	.43133	.43294	.43455	.43615	.43775	.43935	.44095	.44254	.44413
63	.44572	.44731	.44889	.45047	.45205	.45362	.45520	.45677	.45834	.45990
64	.46147	.46303	.46459	.46614	.46770	.46925	.47080	.47235	.47389	.47543
65	.47697	.47851	.48004	.48158	.48311	.48464	.48616	.48768	.48920	.49072
66	.49224	.49375	.49527	.49677	.49828	.49979	.50129	.50279	.50429	.50578
67	.50728	.50877	.51026	.51175	.51323	.51471	.51619	.51767	.51915	.52062
68	.52209	.52356	.52503	.52649	.52796	.52942	.53088	.53233	.53379	.53524
69	.53669	.53814	.53959	.54103	.54247	.54391	.54535	.54679	.54822	.54965
70	6.55108	.55251	.55393	.55536	.55678	.55820	.55962	.56103	.56244	.56386
71	.56526	.56667	.56808	.56948	.57088	.57228	.57368	.57508	.57647	.57786
72	.57925	.58064	.58203	.58341	.58479	.58617	.58755	.58893	.59030	.59167
73	.59304	.59441	.59578	.59715	.59851	.59987	.60123	.60259	.60394	.60530
74	.60665	.60800	.60935	.61070	.61204	.61338	.61473	.61607	.61740	.61874
75	.62007	.62141	.62274	.62407	.62539	.62672	.62804	.62936	.63068	.63200
76	.63332	.63463	.63595	.63726	.63857	.63988	.64118	.64249	.64379	.64509
77	.64639	.64769	.64898	.65028	.65157	.65286	.65415	.65544	.65673	.65801
78	.65929	.66058	.66185	.66313	.66441	.66568	.66696	.66823	.66950	.67077
79	.67203	.67330	.67456	.67582	.67708	.67834	.67960	.68085	.68211	.68336
80	6.68461	.68586	.68711	.68835	.68960	.69084	.69208	.69332	.69456	.69580
81	.69703	.69827	.69950	.70073	.70196	.70319	.70441	.70564	.70686	.70808
82	.70930	.71052	.71174	.71296	.71417	.71538	.71659	.71780	.71901	.72022
83	.72143	.72263	.72383	.72503	.72623	.72743	.72863	.72982	.73102	.73221
84	.73340	.73459	.73578	.73697	.73815	.73934	.74052	.74170	.74288	.74406
85	.74524	.74641	.74759	.74876	.74993	.75110	.75227	.75344	.75460	.75577
86	.75693	.75809	.75926	.76041	.76157	.76273	.76388	.76504	.76619	.76734
87	.76849	.76964	.77079	.77194	.77308	.77422	.77537	.77651	.77765	.77878
88	.77992	.78106	.78219	.78333	.78446	.78559	.78672	.78784	.78897	.79010
89	.79122	.79234	.79347	.79459	.79571	.79682	.79794	.79906	.80017	.80128
90	6.80239	.80351	.80461	.80572	.80683	.80793	.80904	.81014	.81124	.81235
91	.81344	.81454	.81564	.81674	.81783	.81892	.82002	.82111	.82220	.82329
92	.82437	.82546	.82655	.82763	.82871	.82979	.83087	.83195	.83303	.83411
93	.83518	.83626	.83733	.83841	.83948	.84055	.84162	.84268	.84375	.84482
94	.84588	.84694	.84801	.84907	.85013	.85118	.85224	.85330	.85435	.85541
95	.85646	.85751	.85857	.85961	.86066	.86171	.86276	.86380	.86485	.86589
96	.86693	.86797	.86901	.87005	.87109	.87213	.87316	.87420	.87523	.87626
97	.87730	.87833	.87936	.88038	.88141	.88244	.88346	.88449	.88551	.88653
98	.88755	.88857	.88959	.89061	.89163	.89264	.89366	.89467	.89568	.89669
99	.89770	.89871	.89972	.90073	.90174	.90274	.90375	.90475	.90575	.90675

EXPONENTIAL FUNCTIONS

Values of e^x, log e^x and e^{-x} where e is the base of the natural system of logarithms 2.71828...
and x has values from 0 to 10. Facilitating the solution of exponential equations, these tables also
serve as a table of natural or Naperian antilogarithms. For instance, if the logarithm or exponent
$x = 3.26$, the corresponding number or value of e^x is 26.050. Its reciprocal e^{-x} is .038388.

x	e^x	$Log_{10}(e^x)$	e^{-x}	x	e^x	$Log_{10}(e^x)$	e^{-x}
0.00	1.0000	0.00000	1.000000	**0.50**	1.6487	0.21715	0.606531
0.01	1.0101	.00434	0.990050	0.51	1.6653	.22149	.600496
0.02	1.0202	.00869	.980199	0.52	1.6820	.22583	.594521
0.03	1.0305	.01303	.970446	0.53	1.6989	.23018	.588605
0.04	1.0408	.01737	.960789	0.54	1.7160	.23452	.582748
0.05	1.0513	0.02171	0.951229	**0.55**	1.7333	0.23886	0.576950
0.06	1.0618	.02606	.941765	0.56	1.7507	.24320	.571209
0.07	1.0725	.03040	.932394	0.57	1.7683	.24755	.565525
0.08	1.0833	.03474	.923116	0.58	1.7860	.25189	.559898
0.09	1.0942	.03909	.913931	0.59	1.8040	.25623	.554327
0.10	1.1052	0.04343	0.904837	**0.60**	1.8221	0.26058	0.548812
0.11	1.1163	.04777	.895834	0.61	1.8404	.26492	.543351
0.12	1.1275	.05212	.886920	0.62	1.8589	.26926	.537944
0.13	1.1388	.05646	.878095	0.63	1.8776	.27361	.532592
0.14	1.1503	.06080	.869358	0.64	1.8965	.27795	.527292
0.15	1.1618	0.06514	0.860708	**0.65**	1.9155	0.28229	0.522046
0.16	1.1735	.06949	.852144	0.66	1.9348	.28663	.516851
0.17	1.1853	.07383	.843665	0.67	1.9542	.29098	.511709
0.18	1.1972	.07817	.835270	0.68	1.9739	.29532	.506617
0.19	1.2092	.08252	.826959	0.69	1.9937	.29966	.501576
0.20	1.2214	0.08686	0.818731	**0.70**	2.0138	0.30401	0.496585
0.21	1.2337	.09120	.810584	0.71	2.0340	.30835	.491644
0.22	1.2461	.09554	.802519	0.72	2.0544	.31269	.486752
0.23	1.2586	.09989	.794534	0.73	2.0751	.31703	.481909
0.24	1.2712	.10423	.786628	0.74	2.0959	.32138	.477114
0.25	1.2840	0.10857	0.778801	**0.75**	2.1170	0.32572	0.472367
0.26	1.2969	.11292	.771052	0.76	2.1383	.33006	.467666
0.27	1.3100	.11726	.763379	0.77	2.1598	.33441	.463013
0.28	1.3231	.12160	.755784	0.78	2.1815	.33875	.458406
0.29	1.3364	.12595	.748264	0.79	2.2034	.34309	.453845
0.30	1.3499	0.13029	0.740818	**0.80**	2.2255	0.34744	0.449329
0.31	1.3634	.13463	.733447	0.81	2.2479	.35178	.444858
0.32	1.3771	.13897	.726149	0.82	2.2705	.35612	.440432
0.33	1.3910	.14332	.718924	0.83	2.2933	.36046	.436049
0.34	1.4049	.14766	.711770	0.84	2.3164	.36481	.431711
0.35	1.4191	0.15200	0.704688	**0.85**	2.3396	0.36915	0.427415
0.36	1.4333	.15635	.697676	0.86	2.3632	.37349	.423162
0.37	1.4477	.16069	.690734	0.87	2.3869	.37784	.418952
0.38	1.4623	.16503	.683861	0.88	2.4109	.38218	.414783
0.39	1.4770	.16937	.677057	0.89	2.4351	.38652	.410656
0.40	1.4918	0.17372	0.670320	**0.90**	2.4596	0.39087	0.406570
0.41	1.5068	.17806	.663650	0.91	2.4843	.39521	.402524
0.42	1.5220	.18240	.657047	0.92	2.5093	.39955	.398519
0.43	1.5373	.18675	.650509	0.93	2.5345	.40389	.394554
0.44	1.5527	.19109	.644036	0.94	2.5600	.40824	.390628
0.45	1.5683	0.19543	0.637628	**0.95**	2.5857	0.41258	0.386741
0.46	1.5841	.19978	.631284	0.96	2.6117	.41692	.382893
0.47	1.6000	.20412	.625002	0.97	2.6379	.42127	.379083
0.48	1.6161	.20846	.618783	0.98	2.6645	.42561	.375311
0.49	1.6323	.21280	.612626	0.99	2.6912	.42995	.371577
0.50	1.6487	0.21715	0.606531	**1.00**	2.7183	0.43429	0.367879

EXPONENTIAL FUNCTIONS (Continued)

x	e^x	$\text{Log}_{10}(e^x)$	e^{-x}	x	e^x	$\text{Log}_{10}(e^x)$	e^{-x}
1.00	2.7183	0.43429	0.367879	**1.50**	4.4817	0.65144	0.223130
1.01	2.7456	.43864	.364219	1.51	4.5267	.65578	.220910
1.02	2.7732	.44298	.360595	1.52	4.5722	.66013	.218712
1.03	2.8011	.44732	.357007	1.53	4.6182	.66447	.216536
1.04	2.8292	.45167	.353455	1.54	4.6646	.66881	.214381
1.05	2.8577	0.45601	0.349938	**1.55**	4.7115	0.67316	0.212248
1.06	2.8864	.46035	.346456	1.56	4.7588	.67750	.210136
1.07	2.9154	.46470	.343009	1.57	4.8066	.68184	.208045
1.08	2.9447	.46904	.339596	1.58	4.8550	.68619	.205975
1.09	2.9743	.47338	.336216	1.59	4.9037	.69053	.203926
1.10	3.0042	0.47772	0.332871	**1.60**	4.9530	0.69487	0.201897
1.11	3.0344	.48207	.329559	1.61	5.0028	.69921	.199888
1.12	3.0649	.48641	.326280	1.62	5.0531	.70356	.197899
1.13	3.0957	.49075	.323033	1.63	5.1039	.70790	.195930
1.14	3.1268	.49510	.319819	1.64	5.1552	.71224	.193980
1.15	3.1582	0.49944	0.316637	**1.65**	5.2070	0.71659	0.192050
1.16	3.1899	.50378	.313486	1.66	5.2593	.72093	.190139
1.17	3.2220	.50812	.310367	1.67	5.3122	.72527	.188247
1.18	3.2544	.51247	.307279	1.68	5.3656	.72961	.186374
1.19	3.2871	.51681	.304221	1.69	5.4195	.73396	.184520
1.20	3.3201	0.52115	0.301194	**1.70**	5.4739	0.73830	0.182684
1.21	3.3535	.52550	.298197	1.71	5.5290	.74264	.180866
1.22	3.3872	.52984	.295230	1.72	5.5845	.74699	.179066
1.23	3.4212	.53418	.292293	1.73	5.6407	.75133	.177284
1.24	3.4556	.53853	.289384	1.74	5.6973	.75567	.175520
1.25	3.4903	0.54287	0.286505	**1.75**	5.7546	0.76002	0.173774
1.26	3.5254	.54721	.283654	1.76	5.8124	.76436	.172045
1.27	3.5609	.55155	.280832	1.77	5.8709	.76870	.170333
1.28	3.5966	.55590	.278037	1.78	5.9299	.77304	.168638
1.29	3.6328	.56024	.275271	1.79	5.9895	.77739	.166960
1.30	3.6693	0.56458	0.272532	**1.80**	6.0496	0.78173	0.165299
1.31	3.7062	.56893	.269820	1.81	6.1104	.78607	.163654
1.32	3.7434	.57327	.267135	1.82	6.1719	.79042	.162026
1.33	3.7810	.57761	.264477	1.83	6.2339	.79476	.160414
1.34	3.8190	.58195	.261846	1.84	6.2965	.79910	.158817
1.35	3.8574	0.58630	0.259240	**1.85**	6.3598	0.80344	0.157237
1.36	3.8962	.59064	.256661	1.86	6.4237	.80779	.155673
1.37	3.9354	.59498	.254107	1.87	6.4883	.81213	.154124
1.38	3.9749	.59933	.251579	1.88	6.5535	.81647	.152590
1.39	4.0149	.60367	.249075	1.89	6.6194	.82082	.151072
1.40	4.0552	0.60801	0.246597	**1.90**	6.6859	0.82516	0.149569
1.41	4.0960	.61236	.244143	1.91	6.7531	.82950	.148080
1.42	4.1371	.61670	.241714	1.92	6.8210	.83385	.146607
1.43	4.1787	.62104	.239309	1.93	6.8895	.83819	.145148
1.44	4.2207	.62538	.236928	1.94	6.9588	.84253	.143704
1.45	4.2631	0.62973	0.234570	**1.95**	7.0287	0.84687	0.142274
1.46	4.3060	.63407	.232236	1.96	7.0993	.85122	.140858
1.47	4.3492	.63841	.229925	1.97	7.1707	.85556	.139457
1.48	4.3929	.64276	.227638	1.98	7.2427	.85990	.138069
1.49	4.4371	.64710	.225373	1.99	7.3155	.86425	.136695
1.50	4.4817	0.65144	0.223130	**2.00**	7.3891	0.86859	0.135335

EXPONENTIAL FUNCTIONS (Continued)

x	e^x	$\text{Log}_{10}(e^x)$	e^{-x}	x	e^x	$\text{Log}_{10}(e^x)$	e^{-x}
2.00	7.3891	0.86859	0.135335	**2.50**	12.182	1.08574	0.082085
2.01	7.4633	.87293	.133989	2.51	12.305	1.09008	.081268
2.02	7.5383	.87727	.132655	2.52	12.429	1.09442	.080460
2.03	7.6141	.88162	.131336	2.53	12.554	1.09877	.079659
2.04	7.6906	.88596	.130029	2.54	12.680	1.10311	.078866
2.05	7.7679	0.89030	0.128735	**2.55**	12.807	1.10745	0.078082
2.06	7.8460	.89465	.127454	2.56	12.936	1.11179	.077305
2.07	7.9248	.89899	.126186	2.57	13.066	1.11614	.076536
2.08	8.0045	.90333	.124930	2.58	13.197	1.12048	.075774
2.09	8.0849	.90768	.123687	2.59	13.330	1.12482	.075020
2.10	8.1662	0.91202	0.122456	**2.60**	13.464	1.12917	0.074274
2.11	8.2482	.91636	.121238	2.61	13.599	1.13351	.073535
2.12	8.3311	.92070	.120032	2.62	13.736	1.13785	.072803
2.13	8.4149	.92505	.118837	2.63	13.874	1.14219	.072078
2.14	8.4994	.92939	.117655	2.64	14.013	1.14654	.071361
2.15	8.5849	0.93373	0.116484	**2.65**	14.154	1.15088	0.070651
2.16	8.6711	.93808	.115325	2.66	14.296	1.15522	.069948
2.17	8.7583	.94242	.114178	2.67	14.440	1.15957	.069252
2.18	8.8463	.94676	.113042	2.68	14.585	1.16391	.068563
2.19	8.9352	.95110	.111917	2.69	14.732	1.16825	.067881
2.20	9.0250	0.95545	0.110803	**2.70**	14.880	1.17260	0.067206
2.21	9.1157	.95979	.109701	2.71	15.029	1.17694	.066537
2.22	9.2073	.96413	.108609	2.72	15.180	1.18128	.065875
2.23	9.2999	.96848	.107528	2.73	15.333	1.18562	.065219
2.24	9.3933	.97282	.106459	2.74	15.487	1.18997	.064570
2.25	9.4877	0.97716	0.105399	**2.75**	15.643	1.19431	0.063928
2.26	9.5831	.98151	.104350	2.76	15.800	1.19865	.063292
2.27	9.6794	.98585	.103312	2.77	15.959	1.20300	.062662
2.28	9.7767	.99019	.102284	2.78	16.119	1.20734	.062039
2.29	9.8749	.99453	.101266	2.79	16.281	1.21168	.061421
2.30	9.9742	0.99888	0.100259	**2.80**	16.445	1.21602	0.060810
2.31	10.074	1.00322	.099261	2.81	16.610	1.22037	.060205
2.32	10.176	1.00756	.098274	2.82	16.777	1.22471	.059606
2.33	10.278	1.01191	.097296	2.83	16.945	1.22905	.059013
2.34	10.381	1.01625	.096328	2.84	17.116	1.23340	.058426
2.35	10.486	1.02059	0.095369	**2.85**	17.288	1.23774	0.057844
2.36	10.591	1.02493	.094420	2.86	17.462	1.24208	.057269
2.37	10.697	1.02928	.093481	2.87	17.637	1.24643	.056699
2.38	10.805	1.03362	.092551	2.88	17.814	1.25077	.056135
2.39	10.913	1.03796	.091630	2.89	17.993	1.25511	.055576
2.40	11.023	1.04231	0.090718	**2.90**	18.174	1.25945	0.055023
2.41	11.134	1.04665	.089815	2.91	18.357	1.26380	.054476
2.42	11.246	1.05099	.088922	2.92	18.541	1.26814	.053934
2.43	11.359	1.05534	.088037	2.93	18.728	1.27248	.053397
2.44	11.473	1.05968	.087161	2.94	18.916	1.27683	.052866
2.45	11.588	1.06402	0.086294	**2.95**	19.106	1.28117	0.052340
2.46	11.705	1.06836	.085435	2.96	19.298	1.28551	.051819
2.47	11.822	1.07271	.084585	2.97	19.492	1.28985	.051303
2.48	11.941	1.07705	.083743	2.98	19.688	1.29420	.050793
2.49	12.061	1.08139	.082910	2.99	19.886	1.29854	.050287
2.50	12.182	1.08574	0.082085	**3.00**	20.086	1.30288	0.049787

EXPONENTIAL FUNCTIONS (Continued)

x	e^x	$Log_{10}(e^x)$	e^{-x}	x	e^x	$Log_{10}(e^x)$	e^{-x}
3.00	20.086	1.30288	0.049787	**3.50**	33.115	1.52003	0.030197
3.01	20.287	1.30723	.049292	3.51	33.448	1.52437	.029897
3.02	20.491	1.31157	.048801	3.52	33.784	1.52872	.029599
3.03	20.697	1.31591	.048316	3.53	34.124	1.53306	.029305
3.04	20.905	1.32026	.047835	3.54	34.467	1.53740	.029013
3.05	21.115	1.32460	0.047359	**3.55**	34.813	1.54175	0.028725
3.06	21.328	1.32894	.046888	3.56	35.163	1.54609	.028439
3.07	21.542	1.33328	.046421	3.57	35.517	1.55043	.028156
3.08	21.758	1.33763	.045959	3.58	35.874	1.55477	.027876
3.09	21.977	1.34197	.045502	3.59	36.234	1.55912	.027598
3.10	22.198	1.34631	0.045049	**3.60**	36.598	1.56346	0.027324
3.11	22.421	1.35066	.044601	3.61	36.966	1.56780	.027052
3.12	22.646	1.35500	.044157	3.62	37.338	1.57215	.026783
3.13	22.874	1.35934	.043718	3.63	37.713	1.57649	.026516
3.14	23.104	1.36368	.043283	3.64	38.092	1.58083	.026252
3.15	23.336	1.36803	0.042852	**3.65**	38.475	1.58517	0.025991
3.16	23.571	1.37237	.042426	3.66	38.861	1.58952	.025733
3.17	23.807	1.37671	.042004	3.67	39.252	1.59386	.025476
3.18	24.047	1.38106	.041586	3.68	39.646	1.59820	.025223
3.19	24.288	1.38540	.041172	3.69	40.045	1.60255	.024972
3.20	24.533	1.38974	0.040762	**3.70**	40.447	1.60689	0.024724
3.21	24.779	1.39409	.040357	3.71	40.854	1.61123	.024478
3.22	25.028	1.39843	.039955	3.72	41.264	1.61558	.024234
3.23	25.280	1.40277	.039557	3.73	41.679	1.61992	.023993
3.24	25.534	1.40711	.039164	3.74	42.098	1.62426	.023754
3.25	25.790	1.41146	0.038774	**3.75**	42.521	1.62860	0.023518
3.26	26.050	1.41580	.038388	3.76	42.948	1.63295	.023284
3.27	26.311	1.42014	.038006	3.77	43.380	1.63729	.023052
3.28	26.576	1.42449	.037628	3.78	43.816	1.64163	.022823
3.29	26.843	1.42883	.037254	3.79	44.256	1.64598	.022596
3.30	27.113	1.43317	0.036883	**3.80**	44.701	1.65032	0.022371
3.31	27.385	1.43751	.036516	3.81	45.150	1.65466	.022148
3.32	27.660	1.44186	.036153	3.82	45.604	1.65900	.021928
3.33	27.938	1.44620	.035793	3.83	46.063	1.66335	.021710
3.34	28.219	1.45054	.035437	3.84	46.525	1.66769	.021494
3.35	28.503	1.45489	0.035084	**3.85**	46.993	1.67203	0.021280
3.36	28.789	1.45923	.034735	3.86	47.465	1.67638	.021068
3.37	29.079	1.46357	.034390	3.87	47.942	1.68072	.020858
3.38	29.371	1.46792	.034047	3.88	48.424	1.68506	.020651
3.39	29.666	1.47226	.033709	3.89	48.911	1.68941	.020445
3.40	29.964	1.47660	0.033373	**3.90**	49.402	1.69375	0.020242
3.41	30.265	1.48094	.033041	3.91	49.899	1.69809	.020041
3.42	30.569	1.48529	.032712	3.92	50.400	1.70243	.019841
3.43	30.877	1.48963	.032387	3.93	50.907	1.70678	.019644
3.44	31.187	1.49397	.032065	3.94	51.419	1.71112	.019448
3.45	31.500	1.49832	0.031746	**3.95**	51.935	1.71546	0.019255
3.46	31.817	1.50266	.031430	3.96	52.457	1.71981	.019063
3.47	32.137	1.50700	.031117	3.97	52.985	1.72415	.018873
3.48	32.460	1.51134	.030807	3.98	53.517	1.72849	.018686
3.49	32.786	1.51569	.030501	3.99	54.055	1.73283	.018500
3.50	33.115	1.52003	0.030197	**4.00**	54.598	1.73718	0.018316

EXPONENTIAL FUNCTIONS (Continued)

x	e^x	$Log_{10}(e^x)$	e^{-x}	x	e^x	$Log_{10}(e^x)$	e^{-x}
4.00	54.598	1.73718	0.018316	**4.50**	90.017	1.95433	0.011109
4.01	55.147	1.74152	.018133	4.51	90.922	1.95867	.010998
4.02	55.701	1.74586	.017953	4.52	91.836	1.96301	.010889
4.03	56.261	1.75021	.017774	4.53	92.759	1.96735	.010781
4.04	56.826	1.75455	.017597	4.54	93.691	1.97170	.010673
4.05	57.397	1.75889	0.017422	**4.55**	94.632	1.97604	0.010567
4.06	57.974	1.76324	.017249	4.56	95.583	1.98038	.010462
4.07	58.557	1.76758	.017077	4.57	96.544	1.98473	.010358
4.08	59.145	1.77192	.016907	4.58	97.514	1.98907	.010255
4.09	59.740	1.77626	.016739	4.59	98.494	1.99341	.010153
4.10	60.340	1.78061	0.016573	**4.60**	99.484	1.99775	0.010052
4.11	60.947	1.78495	.016408	4.61	100.48	2.00210	.009952
4.12	61.559	1.78929	.016245	4.62	101.49	2.00644	.009853
4.13	62.178	1.79364	.016083	4.63	102.51	2.01078	.009755
4.14	62.803	1.79798	.015923	4.64	103.54	2.01513	.009658
4.15	63.434	1.80232	0.015764	**4.65**	104.58	2.01947	0.009562
4.16	64.072	1.80667	.015608	4.66	105.64	2.02381	.009466
4.17	64.715	1.81101	.015452	4.67	106.70	2.02816	.009372
4.18	65.366	1.81535	.015299	4.68	107.77	2.03250	.009279
4.19	66.023	1.81969	.015146	4.69	108.85	2.03684	.009187
4.20	66.686	1.82404	0.014996	**4.70**	109.95	2.04118	0.009095
4.21	67.357	1.82838	.014846	4.71	111.05	2.04553	.009005
4.22	68.033	1.83272	.014699	4.72	112.17	2.04987	.008915
4.23	68.717	1.83707	.014552	4.73	113.30	2.05421	.008826
4.24	69.408	1.84141	.014408	4.74	114.43	2.05856	.008739
4.25	70.105	1.84575	0.014264	**4.75**	115.58	2.06290	0.008652
4.26	70.810	1.85009	.014122	4.76	116.75	2.06724	.008566
4.27	71.522	1.85444	.013982	4.77	117.92	2.07158	.008480
4.28	72.240	1.85878	.013843	4.78	119.10	2.07593	.008396
4.29	72.966	1.86312	.013705	4.79	120.30	2.08027	.008312
4.30	73.700	1.86747	0.013569	**4.80**	121.51	2.08461	0.008230
4.31	74.440	1.87181	.013434	4.81	122.73	2.08896	.008148
4.32	75.189	1.87615	.013300	4.82	123.97	2.09330	.008067
4.33	75.944	1.88050	.013168	4.83	125.21	2.09764	.007987
4.34	76.708	1.88484	.013037	4.84	126.47	2.10199	.007907
4.35	77.478	1.88918	0.012907	**4.85**	127.74	2.10633	0.007828
4.36	78.257	1.89352	.012778	4.86	129.02	2.11067	.007750
4.37	79.044	1.89787	.012651	4.87	130.32	2.11501	.007673
4.38	79.838	1.90221	.012525	4.88	131.63	2.11936	.007597
4.39	80.640	1.90655	.012401	4.89	132.95	2.12370	.007521
4.40	81.451	1.91090	0.012277	**4.90**	134.29	2.12804	0.007447
4.41	82.269	1.91524	.012155	4.91	135.64	2.13239	.007372
4.42	83.096	1.91958	.012034	4.92	137.00	2.13673	.007299
4.43	83.931	1.92392	.011914	4.93	138.38	2.14107	.007227
4.44	84.775	1.92827	.011796	4.94	139.77	2.14541	.007155
4.45	85.627	1.93261	0.011679	**4.95**	141.17	2.14976	0.007083
4.46	86.488	1.93695	.011562	4.96	142.59	2.15410	.007013
4.47	87.357	1.94130	.011447	4.97	144.03	2.15844	.006943
4.48	88.235	1.94564	.011333	4.98	145.47	2.16279	.006874
4.49	89.121	1.94998	.011221	4.99	146.94	2.16713	.006806
4.50	90.017	1.95433	0.011109	**5.00**	148.41	2.17147	0.006738

EXPONENTIAL FUNCTIONS (Continued)

x	e^x	$\text{Log}_{10}(e^x)$	e^{-x}	x	e^x	$\text{Log}_{10}(e^x)$	e^{-x}
5.00	148.41	2.17147	0.006738	**5.50**	244.69	2.38862	0.0040868
5.01	149.90	2.17582	.006671	5.55	257.24	2.41033	.0038875
5.02	151.41	2.18016	.006605	5.60	270.43	2.43205	.0036979
5.03	152.93	2.18450	.006539	5.65	284.29	2.45376	.0035175
5.04	154.47	2.18884	.006474	5.70	298.87	2.47548	.0033460
5.05	156.02	2.19319	0.006409	**5.75**	314.19	2.49719	0.0031828
5.06	157.59	2.19753	.006346	5.80	330.30	2.51891	.0030276
5.07	159.17	2.20187	.006282	5.85	347.23	2.54062	.0028799
5.08	160.77	2.20622	.006220	5.90	365.04	2.56234	.0027394
5.09	162.39	2.21056	.006158	5.95	383.75	2.58405	.0026058
5.10	164.02	2.21490	0.006097	**6.00**	403.43	2.60577	0.0024788
5.11	165.67	2.21924	.006036	6.05	424.11	2.62748	.0023579
5.12	167.34	2.22359	.005976	6.10	445.86	2.64920	.0022429
5.13	169.02	2.22793	.005917	6.15	468.72	2.67091	.0021335
5.14	170.72	2.23227	.005858	6.20	492.75	2.69263	.0020294
5.15	172.43	2.23662	0.005799	**6.25**	518.01	2.71434	0.0019305
5.16	174.16	2.24096	.005742	6.30	544.57	2.73606	.0018363
5.17	175.91	2.24530	.005685	6.35	572.49	2.75777	.0017467
5.18	177.68	2.24965	.005628	6.40	601.85	2.77948	.0016616
5.19	179.47	2.25399	.005572	6.45	632.70	2.80120	.0015805
5.20	181.27	2.25833	0.005517	**6.50**	665.14	2.82291	0.0015034
5.21	183.09	2.26267	.005462	6.55	699.24	2.84463	.0014301
5.22	184.93	2.26702	.005407	6.60	735.10	2.86634	.0013604
5.23	186.79	2.27136	.005354	6.65	772.78	2.88806	.0012940
5.24	188.67	2.27570	.005300	6.70	812.41	2.90977	.0012309
5.25	190.57	2.28005	0.005248	**6.75**	854.06	2.93149	0.0011709
5.26	192.48	2.28439	.005195	6.80	897.85	2.95320	.0011138
5.27	194.42	2.28873	.005144	6.85	943.88	2.97492	.0010595
5.28	196.37	2.29307	.005092	6.90	992.27	2.99663	.0010078
5.29	198.34	2.29742	.005042	6.95	1043.1	3.01835	.0009586
5.30	200.34	2.30176	0.004992	**7.00**	1096.6	3.04006	0.0009119
5.31	202.35	2.30610	.004942	7.05	1152.9	3.06178	.0008674
5.32	204.38	2.31045	.004893	7.10	1212.0	3.08349	.0008251
5.33	206.44	2.31479	.004844	7.15	1274.1	3.10521	.0007849
5.34	208.51	2.31913	.004796	7.20	1339.4	3.12692	.0007466
5.35	210.61	2.32348	0.004748	**7.25**	1408.1	3.14863	0.0007102
5.36	212.72	2.32782	.004701	7.30	1480.3	3.17035	.0006755
5.37	214.86	2.33216	.004654	7.35	1556.2	3.19206	.0006426
5.38	217.02	2.33650	.004608	7.40	1636.0	3.21378	.0006113
5.39	219.20	2.34085	.004562	7.45	1719.9	3.23549	.0005814
5.40	221.41	2.34519	0.004517	**7.50**	1808.0	3.25721	0.0005531
5.41	223.63	2.34953	.004472	7.55	1900.7	3.27892	.0005261
5.42	225.88	2.35388	.004427	7.60	1998.2	3.30064	.0005005
5.43	228.15	2.35822	.004383	7.65	2100.6	3.32235	.0004760
5.44	230.44	2.36256	.004339	7.70	2208.3	3.34407	.0004528
5.45	232.76	2.36690	0.004296	**7.75**	2321.6	3.36578	0.0004307
5.46	235.10	2.37125	.004254	7.80	2440.6	3.38750	.0004097
5.47	237.46	2.37559	.004211	7.85	2565.7	3.40921	.0003898
5.48	239.85	2.37993	.004169	7.90	2697.3	3.43093	.0003707
5.49	242.26	2.38428	.004128	7.95	2835.6	3.45264	.0003527
5.50	244.69	2.38862	0.004087	**8.00**	2981.0	3.47436	0.0003355

EXPONENTIAL FUNCTIONS (Continued)

x	e^x	$\text{Log}_{10}(e^x)$	e^{-x}
8.00	2981.0	3.47436	0.0003355
8.05	3133.8	3.49607	.0003191
8.10	3294.5	3.51779	.0003035
8.15	3463.4	3.53950	.0002887
8.20	3641.0	3.56121	.0002747
8.25	3827.6	3.58293	0.0002613
8.30	4023.9	3.60464	.0002485
8.35	4230.2	3.62636	.0002364
8.40	4447.1	3.64807	.0002249
8.45	4675.1	3.66979	.0002139
8.50	4914.8	3.69150	0.0002035
8.55	5166.8	3.71322	.0001935
8.60	5431.7	3.73493	.0001841
8.65	5710.1	3.75665	.0001751
8.70	6002.9	3.77836	.0001666
8.75	6310.7	3.80008	0.0001585
8.80	6634.2	3.82179	.0001507
8.85	6974.4	3.84351	.0001434
8.90	7332.0	3.86522	.0001364
8.95	7707.9	3.88694	.0001297
9.00	8103.1	3.90865	0.0001234
9.05	8518.5	3.93037	.0001174
9.10	8955.3	3.95208	.0001117
9.15	9414.4	3.97379	.0001062
9.20	9897.1	3.99551	.0001010
9.25	10405	4.01722	0.0000961
9.30	10938	4.03894	.0000914
9.35	11499	4.06065	.0000870
9.40	12088	4.08237	.0000827
9.45	12708	4.10408	.0000787
9.50	13360	4.12580	0.0000749
9.55	14045	4.14751	.0000712
9.60	14765	4.16923	.0000677
9.65	15522	4.19094	.0000644
9.70	16318	4.21266	.0000613
9.75	17154	4.23437	0.0000583
9.80	18034	4.25609	.0000555
9.85	18958	4.27780	.0000527
9.90	19930	4.29952	.0000502
9.95	20952	4.32123	0.0000477
10.00	22026	4.34294	0.0000454

TRIGONOMETRY

DR. HOWARD EVES

PLANE TRIGONOMETRY

Angle

That part of a straight line lying entirely to one side of a point O on the line is called a *ray* (or a *half-line*); the point O is called the *origin* of the ray. A ray of origin O is identified by the notation OA, where A is any point of the ray.

If a ray OA is rotated, in a plane, about its origin O onto ray OB, an *angle AOB* is said to be generated. Ray OA is called the *initial side*, ray OB the *terminal side*, and point O the *vertex* of the angle. The angle is said to be *positive* or *negative* according as the generating rotation is counterclockwise or clockwise.

An angle is said to be in *standard position* if its vertex is at the origin O and its initial side is on the positive x-axis of a rectangular Cartesian coordinate system (see p. 496). If the terminal side of the angle falls on a coordinate axis, the angle is called a *quadrantal angle*; otherwise the angle is called a *first, second, third,* or *fourth quadrant angle* according as the terminal side falls in the first, second, third, or fourth quadrant of the coordinate system.

An angle of one *degree* is an angle in which the rotation is $1/360$ of one complete rotation.

A *straight angle* is an angle of 180° (180 degrees).

A *right angle* is an angle of 90°.

An *acute angle* is an angle between 0° and 90°.

An *obtuse angle* is an angle between 90° and 180°.

A *radian* is an angle subtended at the center of a circle by an arc whose length is equal to that of the radius.

$$180° = \pi \text{ radians}; \quad 1° = \frac{\pi}{180} \text{ radians}; \quad 1 \text{ radian} = \frac{180}{\pi} \text{ degrees}.$$

The Trigonometric Functions of an Acute Angle

In the right triangle ABC,

sine $A = \sin A = a/c$

cosine $A = \cos A = b/c$

tangent $A = \tan A = a/b$

cosecant $A = \csc A = c/a$

secant $A = \sec A = c/b$

cotangent $A = \cot A = \operatorname{ctn} A = b/a$

exsecant $A = \operatorname{exsec} A = \sec A - 1$

versine $A = \operatorname{vers} A = 1 - \cos A$

coversine $A = \operatorname{covers} A = 1 - \sin A$

haversine $A = \operatorname{hav} A = \frac{1}{2}\operatorname{vers} A$

225

The Trigonometric Functions of an Arbitrary Angle

Let α be any angle in standard position and let $P(x,y)$ be any point on the terminal side of the angle. Denote the positive distance OP by r. Then

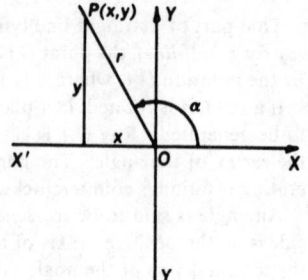

$\sin \alpha = y/r$ $\csc \alpha = r/y$

$\cos \alpha = x/r$ $\sec \alpha = r/x$

$\tan \alpha = y/x$ $\cot \alpha = \text{ctn } \alpha = x/y$

$\text{exsec } \alpha = \sec \alpha - 1$ $\text{covers } \alpha = 1 - \sin \alpha$

$\text{vers } \alpha = 1 - \cos \alpha$ $\text{hav } \alpha = \frac{1}{2} \text{vers } \alpha$

$\text{cis } \alpha = \cos \alpha + i \sin \alpha = e^{i\alpha}, \alpha \text{ in radians}, i = \sqrt{-1}$

RELATIONS BETWEEN CIRCULAR (OR INVERSE CIRCULAR) FUNCTIONS

$$\left(0 \leq x \leq \frac{\pi}{2}\right)$$

	$\sin x = a$	$\cos x = a$	$\tan x = a$
$\sin x$	a	$(1 - a^2)^{1/2}$	$a(1 + a^2)^{-1/2}$
$\cos x$	$(1 - a^2)^{1/2}$	a	$(1 + a^2)^{-1/2}$
$\tan x$	$a(1 - a^2)^{-1/2}$	$a^{-1}(1 - a^2)^{1/2}$	a
$\csc x$	a^{-1}	$(1 - a^2)^{-1/2}$	$a^{-1}(1 + a^2)^{1/2}$
$\sec x$	$(1 - a^2)^{-1/2}$	a^{-1}	$(1 + a^2)^{1/2}$
$\cot x$	$a^{-1}(1 - a^2)^{1/2}$	$a(1 - a^2)^{-1/2}$	a^{-1}

	$\csc x = a$	$\sec x = a$	$\cot x = a$,
$\sin x$	a^{-1}	$a^{-1}(a^2 - 1)^{1/2}$	$(1 + a^2)^{-1/2}$
$\cos x$	$a^{-1}(a^2 - 1)^{1/2}$	a^{-1}	$a(1 + a^2)^{-1/2}$
$\tan x$	$(a^2 - 1)^{-1/2}$	$(a^2 - 1)^{1/2}$	a^{-1}
$\csc x$	a	$a(a^2 - 1)^{-1/2}$	$(1 + a^2)^{1/2}$
$\sec x$	$a(a^2 - 1)^{-1/2}$	a	$a^{-1}(1 + a^2)^{1/2}$
$\cot x$	$(a^2 - 1)^{1/2}$	$(a^2 - 1)^{-1/2}$	a

Examples:

    If $\sec x = a$, then $\tan x = (a^2 - 1)^{1/2}$

    $\text{arc tan } a = \text{arc cos } (1 + a^2)^{-1/2}$

SIGNS OF THE TRIGONOMETRIC FUNCTIONS

Quadrant	sin	cos	tan	cot	sec	csc
I	+	+	+	+	+	+
II	+	−	−	−	−	+
III	−	−	+	+	−	−
IV	−	+	−	−	+	−

VARIATIONS OF THE TRIGONOMETRIC FUNCTIONS

Quadrant	sin	cos	tan	cot	sec	csc
I	$0 \to +1$	$+1 \to 0$	$0 \to +\infty$	$+\infty \to 0$	$+1 \to +\infty$	$+\infty \to +1$
II	$+1 \to 0$	$0 \to -1$	$-\infty \to 0$	$0 \to -\infty$	$-\infty \to -1$	$+1 \to +\infty$
III	$0 \to -1$	$-1 \to 0$	$0 \to +\infty$	$+\infty \to 0$	$-1 \to -\infty$	$-\infty \to -1$
IV	$-1 \to 0$	$0 \to +1$	$-\infty \to 0$	$0 \to -\infty$	$+\infty \to +1$	$-1 \to -\infty$

TRIGONOMETRIC FUNCTIONS OF SOME SPECIAL ANGLES

Angle	sin	cos	tan	cot	sec	csc
$0° = 0$	0	1	0	$\cdots$	1	$\cdots$
$15° = \dfrac{\pi}{12}$	$\dfrac{\sqrt{2}}{4}(\sqrt{3}-1)$	$\dfrac{\sqrt{2}}{4}(\sqrt{3}+1)$	$2-\sqrt{3}$	$2+\sqrt{3}$	$\sqrt{2}(\sqrt{3}-1)$	$\sqrt{2}(\sqrt{3}+1)$
$30° = \dfrac{\pi}{6}$	$1/2$	$\sqrt{3}/2$	$\sqrt{3}/3$	$\sqrt{3}$	$2\sqrt{3}/3$	2
$45° = \dfrac{\pi}{4}$	$\sqrt{2}/2$	$\sqrt{2}/2$	1	1	$\sqrt{2}$	$\sqrt{2}$
$60° = \dfrac{\pi}{3}$	$\sqrt{3}/2$	$1/2$	$\sqrt{3}$	$\sqrt{3}/3$	2	$2\sqrt{3}/3$
$75° = \dfrac{5\pi}{12}$	$\dfrac{\sqrt{2}}{4}(\sqrt{3}+1)$	$\dfrac{\sqrt{2}}{4}(\sqrt{3}-1)$	$2+\sqrt{3}$	$2-\sqrt{3}$	$\sqrt{2}(\sqrt{3}+1)$	$\sqrt{2}(\sqrt{3}-1)$
$90° = \dfrac{\pi}{2}$	1	0	$\cdots$	0	$\cdots$	1
$105° = \dfrac{7\pi}{12}$	$\dfrac{\sqrt{2}}{4}(\sqrt{3}+1)$	$-\dfrac{\sqrt{2}}{4}(\sqrt{3}-1)$	$-(2+\sqrt{3})$	$-(2-\sqrt{3})$	$-2(\sqrt{3}+1)$	$\sqrt{2}(\sqrt{3}-1)$
$120° = \dfrac{2\pi}{3}$	$\sqrt{3}/2$	$-1/2$	$-\sqrt{3}$	$-\sqrt{3}/3$	-2	$2\sqrt{3}/3$
$135° = \dfrac{3\pi}{4}$	$\sqrt{2}/2$	$-\sqrt{2}/2$	-1	-1	$-\sqrt{2}$	$\sqrt{2}$
$150° = \dfrac{5\pi}{6}$	$1/2$	$-\sqrt{3}/2$	$-\sqrt{3}/3$	$-\sqrt{3}$	$-2\sqrt{3}/3$	2
$165° = \dfrac{11\pi}{12}$	$\dfrac{\sqrt{2}}{4}(\sqrt{3}-1)$	$-\dfrac{\sqrt{2}}{4}(\sqrt{3}+1)$	$-(2-\sqrt{3})$	$-(2+\sqrt{3})$	$-\sqrt{2}(\sqrt{3}-1)$	$\sqrt{2}(\sqrt{3}+1)$
$180° = \pi$	0	-1	0	$\cdots$	-1	$\cdots$
$270° = \dfrac{3\pi}{2}$	-1	0	$\cdots$	0	$\cdots$	-1

Relations of the Functions

$$\sin x = \frac{1}{\csc x}$$

$$\csc x = \frac{1}{\sin x}$$

$$\cos x = \frac{1}{\sec x}$$

$$\sec x = \frac{1}{\cos x}$$

$$\tan x = \frac{1}{\cot x} = \frac{\sin x}{\cos x}$$

$$\sin^2 x + \cos^2 x = 1$$

$$1 + \tan^2 x = \sec^2 x$$

$$\cot x = \frac{1}{\tan x} = \frac{\cos x}{\sin x}$$

$$1 + \cot^2 x = \csc^2 x$$

$$*\sin x = \pm \sqrt{1 - \cos^2 x}$$
$$*\tan x = \pm \sqrt{\sec^2 x - 1}$$
$$*\cot x = \pm \sqrt{\csc^2 x - 1}$$

$$*\cos x = \pm \sqrt{1 - \sin^2 x}$$
$$*\sec x = \pm \sqrt{\tan^2 x + 1}$$
$$*\csc x = \pm \sqrt{\cot^2 x + 1}$$

$$\sin x = \cos (90° - x) = \sin (180° - x)$$
$$\cos x = \sin (90° - x) = -\cos (180° - x)$$
$$\tan x = \cot (90° - x) = -\tan (180° - x)$$
$$\cot x = \tan (90° - x) = -\cot (180° - x)$$

$$\csc x = \cot \frac{x}{2} - \cot x$$

*The sign in front of radical depends on quadrant in which x falls.

Reduction Formulas

$$\sin \alpha = + \cos(\alpha - 90°) = - \sin(\alpha - 180°) = - \cos(\alpha - 270°)$$
$$\cos \alpha = - \sin(\alpha - 90°) = - \cos(\alpha - 180°) = + \sin(\alpha - 270°)$$
$$\tan \alpha = - \cot(\alpha - 90°) = + \tan(\alpha - 180°) = - \cot(\alpha - 270°)$$
$$\cot \alpha = - \tan(\alpha - 90°) = + \cot(\alpha - 180°) = - \tan(\alpha - 270°)$$
$$\sec \alpha = - \csc(\alpha - 90°) = - \sec(\alpha - 180°) = + \csc(\alpha - 270°)$$
$$\csc \alpha = + \sec(\alpha - 90°) = - \csc(\alpha - 180°) = - \sec(\alpha - 270°)$$

FURTHER REDUCTION FORMULAS

	sin	cos	tan	cot	sec	csc
$-\alpha$	$-\sin \alpha$	$+\cos \alpha$	$-\tan \alpha$	$-\cot \alpha$	$+\sec \alpha$	$-\csc \alpha$
$90° + \alpha$	$+\cos \alpha$	$-\sin \alpha$	$-\cot \alpha$	$-\tan \alpha$	$-\csc \alpha$	$+\sec \alpha$
$90° - \alpha$	$+\cos \alpha$	$+\sin \alpha$	$+\cot \alpha$	$+\tan \alpha$	$+\csc \alpha$	$+\sec \alpha$
$180° + \alpha$	$-\sin \alpha$	$-\cos \alpha$	$+\tan \alpha$	$+\cot \alpha$	$-\sec \alpha$	$-\csc \alpha$
$180° - \alpha$	$+\sin \alpha$	$-\cos \alpha$	$-\tan \alpha$	$-\cot \alpha$	$-\sec \alpha$	$+\csc \alpha$
$270° + \alpha$	$-\cos \alpha$	$+\sin \alpha$	$-\cot \alpha$	$-\tan \alpha$	$+\csc \alpha$	$-\sec \alpha$
$270° - \alpha$	$-\cos \alpha$	$-\sin \alpha$	$+\cot \alpha$	$+\tan \alpha$	$-\csc \alpha$	$-\sec \alpha$
$360° + \alpha$	$+\sin \alpha$	$+\cos \alpha$	$+\tan \alpha$	$+\cot \alpha$	$+\sec \alpha$	$+\csc \alpha$
$360° - \alpha$	$-\sin \alpha$	$+\cos \alpha$	$-\tan \alpha$	$-\cot \alpha$	$+\sec \alpha$	$-\csc \alpha$

The above table may be summarized and extended by the following easily remembered rule:

$$f(\pm\alpha + n90°) = \pm g(\alpha)$$

where n may be any integer, positive, negative, or zero

     f is any one of the six trigonometric functions: sin, cos, tan, cot, sec, or csc

     α may be any real angle measure

If n is even, then g is the same function as f. If n is odd, then g is the *cofunction* of f.

   (Sine and cosine, tangent and cotangent, secant and cosecant, are cofunctions of each other.)

   The second $\pm$ sign is not necessarily the same as the first one, but is determined as follows: For a given function f, a given value of n, and a given choice of the first $\pm$ sign, the second $\pm$ sign will be the same for all values of α. Thus it is only necessary to check the sign for any one value of α, and the formula will be complete.

EXAMPLES:

    $\tan (\alpha + 270°) = \pm \cot \alpha$. Since $n(=3)$ is odd, we use the cofunction. To determine the sign, assume a value of α in the first quadrant. Then $\alpha + 270°$ is in the fourth quadrant, where the tangent is negative, so a minus sign is required. Thus the formula becomes

$$\tan (\alpha + 270°) = - \cot \alpha, \quad \text{valid for all values of } \alpha.$$

    $\cos (\alpha - 450°) = \pm \sin \alpha$. Again assuming a value of α in the first quadrant, we find that $\alpha - 450°$ is in the fourth quadrant. Thus $\cos (\alpha - 450°)$ would be positive, and no minus sign is needed. Hence the formula becomes

$$\cos (\alpha - 450°) = \sin \alpha.$$

    $\sec (180° - \alpha) = \pm \sec \alpha$. Here $n(=2)$ is even, so we use the same function. To determine the sign, again assume a value of α in the first quadrant. Then $180° - \alpha$ is in the second quadrant, where the secant is negative. Thus the formula, valid for all values of α, is

$$\sec (180° - \alpha) = - \sec \alpha.$$

Fundamental Identities

   Where a double sign appears in the following, the choice of sign depends upon the quadrant in which the angle terminates.

Reciprocal relations

$$\sin \alpha = \frac{1}{\csc \alpha}, \quad \cos \alpha = \frac{1}{\sec \alpha}, \quad \tan \alpha = \frac{1}{\cot \alpha}$$

$$\csc \alpha = \frac{1}{\sin \alpha}, \quad \sec \alpha = \frac{1}{\cos \alpha}, \quad \cot \alpha = \frac{1}{\tan \alpha}$$

Product relations

$$\sin \alpha = \tan \alpha \cos \alpha, \quad \cos \alpha = \cot \alpha \sin \alpha$$
$$\tan \alpha = \sin \alpha \sec \alpha, \quad \cot \alpha = \cos \alpha \csc \alpha$$
$$\sec \alpha = \csc \alpha \tan \alpha, \quad \csc \alpha = \sec \alpha \cot \alpha$$

Quotient relations

$$\sin \alpha = \frac{\tan \alpha}{\sec \alpha}, \quad \cos \alpha = \frac{\cot \alpha}{\csc \alpha}, \quad \tan \alpha = \frac{\sin \alpha}{\cos \alpha}$$

$$\csc \alpha = \frac{\sec \alpha}{\tan \alpha}, \quad \sec \alpha = \frac{\csc \alpha}{\cot \alpha}, \quad \cot \alpha = \frac{\cos \alpha}{\sin \alpha}$$

Pythagorean relations

$$\sin^2\alpha + \cos^2\alpha = 1, \qquad 1 + \tan^2\alpha = \sec^2\alpha, \qquad 1 + \cot^2\alpha = \csc^2\alpha$$

Angle-sum and angle-difference relations

$$\sin(\alpha + \beta) = \sin\alpha\cos\beta + \cos\alpha\sin\beta$$
$$\sin(\alpha - \beta) = \sin\alpha\cos\beta - \cos\alpha\sin\beta$$
$$\cos(\alpha + \beta) = \cos\alpha\cos\beta - \sin\alpha\sin\beta$$
$$\cos(\alpha - \beta) = \cos\alpha\cos\beta + \sin\alpha\sin\beta$$
$$\tan(\alpha + \beta) = \frac{\tan\alpha + \tan\beta}{1 - \tan\alpha\tan\beta}$$
$$\tan(\alpha - \beta) = \frac{\tan\alpha - \tan\beta}{1 + \tan\alpha\tan\beta}$$
$$\cot(\alpha + \beta) = \frac{\cot\beta\cot\alpha - 1}{\cot\beta + \cot\alpha}$$
$$\cot(\alpha - \beta) = \frac{\cot\beta\cot\alpha + 1}{\cot\beta - \cot\alpha}$$
$$\sin(\alpha + \beta)\sin(\alpha - \beta) = \sin^2\alpha - \sin^2\beta = \cos^2\beta - \cos^2\alpha$$
$$\cos(\alpha + \beta)\cos(\alpha - \beta) = \cos^2\alpha - \sin^2\beta = \cos^2\beta - \sin^2\alpha$$

Double-angle relations

$$\sin 2\alpha = 2\sin\alpha\cos\alpha = \frac{2\tan\alpha}{1 + \tan^2\alpha}$$

$$\cos 2\alpha = \cos^2\alpha - \sin^2\alpha = 2\cos^2\alpha - 1 = 1 - 2\sin^2\alpha = \frac{1 - \tan^2\alpha}{1 + \tan^2\alpha}$$

$$\tan 2\alpha = \frac{2\tan\alpha}{1 - \tan^2\alpha}, \qquad \cot 2\alpha = \frac{\cot^2\alpha - 1}{2\cot\alpha}$$

Multiple-angle relations

$$\sin 3\alpha = 3\sin\alpha - 4\sin^3\alpha$$
$$\cos 3\alpha = 4\cos^3\alpha - 3\cos\alpha$$
$$\sin 4\alpha = 4\sin\alpha\cos\alpha - 8\sin^3\alpha\cos\alpha$$
$$\cos 4\alpha = 8\cos^4\alpha - 8\cos^2\alpha + 1$$
$$\sin 5\alpha = 5\sin\alpha - 20\sin^3\alpha + 16\sin^5\alpha$$
$$\cos 5\alpha = 16\cos^5\alpha - 20\cos^3\alpha + 5\cos\alpha$$
$$\sin 6\alpha = 32\cos^5\alpha\sin\alpha - 32\cos^3\alpha\sin\alpha + 6\cos\alpha\sin\alpha$$
$$\cos 6\alpha = 32\cos^6\alpha - 48\cos^4\alpha + 18\cos^2\alpha - 1$$
$$\sin n\alpha = 2\sin(n-1)\alpha\cos\alpha - \sin(n-2)\alpha$$
$$\cos n\alpha = 2\cos(n-1)\alpha\cos\alpha - \cos(n-2)\alpha$$
$$\tan 3\alpha = \frac{3\tan\alpha - \tan^3\alpha}{1 - 3\tan^2\alpha}$$
$$\tan 4\alpha = \frac{4\tan\alpha - 4\tan^3\alpha}{1 - 6\tan^2\alpha + \tan^4\alpha}$$
$$\tan n\alpha = \frac{\tan(n-1)\alpha + \tan\alpha}{1 - \tan(n-1)\alpha\tan\alpha}$$

Function-product relations

$$\sin \alpha \sin \beta = \tfrac{1}{2}\cos(\alpha - \beta) - \tfrac{1}{2}\cos(\alpha + \beta)$$
$$\cos \alpha \cos \beta = \tfrac{1}{2}\cos(\alpha - \beta) + \tfrac{1}{2}\cos(\alpha + \beta)$$
$$\sin \alpha \cos \beta = \tfrac{1}{2}\sin(\alpha + \beta) + \tfrac{1}{2}\sin(\alpha - \beta)$$
$$\cos \alpha \sin \beta = \tfrac{1}{2}\sin(\alpha + \beta) - \tfrac{1}{2}\sin(\alpha - \beta)$$

Function-sum and function-difference relations

$$\sin \alpha + \sin \beta = 2 \sin \tfrac{1}{2}(\alpha + \beta) \cos \tfrac{1}{2}(\alpha - \beta)$$
$$\sin \alpha - \sin \beta = 2 \cos \tfrac{1}{2}(\alpha + \beta) \sin \tfrac{1}{2}(\alpha - \beta)$$
$$\cos \alpha + \cos \beta = 2 \cos \tfrac{1}{2}(\alpha + \beta) \cos \tfrac{1}{2}(\alpha - \beta)$$
$$\cos \alpha - \cos \beta = -2 \sin \tfrac{1}{2}(\alpha + \beta) \sin \tfrac{1}{2}(\alpha - \beta)$$

$$\tan \alpha + \tan \beta = \frac{\sin(\alpha + \beta)}{\cos \alpha \cos \beta}, \qquad \tan \alpha - \tan \beta = \frac{\sin(\alpha - \beta)}{\cos \alpha \cos \beta}$$

$$\cot \alpha + \cot \beta = \frac{\sin(\alpha + \beta)}{\sin \alpha \sin \beta}, \qquad \cot \alpha - \cot \beta = \frac{\sin(\beta - \alpha)}{\sin \alpha \sin \beta}$$

$$\frac{\sin \alpha + \sin \beta}{\sin \alpha - \sin \beta} = \frac{\tan \tfrac{1}{2}(\alpha + \beta)}{\tan \tfrac{1}{2}(\alpha - \beta)}, \qquad \frac{\sin \alpha + \sin \beta}{\cos \alpha - \cos \beta} = \cot \tfrac{1}{2}(\beta - \alpha)$$

$$\frac{\sin \alpha + \sin \beta}{\cos \alpha + \cos \beta} = \tan \tfrac{1}{2}(\alpha + \beta), \qquad \frac{\sin \alpha - \sin \beta}{\cos \alpha + \cos \beta} = \tan \tfrac{1}{2}(\alpha - \beta)$$

Half-angle relations

$$\sin \frac{\alpha}{2} = \pm\sqrt{\frac{1 - \cos \alpha}{2}}, \qquad \cos \frac{\alpha}{2} = \pm\sqrt{\frac{1 + \cos \alpha}{2}}$$

$$\tan \frac{\alpha}{2} = \pm\sqrt{\frac{1 - \cos \alpha}{1 + \cos \alpha}} = \frac{1 - \cos \alpha}{\sin \alpha} = \frac{\sin \alpha}{1 + \cos \alpha}$$

$$\cot \frac{\alpha}{2} = \pm\sqrt{\frac{1 + \cos \alpha}{1 - \cos \alpha}} = \frac{1 + \cos \alpha}{\sin \alpha} = \frac{\sin \alpha}{1 - \cos \alpha}$$

Power relations

$$\sin^2\alpha = \tfrac{1}{2}(1 - \cos 2\alpha), \qquad \sin^3\alpha = \tfrac{1}{4}(3 \sin \alpha - \sin 3\alpha)$$
$$\sin^4\alpha = \tfrac{1}{8}(3 - 4 \cos 2\alpha + \cos 4\alpha)$$
$$\cos^2\alpha = \tfrac{1}{2}(1 + \cos 2\alpha), \qquad \cos^3\alpha = \tfrac{1}{4}(3 \cos \alpha + \cos 3\alpha)$$
$$\cos^4\alpha = \tfrac{1}{8}(3 + 4 \cos 2\alpha + \cos 4\alpha)$$

$$\tan^2\alpha = \frac{1 - \cos 2\alpha}{1 + \cos 2\alpha}, \qquad \cot^2\alpha = \frac{1 + \cos 2\alpha}{1 - \cos 2\alpha}$$

Exponential relations (α in radians), Euler's equation

$$e^{i\alpha} = \cos \alpha + i \sin \alpha, \qquad i = \sqrt{-1}$$

$$\sin \alpha = \frac{e^{i\alpha} - e^{-i\alpha}}{2i}, \qquad \cos \alpha = \frac{e^{i\alpha} + e^{-i\alpha}}{2}$$

$$\tan \alpha = -i\left(\frac{e^{i\alpha} - e^{-i\alpha}}{e^{i\alpha} + e^{-i\alpha}}\right) = -i\left(\frac{e^{2i\alpha} - 1}{e^{2i\alpha} + 1}\right)$$

THE TRIGONOMETRIC FUNCTIONS IN TERMS OF ONE ANOTHER

Function	$\sin \alpha$	$\cos \alpha$	$\tan \alpha$	$\cot \alpha$	$\sec \alpha$	$\csc \alpha$
$\sin \alpha$	$\sin \alpha$	$\pm \sqrt{1 - \cos^2\alpha}$	$\dfrac{\tan \alpha}{\pm \sqrt{1 + \tan^2\alpha}}$	$\dfrac{1}{\pm \sqrt{1 + \cot^2\alpha}}$	$\dfrac{\pm \sqrt{\sec^2\alpha - 1}}{\sec \alpha}$	$\dfrac{1}{\csc \alpha}$
$\cos \alpha$	$\pm \sqrt{1 - \sin^2\alpha}$	$\cos \alpha$	$\dfrac{1}{\pm \sqrt{1 + \tan^2\alpha}}$	$\dfrac{\cot \alpha}{\pm \sqrt{1 + \cot^2\alpha}}$	$\dfrac{1}{\sec \alpha}$	$\dfrac{\pm \sqrt{\csc^2\alpha - 1}}{\csc \alpha}$
$\tan \alpha$	$\dfrac{\sin \alpha}{\pm \sqrt{1 - \sin^2\alpha}}$	$\dfrac{\pm \sqrt{1 - \cos^2\alpha}}{\cos \alpha}$	$\tan \alpha$	$\dfrac{1}{\cot \alpha}$	$\pm \sqrt{\sec^2\alpha - 1}$	$\dfrac{1}{\pm \sqrt{\csc^2\alpha - 1}}$
$\cot \alpha$	$\dfrac{\pm \sqrt{1 - \sin^2\alpha}}{\sin \alpha}$	$\dfrac{\cos \alpha}{\pm \sqrt{1 - \cos^2\alpha}}$	$\dfrac{1}{\tan \alpha}$	$\cot \alpha$	$\dfrac{1}{\pm \sqrt{\sec^2\alpha - 1}}$	$\pm \sqrt{\csc^2\alpha - 1}$
$\sec \alpha$	$\dfrac{1}{\pm \sqrt{1 - \sin^2\alpha}}$	$\dfrac{1}{\cos \alpha}$	$\pm \sqrt{1 + \tan^2\alpha}$	$\dfrac{\pm \sqrt{1 + \cot^2\alpha}}{\cot \alpha}$	$\sec \alpha$	$\dfrac{\csc \alpha}{\pm \sqrt{\csc^2\alpha - 1}}$
$\csc \alpha$	$\dfrac{1}{\sin \alpha}$	$\dfrac{1}{\pm \sqrt{1 - \cos^2\alpha}}$	$\dfrac{\pm \sqrt{1 + \tan^2\alpha}}{\tan \alpha}$	$\pm \sqrt{1 + \cot^2\alpha}$	$\dfrac{\sec \alpha}{\pm \sqrt{\sec^2\alpha - 1}}$	$\csc \alpha$

Note. The choice of sign depends upon the quadrant in which the angle terminates.

Principal Values of the Inverse Trigonometric Functions

The notation arcsin x (or $\sin^{-1}x$) is used to denote any angle whose sine is x; Arcsin x (or $\mathrm{Sin}^{-1}x$) is usually used to denote the *principal value*. Similar notation is used for the other inverse trigonometric functions. The principal values of the inverse trigonometric functions are defined as follows:

$$-\pi/2 \le \mathrm{Arcsin}\, x \le \pi/2, \qquad -1 \le x \le 1$$

$$0 \le \mathrm{Arccos}\, x \le \pi, \qquad -1 \le x \le 1$$

$$-\pi/2 < \mathrm{Arctan}\, x < \pi/2, \qquad -\infty < x < \infty$$

$$0 < \mathrm{Arccsc}\, x \le \pi/2, \qquad x \ge 1$$
$$-\pi < \mathrm{Arccsc}\, x \le -\pi/2, \qquad x \le -1$$

$$0 \le \mathrm{Arcsec}\, x < \pi/2, \qquad x \ge 1$$
$$-\pi \le \mathrm{Arcsec}\, x < -\pi/2, \qquad x \le -1$$

$$0 < \mathrm{Arccot}\, x < \pi, \qquad -\infty < x < \infty$$

Note. There is no uniform agreement on the definitions of Arccsc x, Arcsec x, Arccot x for negative values of x.

Fundamental Identities Involving Principal Values

$$\mathrm{Arcsin}\, x + \mathrm{Arccos}\, x = \pi/2$$
$$\mathrm{Arctan}\, x + \mathrm{Arccot}\, x = \pi/2$$

If $\alpha = \mathrm{Arcsin}\, x$, then

$$\sin \alpha = x, \qquad \cos \alpha = \sqrt{1 - x^2}, \qquad \tan \alpha = \frac{x}{\sqrt{1 - x^2}}$$

$$\csc \alpha = \frac{1}{x}, \qquad \sec \alpha = \frac{1}{\sqrt{1 - x^2}}, \qquad \cot \alpha = \frac{\sqrt{1 - x^2}}{x}$$

If $\alpha = \text{Arccos } x$, then

$$\sin \alpha = \sqrt{1 - x^2}, \qquad \cos \alpha = x, \qquad \tan \alpha = \frac{\sqrt{1 - x^2}}{x}$$

$$\csc \alpha = \frac{1}{\sqrt{1 - x^2}}, \qquad \sec \alpha = \frac{1}{x}, \qquad \cot \alpha = \frac{x}{\sqrt{1 - x^2}}$$

If $\alpha = \text{Arctan } x$, then

$$\sin \alpha = \frac{x}{\sqrt{1 + x^2}}, \qquad \cos \alpha = \frac{1}{\sqrt{1 + x^2}}, \qquad \tan \alpha = x$$

$$\csc \alpha = \frac{\sqrt{1 + x^2}}{x}, \qquad \sec \alpha = \sqrt{1 + x^2}, \qquad \cot \alpha = \frac{1}{x}$$

Relations Between Principal Values of Inverse Trigonometric Functions

The following additional relations between principal values of the inverse trigonometric functions are useful:

$$\text{Arcsin } x = \text{Arccos}(-x) - \frac{\pi}{2} = \frac{\pi}{2} - \text{Arccos } x$$

$$= -\text{Arcsin}(-x) = \text{Arctan } \frac{x}{\sqrt{1 - x^2}}$$

$$= \frac{\pi}{2} - \text{Arccot } \frac{x}{\sqrt{1 - x^2}}$$

$$\text{Arctan } x = \text{Arccot}(-x) - \frac{\pi}{2} = \frac{\pi}{2} - \text{Arccot } x$$

$$= -\text{Arctan}(-x) = \text{Arcsin } \frac{x}{\sqrt{x^2 + 1}}$$

$$= \frac{\pi}{2} - \text{Arccos } \frac{x}{\sqrt{x^2 + 1}}$$

$$\text{Arccos } x = \frac{\pi}{2} + \text{Arcsin}(-x) = \frac{\pi}{2} - \text{Arcsin } x$$

$$= \pi - \text{Arccos}(-x) = \text{Arccot } \frac{x}{\sqrt{1 - x^2}}$$

$$= \frac{\pi}{2} - \text{Arctan } \frac{x}{\sqrt{1 - x^2}}$$

$$\text{Arccot } x = \frac{\pi}{2} + \text{Arctan}(-x) = \frac{\pi}{2} - \text{Arctan } x$$

$$= \pi - \text{Arccot}(-x) = \text{Arccos } \frac{x}{\sqrt{x^2 + 1}}$$

$$= \frac{\pi}{2} - \text{Arcsin } \frac{x}{\sqrt{x^2 + 1}}$$

$$\text{Arccsc } x = \text{Arcsec } \frac{x}{\sqrt{x^2 - 1}}$$

$$\text{Arcsec } x = \text{Arccsc } \frac{x}{\sqrt{x^2 - 1}}$$

$$\cos(\text{Arcsin } x) = \sin(\text{Arccos } x) = \sqrt{1 - x^2}$$

$$\sec(\text{Arctan } x) = \csc(\text{Arccot } x) = \sqrt{x^2 + 1}$$

$$\tan(\text{Arcsec } x) = \cot(\text{Arccsc } x) = \sqrt{x^2 - 1}$$

The above are valid for x positive or negative. The following are valid only for $x \geq 0$.

$$\text{Arcsin } x = \text{Arccos } \sqrt{1 - x^2} = \text{Arccot } \frac{\sqrt{1 - x^2}}{x}$$

$$= \text{Arcsec } \frac{1}{\sqrt{1 - x^2}} = \text{Arccsc } \frac{1}{x}$$

$$= \frac{\pi}{2} - \text{Arcsin } \sqrt{1 - x^2}$$

$$\text{Arccos } x = \text{Arcsin } \sqrt{1 - x^2} = \text{Arctan } \frac{\sqrt{1 - x^2}}{x}$$

$$= \text{Arcsec } \frac{1}{x} = \text{Arccsc } \frac{1}{\sqrt{1 - x^2}}$$

$$= \frac{\pi}{2} - \text{Arccos } \sqrt{1 - x^2}$$

$$\text{Arctan } x = \text{Arccot } \frac{1}{x} = \text{Arccos } \frac{1}{\sqrt{x^2 + 1}}$$

$$= \text{Arcsec } \sqrt{x^2 + 1} = \text{Arccsc } \frac{\sqrt{x^2 + 1}}{x}$$

$$= \frac{\pi}{2} - \text{Arctan } \frac{1}{x}$$

$$\text{Arccot } x = \text{Arctan } \frac{1}{x} = \text{Arcsin } \frac{1}{\sqrt{x^2 + 1}}$$

$$= \text{Arcsec } \frac{\sqrt{x^2 + 1}}{x} = \text{Arccsc } \sqrt{x^2 + 1}$$

$$= \frac{\pi}{2} - \text{Arccot } \frac{1}{x}$$

$$\text{Arcsec } x = \text{Arctan } \sqrt{x^2 - 1} = \text{Arccot } \frac{1}{\sqrt{x^2 - 1}}$$

$$= \text{Arcsin } \frac{\sqrt{x^2 - 1}}{x} = \text{Arccos } \frac{1}{x} = \pi + \text{Arcsec}(-x)$$

$$= \frac{\pi}{2} - \text{Arccsc } x = -\frac{\pi}{2} - \text{Arccsc}(-x)$$

$$\text{Arccsc } x = \text{Arctan } \frac{1}{\sqrt{x^2 - 1}} = \text{Arccot } \sqrt{x^2 - 1}$$

$$= \text{Arcsin } \frac{1}{x} = \text{Arccos } \frac{\sqrt{x^2 - 1}}{x} = \pi + \text{Arccsc}(-x)$$

$$= \frac{\pi}{2} - \text{Arcsec } x = -\frac{\pi}{2} - \text{Arcsec}(-x)$$

The following are valid if $x < 0$.

$$\text{Arcsin } x = -\text{Arccos } \sqrt{1 - x^2} = \text{Arccot } \frac{\sqrt{1 - x^2}}{x} - \pi$$

$$= -\pi - \text{Arccsc } \frac{1}{x} = -\text{Arcsec } \frac{1}{\sqrt{1 - x^2}}$$

$$= \text{Arcsin } \sqrt{1 - x^2} - \frac{\pi}{2}$$

$$\text{Arccos } x = \pi - \text{Arcsin } \sqrt{1 - x^2} = \pi + \text{Arctan } \frac{\sqrt{1 - x^2}}{x}$$

$$= \pi - \text{Arccsc } \frac{1}{\sqrt{1 - x^2}} = -\text{Arcsec } \frac{1}{x}$$

$$= \text{Arccos } \sqrt{1 - x^2} + \frac{\pi}{2}$$

$$\text{Arctan } x = \text{Arccot } \frac{1}{x} - \pi = -\text{Arccos } \frac{1}{\sqrt{x^2 + 1}}$$

$$= -\text{Arcsec } \sqrt{x^2 + 1} = -\pi - \text{Arccsc } \frac{\sqrt{x^2 + 1}}{x}$$

$$= -\frac{\pi}{2} - \text{Arctan } \frac{1}{x}$$

$$\text{Arccot } x = \pi + \text{Arctan } \frac{1}{x} = \pi - \text{Arcsin } \frac{1}{\sqrt{x^2 + 1}}$$

$$= -\text{Arcsec } \frac{\sqrt{x^2 + 1}}{x} = \pi - \text{Arccsc } \sqrt{x^2 + 1}$$

$$= \frac{3\pi}{2} - \text{Arccot } \frac{1}{x}$$

$$\text{Arcsec } x = \text{Arctan } \sqrt{x^2 - 1} - \pi = \text{Arccot } \frac{1}{\sqrt{x^2 - 1}} - \pi$$

$$= -\pi - \text{Arcsin } \frac{\sqrt{x^2 - 1}}{x} = -\text{Arccos } \frac{1}{x} = \text{Arcsec}(-x) - \pi$$

$$= -\frac{3\pi}{2} - \text{Arccsc } x = -\frac{\pi}{2} - \text{Arccsc}(-x)$$

$$\text{Arccsc } x = \text{Arctan } \frac{1}{\sqrt{x^2 - 1}} - \pi = \text{Arccot } \sqrt{x^2 - 1} - \pi$$

$$= -\pi - \text{Arcsin } \frac{1}{x} = -\text{Arccos } \frac{\sqrt{x^2 - 1}}{x} = \text{Arccsc}(-x) - \pi$$

$$= -\frac{3\pi}{2} - \text{Arcsec } x = -\frac{\pi}{2} - \text{Arcsec}(-x)$$

Plane Triangle Formulas

In the following, A, B, C denote the angles of any plane triangle, a, b, c the corresponding opposite sides, and $s = \frac{1}{2}(a + b + c)$.

Radius of inscribed circle:

$$r = \sqrt{\frac{(s - a)(s - b)(s - c)}{s}}$$

Radius of circumscribed circle:

$$R = \frac{a}{2 \sin A} = \frac{b}{2 \sin B} = \frac{c}{2 \sin C}$$

Law of sines:

$$\frac{a}{\sin A} = \frac{b}{\sin B} = \frac{c}{\sin C}$$

Law of cosines:

$$a^2 = b^2 + c^2 - 2bc \cos A, \qquad \cos A = \frac{b^2 + c^2 - a^2}{2bc}$$

$$b^2 = c^2 + a^2 - 2ca \cos B, \qquad \cos B = \frac{c^2 + a^2 - b^2}{2ca}$$

$$c^2 = a^2 + b^2 - 2ab \cos C, \qquad \cos C = \frac{a^2 + b^2 - c^2}{2ab}$$

Law of tangents:

$$\frac{b - c}{b + c} = \frac{\tan \frac{1}{2}(B - C)}{\tan \frac{1}{2}(B + C)}, \qquad \frac{c - a}{c + a} = \frac{\tan \frac{1}{2}(C - A)}{\tan \frac{1}{2}(C + A)}$$

$$\frac{a - b}{a + b} = \frac{\tan \frac{1}{2}(A - B)}{\tan \frac{1}{2}(A + B)}$$

Half-angle formulas:

$$\tan \tfrac{1}{2}A = \frac{r}{s - a}, \qquad \tan \tfrac{1}{2}B = \frac{r}{s - b}, \qquad \tan \tfrac{1}{2}C = \frac{r}{s - c}$$

$$\sin \tfrac{1}{2}A = \sqrt{\frac{(s - b)(s - c)}{bc}}, \qquad \cos \tfrac{1}{2}A = \sqrt{\frac{s(s - a)}{bc}}$$

$$\sin \tfrac{1}{2}B = \sqrt{\frac{(s - c)(s - a)}{ca}}, \qquad \cos \tfrac{1}{2}B = \sqrt{\frac{s(s - b)}{ca}}$$

$$\sin \tfrac{1}{2}C = \sqrt{\frac{(s - a)(s - b)}{ab}}, \qquad \cos \tfrac{1}{2}C = \sqrt{\frac{s(s - c)}{ab}}$$

Area:

$$K = \tfrac{1}{2}bc \sin A = \tfrac{1}{2}ca \sin B = \tfrac{1}{2}ab \sin C$$

$$K = \frac{a^2 \sin B \sin C}{2 \sin A} = \frac{b^2 \sin C \sin A}{2 \sin B} = \frac{c^2 \sin A \sin B}{2 \sin C}$$

$$K = \sqrt{s(s - a)(s - b)(s - c)} = rs = \frac{abc}{4R}$$

Mollweide's formulas:

$$\frac{b - c}{a} = \frac{\sin \tfrac{1}{2}(B - C)}{\cos \tfrac{1}{2}A}, \quad \frac{c - a}{b} = \frac{\sin \tfrac{1}{2}(C - A)}{\cos \tfrac{1}{2}B}$$

$$\frac{a - b}{c} = \frac{\sin \tfrac{1}{2}(A - B)}{\cos \tfrac{1}{2}C}$$

Newton's formulas:

$$\frac{b + c}{a} = \frac{\cos \tfrac{1}{2}(B - C)}{\sin \tfrac{1}{2}A}, \quad \frac{c + a}{b} = \frac{\cos \tfrac{1}{2}(C - A)}{\sin \tfrac{1}{2}B}$$

$$\frac{a + b}{c} = \frac{\cos \tfrac{1}{2}(A - B)}{\sin \tfrac{1}{2}C}$$

Solution of Right Triangles

(a) Given acute angle A and opposite leg a.

$$B = 90° - A, \quad b = a/\tan A = a \cot A, \quad c = a/\sin A = a \csc A$$

(b) Given acute angle A and adjacent leg b.

$$B = 90° - A, \quad a = b \tan A, \quad c = b/\cos A = b \sec A$$

(c) Given acute angle A and hypotenuse c.

$$B = 90° - A, \quad a = c \sin A, \quad b = c \cos A$$

(d) Given legs a and b.

$$c = \sqrt{a^2 + b^2}, \quad \tan A = a/b, \quad B = 90° - A$$

(e) Given hypotenuse c and leg a.

$$b = \sqrt{(c + a)(c - a)}, \quad \sin A = a/c, \quad B = 90° - A$$

Solution of Oblique Triangles

(a) Given sides b and c and included angle A.

Nonlogarithmic solution

$$a^2 = b^2 + c^2 - 2bc \cos A, \quad \cos B = (c^2 + a^2 - b^2)/2ca,$$
$$\cos C = (a^2 + b^2 - c^2)/2ab$$

Logarithmic solution

$$\tfrac{1}{2}(B + C) = 90° - \tfrac{1}{2}A, \quad \tan \tfrac{1}{2}(B - C) = \frac{b - c}{b + c}\tan \tfrac{1}{2}(B + C),$$
$$B = \tfrac{1}{2}(B + C) + \tfrac{1}{2}(B - C), \quad C = \tfrac{1}{2}(B + C) - \tfrac{1}{2}(B - C),$$
$$a = (b \sin A)/\sin B, \quad K = \tfrac{1}{2}bc \sin A$$

Check. $A + B + C = 180°$, or use Newton's formula or law of sines.

(b) Given angles B and C and included side a.

$$A = 180° - (B + C), \quad b = (a \sin B)/\sin A,$$
$$c = (a \sin C)/\sin A, \quad K = \frac{a^2 \sin B \sin C}{2 \sin A}$$

Check. $a = b \cos C + c \cos B$, or use Newton's formula or law of tangents.

(c) Given sides a and c and opposite angle A.

$$\sin C = (c \sin A)/a, \quad B = 180° - (A + C),$$
$$b = (a \sin B)/\sin A, \quad K = \tfrac{1}{2}ac \sin B$$

Check. $a = b \cos C + c \cos B$, or use Newton's formula or law of tangents.
Note. In this case there may be two solutions, for C may have two values:

$C_1 < 90°$ and $C_2 = 180° - C_1 > 90°$. If $A + C_2 > 180°$, use only C_1.

(d) Given the three sides a, b, c.

Nonlogarithmic solution

$$\cos A = (b^2 + c^2 - a^2)/2bc, \quad \cos B = (c^2 + a^2 - b^2)/2ca,$$
$$\cos C = (a^2 + b^2 - c^2)/2ab$$

Logarithmic solution

$$s = \tfrac{1}{2}(a + b + c), \quad r = \sqrt{\frac{(s - a)(s - b)(s - c)}{s}},$$
$$\tan \tfrac{1}{2}A = \frac{r}{s - a}, \quad \tan \tfrac{1}{2}B = \frac{r}{s - b}, \quad \tan \tfrac{1}{2}C = \frac{r}{s - c},$$
$$K = \sqrt{s(s - a)(s - b)(s - c)}$$

Check. $A + B + C = 180°$.

Relations Between Accuracy of Computed Lengths and Angles

When solving a triangle for any of its parts, the following should be observed:

Significant figures for sides	Angles to the nearest
2	degree
3	ten minutes
4	minute
5	tenth of a minute

SPHERICAL TRIGONOMETRY

Right Spherical Triangles

Let a, b, c be the sides of a right spherical triangle with opposite angles $A, B, C = 90°$, respectively, where each side is measured by the angle subtended at the center of the sphere.

$$\sin a = \tan b \cot B, \quad\quad \sin a = \sin A \sin c$$
$$\sin b = \tan a \cot A, \quad\quad \sin b = \sin B \sin c$$
$$\cos A = \tan b \cot c, \quad\quad \cos A = \cos a \sin B$$
$$\cos B = \tan a \cot c, \quad\quad \cos B = \cos b \sin A$$
$$\cos c = \cot A \cot B, \quad\quad \cos c = \cos a \cos b$$

Napier's Rules of Circular Parts

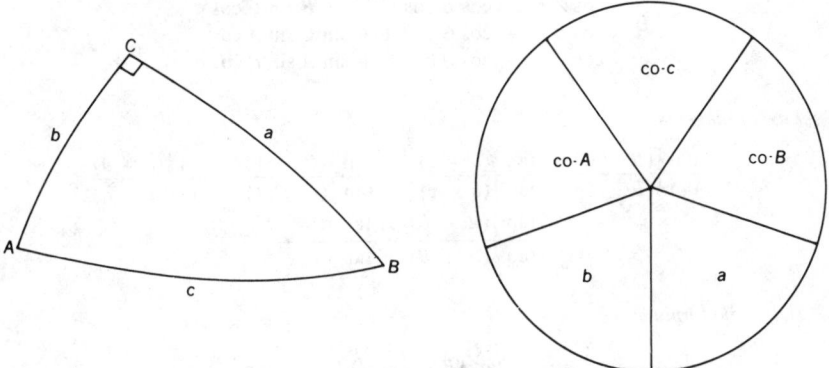

Arrange the five quantities a, b, co-A (complement of A), co-c, co-B of a right spherical triangle right-angled at C in cyclic order as pictured. If any one of these quantities is designated a *middle* part, then two of the other parts are *adjacent* to it, and the remaining two parts are *opposite* to it. The above formulas for a right spherical triangle may be recalled by the following two rules:

(a) The sine of any middle part is equal to the product of the *tangents* of the two *adjacent* parts.

(b) The sine of any middle part is equal to the product of the *cosines* of the two *opposite* parts.

Rules for Determining the Quadrant of a Calculated Part of a Right Spherical Triangle

(a) A leg and the angle opposite it are always of the same quadrant.

(b) If the hypotenuse if less than 90° the legs are of the same quadrant.

(c) If the hypotenuse is greater than 90°, the legs are of unlike quadrants.

Oblique Spherical Triangles

In the following, a, b, c represent the sides of any spherical triangle, A, B, C the corresponding opposite angles, $s = \frac{1}{2}(a + b + c)$, $S = \frac{1}{2}(A + B + C)$, $\Delta =$ area of triangle, $E =$ spherical excess of triangle, $R =$ radius of the sphere upon which the triangle lies, and a', b', c', A', B', C' are the corresponding parts of the polar triangle.

$$0° < a + b + c < 360°, \qquad 180° < A + B + C < 540°$$
$$E = A + B + C - 180°, \qquad \Delta = \pi R^2 E / 180$$
$$\tan \tfrac{1}{4}E = \sqrt{\tan \tfrac{s}{2} \tan \tfrac{1}{2}(s - a) \tan \tfrac{1}{2}(s - b) \tan \tfrac{1}{2}(s - c)}$$
$$A = 180° - a', \qquad B = 180° - b', \qquad C = 180° - c'$$
$$a = 180° - A', \qquad b = 180° - B', \qquad c = 180° - C'$$

Law of sines:

$$\frac{\sin a}{\sin A} = \frac{\sin b}{\sin B} = \frac{\sin c}{\sin C}$$

Law of cosines for sides:

$$\cos a = \cos b \cos c + \sin b \sin c \cos A$$
$$\cos b = \cos c \cos a + \sin c \sin a \cos B$$
$$\cos c = \cos a \cos b + \sin a \sin b \cos C$$

Law of cosines for angles:

$$\cos A = -\cos B \cos C + \sin B \sin C \cos a$$
$$\cos B = -\cos C \cos A + \sin C \sin A \cos b$$
$$\cos C = -\cos A \cos B + \sin A \sin B \cos c$$

Law of tangents:

$$\frac{\tan \frac{1}{2}(B - C)}{\tan \frac{1}{2}(B + C)} = \frac{\tan \frac{1}{2}(b - c)}{\tan \frac{1}{2}(b + c)}, \qquad \frac{\tan \frac{1}{2}(C - A)}{\tan \frac{1}{2}(C + A)} = \frac{\tan \frac{1}{2}(c - a)}{\tan \frac{1}{2}(c + a)}$$

$$\frac{\tan \frac{1}{2}(A - B)}{\tan \frac{1}{2}(A + B)} = \frac{\tan \frac{1}{2}(a - b)}{\tan \frac{1}{2}(a + b)}$$

Half-angle formulas:

$$\tan \tfrac{1}{2}A = \frac{k}{\sin(s - a)}, \qquad \tan \tfrac{1}{2}B = \frac{k}{\sin(s - b)}, \qquad \tan \tfrac{1}{2}C = \frac{k}{\sin(s - c)},$$

where

$$k^2 = \frac{\sin(s - a) \sin(s - b) \sin(s - c)}{\sin s} = (\tan r)^2$$

Half-side formulas:

$$\tan \tfrac{1}{2}\alpha = K \cos(S - A), \qquad \tan \tfrac{1}{2}b = K \cos(S - B),$$
$$\tan \tfrac{1}{2}c = K \cos(S - C),$$

where

$$K^2 = \frac{-\cos S}{\cos(S - A) \cos(S - B) \cos(S - C)} = (\tan R)^2$$

Gauss's formulas:

$$\frac{\sin \frac{1}{2}(a - b)}{\sin \frac{1}{2}c} = \frac{\sin \frac{1}{2}(A - B)}{\cos \frac{1}{2}C}, \qquad \frac{\cos \frac{1}{2}(a - b)}{\cos \frac{1}{2}c} = \frac{\sin \frac{1}{2}(A + B)}{\cos \frac{1}{2}C}$$

$$\frac{\sin \frac{1}{2}(a + b)}{\sin \frac{1}{2}c} = \frac{\cos \frac{1}{2}(A - B)}{\sin \frac{1}{2}C}, \qquad \frac{\cos \frac{1}{2}(a + b)}{\cos \frac{1}{2}c} = \frac{\cos \frac{1}{2}(A + B)}{\sin \frac{1}{2}C}$$

Napier's analogies:

$$\frac{\sin \frac{1}{2}(A - B)}{\sin \frac{1}{2}(A + B)} = \frac{\tan \frac{1}{2}(a - b)}{\tan \frac{1}{2}c}, \qquad \frac{\sin \frac{1}{2}(a - b)}{\sin \frac{1}{2}(a + b)} = \frac{\tan \frac{1}{2}(A - B)}{\cot \frac{1}{2}C}$$

$$\frac{\cos \frac{1}{2}(A - B)}{\cos \frac{1}{2}(A + B)} = \frac{\tan \frac{1}{2}(a + b)}{\tan \frac{1}{2}c}, \qquad \frac{\cos \frac{1}{2}(a - b)}{\cos \frac{1}{2}(a + b)} = \frac{\tan \frac{1}{2}(A + B)}{\cot \frac{1}{2}C}$$

Haversine formulas:

$$\operatorname{hav} a = \operatorname{hav}(b - c) + \sin b \sin c \operatorname{hav} A$$

$$\operatorname{hav} A = \frac{\sin(s - b) \sin(s - c)}{\sin b \sin c}$$

$$= \frac{\operatorname{hav} a - \operatorname{hav}(b - c)}{\sin b \sin c}$$

$$= \operatorname{hav}[180° - (B + C)] + \sin B \sin C \operatorname{hav} a$$

Rules for Determining the Quadrant of a Calculated Part of an Oblique Spherical Triangle

(a) If $A > B > C$, then $a > b > c$.

(b) A side (angle) which differs more from 90° than does another side (angle) is in the same quadrant as its opposite angle (side).

(c) Half the sum of any two sides and half the sum of the opposite angles are in the same quadrant.

SUMMARY OF SOLUTION OF OBLIQUE SPHERICAL TRIANGLES

Given	Solution	Check
Three sides	Half-angle formulas.	Law of sines
Three angles	Half-side formulas.	Law of sines
Two sides and included angle	Napier's analogies (to find sum and difference of unknown angles), then law of sines (to find remaining side).	Gauss's formula
Two angles and included side	Napier's analogies (to find sum and difference of unknown sides), then law of sines (to find remaining angle).	Gauss's formula
Two sides and an opposite angle	Law of sines (to find an angle), then Napier's analogies (to find remaining angle and side). Note number of solutions.	Gauss's formula
Two angles and an opposite side	Law of sines (to find a side), then Napier's analogies (to find remaining side and angle). Note number of solutions.	Gauss's formula

DEGREES, MINUTES, AND SECONDS TO RADIANS

Units in degrees, minutes or seconds	Degrees to Radians	Minutes to Radians	Seconds to Radians
10	0.174 5329	0.002 9089	0.000 0485
20	0.349 0659	0.005 8178	0.000 0970
30	0.523 5988	0.008 7266	0.000 1454
40	0.698 1317	0.011 6355	0.000 1939
50	0.872 6646	0.014 5444	0.000 2424
60	1.047 1976	0.017 4533	0.000 2909
70	1.221 7305	(0.020 3622)	(0.000 3394)
80	1.396 2634	(0.023 2711)	(0.000 3879)
90	1.570 7963	(0.026 1799)	(0.000 4363)
100	1.745 3293	....	....
200	3.490 6585	....	....
300	5.235 9878	....	....

where n = 1, 2, 3, 4, etc. n (100°) = n (1.745 3293)

RADIANS TO DEGREES, MINUTES, AND SECONDS

Radians	1.0	0.1	0.01	0.001	0.0001
1	57° 17' 44.8"	5° 43' 46.5"	0° 34' 22.6"	0° 03' 26.3"	0° 00' 20.6"
2	114° 35' 29.6"	11° 27' 33.0"	1° 08' 45.3"	0° 06' 52.5"	0° 00' 41.3"
3	171° 53' 14.4"	17° 11' 19.4"	1° 43' 07.9'	0° 10' 18.8"	0° 01' 01.9"
4	229° 10' 59.2"	22° 55' 05.9"	2° 17' 30.6"	0° 13' 45.1'	0° 01' 22.5"
5	286° 28' 44.0"	28° 38' 52.4"	2° 51' 53.2"	0° 17' 11.3"	0° 01' 43.1"
6	343° 46' 28.8"	34° 22' 38.9"	3° 26' 15.9"	0° 20' 37.6"	0° 02' 03.8"
7	401° 04' 13.6"	40° 06' 25.4"	4° 00' 38.5"	0° 24' 03.9"	0° 02' 24.4"
8	458° 21' 58.4"	45° 50' 11.8"	4° 35' 01.2"	0° 27' 30.1"	0° 02' 45.0"
9	515° 39' 43.3"	51° 33' 58.3"	5° 09' 23.8"	0° 30' 56.4"	0° 03' 05.6"

Example: If 3.214 is desired in degrees, minutes and seconds it is obtained as follows:

$$
\begin{aligned}
3 &= 171° \ 53' \ 14.4" \\
.2 &= \ \ 11° \ 27' \ 33.0" \\
.01 &= \ \ \ \ 0° \ 34' \ 22.6" \\
.004 &= \ \ \ \ 0° \ 13' \ 45.1" \\
\hline
3.214 &= 184° \ \ \ 8' \ 55.1"
\end{aligned}
$$

MILS—RADIANS—DEGREES

1 mil = 0.00098175 radians = 0.05625° = 3.375' = 202.5"
1000 mils = 0.98175 radians = 56.25°
6400 mils = 360° = 2π radians
1 radian = 1018.6 mils
1° = 17.777778 mils
1' = 0.296296 mils
1" = 0.0049383 mils

DEGREES—RADIANS
1 radian = 57° 17' 44" .80625

		log
1 radian =	57.29577 95131 degrees	1.75812 26324
1 radian =	3437.74677 07849 minutes	3.53627 38828
1 radian =	206264.80625 seconds	5.31442 51332
1 degree =	0.01745 32925 19943 radians	8.24187 73676—10
1 minute =	0.00029 08882 08666 radians	6.46372 61172—10
1 second =	0.00000 48481 36811 radians	4.68557 48668—10

DEGREES—RADIANS

The table gives in radians the angle which is expressed in degrees and minutes at the side and top. Angles expressed to the nearest minute and second can readily be converted to radians by adding to the equivalent of the whole number of degrees the equivalents of the minutes and seconds found on the third page of this table.

°	00′	10	20	30	40	50
0	0.00000	0.00291	0.00582	0.00873	0.01164	0.01454
1	0.01745	0.02036	0.02327	0.02618	0.02909	0.03200
2	0.03491	0.03782	0.04072	0.04363	0.04654	0.04945
3	0.05236	0.05527	0.05818	0.06109	0.06400	0.06690
4	0.06981	0.07272	0.07563	0.07854	0.08145	0.08436
5	0.08727	0.09018	0.09308	0.09599	0.09890	0.10181
6	0.10472	0.10763	0.11054	0.11345	0.11636	0.11926
7	0.12217	0.12508	0.12799	0.13090	0.13381	0.13672
8	0.13963	0.14254	0.14544	0.14835	0.15126	0.15417
9	0.15708	0.15999	0.16290	0.16581	0.16872	0.17162
10	0.17453	0.17744	0.18035	0.18326	0.18617	0.18908
11	0.19199	0.19490	0.19780	0.20071	0.20362	0.20653
12	0.20944	0.21235	0.21526	0.21817	0.22108	0.22398
13	0.22689	0.22980	0.23271	0.23562	0.23853	0.24144
14	0.24435	0.24725	0.25016	0.25307	0.25598	0.25889
15	0.26180	0.26471	0.26762	0.27053	0.27343	0.27634
16	0.27925	0.28216	0.28507	0.28798	0.29089	0.29380
17	0.29671	0.29961	0.30252	0.30543	0.30834	0.31125
18	0.31416	0.31707	0.31998	0.32289	0.32579	0.32870
19	0.33161	0.33452	0.33743	0.34034	0.34325	0.34616
20	0.34907	0.35197	0.35488	0.35779	0.36070	0.36361
21	0.36652	0.36943	0.37234	0.37525	0.37815	0.38106
22	0.38397	0.38688	0.38979	0.39270	0.39561	0.39852
23	0.40143	0.40433	0.40724	0.41015	0.41306	0.41597
24	0.41888	0.42179	0.42470	0.42761	0.43051	0.43342
25	0.43633	0.43924	0.44215	0.44506	0.44797	0.45088
26	0.45379	0.45669	0.45960	0.46251	0.46542	0.46833
27	0.47124	0.47415	0.47706	0.47997	0.48287	0.48578
28	0.48869	0.49160	0.49451	0.49742	0.50033	0.50324
29	0.50615	0.50905	0.51196	0.51487	0.51778	0.52069
30	0.52360	0.52651	0.52942	0.53233	0.53523	0.53814
31	0.54105	0.54396	0.54687	0.54978	0.55269	0.55560
32	0.55851	0.56141	0.56432	0.56723	0.57014	0.57305
33	0.57596	0.57887	0.58178	0.58469	0.58759	0.59050
34	0.59341	0.59632	0.59923	0.60214	0.60505	0.60796
35	0.61087	0.61377	0.61668	0.61959	0.62250	0.62541
36	0.62832	0.63123	0.63414	0.63705	0.63995	0.64286
37	0.64577	0.64868	0.65159	0.65450	0.65741	0.66032
38	0.66323	0.66613	0.66904	0.67195	0.67486	0.67777
39	0.68068	0.68359	0.68650	0.68941	0.69231	0.69522
40	0.69813	0.70104	0.70395	0.70686	0.70977	0.71268
41	0.71558	0.71849	0.72140	0.72431	0.72722	0.73013
42	0.73304	0.73595	0.73886	0.74176	0.74467	0.74758
43	0.75049	0.75340	0.75631	0.75922	0.76213	0.76504
44	0.76794	0.77085	0.77376	0.77667	0.77958	0.78249
45	0.78540	0.78831	0.79122	0.79412	0.79703	0.79994
46	0.80285	0.80576	0.80867	0.81158	0.81449	0.81740
47	0.82030	0.82321	0.82612	0.82903	0.83194	0.83485
48	0.83776	0.84067	0.84358	0.84648	0.84939	0.85230
49	0.85521	0.85812	0.86103	0.86394	0.86685	0.86976

Tables for Use in Trigonometry

DEGREES—RADIANS (Continued)

°	00′	10	20	30	40	50
50	0.87266	0.87557	0.87848	0.88139	0.88430	0.88721
51	0.89012	0.89303	0.89594	0.89884	0.90175	0.90466
52	0.90757	0.91048	0.91339	0.91630	0.91921	0.92212
53	0.92502	0.92793	0.93084	0.93375	0.93666	0.93957
54	0.94248	0.94539	0.94830	0.95120	0.95411	0.95702
55	0.95993	0.96284	0.96575	0.96866	0.97157	0.97448
56	0.97738	0.98029	0.98320	0.98611	0.98902	0.99193
57	0.99484	0.99775	1.00066	1.00356	1.00647	1.00938
58	1.01229	1.01520	1.01811	1.02102	1.02393	1.02684
59	1.02974	1.03265	1.03556	1.03847	1.04138	1.04429
60	1.04720	1.05011	1.05302	1.05592	1.05883	1.06174
61	1.06465	1.06756	1.07047	1.07338	1.07629	1.07920
62	1.08210	1.08501	1.08792	1.09083	1.09374	1.09665
63	1.09956	1.10247	1.10538	1.10828	1.11119	1.11410
64	1.11701	1.11992	1.12283	1.12574	1.12865	1.13156
65	1.13446	1.13737	1.14028	1.14319	1.14610	1.14901
66	1.15192	1.15483	1.15774	1.16064	1.16355	1.16646
67	1.16937	1.17228	1.17519	1.17810	1.18101	1.18392
68	1.18682	1.18973	1.19264	1.19555	1.19846	1.20137
69	1.20428	1.20719	1.21009	1.21300	1.21591	1.21882
70	1.22173	1.22464	1.22755	1.23046	1.23337	1.23627
71	1.23918	1.24209	1.24500	1.24791	1.25082	1.25373
72	1.25664	1.25955	1.26245	1.26536	1.26827	1.27118
73	1.27409	1.27700	1.27991	1.28282	1.28573	1.28863
74	1.29154	1.29445	1.29736	1.30027	1.30318	1.30609
75	1.30900	1.31191	1.31481	1.31772	1.32063	1.32354
76	1.32645	1.32936	1.33227	1.33518	1.33809	1.34099
77	1.34390	1.34681	1.34972	1.35263	1.35554	1.35845
78	1.36136	1.36427	1.36717	1.37008	1.37299	1.37590
79	1.37881	1.38172	1.38463	1.38754	1.39045	1.39335
80	1.39626	1.39917	1.40208	1.40499	1.40790	1.41081
81	1.41372	1.41663	1.41953	1.42244	1.42535	1.42826
82	1.43117	1.43408	1.43699	1.43990	1.44281	1.44571
83	1.44862	1.45153	1.45444	1.45735	1.46026	1.46317
84	1.46608	1.46899	1.47189	1.47480	1.47771	1.48062
85	1.48353	1.48644	1.48935	1.49226	1.49517	1.49807
86	1.50098	1.50389	1.50680	1.50971	1.51262	1.51553
87	1.51844	1.52135	1.52425	1.52716	1.53007	1.53298
88	1.53589	1.53880	1.54171	1.54462	1.54753	1.55043
89	1.55334	1.55625	1.55916	1.56207	1.56498	1.56789
90	1.57080	1.57371	1.57661	1.57952	1.58243	1.58534
91	1.58825	1.59116	1.59407	1.59698	1.59989	1.60279
92	1.60570	1.60861	1.61152	1.61443	1.61734	1.62025
93	1.62316	1.62607	1.62897	1.63188	1.63479	1.63770
94	1.64061	1.64352	1.64643	1.64934	1.65225	1.65515
95	1.65806	1.66097	1.66388	1.66679	1.66970	1.67261
96	1.67552	1.67842	1.68133	1.68424	1.68715	1.69006
97	1.69297	1.69588	1.69879	1.70170	1.70460	1.70751
98	1.71042	1.71333	1.71624	1.71915	1.72206	1.72497
99	1.72788	1.73078	1.73369	1.73660	1.73951	1.74242
100	1.74533	1.74824	1.75115	1.75406	1.75696	1.75987
101	1.76278	1.76569	1.76860	1.77151	1.77442	1.77733
102	1.78024	1.78314	1.78605	1.78896	1.79187	1.79478
103	1.79769	1.80060	1.80351	1.80642	1.80932	1.81223
104	1.81514	1.81805	1.82096	1.82387	1.82678	1.82969
105	1.83260	1.83550	1.83841	1.84132	1.84423	1.84714
106	1.85005	1.85296	1.85587	1.85878	1.86168	1.86459
107	1.86750	1.87041	1.87332	1.87623	1.87914	1.88205
108	1.88496	1.88786	1.89077	1.89368	1.89659	1.89950
109	1.90241	1.90532	1.90823	1.91114	1.91404	1.91695
110	1.91986	1.92277	1.92568	1.92859	1.93150	1.93441

DEGREES—RADIANS (Continued)

Deg.	Radians	Deg.	Radians	Min.	Radians	Sec.	Radians
90	1.57080	**150**	2.61799	**0**	0.00000	**0**	0.00000
91	1.58825	151	2.63545	1	0.00029	1	0.00000
92	1.60570	152	2.65290	2	0.00058	2	0.00001
93	1.62316	153	2.67035	3	0.00087	3	0.00001
94	1.64061	154	2.68781	4	0.00116	4	0.00002
95	1.65806	**155**	2.70526	**5**	0.00145	**5**	0.00002
96	1.67552	156	2.72271	6	0.00175	6	0.00003
97	1.69297	157	2.74017	7	0.00204	7	0.00003
98	1.71042	158	2.75762	8	0.00233	8	0.00004
99	1.72788	159	2.77507	9	0.00262	9	0.00004
100	1.74533	**160**	2.79253	**10**	0.00291	**10**	0.00005
101	1.76278	161	2.80998	11	0.00320	11	0.00005
102	1.78024	162	2.82743	12	0.00349	12	0.00006
103	1.79769	163	2.84489	13	0.00378	13	0.00006
104	1.81514	164	2.86234	14	0.00407	14	0.00007
105	1.83260	**165**	2.87979	**15**	0.00436	**15**	0.00007
106	1.85005	166	2.89725	16	0.00465	16	0.00008
107	1.86750	167	2.91470	17	0.00495	17	0.00008
108	1.88496	168	2.93215	18	0.00524	18	0.00009
109	1.90241	169	2.94961	19	0.00553	19	0.00009
110	1.91986	**170**	2.96706	**20**	0.00582	**20**	0.00010
111	1.93732	171	2.98451	21	0.00611	21	0.00010
112	1.95477	172	3.00197	22	0.00640	22	0.00011
113	1.97222	173	3.01942	23	0.00669	23	0.00011
114	1.98968	174	3.03687	24	0.00698	24	0.00012
115	2.00713	**175**	3.05433	**25**	0.00727	**25**	0.00012
116	2.02458	176	3.07178	26	0.00756	26	0.00013
117	2.04204	177	3.08923	27	0.00785	27	0.00013
118	2.05949	178	3.10668	28	0.00814	28	0.00014
119	2.07694	179	3.12414	29	0.00844	29	0.00014
120	2.09440	**180**	3.14159	**30**	0.00873	**30**	0.00015
121	2.11185	190	3.31613	31	0.00902	31	0.00015
122	2.12930	200	3.49066	32	0.00931	32	0.00016
123	2.14675	210	3.66519	33	0.00960	33	0.00016
124	2.16421	220	3.83972	34	0.00989	34	0.00016
125	2.18166	**230**	4.01426	**35**	0.01018	**35**	0.00017
126	2.19911	240	4.18879	36	0.01047	36	0.00017
127	2.21657	250	4.36332	37	0.01076	37	0.00018
128	2.23402	260	4.53786	38	0.01105	38	0.00018
129	2.25147	270	4.71239	39	0.01134	39	0.00019
130	2.26893	**280**	4.88692	**40**	0.01164	**40**	0.00019
131	2.28638	290	5.06145	41	0.01193	41	0.00020
132	2.30383	300	5.23599	42	0.01222	42	0.00020
133	2.32129	310	5.41052	43	0.01251	43	0.00021
134	2.33874	320	5.58505	44	0.01280	44	0.00021
135	2.35619	**330**	5.75959	**45**	0.01309	**45**	0.00022
136	2.37365	340	5.93412	46	0.01338	46	0.00022
137	2.39110	350	6.10865	47	0.01367	47	0.00023
138	2.40855	360	6.28319	48	0.01396	48	0.00023
139	2.42601	370	6.45772	49	0.01425	49	0.00024
140	2.44346	**380**	6.63225	**50**	0.01454	**50**	0.00024
141	2.46091	390	6.80678	51	0.01484	51	0.00025
142	2.47837	400	6.98132	52	0.01513	52	0.00025
143	2.49582	410	7.15585	53	0.01542	53	0.00026
144	2.51327	420	7.33038	54	0.01571	54	0.00026
145	2.53073	**430**	7.50492	**55**	0.01600	**55**	0.00027
146	2.54818	440	7.67945	56	0.01629	56	0.00027
147	2.56563	450	7.85398	57	0.01658	57	0.00028
148	2.58309	460	8.02851	58	0.01687	58	0.00028
149	2.60054	470	8.20305	59	0.01716	59	0.00029
150	2.61799	**480**	8.37758	**60**	0.01745	**60**	0.00029

DEGREES AND DECIMAL FRACTIONS TO RADIANS

The table below facilitates conversion of an angle expressed in degrees and decimal fractions into radians. To convert 25.78 into radians, find the equivalents, successively, of 20°, 5°, 0°.7, 0°.08 and add.

Deg.	Radians	Deg.	Radians	Deg.	Radians	Deg.	Radians	Deg.	Radians
10	0.174533	1	0.017453	0.1	0.001745	0.01	0.000175	0.001	0.000017
20	0.349066	2	.034907	.2	.003491	.02	.000349	.002	.000035
30	0.523599	3	.052360	.3	.005236	.03	.000524	.003	.000052
40	0.698132	4	.069813	.4	.006981	.04	.000698	.004	.000070
50	0.872665	5	.087266	.5	.008727	.05	.000873	.005	.000087
60	1.047198	6	.104720	.6	.010472	.06	.001047	.006	.000105
70	1.221730	7	.122173	.7	.012217	.07	.001222	.007	.000122
80	1.396263	8	.139626	.8	.013963	.08	.001396	.008	.000140
90	1.570796	9	.157080	.9	.015708	.09	.001571	.009	.000157

RADIANS TO DEGREES AND DECIMALS

Radians	Degrees	Radians	Degrees	Radians	Degrees	Radians	Degrees
1	57.2958	0.1	5.7296	0.01	0.5730	0.001	0.0573
2	114.5916	.2	11.4592	.02	1.1459	.002	.1146
3	171.8873	.3	17.1887	.03	1.7189	.003	.1719
4	229.1831	.4	22.9183	.04	2.2918	.004	.2292
5	286.4789	.5	28.6479	.05	2.8648	.005	.2865
6	343.7747	.6	34.3775	.06	3.4377	.006	.3438
7	401.0705	.7	40.1070	.07	4.0107	.007	.4011
8	458.3662	.8	45.8366	.08	4.5837	.008	.4584
9	515.6620	.9	51.5662	.09	5.1566	.009	.5157
10	572.9578	1.0	57.2958	.10	5.7296	.010	.5730

RADIANS—DEGREES
Multiples and Fractions of π Radians in Degrees

Radians	Radians	Deg.	Radians	Radians	Deg.	Radians	Radians	Deg.
π	3.1416	180	$\pi/2$	1.5708	90	$2\pi/3$	2.0944	120
2π	6.2832	360	$\pi/3$	1.0472	60	$3\pi/4$	2.3562	135
3π	9.4248	540	$\pi/4$	0.7854	45	$5\pi/6$	2.6180	150
4π	12.5664	720	$\pi/5$	0.6283	36	$7\pi/6$	3.6652	210
5π	15.7080	900	$\pi/6$	0.5236	30	$5\pi/4$	3.9270	225
6π	18.8496	1080	$\pi/7$	0.4488	25.714	$4\pi/3$	4.1888	240
7π	21.9911	1260	$\pi/8$	0.3927	22.5	$3\pi/2$	4.7124	270
8π	25.1327	1440	$\pi/9$	0.3491	20	$5\pi/3$	5.2360	300
9π	28.2743	1620	$\pi/10$	0.3142	18	$7\pi/4$	5.4978	315
10π	31.4159	1800	$\pi/12$	0.2618	15	$11\pi/6$	5.7596	330

CONVERSION OF ANGLES FROM ARC TO TIME

Arc	Time	Arc	Time	Arc	Time	Arc	Time
°	h m	°	h m	″	s	″	s
′	m s	′	m s				
0	0 00	20	1 20	0	0.00	8	0.53
1	0 04	30	2 00	1	0.07	9	0.60
2	0 08	40	2 40	2	0.13	10	0.67
3	0 12	50	3 20	3	0.20	20	1.33
4	0 16	60	4 00	4	0.27	30	2.00
5	0 20	70	4 40	5	0.33	40	2.67
6	0 24	80	5 20	6	0.40	50	3.33
7	0 28	90	6 00	7	0.47	60	4.00
8	0 32	100	6 40				
9	0 36	200	13 20				
10	0 40	300	20 00				

MINUTES AND SECONDS TO DECIMAL PARTS OF A DEGREE

MINUTES AND SECONDS TO DECIMAL PARTS OF A DEG.				DECIMAL PARTS OF A DEGREE TO MINUTES AND SECONDS					
Min.	Degrees	Sec.	Degrees	Deg.	'	"	Deg.	'	"
0	0.00000	0	0.00000	0.00	0	00	0.60	36	
1	.01667	1	.00028	.01	0	36	.61	36	36
2	.03333	2	.00056	.02	1	12	.62	37	12
3	.05	3	.00083	.03	1	48	.63	37	48
4	.06667	4	.00111	.04	2	24	.64	38	24
5	.08333	5	.00139	.05	3		.65	39	
6	.10	6	.00167	.06	3	36	.66	39	36
7	.11667	7	.00194	.07	4	12	.67	40	12
8	.13333	8	.00222	.08	4	48	.68	40	48
9	.15	9	.0025	.09	5	24	.69	41	24
10	0.16667	10	0.00278	0.10	6		0.70	42	
11	.18333	11	.00306	.11	6	36	.71	42	36
12	.20	12	.00333	.12	7	12	.72	43	12
13	.21667	13	.00361	.13	7	48	.73	43	48
14	.23333	14	.00389	.14	8	24	.74	44	24
15	.25	15	.00417	.15	9		.75	45	
16	.26667	16	.00444	.16	9	36	.76	45	36
17	.28333	17	.00472	.17	10	12	.77	46	12
18	.30	18	.005	.18	10	48	.78	46	48
19	.31667	19	.00528	.19	11	24	.79	47	24
20	0.33333	20	0.00556	0.20	12		0.80	48	
21	.35	21	.00583	.21	12	36	.81	48	36
22	.36667	22	.00611	.22	13	12	.82	49	12
23	.38333	23	.00639	.23	13	48	.83	49	48
24	.40	24	.00667	.24	14	24	.84	50	24
25	.41667	25	.00694	.25	15		.85	51	
26	.43333	26	.00722	.26	15	36	.86	51	36
27	.45	27	.0075	.27	16	12	.87	52	12
28	.46667	28	.00778	.28	16	48	.88	52	48
29	.48333	29	.00806	.29	17	24	.89	53	24
30	0.50	30	0.00833	0.30	18		0.90	54	
31	.51667	31	.00861	.31	18	36	.91	54	36
32	.53333	32	.00889	.32	19	12	.92	55	12
33	.55	33	.00917	.33	19	48	.93	55	48
34	.56667	34	.00944	.34	20	24	94	56	24
35	.58333	35	.00972	.35	21		.95	57	
36	.60	36	.01	.36	21	36	.96	57	36
37	.61667	37	.01028	.37	22	12	.97	58	12
38	.63333	38	.01056	.38	22	48	.98	58	48
39	.65	39	.01083	.39	23	24	.99	59	24
40	0.66667	40	0.01111	0.40	24		1.00	60	
41	.68333	41	.01139	.41	24	36			
42	.70	42	.01167	.42	25	12			
43	.71667	43	.01194	.43	25	48			
44	.73333	44	.01222	.44	26	24			
45	.75	45	.0125	.45	27				
46	.76667	46	.01278	.46	27	36			
47	.78333	47	.01306	.47	28	12			
48	.80	48	.01333	.48	28	48			
49	.81667	49	.01361	.49	29	24			
50	0.83333	50	0.01389	0.50	30				
51	.85	51	.01417	.51	30	36			
52	.86667	52	.01444	.52	31	12			
53	.88333	53	.01472	.53	31	48			
54	.90	54	.015	.54	32	24			
55	.91667	55	.01528	.55	33				
56	.93333	56	.01556	.56	33	36			
57	.95	57	.01583	.57	34	12			
58	.96667	58	.01611	.58	34	48			
59	.98333	59	.01639	.59	35	24			
60	1.00	60	0.01667	0.60	36				

Deg.	Sec.
0.000	0.0
.001	3.6
.002	7.2
.003	10.8
.004	14.4
.005	18.
.006	21.6
.007	25.2
.008	28.8
.009	32.4
0.010	36.

NATURAL TRIGONOMETRIC FUNCTIONS
TO FIVE PLACES

Values of the trigonometric functions sin, cos, tan, cot of angles for each minute from 0–360°.

For degrees indicated at the top of the page use the column headings at the top. For degrees indicated at the bottom use the column indications at the bottom.

With degrees at the left of each block (top or bottom), use the minute column at the left and with degrees at the right of each block use the minute column at the right.

If natural trigonometric function tables are used for angle measures greater than 90° and less than 360°, appropriate signs for the functions must be supplied in accordance with the quadrant in which the angle measure belongs.

Linear interpolation may be used to obtain values of the functions for seconds or other fractions of a minute, except in regions where the functions are rapidly changing. See section on "Use of Logarithm Tables" for further discussion in interpolation practice.

NATURAL TRIGONOMETRIC FUNCTIONS
TO FIVE PLACES

(359)° 179°   1° (181°)   (358)° 178°

Sin	Tan	Cot	Cos	Sec	Csc	'
.00000	.00000	———	1.0000	1.0000	———	60
.00029	.00029	3437.7	1.0000	1.0000	3437.7	59
.00058	.00058	1718.9	1.0000	1.0000	1718.9	58
.00087	.00087	1145.9	1.0000	1.0000	1145.9	57
.00116	.00116	859.44	1.0000	1.0000	859.44	56
.00145	.00145	687.55	1.0000	1.0000	687.55	55
.00175	.00175	572.96	1.0000	1.0000	572.96	54
.00204	.00204	491.11	1.0000	1.0000	491.11	53
.00233	.00233	429.72	1.0000	1.0000	429.72	52
.00262	.00262	381.97	1.0000	1.0000	381.97	51
.00291	.00291	343.77	1.0000	1.0000	343.78	50
.00320	.00320	312.52	.99999	1.0000	312.52	49
.00349	.00349	286.48	.99999	1.0000	286.48	48
.00378	.00378	264.44	.99999	1.0000	264.44	47
.00407	.00407	245.55	.99999	1.0000	245.55	46
.00436	.00436	229.18	.99999	1.0000	229.18	45
.00465	.00465	214.86	.99999	1.0000	214.86	44
.00495	.00495	202.22	.99999	1.0000	202.22	43
.00524	.00524	190.98	.99999	1.0000	190.99	42
.00553	.00553	180.93	.99998	1.0000	180.93	41
.00582	.00582	171.89	.99998	1.0000	171.89	40
.00611	.00611	163.70	.99998	1.0000	163.70	39
.00640	.00640	156.26	.99998	1.0000	156.26	38
.00669	.00669	149.47	.99998	1.0000	149.47	37
.00698	.00698	143.24	.99998	1.0000	143.24	36
.00727	.00727	137.51	.99997	1.0000	137.51	35
.00756	.00756	132.22	.99997	1.0000	132.22	34
.00785	.00785	127.32	.99997	1.0000	127.33	33
.00814	.00815	122.77	.99997	1.0000	122.78	32
.00844	.00844	118.54	.99996	1.0000	118.54	31
.00873	.00873	114.59	.99996	1.0000	114.59	30
.00902	.00902	110.89	.99996	1.0000	110.90	29
.00931	.00931	107.43	.99996	1.0000	107.43	28
.00960	.00960	104.17	.99995	1.0000	104.18	27
.00989	.00989	101.11	.99995	1.0000	101.11	26
.01018	.01018	98.218	.99995	1.0001	98.223	25
.01047	.01047	95.489	.99995	1.0001	95.495	24
.01076	.01076	92.908	.99994	1.0001	92.914	23
.01105	.01105	90.463	.99994	1.0001	90.469	22
.01134	.01135	88.144	.99994	1.0001	88.149	21
.01164	.01164	85.940	.99993	1.0001	85.946	20
.01193	.01193	83.844	.99993	1.0001	83.849	19
.01222	.01222	81.847	.99993	1.0001	81.853	18
.01251	.01251	79.943	.99992	1.0001	79.950	17
.01280	.01280	78.126	.99992	1.0001	78.133	16
.01309	.01309	76.390	.99991	1.0001	76.397	15
.01338	.01338	74.729	.99991	1.0001	74.736	14
.01367	.01367	73.139	.99991	1.0001	73.146	13
.01396	.01396	71.615	.99990	1.0001	71.622	12
.01425	.01425	70.153	.99990	1.0001	70.160	11
.01454	.01455	68.750	.99989	1.0001	68.757	10
.01483	.01484	67.402	.99989	1.0001	67.409	9
.01513	.01513	66.105	.99989	1.0001	66.113	8
.01542	.01542	64.858	.99988	1.0001	64.866	7
.01571	.01571	63.657	.99988	1.0001	63.665	6
.01600	.01600	62.499	.99987	1.0001	62.507	5
.01629	.01629	61.383	.99987	1.0001	61.391	4
.01658	.01658	60.306	.99986	1.0001	60.314	3
.01687	.01687	59.266	.99986	1.0001	59.274	2
.01716	.01716	58.261	.99985	1.0001	58.270	1
.01745	.01746	57.290	.99985	1.0002	57.299	0
Cos	Cot	Tan	Sin	Csc	Sec	'

(269)° 89°

'	Sin	Tan	Cot	Cos	Sec	Csc	'
0	.01745	.01746	57.290	.99985	1.0002	57.299	60
1	.01774	.01775	56.351	.99984	1.0002	56.359	59
2	.01803	.01804	55.442	.99984	1.0002	55.451	58
3	.01832	.01833	54.561	.99983	1.0002	54.570	57
4	.01862	.01862	53.709	.99983	1.0002	53.718	56
5	.01891	.01891	52.882	.99982	1.0002	52.892	55
6	.01920	.01920	52.081	.99982	1.0002	52.090	54
7	.01949	.01949	51.303	.99981	1.0002	51.313	53
8	.01978	.01978	50.549	.99980	1.0002	50.558	52
9	.02007	.02007	49.816	.99980	1.0002	49.826	51
10	.02036	.02036	49.104	.99979	1.0002	49.114	50
11	.02065	.02066	48.412	.99979	1.0002	48.422	49
12	.02094	.02095	47.740	.99978	1.0002	47.750	48
13	.02123	.02124	47.085	.99977	1.0002	47.096	47
14	.02152	.02153	46.449	.99977	1.0002	46.460	46
15	.02181	.02182	45.829	.99976	1.0002	45.840	45
16	.02211	.02211	45.226	.99976	1.0002	45.237	44
17	.02240	.02240	44.639	.99975	1.0003	44.650	43
18	.02269	.02269	44.066	.99974	1.0003	44.077	42
19	.02298	.02298	43.508	.99974	1.0003	43.520	41
20	.02327	.02328	42.964	.99973	1.0003	42.976	40
21	.02356	.02357	42.433	.99972	1.0003	42.445	39
22	.02385	.02386	41.916	.99972	1.0003	41.928	38
23	.02414	.02415	41.411	.99971	1.0003	41.423	37
24	.02443	.02444	40.917	.99970	1.0003	40.930	36
25	.02472	.02473	40.436	.99969	1.0003	40.448	35
26	.02501	.02502	39.965	.99969	1.0003	39.978	34
27	.02530	.02531	39.506	.99968	1.0003	39.519	33
28	.02560	.02560	39.057	.99967	1.0003	39.070	32
29	.02589	.02589	38.618	.99966	1.0003	38.631	31
30	.02618	.02619	38.188	.99966	1.0003	38.202	30
31	.02647	.02648	37.769	.99965	1.0004	37.782	29
32	.02676	.02677	37.358	.99964	1.0004	37.371	28
33	.02705	.02706	36.956	.99963	1.0004	36.970	27
34	.02734	.02735	36.563	.99963	1.0004	36.576	26
35	.02763	.02764	36.178	.99962	1.0004	36.191	25
36	.02792	.02793	35.801	.99961	1.0004	35.815	24
37	.02821	.02822	35.431	.99960	1.0004	35.445	23
38	.02850	.02851	35.070	.99959	1.0004	35.084	22
39	.02879	.02881	34.715	.99959	1.0004	34.730	21
40	.02908	.02910	34.368	.99958	1.0004	34.382	20
41	.02938	.02939	34.027	.99957	1.0004	34.042	19
42	.02967	.02968	33.694	.99956	1.0004	33.708	18
43	.02996	.02997	33.366	.99955	1.0004	33.381	17
44	.03025	.03026	33.045	.99954	1.0005	33.060	16
45	.03054	.03055	32.730	.99953	1.0005	32.746	15
46	.03083	.03084	32.421	.99952	1.0005	32.437	14
47	.03112	.03114	32.118	.99952	1.0005	32.134	13
48	.03141	.03143	31.821	.99951	1.0005	31.836	12
49	.03170	.03172	31.528	.99950	1.0005	31.544	11
50	.03199	.03201	31.242	.99949	1.0005	31.258	10
51	.03228	.03230	30.960	.99948	1.0005	30.976	9
52	.03257	.03259	30.683	.99947	1.0005	30.700	8
53	.03286	.03288	30.412	.99946	1.0005	30.428	7
54	.03316	.03317	30.145	.99945	1.0006	30.161	6
55	.03345	.03346	29.882	.99944	1.0006	29.899	5
56	.03374	.03376	29.624	.99943	1.0006	29.641	4
57	.03403	.03405	29.371	.99942	1.0006	29.388	3
58	.03432	.03434	29.122	.99941	1.0006	29.139	2
59	.03461	.03463	28.877	.99940	1.0006	28.894	1
60	.03490	.03492	28.636	.99939	1.0006	28.654	0
'	Cos	Cot	Tan	Sin	Csc	Sec	'

91° (271°)   (268°) 88°

Tables for Use in Trigonometry

NATURAL TRIGONOMETRIC FUNCTIONS
TO FIVE PLACES

2° (182°) (357°) 177°   **3° (183°)** (356°)

'	Sin	Tan	Cot	Cos	Sec	Csc	'
0	.03490	.03492	28.636	.99939	1.0006	28.654	60
1	.03519	.03521	28.399	.99938	1.0006	28.417	59
2	.03548	.03550	28.166	.99937	1.0006	28.184	58
3	.03577	.03579	27.937	.99936	1.0006	27.955	57
4	.03606	.03609	27.712	.99935	1.0007	27.730	56
5	.03635	.03638	27.490	.99934	1.0007	27.508	55
6	.03664	.03667	27.271	.99933	1.0007	27.290	54
7	.03693	.03696	27.057	.99932	1.0007	27.075	53
8	.03723	.03725	26.845	.99931	1.0007	26.864	52
9	.03752	.03754	26.637	.99930	1.0007	26.655	51
10	.03781	.03783	26.432	.99929	1.0007	26.451	50
11	.03810	.03812	26.230	.99927	1.0007	26.249	49
12	.03839	.03842	26.031	.99926	1.0007	26.050	48
13	.03868	.03871	25.835	.99925	1.0007	25.854	47
14	.03897	.03900	25.642	.99924	1.0008	25.661	46
15	.03926	.03929	25.452	.99923	1.0008	25.471	45
16	.03955	.03958	25.264	.99922	1.0008	25.284	44
17	.03984	.03987	25.080	.99921	1.0008	25.100	43
18	.04013	.04016	24.898	.99919	1.0008	24.918	42
19	.04042	.04046	24.719	.99918	1.0008	24.739	41
20	.04071	.04075	24.542	.99917	1.0008	24.562	40
21	.04100	.04104	24.368	.99916	1.0008	24.388	39
22	.04129	.04133	24.196	.99915	1.0009	24.216	38
23	.04159	.04162	24.026	.99913	1.0009	24.047	37
24	.04188	.04191	23.859	.99912	1.0009	23.880	36
25	.04217	.04220	23.695	.99911	1.0009	23.716	35
26	.04246	.04250	23.532	.99910	1.0009	23.553	34
27	.04275	.04279	23.372	.99909	1.0009	23.393	33
28	.04304	.04308	23.214	.99907	1.0009	23.235	32
29	.04333	.04337	23.058	.99906	1.0009	23.079	31
30	.04362	.04366	22.904	.99905	1.0010	22.926	30
31	.04391	.04395	22.752	.99904	1.0010	22.774	29
32	.04420	.04424	22.602	.99902	1.0010	22.624	28
33	.04449	.04454	22.454	.99901	1.0010	22.476	27
34	.04478	.04483	22.308	.99900	1.0010	22.330	26
35	.04507	.04512	22.164	.99898	1.0010	22.187	25
36	.04536	.04541	22.022	.99897	1.0010	22.044	24
37	.04565	.04570	21.881	.99896	1.0010	21.904	23
38	.04594	.04599	21.743	.99894	1.0011	21.766	22
39	.04623	.04628	21.606	.99893	1.0011	21.629	21
40	.04653	.04658	21.470	.99892	1.0011	21.494	20
41	.04682	.04687	21.337	.99890	1.0011	21.360	19
42	.04711	.04716	21.205	.99889	1.0011	21.229	18
43	.04740	.04745	21.075	.99888	1.0011	21.098	17
44	.04769	.04774	20.946	.99886	1.0011	20.970	16
45	.04798	.04803	20.819	.99885	1.0012	20.843	15
46	.04827	.04833	20.693	.99883	1.0012	20.717	14
47	.04856	.04862	20.569	.99882	1.0012	20.593	13
48	.04885	.04891	20.446	.99881	1.0012	20.471	12
49	.04914	.04920	20.325	.99879	1.0012	20.350	11
50	.04943	.04949	20.206	.99878	1.0012	20.230	10
51	.04972	.04978	20.087	.99876	1.0012	20.112	9
52	.05001	.05007	19.970	.99875	1.0013	19.995	8
53	.05030	.05037	19.855	.99873	1.0013	19.880	7
54	.05059	.05066	19.740	.99872	1.0013	19.766	6
55	.05088	.05095	19.627	.99870	1.0013	19.653	5
56	.05117	.05124	19.516	.99869	1.0013	19.541	4
57	.05146	.05153	19.405	.99867	1.0013	19.431	3
58	.05175	.05182	19.296	.99866	1.0013	19.322	2
59	.05205	.05212	19.188	.99864	1.0014	19.214	1
60	.05234	.05241	19.081	.99863	1.0014	19.107	0
'	Cos	Cot	Tan	Sin	Csc	Sec	'

92° (272°) (267°) 87°

'	Sin	Tan	Cot	Cos	Sec	Csc
0	.05234	.05241	19.081	.99863	1.0014	19.107
1	.05263	.05270	18.976	.99861	1.0014	19.002
2	.05292	.05299	18.871	.99860	1.0014	18.898
3	.05321	.05328	18.768	.99858	1.0014	18.794
4	.05350	.05357	18.666	.99857	1.0014	18.692
5	.05379	.05387	18.564	.99855	1.0014	18.591
6	.05408	.05416	18.464	.99854	1.0015	18.492
7	.05437	.05445	18.366	.99852	1.0015	18.393
8	.05466	.05474	18.268	.99851	1.0015	18.295
9	.05495	.05503	18.171	.99849	1.0015	18.198
10	.05524	.05533	18.075	.99847	1.0015	18.103
11	.05553	.05562	17.980	.99846	1.0015	18.008
12	.05582	.05591	17.886	.99844	1.0016	17.914
13	.05611	.05620	17.793	.99842	1.0016	17.822
14	.05640	.05649	17.702	.99841	1.0016	17.730
15	.05669	.05678	17.611	.99839	1.0016	17.639
16	.05698	.05708	17.521	.99838	1.0016	17.549
17	.05727	.05737	17.431	.99836	1.0016	17.460
18	.05756	.05766	17.343	.99834	1.0017	17.372
19	.05785	.05795	17.256	.99833	1.0017	17.285
20	.05814	.05824	17.169	.99831	1.0017	17.198
21	.05844	.05854	17.084	.99829	1.0017	17.113
22	.05873	.05883	16.999	.99827	1.0017	17.028
23	.05902	.05912	16.915	.99826	1.0017	16.945
24	.05931	.05941	16.832	.99824	1.0018	16.862
25	.05960	.05970	16.750	.99822	1.0018	16.779
26	.05989	.05999	16.668	.99821	1.0018	16.698
27	.06018	.06029	16.587	.99819	1.0018	16.618
28	.06047	.06058	16.507	.99817	1.0018	16.538
29	.06076	.06087	16.428	.99815	1.0019	16.459
30	.06105	.06116	16.350	.99813	1.0019	16.380
31	.06134	.06145	16.272	.99812	1.0019	16.303
32	.06163	.06175	16.195	.99810	1.0019	16.226
33	.06192	.06204	16.119	.99808	1.0019	16.150
34	.06221	.06233	16.043	.99806	1.0019	16.075
35	.06250	.06262	15.969	.99804	1.0020	16.000
36	.06279	.06291	15.895	.99803	1.0020	15.926
37	.06308	.06321	15.821	.99801	1.0020	15.853
38	.06337	.06350	15.748	.99799	1.0020	15.780
39	.06366	.06379	15.676	.99797	1.0020	15.708
40	.06395	.06408	15.605	.99795	1.0021	15.637
41	.06424	.06438	15.534	.99793	1.0021	15.566
42	.06453	.06467	15.464	.99792	1.0021	15.496
43	.06482	.06496	15.394	.99790	1.0021	15.427
44	.06511	.06525	15.325	.99788	1.0021	15.358
45	.06540	.06554	15.257	.99786	1.0021	15.290
46	.06569	.06584	15.189	.99784	1.0022	15.222
47	.06598	.06613	15.122	.99782	1.0022	15.155
48	.06627	.06642	15.056	.99780	1.0022	15.089
49	.06656	.06671	14.990	.99778	1.0022	15.023
50	.06685	.06700	14.924	.99776	1.0022	14.958
51	.06714	.06730	14.860	.99774	1.0023	14.893
52	.06743	.06759	14.795	.99772	1.0023	14.829
53	.06773	.06788	14.732	.99770	1.0023	14.766
54	.06802	.06817	14.669	.99768	1.0023	14.703
55	.06831	.06847	14.606	.99766	1.0023	14.640
56	.06860	.06876	14.544	.99764	1.0024	14.578
57	.06889	.06905	14.482	.99762	1.0024	14.517
58	.06918	.06934	14.421	.99760	1.0024	14.456
59	.06947	.06963	14.361	.99758	1.0024	14.395
60	.06976	.06993	14.301	.99756	1.0024	14.336
'	Cos	Cot	Tan	Sin	Csc	Sec

93° (273°) (266°)

NATURAL TRIGONOMETRIC FUNCTIONS
TO FIVE PLACES

(355°) 175°   5° (185°)   (354°) 174°

Sin	Tan	Cot	Cos	Sec	Csc	'
.06976	.06993	14.301	.99756	1.0024	14.336	60
.07005	.07022	14.241	.99754	1.0025	14.276	59
.07034	.07051	14.182	.99752	1.0025	14.217	58
.07063	.07080	14.124	.99750	1.0025	14.159	57
.07092	.07110	14.065	.99748	1.0025	14.101	56
.07121	.07139	14.008	.99746	1.0025	14.044	55
.07150	.07168	13.951	.99744	1.0026	13.987	54
.07179	.07197	13.894	.99742	1.0026	13.930	53
.07208	.07227	13.838	.99740	1.0026	13.874	52
.07237	.07256	13.782	.99738	1.0026	13.818	51
.07266	.07285	13.727	.99736	1.0027	13.763	50
.07295	.07314	13.672	.99734	1.0027	13.708	49
.07324	.07344	13.617	.99731	1.0027	13.654	48
.07353	.07373	13.563	.99729	1.0027	13.600	47
.07382	.07402	13.510	.99727	1.0027	13.547	46
.07411	.07431	13.457	.99725	1.0028	13.494	45
.07440	.07461	13.404	.99723	1.0028	13.441	44
.07469	.07490	13.352	.99721	1.0028	13.389	43
.07498	.07519	13.300	.99719	1.0028	13.337	42
.07527	.07548	13.248	.99716	1.0028	13.286	41
.07556	.07578	13.197	.99714	1.0029	13.235	40
.07585	.07607	13.146	.99712	1.0029	13.184	39
.07614	.07636	13.096	.99710	1.0029	13.134	38
.07643	.07665	13.046	.99708	1.0029	13.084	37
.07672	.07695	12.996	.99705	1.0030	13.035	36
.07701	.07724	12.947	.99703	1.0030	12.985	35
.07730	.07753	12.898	.99701	1.0030	12.937	34
.07759	.07782	12.850	.99699	1.0030	12.888	33
.07788	.07812	12.801	.99696	1.0030	12.840	32
.07817	.07841	12.754	.99694	1.0031	12.793	31
.07846	.07870	12.706	.99692	1.0031	12.745	30
.07875	.07899	12.659	.99689	1.0031	12.699	29
.07904	.07929	12.612	.99687	1.0031	12.652	28
.07933	.07958	12.566	.99685	1.0032	12.606	27
.07962	.07987	12.520	.99683	1.0032	12.560	26
.07991	.08017	12.474	.99680	1.0032	12.514	25
.08020	.08046	12.429	.99678	1.0032	12.469	24
.08049	.08075	12.384	.99676	1.0033	12.424	23
.08078	.08104	12.339	.99673	1.0033	12.379	22
.08107	.08134	12.295	.99671	1.0033	12.335	21
.08136	.08163	12.251	.99668	1.0033	12.291	20
.08165	.08192	12.207	.99666	1.0034	12.248	19
.08194	.08221	12.163	.99664	1.0034	12.204	18
.08223	.08251	12.120	.99661	1.0034	12.161	17
.08252	.08280	12.077	.99659	1.0034	12.119	16
.08281	.08309	12.035	.99657	1.0034	12.076	15
.08310	.08339	11.992	.99654	1.0035	12.034	14
.08339	.08368	11.950	.99652	1.0035	11.992	13
.08368	.08397	11.909	.99649	1.0035	11.951	12
.08397	.08427	11.867	.99647	1.0035	11.909	11
.08426	.08456	11.826	.99644	1.0036	11.868	10
.08455	.08485	11.785	.99642	1.0036	11.828	9
.08484	.08514	11.745	.99639	1.0036	11.787	8
.08513	.08544	11.705	.99637	1.0036	11.747	7
.08542	.08573	11.664	.99635	1.0037	11.707	6
.08571	.08602	11.625	.99632	1.0037	11.668	5
.08600	.08632	11.585	.99630	1.0037	11.628	4
.08629	.08661	11.546	.99627	1.0037	11.589	3
.08658	.08690	11.507	.99625	1.0038	11.551	2
.08687	.08720	11.468	.99622	1.0038	11.512	1
.08716	.08749	11.430	.99619	1.0038	11.474	0
Cos	Cot	Tan	Sin	Csc	Sec	'

'	Sin	Tan	Cot	Cos	Sec	Csc	'
0	.08716	.08749	11.430	.99619	1.0038	11.474	60
1	.08745	.08778	11.392	.99617	1.0038	11.436	59
2	.08774	.08807	11.354	.99614	1.0039	11.398	58
3	.08803	.08837	11.316	.99612	1.0039	11.360	57
4	.08831	.08866	11.279	.99609	1.0039	11.323	56
5	.08860	.08895	11.242	.99607	1.0039	11.286	55
6	.08889	.08925	11.205	.99604	1.0040	11.249	54
7	.08918	.08954	11.168	.99602	1.0040	11.213	53
8	.08947	.08983	11.132	.99599	1.0040	11.176	52
9	.08976	.09013	11.095	.99596	1.0041	11.140	51
10	.09005	.09042	11.059	.99594	1.0041	11.105	50
11	.09034	.09071	11.024	.99591	1.0041	11.069	49
12	.09063	.09101	10.988	.99588	1.0041	11.034	48
13	.09092	.09130	10.953	.99586	1.0042	10.998	47
14	.09121	.09159	10.918	.99583	1.0042	10.963	46
15	.09150	.09189	10.883	.99580	1.0042	10.929	45
16	.09179	.09218	10.848	.99578	1.0042	10.894	44
17	.09208	.09247	10.814	.99575	1.0043	10.860	43
18	.09237	.09277	10.780	.99572	1.0043	10.826	42
19	.09266	.09306	10.746	.99570	1.0043	10.792	41
20	.09295	.09335	10.712	.99567	1.0043	10.758	40
21	.09324	.09365	10.678	.99564	1.0044	10.725	39
22	.09353	.09394	10.645	.99562	1.0044	10.692	38
23	.09382	.09423	10.612	.99559	1.0044	10.659	37
24	.09411	.09453	10.579	.99556	1.0045	10.626	36
25	.09440	.09482	10.546	.99553	1.0045	10.593	35
26	.09469	.09511	10.514	.99551	1.0045	10.561	34
27	.09498	.09541	10.481	.99548	1.0045	10.529	33
28	.09527	.09570	10.449	.99545	1.0046	10.497	32
29	.09556	.09600	10.417	.99542	1.0046	10.465	31
30	.09585	.09629	10.385	.99540	1.0046	10.433	30
31	.09614	.09658	10.354	.99537	1.0047	10.402	29
32	.09642	.09688	10.322	.99534	1.0047	10.371	28
33	.09671	.09717	10.291	.99531	1.0047	10.340	27
34	.09700	.09746	10.260	.99528	1.0047	10.309	26
35	.09729	.09776	10.229	.99526	1.0048	10.278	25
36	.09758	.09805	10.199	.99523	1.0048	10.248	24
37	.09787	.09834	10.168	.99520	1.0048	10.217	23
38	.09816	.09864	10.138	.99517	1.0049	10.187	22
39	.09845	.09893	10.108	.99514	1.0049	10.157	21
40	.09874	.09923	10.078	.99511	1.0049	10.128	20
41	.09903	.09952	10.048	.99508	1.0049	10.098	19
42	.09932	.09981	10.019	.99506	1.0050	10.068	18
43	.09961	.10011	9.9893	.99503	1.0050	10.039	17
44	.09990	.10040	9.9601	.99500	1.0050	10.010	16
45	.10019	.10069	9.9310	.99497	1.0051	9.9812	15
46	.10048	.10099	9.9021	.99494	1.0051	9.9525	14
47	.10077	.10128	9.8734	.99491	1.0051	9.9239	13
48	.10106	.10158	9.8448	.99488	1.0051	9.8955	12
49	.10135	.10187	9.8164	.99485	1.0052	9.8672	11
50	.10164	.10216	9.7882	.99482	1.0052	9.8391	10
51	.10192	.10246	9.7601	.99479	1.0052	9.8112	9
52	.10221	.10275	9.7322	.99476	1.0053	9.7834	8
53	.10250	.10305	9.7044	.99473	1.0053	9.7558	7
54	.10279	.10334	9.6768	.99470	1.0053	9.7283	6
55	.10308	.10363	9.6493	.99467	1.0054	9.7010	5
56	.10337	.10393	9.6220	.99464	1.0054	9.6739	4
57	.10366	.10422	9.5949	.99461	1.0054	9.6469	3
58	.10395	.10452	9.5679	.99458	1.0054	9.6200	2
59	.10424	.10481	9.5411	.99455	1.0055	9.5933	1
60	.10453	.10510	9.5144	.99452	1.0055	9.5668	0
'	Cos	Cot	Tan	Sin	Csc	Sec	'

Tables for Use in Trigonometry

NATURAL TRIGONOMETRIC FUNCTIONS
TO FIVE PLACES

6° (186°)   (353°) 173°   **7° (187°)**   (352

′	Sin	Tan	Cot	Cos	Sec	Csc	′
0	.10453	.10510	9.5144	.99452	1.0055	9.5668	60
1	.10482	.10540	9.4878	.99449	1.0055	9.5404	59
2	.10511	.10569	9.4614	.99446	1.0056	9.5141	58
3	.10540	.10599	9.4352	.99443	1.0056	9.4880	57
4	.10569	.10628	9.4090	.99440	1.0056	9.4620	56
5	.10597	.10657	9.3831	.99437	1.0057	9.4362	55
6	.10626	.10687	9.3572	.99434	1.0057	9.4105	54
7	.10655	.10716	9.3315	.99431	1.0057	9.3850	53
8	.10684	.10746	9.3060	.99428	1.0058	9.3596	52
9	.10713	.10775	9.2806	.99424	1.0058	9.3343	51
10	.10742	.10805	9.2553	.99421	1.0058	9.3092	50
11	.10771	.10834	9.2302	.99418	1.0059	9.2842	49
12	.10800	.10863	9.2052	.99415	1.0059	9.2593	48
13	.10829	.10893	9.1803	.99412	1.0059	9.2346	47
14	.10858	.10922	9.1555	.99409	1.0059	9.2100	46
15	.10887	.10952	9.1309	.99406	1.0060	9.1855	45
16	.10916	.10981	9.1065	.99402	1.0060	9.1612	44
17	.10945	.11011	9.0821	.99399	1.0060	9.1370	43
18	.10973	.11040	9.0579	.99396	1.0061	9.1129	42
19	.11002	.11070	9.0338	.99393	1.0061	9.0890	41
20	.11031	.11099	9.0098	.99390	1.0061	9.0652	40
21	.11060	.11128	8.9860	.99386	1.0062	9.0415	39
22	.11089	.11158	8.9623	.99383	1.0062	9.0179	38
23	.11118	.11187	8.9387	.99380	1.0062	8.9944	37
24	.11147	.11217	8.9152	.99377	1.0063	8.9711	36
25	.11176	.11246	8.8919	.99374	1.0063	8.9479	35
26	.11205	.11276	8.8686	.99370	1.0063	8.9248	34
27	.11234	.11305	8.8455	.99367	1.0064	8.9019	33
28	.11263	.11335	8.8225	.99364	1.0064	8.8790	32
29	.11291	.11364	8.7996	.99360	1.0064	8.8563	31
30	.11320	.11394	8.7769	.99357	1.0065	8.8337	30
31	.11349	.11423	8.7542	.99354	1.0065	8.8112	29
32	.11378	.11452	8.7317	.99351	1.0065	8.7888	28
33	.11407	.11482	8.7093	.99347	1.0066	8.7665	27
34	.11436	.11511	8.6870	.99344	1.0066	8.7444	26
35	.11465	.11541	8.6648	.99341	1.0066	8.7223	25
36	.11494	.11570	8.6427	.99337	1.0067	8.7004	24
37	.11523	.11600	8.6208	.99334	1.0067	8.6786	23
38	.11552	.11629	8.5989	.99331	1.0067	8.6569	22
39	.11580	.11659	8.5772	.99327	1.0068	8.6353	21
40	.11609	.11688	8.5555	.99324	1.0068	8.6138	20
41	.11638	.11718	8.5340	.99320	1.0068	8.5924	19
42	.11667	.11747	8.5126	.99317	1.0069	8.5711	18
43	.11696	.11777	8.4913	.99314	1.0069	8.5500	17
44	.11725	.11806	8.4701	.99310	1.0069	8.5289	16
45	.11754	.11836	8.4490	.99307	1.0070	8.5079	15
46	.11783	.11865	8.4280	.99303	1.0070	8.4871	14
47	.11812	.11895	8.4071	.99300	1.0070	8.4663	13
48	.11840	.11924	8.3863	.99297	1.0071	8.4457	12
49	.11869	.11954	8.3656	.99293	1.0071	8.4251	11
50	.11898	.11983	8.3450	.99290	1.0072	8.4047	10
51	.11927	.12013	8.3245	.99286	1.0072	8.3843	9
52	.11956	.12042	8.3041	.99283	1.0072	8.3641	8
53	.11985	.12072	8.2838	.99279	1.0073	8.3439	7
54	.12014	.12101	8.2636	.99276	1.0073	8.3238	6
55	.12043	.12131	8.2434	.99272	1.0073	8.3039	5
56	.12071	.12160	8.2234	.99269	1.0074	8.2840	4
57	.12100	.12190	8.2035	.99265	1.0074	8.2642	3
58	.12129	.12219	8.1837	.99262	1.0074	8.2446	2
59	.12158	.12249	8.1640	.99258	1.0075	8.2250	1
60	.12187	.12278	8.1443	.99255	1.0075	8.2055	0
′	Cos	Cot	Tan	Sin	Csc	Sec	′

′	Sin	Tan	Cot	Cos	Sec	Csc
0	.12187	.12278	8.1443	.99255	1.0075	8.2055
1	.12216	.12308	8.1248	.99251	1.0075	8.1861
2	.12245	.12338	8.1054	.99248	1.0076	8.1668
3	.12274	.12367	8.0860	.99244	1.0076	8.1476
4	.12302	.12397	8.0667	.99240	1.0077	8.1285
5	.12331	.12426	8.0476	.99237	1.0077	8.1095
6	.12360	.12456	8.0285	.99233	1.0077	8.0905
7	.12389	.12485	8.0095	.99230	1.0078	8.0717
8	.12418	.12515	7.9906	.99226	1.0078	8.0529
9	.12447	.12544	7.9718	.99222	1.0078	8.0342
10	.12476	.12574	7.9530	.99219	1.0079	8.0156
11	.12504	.12603	7.9344	.99215	1.0079	7.9971
12	.12533	.12633	7.9158	.99211	1.0079	7.9787
13	.12562	.12662	7.8973	.99208	1.0080	7.9604
14	.12591	.12692	7.8789	.99204	1.0080	7.9422
15	.12620	.12722	7.8606	.99200	1.0081	7.9240
16	.12649	.12751	7.8424	.99197	1.0081	7.9059
17	.12678	.12781	7.8243	.99193	1.0081	7.8879
18	.12706	.12810	7.8062	.99189	1.0082	7.8700
19	.12735	.12840	7.7882	.99186	1.0082	7.8522
20	.12764	.12869	7.7704	.99182	1.0082	7.8344
21	.12793	.12899	7.7525	.99178	1.0083	7.8168
22	.12822	.12929	7.7348	.99175	1.0083	7.7992
23	.12851	.12958	7.7171	.99171	1.0084	7.7817
24	.12880	.12988	7.6996	.99167	1.0084	7.7642
25	.12908	.13017	7.6821	.99163	1.0084	7.7469
26	.12937	.13047	7.6647	.99160	1.0085	7.7296
27	.12966	.13076	7.6473	.99156	1.0085	7.7124
28	.12995	.13106	7.6301	.99152	1.0086	7.6953
29	.13024	.13136	7.6129	.99148	1.0086	7.6783
30	.13053	.13165	7.5958	.99144	1.0086	7.6613
31	.13081	.13195	7.5787	.99141	1.0087	7.6444
32	.13110	.13224	7.5618	.99137	1.0087	7.6276
33	.13139	.13254	7.5449	.99133	1.0087	7.6109
34	.13168	.13284	7.5281	.99129	1.0088	7.5942
35	.13197	.13313	7.5113	.99125	1.0088	7.5776
36	.13226	.13343	7.4947	.99122	1.0089	7.5611
37	.13254	.13372	7.4781	.99118	1.0089	7.5446
38	.13283	.13402	7.4615	.99114	1.0089	7.5282
39	.13312	.13432	7.4451	.99110	1.0090	7.5119
40	.13341	.13461	7.4287	.99106	1.0090	7.4957
41	.13370	.13491	7.4124	.99102	1.0091	7.4795
42	.13399	.13521	7.3962	.99098	1.0091	7.4635
43	.13427	.13550	7.3800	.99094	1.0091	7.4474
44	.13456	.13580	7.3639	.99091	1.0092	7.4315
45	.13485	.13609	7.3479	.99087	1.0092	7.4156
46	.13514	.13639	7.3319	.99083	1.0093	7.3998
47	.13543	.13669	7.3160	.99079	1.0093	7.3840
48	.13572	.13698	7.3002	.99075	1.0093	7.3684
49	.13600	.13728	7.2844	.99071	1.0094	7.3527
50	.13629	.13758	7.2687	.99067	1.0094	7.3372
51	.13658	.13787	7.2531	.99063	1.0095	7.3217
52	.13687	.13817	7.2375	.99059	1.0095	7.3063
53	.13716	.13846	7.2220	.99055	1.0095	7.2909
54	.13744	.13876	7.2066	.99051	1.0096	7.2757
55	.13773	.13906	7.1912	.99047	1.0096	7.2604
56	.13802	.13935	7.1759	.99043	1.0097	7.2453
57	.13831	.13965	7.1607	.99039	1.0097	7.2302
58	.13860	.13995	7.1455	.99035	1.0097	7.2152
59	.13889	.14024	7.1304	.99031	1.0098	7.2002
60	.13917	.14054	7.1154	.99027	1.0098	7.1853
′	Cos	Cot	Tan	Sin	Csc	Sec

96° (276°)   (263°) 83°   **97° (277°)**   (262

NATURAL TRIGONOMETRIC FUNCTIONS
TO FIVE PLACES

8°) (351°) 171°   9° (189°) (350°) 170°

Sin	Tan	Cot	Cos	Sec	Csc	'
.13917	.14054	7.1154	.99027	1.0098	7.1853	60
.13946	.14084	7.1004	.99023	1.0099	7.1705	59
.13975	.14113	7.0855	.99019	1.0099	7.1557	58
.14004	.14143	7.0706	.99015	1.0100	7.1410	57
.14033	.14173	7.0558	.99011	1.0100	7.1263	56
.14061	.14202	7.0410	.99006	1.0100	7.1117	55
.14090	.14232	7.0264	.99002	1.0101	7.0972	54
.14119	.14262	7.0117	.98998	1.0101	7.0827	53
.14148	.14291	6.9972	.98994	1.0102	7.0683	52
.14177	.14321	6.9827	.98990	1.0102	7.0539	51
.14205	.14351	6.9682	.98986	1.0102	7.0396	50
.14234	.14381	6.9538	.98982	1.0103	7.0254	49
.14263	.14410	6.9395	.98978	1.0103	7.0112	48
.14292	.14440	6.9252	.98973	1.0104	6.9971	47
.14320	.14470	6.9110	.98969	1.0104	6.9830	46
.14349	.14499	6.8969	.98965	1.0105	6.9690	45
.14378	.14529	6.8828	.98961	1.0105	6.9550	44
.14407	.14559	6.8687	.98957	1.0105	6.9411	43
.14436	.14588	6.8548	.98953	1.0106	6.9273	42
.14464	.14618	6.8408	.98948	1.0106	6.9135	41
.14493	.14648	6.8269	.98944	1.0107	6.8998	40
.14522	.14678	6.8131	.98940	1.0107	6.8861	39
.14551	.14707	6.7994	.98936	1.0108	6.8725	38
.14580	.14737	6.7856	.98931	1.0108	6.8589	37
.14608	.14767	6.7720	.98927	1.0108	6.8454	36
.14637	.14796	6.7584	.98923	1.0109	6.8320	35
.14666	.14826	6.7448	.98919	1.0109	6.8186	34
.14695	.14856	6.7313	.98914	1.0110	6.8052	33
.14723	.14886	6.7179	.98910	1.0110	6.7919	32
.14752	.14915	6.7045	.98906	1.0111	6.7787	31
.14781	.14945	6.6912	.98902	1.0111	6.7655	30
.14810	.14975	6.6779	.98897	1.0112	6.7523	29
.14838	.15005	6.6646	.98893	1.0112	6.7392	28
.14867	.15034	6.6514	.98889	1.0112	6.7262	27
.14896	.15064	6.6383	.98884	1.0113	6.7132	26
.14925	.15094	6.6252	.98880	1.0113	6.7003	25
.14954	.15124	6.6122	.98876	1.0114	6.6874	24
.14982	.15153	6.5992	.98871	1.0114	6.6745	23
.15011	.15183	6.5863	.98867	1.0115	6.6618	22
.15040	.15213	6.5734	.98863	1.0115	6.6490	21
.15069	.15243	6.5606	.98858	1.0116	6.6363	20
.15097	.15272	6.5478	.98854	1.0116	6.6237	19
.15126	.15302	6.5350	.98849	1.0116	6.6111	18
.15155	.15332	6.5223	.98845	1.0117	6.5986	17
.15184	.15362	6.5097	.98841	1.0117	6.5861	16
.15212	.15391	6.4971	.98836	1.0118	6.5736	15
.15241	.15421	6.4846	.98832	1.0118	6.5612	14
.15270	.15451	6.4721	.98827	1.0119	6.5489	13
.15299	.15481	6.4596	.98823	1.0119	6.5366	12
.15327	.15511	6.4472	.98818	1.0120	6.5243	11
.15356	.15540	6.4348	.98814	1.0120	6.5121	10
.15385	.15570	6.4225	.98809	1.0120	6.4999	9
.15414	.15600	6.4103	.98805	1.0121	6.4878	8
.15442	.15630	6.3980	.98800	1.0121	6.4757	7
.15471	.15660	6.3859	.98796	1.0122	6.4637	6
.15500	.15689	6.3737	.98791	1.0122	6.4517	5
.15529	.15719	6.3617	.98787	1.0123	6.4398	4
.15557	.15749	6.3496	.98782	1.0123	6.4279	3
.15586	.15779	6.3376	.98778	1.0124	6.4160	2
.15615	.15809	6.3257	.98773	1.0124	6.4042	1
.15643	.15838	6.3138	.98769	1.0125	6.3925	0
Cos	Cot	Tan	Sin	Csc	Sec	'

'	Sin	Tan	Cot	Cos	Sec	Csc	'
0	.15643	.15838	6.3138	.98769	1.0125	6.3925	60
1	.15672	.15868	6.3019	.98764	1.0125	6.3807	59
2	.15701	.15898	6.2901	.98760	1.0126	6.3691	58
3	.15730	.15928	6.2783	.98755	1.0126	6.3574	57
4	.15758	.15958	6.2666	.98751	1.0127	6.3458	56
5	.15787	.15988	6.2549	.98746	1.0127	6.3343	55
6	.15816	.16017	6.2432	.98741	1.0127	6.3228	54
7	.15845	.16047	6.2316	.98737	1.0128	6.3113	53
8	.15873	.16077	6.2200	.98732	1.0128	6.2999	52
9	.15902	.16107	6.2085	.98728	1.0129	6.2885	51
10	.15931	.16137	6.1970	.98723	1.0129	6.2772	50
11	.15959	.16167	6.1856	.98718	1.0130	6.2659	49
12	.15988	.16196	6.1742	.98714	1.0130	6.2546	48
13	.16017	.16226	6.1628	.98709	1.0131	6.2434	47
14	.16046	.16256	6.1515	.98704	1.0131	6.2323	46
15	.16074	.16286	6.1402	.98700	1.0132	6.2211	45
16	.16103	.16316	6.1290	.98695	1.0132	6.2100	44
17	.16132	.16346	6.1178	.98690	1.0133	6.1990	43
18	.16160	.16376	6.1066	.98686	1.0133	6.1880	42
19	.16189	.16405	6.0955	.98681	1.0134	6.1770	41
20	.16218	.16435	6.0844	.98676	1.0134	6.1661	40
21	.16246	.16465	6.0734	.98671	1.0135	6.1552	39
22	.16275	.16495	6.0624	.98667	1.0135	6.1443	38
23	.16304	.16525	6.0514	.98662	1.0136	6.1335	37
24	.16333	.16555	6.0405	.98657	1.0136	6.1227	36
25	.16361	.16585	6.0296	.98652	1.0137	6.1120	35
26	.16390	.16615	6.0188	.98648	1.0137	6.1013	34
27	.16419	.16645	6.0080	.98643	1.0138	6.0906	33
28	.16447	.16674	5.9972	.98638	1.0138	6.0800	32
29	.16476	.16704	5.9865	.98633	1.0139	6.0694	31
30	.16505	.16734	5.9758	.98629	1.0139	6.0589	30
31	.16533	.16764	5.9651	.98624	1.0140	6.0483	29
32	.16562	.16794	5.9545	.98619	1.0140	6.0379	28
33	.16591	.16824	5.9439	.98614	1.0141	6.0274	27
34	.16620	.16854	5.9333	.98609	1.0141	6.0170	26
35	.16648	.16884	5.9228	.98604	1.0142	6.0067	25
36	.16677	.16914	5.9124	.98600	1.0142	5.9963	24
37	.16706	.16944	5.9019	.98595	1.0143	5.9860	23
38	.16734	.16974	5.8915	.98590	1.0143	5.9758	22
39	.16763	.17004	5.8811	.98585	1.0144	5.9656	21
40	.16792	.17033	5.8708	.98580	1.0144	5.9554	20
41	.16820	.17063	5.8605	.98575	1.0145	5.9452	19
42	.16849	.17093	5.8502	.98570	1.0145	5.9351	18
43	.16878	.17123	5.8400	.98565	1.0146	5.9250	17
44	.16906	.17153	5.8298	.98561	1.0146	5.9150	16
45	.16935	.17183	5.8197	.98556	1.0147	5.9049	15
46	.16964	.17213	5.8095	.98551	1.0147	5.8950	14
47	.16992	.17243	5.7994	.98546	1.0148	5.8850	13
48	.17021	.17273	5.7894	.98541	1.0148	5.8751	12
49	.17050	.17303	5.7794	.98536	1.0149	5.8652	11
50	.17078	.17333	5.7694	.98531	1.0149	5.8554	10
51	.17107	.17363	5.7594	.98526	1.0150	5.8456	9
52	.17136	.17393	5.7495	.98521	1.0150	5.8358	8
53	.17164	.17423	5.7396	.98516	1.0151	5.8261	7
54	.17193	.17453	5.7297	.98511	1.0151	5.8164	6
55	.17222	.17483	5.7199	.98506	1.0152	5.8067	5
56	.17250	.17513	5.7101	.98501	1.0152	5.7970	4
57	.17279	.17543	5.7004	.98496	1.0153	5.7874	3
58	.17308	.17573	5.6906	.98491	1.0153	5.7778	2
59	.17336	.17603	5.6809	.98486	1.0154	5.7683	1
60	.17365	.17633	5.6713	.98481	1.0154	5.7588	0
'	Cos	Cot	Tan	Sin	Csc	Sec	'

78°) (261°) 81°   99° (279°) (260°) 80°

Tables for Use in Trigonometry

NATURAL TRIGONOMETRIC FUNCTIONS
TO FIVE PLACES

10° (190°)   (349°) 169°   **11° (191°)**   (34

′	Sin	Tan	Cot	Cos	Sec	Csc	′		′	Sin	Tan	Cot	Cos	Sec	Csc
0	.17365	.17633	5.6713	.98481	1.0154	5.7588	60		0	.19081	.19438	5.1446	.98163	1.0187	5.2408
1	.17393	.17663	5.6617	.98476	1.0155	5.7493	59		1	.19109	.19468	5.1366	.98157	1.0188	5.2330
2	.17422	.17693	5.6521	.98471	1.0155	5.7398	58		2	.19138	.19498	5.1286	.98152	1.0188	5.2252
3	.17451	.17723	5.6425	.98466	1.0156	5.7304	57		3	.19167	.19529	5.1207	.98146	1.0189	5.2174
4	.17479	.17753	5.6329	.98461	1.0156	5.7210	56		4	.19195	.19559	5.1128	.98140	1.0189	5.2097
5	.17508	.17783	5.6234	.98455	1.0157	5.7117	55		5	.19224	.19589	5.1049	.98135	1.0190	5.2019
6	.17537	.17813	5.6140	.98450	1.0157	5.7023	54		6	.19252	.19619	5.0970	.98129	1.0191	5.1942
7	.17565	.17843	5.6045	.98445	1.0158	5.6930	53		7	.19281	.19649	5.0892	.98124	1.0191	5.1865
8	.17594	.17873	5.5951	.98440	1.0158	5.6838	52		8	.19309	.19680	5.0814	.98118	1.0192	5.1789
9	.17623	.17903	5.5857	.98435	1.0159	5.6745	51		9	.19338	.19710	5.0736	.98112	1.0192	5.1712
10	.17651	.17933	5.5764	.98430	1.0160	5.6653	50		10	.19366	.19740	5.0658	.98107	1.0193	5.1636
11	.17680	.17963	5.5671	.98425	1.0160	5.6562	49		11	.19395	.19770	5.0581	.98101	1.0194	5.1560
12	.17708	.17993	5.5578	.98420	1.0161	5.6470	48		12	.19423	.19801	5.0504	.98096	1.0194	5.1484
13	.17737	.18023	5.5485	.98414	1.0161	5.6379	47		13	.19452	.19831	5.0427	.98090	1.0195	5.1409
14	.17766	.18053	5.5393	.98409	1.0162	5.6288	46		14	.19481	.19861	5.0350	.98084	1.0195	5.1333
15	.17794	.18083	5.5301	.98404	1.0162	5.6198	45		15	.19509	.19891	5.0273	.98079	1.0196	5.1258
16	.17823	.18113	5.5209	.98399	1.0163	5.6107	44		16	.19538	.19921	5.0197	.98073	1.0197	5.1183
17	.17852	.18143	5.5118	.98394	1.0163	5.6017	43		17	.19566	.19952	5.0121	.98067	1.0197	5.1109
18	.17880	.18173	5.5026	.98389	1.0164	5.5928	42		18	.19595	.19982	5.0045	.98061	1.0198	5.1034
19	.17909	.18203	5.4936	.98383	1.0164	5.5838	41		19	.19623	.20012	4.9969	.98056	1.0198	5.0960
20	.17937	.18233	5.4845	.98378	1.0165	5.5749	40		20	.19652	.20042	4.9894	.98050	1.0199	5.0886
21	.17966	.18263	5.4755	.98373	1.0165	5.5660	39		21	.19680	.20073	4.9819	.98044	1.0199	5.0813
22	.17995	.18293	5.4665	.98368	1.0166	5.5572	38		22	.19709	.20103	4.9744	.98039	1.0200	5.0739
23	.18023	.18323	5.4575	.98362	1.0166	5.5484	37		23	.19737	.20133	4.9669	.98033	1.0201	5.0666
24	.18052	.18353	5.4486	.98357	1.0167	5.5396	36		24	.19766	.20164	4.9594	.98027	1.0201	5.0593
25	.18081	.18384	5.4397	.98352	1.0168	5.5308	35		25	.19794	.20194	4.9520	.98021	1.0202	5.0520
26	.18109	.18414	5.4308	.98347	1.0168	5.5221	34		26	.19823	.20224	4.9446	.98016	1.0202	5.0447
27	.18138	.18444	5.4219	.98341	1.0169	5.5134	33		27	.19851	.20254	4.9372	.98010	1.0203	5.0375
28	.18166	.18474	5.4131	.98336	1.0169	5.5047	32		28	.19880	.20285	4.9298	.98004	1.0204	5.0302
29	.18195	.18504	5.4043	.98331	1.0170	5.4960	31		29	.19908	.20315	4.9225	.97998	1.0204	5.0230
30	.18224	.18534	5.3955	.98325	1.0170	5.4874	30		30	.19937	.20345	4.9152	.97992	1.0205	5.0159
31	.18252	.18564	5.3868	.98320	1.0171	5.4788	29		31	.19965	.20376	4.9078	.97987	1.0205	5.0087
32	.18281	.18594	5.3781	.98315	1.0171	5.4702	28		32	.19994	.20406	4.9006	.97981	1.0206	5.0016
33	.18309	.18624	5.3694	.98304	1.0172	5.4617	27		33	.20022	.20436	4.8933	.97975	1.0207	4.9944
34	.18338	.18654	5.3607	.98304	1.0173	5.4532	26		34	.20051	.20466	4.8860	.97969	1.0207	4.9873
35	.18367	.18684	5.3521	.98299	1.0173	5.4447	25		35	.20079	.20497	4.8788	.97963	1.0208	4.9803
36	.18395	.18714	5.3435	.98294	1.0174	5.4362	24		36	.20108	.20527	4.8716	.97958	1.0209	4.9732
37	.18424	.18745	5.3349	.98288	1.0174	5.4278	23		37	.20136	.20557	4.8644	.97952	1.0209	4.9662
38	.18452	.18775	5.3263	.98283	1.0175	5.4194	22		38	.20165	.20588	4.8573	.97946	1.0210	4.9591
39	.18481	.18805	5.3178	.98277	1.0175	5.4110	21		39	.20193	.20618	4.8501	.97940	1.0210	4.9521
40	.18509	.18835	5.3093	.98272	1.0176	5.4026	20		40	.20222	.20648	4.8430	.97934	1.0211	4.9452
41	.18538	.18865	5.3008	.98267	1.0176	5.3943	19		41	.20250	.20679	4.8359	.97928	1.0212	4.9382
42	.18567	.18895	5.2924	.98261	1.0177	5.3860	18		42	.20279	.20709	4.8288	.97922	1.0212	4.9313
43	.18595	.18925	5.2839	.98256	1.0178	5.3777	17		43	.20307	.20739	4.8218	.97916	1.0213	4.9244
44	.18624	.18955	5.2755	.98250	1.0178	5.3695	16		44	.20336	.20770	4.8147	.97910	1.0213	4.9175
45	.18652	.18986	5.2672	.98245	1.0179	5.3612	15		45	.20364	.20800	4.8077	.97905	1.0214	4.9106
46	.18681	.19016	5.2588	.98240	1.0179	5.3530	14		46	.20393	.20830	4.8007	.97899	1.0215	4.9037
47	.18710	.19046	5.2505	.98234	1.0180	5.3449	13		47	.20421	.20861	4.7937	.97893	1.0215	4.8969
48	.18738	.19076	5.2422	.98229	1.0180	5.3367	12		48	.20450	.20891	4.7867	.97887	1.0216	4.8901
49	.18767	.19106	5.2339	.98223	1.0181	5.3286	11		49	.20478	.20921	4.7798	.97881	1.0217	4.8833
50	.18795	.19136	5.2257	.98218	1.0181	5.3205	10		50	.20507	.20952	4.7729	.97875	1.0217	4.8765
51	.18824	.19166	5.2174	.98212	1.0182	5.3124	9		51	.20535	.20982	4.7659	.97869	1.0218	4.8697
52	.18852	.19197	5.2092	.98207	1.0183	5.3044	8		52	.20563	.21013	4.7591	.97863	1.0218	4.8630
53	.18881	.19227	5.2011	.98201	1.0183	5.2963	7		53	.20592	.21043	4.7522	.97857	1.0219	4.8563
54	.18910	.19257	5.1929	.98196	1.0184	5.2883	6		54	.20620	.21073	4.7453	.97851	1.0220	4.8496
55	.18938	.19287	5.1848	.98190	1.0184	5.2804	5		55	.20649	.21104	4.7385	.97845	1.0220	4.8429
56	.18967	.19317	5.1767	.98185	1.0185	5.2724	4		56	.20677	.21134	4.7317	.97839	1.0221	4.8362
57	.18995	.19347	5.1686	.98179	1.0185	5.2645	3		57	.20706	.21164	4.7249	.97833	1.0222	4.8296
58	.19024	.19378	5.1606	.98174	1.0186	5.2566	2		58	.20734	.21195	4.7181	.97827	1.0222	4.8229
59	.19052	.19408	5.1526	.98168	1.0187	5.2487	1		59	.20763	.21225	4.7114	.97821	1.0223	4.8163
60	.19081	.19438	5.1446	.98163	1.0187	5.2408	0		60	.20791	.21256	4.7046	.97815	1.0223	4.8097
′	Cos	Cot	Tan	Sin	Csc	Sec	′		′	Cos	Cot	Tan	Sin	Csc	Sec

100° (280°)   (259°) 79°   **101° (281°)**   (258

NATURAL TRIGONOMETRIC FUNCTIONS
TO FIVE PLACES

Sin	Tan	Cot	Cos	Sec	Csc	'		'	Sin	Tan	Cot	Cos	Sec	Csc	'
.20791	.21256	4.7046	.97815	1.0223	4.8097	60		0	.22495	.23087	4.3315	.97437	1.0263	4.4454	60
.20820	.21286	4.6979	.97809	1.0224	4.8032	59		1	.22523	.23117	4.3257	.97430	1.0264	4.4398	59
.20848	.21316	4.6912	.97803	1.0225	4.7966	58		2	.22552	.23148	4.3200	.97424	1.0264	4.4342	58
.20877	.21347	4.6845	.97797	1.0225	4.7901	57		3	.22580	.23179	4.3143	.97417	1.0265	4.4287	57
.20905	.21377	4.6779	.97791	1.0226	4.7836	56		4	.22608	.23209	4.3086	.97411	1.0266	4.4231	56
.20933	.21408	4.6712	.97784	1.0227	4.7771	55		5	.22637	.23240	4.3029	.97404	1.0266	4.4176	55
.20962	.21438	4.6646	.97778	1.0227	4.7706	54		6	.22665	.23271	4.2972	.97398	1.0267	4.4121	54
.20990	.21469	4.6580	.97772	1.0228	4.7641	53		7	.22693	.23301	4.2916	.97391	1.0268	4.4066	53
.21019	.21499	4.6514	.97766	1.0228	4.7577	52		8	.22722	.23332	4.2859	.97384	1.0269	4.4011	52
.21047	.21529	4.6448	.97760	1.0229	4.7512	51		9	.22750	.23363	4.2803	.97378	1.0269	4.3956	51
.21076	.21560	4.6382	.97754	1.0230	4.7448	50		10	.22778	.23393	4.2747	.97371	1.0270	4.3901	50
.21104	.21590	4.6317	.97748	1.0230	4.7384	49		11	.22807	.23424	4.2691	.97365	1.0271	4.3847	49
.21132	.21621	4.6252	.97742	1.0231	4.7321	48		12	.22835	.23455	4.2635	.97358	1.0271	4.3792	48
.21161	.21651	4.6187	.97735	1.0232	4.7257	47		13	.22863	.23485	4.2580	.97351	1.0272	4.3738	47
.21189	.21682	4.6122	.97729	1.0232	4.7194	46		14	.22892	.23516	4.2524	.97345	1.0273	4.3684	46
.21218	.21712	4.6057	.97723	1.0233	4.7130	45		15	.22920	.23547	4.2468	.97338	1.0273	4.3630	45
.21246	.21743	4.5993	.97717	1.0234	4.7067	44		16	.22948	.23578	4.2413	.97331	1.0274	4.3576	44
.21275	.21773	4.5928	.97711	1.0234	4.7004	43		17	.22977	.23608	4.2358	.97325	1.0275	4.3522	43
.21303	.21804	4.5864	.97705	1.0235	4.6942	42		18	.23005	.23639	4.2303	.97318	1.0276	4.3469	42
.21331	.21834	4.5800	.97698	1.0236	4.6879	41		19	.23033	.23670	4.2248	.97311	1.0276	4.3415	41
.21360	.21864	4.5736	.97692	1.0236	4.6817	40		20	.23062	.23700	4.2193	.97304	1.0277	4.3362	40
.21388	.21895	4.5673	.97686	1.0237	4.6755	39		21	.23090	.23731	4.2139	.97298	1.0278	4.3309	39
.21417	.21925	4.5609	.97680	1.0238	4.6693	38		22	.23118	.23762	4.2084	.97291	1.0278	4.3256	38
.21445	.21956	4.5546	.97673	1.0238	4.6631	37		23	.23146	.23793	4.2030	.97284	1.0279	4.3203	37
.21474	.21986	4.5483	.97667	1.0239	4.6569	36		24	.23175	.23823	4.1976	.97278	1.0280	4.3150	36
.21502	.22017	4.5420	.97661	1.0240	4.6507	35		25	.23203	.23854	4.1922	.97271	1.0281	4.3098	35
.21530	.22047	4.5357	.97655	1.0240	4.6446	34		26	.23231	.23885	4.1868	.97264	1.0281	4.3045	34
.21559	.22078	4.5294	.97648	1.0241	4.6385	33		27	.23260	.23916	4.1814	.97257	1.0282	4.2993	33
.21587	.22108	4.5232	.97642	1.0241	4.6324	32		28	.23288	.23946	4.1760	.97251	1.0283	4.2941	32
.21616	.22139	4.5169	.97636	1.0242	4.6263	31		29	.23316	.23977	4.1706	.97244	1.0283	4.2889	31
.21644	.22169	4.5107	.97630	1.0243	4.6202	30		30	.23345	.24008	4.1653	.97237	1.0284	4.2837	30
.21672	.22200	4.5045	.97623	1.0243	4.6142	29		31	.23373	.24039	4.1600	.97230	1.0285	4.2785	29
.21701	.22231	4.4983	.97617	1.0244	4.6081	28		32	.23401	.24069	4.1547	.97223	1.0286	4.2733	28
.21729	.22261	4.4922	.97611	1.0245	4.6021	27		33	.23429	.24100	4.1493	.97217	1.0286	4.2681	27
.21758	.22292	4.4860	.97604	1.0245	4.5961	26		34	.23458	.24131	4.1441	.97210	1.0287	4.2630	26
.21786	.22322	4.4799	.97598	1.0246	4.5901	25		35	.23486	.24162	4.1388	.97203	1.0288	4.2579	25
.21814	.22353	4.4737	.97592	1.0247	4.5841	24		36	.23514	.24193	4.1335	.97196	1.0288	4.2527	24
.21843	.22383	4.4676	.97585	1.0247	4.5782	23		37	.23542	.24223	4.1282	.97189	1.0289	4.2476	23
.21871	.22414	4.4615	.97579	1.0248	4.5722	22		38	.23571	.24254	4.1230	.97182	1.0290	4.2425	22
.21899	.22444	4.4555	.97573	1.0249	4.5663	21		39	.23599	.24285	4.1178	.97176	1.0291	4.2375	21
.21928	.22475	4.4494	.97566	1.0249	4.5604	20		40	.23627	.24316	4.1126	.97169	1.0291	4.2324	20
.21956	.22505	4.4434	.97560	1.0250	4.5545	19		41	.23656	.24347	4.1074	.97162	1.0292	4.2273	19
.21985	.22536	4.4373	.97553	1.0251	4.5486	18		42	.23684	.24377	4.1022	.97155	1.0293	4.2223	18
.22013	.22567	4.4313	.97547	1.0251	4.5428	17		43	.23712	.24408	4.0970	.97148	1.0294	4.2173	17
.22041	.22597	4.4253	.97541	1.0252	4.5369	16		44	.23740	.24439	4.0918	.97141	1.0294	4.2122	16
.22070	.22628	4.4194	.97534	1.0253	4.5311	15		45	.23769	.24470	4.0867	.97134	1.0295	4.2072	15
.22098	.22658	4.4134	.97528	1.0253	4.5253	14		46	.23797	.24501	4.0815	.97127	1.0296	4.2022	14
.22126	.22689	4.4075	.97521	1.0254	4.5195	13		47	.23825	.24532	4.0764	.97120	1.0297	4.1973	13
.22155	.22719	4.4015	.97515	1.0255	4.5137	12		48	.23853	.24562	4.0713	.97113	1.0297	4.1923	12
.22183	.22750	4.3956	.97508	1.0256	4.5079	11		49	.23882	.24593	4.0662	.97106	1.0298	4.1873	11
.22212	.22781	4.3897	.97502	1.0256	4.5022	10		50	.23910	.24624	4.0611	.97100	1.0299	4.1824	10
.22240	.22811	4.3838	.97496	1.0257	4.4964	9		51	.23938	.24655	4.0560	.97093	1.0299	4.1774	9
.22268	.22842	4.3779	.97489	1.0258	4.4907	8		52	.23966	.24686	4.0509	.97086	1.0300	4.1725	8
.22297	.22872	4.3721	.97483	1.0258	4.4850	7		53	.23995	.24717	4.0459	.97079	1.0301	4.1676	7
.22325	.22903	4.3662	.97476	1.0259	4.4793	6		54	.24023	.24747	4.0408	.97072	1.0302	4.1627	6
.22353	.22934	4.3604	.97470	1.0260	4.4736	5		55	.24051	.24778	4.0358	.97065	1.0302	4.1578	5
.22382	.22964	4.3546	.97463	1.0260	4.4679	4		56	.24079	.24809	4.0308	.97058	1.0303	4.1529	4
.22410	.22995	4.3488	.97457	1.0261	4.4623	3		57	.24108	.24840	4.0257	.97051	1.0304	4.1481	3
.22438	.23026	4.3430	.97450	1.0262	4.4566	2		58	.24136	.24871	4.0207	.97044	1.0305	4.1432	2
.22467	.23056	4.3372	.97444	1.0262	4.4510	1		59	.24164	.24902	4.0158	.97037	1.0305	4.1384	1
.22495	.23087	4.3315	.97437	1.0263	4.4454	0		60	.24192	.24933	4.0108	.97030	1.0306	4.1336	0
Cos	Cot	Tan	Sin	Csc	Sec	'		'	Cos	Cot	Tan	Sin	Csc	Sec	'

256

Tables for Use in Trigonometry

NATURAL TRIGONOMETRIC FUNCTIONS
TO FIVE PLACES

14° (194°) — **(345°) 165°**

'	Sin	Tan	Cot	Cos	Sec	Csc	'
0	.24192	.24933	4.0108	.97030	1.0306	4.1336	60
1	.24220	.24964	4.0058	.97023	1.0307	4.1287	59
2	.24249	.24995	4.0009	.97015	1.0308	4.1239	58
3	.24277	.25026	3.9959	.97008	1.0308	4.1191	57
4	.24305	.25056	3.9910	.97001	1.0309	4.1144	56
5	.24333	.25087	3.9861	.96994	1.0310	4.1096	55
6	.24362	.25118	3.9812	.96987	1.0311	4.1048	54
7	.24390	.25149	3.9763	.96980	1.0311	4.1001	53
8	.24418	.25180	3.9714	.96973	1.0312	4.0954	52
9	.24446	.25211	3.9665	.96966	1.0313	4.0906	51
10	.24474	.25242	3.9617	.96959	1.0314	4.0859	50
11	.24503	.25273	3.9568	.96952	1.0314	4.0812	49
12	.24531	.25304	3.9520	.96945	1.0315	4.0765	48
13	.24559	.25335	3.9471	.96937	1.0316	4.0718	47
14	.24587	.25366	3.9423	.96930	1.0317	4.0672	46
15	.24615	.25397	3.9375	.96923	1.0317	4.0625	45
16	.24644	.25428	3.9327	.96916	1.0318	4.0579	44
17	.24672	.25459	3.9279	.96909	1.0319	4.0532	43
18	.24700	.25490	3.9232	.96902	1.0320	4.0486	42
19	.24728	.25521	3.9184	.96894	1.0321	4.0440	41
20	.24756	.25552	3.9136	.96887	1.0321	4.0394	40
21	.24784	.25583	3.9089	.96880	1.0322	4.0348	39
22	.24813	.25614	3.9042	.96873	1.0323	4.0302	38
23	.24841	.25645	3.8995	.96866	1.0324	4.0256	37
24	.24869	.25676	3.8947	.96858	1.0324	4.0211	36
25	.24897	.25707	3.8900	.96851	1.0325	4.0165	35
26	.24925	.25738	3.8854	.96844	1.0326	4.0120	34
27	.24954	.25769	3.8807	.96837	1.0327	4.0075	33
28	.24982	.25800	3.8760	.96829	1.0327	4.0029	32
29	.25010	.25831	3.8714	.96822	1.0328	3.9984	31
30	.25038	.25862	3.8667	.96815	1.0329	3.9939	30
31	.25066	.25893	3.8621	.96807	1.0330	3.9894	29
32	.25094	.25924	3.8575	.96800	1.0331	3.9850	28
33	.25122	.25955	3.8528	.96793	1.0331	3.9805	27
34	.25151	.25986	3.8482	.96786	1.0332	3.9760	26
35	.25179	.26017	3.8436	.96778	1.0333	3.9716	25
36	.25207	.26048	3.8391	.96771	1.0334	3.9672	24
37	.25235	.26079	3.8345	.96764	1.0334	3.9627	23
38	.25263	.26110	3.8299	.96756	1.0335	3.9583	22
39	.25291	.26141	3.8254	.96749	1.0336	3.9539	21
40	.25320	.26172	3.8208	.96742	1.0337	3.9495	20
41	.25348	.26203	3.8163	.96734	1.0338	3.9451	19
42	.25376	.26235	3.8118	.96727	1.0338	3.9408	18
43	.25404	.26266	3.8073	.96719	1.0339	3.9364	17
44	.25432	.26297	3.8028	.96712	1.0340	3.9320	16
45	.25460	.26328	3.7983	.96705	1.0341	3.9277	15
46	.25488	.26359	3.7938	.96697	1.0342	3.9234	14
47	.25516	.26390	3.7893	.96690	1.0342	3.9190	13
48	.25545	.26421	3.7848	.96682	1.0343	3.9147	12
49	.25573	.26452	3.7804	.96675	1.0344	3.9104	11
50	.25601	.26483	3.7760	.96667	1.0345	3.9061	10
51	.25629	.26515	3.7715	.96660	1.0346	3.9018	9
52	.25657	.26546	3.7671	.96653	1.0346	3.8976	8
53	.25685	.26577	3.7627	.96645	1.0347	3.8933	7
54	.25713	.26608	3.7583	.96638	1.0348	3.8890	6
55	.25741	.26639	3.7539	.96630	1.0349	3.8848	5
56	.25769	.26670	3.7495	.96623	1.0350	3.8806	4
57	.25798	.26701	3.7451	.96615	1.0350	3.8763	3
58	.25826	.26733	3.7408	.96608	1.0351	3.8721	2
59	.25854	.26764	3.7364	.96600	1.0352	3.8679	1
60	.25882	.26795	3.7321	.96593	1.0353	3.8637	0
'	Cos	Cot	Tan	Sin	Csc	Sec	'

15° (195°) — **(344°)**

'	Sin	Tan	Cot	Cos	Sec	Csc	'
0	.25882	.26795	3.7321	.96593	1.0353	3.8637	
1	.25910	.26826	3.7277	.96585	1.0354	3.8595	
2	.25938	.26857	3.7234	.96578	1.0354	3.8553	
3	.25966	.26888	3.7191	.96570	1.0355	3.8512	
4	.25994	.26920	3.7148	.96562	1.0356	3.8470	
5	.26022	.26951	3.7105	.96555	1.0357	3.8428	
6	.26050	.26982	3.7062	.96547	1.0358	3.8387	
7	.26079	.27013	3.7019	.96540	1.0358	3.8346	
8	.26107	.27044	3.6976	.96532	1.0359	3.8304	
9	.26135	.27076	3.6933	.96524	1.0360	3.8263	
10	.26163	.27107	3.6891	.96517	1.0361	3.8222	
11	.26191	.27138	3.6848	.96509	1.0362	3.8181	
12	.26219	.27169	3.6806	.96502	1.0363	3.8140	
13	.26247	.27201	3.6764	.96494	1.0363	3.8100	
14	.26275	.27232	3.6722	.96486	1.0364	3.8059	
15	.26303	.27263	3.6680	.96479	1.0365	3.8018	
16	.26331	.27294	3.6638	.96471	1.0366	3.7978	
17	.26359	.27326	3.6596	.96463	1.0367	3.7937	
18	.26387	.27357	3.6554	.96456	1.0367	3.7897	
19	.26415	.27388	3.6512	.96448	1.0368	3.7857	
20	.26443	.27419	3.6470	.96440	1.0369	3.7817	
21	.26471	.27451	3.6429	.96433	1.0370	3.7777	
22	.26500	.27482	3.6387	.96425	1.0371	3.7737	
23	.26528	.27513	3.6346	.96417	1.0372	3.7697	
24	.26556	.27545	3.6305	.96410	1.0372	3.7657	
25	.26584	.27576	3.6264	.96402	1.0373	3.7617	
26	.26612	.27607	3.6222	.96394	1.0374	3.7577	
27	.26640	.27638	3.6181	.96386	1.0375	3.7538	
28	.26668	.27670	3.6140	.96379	1.0376	3.7498	
29	.26696	.27701	3.6100	.96371	1.0377	3.7459	
30	.26724	.27732	3.6059	.96363	1.0377	3.7420	
31	.26752	.27764	3.6018	.96355	1.0378	3.7381	
32	.26780	.27795	3.5978	.96347	1.0379	3.7341	
33	.26808	.27826	3.5937	.96340	1.0380	3.7302	
34	.26836	.27858	3.5897	.96332	1.0381	3.7263	
35	.26864	.27889	3.5856	.96324	1.0382	3.7225	
36	.26892	.27921	3.5816	.96316	1.0382	3.7186	
37	.26920	.27952	3.5776	.96308	1.0383	3.7147	
38	.26948	.27983	3.5736	.96301	1.0384	3.7108	
39	.26976	.28015	3.5696	.96293	1.0385	3.7070	
40	.27004	.28046	3.5656	.96285	1.0386	3.7032	
41	.27032	.28077	3.5616	.96277	1.0387	3.6993	
42	.27060	.28109	3.5576	.96269	1.0388	3.6955	
43	.27088	.28140	3.5536	.96261	1.0388	3.6917	
44	.27116	.28172	3.5497	.96253	1.0389	3.6879	
45	.27144	.28203	3.5457	.96246	1.0390	3.6840	
46	.27172	.28234	3.5418	.96238	1.0391	3.6803	
47	.27200	.28266	3.5379	.96230	1.0392	3.6765	
48	.27228	.28297	3.5339	.96222	1.0393	3.6727	
49	.27256	.28329	3.5300	.96214	1.0394	3.6689	
50	.27284	.28360	3.5261	.96206	1.0394	3.6652	
51	.27312	.28391	3.5222	.96198	1.0395	3.6614	
52	.27340	.28423	3.5183	.96190	1.0396	3.6575	
53	.27368	.28454	3.5144	.96182	1.0397	3.6539	
54	.27396	.28486	3.5105	.96174	1.0398	3.6502	
55	.27424	.28517	3.5067	.96166	1.0399	3.6465	
56	.27452	.28549	3.5028	.96158	1.0400	3.6427	
57	.27480	.28580	3.4989	.96150	1.0400	3.6390	
58	.27508	.28612	3.4951	.96142	1.0401	3.6353	
59	.27536	.28643	3.4912	.96134	1.0402	3.6316	
60	.27564	.28675	3.4874	.96126	1.0403	3.6280	
'	Cos	Cot	Tan	Sin	Csc	Sec	'

104° (284°) — **(255°) 75°**

105° (285°) — **(254°)**

NATURAL TRIGONOMETRIC FUNCTIONS
TO FIVE PLACES

(196°)   (343°) 163°   17° (197°)   (342°) 162°

	Sin	Tan	Cot	Cos	Sec	Csc	'
	.27564	.28675	3.4874	.96126	1.0403	3.6280	60
	.27592	.28706	3.4836	.96118	1.0404	3.6243	59
	.27620	.28738	3.4798	.96110	1.0405	3.6206	58
	.27648	.28769	3.4760	.96102	1.0406	3.6169	57
	.27676	.28801	3.4722	.96094	1.0406	3.6133	56
	.27704	.28832	3.4684	.96086	1.0407	3.6097	55
	.27731	.28864	3.4646	.96078	1.0408	3.6060	54
	.27759	.28895	3.4608	.96070	1.0409	3.6024	53
	.27787	.28927	3.4570	.96062	1.0410	3.5988	52
	.27815	.28958	3.4533	.96054	1.0411	3.5951	51
	.27843	.28990	3.4495	.96046	1.0412	3.5915	50
	.27871	.29021	3.4458	.96037	1.0413	3.5879	49
	.27899	.29053	3.4420	.96029	1.0413	3.5843	48
	.27927	.29084	3.4383	.96021	1.0414	3.5808	47
	.27955	.29116	3.4346	.96013	1.0415	3.5772	46
	.27983	.29147	3.4308	.96005	1.0416	3.5736	45
	.28011	.29179	3.4271	.95997	1.0417	3.5700	44
	.28039	.29210	3.4234	.95989	1.0418	3.5665	43
	.28067	.29242	3.4197	.95981	1.0419	3.5629	42
	.28095	.29274	3.4160	.95972	1.0420	3.5594	41
	.28123	.29305	3.4124	.95964	1.0421	3.5559	40
	.28150	.29337	3.4087	.95956	1.0421	3.5523	39
	.28178	.29368	3.4050	.95948	1.0422	3.5488	38
	.28206	.29400	3.4014	.95940	1.0423	3.5453	37
	.28234	.29432	3.3977	.95931	1.0424	3.5418	36
	.28262	.29463	3.3941	.95923	1.0425	3.5383	35
	.28290	.29495	3.3904	.95915	1.0426	3.5348	34
	.28318	.29526	3.3868	.95907	1.0427	3.5313	33
	.28346	.29558	3.3832	.95898	1.0428	3.5279	32
	.28374	.29590	3.3796	.95890	1.0429	3.5244	31
	.28402	.29621	3.3759	.95882	1.0429	3.5209	30
	.28429	.29653	3.3723	.95874	1.0430	3.5175	29
	.28457	.29685	3.3687	.95865	1.0431	3.5140	28
	.28485	.29716	3.3652	.95857	1.0432	3.5106	27
	.28513	.29748	3.3616	.95849	1.0433	3.5072	26
	.28541	.29780	3.3580	.95841	1.0434	3.5037	25
	.28569	.29811	3.3544	.95832	1.0435	3.5003	24
	.28597	.29843	3.3509	.95824	1.0436	3.4969	23
	.28625	.29875	3.3473	.95816	1.0437	3.4935	22
	.28652	.29906	3.3438	.95807	1.0438	3.4901	21
	.28680	.29938	3.3402	.95799	1.0439	3.4867	20
	.28708	.29970	3.3367	.95791	1.0439	3.4833	19
	.28736	.30001	3.3332	.95782	1.0440	3.4799	18
	.28764	.30033	3.3297	.95774	1.0441	3.4766	17
	.28792	.30065	3.3261	.95766	1.0442	3.4732	16
	.28820	.30097	3.3226	.95757	1.0443	3.4699	15
	.28847	.30128	3.3191	.95749	1.0444	3.4665	14
	.28875	.30160	3.3156	.95740	1.0445	3.4632	13
	.28903	.30192	3.3122	.95732	1.0446	3.4598	12
	.28931	.30224	3.3087	.95724	1.0447	3.4565	11
	.28959	.30255	3.3052	.95715	1.0448	3.4532	10
	.28987	.30287	3.3017	.95707	1.0449	3.4499	9
	.29015	.30319	3.2983	.95698	1.0450	3.4465	8
	.29042	.30351	3.2948	.95690	1.0450	3.4432	7
	.29070	.30382	3.2914	.95681	1.0451	3.4399	6
	.29098	.30414	3.2879	.95673	1.0452	3.4367	5
	.29126	.30446	3.2845	.95664	1.0453	3.4334	4
	.29154	.30478	3.2811	.95656	1.0454	3.4301	3
	.29182	.30509	3.2777	.95647	1.0455	3.4268	2
	.29209	.30541	3.2743	.95639	1.0456	3.4236	1
	.29237	.30573	3.2709	.95630	1.0457	3.4203	0
	Cos	Cot	Tan	Sin	Csc	Sec	'

'	Sin	Tan	Cot	Cos	Sec	Csc	'
0	.29237	.30573	3.2709	.95630	1.0457	3.4203	60
1	.29265	.30605	3.2675	.95622	1.0458	3.4171	59
2	.29293	.30637	3.2641	.95613	1.0459	3.4138	58
3	.29321	.30669	3.2607	.95605	1.0460	3.4106	57
4	.29348	.30700	3.2573	.95596	1.0461	3.4073	56
5	.29376	.30732	3.2539	.95588	1.0462	3.4041	55
6	.29404	.30764	3.2506	.95579	1.0463	3.4009	54
7	.29432	.30796	3.2472	.95571	1.0463	3.3977	53
8	.29460	.30828	3.2438	.95562	1.0464	3.3945	52
9	.29487	.30860	3.2405	.95554	1.0465	3.3913	51
10	.29515	.30891	3.2371	.95545	1.0466	3.3881	50
11	.29543	.30923	3.2338	.95536	1.0467	3.3849	49
12	.29571	.30955	3.2305	.95528	1.0468	3.3817	48
13	.29599	.30987	3.2272	.95519	1.0469	3.3785	47
14	.29626	.31019	3.2238	.95511	1.0470	3.3754	46
15	.29654	.31051	3.2205	.95502	1.0471	3.3722	45
16	.29682	.31083	3.2172	.95493	1.0472	3.3691	44
17	.29710	.31115	3.2139	.95485	1.0473	3.3659	43
18	.29737	.31147	3.2106	.95476	1.0474	3.3628	42
19	.29765	.31178	3.2073	.95467	1.0475	3.3596	41
20	.29793	.31210	3.2041	.95459	1.0476	3.3565	40
21	.29821	.31242	3.2008	.95450	1.0477	3.3534	39
22	.29849	.31274	3.1975	.95441	1.0478	3.3502	38
23	.29876	.31306	3.1943	.95433	1.0479	3.3471	37
24	.29904	.31338	3.1910	.95424	1.0480	3.3440	36
25	.29932	.31370	3.1878	.95415	1.0480	3.3409	35
26	.29960	.31402	3.1845	.95407	1.0481	3.3378	34
27	.29987	.31434	3.1813	.95398	1.0482	3.3347	33
28	.30015	.31466	3.1780	.95389	1.0483	3.3317	32
29	.30043	.31498	3.1748	.95380	1.0484	3.3286	31
30	.30071	.31530	3.1716	.95372	1.0485	3.3255	30
31	.30098	.31562	3.1684	.95363	1.0486	3.3224	29
32	.30126	.31594	3.1652	.95354	1.0487	3.3194	28
33	.30154	.31626	3.1620	.95345	1.0488	3.3163	27
34	.30182	.31658	3.1588	.95337	1.0489	3.3133	26
35	.30209	.31690	3.1556	.95328	1.0490	3.3102	25
36	.30237	.31722	3.1524	.95319	1.0491	3.3072	24
37	.30265	.31754	3.1492	.95310	1.0492	3.3042	23
38	.30292	.31786	3.1460	.95301	1.0493	3.3012	22
39	.30320	.31818	3.1429	.95293	1.0494	3.2981	21
40	.30348	.31850	3.1397	.95284	1.0495	3.2951	20
41	.30376	.31882	3.1366	.95275	1.0496	3.2921	19
42	.30403	.31914	3.1334	.95266	1.0497	3.2891	18
43	.30431	.31946	3.1303	.95257	1.0498	3.2861	17
44	.30459	.31978	3.1271	.95248	1.0499	3.2831	16
45	.30486	.32010	3.1240	.95240	1.0500	3.2801	15
46	.30514	.32042	3.1209	.95231	1.0501	3.2772	14
47	.30542	.32074	3.1178	.95222	1.0502	3.2742	13
48	.30570	.32106	3.1146	.95213	1.0503	3.2712	12
49	.30597	.32139	3.1115	.95204	1.0504	3.2683	11
50	.30625	.32171	3.1084	.95195	1.0505	3.2653	10
51	.30653	.32203	3.1053	.95186	1.0506	3.2624	9
52	.30680	.32235	3.1022	.95177	1.0507	3.2594	8
53	.30708	.32267	3.0991	.95168	1.0508	3.2565	7
54	.30736	.32299	3.0961	.95159	1.0509	3.2535	6
55	.30763	.32331	3.0930	.95150	1.0510	3.2506	5
56	.30791	.32363	3.0899	.95142	1.0511	3.2477	4
57	.30819	.32396	3.0868	.95133	1.0512	3.2448	3
58	.30846	.32428	3.0838	.95124	1.0513	3.2419	2
59	.30874	.32460	3.0807	.95115	1.0514	3.2390	1
60	.30902	.32492	3.0777	.95106	1.0515	3.2361	0
'	Cos	Cot	Tan	Sin	Csc	Sec	'

(286°)   (253°) 73°   107° (287°)   (252°) 72°

Tables for Use in Trigonometry

NATURAL TRIGONOMETRIC FUNCTIONS
TO FIVE PLACES

18° (198°)　　　　　　　　　　　　　　　　(341°) **161°**　　　**19° (199°)**　　　　　　　　　　　　(340°)

′	Sin	Tan	Cot	Cos	Sec	Csc	′		′	Sin	Tan	Cot	Cos	Sec	Csc
0	.30902	.32492	3.0777	.95106	1.0515	3.2361	60		0	.32557	.34433	2.9042	.94552	1.0576	3.0716
1	.30929	.32524	3.0746	.95097	1.0516	3.2332	59		1	.32584	.34465	2.9015	.94542	1.0577	3.0690
2	.30957	.32556	3.0716	.95088	1.0517	3.2303	58		2	.32612	.34498	2.8987	.94533	1.0578	3.0664
3	.30985	.32588	3.0686	.95079	1.0518	3.2274	57		3	.32639	.34530	2.8960	.94523	1.0579	3.0638
4	.31012	.32621	3.0655	.95070	1.0519	3.2245	56		4	.32667	.34563	2.8933	.94514	1.0580	3.0612
5	.31040	.32653	3.0625	.95061	1.0520	3.2217	55		5	.32694	.34596	2.8905	.94504	1.0582	3.0586
6	.31068	.32685	3.0595	.95052	1.0521	3.2188	54		6	.32722	.34628	2.8878	.94495	1.0583	3.0561
7	.31095	.32717	3.0565	.95043	1.0522	3.2159	53		7	.32749	.34661	2.8851	.94485	1.0584	3.0535
8	.31123	.32749	3.0535	.95033	1.0523	3.2131	52		8	.32777	.34693	2.8824	.94476	1.0585	3.0509
9	.31151	.32782	3.0505	.95024	1.0524	3.2102	51		9	.32804	.34726	2.8797	.94466	1.0586	3.0484
10	.31178	.32814	3.0475	.95015	1.0525	3.2074	50		10	.32832	.34758	2.8770	.94457	1.0587	3.0458
11	.31206	.32846	3.0445	.95006	1.0526	3.2045	49		11	.32859	.34791	2.8743	.94447	1.0588	3.0433
12	.31233	.32878	3.0415	.94997	1.0527	3.2017	48		12	.32887	.34824	2.8716	.94438	1.0589	3.0407
13	.31261	.32911	3.0385	.94988	1.0528	3.1989	47		13	.32914	.34856	2.8689	.94428	1.0590	3.0382
14	.31289	.32943	3.0356	.94979	1.0529	3.1960	46		14	.32942	.34889	2.8662	.94418	1.0591	3.0357
15	.31316	.32975	3.0326	.94970	1.0530	3.1932	45		15	.32969	.34922	2.8636	.94409	1.0592	3.0331
16	.31344	.33007	3.0296	.94961	1.0531	3.1904	44		16	.32997	.34954	2.8609	.94399	1.0593	3.0306
17	.31372	.33040	3.0267	.94952	1.0532	3.1876	43		17	.33024	.34987	2.8582	.94390	1.0594	3.0281
18	.31399	.33072	3.0237	.94943	1.0533	3.1848	42		18	.33051	.35020	2.8556	.94380	1.0595	3.0256
19	.31427	.33104	3.0208	.94933	1.0534	3.1820	41		19	.33079	.35052	2.8529	.94370	1.0597	3.0231
20	.31454	.33136	3.0178	.94924	1.0535	3.1792	40		20	.33106	.35085	2.8502	.94361	1.0598	3.0206
21	.31482	.33169	3.0149	.94915	1.0536	3.1764	39		21	.33134	.35118	2.8476	.94351	1.0599	3.0181
22	.31510	.33201	3.0120	.94906	1.0537	3.1736	38		22	.33161	.35150	2.8449	.94342	1.0600	3.0156
23	.31537	.33233	3.0090	.94897	1.0538	3.1708	37		23	.33189	.35183	2.8423	.94332	1.0601	3.0131
24	.31565	.33266	3.0061	.94888	1.0539	3.1681	36		24	.33216	.35216	2.8397	.94322	1.0602	3.0106
25	.31593	.33298	3.0032	.94878	1.0540	3.1653	35		25	.33244	.35248	2.8370	.94313	1.0603	3.0081
26	.31620	.33330	3.0003	.94869	1.0541	3.1625	34		26	.33271	.35281	2.8344	.94303	1.0604	3.0056
27	.31648	.33363	2.9974	.94860	1.0542	3.1598	33		27	.33298	.35314	2.8318	.94293	1.0605	3.0031
28	.31675	.33395	2.9945	.94851	1.0543	3.1570	32		28	.33326	.35346	2.8291	.94284	1.0606	3.0007
29	.31703	.33427	2.9916	.94842	1.0544	3.1543	31		29	.33353	.35379	2.8265	.94274	1.0607	2.9982
30	.31730	.33460	2.9887	.94832	1.0545	3.1515	30		30	.33381	.35412	2.8239	.94264	1.0608	2.9957
31	.31758	.33492	2.9858	.94823	1.0546	3.1488	29		31	.33408	.35445	2.8213	.94254	1.0610	2.9933
32	.31786	.33524	2.9829	.94814	1.0547	3.1461	28		32	.33436	.35477	2.8187	.94245	1.0611	2.9908
33	.31813	.33557	2.9800	.94805	1.0548	3.1433	27		33	.33463	.35510	2.8161	.94235	1.0612	2.9884
34	.31841	.33589	2.9772	.94795	1.0549	3.1406	26		34	.33490	.35543	2.8135	.94225	1.0613	2.9859
35	.31868	.33621	2.9743	.94786	1.0550	3.1379	25		35	.33518	.35576	2.8109	.94215	1.0614	2.9835
36	.31896	.33654	2.9714	.94777	1.0551	3.1352	24		36	.33545	.35608	2.8083	.94206	1.0615	2.9811
37	.31923	.33686	2.9686	.94768	1.0552	3.1325	23		37	.33573	.35641	2.8057	.94196	1.0616	2.9786
38	.31951	.33718	2.9657	.94758	1.0553	3.1298	22		38	.33600	.35674	2.8032	.94186	1.0617	2.9762
39	.31979	.33751	2.9629	.94749	1.0554	3.1271	21		39	.33627	.35707	2.8006	.94176	1.0618	2.9738
40	.32006	.33783	2.9600	.94740	1.0555	3.1244	20		40	.33655	.35740	2.7980	.94167	1.0619	2.9713
41	.32034	.33816	2.9572	.94730	1.0556	3.1217	19		41	.33682	.35772	2.7955	.94157	1.0621	2.9689
42	.32061	.33848	2.9544	.94721	1.0557	3.1190	18		42	.33710	.35805	2.7929	.94147	1.0622	2.9665
43	.32089	.33881	2.9515	.94712	1.0558	3.1163	17		43	.33737	.35838	2.7903	.94137	1.0623	2.9641
44	.32116	.33913	2.9487	.94702	1.0559	3.1137	16		44	.33764	.35871	2.7878	.94127	1.0624	2.9617
45	.32144	.33945	2.9459	.94693	1.0560	3.1110	15		45	.33792	.35904	2.7852	.94118	1.0625	2.9593
46	.32171	.33978	2.9431	.94684	1.0561	3.1083	14		46	.33819	.35937	2.7827	.94108	1.0626	2.9569
47	.32199	.34010	2.9403	.94674	1.0563	3.1057	13		47	.33846	.35969	2.7801	.94098	1.0627	2.9545
48	.32227	.34043	2.9375	.94665	1.0564	3.1030	12		48	.33874	.36002	2.7776	.94088	1.0628	2.9521
49	.32254	.34075	2.9347	.94656	1.0565	3.1004	11		49	.33901	.36035	2.7751	.94078	1.0629	2.9498
50	.32282	.34108	2.9319	.94646	1.0566	3.0977	10		50	.33929	.36068	2.7725	.94068	1.0631	2.9474
51	.32309	.34140	2.9291	.94637	1.0567	3.0951	9		51	.33956	.36101	2.7700	.94058	1.0632	2.9450
52	.32337	.34173	2.9263	.94627	1.0568	3.0925	8		52	.33983	.36134	2.7675	.94049	1.0633	2.9426
53	.32364	.34205	2.9235	.94618	1.0569	3.0898	7		53	.34011	.36167	2.7650	.94039	1.0634	2.9403
54	.32392	.34238	2.9208	.94609	1.0570	3.0872	6		54	.34038	.36199	2.7625	.94029	1.0635	2.9379
55	.32419	.34270	2.9180	.94599	1.0571	3.0846	5		55	.34065	.36232	2.7600	.94019	1.0636	2.9355
56	.32447	.34303	2.9152	.94590	1.0572	3.0820	4		56	.34093	.36265	2.7575	.94009	1.0637	2.9332
57	.32474	.34335	2.9125	.94580	1.0573	3.0794	3		57	.34120	.36298	2.7550	.93999	1.0638	2.9308
58	.32502	.34368	2.9097	.94571	1.0574	3.0768	2		58	.34147	.36331	2.7525	.93989	1.0640	2.9285
59	.32529	.34400	2.9070	.94561	1.0575	3.0742	1		59	.34175	.36364	2.7500	.93979	1.0641	2.9261
60	.32557	.34433	2.9042	.94552	1.0576	3.0716	0		60	.34202	.36397	2.7475	.93969	1.0642	2.9238
′	Cos	Cot	Tan	Sin	Csc	Sec	′		′	Cos	Cot	Tan	Sin	Csc	Sec

108° (288°)　　　　　　　　　　　　　　　　(251°) **71°**　　**109° (289°)**　　　　　　　　　　　　(250°)

NATURAL TRIGONOMETRIC FUNCTIONS
TO FIVE PLACES

Sin	Tan	Cot	Cos	Sec	Csc	′
.34202	.36397	2.7475	.93969	1.0642	2.9238	60
.34229	.36430	2.7450	.93959	1.0643	2.9215	59
.34257	.36463	2.7425	.93949	1.0644	2.9191	58
.34284	.36496	2.7400	.93939	1.0645	2.9168	57
.34311	.36529	2.7376	.93929	1.0646	2.9145	56
.34339	.36562	2.7351	.93919	1.0647	2.9122	55
.34366	.36595	2.7326	.93909	1.0649	2.9099	54
.34393	.36628	2.7302	.93899	1.0650	2.9075	53
.34421	.36661	2.7277	.93889	1.0651	2.9052	52
.34448	.36694	2.7253	.93879	1.0652	2.9029	51
.34475	.36727	2.7228	.93869	1.0653	2.9006	50
.34503	.36760	2.7204	.93859	1.0654	2.8983	49
.34530	.36793	2.7179	.93849	1.0655	2.8960	48
.34557	.36826	2.7155	.93839	1.0657	2.8938	47
.34584	.36859	2.7130	.93829	1.0658	2.8915	46
.34612	.36892	2.7106	.93819	1.0659	2.8892	45
.34639	.36925	2.7082	.93809	1.0660	2.8869	44
.34666	.36958	2.7058	.93799	1.0661	2.8846	43
.34694	.36991	2.7034	.93789	1.0662	2.8824	42
.34721	.37024	2.7009	.93779	1.0663	2.8801	41
.34748	.37057	2.6985	.93769	1.0665	2.8779	40
.34775	.37090	2.6961	.93759	1.0666	2.8756	39
.34803	.37123	2.6937	.93748	1.0667	2.8733	38
.34830	.37157	2.6913	.93738	1.0668	2.8711	37
.34857	.37190	2.6889	.93728	1.0669	2.8688	36
.34884	.37223	2.6865	.93718	1.0670	2.8666	35
.34912	.37256	2.6841	.93708	1.0671	2.8644	34
.34939	.37289	2.6818	.93698	1.0673	2.8621	33
.34966	.37322	2.6794	.93688	1.0674	2.8599	32
.34993	.37355	2.6770	.93677	1.0675	2.8577	31
.35021	.37388	2.6746	.93667	1.0676	2.8555	30
.35048	.37422	2.6723	.93657	1.0677	2.8532	29
.35075	.37455	2.6699	.93647	1.0678	2.8510	28
.35102	.37488	2.6675	.93637	1.0680	2.8488	27
.35130	.37521	2.6652	.93626	1.0681	2.8466	26
.35157	.37554	2.6628	.93616	1.0682	2.8444	25
.35184	.37588	2.6605	.93606	1.0683	2.8422	24
.35211	.37621	2.6581	.93596	1.0684	2.8400	23
.35239	.37654	2.6558	.93585	1.0685	2.8378	22
.35266	.37687	2.6534	.93575	1.0687	2.8356	21
.35293	.37720	2.6511	.93565	1.0688	2.8334	20
.35320	.37754	2.6488	.93555	1.0689	2.8312	19
.35347	.37787	2.6464	.93544	1.0690	2.8291	18
.35375	.37820	2.6441	.93534	1.0691	2.8269	17
.35402	.37853	2.6418	.93524	1.0692	2.8247	16
.35429	.37887	2.6395	.93514	1.0694	2.8225	15
.35456	.37920	2.6371	.93503	1.0695	2.8204	14
.35484	.37953	2.6348	.93493	1.0696	2.8182	13
.35511	.37986	2.6325	.93483	1.0697	2.8161	12
.35538	.38020	2.6302	.93472	1.0698	2.8139	11
.35565	.38053	2.6279	.93462	1.0700	2.8117	10
.35592	.38086	2.6256	.93452	1.0701	2.8096	9
.35619	.38120	2.6233	.93441	1.0702	2.8075	8
.35647	.38153	2.6210	.93431	1.0703	2.8053	7
.35674	.38186	2.6187	.93420	1.0704	2.8032	6
.35701	.38220	2.6165	.93410	1.0705	2.8010	5
.35728	.38253	2.6142	.93400	1.0707	2.7989	4
.35755	.38286	2.6119	.93389	1.0708	2.7968	3
.35782	.38320	2.6096	.93379	1.0709	2.7947	2
.35810	.38353	2.6074	.93368	1.0710	2.7925	1
.35837	.38386	2.6051	.93358	1.0711	2.7904	0
Cos	Cot	Tan	Sin	Csc	Sec	′

(339°) 159°   (290°)   (249°) 69°

21° (201°)   (338°) 158°

′	Sin	Tan	Cot	Cos	Sec	Csc	′
0	.35837	.38386	2.6051	.93358	1.0711	2.7904	60
1	.35864	.38420	2.6028	.93348	1.0713	2.7883	59
2	.35891	.38453	2.6006	.93337	1.0714	2.7862	58
3	.35918	.38487	2.5983	.93327	1.0715	2.7841	57
4	.35945	.38520	2.5961	.93316	1.0716	2.7820	56
5	.35973	.38553	2.5938	.93306	1.0717	2.7799	55
6	.36000	.38587	2.5916	.93295	1.0719	2.7778	54
7	.36027	.38620	2.5893	.93285	1.0720	2.7757	53
8	.36054	.38654	2.5871	.93274	1.0721	2.7736	52
9	.36081	.38687	2.5848	.93264	1.0722	2.7715	51
10	.36108	.38721	2.5826	.93253	1.0723	2.7695	50
11	.36135	.38754	2.5804	.93243	1.0725	2.7674	49
12	.36162	.38787	2.5782	.93232	1.0726	2.7653	48
13	.36190	.38821	2.5759	.93222	1.0727	2.7632	47
14	.36217	.38854	2.5737	.93211	1.0728	2.7612	46
15	.36244	.38888	2.5715	.93201	1.0730	2.7591	45
16	.36271	.38921	2.5693	.93190	1.0731	2.7570	44
17	.36298	.38955	2.5671	.93180	1.0732	2.7550	43
18	.36325	.38988	2.5649	.93169	1.0733	2.7529	42
19	.36352	.39022	2.5627	.93159	1.0734	2.7509	41
20	.36379	.39055	2.5605	.93148	1.0736	2.7488	40
21	.36406	.39089	2.5583	.93137	1.0737	2.7468	39
22	.36434	.39122	2.5561	.93127	1.0738	2.7447	38
23	.36461	.39156	2.5539	.93116	1.0739	2.7427	37
24	.36488	.39190	2.5517	.93106	1.0740	2.7407	36
25	.36515	.39223	2.5495	.93095	1.0742	2.7386	35
26	.36542	.39257	2.5473	.93084	1.0743	2.7366	34
27	.36569	.39290	2.5452	.93074	1.0744	2.7346	33
28	.36596	.39324	2.5430	.93063	1.0745	2.7325	32
29	.36623	.39357	2.5408	.93052	1.0747	2.7305	31
30	.36650	.39391	2.5386	.93042	1.0748	2.7285	30
31	.36677	.39425	2.5365	.93031	1.0749	2.7265	29
32	.36704	.39458	2.5343	.93020	1.0750	2.7245	28
33	.36731	.39492	2.5322	.93010	1.0752	2.7225	27
34	.36758	.39526	2.5300	.92999	1.0753	2.7205	26
35	.36785	.39559	2.5279	.92988	1.0754	2.7185	25
36	.36812	.39593	2.5257	.92978	1.0755	2.7165	24
37	.36839	.39626	2.5236	.92967	1.0757	2.7145	23
38	.36867	.39660	2.5214	.92956	1.0758	2.7125	22
39	.36894	.39694	2.5193	.92945	1.0759	2.7105	21
40	.36921	.39727	2.5172	.92935	1.0760	2.7085	20
41	.36948	.39761	2.5150	.92924	1.0761	2.7065	19
42	.36975	.39795	2.5129	.92913	1.0763	2.7046	18
43	.37002	.39829	2.5108	.92902	1.0764	2.7026	17
44	.37029	.39862	2.5086	.92892	1.0765	2.7006	16
45	.37056	.39896	2.5065	.92881	1.0766	2.6986	15
46	.37083	.39930	2.5044	.92870	1.0768	2.6967	14
47	.37110	.39963	2.5023	.92859	1.0769	2.6947	13
48	.37137	.39997	2.5002	.92849	1.0770	2.6927	12
49	.37164	.40031	2.4981	.92838	1.0771	2.6908	11
50	.37191	.40065	2.4960	.92827	1.0773	2.6888	10
51	.37218	.40098	2.4939	.92816	1.0774	2.6869	9
52	.37245	.40132	2.4918	.92805	1.0775	2.6849	8
53	.37272	.40166	2.4897	.92794	1.0777	2.6830	7
54	.37299	.40200	2.4876	.92784	1.0778	2.6811	6
55	.37326	.40234	2.4855	.92773	1.0779	2.6791	5
56	.37353	.40267	2.4834	.92762	1.0780	2.6772	4
57	.37380	.40301	2.4813	.92751	1.0782	2.6752	3
58	.37407	.40335	2.4792	.92740	1.0783	2.6733	2
59	.37434	.40369	2.4772	.92729	1.0784	2.6714	1
60	.37461	.40403	2.4751	.92718	1.0785	2.6695	0
′	Cos	Cot	Tan	Sin	Csc	Sec	′

111° (291°)   (248°) 68°

NATURAL TRIGONOMETRIC FUNCTIONS
TO FIVE PLACES

22° (202°)   (337°) 157°

′	Sin	Tan	Cot	Cos	Sec	Csc	′
0	.37461	.40403	2.4751	.92718	1.0785	2.6695	60
1	.37488	.40436	2.4730	.92707	1.0787	2.6675	59
2	.37515	.40470	2.4709	.92697	1.0788	2.6656	58
3	.37542	.40504	2.4689	.92686	1.0789	2.6637	57
4	.37569	.40538	2.4668	.92675	1.0790	2.6618	56
5	.37595	.40572	2.4648	.92664	1.0792	2.6599	55
6	.37622	.40606	2.4627	.92653	1.0793	2.6580	54
7	.37649	.40640	2.4606	.92642	1.0794	2.6561	53
8	.37676	.40674	2.4586	.92631	1.0796	2.6542	52
9	.37703	.40707	2.4566	.92620	1.0797	2.6523	51
10	.37730	.40741	2.4545	.92609	1.0798	2.6504	50
11	.37757	.40775	2.4525	.92598	1.0799	2.6485	49
12	.37784	.40809	2.4504	.92587	1.0801	2.6466	48
13	.37811	.40843	2.4484	.92576	1.0802	2.6447	47
14	.37838	.40877	2.4464	.92565	1.0803	2.6429	46
15	.37865	.40911	2.4443	.92554	1.0804	2.6410	45
16	.37892	.40945	2.4423	.92543	1.0806	2.6391	44
17	.37919	.40979	2.4403	.92532	1.0807	2.6372	43
18	.37946	.41013	2.4383	.92521	1.0808	2.6354	42
19	.37973	.41047	2.4362	.92510	1.0810	2.6335	41
20	.37999	.41081	2.4342	.92499	1.0811	2.6316	40
21	.38026	.41115	2.4322	.92488	1.0812	2.6298	39
22	.38053	.41149	2.4302	.92477	1.0814	2.6279	38
23	.38080	.41183	2.4282	.92466	1.0815	2.6260	37
24	.38107	.41217	2.4262	.92455	1.0816	2.6242	36
25	.38134	.41251	2.4242	.92444	1.0817	2.6223	35
26	.38161	.41285	2.4222	.92432	1.0819	2.6205	34
27	.38188	.41319	2.4202	.92421	1.0820	2.6186	33
28	.38215	.41353	2.4182	.92410	1.0821	2.6168	32
29	.38241	.41387	2.4162	.92399	1.0823	2.6150	31
30	.38268	.41421	2.4142	.92388	1.0824	2.6131	30
31	.38295	.41455	2.4122	.92377	1.0825	2.6113	29
32	.38322	.41490	2.4102	.92366	1.0827	2.6095	28
33	.38349	.41524	2.4083	.92355	1.0828	2.6076	27
34	.38376	.41558	2.4063	.92343	1.0829	2.6058	26
35	.38403	.41592	2.4043	.92332	1.0830	2.6040	25
36	.38430	.41626	2.4023	.92321	1.0832	2.6022	24
37	.38456	.41660	2.4004	.92310	1.0833	2.6003	23
38	.38483	.41694	2.3984	.92299	1.0834	2.5985	22
39	.38510	.41728	2.3964	.92287	1.0836	2.5967	21
40	.38537	.41763	2.3945	.92276	1.0837	2.5949	20
41	.38564	.41797	2.3925	.92265	1.0838	2.5931	19
42	.38591	.41831	2.3906	.92254	1.0840	2.5913	18
43	.38617	.41865	2.3886	.92243	1.0841	2.5895	17
44	.38644	.41899	2.3867	.92231	1.0842	2.5877	16
45	.38671	.41933	2.3847	.92220	1.0844	2.5859	15
46	.38698	.41968	2.3828	.92209	1.0845	2.5841	14
47	.38725	.42002	2.3808	.92198	1.0846	2.5823	13
48	.38752	.42036	2.3789	.92186	1.0848	2.5805	12
49	.38778	.42070	2.3770	.92175	1.0849	2.5788	11
50	.38805	.42105	2.3750	.92164	1.0850	2.5770	10
51	.38832	.42139	2.3731	.92152	1.0852	2.5752	9
52	.38859	.42173	2.3712	.92141	1.0853	2.5734	8
53	.38886	.42207	2.3693	.92130	1.0854	2.5716	7
54	.38912	.42242	2.3673	.92119	1.0856	2.5699	6
55	.38939	.42276	2.3654	92107	1.0857	2.5681	5
56	.38966	.42310	2.3635	92096	1.0858	2.5663	4
57	.38993	.42345	2.3616	92085	1.0860	2.5646	3
58	.39020	.42379	2.3597	92073	1.0861	2.5628	2
59	.39046	.42413	2.3578	92062	1.0862	2.5611	1
60	.39073	.42447	2.3559	.92050	1.0864	2.5593	0
′	Cos	Cot	Tan	Sin	Csc	Sec	′

112° (292°)   (247°) 67°

23° (203°)   (336

′	Sin	Tan	Cot	Cos	Sec	Csc
0	.39073	.42447	2.3559	.92050	1.0864	2.5593
1	.39100	.42482	2.3539	.92039	1.0865	2.5576
2	.39127	.42516	2.3520	.92028	1.0866	2.5558
3	.39153	.42551	2.3501	.92016	1.0868	2.5541
4	.39180	.42585	2 3483	92005	1.0869	2.5523
5	.39207	.42619	2.3464	.91994	1.0870	2.5506
6	.39234	.42654	2.3445	.91982	1.0872	2.5488
7	.39260	.42688	2.3426	.91971	1.0873	2.5471
8	.39287	.42722	2.3407	.91959	1.0874	2.5454
9	.39314	.42757	2.3388	.91948	1.0876	2.5436
10	.39341	.42791	2.3369	.91936	1.0877	2.5419
11	.39367	.42826	2.3351	.91925	1.0878	2.5402
12	.39394	.42860	2.3332	.91914	1.0880	2.5384
13	.39421	.42894	2.3313	.91902	1.0881	2.5367
14	.39448	.42929	2.3294	.91891	1.0883	2.5350
15	.39474	.42963	2.3276	.91879	1.0884	2.5333
16	.39501	.42998	2.3257	.91868	1.0885	2.5316
17	.39528	.43032	2.3238	.91856	1.0887	2.5299
18	.39555	.43067	2.3220	.91845	1.0888	2.5282
19	.39581	.43101	2.3201	.91833	1.0889	2.5264
20	.39608	.43136	2.3183	.91822	1.0891	2.5247
21	.39635	.43170	2.3164	.91810	1.0892	2.5230
22	.39661	.43205	2.3146	.91799	1.0893	2.5213
23	.39688	.43239	2.3127	.91787	1.0895	2.5196
24	.39715	.43274	2.3109	.91775	1.0896	2.5180
25	.39741	.43308	2.3090	.91764	1.0898	2.5163
26	.39768	.43343	2.3072	.91752	1.0899	2.5146
27	.39795	.43378	2.3053	.91741	1.0900	2.5129
28	.39822	.43412	2.3035	.91729	1.0902	2.5112
29	.39848	.43447	2.3017	.91718	1.0903	2.5095
30	.39875	.43481	2.2998	.91706	1.0904	2.5078
31	.39902	.43516	2.2980	.91694	1.0906	2.5062
32	.39928	.43550	2.2962	.91683	1.0907	2.5045
33	.39955	.43585	2.2944	.91671	1.0909	2.5028
34	.39982	.43620	2.2925	.91660	1.0910	2.5012
35	.40008	.43654	2.2907	.91648	1.0911	2.4995
36	.40035	.43689	2.2889	.91636	1.0913	2.4978
37	.40062	.43724	2.2871	.91625	1.0914	2.4962
38	.40088	.43758	2.2853	.91613	1.0915	2.4945
39	.40115	.43793	2.2835	.91601	1.0917	2.4928
40	.40141	.43828	2.2817	.91590	1.0918	2.4912
41	.40168	.43862	2.2799	.91578	1.0920	2.4895
42	.40195	.43897	2.2781	.91566	1.0921	2.4879
43	.40221	.43932	2.2763	.91555	1.0922	2.4862
44	.40248	.43966	2.2745	.91543	1.0924	2.4846
45	.40275	.44001	2.2727	.91531	1.0925	2.4830
46	.40301	.44036	2.2709	.91519	1.0927	2.4813
47	.40328	.44071	2.2691	.91508	1.0928	2.4797
48	.40355	.44105	2.2673	.91496	1.0929	2.4780
49	.40381	.44140	2.2655	.91484	1.0931	2.4764
50	.40408	.44175	2.2637	.91472	1.0932	2.4748
51	.40434	.44210	2.2620	.91461	1.0934	2.4731
52	.40461	.44244	2.2602	.91449	1.0935	2.4715
53	.40488	.44279	2.2584	.91437	1.0936	2.4699
54	.40514	.44314	2.2566	.91425	1.0938	2.4683
55	.40541	.44349	2.2549	.91414	1.0939	2.4667
56	.40567	.44384	2.2531	.91402	1.0941	2.4650
57	.40594	.44418	2.2513	.91390	1.0942	2.4634
58	.40621	.44453	2.2496	.91378	1.0944	2.4618
59	.40647	.44488	2.2478	.91366	1.0945	2.4602
60	.40674	.44523	2.2460	.91355	1.0946	2.4586
′	Cos	Cot	Tan	Sin	Csc	Sec

113° (293°)   (246°

NATURAL TRIGONOMETRIC FUNCTIONS
TO FIVE PLACES

4°)   (335°) 155°   25° (205°)   (334°) 154°

Sin	Tan	Cot	Cos	Sec	Csc	'
.40674	.44523	2.2460	.91355	1.0946	2.4586	60
.40700	.44558	2.2443	.91343	1.0948	2.4570	59
.40727	.44593	2.2425	.91331	1.0949	2.4554	58
.40753	.44627	2.2408	.91319	1.0951	2.4538	57
.40780	.44662	2.2390	.91307	1.0952	2.4522	56
.40806	.44697	2.2373	.91295	1.0953	2.4506	55
.40833	.44732	2.2355	.91283	1.0955	2.4490	54
.40860	.44767	2.2338	.91272	1.0956	2.4474	53
.40886	.44802	2.2320	.91260	1.0958	2.4458	52
.40913	.44837	2.2303	.91248	1.0959	2.4442	51
.40939	.44872	2.2286	.91236	1.0961	2.4426	50
.40966	.44907	2.2268	.91224	1.0962	2.4411	49
.40992	.44942	2.2251	.91212	1.0963	2.4395	48
.41019	.44977	2.2234	.91200	1.0965	2.4379	47
.41045	.45012	2.2216	.91188	1.0966	2.4363	46
.41072	.45047	2.2199	.91176	1.0968	2.4348	45
.41098	.45082	2.2182	.91164	1.0969	2.4332	44
.41125	.45117	2.2165	.91152	1.0971	2.4316	43
.41151	.45152	2.2148	.91140	1.0972	2.4300	42
.41178	.45187	2.2130	.91128	1.0974	2.4285	41
.41204	.45222	2.2113	.91116	1.0975	2.4269	40
.41231	.45257	2.2096	.91104	1.0976	2.4254	39
.41257	.45292	2.2079	.91092	1.0978	2.4238	38
.41284	.45327	2.2062	.91080	1.0979	2.4222	37
.41310	.45362	2.2045	.91068	1.0981	2.4207	36
.41337	.45397	2.2028	.91056	1.0982	2.4191	35
.41363	.45432	2.2011	.91044	1.0984	2.4176	34
.41390	.45467	2.1994	.91032	1.0985	2.4160	33
.41416	.45502	2.1977	.91020	1.0987	2.4145	32
.41443	.45538	2.1960	.91008	1.0988	2.4130	31
.41469	.45573	2.1943	.90996	1.0989	2.4114	30
.41496	.45608	2.1926	.90984	1.0991	2.4099	29
.41522	.45643	2.1909	.90972	1.0992	2.4083	28
.41549	.45678	2.1892	.90960	1.0994	2.4068	27
.41575	.45713	2.1876	.90948	1.0995	2.4053	26
.41602	.45748	2.1859	.90936	1.0997	2.4038	25
.41628	.45784	2.1842	.90924	1.0998	2.4022	24
.41655	.45819	2.1825	.90911	1.1000	2.4007	23
.41681	.45854	2.1808	.90899	1.1001	2.3992	22
.41707	.45889	2.1792	.90887	1.1003	2.3977	21
.41734	.45924	2.1775	.90875	1.1004	2.3961	20
.41760	.45960	2.1758	.90863	1.1006	2.3946	19
.41787	.45995	2.1742	.90851	1.1007	2.3931	18
.41813	.46030	2.1725	.90839	1.1009	2.3916	17
.41840	.46065	2.1708	.90826	1.1010	2.3901	16
.41866	.46101	2.1692	.90814	1.1011	2.3886	15
.41892	.46136	2.1675	.90802	1.1013	2.3871	14
.41919	.46171	2.1659	.90790	1.1014	2.3856	13
.41945	.46206	2.1642	.90778	1.1016	2.3841	12
.41972	.46242	2.1625	.90766	1.1017	2.3826	11
.41998	.46277	2.1609	.90753	1.1019	2.3811	10
.42024	.46312	2.1592	.90741	1.1020	2.3796	9
.42051	.46348	2.1576	.90729	1.1022	2.3781	8
.42077	.46383	2.1560	.90717	1.1023	2.3766	7
.42104	.46418	2.1543	.90704	1.1025	2.3751	6
.42130	.46454	2.1527	.90692	1.1026	2.3736	5
.42156	.46489	2.1510	.90680	1.1028	2.3721	4
.42183	.46525	2.1494	.90668	1.1029	2.3706	3
.42209	.46560	2.1478	.90655	1.1031	2.3692	2
.42235	.46595	2.1461	.90643	1.1032	2.3677	1
.42262	.46631	2.1445	.90631	1.1034	2.3662	0
Cos	Cot	Tan	Sin	Csc	Sec	'

(294°)   (245°) 65°

'	Sin	Tan	Cot	Cos	Sec	Csc	'
0	.42262	.46631	2.1445	.90631	1.1034	2.3662	60
1	.42288	.46666	2.1429	.90618	1.1035	2.3647	59
2	.42315	.46702	2.1413	.90606	1.1037	2.3633	58
3	.42341	.46737	2.1396	.90594	1.1038	2.3618	57
4	.42367	.46772	2.1380	.90582	1.1040	2.3603	56
5	.42394	.46808	2.1364	.90569	1.1041	2.3588	55
6	.42420	.46843	2.1348	.90557	1.1043	2.3574	54
7	.42446	.46879	2.1332	.90545	1.1044	2.3559	53
8	.42473	.46914	2.1315	.90532	1.1046	2.3545	52
9	.42499	.46950	2.1299	.90520	1.1047	2.3530	51
10	.42525	.46985	2.1283	.90507	1.1049	2.3515	50
11	.42552	.47021	2.1267	.90495	1.1050	2.3501	49
12	.42578	.47056	2.1251	.90483	1.1052	2.3486	48
13	.42604	.47092	2.1235	.90470	1.1053	2.3472	47
14	.42631	.47128	2.1219	.90458	1.1055	2.3457	46
15	.42657	.47163	2.1203	.90446	1.1056	2.3443	45
16	.42683	.47199	2.1187	.90433	1.1058	2.3428	44
17	.42709	.47234	2.1171	.90421	1.1059	2.3414	43
18	.42736	.47270	2.1155	.90408	1.1061	2.3400	42
19	.42762	.47305	2.1139	.90396	1.1062	2.3385	41
20	.42788	.47341	2.1123	.90383	1.1064	2.3371	40
21	.42815	.47377	2.1107	.90371	1.1066	2.3356	39
22	.42841	.47412	2.1092	.90358	1.1067	2.3342	38
23	.42867	.47448	2.1076	.90346	1.1069	2.3328	37
24	.42894	.47483	2.1060	.90334	1.1070	2.3314	36
25	.42920	.47519	2.1044	.90321	1.1072	2.3299	35
26	.42946	.47555	2.1028	.90309	1.1073	2.3285	34
27	.42972	.47590	2.1013	.90296	1.1075	2.3271	33
28	.42999	.47626	2.0997	.90284	1.1076	2.3257	32
29	.43025	.47662	2.0981	.90271	1.1078	2.3242	31
30	.43051	.47698	2.0965	.90259	1.1079	2.3228	30
31	.43077	.47733	2.0950	.90246	1.1081	2.3214	29
32	.43104	.47769	2.0934	.90233	1.1082	2.3200	28
33	.43130	.47805	2.0918	.90221	1.1084	2.3186	27
34	.43156	.47840	2.0903	.90208	1.1085	2.3172	26
35	.43182	.47876	2.0887	.90196	1.1087	2.3158	25
36	.43209	.47912	2.0872	.90183	1.1089	2.3144	24
37	.43235	.47948	2.0856	.90171	1.1090	2.3130	23
38	.43261	.47984	2.0840	.90158	1.1092	2.3115	22
39	.43287	.48019	2.0825	.90146	1.1093	2.3101	21
40	.43313	.48055	2.0809	.90133	1.1095	2.3088	20
41	.43340	.48091	2.0794	.90120	1.1096	2.3074	19
42	.43366	.48127	2.0778	.90108	1.1098	2.3060	18
43	.43392	.48163	2.0763	.90095	1.1099	2.3046	17
44	.43418	.48198	2.0748	.90082	1.1101	2.3032	16
45	.43445	.48234	2.0732	.90070	1.1102	2.3018	15
46	.43471	.48270	2.0717	.90057	1.1104	2.3004	14
47	.43497	.48306	2.0701	.90045	1.1106	2.2990	13
48	.43523	.48342	2.0686	.90032	1.1107	2.2976	12
49	.43549	.48378	2.0671	.90019	1.1109	2.2962	11
50	.43575	.48414	2.0655	.90007	1.1110	2.2949	10
51	.43602	.48450	2.0640	.89994	1.1112	2.2935	9
52	.43628	.48486	2.0625	.89981	1.1113	2.2921	8
53	.43654	.48521	2.0609	.89968	1.1115	2.2907	7
54	.43680	.48557	2.0594	.89956	1.1117	2.2894	6
55	.43706	.48593	2.0579	.89943	1.1118	2.2880	5
56	.43733	.48629	2.0564	.89930	1.1120	2.2866	4
57	.43759	.48665	2.0549	.89918	1.1121	2.2853	3
58	.43785	.48701	2.0533	.89905	1.1123	2.2839	2
59	.43811	.48737	2.0518	.89892	1.1124	2.2825	1
60	.43837	.48773	2.0503	.89879	1.1126	2.2812	0
'	Cos	Cot	Tan	Sin	Csc	Sce	'

115° (295°)   (244°) 64°

NATURAL TRIGONOMETRIC FUNCTIONS
TO FIVE PLACES

26° (206°)   (333°) 153°   27° (207°)   (332

′	Sin	Tan	Cot	Cos	Sec	Csc	′
0	.43837	.48773	2.0503	.89879	1.1126	2.2812	60
1	.43863	.48809	2.0488	.89867	1.1128	2.2798	59
2	.43889	.48845	2.0473	.89854	1.1129	2.2785	58
3	.43916	.48881	2.0458	.89841	1.1131	2.2771	57
4	.43942	.48917	2.0443	.89828	1.1132	2.2757	56
5	.43968	.48953	2.0428	.89816	1.1134	2.2744	55
6	.43994	.48989	2.0413	.89803	1.1136	2.2730	54
7	.44020	.49026	2.0398	.89790	1.1137	2.2717	53
8	.44046	.49062	2.0383	.89777	1.1139	2.2703	52
9	.44072	.49098	2.0368	.89764	1.1140	2.2690	51
10	.44098	.49134	2.0353	.89752	1.1142	2.2677	50
11	.44124	.49170	2.0338	.89739	1.1143	2.2663	49
12	.44151	.49206	2.0323	.89726	1.1145	2.2650	48
13	.44177	.49242	2.0308	.89713	1.1147	2.2636	47
14	.44203	.49278	2.0293	.89700	1.1148	2.2623	46
15	.44229	.49315	2.0278	.89687	1.1150	2.2610	45
16	.44255	.49351	2.0263	.89674	1.1151	2.2596	44
17	.44281	.49387	2.0248	.89662	1.1153	2.2583	43
18	.44307	.49423	2.0233	.89649	1.1155	2.2570	42
19	.44333	.49459	2.0219	.89636	1.1156	2.2556	41
20	.44359	.49495	2.0204	.89623	1.1158	2.2543	40
21	.44385	.49532	2.0189	.89610	1.1159	2.2530	39
22	.44411	.49568	2.0174	.89597	1.1161	2.2517	38
23	.44437	.49604	2.0160	.89584	1.1163	2.2504	37
24	.44464	.49640	2.0145	.89571	1.1164	2.2490	36
25	.44490	.49677	2.0130	.89558	1.1166	2.2477	35
26	.44516	.49713	2.0115	.89545	1.1168	2.2464	34
27	.44542	.49749	2.0101	.89532	1.1169	2.2451	33
28	.44568	.49786	2.0086	.89519	1.1171	2.2438	32
29	.44594	.49822	2.0072	.89506	1.1172	2.2425	31
30	.44620	.49858	2.0057	.89493	1.1174	2.2412	30
31	.44646	.49894	2.0042	.89480	1.1176	2.2399	29
32	.44672	.49931	2.0028	.89467	1.1177	2.2385	28
33	.44698	.49967	2.0013	.89454	1.1179	2.2372	27
34	.44724	.50004	1.9999	.89441	1.1180	2.2359	26
35	.44750	.50040	1.9984	.89428	1.1182	2.2346	25
36	.44776	.50076	1.9970	.89415	1.1184	2.2333	24
37	.44802	.50113	1.9955	.89402	1.1185	2.2320	23
38	.44828	.50149	1.9941	.89389	1.1187	2.2308	22
39	.44854	.50185	1.9926	.89376	1.1189	2.2295	21
40	.44880	.50222	1.9912	.89363	1.1190	2.2282	20
41	.44906	.50258	1.9897	.89350	1.1192	2.2269	19
42	.44932	.50295	1.9883	.89337	1.1194	2.2256	18
43	.44958	.50331	1.9868	.89324	1.1195	2.2243	17
44	.44984	.50368	1.9854	.89311	1.1197	2.2230	16
45	.45010	.50404	1.9840	.89298	1.1198	2.2217	15
46	.45036	.50441	1.9825	.89285	1.1200	2.2205	14
47	.45062	.50477	1.9811	.89272	1.1202	2.2192	13
48	.45088	.50514	1.9797	.89259	1.1203	2.2179	12
49	.45114	.50550	1.9782	.89245	1.1205	2.2166	11
50	.45140	.50587	1.9768	.89232	1.1207	2.2153	10
51	.45166	.50623	1.9754	.89219	1.1208	2.2141	9
52	.45192	.50660	1.9740	.89206	1.1210	2.2128	8
53	.45218	.50696	1.9725	.89193	1.1212	2.2115	7
54	.45243	.50733	1.9711	.89180	1.1213	2.2103	6
55	.45269	.50769	1.9697	.89167	1.1215	2.2090	5
56	.45295	.50806	1.9683	.89153	1.1217	2.2077	4
57	.45321	.50843	1.9669	.89140	1.1218	2.2065	3
58	.45347	.50879	1.9654	.89127	1.1220	2.2052	2
59	.45373	.50916	1.9640	.89114	1.1222	2.2039	1
60	.45399	.50953	1.9626	.89101	1.1223	2.2027	0
′	Cos	Cot	Tan	Sin	Csc	Sec	′

′	Sin	Tan	Cot	Cos	Sec	Csc
0	.45399	.50953	1.9626	.89101	1.1223	2.2027
1	.45425	.50989	1.9612	.89087	1.1225	2.2014
2	.45451	.51026	1.9598	.89074	1.1227	2.2002
3	.45477	.51063	1.9584	.89061	1.1228	2.1989
4	.45503	.51099	1.9570	.89048	1.1230	2.1977
5	.45529	.51136	1.9556	.89035	1.1232	2.1964
6	.45554	.51173	1.9542	.89021	1.1233	2.1952
7	.45580	.51209	1.9528	.89008	1.1235	2.1939
8	.45606	.51246	1.9514	.88995	1.1237	2.1927
9	.45632	.51283	1.9500	.88981	1.1238	2.1914
10	.45658	.51319	1.9486	.88968	1.1240	2.1902
11	.45684	.51356	1.9472	.88955	1.1242	2.1890
12	.45710	.51393	1.9458	.88942	1.1243	2.1877
13	.45736	.51430	1.9444·	.88928	1.1245	2.1865
14	.45762	.51467	1.9430	.88915	1.1247	2.1852
15	.45787	.51503	1.9416	.88902	1.1248	2.1840
16	.45813	.51540	1.9402	.88888	1.1250	2.1828
17	.45839	.51577	1.9388	.88875	1.1252	2.1815
18	.45865	.51614	1.9375	.88862	1.1253	2.1803
19	.45891	.51651	1.9361	.88848	1.1255	2.1791
20	.45917	.51688	1.9347	.88835	1.1257	2.1779
21	.45942	.51724	1.9333	.88822	1.1259	2.1766
22	.45968	.51761	1.9319	.88808	1.1260	2.1754
23	.45994	.51798	1.9306	.88795	1.1262	2.1742
24	.46020	.51835	1.9292	.88782	1.1264	2.1730
25	.46046	.51872	1.9278	.88768	1.1265	2.1718
26	.46072	.51909	1.9265	.88755	1.1267	2.1705
27	.46097	.51946	1.9251	.88741	1.1269	2.1693
28	.46123	.51983	1.9237	.88728	1.1270	2.1681
29	.46149	.52020	1.9223	.88715	1.1272	2.1669
30	.46175	.52057	1.9210	.88701	1.1274	2.1657
31	.46201	.52094	1.9196	.88688	1.1276	2.1645
32	.46226	.52131	1.9183	.88674	1.1277	2.1633
33	.46252	.52168	1.9169	.88661	1.1279	2.1621
34	.46278	.52205	1.9155	.88647	1.1281	2.1609
35	.46304	.52242	1.9142	.88634	1.1282	2.1596
36	.46330	.52279	1.9128	.88620	1.1284	2.1584
37	.46355	.52316	1.9115	.88607	1.1286	2.1572
38	.46381	.52353	1.9101	.88593	1.1288	2.1560
39	.46407	.52390	1.9088	.88580	1.1289	2.1549
40	.46433	.52427	1.9074	.88566	1.1291	2.1537
41	.46458	.52464	1.9061	.88553	1.1293	2.1525
42	.46484	.52501	1.9047	.88539	1.1294	2.1513
43	.46510	.52538	1.9034	.88526	1.1296	2.1501
44	.46536	.52575	1.9020	.88512	1.1298	2.1489
45	.46561	.52613	1.9007	.88499	1.1300	2.1477
46	.46587	.52650	1.8993	.88485	1.1301	2.1465
47	.46613	.52687	1.8980	.88472	1.1303	2.1453
48	.46639	.52724	1.8967	.88458	1.1305	2.1441
49	.46664	.52761	1.8953	.88445	1.1307	2.1430
50	.46690	.52798	1.8940	.88431	1.1308	2.1418
51	.46716	.52836	1.8927	.88417	1.1310	2.1406
52	.46742	.52873	1.8913	.88404	1.1312	2.1394
53	.46767	.52910	1.8900	.88390	1.1313	2.1382
54	.46793	.52947	1.8887	.88377	1.1315	2.1371
55	.46819	.52985	1.8873	.88363	1.1317	2.1359
56	.46844	.53022	1.8860	.88349	1.1319	2.1347
57	.46870	.53059	1.8847	.88336	1.1320	2.1336
58	.46896	.53096	1.8834	.88322	1.1322	2.1324
59	.46921	.53134	1.8820	.88308	1.1324	2.1312
60	.46947	.53171	1.8807	.88295	1.1326	2.1301
′	Cos	Cot	Tan	Sin	Csc	Sec

NATURAL TRIGONOMETRIC FUNCTIONS
TO FIVE PLACES

8°)   (331°) **151°**   **29° (209°)**   (330)° **150°**

Sin	Tan	Cot	Cos	Sec	Csc	'
46947	.53171	1.8807	.88295	1.1326	2.1301	60
46973	.53208	1.8794	.88281	1.1327	2.1289	59
46999	.53246	1.8781	.88267	1.1329	2.1277	58
47024	.53283	1.8768	.88254	1.1331	2.1266	57
47050	.53320	1.8755	.88240	1.1333	2.1254	56
47076	.53358	1.8741	.88226	1.1334	2.1242	55
47101	.53395	1.8728	.88213	1.1336	2.1231	54
47127	.53432	1.8715	.88199	1.1338	2.1219	53
47153	.53470	1.8702	.88185	1.1340	2.1208	52
47178	.53507	1.8689	.88172	1.1342	2.1196	51
47204	.53545	1.8676	.88158	1.1343	2.1185	50
47229	.53582	1.8663	.88144	1.1345	2.1173	49
47255	.53620	1.8650	.88130	1.1347	2.1162	48
47281	.53657	1.8637	.88117	1.1349	2.1150	47
47306	.53694	1.8624	.88103	1.1350	2.1139	46
47332	.53732	1.8611	.88089	1.1352	2.1127	45
47358	.53769	1.8598	.88075	1.1354	2.1116	44
47383	.53807	1.8585	.88062	1.1356	2.1105	43
47409	.53844	1.8572	.88048	1.1357	2.1093	42
47434	.53882	1.8559	.88034	1.1359	2.1082	41
47460	.53920	1.8546	.88020	1.1361	2.1070	40
47486	.53957	1.8533	.88006	1.1363	2.1059	39
47511	.53995	1.8520	.87993	1.1365	2.1048	38
47537	.54032	1.8507	.87979	1.1366	2.1036	37
47562	.54070	1.8495	.87965	1.1368	2.1025	36
47588	.54107	1.8482	.87951	1.1370	2.1014	35
47614	.54145	1.8469	.87937	1.1372	2.1002	34
47639	.54183	1.8456	.87923	1.1374	2.0991	33
47665	.54220	1.8443	.87909	1.1375	2.0980	32
47690	.54258	1.8430	.87896	1.1377	2.0969	31
47716	.54296	1.8418	.87882	1.1379	2.0957	30
47741	.54333	1.8405	.87868	1.1381	2.0946	29
47767	.54371	1.8392	.87854	1.1383	2.0935	28
47793	.54409	1.8379	.87840	1.1384	2.0924	27
47818	.54446	1.8367	.87826	1.1386	2.0913	26
47844	.54484	1.8354	.87812	1.1388	2.0901	25
47869	.54522	1.8341	.87798	1.1390	2.0890	24
47895	.54560	1.8329	.87784	1.1392	2.0879	23
47920	.54597	1.8316	.87770	1.1393	2.0868	22
47946	.54635	1.8303	.87756	1.1395	2.0857	21
47971	.54673	1.8291	.87743	1.1397	2.0846	20
47997	.54711	1.8278	.87729	1.1399	2.0835	19
48022	.54748	1.8265	.87715	1.1401	2.0824	18
48048	.54786	1.8253	.87701	1.1402	2.0813	17
48073	.54824	1.8240	.87687	1.1404	2.0802	16
48099	.54862	1.8228	.87673	1.1406	2.0791	15
48124	.54900	1.8215	.87659	1.1408	2.0779	14
48150	.54938	1.8202	.87645	1.1410	2.0768	13
48175	.54975	1.8190	.87631	1.1412	2.0757	12
48201	.55013	1.8177	.87617	1.1413	2.0747	11
48226	.55051	1.8165	.87603	1.1415	2.0736	10
48252	.55089	1.8152	.87589	1.1417	2.0725	9
48277	.55127	1.8140	.87575	1.1419	2.0714	8
48303	.55165	1.8127	.87561	1.1421	2.0703	7
48328	.55203	1.8115	.87546	1.1423	2.0692	6
48354	.55241	1.8103	.87532	1.1424	2.0681	5
48379	.55279	1.8090	.87518	1.1426	2.0670	4
48405	.55317	1.8078	.87504	1.1428	2.0659	3
48430	.55355	1.8065	.87490	1.1430	2.0648	2
48456	.55393	1.8053	.87476	1.1432	2.0637	1
48481	.55431	1.8040	.87462	1.1434	2.0627	0
Cos	Cot	Tan	Sin	Csc	Sec	'

298°)   (241°) **61°**

'	Sin	Tan	Cot	Cos	Sec	Csc	'
0	.48481	.55431	1.8040	.87462	1.1434	2.0627	60
1	.48506	.55469	1.8028	.87448	1.1435	2.0616	59
2	.48532	.55507	1.8016	.87434	1.1437	2.0605	58
3	.48557	.55545	1.8003	.87420	1.1439	2.0594	57
4	.48583	.55583	1.7991	.87406	1.1441	2.0583	56
5	.48608	.55621	1.7979	.87391	1.1443	2.0573	55
6	.48634	.55659	1.7966	.87377	1.1445	2.0562	54
7	.48659	.55697	1.7954	.87363	1.1446	2.0551	53
8	.48684	.55736	1.7942	.87349	1.1448	2.0540	52
9	.48710	.55774	1.7930	.87335	1.1450	2.0530	51
10	.48735	.55812	1.7917	.87321	1.1452	2.0519	50
11	.48761	.55850	1.7905	.87306	1.1454	2.0508	49
12	.48786	.55888	1.7893	.87292	1.1456	2.0498	48
13	.48811	.55926	1.7881	.87278	1.1458	2.0487	47
14	.48837	.55964	1.7868	.87264	1.1460	2.0476	46
15	.48862	.56003	1.7856	.87250	1.1461	2.0466	45
16	.48888	.56041	1.7844	.87235	1.1463	2.0455	44
17	.48913	.56079	1.7832	.87221	1.1465	2.0445	43
18	.48938	.56117	1.7820	.87207	1.1467	2.0434	42
19	.48964	.56156	1.7808	.87193	1.1469	2.0423	41
20	.48989	.56194	1.7796	.87178	1.1471	2.0413	40
21	.49014	.56232	1.7783	.87164	1.1473	2.0402	39
22	.49040	.56270	1.7771	.87150	1.1474	2.0392	38
23	.49065	.56309	1.7759	.87136	1.1476	2.0381	37
24	.49090	.56347	1.7747	.87121	1.1478	2.0371	36
25	.49116	.56385	1.7735	.87107	1.1480	2.0360	35
26	.49141	.56424	1.7723	.87093	1.1482	2.0350	34
27	.49166	.56462	1.7711	.87079	1.1484	2.0339	33
28	.49192	.56501	1.7699	.87064	1.1486	2.0329	32
29	.49217	.56539	1.7687	.87050	1.1488	2.0318	31
30	.49242	.56577	1.7675	.87036	1.1490	2.0308	30
31	.49268	.56616	1.7663	.87021	1.1491	2.0297	29
32	.49293	.56654	1.7651	.87007	1.1493	2.0287	28
33	.49318	.56693	1.7639	.86993	1.1495	2.0276	27
34	.49344	.56731	1.7627	.86978	1.1497	2.0266	26
35	.49369	.56769	1.7615	.86964	1.1499	2.0256	25
36	.49394	.56808	1.7603	.86949	1.1501	2.0245	24
37	.49419	.56846	1.7591	.86935	1.1503	2.0235	23
38	.49445	.56885	1.7579	.86921	1.1505	2.0225	22
39	.49470	.56923	1.7567	.86906	1.1507	2.0214	21
40	.49495	.56962	1.7556	.86892	1.1509	2.0204	20
41	.49521	.57000	1.7544	.86878	1.1510	2.0194	19
42	.49546	.57039	1.7532	.86863	1.1512	2.0183	18
43	.49571	.57078	1.7520	.86849	1.1514	2.0173	17
44	.49596	.57116	1.7508	.86834	1.1516	2.0163	16
45	.49622	.57155	1.7496	.86820	1.1518	2.0152	15
46	.49647	.57193	1.7485	.86805	1.1520	2.0142	14
47	.49672	.57232	1.7473	.86791	1.1522	2.0132	13
48	.49697	.57271	1.7461	.86777	1.1524	2.0122	12
49	.49723	.57309	1.7449	.86762	1.1526	2.0112	11
50	.49748	.57348	1.7437	.86748	1.1528	2.0101	10
51	.49773	.57386	1.7426	.86733	1.1530	2.0091	9
52	.49798	.57425	1.7414	.86719	1.1532	2.0081	8
53	.49824	.57464	1.7402	.86704	1.1533	2.0071	7
54	.49849	.57503	1.7391	.86690	1.1535	2.0061	6
55	.49874	.57541	1.7379	.86675	1.1537	2.0051	5
56	.49899	.57580	1.7367	.86661	1.1539	2.0040	4
57	.49924	.57619	1.7355	.86646	1.1541	2.0030	3
58	.49950	.57657	1.7344	.86632	1.1543	2.0020	2
59	.49975	.57696	1.7332	.86617	1.1545	2.0010	1
60	.50000	.57735	1.7321	.86603	1.1547	2.0000	0
'	Cos	Cot	Tan	Sin	Csc	Sec	'

119° (299°)   (240°) **60°**

Tables for Use in Trigonometry

NATURAL TRIGONOMETRIC FUNCTIONS
TO FIVE PLACES

30° (210°)   (329°) 149°   **31° (211°)**   (32

′	Sin	Tan	Cot	Cos	Sec	Csc	′
0	.50000	.57735	1.7321	.86603	1.1547	2.0000	60
1	.50025	.57774	1.7309	.86588	1.1549	1.9990	59
2	.50050	.57813	1.7297	.86573	1.1551	1.9980	58
3	.50076	.57851	1.7286	.86559	1.1553	1.9970	57
4	.50101	.57890	1.7274	.86544	1.1555	1.9960	56
5	.50126	.57929	1.7262	.86530	1.1557	1.9950	55
6	.50151	.57968	1.7251	.86515	1.1559	1.9940	54
7	.50176	.58007	1.7239	.86501	1.1561	1.9930	53
8	.50201	.58046	1.7228	.86486	1.1563	1.9920	52
9	.50227	.58085	1.7216	.86471	1.1565	1.9910	51
10	.50252	.58124	1.7205	.86457	1.1566	1.9900	50
11	.50277	.58162	1.7193	.86442	1.1568	1.9890	49
12	.50302	.58201	1.7182	.86427	1.1570	1.9880	48
13	.50327	.58240	1.7170	.86413	1.1572	1.9870	47
14	.50352	.58279	1.7159	.86398	1.1574	1.9860	46
15	.50377	.58318	1.7147	.86384	1.1576	1.9850	45
16	.50403	.58357	1.7136	.86369	1.1578	1.9840	44
17	.50428	.58396	1.7124	.86354	1.1580	1.9830	43
18	.50453	.58435	1.7113	.86340	1.1582	1.9821	42
19	.50478	.58474	1.7102	.86325	1.1584	1.9811	41
20	.50503	.58513	1.7090	.86310	1.1586	1.9801	40
21	.50528	.58552	1.7079	.86295	1.1588	1.9791	39
22	.50553	.58591	1.7067	.86281	1.1590	1.9781	38
23	.50578	.58631	1.7056	.86266	1.1592	1.9771	37
24	.50603	.58670	1.7045	.86251	1.1594	1.9762	36
25	.50628	.58709	1.7033	.86237	1.1596	1.9752	35
26	.50654	.58748	1.7022	.86222	1.1598	1.9742	34
27	.50679	.58787	1.7011	.86207	1.1600	1.9732	33
28	.50704	.58826	1.6999	.86192	1.1602	1.9722	32
29	.50729	.58865	1.6988	.86178	1.1604	1.9713	31
30	.50754	.58905	1.6977	.86163	1.1606	1.9703	30
31	.50779	.58944	1.6965	.86148	1.1608	1.9693	29
32	.50804	.58983	1.6954	.86133	1.1610	1.9684	28
33	.50829	.59022	1.6943	.86119	1.1612	1.9674	27
34	.50854	.59061	1.6932	.86104	1.1614	1.9664	26
35	.50879	.59101	1.6920	.86089	1.1616	1.9654	25
36	.50904	.59140	1.6909	.86074	1.1618	1.9645	24
37	.50929	.59179	1.6898	.86059	1.1620	1.9635	23
38	.50954	.59218	1.6887	.86045	1.1622	1.9625	22
39	.50979	.59258	1.6875	.86030	1.1624	1.9616	21
40	.51004	.59297	1.6864	.86015	1.1626	1.9606	20
41	.51029	.59336	1.6853	.86000	1.1628	1.9597	19
42	.51054	.59376	1.6842	.85985	1.1630	1.9587	18
43	.51079	.59415	1.6831	.85970	1.1632	1.9577	17
44	.51104	.59454	1.6820	.85956	1.1634	1.9568	16
45	.51129	.59494	1.6808	.85941	1.1636	1.9558	15
46	.51154	.59533	1.6797	.85926	1.1638	1.9549	14
47	.51179	.59573	1.6786	.85911	1.1640	1.9539	13
48	.51204	.59612	1.6775	.85896	1.1642	1.9530	12
49	.51229	.59651	1.6764	.85881	1.1644	1.9520	11
50	.51254	.59691	1.6753	.85866	1.1646	1.9511	10
51	.51279	.59730	1.6742	.85851	1.1648	1.9501	9
52	.51304	.59770	1.6731	.85836	1.1650	1.9492	8
53	.51329	.59809	1.6720	.85821	1.1652	1.9482	7
54	.51354	.59849	1.6709	.85806	1.1654	1.9473	6
55	.51379	.59888	1.6698	.85792	1.1656	1.9463	5
56	.51404	.59928	1.6687	.85777	1.1658	1.9454	4
57	.51429	.59967	1.6676	.85762	1.1660	1.9444	3
58	.51454	.60007	1.6665	.85747	1.1662	1.9435	2
59	.51479	.60046	1.6654	.85732	1.1664	1.9425	1
60	.51504	.60086	1.6643	.85717	1.1666	1.9416	0
′	Cos	Cot	Tan	Sin	Csc	Sec	′

120° (300°)   (239°) 59°

′	Sin	Tan	Cot	Cos	Sec	Csc
0	.51504	.60086	1.6643	.85717	1.1666	1.941
1	.51529	.60126	1.6632	.85702	1.1668	1.940
2	.51554	.60165	1.6621	.85687	1.1670	1.939
3	.51579	.60205	1.6610	.85672	1.1672	1.938
4	.51604	.60245	1.6599	.85657	1.1675	1.937
5	.51628	.60284	1.6588	.85642	1.1677	1.936
6	.51653	.60324	1.6577	.85627	1.1679	1.936
7	.51678	.60364	1.6566	.85612	1.1681	1.935
8	.51703	.60403	1.6555	.85597	1.1683	1.934
9	.51728	.60443	1.6545	.85582	1.1685	1.933
10	.51753	.60483	1.6534	.85567	1.1687	1.932
11	.51778	.60522	1.6523	.85551	1.1689	1.931
12	.51803	.60562	1.6512	.85536	1.1691	1.930
13	.51828	.60602	1.6501	.85521	1.1693	1.929
14	.51852	.60642	1.6490	.85506	1.1695	1.928
15	.51877	.60681	1.6479	.85491	1.1697	1.927
16	.51902	.60721	1.6469	.85476	1.1699	1.926
17	.51927	.60761	1.6458	.85461	1.1701	1.925
18	.51952	.60801	1.6447	.85446	1.1703	1.924
19	.51977	.60841	1.6436	.85431	1.1705	1.923
20	.52002	.60881	1.6426	.85416	1.1707	1.923
21	.52026	.60921	1.6415	.85401	1.1710	1.922
22	.52051	.60960	1.6404	.85385	1.1712	1.921
23	.52076	.61000	1.6393	.85370	1.1714	1.920
24	.52101	.61040	1.6383	.85355	1.1716	1.919
25	.52126	.61080	1.6372	.85340	1.1718	1.918
26	.52151	.61120	1.6361	.85325	1.1720	1.917
27	.52175	.61160	1.6351	.85310	1.1722	1.916
28	.52200	.61200	1.6340	.85294	1.1724	1.915
29	.52225	.61240	1.6329	.85279	1.1726	1.914
30	.52250	.61280	1.6319	.85264	1.1728	1.913
31	.52275	.61320	1.6308	.85249	1.1730	1.913
32	.52299	.61360	1.6297	.85234	1.1732	1.912
33	.52324	.61400	1.6287	.85218	1.1735	1.911
34	.52349	.61440	1.6276	.85203	1.1737	1.910
35	.52374	.61480	1.6265	.85188	1.1739	1.909
36	.52399	.61520	1.6255	.85173	1.1741	1.908
37	.52423	.61561	1.6244	.85157	1.1743	1.907
38	.52448	.61601	1.6234	.85142	1.1745	1.906
39	.52473	.61641	1.6223	.85127	1.1747	1.905
40	.52498	.61681	1.6212	.85112	1.1749	1.904
41	.52522	.61721	1.6202	.85096	1.1751	1.903
42	.52547	.61761	1.6191	.85081	1.1753	1.903
43	.52572	.61801	1.6181	.85066	1.1756	1.902
44	.52597	.61842	1.6170	.85051	1.1758	1.901
45	.52621	.61882	1.6160	.85035	1.1760	1.900
46	.52646	.61922	1.6149	.85020	1.1762	1.899
47	.52671	.61962	1.6139	.85005	1.1764	1.898
48	.52696	.62003	1.6128	.84989	1.1766	1.897
49	.52720	.62043	1.6118	.84974	1.1768	1.896
50	.52745	.62083	1.6107	.84959	1.1770	1.895
51	.52770	.62124	1.6097	.84943	1.1773	1.895
52	.52794	.62164	1.6087	.84928	1.1775	1.894
53	.52819	.62204	1.6076	.84913	1.1777	1.893
54	.52844	.62245	1.6066	.84897	1.1779	1.892
55	.52869	.62285	1.6055	.84882	1.1781	1.891
56	.52893	.62325	1.6045	.84866	1.1783	1.890
57	.52918	.62366	1.6034	.84851	1.1785	1.889
58	.52943	.62406	1.6024	.84836	1.1788	1.888
59	.52967	.62446	1.6014	.84820	1.1790	1.888
60	.52992	.62487	1.6003	.84805	1.1792	1.887
′	Cos	Cot	Tan	Sin	Csc	Sec

121° (301°)   (23

NATURAL TRIGONOMETRIC FUNCTIONS
TO FIVE PLACES

2°)   (327°) 147°   33° (213°)   (326°) 146°

Sin	Tan	Cot	Cos	Sec	Csc	'
.52992	.62487	1.6003	.84805	1.1792	1.8871	60
.53017	.62527	1.5993	.84789	1.1794	1.8862	59
.53041	.62568	1.5983	.84774	1.1796	1.8853	58
.53066	.62608	1.5972	.84759	1.1798	1.8844	57
.53091	.62649	1.5962	.84743	1.1800	1.8836	56
.53115	.62689	1.5952	.84728	1.1803	1.8827	55
.53140	.62730	1.5941	.84712	1.1805	1.8818	54
.53164	.62770	1.5931	.84697	1.1807	1.8810	53
.53189	.62811	1.5921	.84681	1.1809	1.8801	52
.53214	.62852	1.5911	.84666	1.1811	1.8792	51
.53238	.62892	1.5900	.84650	1.1813	1.8783	50
.53263	.62933	1.5890	.84635	1.1815	1.8775	49
.53288	.62973	1.5880	.84619	1.1818	1.8766	48
.53312	.63014	1.5869	.84604	1.1820	1.8757	47
.53337	.63055	1.5859	.84588	1.1822	1.8749	46
.53361	.63095	1.5849	.84573	1.1824	1.8740	45
.53386	.63136	1.5839	.84557	1.1826	1.8731	44
.53411	.63177	1.5829	.84542	1.1828	1.8723	43
.53435	.63217	1.5818	.84526	1.1831	1.8714	42
.53460	.63258	1.5808	.84511	1.1833	1.8706	41
.53484	.63299	1.5798	.84495	1.1835	1.8697	40
.53509	.63340	1.5788	.84480	1.1837	1.8688	39
.53534	.63380	1.5778	.84464	1.1830	1.8680	38
.53558	.63421	1.5768	.84448	1.1842	1.8671	37
.53583	.63462	1.5757	.84433	1.1844	1.8663	36
.53607	.63503	1.5747	.84417	1.1846	1.8654	35
.53632	.63544	1.5737	.84402	1.1848	1.8646	34
.53656	.63584	1.5727	.84386	1.1850	1.8637	33
.53681	.63625	1.5717	.84370	1.1852	1.8629	32
.53705	.63666	1.5707	.84355	1.1855	1.8620	31
.53730	.63707	1.5697	.84339	1.1857	1.8612	30
.53754	.63748	1.5687	.84324	1.1859	1.8603	29
.53779	.63789	1.5677	.84308	1.1861	1.8595	28
.53804	.63830	1.5667	.84292	1.1863	1.8586	27
.53828	.63871	1.5657	.84277	1.1866	1.8578	26
.53853	.63912	1.5647	.84261	1.1868	1.8569	25
.53877	.63953	1.5637	.84245	1.1870	1.8561	24
.53902	.63994	1.5627	.84230	1.1872	1.8552	23
.53926	.64035	1.5617	.84214	1.1875	1.8544	22
.53951	.64076	1.5607	.84198	1.1877	1.8535	21
.53975	.64117	1.5597	.84182	1.1879	1.8527	20
.54000	.64158	1.5587	.84167	1.1881	1.8519	19
.54024	.64199	1.5577	.84151	1.1883	1.8510	18
.54049	.64240	1.5567	.84135	1.1886	1.8502	17
.54073	.64281	1.5557	.84120	1.1888	1.8494	16
.54097	.64322	1.5547	.84104	1.1890	1.8485	15
.54122	.64363	1.5537	.84088	1.1892	1.8477	14
.54146	.64404	1.5527	.84072	1.1895	1.8468	13
.54171	.64446	1.5517	.84057	1.1897	1.8460	12
.54195	.64487	1.5507	.84041	1.1899	1.8452	11
.54220	.64528	1.5497	.84025	1.1901	1.8443	10
.54244	.64569	1.5487	.84009	1.1903	1.8435	9
.54269	.64610	1.5477	.83994	1.1906	1.8427	8
.54293	.64652	1.5468	.83978	1.1908	1.8419	7
.54317	.64693	1.5458	.83962	1.1910	1.8410	6
.54342	.64734	1.5448	.83946	1.1912	1.8402	5
.54366	.64775	1.5438	.83930	1.1915	1.8394	4
.54391	.64817	1.5428	.83915	1.1917	1.8385	3
.54415	.64858	1.5418	.83899	1.1919	1.8377	2
.54440	.64899	1.5408	.83883	1.1921	1.8369	1
.54464	.64941	1.5399	.83867	1.1924	1.8361	0
Cos	Cot	Tan	Sin	Csc	Sec	'

'	Sin	Tan	Cot	Cos	Sec	Csc	'
0	.54464	.64941	1.5399	.83867	1.1924	1.8361	60
1	.54488	.64982	1.5389	.83851	1.1926	1.8353	59
2	.54513	.65024	1.5379	.83835	1.1928	1.8344	58
3	.54537	.65065	1.5369	.83819	1.1930	1.8336	57
4	.54561	.65106	1.5359	.83804	1.1933	1.8328	56
5	.54586	.65148	1.5350	.83788	1.1935	1.8320	55
6	.54610	.65189	1.5340	.83772	1.9137	1.8312	54
7	.54635	.65231	1.5330	.83756	1.1939	1.8303	53
8	.54659	.65272	1.5320	.83740	1.1942	1.8295	52
9	.54683	.65314	1.5311	.83724	1.1944	1.8287	51
10	.54708	.65355	1.5301	.83708	1.1946	1.8279	50
11	.54732	.65397	1.5291	.83692	1.1949	1.8271	49
12	.54756	.65438	1.5282	.83676	1.1951	1.8263	48
13	.54781	.65480	1.5272	.83660	1.1953	1.8255	47
14	.54805	.65521	1.5262	.83645	1.1955	1.8247	46
15	.54829	.65563	1.5253	.83629	1.1958	1.8238	45
16	.54854	.65604	1.5243	.83613	1.1960	1.8230	44
17	.54878	.65646	1.5233	.83597	1.1962	1.8222	43
18	.54902	.65688	1.5224	.83581	1.1964	1.8214	42
19	.54927	.65729	1.5214	.83565	1.1967	1.8206	41
20	.54951	.65771	1.5204	.83549	1.1969	1.8198	40
21	.54975	.65813	1.5195	.83533	1.1971	1.8190	39
22	.54999	.65854	1.5185	.83517	1.1974	1.8182	38
23	.55024	.65896	1.5175	.83501	1.1976	1.8174	37
24	.55048	.65938	1.5166	.83485	1.1978	1.8166	36
25	.55072	.65980	1.5156	.83469	1.1981	1.8158	35
26	.55097	.66021	1.5147	.83453	1.1983	1.8150	34
27	.55121	.66063	1.5137	.83437	1.1985	1.8142	33
28	.55145	.66105	1.5127	.83421	1.1987	1.8134	32
29	.55169	.66147	1.5118	.83405	1.1990	1.8126	31
30	.55194	.66189	1.5108	.83389	1.1992	1.8118	30
31	.55218	.66230	1.5099	.83373	1.1994	1.8110	29
32	.55242	.66272	1.5089	.83356	1.1997	1.8102	28
33	.55266	.66314	1.5080	.83340	1.1999	1.8094	27
34	.55291	.66356	1.5070	.83324	1.2001	1.8086	26
35	.55315	.66398	1.5061	.83308	1.2004	1.8078	25
36	.55339	.66440	1.5051	.83292	1.2006	1.8070	24
37	.55363	.66482	1.5042	.83276	1.2008	1.8062	23
38	.55388	.66524	1.5032	.83260	1.2011	1.8055	22
39	.55412	.66566	1.5023	.83244	1.2013	1.8047	21
40	.55436	.66608	1.5013	.83228	1.2015	1.8039	20
41	.55460	.66650	1.5004	.83212	1.2018	1.8031	19
42	.55484	.66692	1.4994	.83195	1.2020	1.8023	18
43	.55509	.66734	1.4985	.83179	1.2022	1.8015	17
44	.55533	.66776	1.4975	.83163	1.2025	1.8007	16
45	.55557	.66818	1.4966	.83147	1.2027	1.8000	15
46	.55581	.66860	1.4957	.83131	1.2029	1.7992	14
47	.55605	.66902	1.4947	.83115	1.2032	1.7984	13
48	.55630	.66944	1.4938	.83098	1.2034	1.7976	12
49	.55654	.66986	1.4928	.83082	1.2036	1.7968	11
50	.55678	.67028	1.4919	.83066	1.2039	1.7960	10
51	.55702	.67071	1.4910	.83050	1.2041	1.7953	9
52	.55726	.67113	1.4900	.83034	1.2043	1.7945	8
53	.55750	.67155	1.4891	.83017	1.2046	1.7937	7
54	.55775	.67197	1.4882	.83001	1.2048	1.7929	6
55	.55799	.67239	1.4872	.82985	1.2050	1.7922	5
56	.55823	.67282	1.4863	.82969	1.2053	1.7914	4
57	.55847	.67324	1.4854	.82953	1.2055	1.7906	3
58	.55871	.67366	1.4844	.82936	1.2057	1.7898	2
59	.55895	.67409	1.4835	.82920	1.2060	1.7891	1
60	.55919	.67451	1.4826	.82904	1.2062	1.7883	0
'	Cos	Cot	Tan	Sin	Csc	Sec	'

Tables for Use in Trigonometry

NATURAL TRIGONOMETRIC FUNCTIONS
TO FIVE PLACES

34° (214°) (325°) 145°   **35° (215°)** (32...

'	Sin	Tan	Cot	Cos	Sec	Csc	'		'	Sin	Tan	Cot	Cos	Sec	Csc
0	.55919	.67451	1.4826	.82904	1.2062	1.7883	60		0	.57358	.70021	1.4281	.81915	1.2208	1.743
1	.55943	.67493	1.4816	.82887	1.2065	1.7875	59		1	.57381	.70064	1.4273	.81899	1.2210	1.7427
2	.55968	.67536	1.4807	.82871	1.2067	1.7868	58		2	.57405	.70107	1.4264	.81882	1.2213	1.742
3	.55992	.67578	1.4798	.82855	1.2069	1.7860	57		3	.57429	.70151	1.4255	.81865	1.2215	1.741
4	.56016	.67620	1.4788	.82839	1.2072	1.7852	56		4	.57453	.70194	1.4246	.81848	1.2218	1.740
5	.56040	.67663	1.4779	.82822	1.2074	1.7844	55		5	.57477	.70238	1.4237	.81832	1.2220	1.7398
6	.56064	.67705	1.4770	.82806	1.2076	1.7837	54		6	.57501	.70281	1.4229	.81815	1.2223	1.7391
7	.56088	.67748	1.4761	.82790	1.2079	1.7829	53		7	.57524	.70325	1.4220	.81798	1.2225	1.738
8	.56112	.67790	1.4751	.82773	1.2081	1.7821	52		8	.57548	.70368	1.4211	.81782	1.2228	1.7372
9	.56136	.67832	1.4742	.82757	1.2084	1.7814	51		9	.57572	.70412	1.4202	.81765	1.2230	1.737
10	.56160	.67875	1.4733	.82741	1.2086	1.7806	50		10	.57596	.70455	1.4193	.81748	1.2233	1.7362
11	.56184	.67917	1.4724	.82724	1.2088	1.7799	49		11	.57619	.70499	1.4185	.81731	1.2235	1.735
12	.56208	.67960	1.4715	.82708	1.2091	1.7791	48		12	.57643	.70542	1.4176	.81714	1.2238	1.734
13	.56232	.68002	1.4705	.82692	1.2093	1.7783	47		13	.57667	.70586	1.4167	.81698	1.2240	1.734
14	.56256	.68045	1.4696	.82675	1.2096	1.7776	46		14	.57691	.70629	1.4158	.81681	1.2243	1.7334
15	.56280	.68088	1.4687	.82659	1.2098	1.7768	45		15	.57715	.70673	1.4150	.81664	1.2245	1.7327
16	.56305	.68130	1.4678	.82643	1.2100	1.7761	44		16	.57738	.70717	1.4141	.81647	1.2248	1.732
17	.56329	.68173	1.4669	.82626	1.2103	1.7753	43		17	.57762	.70760	1.4132	.81631	1.2250	1.7312
18	.56353	.68215	1.4659	.82610	1.2105	1.7745	42		18	.57786	.70804	1.4124	.81614	1.2253	1.730
19	.56377	.68258	1.4650	.82593	1.2108	1.7738	41		19	.57810	.70848	1.4115	.81597	1.2255	1.7298
20	.56401	.68301	1.4641	.82577	1.2110	1.7730	40		20	.57833	.70891	1.4106	.81580	1.2258	1.729
21	.56425	.68343	1.4632	.82561	1.2112	1.7723	39		21	.57857	.70935	1.4097	.81563	1.2260	1.7284
22	.56449	.68386	1.4623	.82544	1.2115	1.7715	38		22	.57881	.70979	1.4089	.81546	1.2263	1.7277
23	.56473	.68429	1.4614	.82528	1.2117	1.7708	37		23	.57904	.71023	1.4080	.81530	1.2265	1.727
24	.56497	.68471	1.4605	.82511	1.2120	1.7700	36		24	.57928	.71066	1.4071	.81513	1.2268	1.7263
25	.56521	.68514	1.4596	.82495	1.2122	1.7693	35		25	.57952	.71110	1.4063	.81496	1.2271	1.725
26	.56545	.68557	1.4586	.82478	1.2124	1.7685	34		26	.57976	.71154	1.4054	.81479	1.2273	1.724
27	.56569	.68600	1.4577	.82462	1.2127	1.7678	33		27	.57999	.71198	1.4045	.81462	1.2276	1.7242
28	.56593	.68642	1.4568	.82446	1.2129	1.7670	32		28	.58023	.71242	1.4037	.81445	1.2278	1.7235
29	.56617	.68685	1.4559	.82429	1.2132	1.7663	31		29	.58047	.71285	1.4028	.81428	1.2281	1.7228
30	.56641	.68728	1.4550	.82413	1.2134	1.7655	30		30	.58070	.71329	1.4019	.81412	1.2283	1.7221
31	.56665	.68771	1.4541	.82396	1.2136	1.7648	29		31	.58094	.71373	1.4011	.81395	1.2286	1.7213
32	.56689	.68814	1.4532	.82380	1.2139	1.7640	28		32	.58118	.71417	1.4002	.81378	1.2288	1.7206
33	.56713	.68857	1.4523	.82363	1.2141	1.7633	27		33	.58141	.71461	1.3994	.81361	1.2291	1.7199
34	.56736	.68900	1.4514	.82347	1.2144	1.7625	26		34	.58165	.71505	1.3985	.81344	1.2293	1.7192
35	.56760	.68942	1.4505	.82330	1.2146	1.7618	25		35	.58189	.71549	1.3976	.81327	1.2296	1.7185
36	.56784	.68985	1.4496	.82314	1.2149	1.7610	24		36	.58212	.71593	1.3968	.81310	1.2299	1.7179
37	.56808	.69028	1.4487	.82297	1.2151	1.7603	23		37	.58236	.71637	1.3959	.81293	1.2301	1.7172
38	.56832	.69071	1.4478	.82281	1.2154	1.7596	22		38	.58260	.71681	1.3951	.81276	1.2304	1.7165
39	.56856	.69114	1.4469	.82264	1.2156	1.7588	21		39	.58283	.71725	1.3942	.81259	1.2306	1.7158
40	.56880	.69157	1.4460	.82248	1.2158	1.7581	20		40	.58307	.71769	1.3934	.81242	1.2309	1.7151
41	.56904	.69200	1.4451	.82231	1.2161	1.7573	19		41	.58330	.71813	1.3925	.81225	1.2311	1.7144
42	.56928	.69243	1.4442	.82214	1.2163	1.7566	18		42	.58354	.71857	1.3916	.81208	1.2314	1.7137
43	.56952	.69286	1.4433	.82198	1.2166	1.7559	17		43	.58378	.71901	1.3908	.81191	1.2317	1.7130
44	.56976	.69329	1.4424	.82181	1.2168	1.7551	16		44	.58401	.71946	1.3899	.81174	1.2319	1.7123
45	.57000	.69372	1.4415	.82165	1.2171	1.7544	15		45	.58425	.71990	1.3891	.81157	1.2322	1.7116
46	.57024	.69416	1.4406	.82148	1.2173	1.7537	14		46	.58449	.72034	1.3882	.81140	1.2324	1.7109
47	.57047	.69459	1.4397	.82132	1.2176	1.7529	13		47	.58472	.72078	1.3874	.81123	1.2327	1.7102
48	.57071	.69502	1.4388	.82115	1.2178	1.7522	12		48	.58496	.72122	1.3865	.81106	1.2329	1.7095
49	.57095	.69545	1.4379	.82098	1.2181	1.7515	11		49	.58519	.72167	1.3857	.81089	1.2332	1.7088
50	.57119	.69588	1.4370	.82082	1.2183	1.7507	10		50	.58543	.72211	1.3848	.81072	1.2335	1.7081
51	.57143	.69631	1.4361	.82065	1.2185	1.7500	9		51	.58567	.72255	1.3840	.81055	1.2337	1.7075
52	.57167	.69675	1.4352	.82048	1.2188	1.7493	8		52	.58590	.72299	1.3831	.81038	1.2340	1.7068
53	.57191	.69718	1.4344	.82032	1.2190	1.7485	7		53	.58614	.72344	1.3823	.81021	1.2342	1.7061
54	.57215	.69761	1.4335	.82015	1.2193	1.7478	6		54	.58637	.72388	1.3814	.81004	1.2345	1.7054
55	.57238	.69804	1.4326	.81999	1.2195	1.7471	5		55	.58661	.72432	1.3806	.80987	1.2348	1.7047
56	.57262	.69847	1.4317	.81982	1.2198	1.7463	4		56	.58684	.72477	1.3798	.80970	1.2350	1.7040
57	.57286	.69891	1.4308	.81965	1.2200	1.7456	3		57	.58708	.72521	1.3789	.80953	1.2353	1.7033
58	.57310	.69934	1.4299	.81949	1.2203	1.7449	2		58	.58731	.72565	1.3781	.80936	1.2355	1.7027
59	.57334	.69977	1.4290	.81932	1.2205	1.7442	1		59	.58755	.72610	1.3772	.80919	1.2358	1.7020
60	.57358	.70021	1.4281	.81915	1.2208	1.7434	0		60	.58779	.72654	1.3764	.80902	1.2361	1.7013
'	Cos	Cot	Tan	Sin	Csc	Sec	'		'	Cos	Cot	Tan	Sin	Csc	Sec

124° (304°) (235°) 55°   **125° (305°)** (23...

NATURAL TRIGONOMETRIC FUNCTIONS
TO FIVE PLACES

(36°)   **(323°) 143°**   **37° (217°)**   **(322°) 142°**

Sin	Tan	Cot	Cos	Sec	Csc	′
.58779	.72654	1.3764	.80902	1.2361	1.7013	60
.58802	.72699	1.3755	.80885	1.2363	1.7006	59
.58826	.72743	1.3747	.80867	1.2366	1.6999	58
.58849	.72788	1.3739	.80850	1.2369	1.6993	57
.58873	.72832	1.3730	.80833	1.2371	1.6986	56
.58896	.72877	1.3722	.80816	1.2374	1.6979	55
.58920	.72921	1.3713	.80799	1.2376	1.6972	54
.58943	.72966	1.3705	.80782	1.2379	1.6966	53
.58967	.73010	1.3697	.80765	1.2382	1.6959	52
.58990	.73055	1.3688	.80748	1.2384	1.6952	51
.59014	.73100	1.3680	.80730	1.2387	1.6945	50
.59037	.73144	1.3672	.80713	1.2390	1.6939	49
.59061	.73189	1.3663	.80696	1.2392	1.6932	48
.59084	.73234	1.3655	.80679	1.2395	1.6925	47
.59108	.73278	1.3647	.80662	1.2397	1.6918	46
.59131	.73323	1.3638	.80644	1.2400	1.6912	45
.59154	.73368	1.3630	.80627	1.2403	1.6905	44
.59178	.73413	1.3622	.80610	1.2405	1.6898	43
.59201	.73457	1.3613	.80593	1.2408	1.6892	42
.59225	.73502	1.3605	.80576	1.2411	1.6885	41
.59248	.73547	1.3597	.80558	1.2413	1.6878	40
.59272	.73592	1.3588	.80541	1.2416	1.6871	39
.59295	.73637	1.3580	.80524	1.2419	1.6865	38
.59318	.73681	1.3572	.80507	1.2421	1.6858	37
.59342	.73726	1.3564	.80489	1.2424	1.6852	36
.59365	.73771	1.3555	.80472	1.2427	1.6845	35
.59389	.73816	1.3547	.80455	1.2429	1.6838	34
.59412	.73861	1.3539	.80438	1.2432	1.6832	33
.59436	.73906	1.3531	.80420	1.2435	1.6825	32
.59459	.73951	1.3522	.80403	1.2437	1.6818	31
.59482	.73996	1.3514	.80386	1.2440	1.6812	30
.59506	.74041	1.3506	.80368	1.2443	1.6805	29
.59529	.74086	1.3498	.80351	1.2445	1.6799	28
.59552	.74131	1.3490	.80334	1.2448	1.6792	27
.59576	.74176	1.3481	.80316	1.2451	1.6785	26
.59599	.74221	1.3473	.80299	1.2453	1.6779	25
.59622	.74267	1.3465	.80282	1.2456	1.6772	24
.59646	.74312	1.3457	.80264	1.2459	1.6766	23
.59669	.74357	1.3449	.80247	1.2462	1.6759	22
.59693	.74402	1.3440	.80230	1.2464	1.6753	21
.59716	.74447	1.3432	.80212	1.2467	1.6746	20
.59739	.74492	1.3424	.80195	1.2470	1.6739	19
.59763	.74538	1.3416	.80178	1.2472	1.6733	18
.59786	.74583	1.3408	.80160	1.2475	1.6726	17
.59809	.74628	1.3400	.80143	1.2478	1.6720	16
.59832	.74674	1.3392	.80125	1.2480	1.6713	15
.59856	.74719	1.3384	.80108	1.2483	1.6707	14
.59879	.74764	1.3375	.80091	1.2486	1.6700	13
.59902	.74810	1.3367	.80073	1.2489	1.6694	12
.59926	.74855	1.3359	.80056	1.2491	1.6687	11
.59949	.74900	1.3351	.80038	1.2494	1.6681	10
.59972	.74946	1.3343	.80021	1.2497	1.6674	9
.59995	.74991	1.3335	.80003	1.2499	1.6668	8
.60019	.75037	1.3327	.79986	1.2502	1.6661	7
.60042	.75082	1.3319	.79968	1.2505	1.6655	6
.60065	.75128	1.3311	.79951	1.2508	1.6649	5
.60089	.75173	1.3303	.79934	1.2510	1.6642	4
.60112	.75219	1.3295	.79916	1.2513	1.6636	3
.60135	.75264	1.3287	.79899	1.2516	1.6629	2
.60158	.75310	1.3278	.79881	1.2519	1.6623	1
.60182	.75355	1.3270	.79864	1.2521	1.6616	0

| Cos | Cot | Tan | Sin | Csc | Sec | ′ |

′	Sin	Tan	Cot	Cos	Sec	Csc	′
0	.60182	.75355	1.3270	.79864	1.2521	1.6616	60
1	.60205	.75401	1.3262	.79846	1.2524	1.6610	59
2	.60228	.75447	1.3254	.79829	1.2527	1.6604	58
3	.60251	.75492	1.3246	.79811	1.2530	1.6597	57
4	.60274	.75538	1.3238	.79793	1.2532	1.6591	56
5	.60298	.75584	1.3230	.79776	1.2535	1.6584	55
6	.60321	.75629	1.3222	.79758	1.2538	1.6578	54
7	.60344	.75675	1.3214	.79741	1.2541	1.6572	53
8	.60367	.75721	1.3206	.79723	1.2543	1.6565	52
9	.60390	.75767	1.3198	.79706	1.2546	1.6559	51
10	.60414	.75812	1.3190	.79688	1.2549	1.6553	50
11	.60437	.75858	1.3182	.79671	1.2552	1.6546	49
12	.60460	.75904	1.3175	.79653	1.2554	1.6540	48
13	.60483	.75950	1.3167	.79635	1.2557	1.6534	47
14	.60506	.75996	1.3159	.79618	1.2560	1.6527	46
15	.60529	.76042	1.3151	.79600	1.2563	1.6521	45
16	.60553	.76088	1.3143	.79583	1.2566	1.6515	44
17	.60576	.76134	1.3135	.79565	1.2568	1.6508	43
18	.60599	.76180	1.3127	.79547	1.2571	1.6502	42
19	.60622	.76226	1.3119	.79530	1.2574	1.6496	41
20	.60645	.76272	1.3111	.79512	1.2577	1.6489	40
21	.60668	.76318	1.3103	.79494	1.2579	1.6483	39
22	.60691	.76364	1.3095	.79477	1.2582	1.6477	38
23	.60714	.76410	1.3087	.79459	1.2585	1.6471	37
24	.60738	.76456	1.3079	.79441	1.2588	1.6464	36
25	.60761	.76502	1.3072	.79424	1.2591	1.6458	35
26	.60784	.76548	1.3064	.79406	1.2593	1.6452	34
27	.60807	.76594	1.3056	.79388	1.2596	1.6446	33
28	.60830	.76640	1.3048	.79371	1.2599	1.6439	32
29	.60853	.76686	1.3040	.79353	1.2602	1.6433	31
30	.60876	.76733	1.3032	.79335	1.2605	1.6427	30
31	.60899	.76779	1.3024	.79318	1.2608	1.6421	29
32	.60922	.76825	1.3017	.79300	1.2610	1.6414	28
33	.60945	.76871	1.3009	.79282	1.2613	1.6408	27
34	.60968	.76918	1.3001	.79264	1.2616	1.6402	26
35	.60991	.76964	1.2993	.79247	1.2619	1.6396	25
36	.61015	.77010	1.2985	.79229	1.2622	1.6390	24
37	.61038	.77057	1.2977	.79211	1.2624	1.6383	23
38	.61061	.77103	1.2970	.79193	1.2627	1.6377	22
39	.61084	.77149	1.2962	.79176	1.2630	1.6371	21
40	.61107	.77196	1.2954	.79158	1.2633	1.6365	20
41	.61130	.77242	1.2946	.79140	1.2636	1.6359	19
42	.61153	.77289	1.2938	.79122	1.2639	1.6353	18
43	.61176	.77335	1.2931	.79105	1.2641	1.6346	17
44	.61199	.77382	1.2923	.79087	1.2644	1.6340	16
45	.61222	.77428	1.2915	.79069	1.2647	1.6334	15
46	.61245	.77475	1.2907	.79051	1.2650	1.6328	14
47	.61268	.77521	1.2900	.79033	1.2653	1.6322	13
48	.61291	.77568	1.2892	.79016	1.2656	1.6316	12
49	.61314	.77615	1.2884	.78998	1.2659	1.6310	11
50	.61337	.77661	1.2876	.78980	1.2661	1.6303	10
51	.61360	.77708	1.2869	.78962	1.2664	1.6297	9
52	.61383	.77754	1.2861	.78944	1.2667	1.6291	8
53	.61406	.77801	1.2853	.78926	1.2670	1.6285	7
54	.61429	.77848	1.2846	.78908	1.2673	1.6279	6
55	.61451	.77895	1.2838	.78891	1.2676	1.6273	5
56	.61474	.77941	1.2830	.78873	1.2679	1.6267	4
57	.61497	.77988	1.2822	.78855	1.2682	1.6261	3
58	.61520	.78035	1.2815	.78837	1.2684	1.6255	2
59	.61543	.78082	1.2807	.78819	1.2687	1.6249	1
60	.61566	.78129	1.2799	.78801	1.2690	1.6243	0

| ′ | Cos | Cot | Tan | Sin | Csc | Sec | ′ |

NATURAL TRIGONOMETRIC FUNCTIONS
TO FIVE PLACES

38° (218°)   **(321°) 141°**   **39° (219°)**   **(32(**

′	Sin.	Tan	Cot	Cos	Sec	Csc	′	′	Sin	Tan	Cot	Cos	Sec	Csc
0	.61566	.78129	1.2799	.78801	1.2690	1.6243	60	0	.62932	.80978	1.2349	.77715	1.2868	1.5890
1	.61589	.78175	1.2792	.78783	1.2693	1.6237	59	1	.62955	.81027	1.2342	.77696	1.2871	1.5884
2	.61612	.78222	1.2784	.78765	1.2696	1.6231	58	2	.62977	.81075	1.2334	.77678	1.2874	1.5879
3	.61635	.78269	1.2776	.78747	1.2699	1.6225	57	3	.63000	.81123	1.2327	.77660	1.2877	1.5873
4	.61658	.78316	1.2769	.78729	1.2702	1.6219	56	4	.63022	.81171	1.2320	.77641	1.2880	1.5867
5	.61681	.78363	1.2761	.78711	1.2705	1.6213	55	5	.63045	.81220	1.2312	.77623	1.2883	1.5862
6	.61704	.78410	1.2753	.78694	1.2708	1.6207	54	6	.63068	.81268	1.2305	.77605	1.2886	1.5856
7	.61726	.78457	1.2746	.78676	1.2710	1.6201	53	7	.63090	.81316	1.2298	.77586	1.2889	1.5850
8	.61749	.78504	1.2738	.78658	1.2713	1.6195	52	8	.63113	.81364	1.2290	.77568	1.2892	1.5845
9	.61772	.78551	1.2731	.78640	1.2716	1.6189	51	9	.63135	.81413	1.2283	.77550	1.2895	1.5839
10	.61795	.78598	1.2723	.78622	1.1719	1.6183	50	10	.63158	.81461	1.2276	.77531	1.2898	1.5833
11	.61818	.78645	1.2715	.78604	1.2722	1.6177	49	11	.63180	.81510	1.2268	.77513	1.2901	1.5828
12	.61841	.78692	1.2708	.78586	1.2725	1.6171	48	12	.63203	.81558	1.2261	.77494	1.2904	1.5822
13	.61864	.78739	1.2700	.78568	1.2728	1.6165	47	13	.63225	.81606	1.2254	.77476	1.2907	1.5816
14	.61887	.78786	1.2693	.78550	1.2731	1.6159	46	14	.63248	.81655	1.2247	.77458	1.2910	1.581
15	.61909	.78834	1.2685	.78532	1.2734	1.6153	45	15	.63271	.81703	1.2239	.77439	1.2913	1.580
16	.61932	.78881	1.2677	.78514	1.2737	1.6147	44	16	.63293	.81752	1.2232	.77421	1.2916	1.5800
17	.61955	.78928	1.2670	.78496	1.2740	1.6141	43	17	.63316	.81800	1.2225	.77402	1.2919	1.5794
18	.61978	.78975	1.2662	.78478	1.2742	1.6135	42	18	.63338	.81849	1.2218	.77384	1.2923	1.5788
19	.62001	.79022	1.2655	.78460	1.2745	1.6129	41	19	.63361	.81898	1.2210	.77366	1.2926	1.5783
20	.62024	.79070	1.2647	.78442	1.2748	1.6123	40	20	.63383	.81946	1.2203	.77347	1.2929	1.5777
21	.62046	.79117	1.2640	.78424	1.2751	1.6117	39	21	.63406	.81995	1.2196	.77329	1.2932	1.5771
22	.62069	.79164	1.2632	.78405	1.2754	1.6111	38	22	.63428	.82044	1.2189	.77310	1.2935	1.5766
23	.62092	.79212	1.2624	.78387	1.2757	1.6105	37	23	.63451	.82092	1.2181	.77292	1.2938	1.5760
24	.62115	.79259	1.2617	.78369	1.2760	1.6099	36	24	.63473	.82141	1.2174	.77273	1.2941	1.5755
25	.62138	.79306	1.2609	.78351	1.2763	1.6093	35	25	.63496	.82190	1.2167	.77255	1.2944	1.5749
26	.62160	.79354	1.2602	.78333	1.2766	1.6087	34	26	.63518	.82238	1.2160	.77236	1.2947	1.5744
27	.62183	.79401	1.2594	.78315	1.2769	1.6082	33	27	.63540	.82287	1.2153	.77218	1.2950	1.5738
28	.62206	.79449	1.2587	.78297	1.2772	1.6076	32	28	.63563	.82336	1.2145	.77199	1.2953	1.5732
29	.62229	.79496	1.2579	.78279	1.2775	1.6070	31	29	.63585	.82385	1.2138	.77181	1.2957	1.5727
30	.62251	.79544	1.2572	.78261	1.2778	1.6064	30	30	.63608	.82434	1.2131	.77162	1.2960	1.5721
31	.62274	.79591	1.2564	.78243	1.2781	1.6058	29	31	.63630	.82483	1.2124	.77144	1.2963	1.5716
32	.62297	.79639	1.2557	.78225	1.2784	1.6052	28	32	.63653	.82531	1.2117	.77125	1.2966	1.5710
33	.62320	.79686	1.2549	.78206	1.2787	1.6046	27	33	.63675	.82580	1.2109	.77107	1.2969	1.5705
34	.62342	.79734	1.2542	.78188	1.2790	1.6040	26	34	.63698	.82629	1.2102	.77088	1.2972	1.5699
35	.62365	.79781	1.2534	.78170	1.2793	1.6035	25	35	.63720	.82678	1.2095	.77070	1.2975	1.5694
36	.62388	.79829	1.2527	.78152	1.2796	1.6029	24	36	.63742	.82727	1.2088	.77051	1.2978	1.5688
37	.62411	.79877	1.2519	.78134	1.2799	1.6023	23	37	.63765	.82776	1.2081	.77033	1.2981	1.5683
38	.62433	.79924	1.2512	.78116	1.2802	1.6017	22	38	.63787	.82825	1.2074	.77014	1.2985	1.5677
39	.62456	.79972	1.2504	.78098	1.2804	1.6011	21	39	.63810	.82874	1.2066	.76996	1.2988	1.5672
40	.62479	.80020	1.2497	.78079	1.2807	1.6005	20	40	.63832	.82923	1.2059	.76977	1.2991	1.5666
41	.62502	.80067	1.2489	.78061	1.2810	1.6000	19	41	.63854	.82972	1.2052	.76959	1.2994	1.5661
42	.62524	.80115	1.2482	.78043	1.2813	1.5994	18	42	.63877	.83022	1.2045	.76940	1.2997	1.5655
43	.62547	.80163	1.2475	.78025	1.2816	1.5988	17	43	.63899	.83071	1.2038	.76921	1.3000	1.5650
44	.62570	.80211	1.2467	.78007	1.2819	1.5982	16	44	.63922	.83120	1.2031	.76903	1.3003	1.5644
45	.62592	.80258	1.2460	.77988	1.2822	1.5976	15	45	.63944	.83169	1.2024	.76884	1.3007	1.5639
46	.62615	.80306	1.2452	.77970	1.2825	1.5971	14	46	.63966	.83218	1.2017	.76866	1.3010	1.5633
47	.62638	.80354	1.2445	.77952	1.2828	1.5965	13	47	.63989	.83268	1.2009	.76847	1.3013	1.5628
48	.62660	.80402	1.2437	.77934	1.2831	1.5959	12	48	.64011	.83317	1.2002	.76828	1.3016	1.5622
49	.62683	.80450	1.2430	.77916	1.2834	1.5953	11	49	.64033	.83366	1.1995	.76810	1.3019	1.5617
50	.62706	.80498	1.2423	.77897	1.2837	1.5948	10	50	.64056	.83415	1.1988	.76791	1.3022	1.5611
51	.62728	.80546	1.2415	.77879	1.2840	1.5942	9	51	.64078	.83465	1.1981	.76772	1.3026	1.5606
52	.62751	.80594	1.2408	.77861	1.2843	1.5936	8	52	.64100	.83514	1.1974	.76754	1.3029	1.5601
53	.62774	.80642	1.2401	.77843	1.2846	1.5930	7	53	.64123	.83564	1.1967	.76735	1.3032	1.5595
54	.62796	.80690	1.2393	.77824	1.2849	1.5925	6	54	.64145	.83613	1.1960	.76717	1.3035	1.5590
55	.62819	.80738	1.2386	.77806	1.2852	1.5919	5	55	.64167	.83662	1.1953	.76698	1.3038	1.5584
56	.62842	.80786	1.2378	.77788	1.2855	1.5913	4	56	.64190	.83712	1.1946	.76679	1.3041	1.5579
57	.62864	.80834	1.2371	.77769	1.2859	1.5907	3	57	.64212	.83761	1.1939	.76661	1.3045	1.5573
58	.62887	.80882	1.2364	.77751	1.2862	1.5902	2	58	.64234	.83811	1.1932	.76642	1.3048	1.5568
59	.62909	.80930	1.2356	.77733	1.2865	1.5896	1	59	.64256	.83860	1.1925	.76623	1.3051	1.5563
60	.62932	.80978	1.2349	.77715	1.2868	1.5890	0	60	.64279	.83910	1 1918	.76604	1.3054	1.5557
′	Cos	Cot	Tan	Sin	Csc	Sec	′	′	Cos	Cot	Tan	Sin	Csc	Sec

128° (308°)   **(231°) 51°**   **129° (309°)**   **(23(**

NATURAL TRIGONOMETRIC FUNCTIONS
TO FIVE PLACES

Sin	Tan	Cot	Cos	Sec	Csc	′
.64279	.83910	1.1918	.76604	1.3054	1.5557	60
.64301	.83960	1.1910	.76586	1.3057	1.5552	59
.64323	.84009	1.1903	.76567	1.3060	1.5546	58
.64346	.84059	1.1896	.76548	1.3064	1.5541	57
.64368	.84108	1.1889	.76530	1.3067	1.5536	56
.64390	.84158	1.1882	.76511	1.3070	1.5530	55
.64412	.84208	1.1875	.76492	1.3073	1.5525	54
.64435	.84258	1.1868	.76473	1.3076	1.5520	53
.64457	.84307	1.1861	.76455	1.3080	1.5514	52
.64479	.84357	1.1854	.76436	1.3083	1.5509	51
.64501	.84407	1.1847	.76417	1.3086	1.5504	50
.64524	.84457	1.1840	.76398	1.3089	1.5498	49
.64546	.84507	1.1833	.76380	1.3093	1.5493	48
.64568	.84556	1.1826	.76361	1.3096	1.5488	47
.64590	.84606	1.1819	.76342	1.3099	1.5482	46
.64612	.84656	1.1812	.76323	1.3102	1.5477	45
.64635	.84706	1.1806	.76304	1.3105	1.5472	44
.64657	.84756	1.1799	.76286	1.3109	1.5466	43
.64679	.84806	1.1792	.76267	1.3112	1.5461	42
.64701	.84856	1.1785	.76248	1.3115	1.5456	41
.64723	.84906	1.1778	.76229	1.3118	1.5450	40
.64746	.84956	1.1771	.76210	1.3122	1.5445	39
.64768	.85006	1.1764	.76192	1.3125	1.5440	38
.64790	.85057	1.1757	.76173	1.3128	1.5435	37
.64812	.85107	1.1750	.76154	1.3131	1.5429	36
.64834	.85157	1.1743	.76135	1.3135	1.5424	35
.64856	.85207	1.1736	.76116	1.3138	1.5419	34
.64878	.85257	1.1729	.76097	1.3141	1.5413	33
.64901	.85308	1.1722	.76078	1.3144	1.5408	32
.64923	.85358	1.1715	.76059	1.3148	1.5403	31
.64945	.85408	1.1708	.76041	1.3151	1.5398	30
.64967	.85458	1.1702	.76022	1.3154	1.5392	29
.64989	.85509	1.1695	.76003	1.3157	1.5387	28
.65011	.85559	1.1688	.75984	1.3161	1.5382	27
.65033	.85609	1.1681	.75965	1.3164	1.5377	26
.65055	.85660	1.1674	.75946	1.3167	1.5372	25
.65077	.85710	1.1667	.75927	1.3171	1.5366	24
.65100	.85761	1.1660	.75908	1.3174	1.5361	23
.65122	.85811	1.1653	.75889	1.3177	1.5356	22
.65144	.85862	1.1647	.75870	1.3180	1.5351	21
.65166	.85912	1.1640	.75851	1.3184	1.5345	20
.65188	.85963	1.1633	.75832	1.3187	1.5340	19
.65210	.86014	1.1626	.75813	1.3190	1.5335	18
.65232	.86064	1.1619	.75794	1.3194	1.5330	17
.65254	.86115	1.1612	.75775	1.3197	1.5325	16
.65276	.86166	1.1606	.75756	1.3200	1.5320	15
.65298	.86216	1.1599	.75738	1.3203	1.5314	14
.65320	.86267	1.1592	.75719	1.3207	1.5309	13
.65342	.86318	1.1585	.75700	1.3210	1.5304	12
.65364	.86368	1.1578	.75680	1.3213	1.5299	11
.65386	.86419	1.1571	.75661	1.3217	1.5294	10
.65408	.86470	1.1565	.75642	1.3220	1.5289	9
.65430	.86521	1.1558	.75623	1.3223	1.5283	8
.65452	.86572	1.1551	.75604	1.3227	1.5278	7
.65474	.86623	1.1544	.75585	1.3230	1.5273	6
.65496	.86674	1.1538	.75566	1.3233	1.5268	5
.65518	.86725	1.1531	.75547	1.3237	1.5263	4
.65540	.86776	1.1524	.75528	1.3240	1.5258	3
.65562	.86827	1.1517	.75509	1.3243	1.5253	2
.65584	.86878	1.1510	.75490	1.3247	1.5248	1
.65606	.86929	1.1504	.75471	1.3250	1.5243	0
Cos	Cot	Tan	Sin	Csc	Sec	′

′	Sin	Tan	Cot	Cos	Sec	Csc	′
0	.65606	.86929	1.1504	.75471	1.3250	1.5243	60
1	.65628	.86980	1.1497	.75452	1.3253	1.5237	59
2	.65650	.87031	1.1490	.75433	1.3257	1.5232	58
3	.65672	.87082	1.1483	.75414	1.3260	1.5227	57
4	.65694	.87133	1.1477	.75395	1.3264	1.5222	56
5	.65716	.87184	1.1470	.75375	1.3267	1.5217	55
6	.65738	.87236	1.1463	.75356	1.3270	1.5212	54
7	.65759	.87287	1.1456	.75337	1.3274	1.5207	53
8	.65781	.87338	1.1450	.75318	1.3277	1.5202	52
9	.65803	.87389	1.1443	.75299	1.3280	1.5197	51
10	.65825	.87441	1.1436	.75280	1.3284	1.5192	50
11	.65847	.87492	1.1430	.75261	1.3287	1.5187	49
12	.65869	.87543	1.1423	.75241	1.3291	1.5182	48
13	.65891	.87595	1.1416	.75222	1.3294	1.5177	47
14	.65913	.87646	1.1410	.75203	1.3297	1.5172	46
15	.65935	.87698	1.1403	.75184	1.3301	1.5167	45
16	.65956	.87749	1.1396	.75165	1.3304	1.5162	44
17	.65978	.87801	1.1389	.75146	1.3307	1.5156	43
18	.66000	.87852	1.1383	.75126	1.3311	1.5151	42
19	.66022	.87904	1.1376	.75107	1.3314	1.5146	41
20	.66044	.87955	1.1369	.75088	1.3318	1.5141	40
21	.66066	.88007	1.1363	.75069	1.3321	1.5136	39
22	.66088	.88059	1.1356	.75050	1.3325	1.5131	38
23	.66109	.88110	1.1349	.75030	1.3328	1.5126	37
24	.66131	.88162	1.1343	.75011	1.3331	1.5121	36
25	.66153	.88214	1.1336	.74992	1.3335	1.5116	35
26	.66175	.88265	1.1329	.74973	1.3338	1.5111	34
27	.66197	.88317	1.1323	.74953	1.3342	1.5107	33
28	.66218	.88369	1.1316	.74934	1.3345	1.5102	32
29	.66240	.88421	1.1310	.74915	1.3348	1.5097	31
30	.66262	.88473	1.1303	.74896	1.3352	1.5092	30
31	.66284	.88524	1.1296	.74876	1.3355	1.5087	29
32	.66306	.88576	1.1290	.74857	1.3359	1.5082	28
33	.66327	.88628	1.1283	.74838	1.3362	1.5077	27
34	.66349	.88680	1.1276	.74818	1.3366	1.5072	26
35	.66371	.88732	1.1270	.74799	1.3369	1.5067	25
36	.66393	.88784	1.1263	.74780	1.3373	1.5062	24
37	.66414	.88836	1.1257	.74760	1.3376	1.5057	23
38	.66436	.88888	1.1250	.74741	1.3380	1.5052	22
39	.66458	.88940	1.1243	.74722	1.3383	1.5047	21
40	.66480	.88992	1.1237	.74703	1.3386	1.5042	20
41	.66501	.89045	1.1230	.74683	1.3390	1.5037	19
42	.66523	.89097	1.1224	.74664	1.3393	1.5032	18
43	.66545	.89149	1.1217	.74644	1.3397	1.5027	17
44	.66566	.89201	1.1211	.74625	1.3400	1.5023	16
45	.66588	.89253	1.1204	.74606	1.3404	1.5018	15
46	.66610	.89306	1.1197	.74586	1.3407	1.5013	14
47	.66632	.89358	1.1191	.74567	1.3411	1.5008	13
48	.66653	.89410	1.1184	.74548	1.3414	1.5003	12
49	.66675	.89463	1.1178	.74528	1.3418	1.4998	11
50	.66697	.89515	1.1171	.74509	1.3421	1.4993	10
51	.66718	.89567	1.1165	.74489	1.3425	1.4988	9
52	.66740	.89620	1.1158	.74470	1.3428	1.4984	8
53	.66762	.89672	1.1152	.74451	1.3432	1.4979	7
54	.66783	.89725	1.1145	.74431	1.3435	1.4974	6
55	.66805	.89777	1.1139	.74412	1.3439	1.4969	5
56	.66827	.89830	1.1132	.74392	1.3442	1.4964	4
57	.66848	.89883	1.1126	.74373	1.3446	1.4959	3
58	.66870	.89935	1.1119	.74353	1.3449	1.4954	2
59	.66891	.89988	1.1113	.74334	1.3453	1.4950	1
60	.66913	.90040	1.1106	.74314	1.3456	1.4945	0
′	Cos	Cot	Tan	Sin	Csc	Sec	′

NATURAL TRIGONOMETRIC FUNCTIONS
TO FIVE PLACES

42° (222°)   **(317°) 137°**   **43° (223°)**   **(316**

′	Sin	Tan	Cot	Cos	Sec	Csc	′	′	Sin	Tan	Cot	Cos	Sec	Csc
0	.66913	.90040	1.1106	.74314	1.3456	1.4945	60	0	.68200	.93252	1.0724	.73135	1.3673	1.4663
1	.66935	.90093	1.1100	.74295	1.3460	1.4940	59	1	.68221	.93306	1.0717	.73116	1.3677	1.4658
2	.66956	.90146	1.1093	.74276	1.3463	1.4935	58	2	.68242	.93360	1.0711	.73096	1.3681	1.4654
3	.66978	.90199	1.1087	.74256	1.3467	1.4930	57	3	.68264	.93415	1.0705	.73076	1.3684	1.4649
4	.66999	.90251	1.1080	.74237	1.3470	1.4925	56	4	.68285	.93469	1.0699	.73056	1.3688	1.4645
5	.67021	.90304	1.1074	.74217	1.3474	1.4921	55	5	.68306	.93524	1.0692	.73036	1.3692	1.4640
6	.67043	.90357	1.1067	.74198	1.3478	1.4916	54	6	.68327	.93578	1.0686	.73016	1.3696	1.4635
7	.67064	.90410	1.1061	.74178	1.3481	1.4911	53	7	.68349	.93633	1.0680	.72996	1.3699	1.4631
8	.67086	.90463	1.1054	.74159	1.3485	1.4906	52	8	.68370	.93688	1.0674	.72976	1.3703	1.4626
9	.67107	.90516	1.1048	.74139	1.3488	1.4901	51	9	.68391	.93742	1.0668	.72957	1.3707	1.4622
10	.67129	.90569	1.1041	.74120	1.3492	1.4897	50	10	.68412	.93797	1.0661	.72937	1.3711	1.4617
11	.67151	.90621	1.1035	.74100	1.3495	1.4892	49	11	.68434	.93852	1.0655	.72917	1.3714	1.4613
12	.67172	.90674	1.1028	.74080	1.3499	1.4887	48	12	.68455	.93906	1.0649	.72897	1.3718	1.4608
13	.67194	.90727	1.1022	.74061	1.3502	1.4882	47	13	.68476	.93961	1.0643	.72877	1.3722	1.4604
14	.67215	.90781	1.1016	.74041	1.3506	1.4878	46	14	.68497	.94016	1.0637	.72857	1.3726	1.4599
15	.67237	.90834	1.1009	.74022	1.3510	1.4873	45	15	.68518	.94071	1.0630	.72837	1.3729	1.4595
16	.67258	.90887	1.1003	.74002	1.3513	1.4868	44	16	.68539	.94125	1.0624	.72817	1.3733	1.4590
17	.67280	.90940	1.0996	.73983	1.3517	1.4863	43	17	.68561	.94180	1.0618	.72797	1.3737	1.4586
18	.67301	.90993	1.0990	.73963	1.3520	1.4859	42	18	.68582	.94235	1.0612	.72777	1.3741	1.4581
19	.67323	.91046	1.0983	.73944	1.3524	1.4854	41	19	.68603	.94290	1.0606	.72757	1.3744	1.4577
20	.67344	.91099	1.0977	.73924	1.3527	1.4849	40	20	.68624	.94345	1.0599	.72737	1.3748	1.4572
21	.67366	.91153	1.0971	.73904	1.3531	1.4844	39	21	.68645	.94400	1.0593	.72717	1.3752	1.4568
22	.67387	.91206	1.0964	.73885	1.3535	1.4840	38	22	.68666	.94455	1.0587	.72697	1.3756	1.4563
23	.67409	.91259	1.0958	.73865	1.3538	1.4835	37	23	.68688	.94510	1.0581	.72677	1.3759	1.4559
24	.67430	.91313	1.0951	.73846	1.3542	1.4830	36	24	.68709	.94565	1.0575	.72657	1.3763	1.4554
25	.67452	.91366	1.0945	.73826	1.3545	1.4825	35	25	.68730	.94620	1.0569	.72637	1.3767	1.4550
26	.67473	.91419	1.0939	.73806	1.3549	1.4821	34	26	.68751	.94676	1.0562	.72617	1.3771	1.4545
27	.67495	.91473	1.0932	.73787	1.3553	1.4816	33	27	.68772	.94731	1.0556	.72597	1.3775	1.4541
28	.67516	.91526	1.0926	.73767	1.3556	1.4811	32	28	.68793	.94786	1.0550	.72577	1.3778	1.4536
29	.67538	.91580	1.0919	.73747	1.3560	1.4807	31	29	.68814	.94841	1.0544	.72557	1.3782	1.4532
30	.67559	.91633	1.0913	.73728	1.3563	1.4802	30	30	.68835	.94896	1.0538	.72537	1.3786	1.4527
31	.67580	.91687	1.0907	.73708	1.3567	1.4797	29	31	.68857	.94952	1.0532	.72517	1.3790	1.4523
32	.67602	.91740	1.0900	.73688	1.3571	1.4792	28	32	.68878	.95007	1.0526	.72497	1.3794	1.4518
33	.67623	.91794	1.0894	.73669	1.3574	1.4788	27	33	.68899	.95062	1.0519	.72477	1.3797	1.4514
34	.67645	.91847	1.0888	.73649	1.3578	1.4783	26	34	.68920	.95118	1.0513	.72457	1.3801	1.4510
35	.67666	.91901	1.0881	.73629	1.3582	1.4778	25	35	.68941	.95173	1.0507	.72437	1.3805	1.4505
36	.67688	.91955	1.0875	.73610	1.3585	1.4774	24	36	.68962	.95229	1.0501	.72417	1.3809	1.4501
37	.67709	.92008	1.0869	.73590	1.3589	1.4769	23	37	.68983	.95284	1.0495	.72397	1.3813	1.4496
38	.67730	.92062	1.0862	.73570	1.3592	1.4764	22	38	.69004	.95340	1.0489	.72377	1.3817	1.4492
39	.67752	.92116	1.0856	.73551	1.3596	1.4760	21	39	.69025	.95395	1.0483	.72357	1.3820	1.4487
40	.67773	.92170	1.0850	.73531	1.3600	1.4755	20	40	.69046	.95451	1.0477	.72337	1.3824	1.4483
41	.67795	.92224	1.0843	.73511	1.3603	1.4750	19	41	.69067	.95506	1.0470	.72317	1.3828	1.4479
42	.67816	.92277	1.0837	.73491	1.3607	1.4746	18	42	.69088	.95562	1.0464	.72297	1.3832	1.4474
43	.67837	.92331	1.0831	.73472	1.3611	1.4741	17	43	.69109	.95618	1.0458	.72277	1.3836	1.4470
44	.67859	.92385	1.0824	.73452	1.3614	1.4737	16	44	.69130	.95673	1.0452	.72257	1.3840	1.4465
45	.67880	.92439	1.0818	.73432	1.3618	1.4732	15	45	.69151	.95729	1.0446	.72236	1.3843	1.4461
46	.67901	.92493	1.0812	.73413	1.3622	1.4727	14	46	.69172	.95785	1.0440	.72216	1.3847	1.4457
47	.67923	.92547	1.0805	.73393	1.3625	1.4723	13	47	.69193	.95841	1.0434	.72196	1.3851	1.4452
48	.67944	.92601	1.0799	.73373	1.3629	1.4718	12	48	.69214	.95897	1.0428	.72176	1.3855	1.4448
49	.67965	.92655	1.0793	.73353	1.3633	1.4713	11	49	.69235	.95952	1.0422	.72156	1.3859	1.4443
50	.67987	.92709	1.0786	.73333	1.3636	1.4709	10	50	.69256	.96008	1.0416	.72136	1.3863	1.4439
51	.68008	.92763	1.0780	.73314	1.3640	1.4704	9	51	.69277	.96064	1.0410	.72116	1.3867	1.4435
52	.68029	.92817	1.0774	.73294	1.3644	1.4700	8	52	.69298	.96120	1.0404	.72095	1.3871	1.4430
53	.68051	.92872	1.0768	.73274	1.3647	1.4695	7	53	.69319	.96176	1.0398	.72075	1.3874	1.4426
54	.68072	.92926	1.0761	.73254	1.3651	1.4690	6	54	.69340	.96232	1.0392	.72055	1.3878	1.4422
55	.68093	.92980	1.0755	.73234	1.3655	1.4686	5	55	.69361	.96288	1.0385	.72035	1.3882	1.4417
56	.68115	.93034	1.0749	.73215	1.3658	1.4681	4	56	.69382	.96344	1.0379	.72015	1.3886	1.4413
57	.68136	.93088	1.0742	.73195	1.3662	1.4677	3	57	.69403	.96400	1.0373	.71995	1.3890	1.4409
58	.68157	.93143	1.0736	.73175	1.3666	1.4672	2	58	.69424	.96457	1.0367	.71974	1.3894	1.4404
59	.68179	.93197	1.0730	.73155	1.3670	1.4667	1	59	.69445	.96513	1.0361	.71954	1.3898	1.4400
60	.68200	.93252	1.0724	.73135	1.3673	1.4663	0	60	.69466	.96569	1.0355	.71934	1.3902	1.4396
′	Cos	Cot	Tan	Sin	Csc	Sec	′	′	Cos	Cot	Tan	Sin	Csc	Sec

132° (312°)   **(227°) 47°**   **133° (313°)**   **(22**

NATURAL TRIGONOMETRIC FUNCTIONS
TO FIVE PLACES

44° (224°)   (315°) 135°

′	Sin	Tan	Cot	Cos	Sec	Csc	′
0	.69466	.96569	1.0355	.71934	1.3902	1.4396	60
1	.69487	.96625	1.0349	.71914	1.3906	1.4391	59
2	.69508	.96681	1.0343	.71894	1.3909	1.4387	58
3	.69529	.96738	1.0337	.71873	1.3913	1.4383	57
4	.69549	.96794	1.0331	.71853	1.3917	1.4378	56
5	.69570	.96850	1.0325	.71833	1.3921	1.4374	55
6	.69591	.96907	1.0319	.71813	1.3925	1.4370	54
7	.69612	.96963	1.0313	.71792	1.3929	1.4365	53
8	.69633	.97020	1.0307	.71772	1.3933	1.4361	52
9	.69654	.97076	1.0301	.71752	1.3937	1.4357	51
10	.69675	.97133	1.0295	.71732	1.3941	1.4352	50
11	.69696	.97189	1.0289	.71711	1.3945	1.4348	49
12	.69717	.97246	1.0283	.71691	1.3949	1.4344	48
13	.69737	.97302	1.0277	.71671	1.3953	1.4340	47
14	.69758	.97359	1.0271	.71650	1.3957	1.4335	46
15	.69779	.97416	1.0265	.71630	1.3961	1.4331	45
16	.69800	.97472	1.0259	.71610	1.3965	1.4327	44
17	.69821	.97529	1.0253	.71590	1.3969	1.4322	43
18	.69842	.97586	1.0247	.71569	1.3972	1.4318	42
19	.69862	.97643	1.0241	.71549	1.3976	1.4314	41
20	.69883	.97700	1.0235	.71529	1.3980	1.4310	40
21	.69904	.97756	1.0230	.71508	1.3984	1.4305	39
22	.69925	.97813	1.0224	.71488	1.3988	1.4301	38
23	.69946	.97870	1.0218	.71468	1.3992	1.4297	37
24	.69966	.97927	1.0212	.71447	1.3996	1.4293	36
25	.69987	.97984	1.0206	.71427	1.4000	1.4288	35
26	.70008	.98041	1.0200	.71407	1.4004	1.4284	34
27	.70029	.98098	1.0194	.71386	1.4008	1.4280	33
28	.70049	.98155	1.0188	.71366	1.4012	1.4276	32
29	.70070	.98213	1.0182	.71345	1.4016	1.4271	31
30	.70091	.98270	1.0176	.71325	1.4020	1.4267	30
31	.70112	.98327	1.0170	.71305	1.4024	1.4263	29
32	.70132	.98384	1.0164	.71284	1.4028	1.4259	28
33	.70153	.98441	1.0158	.71264	1.4032	1.4255	27
34	.70174	.98499	1.0152	.71243	1.4036	1.4250	26
35	.70195	.98556	1.0147	.71223	1.4040	1.4246	25
36	.70215	.98613	1.0141	.71203	1.4044	1.4242	24
37	.70236	.98671	1.0135	.71182	1.4048	1.4238	23
38	.70257	.98728	1.0129	.71162	1.4052	1.4234	22
39	.70277	.98786	1.0123	.71141	1.4057	1.4229	21
40	.70298	.98843	1.0117	.71121	1.4061	1.4225	20
41	.70319	.98901	1.0111	.71100	1.4065	1.4221	19
42	.70339	.98958	1.0105	.71080	1.4069	1.4217	18
43	.70360	.99016	1.0099	.71059	1.4073	1.4213	17
44	.70381	.99073	1.0094	.71039	1.4077	1.4208	16
45	.70401	.99131	1.0088	.71019	1.4081	1.4204	15
46	.70422	.99189	1.0082	.70998	1.4085	1.4200	14
47	.70443	.99247	1.0076	.70978	1.4089	1.4196	13
48	.70463	.99304	1.0070	.70957	1.4093	1.4192	12
49	.70484	.99362	1.0064	.70937	1.4097	1.4188	11
50	.70505	.99420	1.0058	.70916	1.4101	1.4183	10
51	.70525	.99478	1.0052	.70896	1.4105	1.4179	9
52	.70546	.99536	1.0047	.70875	1.4109	1.4175	8
53	.70567	.99594	1.0041	.70855	1.4113	1.4171	7
54	.70587	.99652	1.0035	.70834	1.4118	1.4167	6
55	.70608	.99710	1.0029	.70813	1.4122	1.4163	5
56	.70628	.99768	1.0023	.70793	1.4126	1.4159	4
57	.70649	.99826	1.0017	.70772	1.4130	1.4154	3
58	.70670	.99884	1.0012	.70752	1.4134	1.4150	2
59	.70690	.99942	1.0006	.70731	1.4138	1.4146	1
60	.70711	1.0000	1.0000	.70711	1.4142	1.4142	0
′	Cos	Cot	Tan	Sin	Csc	Sec	′

134° (314°)   (225°) 45°

NATURAL TRIGONOMETRIC FUNCTIONS
SINE, COSINE, TANGENT, COTANGENT,
FOR ANGLES IN DEGREES AND DECIMALS

The table that follows, NATURAL TRIGONOMETRIC FUNCTIONS, SINE, COSINE, TANGENT, COTANGENT, FOR ANGLES IN DEGREES AND DECIMALS, gives the values of the sine, cosine, tangent, and cotangent for each tenth of a degree from 0° to 90° where the entries are correct to five significant digits.

For angle values in the left column, use the column headings at the top of each column. For angle values in the right column, use the column headings at the bottom of each column.

Linear interpolation may be used to obtain functional values for angles expressed to hundredths of a degree, except where the functions are rapidly varying.

This is followed by the table NATURAL TRIGONOMETRIC FUNCTIONS TO FIVE TENTHS OF A DEGREE (SECANTS AND COSECANTS), which gives the values of the secant and cosecant for equally spaced intervals of one-half degree from 0° to 90°, and the entries are correct to six significant digits.

NATURAL TRIGONOMETRIC FUNCTIONS
SINE, COSINE, TANGENT, COTANGENT,
FOR ANGLES IN DEGREES AND DECIMALS

Deg.	Sin	Tan	*Cot	Cos	
0.0	0 00000	0.00000	∞	1.0000	**90.0**
.1	.00175	00175	573.0	1.0000	89.9
.2	.00349	00349	286.5	1.0000	.8
.3	.00524	00524	191.0	1.0000	.7
.4	.00698	.00698	143.24	1 0000	.6
.5	00873	.00873	114.59	1.0000	.5
.6	.01047	.01047	95.49	0.9999	.4
.7	.01222	.01222	81 85	.9999	.3
.8	.01396	.01396	71.62	.9999	.2
.9	.01571	.01571	63.66	.9999	89.1
1.0	0.01745	0.01746	57.29	0.9998	**89.0**
.1	.01920	.01920	52.08	9998	88.9
.2	02094	02095	47.74	.9998	.8
.3	.02269	02269	44.07	.9997	.7
.4	.02443	.02444	40.92	.9997	.6
.5	.02618	.02619	38.19	.9997	.5
.6	02792	.02793	35.80	.9996	.4
.7	.02967	.02968	33.69	.9996	.3
.8	03141	.03143	31.82	.9995	.2
.9	.03316	.03317	30.14	.9995	88.1
2.0	0.03490	0.03492	28.64	0.9994	**88.0**
.1	.03664	03667	27.27	.9993	87.9
.2	.03839	03842	26.03	.9993	.8
.3	.04013	.04016	24.90	.9992	.7
.4	.04188	04191	23.86	.9991	.6
.5	.04362	.04366	22.90	.9990	.5
.6	.04536	.04541	22 02	.9990	.4
.7	.04711	.04716	21.20	.9989	.3
.8	.04885	.04891	20.45	.9988	.2
.9	.05059	.05066	19.74	.9987	87.1
3.0	0.05234	0.05241	19.081	0.9986	**87.0**
.1	.05408	.05416	18.464	.9985	86.9
.2	.05582	.05591	17.886	.9984	.8
.3	.05756	.05766	17.343	.9983	.7
.4	.05931	.05941	16.832	9982	.6
.5	.06105	.06116	16.350	.9981	.5
.6	06279	.06291	15.895	.9980	.4
.7	.06453	.06467	15.464	.9979	.3
.8	.06627	.06642	15.056	.9978	.2
.9	.06802	.06817	14.669	.9977	86.1
4.0	0.06976	0.06993	14.301	0.9976	**86.0**
.1	.07150	.07168	13.951	.9974	85.9
.2	.07324	.07344	13.617	.9973	.8
.3	07498	.07519	13.300	.9972	.7
.4	07672	.07695	12.996	.9971	.6
.5	.07846	.07870	12.706	.9969	.5
.6	.08020	.08046	12.429	.9968	.4
.7	.08194	.08221	12.163	.9966	.3
.8	.08368	.08397	11.909	.9965	.2
.9	.08542	.08573	11.664	.9963	85.1
5.0	0.08716	0.08749	11.430	0.9962	**85.0**
.1	.08889	.08925	11.205	.9960	84.9
.2	.09063	.09101	10.988	.9959	.8
.3	.09237	.09277	10.780	.9957	.7
.4	.09411	.09453	10.579	.9956	.6
.5	.09585	.09629	10.385	.9954	.5
.6	.09758	.09805	10.199	.9952	4
.7	.09932	.09981	10.019	.9951	.3
.8	.10106	.10158	9.845	.9949	.2
.9	.10279	.10334	9.677	.9947	84.1
6.0	0.10453	0.10510	9.514	0.9945	**84.0**
	Cos	Cot	*Tan	Sin	Deg.

Deg.	Sin	Tan	Cot	Cos	
6.0	0.10453	0.10510	9 514	0.9945	**84.0**
.1	.10626	.10687	9.357	.9943	83.9
.2	.10800	10863	9.205	.9942	.8
.3	.10973	.11040	9.058	9940	.7
.4	.11147	.11217	8.915	9938	.6
.5	.11320	.11394	8.777	.9936	.5
.6	.11494	.11570	8.643	9934	.4
.7	.11667	11747	8.513	9932	.3
.8	.11840	.11924	8.386	.9930	.2
.9	.12014	.12101	8.264	.9928	83.1
7.0	0.12187	0.12278	8.144	0.9925	**83.0**
.1	.12360	.12456	8.028	.9923	82.9
.2	.12533	.12633	7.916	.9921	.8
.3	.12706	.12810	7.806	.9919	.7
.4	.12880	.12988	7.700	.9917	.6
.5	.13053	.13165	7 596	.9914	.5
.6	.13226	13343	7.495	.9912	.4
.7	.13399	.13521	7.396	.9910	.3
.8	.13572	.13698	7.300	.9907	.2
.9	.13744	.13876	7.207	.9905	82.1
8.0	0.13917	0.14054	7.115	0.9903	**82.0**
.1	.14090	.14232	7.026	.9900	81.9
.2	.14263	.14410	6.940	.9898	.8
.3	.14436	.14588	6.855	.9895	.7
.4	.14608	.14767	6.772	.9893	.6
.5	.14781	.14945	6.691	.9890	.5
.6	.14954	.15124	6.612	.9888	.4
.7	.15126	.15302	6.535	.9885	.3
.8	.15299	.15481	6.460	.9882	.2
.9	.15471	.15660	6.386	.9880	81.1
9.0	0.15643	0.15838	6.314	0.9877	**81.0**
.1	.15816	.16017	6.243	.9874	80.9
.2	.15988	.16196	6.174	.9871	.8
.3	.16160	.16376	6.107	.9869	.7
.4	.16333	.16555	6.041	.9866	.6
.5	.16505	.16734	5.976	.9863	.5
.6	.16677	.16914	5.912	.9860	.4
.7	.16849	.17093	5.850	.9857	.3
.8	.17021	.17273	5.789	.9854	.2
.9	.17193	.17453	5.730	.9851	80.1
10.0	0.1736	0.1763	5.671	0.9848	**80.0**
.1	.1754	.1781	5.614	.9845	79.9
.2	.1771	.1799	5.558	.9842	.8
.3	.1788	.1817	5.503	.9839	.7
.4	.1805	.1835	5.449	.9836	.6
.5	.1822	.1853	5.396	.9833	.5
.6	.1840	.1871	5.343	.9829	.4
.7	.1857	.1890	5.292	.9826	.3
.8	.1874	.1908	5.242	.9823	.2
.9	.1891	.1926	5.193	.9820	79.1
11.0	0.1908	0.1944	5.145	0.9816	**79.0**
.1	.1925	.1962	5.097	.9813	78.9
.2	.1942	.1980	5.050	.9810	.8
.3	.1959	.1998	5.005	.9806	.7
.4	.1977	.2016	4.959	.9803	.6
.5	.1994	.2035	4.915	.9799	.5
.6	.2011	.2053	4.872	.9796	.4
.7	.2028	.2071	4.829	.9792	.3
.8	.2045	.2089	4.787	.9789	.2
.9	.2062	.2107	4.745	.9785	78.1
12.0	0.2079	0.2126	4.705	0.9781	**78.0**
	Cos	Cot	Tan	Sin	Deg.

* Interpolation in this section of the table is inaccurate.

NATURAL TRIGONOMETRIC FUNCTIONS
SINE, COSINE, TANGENT, COTANGENT,
FOR ANGLES IN DEGREES AND DECIMALS (Continued)

Deg.	Sin	Tan	Cot	Cos	
12.0	0.2079	0.2126	4.705	0.9781	**78.0**
.1	.2096	.2144	4.665	.9778	77.9
.2	.2113	.2162	4.625	.9774	.8
.3	.2130	.2180	4.586	.9770	.7
.4	.2147	.2199	4.548	.9767	.6
.5	.2164	.2217	4.511	.9763	.5
.6	.2181	.2235	4.474	.9759	.4
.7	.2198	.2254	4.437	.9755	.3
.8	.2215	.2272	4.402	.9751	.2
.9	.2233	.2290	4.366	.9748	77.1
13.0	0.2250	0.2309	4.331	0.9744	**77.0**
.1	.2267	.2327	4.297	.9740	76.9
.2	.2284	.2345	4.264	.9736	.8
.3	.2300	.2364	4.230	.9732	.7
.4	.2317	.2382	4.198	.9728	.6
.5	.2334	.2401	4.165	.9724	.5
.6	.2351	.2419	4.134	.9720	.4
.7	.2368	.2438	4.102	.9715	.3
.8	.2385	.2456	4.071	.9711	.2
.9	.2402	.2475	4.041	.9707	76.1
14.0	0.2419	0.2493	4.011	0.9703	**76.0**
.1	.2436	.2512	3.981	.9699	75.9
.2	.2453	.2530	3.952	.9694	.8
.3	.2470	.2549	3.923	.9690	.7
.4	.2487	.2568	3.895	.9686	.6
.5	.2504	.2586	3.867	.9681	.5
.6	.2521	.2605	3.839	.9677	.4
.7	.2538	.2623	3.812	.9673	.3
.8	.2554	.2642	3.785	.9668	.2
.9	.2571	.2661	3.758	.9664	75.1
15.0	0.2588	0.2679	3.732	0.9659	**75.0**
.1	.2605	.2698	3.706	.9655	74.9
.2	.2622	.2717	3.681	.9650	.8
.3	.2639	.2736	3.655	.9646	.7
.4	.2656	.2754	3.630	.9641	.6
.5	.2672	.2773	3.606	.9636	.5
.6	.2689	.2792	3.582	.9632	.4
.7	.2706	.2811	3.558	.9627	.3
.8	.2723	.2830	3.534	.9622	.2
.9	.2740	.2849	3.511	.9617	74.1
16.0	0.2756	0.2867	3.487	0.9613	**74.0**
.1	.2773	.2886	3.465	.9608	73.9
.2	.2790	.2905	3.442	.9603	.8
.3	.2807	.2924	3.420	.9598	.7
.4	.2823	.2943	3.398	.9593	.6
.5	.2840	.2962	3.376	.9588	.5
.6	.2857	.2981	3.354	.9583	.4
.7	.2874	.3000	3.333	.9578	.3
.8	.2890	.3019	3.312	.9573	.2
.9	.2907	.3038	3.291	.9568	73.1
17.0	0.2924	0.3057	3.271	0.9563	**73.0**
.1	.2940	.3076	3.251	.9558	72.9
.2	.2957	.3096	3.230	.9553	.8
.3	.2974	.3115	3.211	.9548	.7
.4	.2990	.3134	3.191	.9542	.6
.5	.3007	.3153	3.172	.9537	.5
.6	.3024	.3172	3.152	.9532	.4
.7	.3040	.3191	3.133	.9527	.3
.8	.3057	.3211	3.115	.9521	.2
.9	.3074	.3230	3.096	.9516	72.1
18.0	0.3090	0.3249	3.078	0.9511	**72.0**
	Cos	Cot	Tan	Sin	Deg.

Deg.	Sin	Tan	Cot	Cos	
18.0	0.3090	0.3249	3.078	0.9511	**72.0**
.1	.3107	.3269	3.060	.9505	71.9
.2	.3123	.3288	3.042	.9500	.8
.3	.3140	.3307	3.024	.9494	.7
.4	.3156	.3327	3.006	.9489	.6
.5	.3173	.3346	2.989	.9483	.5
.6	.3190	.3365	2.971	.9478	.4
.7	.3206	.3385	2.954	.9472	.3
.8	.3223	.3404	2.937	.9466	.2
.9	.3239	.3424	2.921	.9461	71.1
19.0	0.3256	0.3443	2.904	0.9455	**71.0**
.1	.3272	.3463	2.888	.9449	70.9
.2	.3289	.3482	2.872	.9444	.8
.3	.3305	.3502	2.856	.9438	.7
.4	.3322	.3522	2.840	.9432	.6
.5	.3338	.3541	2.824	.9426	.5
.6	.3355	.3561	2.808	.9421	.4
.7	.3371	.3581	2.793	.9415	.3
.8	.3387	.3600	2.778	.9409	.2
.9	.3404	.3620	2.762	.9403	70.1
20.0	0.3420	0.3640	2.747	0.9397	**70.0**
.1	.3437	.3659	2.733	.9391	69.9
.2	.3453	.3679	2.718	.9385	.8
.3	.3469	.3699	2.703	.9379	.7
.4	.3486	.3719	2.689	.9373	.6
.5	.3502	.3739	2.675	.9367	.5
.6	.3518	.3759	2.660	.9361	.4
.7	.3535	.3779	2.646	.9354	.3
.8	.3551	.3799	2.633	.9348	.2
.9	.3567	.3819	2.619	.9342	69.1
21.0	0.3584	0.3839	2.605	0.9336	**69.0**
.1	.3600	.3859	2.592	.9330	68.9
.2	.3616	.3879	2.578	.9323	.8
.3	.3633	.3899	2.565	.9317	.7
.4	.3649	.3919	2.552	.9311	.6
.5	.3665	.3939	2.539	.9304	.5
.6	.3681	.3959	2.526	.9298	.4
.7	.3697	.3979	2.513	.9291	.3
.8	.3714	.4000	2.500	.9285	.2
.9	.3730	.4020	2.488	.9278	68.1
22.0	0.3746	0.4040	2.475	0.9272	**68.0**
.1	.3762	.4061	2.463	.9265	67.9
.2	.3778	.4081	2.450	.9259	.8
.3	.3795	.4101	2.438	.9252	.7
.4	.3811	.4122	2.426	.9245	.6
.5	.3827	.4142	2.414	.9239	.5
.6	.3843	.4163	2.402	.9232	.4
.7	.3859	.4183	2.391	.9225	.3
.8	.3875	.4204	2.379	.9219	.2
.9	.3891	.4224	2.367	.9212	67.1
23.0	0.3907	0.4245	2.356	0.9205	**67.0**
.1	.3923	.4265	2.344	.9198	66.9
.2	.3939	.4286	2.333	.9191	.8
.3	.3955	.4307	2.322	.9184	.7
.4	.3971	.4327	2.311	.9178	.6
.5	.3987	.4348	2.300	.9171	.5
.6	.4003	.4369	2.289	.9164	.4
.7	.4019	.4390	2.278	.9157	.3
.8	.4035	.4411	2.267	.9150	.2
.9	.4051	.4431	2.257	.9143	66.1
24.0	0.4067	0.4452	2.246	0.9135	**66.0**
	Cos	Cot	Tan	Sin	Deg.

NATURAL TRIGONOMETRIC FUNCTIONS
SINE, COSINE, TANGENT, COTANGENT,
FOR ANGLES IN DEGREES AND DECIMALS (Continued)

Deg.	Sin	Tan	Cot	Cos	
24.0	0.4067	0.4452	2.246	0.9135	**66.0**
.1	.4083	.4473	2.236	.9128	65.9
.2	.4099	.4494	2.225	.9121	.8
.3	.4115	.4515	2.215	.9114	.7
.4	.4131	.4536	2.204	.9107	.6
.5	.4147	.4557	2.194	.9100	.5
.6	.4163	.4578	2.184	.9092	.4
.7	.4179	.4599	2.174	.9085	.3
.8	.4195	.4621	2.164	.9078	.2
.9	.4210	.4642	2.154	.9070	65.1
25.0	0.4226	0.4663	2.145	0.9063	**65.0**
.1	.4242	.4684	2.135	.9056	64.9
.2	.4258	.4706	2.125	.9048	.8
.3	.4274	.4727	2.116	.9041	.7
.4	.4289	.4748	2.106	.9033	.6
.5	.4305	.4770	2.097	.9026	.5
.6	.4321	.4791	2.087	.9018	.4
.7	.4337	.4813	2.078	.9011	.3
.8	.4352	.4834	2.069	.9003	.2
.9	.4368	.4856	2.059	.8996	64.1
26.0	0.4384	0.4877	2.050	0.8988	**64.0**
.1	.4399	.4899	2.041	.8980	63.9
.2	.4415	.4921	2.032	.8973	.8
.3	.4431	.4942	2.023	.8965	.7
.4	.4446	.4964	2.014	.8957	.6
.5	.4462	.4986	2.006	.8949	.5
.6	.4478	.5008	1.997	.8942	.4
.7	.4493	.5029	1.988	.8934	.3
.8	.4509	.5051	1.980	.8926	.2
.9	.4524	.5073	1.971	.8918	63.1
27.0	0.4540	0.5095	1.963	0.8910	**63.0**
.1	.4555	.5117	1.954	.8902	62.9
.2	.4571	.5139	1.946	.8894	.8
.3	.4586	.5161	1.937	.8886	.7
.4	.4602	.5184	1.929	.8878	.6
.5	.4617	.5206	1.921	.8870	.5
.6	.4633	.5228	1.913	.8862	.4
.7	.4648	.5250	1.905	.8854	.3
.8	.4664	.5272	1.897	.8846	.2
.9	.4679	.5295	1.889	.8838	62.1
28.0	0.4695	0.5317	1.881	0.8829	**62.0**
.1	.4710	.5340	1.873	.8821	61.9
.2	.4726	.5362	1.865	.8813	.8
.3	.4741	.5384	1.857	.8805	.7
.4	.4756	.5407	1.849	.8796	.6
.5	.4772	.5430	1.842	.8788	.5
.6	.4787	.5452	1.834	.8780	.4
.7	.4802	.5475	1.827	.8771	.3
.8	.4818	.5498	1.819	.8763	.2
.9	.4833	.5520	1.811	.8755	61.1
29.0	0.4848	0.5543	1.804	0.8746	**61.0**
.1	.4863	.5566	1.797	.8738	60.9
.2	.4879	.5589	1.789	.8729	.8
.3	.4894	.5612	1.782	.8721	.7
.4	.4909	.5635	1.775	.8712	.6
.5	.4924	.5658	1.767	.8704	.5
.6	.4939	.5681	1.760	.8695	.4
.7	.4955	.5704	1.753	.8686	.3
.8	.4970	.5727	1.746	.8678	.2
.9	.4985	.5750	1.739	.8669	60.1
30.0	0.5000	0.5774	1.732	0.8660	**60.0**
	Cos	Cot	Tan	Sin	Deg.

Deg.	Sin	Tan	Cot	Cos	
30.0	0.5000	0.5774	1.7321	0.8660	**60.0**
.1	.5015	.5797	1.7251	.8652	59.9
.2	.5030	.5820	1.7182	.8643	.8
.3	.5045	.5844	1.7113	.8634	.7
.4	.5060	.5867	1.7045	.8625	.6
.5	.5075	.5890	1.6977	.8616	.5
.6	.5090	.5914	1.6909	.8607	.4
.7	.5105	.5938	1.6842	.8599	.3
.8	.5120	.5961	1.6775	.8590	.2
.9	.5135	.5985	1.6709	.8581	59.1
31.0	0.5150	0.6009	1.6643	0.8572	**59.0**
.1	.5165	.6032	1.6577	.8563	58.9
.2	.5180	.6056	1.6512	.8554	.8
.3	.5195	.6080	1.6447	.8545	.7
.4	.5210	.6104	1.6383	.8536	.6
.5	.5225	.6128	1.6319	.8526	.5
.6	.5240	.6152	1.6255	.8517	.4
.7	.5255	.6176	1.6191	.8508	.3
.8	.5270	.6200	1.6128	.8499	.2
.9	.5284	.6224	1.6066	.8490	58.1
32.0	0.5299	0.6249	1.6003	0.8480	**58.0**
.1	.5314	.6273	1.5941	.8471	57.9
.2	.5329	.6297	1.5880	.8462	.8
.3	.5344	.6322	1.5818	.8453	.7
.4	.5358	.6346	1.5757	.8443	.6
.5	.5373	.6371	1.5697	.8434	.5
.6	.5388	.6395	1.5637	.8425	.4
.7	.5402	.6420	1.5577	.8415	.3
.8	.5417	.6445	1.5517	.8406	.2
.9	.5432	.6469	1.5458	.8396	57.1
33.0	0.5446	0.6494	1.5399	0.8387	**57.0**
.1	.5461	.6519	1.5340	.8377	56.9
.2	.5476	.6544	1.5282	.8368	.8
.3	.5490	.6569	1.5224	.8358	.7
.4	.5505	.6594	1.5166	.8348	.6
.5	.5519	.6619	1.5108	.8339	.5
.6	.5534	.6644	1.5051	.8329	.4
.7	.5548	.6669	1.4994	.8320	.3
.8	.5563	.6694	1.4938	.8310	.2
.9	.5577	.6720	1.4882	.8300	56.1
34.0	0.5592	0.6745	1.4826	0.8290	**56.0**
.1	.5606	.6771	1.4770	.8281	55.9
.2	.5621	.6796	1.4715	.8271	.8
.3	.5635	.6822	1.4659	.8261	.7
.4	.5650	.6847	1.4605	.8251	.6
.5	.5664	.6873	1.4550	.8241	.5
.6	.5678	.6899	1.4496	.8231	.4
.7	.5693	.6924	1.4442	.8221	.3
.8	.5707	.6950	1.4388	.8211	.2
.9	.5721	.6976	1.4335	.8202	55.1
35.0	0.5736	0.7002	1.4281	0.8192	**55.0**
.1	.5750	.7028	1.4229	.8181	54.9
.2	.5764	.7054	1.4176	.8171	.8
.3	.5779	.7080	1.4124	.8161	.7
.4	.5793	.7107	1.4071	.8151	.6
.5	.5807	.7133	1.4019	.8141	.5
.6	.5821	.7159	1.3968	.8131	.4
.7	.5835	.7186	1.3916	.8121	.3
.8	.5850	.7212	1.3865	.8111	.2
.9	.5864	.7239	1.3814	.8100	54.1
36.0	0.5878	0.7265	1.3764	0.8090	**54.0**
	Cos	Cot	Tan	Sin	Deg.

NATURAL TRIGONOMETRIC FUNCTIONS
SINE, COSINE, TANGENT, COTANGENT,
FOR ANGLES IN DEGREES AND DECIMALS (Continued)

Deg.	Sin	Tan	Cot	Cos		Deg.	Sin	Tan	Cot	Cos	
36.0	0.5878	0.7265	1.3764	0.8090	**54.0**	**40.5**	0.6494	0.8541	1.1708	0.7604	**49.5**
.1	.5892	.7292	1.3713	.8080	53.9	.6	.6508	.8571	1.1667	.7593	.4
.2	.5906	.7319	1.3663	.8070	.8	.7	.6521	.8601	1.1626	.7581	.3
.3	.5920	.7346	1.3613	.8059	.7	.8	.6534	.8632	1.1585	.7570	.2
.4	.5934	.7373	1.3564	.8049	.6	.9	.6547	.8662	1.1544	.7559	49.1
.5	.5948	.7400	1.3514	.8039	.5	**41.0**	0.6561	0.8693	1.1504	0.7547	**49.0**
.6	.5962	.7427	1.3465	.8028	.4	.1	.6574	.8724	1.1463	.7536	48.9
.7	.5976	.7454	1.3416	.8018	.3	.2	.6587	.8754	1.1423	.7524	.8
.8	.5990	.7481	1.3367	.8007	.2	.3	.6600	.8785	1.1383	.7513	.7
.9	.6004	.7508	1.3319	.7997	53.1	.4	.6613	.8816	1.1343	.7501	.6
37.0	0.6018	0.7536	1.3270	0.7986	**53.0**	.5	.6626	.8847	1.1303	.7490	.5
.1	.6032	.7563	1.3222	.7976	52.9	.6	.6639	.8878	1.1263	.7478	.4
.2	.6046	.7590	1.3175	.7965	.8	.7	.6652	.8910	1.1224	.7466	.3
.3	.6060	.7618	1.3127	.7955	.7	.8	.6665	.8941	1.1184	.7455	.2
.4	.6074	.7646	1.3079	.7944	.6	.9	.6678	.8972	1.1145	.7443	48.1
.5	.6088	.7673	1.3032	.7934	.5	**42.0**	0.6691	0.9004	1.1106	0.7431	**48.0**
.6	.6101	.7701	1.2985	.7923	.4	.1	.6704	.9036	1.1067	.7420	47.9
.7	.6115	.7729	1.2938	.7912	.3	.2	.6717	.9067	1.1028	.7408	.8
.8	.6129	.7757	1.2892	.7902	.2	.3	.6730	.9099	1.0990	.7396	.7
.9	.6143	.7785	1.2846	.7891	52.1	.4	.6743	.9131	1.0951	.7385	.6
38.0	0.6157	0.7813	1.2799	0.7880	**52.0**	.5	.6756	.9163	1.0913	.7373	.5
.1	.6170	.7841	1.2753	.7869	51.9	.6	.6769	.9195	1.0875	.7361	.4
.2	.6184	.7869	1.2708	.7859	.8	.7	.6782	.9228	1.0837	.7349	.3
.3	.6198	.7898	1.2662	.7848	.7	.8	.6794	.9260	1.0799	.7337	.2
.4	.6211	.7926	1.2617	.7837	.6	.9	.6807	.9293	1.0761	.7325	47.1
.5	.6225	.7954	1.2572	.7826	.5	**43.0**	0.6820	0.9325	1.0724	0.7314	**47.0**
.6	.6239	.7983	1.2527	.7815	.4	.1	.6833	.9358	1.0686	.7302	46.9
.7	.6252	.8012	1.2482	.7804	.3	.2	.6845	.9391	1.0649	.7290	.8
.8	.6266	.8040	1.2437	.7793	.2	.3	.6858	.9424	1.0612	.7278	.7
.9	.6280	.8069	1.2393	.7782	51.1	.4	.6871	9457	1.0575	.7266	.6
39.0	0.6293	0.8098	1.2349	0.7771	**51.0**	.5	.6884	.9490	1.0538	.7254	.5
.1	.6307	.8127	1.2305	.7760	50.9	.6	.6896	.9523	1.0501	.7242	.4
.2	.6320	.8156	1.2261	.7749	.8	.7	.6909	.9556	1.0464	.7230	.3
.3	.6334	.8185	1.2218	.7738	.7	.8	.6921	.9590	1.0428	.7218	.2
.4	.6347	.8214	1.2174	.7727	.6	.9	.6934	.9623	1.0392	.7206	46.1
.5	.6361	.8243	1.2131	.7716	.5	**44.0**	0.6947	0.9657	1.0355	0.7193	**46.0**
.6	.6374	.8273	1.2088	.7705	.4	.1	.6959	.9691	1.0319	.7181	45.9
.7	.6388	.8302	1.2045	.7694	.3	.2	.6972	.9725	1.0283	.7169	.8
.8	.6401	.8332	1.2002	.7683	.2	.3	.6984	.9759	1.0247	.7157	.7
.9	.6414	.8361	1.1960	.7672	50.1	.4	.6997	.9793	1.0212	.7145	.6
40.0	0.6428	0.8391	1.1918	0.7660	**50.0**	.5	.7009	.9827	1.0176	.7133	.5
.1	.6441	.8421	1.1875	.7649	49.9	.6	.7022	.9861	1.0141	.7120	.4
.2	.6455	.8451	1.1833	.7638	.8	.7	.7034	.9896	1.0105	.7108	.3
.3	.6468	.8481	1.1792	.7627	.7	.8	.7046	.9930	1.0070	.7096	.2
.4	.6481	.8511	1.1750	.7615	.6	.9	.7059	.9965	1.0035	.7083	45.1
40.5	0.6494	0.8541	1.1708	0.7604	**49.5**	**45.0**	0.7071	1.0000	1.0000	0.7071	**45.0**
	Cos	Cot	Tan	Sin	Deg.		Cos	Cot	Tan	Sin	Deg.

NATURAL TRIGONOMETRIC FUNCTIONS TO FIVE TENTHS OF A DEGREE
(SECANTS AND COSECANTS)

Deg.	Sec	Csc	Deg.		Deg.	Sec	Csc	Deg.
0.0	1.00000	∞	90.0		22.5	1.08239	2.61313	67.5
0.5	1.00004	114.59301	89.5		23.0	1.08636	2.55930	67.0
1.0	1.00015	57.29869	89.0		23.5	1.09044	2.50784	66.5
1.5	1.00034	38.20155	88.5		24.0	1.09464	2.45859	66.0
2.0	1.00061	28.65371	88.0		24.5	1.09895	2.41142	65.5
2.5	1.00095	22.92559	87.5		25.0	1.10338	2.36620	65.0
3.0	1.00137	19.10732	87.0		25.5	1.10793	2.32282	64.5
3.5	1.00187	16.38041	86.5		26.0	1.11260	2.28117	64.0
4.0	1.00244	14.33559	86.0		26.5	1.11740	2.24116	63.5
4.5	1.00309	12.74549	85.5		27.0	1.12233	2.20269	63.0
5.0	1.00382	11.47371	85.0		27.5	1.12738	2.16568	62.5
5.5	1.00463	10.43343	84.5		28.0	1.13257	2.13005	62.0
6.0	1.00551	9.56677	84.0		28.5	1.13789	2.09574	61.5
6.5	1.00647	8.83367	83.5		29.0	1.14335	2.06267	61.0
7.0	1.00751	8.20551	83.0		29.5	1.14896	2.03077	60.5
7.5	1.00863	7.66130	82.5		30.0	1.15470	2.00000	60.0
8.0	1.00983	7.18530	82.0		30.5	1.16059	1.97029	59.5
8.5	1.01111	6.76547	81.5		31.0	1.16663	1.94160	59.0
9.0	1.01247	6.39245	81.0		31.5	1.17283	1.91388	58.5
9.5	1.01391	6.05886	80.5		32.0	1.17918	1.88708	58.0
10.0	1.01543	5.75877	80.0		32.5	1.18569	1.86116	57.5
10.5	1.01703	5.48740	79.5		33.0	1.19236	1.83608	57.0
11.0	1.01872	5.24084	79.0		33.5	1.19920	1.81180	56.5
11.5	1.02049	5.01585	78.5		34.0	1.20622	1.78829	56.0
12.0	1.02234	4.80973	78.0		34.5	1.21341	1.76552	55.5
12.5	1.02428	4.62023	77.5		35.0	1.22077	1.74345	55.0
13.0	1.02630	4.44541	77.0		35.5	1.22833	1.72205	54.5
13.5	1.02842	4.28366	76.5		36.0	1.23607	1.70130	54.0
14.0	1.03061	4.13357	76.0		36.5	1.24400	1.68117	53.5
14.5	1.03290	3.99393	75.5		37.0	1.25214	1.66164	53.0
15.0	1.03528	3.86370	75.0		37.5	1.26047	1.64268	52.5
15.5	1.03774	3.74198	74.5		38.0	1.26902	1.62427	52.0
16.0	1.04030	3.62796	74.0		38.5	1.27778	1.60639	51.5
16.5	1.04295	3.52094	73.5		39.0	1.28676	1.58902	51.0
17.0	1.04569	3.42030	73.0		39.5	1.29597	1.57213	50.5
17.5	1.04853	3.32551	72.5		40.0	1.30541	1.55572	50.0
18.0	1.05146	3.23607	72.0		40.5	1.31509	1.53977	49.5
18.5	1.05449	3.15155	71.5		41.0	1.32501	1.52425	49.0
19.0	1.05762	3.07155	71.0		41.5	1.33519	1.50916	48.5
19.5	1.06085	2.99574	70.5		42.0	1.34563	1.49448	48.0
20.0	1.06418	2.92380	70.0		42.5	1.35634	1.48019	47.5
20.5	1.06761	2.85545	69.5		43.0	1.36733	1.46628	47.0
21.0	1.07114	2.79043	69.0		43.5	1.37860	1.45274	46.5
21.5	1.07479	2.72850	68.5		44.0	1.39016	1.43956	46.0
22.0	1.07853	2.66947	68.0		44.5	1.40203	1.42672	45.5
22.5	1.08239	2.61313	67.5		45.0	1.41421	1.41421	45.0
	Csc	Sec				Csc	Sec	

Tables for Use in Trigonometry
NATURAL TRIGONOMETRIC FUNCTIONS
FOR ANGLES IN RADIANS

x	Sin	Tan	Cot	Cos	x	Sin	Tan	Cot	Cos
.00	.00000	.00000	∞	1.00000	**.50**	.47943	.54630	1.8305	.87758
01	.01000	.01000	99.997	0.99995	.51	.48818	.55936	1.7878	.87274
.02	.02000	.02000	49.993	.99980	.52	.49688	.57256	1.7465	.86782
.03	.03000	.03001	33.323	.99955	.53	.50553	.58592	1.7067	.86281
.04	.03999	.04002	24.987	.99920	.54	.51414	.59943	1.6683	.85771
.05	.04998	.05004	19.983	.99875	.55	.52269	.61311	1.6310	.85252
.06	.05996	.06007	16.647	.99820	.56	.53119	.62695	1.5950	.84726
.07	.06994	.07011	14.262	.99755	.57	.53963	.64097	1.5601	.84190
.08	.07991	.08017	12.473	.99680	.58	.54802	.65517	1.5263	.83646
.09	.08988	.09024	11.081	.99595	.59	.55636	.66956	1.4935	.83094
.10	.09983	.10033	9.9666	.99500	**.60**	.56464	.68414	1.4617	.82534
.11	.10978	.11045	9.0542	.99396	.61	.57287	.69892	1.4308	.81965
.12	.11971	.12058	8.2933	.99281	.62	.58104	.71391	1.4007	.81388
.13	.12963	.13074	7.6489	.99156	.63	.58914	.72911	1.3715	.80803
.14	.13954	.14092	7.0961	.99022	.64	.59720	.74454	1.3431	.80210
.15	.14944	.15114	6.6166	.98877	.65	.60519	.76020	1.3154	.79608
.16	.15932	.16138	6.1966	.98723	.66	.61312	.77610	1.2885	.78999
.17	.16918	.17166	5.8256	.98558	.67	.62099	.79225	1.2622	.78382
.18	.17903	.18197	5.4954	.98384	.68	.62879	.80866	1.2366	.77757
.19	.18886	.19232	5.1997	.98200	.69	.63654	.82534	1.2116	.77125
.20	.19867	.20271	4.9332	.98007	**.70**	.64422	.84229	1.1872	.76484
.21	.20846	.21314	4.6917	.97803	.71	.65183	.85953	1.1634	.75836
.22	.21823	.22362	4.4719	.97590	.72	.65938	.87707	1.1402	.75181
.23	.22798	.23414	4.2709	.97367	.73	.66687	.89492	1.1174	.74517
.24	.23770	.24472	4.0864	.97134	.74	.67429	.91309	1.0952	.73847
.25	.24740	.25534	3.9163	.96891	.75	.68164	.93160	1.0734	.73169
.26	.25708	.26602	3.7591	.96639	.76	.68892	.95045	1.0521	.72484
.27	.26673	.27676	3.6133	.96377	.77	.69614	.96967	1.0313	.71791
.28	.27636	.28755	3.4776	.96106	.78	.70328	.98926	1.0109	.71091
.29	.28595	.29841	3.3511	.95824	.79	.71035	1.0092	.99084	.70385
.30	.29552	.30934	3.2327	.95534	**.80**	.71736	1.0296	.97121	.69671
.31	.30506	.32033	3.1218	.95233	.81	.72429	1.0505	.95197	.68950
.32	.31457	.33139	3.0176	.94924	.82	.73115	1.0717	.93309	.68222
.33	.32404	.34252	2.9195	.94604	.83	.73793	1.0934	.91455	.67488
.34	.33349	.35374	2.8270	.94275	.84	.74464	1.1156	.89635	.66746
.35	.34290	.36503	2.7395	.93937	.85	.75128	1.1383	.87848	.65998
.36	.35227	.37640	2.6567	.93590	.86	.75784	1.1616	.86091	.65244
.37	.36162	.38786	2.5782	.93233	.87	.76433	1.1853	.84365	.64483
.38	.37092	.39941	2.5037	.92866	.88	.77074	1.2097	.82668	.63715
.39	.38019	.41105	2.4328	.92491	.89	.77707	1.2346	.80998	.62941
.40	.38942	.42279	2.3652	.92106	**.90**	.78333	1.2602	.79355	.62161
.41	.39861	.43463	2.3008	.91712	.91	.78950	1.2864	.77738	.61375
.42	.40776	.44657	2.2393	.91309	.92	.79560	1.3133	.76146	.60582
.43	.41687	.45862	2.1804	.90897	.93	.80162	1.3409	.74578	.59783
.44	.42594	.47078	2.1241	.90475	.94	.80756	1.3692	.73034	.58979
.45	.43497	.48306	2.0702	.90045	.95	.81342	1.3984	.71511	.58168
.46	.44395	.49545	2.0184	.89605	.96	.81919	1.4284	.70010	.57352
.47	.45289	.50797	1.9686	.89157	.97	.82489	1.4592	.68531	.56530
.48	.46178	.52061	1.9208	.88699	.98	.83050	1.4910	.67071	.55702
.49	.47063	.53339	1.8748	.88233	.99	.83603	1.5237	.65631	.54869
.50	.47943	.54630	1.8305	.87758	**1.00**	.84147	1.5574	.64209	.54030
x	Sin	Tan	Cot	Cos	x	Sin	Tan	Cot	Cos

NATURAL TRIGONOMETRIC FUNCTIONS
FOR ANGLES IN RADIANS (Continued)

x	Sin	Tan	Cot	Cos	x	Sin	Tan	Cot	Cos
1.00	.84147	1.5574	.64209	.54030	1.50	.99749	14.101	.07091	.07074
1.01	.84683	1.5922	.62806	.53186	1.51	.99815	16.428	.06087	.06076
1.02	.85211	1.6281	.61420	.52337	1.52	.99871	19.670	.05084	.05077
1.03	.85730	1.6652	.60051	.51482	1.53	.99917	24.498	.04082	.04079
1.04	.86240	1.7036	.58699	.50622	1.54	.99953	32.461	.03081	.03079
1.05	.86742	1.7433	.57362	.49757	1.55	.99978	48.078	.02080	.02079
1.06	.87236	1.7844	.56040	.48887	1.56	.99994	92.620	.01080	.01080
1.07	.87720	1.8270	.54734	.48012	1.57	1.00000	1255.8	.00080	.00080
1.08	.88196	1.8712	.53441	.47133	1.58	.99996	−108.65	−.00920	−.00920
1.09	.88663	1.9171	.52162	.46249	1.59	.99982	−52.067	−.01921	−.01920
1.10	.89121	1.9648	.50897	.45360	1.60	.99957	−34.233	−.02921	−.02920
1.11	.89570	2.0143	.49644	.44466	1.61	.99923	−25.495	−.03922	−.03919
1.12	.90010	2.0660	.48404	.43568	1.62	.99879	−20.307	−.04924	−.04918
1.13	.90441	2.1198	.47175	.42666	1.63	.99825	−16.871	−.05927	−.05917
1.14	.90863	2.1759	.45959	.41759	1.64	.99761	−14.427	−.06931	−.06915
1.15	.91276	2.2345	.44753	.40849	1.65	.99687	−12.599	−.07397	−.07912
1.16	.91680	2.2958	.43558	.39934	1.66	.99602	−11.181	−.08944	−.08909
1.17	.92075	2.3600	.42373	.39015	1.67	.99508	−10.047	−.09953	−.09904
1.18	.92461	2.4273	.41199	.38092	1.68	.99404	− 9.1208	−.10964	−.10899
1.19	.92837	2.4979	.40034	.37166	1.69	.99290	− 8.3492	−.11977	−.11892
1.20	.93204	2.5722	.38878	.36236	1.70	.99166	− 7.6966	−.12993	−.12884
1.21	.93562	2.6503	.37731	.35302	1.71	.99033	− 7.1373	−.14011	−.13875
1.22	.93910	2.7328	.36593	.34365	1.72	.98889	− 6.6524	−.15032	−.14865
1.23	.94249	2.8198	.35463	.33424	1.73	.98735	− 6.2281	−.16056	−.15853
1.24	.94578	2.9119	.34341	.32480	1.74	.98572	− 5.8535	−.17084	−.16840
1.25	.94898	3.0096	.33227	.31532	1.75	.98399	− 5.5204	−.18115	−.17825
1.26	.95209	3.1133	.32121	.30582	1.76	.98215	− 5.2221	−.19149	−.18808
1.27	.95510	3.2236	.31021	.29628	1.77	.98022	− 4.9534	−.20188	−.19789
1.28	.95802	3.3413	.29928	.28672	1.78	.97820	− 4.7101	−.21231	−.20768
1.29	.96084	3.4672	.28842	.27712	1.79	.97607	− 4.4887	−.22278	−.21745
1.30	.96356	3.6021	.27762	.26750	1.80	.97385	− 4.2863	−.23330	−.22720
1.31	.96618	3.7471	.26687	.25785	1.81	.97153	− 4.1005	−.24387	−.23693
1.32	.96872	3.9033	.25619	.24818	1.82	.96911	− 3.9294	−.25449	−.24663
1.33	.97115	4.0723	.24556	.23848	1.83	.96659	− 3.7712	−.26517	−.25631
1.34	.97348	4.2556	.23498	.22875	1.84	.96398	− 3.6245	−.27590	−.26596
1.35	.97572	4.4552	.22446	.21901	1.85	.96128	− 3.4881	−.28669	−.27559
1.36	.97786	4.6734	.21398	.20924	1.86	.95847	− 3.3608	−.29755	−.28519
1.37	.97991	4.9131	.20354	.19945	1.87	.95557	− 2.2419	−.30846	−.29476
1.38	.98185	5.1774	.19315	.18964	1.88	.95258	− 3.1304	−.31945	−.30430
1.39	.98370	5.4707	.18279	.17981	1.89	.94949	− 3.0257	−.33051	−.31381
1.40	.98545	5.7979	.17248	.16997	1.90	.94630	− 2.9271	−.34164	−.32329
1.41	.98710	6.1654	.16220	.16010	1.91	.94302	− 2.8341	−.35284	−.33274
1.42	.98865	6.5811	.15195	.15023	1.92	.93965	− 2.7463	−.36413	−.34215
1.43	.99010	7.0555	.14173	.14033	1.93	.93618	− 2.6632	−.37549	−.35153
1.44	.99146	7.6018	.13155	.13042	1.94	.93262	− 2.5843	−.38695	−.36087
1.45	.99271	8.2381	.12139	.12050	1.95	.92896	− 2.5095	−.39849	−.37018
1.46	.99387	8.9886	.11125	.11057	1.96	.92521	− 2.4383	−.41012	−.37945
1.47	.99492	9.8874	.10114	.10063	1.97	.92137	− 2.3705	−.42185	−.38868
1.48	.99588	10.983	.09105	.09067	1.98	.91744	− 2.3058	−.43368	−.39788
1.49	.99674	12.350	.08097	.08071	1.99	.91341	− 2.2441	−.44562	−.40703
1.50	.99749	14.101	.07091	.07074	2.00	.90930	− 2.1850	−.45766	−.41615
x	Sin	Tan	Cot	Cos	x	Sin	Tan	Cot	Cos

NATURAL TRIGONOMETRIC FUNCTIONS
SECANTS AND COSECANTS
FOR ANGLES IN RADIANS

x	sec x	csc x	x	sec x	csc x	x	sec x	csc x
0.00	1.00000	∞	0.55	1.17299	1.91319	1.10	2.20460	1.12207
0.01	1.00005	100.00167	0.56	1.18028	1.88258	1.11	2.24890	1.11645
0.02	1.00020	50.00333	0.57	1.18779	1.85311	1.12	2.29525	1.11099
0.03	1.00045	33.33833	0.58	1.19551	1.82474	1.13	2.34379	1.10569
0.04	1.00080	25.00667	0.59	1.20346	1.79739	1.14	2.39467	1.10055
0.05	1.00125	20.00834	0.60	1.21163	1.77103	1.15	2.44806	1.09557
0.06	1.00180	16.67667	0.61	1.22004	1.74560	1.16	2.50413	1.09075
0.07	1.00246	14.29739	0.62	1.22868	1.72107	1.17	2.56311	1.08607
0.08	1.00321	12.51334	0.63	1.23758	1.69738	1.18	2.62519	1.08154
0.09	1.00406	11.12613	0.64	1.24673	1.67449	1.19	2.69063	1.07716
0.10	1.00502	10.01669	0.65	1.25615	1.65238	1.20	2.75970	1.07292
0.11	1.00608	9.10927	0.66	1.26584	1.63101	1.21	2.83271	1.06881
0.12	1.00724	8.35337	0.67	1.27580	1.61034	1.22	2.90997	1.06485
0.13	1.00851	7.71402	0.68	1.28605	1.59035	1.23	2.99188	1.06102
0.14	1.00988	7.16624	0.69	1.29660	1.57100	1.24	3.07885	1.05732
0.15	1.01136	6.69173	0.70	1.30746	1.55227	1.24	3.17136	1.05376
0.16	1.01294	6.27675	0.71	1.31863	1.53413	1.26	3.26993	1.05032
0.17	1.01463	5.91078	0.72	1.33013	1.51657	1.27	3.37518	1.04701
0.18	1.01642	5.58567	0.73	1.34197	1.49954	1.28	3.48778	1.04382
0.19	1.01833	5.29496	0.74	1.35415	1.48305	1.29	3.60853	1.04076
0.20	1.02034	5.03349	0.75	1.36670	1.46705	1.30	3.73833	1.03782
0.21	1.02246	4.79709	0.76	1.37962	1.45154	1.31	3.87822	1.03500
0.22	1.02470	4.58233	0.77	1.39293	1.43650	1.32	4.02941	1.03230
0.23	1.02705	4.38640	0.78	1.40664	1.42191	1.33	4.19329	1.02971
0.24	1.02951	4.20694	0.79	1.42077	1.40775	1.34	4.37153	1.02724
0.25	1.03209	4.04197	0.80	1.43532	1.39401	1.35	4.56607	1.02488
0.26	1.03478	3.88983	0.81	1.45033	1.38067	1.36	4.77923	1.02264
0.27	1.03759	3.74909	0.82	1.46580	1.36772	1.37	5.01379	1.02050
0.28	1.04052	3.61853	0.83	1.48175	1.35514	1.38	5.27313	1.01848
0.29	1.04358	3.49709	0.84	1.49821	1.34293	1.39	5.56133	1.01657
0.30	1.04675	3.38386	0.85	1.51519	1.33106	1.40	5.88349	1.01477
0.31	1.05005	3.27806	0.86	1.53271	1.31954	1.41	6.24593	1.01307
0.32	1.05348	3.17898	0.87	1.55080	1.30834	1.42	6.65666	1.01148
0.33	1.05704	3.08601	0.88	1.56949	1.29746	1.43	7.12598	1.00999
0.34	1.06072	2.99862	0.89	1.58878	1.28688	1.44	7.66732	1.00862
0.35	1.06454	2.91632	0.90	1.60873	1.27661	1.45	8.29856	1.00734
0.36	1.06849	2.83870	0.91	1.62934	1.26662	1.46	9.04406	1.00617
0.37	1.07258	2.76537	0.92	1.65065	1.25691	1.47	9.93782	1.00510
0.38	1.07682	2.69600	0.93	1.67271	1.24747	1.48	11.02881	1.00414
0.39	1.08119	2.63027	0.94	1.69552	1.23830	1.49	12.39028	1.00327
0.40	1.08570	2.56793	0.95	1.71915	1.22938	1.50	14.13683	1.00251
0.41	1.09037	2.50872	0.96	1.74362	1.22072	1.51	16.45850	1.00185
0.42	1.09518	2.45242	0.97	1.76897	1.21229	1.52	19.69493	1.00129
0.43	1.10015	2.39882	0.98	1.79526	1.20410	1.53	24.51881	1.00083
0.44	1.10528	2.34775	0.99	1.82252	1.19614	1.54	32.47654	1.00047
0.45	1.11056	2.29903	1.00	1.85082	1.18840	1.55	48.08888	1.00022
0.46	1.11601	2.25252	1.01	1.88019	1.18087	1.56	92.62589	1.00006
0.47	1.12162	2.20806	1.02	1.91071	1.17356	1.57	+1255.76599	1.00000
0.48	1.12740	2.16554	1.03	1.94243	1.16645	1.58	− 108.65381	1.00004
0.49	1.13336	2.12483	1.04	1.97542	1.15955	1.59	− 52.07657	1.00018
0.50	1.13949	2.08583	1.05	2.00976	1.15284	1.60	− 34.24714	1.00043
0.51	1.14581	2.04844	1.06	2.04552	1.14632			
0.52	1.15231	2.01256	1.07	2.08279	1.13999			
0.53	1.15901	1.97811	1.08	2.12166	1.13384			
0.54	1.16590	1.94501	1.09	2.16223	1.12787			
0.55	1.17299	1.91319	1.10	2.20460	1.12207			

NATURAL TRIGONOMETRIC FUNCTIONS
SINE, TANGENT, COTANGENT, COSINE
FOR ANGLES IN πx RADIANS

x		Sin (πx)	Tan (πx)	Cot (πx)	Cos (πx)
.00 or 1.00		.00000	.00000	inf	1.00000
.01	.99	.03141	.03143	31.821	.99951
.02	.98	.06279	.06291	15.895	.99803
.03	.97	.09411	.09453	10.579	.99556
.04	.96	.12533	.12633	7.9158	.99211
.05	.95	.15643	.15838	6.3138	.98769
.06	.94	.18738	.19076	5.2422	.98229
.07	.93	.21814	.22353	4.4737	.97592
.08	.92	.24869	.25676	3.8947	.96858
.09	.91	.27899	.29053	3.4420	.96029
.10	.90	.30902	.32492	3.0777	.95106
.11	.89	.33874	.36002	2.7776	.94088
.12	.88	.36812	.39593	2.5257	.92978
.13	.87	.39715	.43274	2.3109	.91775
.14	.86	.42578	.47056	2.1251	.90483
.15	.85	.45399	.50953	1.9626	.89101
.16	.84	.48175	.54975	1.8190	.87631
.17	.83	.50904	.59140	1.6909	.86074
.18	.82	.53583	.63462	1.5757	.84433
.19	.81	.56208	.67960	1.4715	.82708
.20	.80	.58779	.72654	1.3764	.80902
.21	.79	.61291	.77568	1.2892	.79016
.22	.78	.63742	.82727	1.2088	.77051
.23	.77	.66131	.88162	1.1343	.75011
.24	.76	.68455	.93906	1.0649	.72897
.25	.75	.70711	1.0000	1.0000	.70711
.26	.74	.72897	1.0649	.93906	.68455
.27	.73	.75011	1.1343	.88162	.66131
.28	.72	.77051	1.2088	.82727	.63742
.29	.71	.79016	1.2892	.77568	.61291
.30	.70	.80902	1.3764	.72654	.58779
.31	.69	.82708	1.4715	.67960	.56208
.32	.68	.84433	1.5757	.63462	.53583
.33	.67	.86074	1.6909	.59140	.50904
.34	.66	.87631	1.8190	.54975	.48175
.35	.65	.89101	1.9626	.50953	.45399
.36	.64	.90483	2.1251	.47056	.42578
.37	.63	.91775	2.3109	.43274	.39715
.38	.62	.92978	2.5257	.39593	.36812
.39	.61	.94088	2.7776	.36002	.33874
.40	.60	.95106	3.0777	.32492	.30902
.41	.59	.96029	3.4420	.29053	.27899
.42	.58	.96858	3.8947	.25676	.24869
.43	.57	.97592	4.4737	.22353	.21814
.44	.56	.98229	5.2422	.19076	.18738
.45	.55	.98769	6.3138	.15838	.15643
.46	.54	.99211	7.9158	.12633	.12533
.47	.53	.99556	10.579	.09453	.09411
.48	.52	.99803	15.895	.06291	.06279
.49	.51	.99951	31.821	.03143	.03141
.50	.50	1.0000	inf	.00000	.00000

These functions are useful in the solution of wave equations such as the displacement equation of a sound wave in the form:

$$y = A \sin 2\pi n x$$

without the necessity of reducing the angular rotation either to radians or to degrees in order to find the value of the function.

The algebraic sign of the function follows the familiar Quadrant Law for the particular function desired. Thus a numerical value of 9.13π radians becomes (by the subtraction of the greatest multiple of 2π radians) 1.13π radians. This is the same as $.13\pi$ radians in the 3rd Quadrant, which would give, from the tables above, a value of the sine function of $-.39715$.

Submitted by J. A. Blythe Jr.

COMMON LOGARITHMS OF THE
TRIGONOMETRIC FUNCTIONS

Logarithms of the functions are given for each minute from 0–360°.

The quantity -10 is to be appended to all logarithms of the sine and cosine, to logarithms of the tangent from 0–45° and of the cotangent from 45–90°.

With degrees indicated at either side of top of the page use the column headings at the top. With degrees stated at bottom of the page use the column designations at the bottom.

With degrees at the left (top or bottom) use the minute column at the left, and with degrees on the right side of the page use the minute column at the right.

To illustrate the proper employment of headings for angles in the four quadrants—

log sin 6° 23′ = 9.04603 − 10	log sin 186° 23′ = 9.04603 − 10
log sin 83° 15′ = 9.99698 − 10	log sin 263° 15′ = 9.99698 − 10
log cos 96° 41′ = 9.06589 − 10	log cos 276° 41′ = 9.06589 − 10
log cos 173° 49′ = 9.99747 − 10	log cos 353° 49′ = 9.99747 − 10

For the accurate determination of values where the tabular differences are large, the values of CS and CT are given. The following equations indicate their use.

To find the logarithm of the functions of an angle:

For angles 0–3°	For angles 87–90°
$\log \sin \theta = \log \theta'' - CS$	$\log \cos \theta = \log (90° - \theta)'' - CS$
$\log \tan \theta = \log \theta'' - CT$	$\log \cot \theta = \log (90° - \theta)'' - CT$
$\log \cot \theta = \text{colog} \tan \theta$	$\log \tan \theta = \text{colog} \cot \theta$

To find the angle:

For angles 0–3°	For angles 87–90°
$\log \theta'' = \log \sin \theta + CS$	$\log (90° - \theta)'' = \log \cos \theta + CS$
$\log \theta'' = \log \tan \theta + CT$	$\log (90° - \theta)'' = \log \cot \theta + CT$

In the above expressions, θ'' and $(90° - \theta)''$ are used to indicate the value of the angles expressed in seconds. The values in the body of the table are the cologarithms and should be used as indicated above.

The values of the logarithms S and T are also given in a separate table. For these the following relations hold:

To find the function of an angle:

$\log \sin \theta = \log \theta'' + S$	$\log \cos \theta = \log (90° - \theta)'' + S$
$\log \tan \theta = \log \theta'' + T$	$\log \cot \theta = \log (90° - \theta)'' + T$

To find the angle:

$\log \theta'' = \log \sin \theta - S$	$\log (90° - \theta)'' = \log \cos \theta - S$
$\log \theta'' = \log \tan \theta - T$	$\log (90° - \theta)'' = \log \cot \theta - T$

Where the values of CS and CT are given, the logarithms of the angles expressed in seconds are given in the supplementary column at the left.

The tabular differences are given under the headings "d." and "c.d.", the latter referring to the common difference for the tangent and cotangent. Tables of proportional parts ("p.p.") facilitate interpolation. At the bottom of each column will be found special proportional parts between the tabular differences for the tangent or cotangent and those for the sine or cosine. These are useful when one function is to be obtained directly from the other without determining the angle.

For example, suppose log tan θ is given as 9.67644 and log cos θ is required. The difference between the given logarithm and that given in the table, 9.67622 (opposite 25° 23′), is 22. The tabular differences of the two logarithmic functions at this place are 32 and 6. In the proportional table for $\frac{6}{32}$, 22 corresponds to 4; this, subtracted from the tabular logarithmic cosine 9.95591, gives the required log cos θ = 9.95587.

The symbols $\bar{5}$ and $\acute{5}$ are used to indicate how the terminal 5 has been derived. For example, the logarithm 8.8307$\bar{5}$ is more fully given as 8.8307495 while the value 9.4082$\acute{5}$ is derived from 9.4082539. Thus, in rounding off to four places, a number ending in $\bar{5}$ should be decreased but a number ending in $\acute{5}$ should be increased.

282

COMMON LOGARITHMS OF THE TRIGONOMETRIC FUNCTIONS
Values of S and T

Min.	Values of S, − 10 to be appended					Values of T, − 10 to be appended					Sec.
	0°	1°	2°	3°	4°	0°	1°	2°	3°	4°	
0′	4.68 557	555	549	538	522	4.68 557	562	575	597	628	0″
1	557	555	549	537	522	557	562	575	598	629	60
2	557	555	548	537	522	557	562	576	598	629	120
3	557	555	548	537	521	557	562	576	599	630	180
4	557	555	548	537	521	558	563	576	599	631	240
5	557	555	548	537	521	558	563	577	599	631	300
6	557	555	548	536	520	558	563	577	600	632	360
7	557	555	548	536	520	558	563	577	600	632	420
8	557	555	548	536	520	558	563	578	601	633	480
9	557	555	547	536	520	558	563	578	601	634	540
10	4.68 557	555	547	535	519	4.68 558	564	578	602	634	600
11	557	554	547	535	519	558	564	579	602	635	660
12	557	554	547	535	519	558	564	579	603	635	720
13	557	554	547	535	518	558	564	579	603	636	780
14	557	554	547	534	518	558	564	580	604	637	840
15	557	554	546	534	518	558	564	580	604	637	900
16	557	554	546	534	517	558	565	580	605	638	960
17	557	554	546	534	517	558	565	581	605	639	1020
18	557	554	546	534	517	558	565	581	606	639	1080
19	557	554	546	533	516	558	565	581	606	640	1140
20	4.68 557	554	546	533	516	4.68 558	565	582	607	640	1200
21	557	554	545	533	516	558	566	582	607	641	1260
22	557	553	545	533	515	558	566	582	608	642	1320
23	557	553	545	532	515	558	566	583	608	642	1380
24	557	553	545	532	515	558	566	583	609	643	1440
25	557	553	545	532	515	558	566	583	609	644	1500
26	557	553	544	532	514	558	567	584	610	644	1560
27	557	553	544	531	514	558	567	584	610	645	1620
28	557	553	544	531	514	558	567	584	611	646	1680
29	557	553	544	531	513	559	567	585	611	646	1740
30	4.68 557	553	544	531	513	4.68 559	567	585	612	647	1800
31	557	552	544	530	513	559	568	585	612	648	1860
32	557	552	543	530	512	559	568	586	613	648	1920
33	557	552	543	530	512	559	568	586	613	649	1980
34	557	552	543	529	512	559	568	587	614	650	2040
35	557	552	543	529	511	559	569	587	614	650	2100
36	557	552	543	529	511	559	569	587	615	651	2160
37	557	552	542	529	511	559	569	588	615	652	2220
38	557	552	542	528	510	559	569	588	616	652	2280
39	557	552	542	528	510	559	570	589	616	653	2340
40	4.68 557	551	542	528	510	4.68 559	570	589	617	654	2400
41	556	551	542	528	509	560	570	589	617	654	2460
42	556	551	541	527	509	560	570	590	618	655	2520
43	556	551	541	527	508	560	571	590	619	656	2580
44	556	551	541	527	508	560	571	591	619	656	2640
45	556	551	541	527	508	560	571	591	620	657	2700
46	556	551	541	526	507	560	571	591	620	658	2760
47	556	551	540	526	507	560	572	592	621	659	2820
48	556	550	540	526	507	560	572	592	621	659	2880
49	556	550	540	525	506	560	572	593	622	660	2940
50	4.68 556	550	540	525	506	4.68 561	572	593	622	661	3000
51	556	550	540	525	506	561	573	593	623	661	3060
52	556	550	539	525	505	561	573	594	624	662	3120
53	556	550	539	524	505	561	573	594	624	663	3180
54	556	550	539	524	505	561	573	595	625	664	3240
55	556	549	539	524	504	561	574	595	625	664	3300
56	556	549	539	523	504	561	574	596	626	665	3360
57	556	549	538	523	503	562	574	596	626	666	3420
58	555	549	538	523	503	562	575	596	627	667	3480
59	555	549	538	523	503	562	575	597	628	667	3540
60	4.68 555	549	538	522	502	4.68 562	575	597	628	668	3600

COMMON LOGARITHMS OF THE TRIGONOMETRIC FUNCTIONS (Continued)

0° (180°)   (359°) **179°**

"	'	L. Sin.	*d.	C. S.	C. T.	L. Tan	*c.d.	L. Cot.	L. Cos.	'
0	0	—		—	—	6.46 373		—	0.00 000	60
60	1	6.46 373	30103	5.31 443	5.31 443	6.46 373	30103	3.53 627	0.00 000	59
120	2	6.76 476	17609	5.31 443	5.31 443	6.76 476	17609	3.23 524	0.00 000	58
180	3	6.94 085	12494	5.31 443	5.31 443	6.94 085	12494	3.05 915	0.00 000	57
240	4	7.06 579	9691	5.31 443	5.31 442	7.06 579	9691	2.93 421	0.00 000	56
300	5	7.16 270	7918	5.31 443	5.31 442	7.16 270	7918	2.83 730	0.00 000	55
360	6	7.24 188	6694	5.31 443	5.31 442	7.24 188	6694	2.75 812	0.00 000	54
420	7	7.30 882	5800	5.31 443	5.31 442	7.30 882	5800	2.69 118	0.00 000	53
480	8	7.36 682	5115	5.31 443	5.31 442	7.36 682	5115	2.63 318	0.00 000	52
540	9	7.41 797	4576	5.31 443	5.31 442	7.41 797	4576	2.58 203	0.00 000	51
600	10	7.46 373	4139	5.31 443	5.31 442	7.46 373	4139	2.53 627	0.00 000	50
660	11	7.50 512	3779	5.31 443	5.31 442	7.50 512	3779	2.49 488	0.00 000	49
720	12	7.54 291	3476	5.31 443	5.31 442	7.54 291	3476	2.45 709	0.00 000	48
780	13	7.57 767	3218	5.31 443	5.31 442	7.57 767	3219	2.42 233	0.00 000	47
840	14	7.60 985	2997	5.31 443	5.31 442	7.60 986	2996	2.39 014	0.00 000	46
900	15	7.63 982	2802	5.31 443	5.31 442	7.63 982	2803	2.36 018	0.00 000	45
960	16	7.66 784	2633	5.31 443	5.31 442	7.66 785	2633	2.33 215	0.00 000	44
1020	17	7.69 417	2483	5.31 443	5.31 442	7.69 417	2482	2.30 582	9.99 999	43
1080	18	7.71 900	2348	5.31 443	5.31 442	7.71 900	2348	2.28 100	9.99 999	42
1140	19	7.74 248	2227	5.31 443	5.31 442	7.74 248	2228	2.25 752	9.99 999	41
1200	20	7.76 475	2119	5.31 443	5.31 442	7.76 476	2119	2.23 524	9.99 999	40
1260	21	7.78 594	2021	5.31 443	5.31 442	7.78 595	2020	2.21 405	9.99 999	39
1320	22	7.80 615	1930	5.31 443	5.31 442	7.80 615	1931	2.19 385	9.99 999	38
1380	23	7.82 545	1848	5.31 443	5.31 442	7.82 546	1848	2.17 454	9.99 999	37
1440	24	7.84 393	1773	5.31 443	5.31 442	7.84 394	1773	2.15 606	9.99 999	36
1500	25	7.86 166	1704	5.31 443	5.31 442	7.86 167	1704	2.13 833	9.99 999	35
1560	26	7.87 870	1639	5.31 443	5.31 442	7.87 871	1639	2.12 129	9.99 999	34
1620	27	7.89 509	1579	5.31 443	5.31 442	7.89 510	1579	2.10 490	9.99 999	33
1680	28	7.91 088	1524	5.31 443	5.31 442	7.91 089	1524	2.08 911	9.99 999	32
1740	29	7.92 612	1472	5.31 443	5.31 441	7.92 613	1473	2.07 387	9.99 998	31
1800	30	7.94 084	1424	5.31 443	5.31 441	7.94 086	1424	2.05 914	9.99 998	30
1860	31	7.95 508	1379	5.31 443	5.31 441	7.95 510	1379	2.04 490	9.99 998	29
1920	32	7.96 887	1336	5.31 443	5.31 441	7.96 889	1336	2.03 111	9.99 998	28
1980	33	7.98 223	1297	5.31 443	5.31 441	7.98 225	1297	2.01 775	9.99 998	27
2040	34	7.99 520	1259	5.31 443	5.31 441	7.99 522	1259	2.00 478	9.99 998	26
2100	35	8.00 779	1223	5.31 443	5.31 441	8.00 781	1223	1.99 219	9.99 998	25
2160	36	8.02 002	1190	5.31 443	5.31 441	8.02 004	1190	1.97 996	9.99 998	24
2220	37	8.03 192	1158	5.31 443	5.31 441	8.03 194	1159	1.96 806	9.99 997	23
2280	38	8.04 350	1128	5.31 443	5.31 441	8.04 353	1128	1.95 647	9.99 997	22
2340	39	8.05 478	1100	5.31 443	5.31 441	8.05 481	1100	1.94 519	9.99 997	21
2400	40	8.06 578	1072	5.31 443	5.31 441	8.06 581	1072	1.93 419	9.99 997	20
2460	41	8.07 650	1046	5.31 443	5.31 440	8.07 653	1047	1.92 347	9.99 997	19
2520	42	8.08 696	1022	5.31 444	5.31 440	8.08 700	1022	1.91 300	9.99 997	18
2580	43	8.09 718	999	5.31 444	5.31 440	8.09 722	998	1.90 278	9.99 997	17
2640	44	8.10 717	976	5.31 444	5.31 440	8.10 720	976	1.89 280	9.99 996	16
2700	45	8.11 693	954	5.31 444	5.31 440	8.11 696	955	1.88 304	9.99 996	15
2760	46	8.12 647	934	5.31 444	5.31 440	8.12 651	934	1.87 349	9.99 996	14
2820	47	8.13 581	914	5.31 444	5.31 440	8.13 585	915	1.86 415	9.99 996	13
2880	48	8.14 495	896	5.31 444	5.31 440	8.14 500	895	1.85 500	9.99 996	12
2940	49	8.15 391	877	5.31 444	5.31 440	8.15 395	878	1.84 605	9.99 996	11
3000	50	8.16 268	860	5.31 444	5.31 439	8.16 273	860	1.83 727	9.99 995	10
3060	51	8.17 128	843	5.31 444	5.31 439	8.17 133	843	1.82 867	9.99 995	9
3120	52	8.17 971	827	5.31 444	5.31 439	8.17 976	828	1.82 024	9.99 995	8
3180	53	8.18 798	812	5.31 444	5.31 439	8.18 804	812	1.81 196	9.99 995	7
3240	54	8.19 610	797	5.31 444	5.31 439	8.19 616	797	1.80 384	9.99 995	6
3300	55	8.20 407	782	5.31 444	5.31 439	8.20 413	782	1.79 587	9.99 994	5
3360	56	8.21 189	769	5.31 444	5.31 439	8.21 195	769	1.78 805	9.99 994	4
3420	57	8.21 958	755	5.31 445	5.31 439	8.21 964	756	1.78 036	9.99 994	3
3480	58	8.22 713	743	5.31 445	5.31 438	8.22 720	742	1.77 280	9.99 994	2
3540	59	8.23 456	730	5.31 445	5.31 438	8.23 462	730	1.76 538	9.99 994	1
3600	60	8.24 186		5.31 445	5.31 438	8.24 192		1.75 808	9.99 993	0
"	'	L. Cos.	d.	C. S.	C. T.	L. Cot.	c.d.	L. Tan.	L. Sin.	'

90° (270°)   (269°) **89°**

* Interpolation in this section of the table is not accurate.

COMMON LOGARITHMS OF THE TRIGONOMETRIC
FUNCTIONS (Continued)

1° (181°)   **(358°) 178°**

"	'	L. Sin.	*d.	C. S.	C. T.	L. Tan.	*c.d.	L. Cot.	L. Cos.	'
3600	0	8.24 186	717	5.31 445	5.31 438	8.24 192	718	1.75 808	9.99 993	60
3660	1	8.24 903	706	5.31 445	5.31 438	8.24 910	706	1.75 090	9.99 993	59
3720	2	8.25 609	695	5.31 445	5.31 438	8.25 616	696	1.74 384	9.99 993	58
3780	3	8.26 304	664	5.31 445	5.31 438	8.26 312	684	1.73 688	9.99 993	57
3840	4	8.26 988	673	5.31 445	5.31 437	8.26 996	673	1.73 004	9.99 992	56
3900	5	8.27 661	663	5.31 445	5.31 437	8.27 669	663	1.72 331	9.99 992	55
3960	6	8.28 324	653	5.31 445	5.31 437	8.28 332	654	1.71 668	9.99 992	54
4020	7	8.28 977	644	5.31 445	5.31 437	8.28 986	643	1.71 014	9.99 992	53
4080	8	8.29 621	634	5.31 445	5.31 437	8.29 629	634	1.70 371	9.99 992	52
4140	9	8.30 255	624	5.31 445	5.31 437	8.30 263	625	1.69 737	9.99 991	51
4200	10	8.30 879	616	5.31 446	5.31 437	8.30 888	617	1.69 112	9.99 991	50
4260	11	8.31 495	608	5.31 446	5.31 436	8.31 505	607	1.68 495	9.99 991	49
4320	12	8.32 103	599	5.31 446	5.31 436	8.32 112	599	1.67 888	9.99 990	48
4380	13	8.32 702	590	5.31 446	5.31 436	8.32 711	591	1.67 289	9.99 990	47
4440	14	8.33 292	583	5.31 446	5.31 436	8.33 302	584	1.66 698	9.99 990	46
4500	15	8.33 875	575	5.31 446	5.31 436	8.33 886	575	1.66 114	9.99 990	45
4560	16	8.34 450	568	5.31 446	5.31 435	8.34 461	568	1.65 539	9.99 989	44
4620	17	8.35 018	560	5.31 446	5.31 435	8.35 029	561	1.64 971	9.99 989	43
4680	18	8.35 578	553	5.31 446	5.31 435	8.35 590	553	1.64 410	9.99 989	42
4740	19	8.36 131	547	5.31 446	5.31 435	8.36 143	546	1.63 857	9.99 989	41
4800	20	8.36 678	539	5.31 446	5.31 435	8.36 689	540	1.63 311	9.99 988	40
4860	21	8.37 217	533	5.31 447	5.31 434	8.37 229	533	1.62 771	9.99 988	39
4920	22	8.37 750	526	5.31 447	5.31 434	8.37 762	527	1.62 238	9.99 988	38
4980	23	8.38 276	520	5.31 447	5.31 434	8.38 289	520	1.61 711	9.99 987	37
5040	24	8.38 796	514	5.31 447	5.31 434	8.38 809	514	1.61 191	9.99 987	36
5100	25	8.39 310	508	5.31 447	5.31 434	8.39 323	509	1.60 677	9.99 987	35
5160	26	8.39 818	502	5.31 447	5.31 433	8.39 832	502	1.60 168	9.99 986	34
5220	27	8.40 320	496	5.31 447	5.31 433	8.40 334	496	1.59 666	9.99 986	33
5280	28	8.40 816	491	5.31 447	5.31 433	8.40 830	491	1.59 170	9.99 986	32
5340	29	8.41 307	485	5.31 447	5.31 433	8.41 321	486	1.58 679	9.99 985	31
5400	30	8.41 792	480	5.31 447	5.31 432	8.41 807	480	1.58 193	9.99 985	30
5460	31	8.42 272	474	5.31 448	5.31 432	8.42 287	475	1.57 713	9.99 985	29
5520	32	8.42 746	470	5.31 448	5.31 432	8.42 762	470	1.57 238	9.99 984	28
5580	33	8.43 216	464	5.31 448	5.31 432	8.43 232	464	1.56 768	9.99 984	27
5640	34	8.43 680	459	5.31 448	5.31 432	8.43 696	460	1.56 304	9.99 984	26
5700	35	8.44 139	455	5.31 448	5.31 431	8.44 156	455	1.55 844	9.99 983	25
5760	36	8.44 594	450	5.31 448	5.31 431	8.44 611	450	1.55 389	9.99 983	24
5820	37	8.45 044	445	5.31 448	5.31 431	8.45 061	446	1.54 939	9.99 983	23
5880	38	8.45 489	441	5.31 449	5.31 431	8.45 507	441	1.54 493	9.99 982	22
5940	39	8.45 930	436	5.31 449	5.31 431	8.45 948	437	1.54 052	9.99 982	21
6000	40	8.46 366	433	5.31 449	5.31 430	8.46 385	432	1.53 615	9.99 982	20
6060	41	8.46 799	427	5.31 449	5.31 430	8.46 817	428	1.53 183	9.99 981	19
6120	42	8.47 226	424	5.31 449	5.31 430	8.47 245	424	1.52 755	9.99 981	18
6180	43	8.47 650	419	5.31 449	5.31 430	8.47 669	420	1.52 331	9.99 981	17
6240	44	8.48 069	416	5.31 449	5.31 429	8.48 089	416	1.51 911	9.99 980	16
6300	45	8.48 485	411	5.31 449	5.31 429	8.48 505	412	1.51 495	9.99 980	15
6360	46	8.48 896	408	5.31 449	5.31 429	8.48 917	408	1.51 083	9.99 979	14
6420	47	8.49 304	404	5.31 450	5.31 428	8.49 325	404	1.50 675	9.99 979	13
6480	48	8.49 708	400	5.31 450	5.31 428	8.49 729	401	1.50 271	9.99 979	12
6540	49	8.50 108	396	5.31 450	5.31 428	8.50 130	397	1.49 870	9.99 978	11
6600	50	8.50 504	393	5.31 450	5.31 428	8.50 527	393	1.49 473	9.99 978	10
6660	51	8.50 897	390	5.31 450	5.31 427	8.50 920	390	1.49 080	9.99 977	9
6720	52	8.51 287	386	5.31 450	5.31 427	8.51 310	386	1.48 690	9.99 977	8
6780	53	8.51 673	382	5.31 450	5.31 427	8.51 696	383	1.48 304	9.99 977	7
6840	54	8.52 055	379	5.31 450	5.31 427	8.52 079	380	1.47 921	9.99 976	6
6900	55	8.52 434	376	5.31 451	5.31 426	8.52 459	376	1.47 541	9.99 976	5
6960	56	8.52 810	373	5.31 451	5.31 426	8.52 835	373	1.47 165	9.99 975	4
7020	57	8.53 183	369	5.31 451	5.31 426	8.53 208	370	1.46 792	9.99 975	3
7080	58	8.53 552	367	5.31 451	5.31 425	8.53 578	367	1.46 422	9.99 974	2
7140	59	8.53 919	363	5.31 451	5.31 425	8.53 945	363	1.46 055	9.99 974	1
7200	60	8.54 282		5.31 451	5.31 425	8.54 308		1.45 692	9.99 974	0
"	'	L. Cos.	d.	C. S.	C. T.	L. Cot.	c.d.	L. Tan.	L. Sin.	'

91° (271°)   **(268°) 88°**

* Interpolation in this section of the table is not accurate.

COMMON LOGARITHMS OF THE TRIGONOMETRIC
FUNCTIONS (Continued)

2° (182°)   **(357°) 177°**

"	′	L. Sin.	*d.	C. S.	C. T.	L. Tan.	*c.d.	L. Cot.	L. Cos.	′
7200	0	8.54 282	360	5.31 451	5.31 425	8.54 308	361	1.45 692	9.99 974	60
7260	1	8.54 642	357	5.31 451	5.31 425	8.54 669	358	1.45 331	9.99 973	59
7320	2	8.54 999	355	5.31 452	5.31 424	8.55 027	355	1.44 973	9.99 973	58
7380	3	8.55 354	351	5.31 452	5.31 424	8.55 382	352	1.44 618	9.99 972	57
7440	4	8.55 705	349	5.31 452	5.31 424	8.55 734	349	1.44 266	9.99 972	56
7500	5	8.56 054	346	5.31 452	5.31 423	8.56 083	346	1.43 917	9.99 971	55
7560	6	8.56 400	343	5.31 452	5.31 423	8.56 429	344	1.43 571	9.99 971	54
7620	7	8.56 743	341	5.31 452	5.31 423	8.56 773	341	1.43 227	9.99 970	53
7680	8	8.57 084	337	5.31 453	5.31 422	8.57 114	338	1.42 886	9.99 970	52
7740	9	8.57 421	336	5.31 453	5.31 422	8.57 452	336	1.42 548	9.99 969	51
7800	10	8.57 757	332	5.31 453	5.31 422	8.57 788	333	1.42 212	9.99 969	50
7860	11	8.58 089	330	5.31 453	5.31 421	8.58 121	330	1.41 879	9.99 968	49
7920	12	8.58 419	328	5.31 453	5.31 421	8.58 451	328	1.41 549	9.99 968	48
7980	13	8.58 747	325	5.31 454	5.31 421	8.58 779	326	1.41 221	9.99 967	47
8040	14	8.59 072	323	5.31 454	5.31 421	8.59 105	323	1.40 895	9.99 967	46
8100	15	8.59 395	320	5.31 454	5.31 420	8.59 428	321	1.40 572	9.99 967	45
8160	16	8.59 715	318	5.31 454	5.31 420	8.59 749	319	1.40 251	9.99 966	44
8220	17	8.60 033	316	5.31 454	5.31 420	8.60 068	316	1.39 932	9.99 966	43
8280	18	8.60 349	313	5.31 454	5.31 419	8.60 384	314	1.39 616	9.99 965	42
8340	19	8.60 662	311	5.31 454	5.31 419	8.60 698	311	1.39 302	9.99 964	41
8400	20	8.60 973	309	5.31 455	5.31 418	8.61 009	310	1.38 991	9.99 964	40
8460	21	8.61 282	307	5.31 455	5.31 418	8.61 319	307	1.38 681	9.99 963	39
8520	22	8.61 589	305	5.31 455	5.31 418	8.61 626	305	1.38 374	9.99 963	38
8580	23	8.61 894	302	5.31 455	5.31 417	8.61 931	303	1.38 069	9.99 962	37
8640	24	8.62 196	301	5.31 455	5.31 417	8.62 234	301	1.37 766	9.99 962	36
8700	25	8.62 497	298	5.31 455	5.31 417	8.62 535	299	1.37 465	9.99 961	35
8760	26	8.62 795	296	5.31 455	5.31 416	8.62 834	297	1.37 166	9.99 961	34
8820	27	8.63 091	294	5.31 456	5.31 416	8.63 131	295	1.36 869	9.99 960	33
8880	28	8.63 385	293	5.31 456	5.31 416	8.63 426	292	1.36 574	9.99 960	32
8940	29	8.63 678	290	5.31 456	5.31 415	8.63 718	291	1.36 282	9.99 959	31
9000	30	8.63 968	288	5.31 456	5.31 415	8.64 009	289	1.35 991	9.99 959	30
9060	31	8.64 256	287	5.31 456	5.31 415	8.64 298	287	1.35 702	9.99 958	29
9120	32	8.64 543	284	5.31 457	5.31 414	8.64 585	285	1.35 415	9.99 958	28
9180	33	8.64 827	283	5.31 457	5.31 414	8.64 870	284	1.35 130	9.99 957	27
9240	34	8.65 110	281	5.31 457	5.31 413	8.65 154	281	1.34 846	9.99 956	26
9300	35	8.65 391	279	5.31 457	5.31 413	8.65 435	280	1.34 565	9.99 956	25
9360	36	8.65 670	277	5.31 457	5.31 413	8.65 715	278	1.34 285	9.99 955	24
9420	37	8.65 947	276	5.31 458	5.31 412	8.65 993	276	1.34 007	9.99 955	23
9480	38	8.66 223	274	5.31 458	5.31 412	8.66 269	274	1.33 731	9.99 954	22
9540	39	8.66 497	272	5.31 458	5.31 412	8.66 543	273	1.33 457	9.99 954	21
9600	40	8.66 769	270	5.31 458	5.31 411	8.66 816	271	1.33 184	9.99 953	20
9660	41	8.67 039	269	5.31 458	5.31 411	8.67 087	269	1.32 913	9.99 952	19
9720	42	8.67 308	267	5.31 459	5.31 410	8.67 356	268	1.32 644	9.99 952	18
9780	43	8.67 575	266	5.31 459	5.31 410	8.67 624	266	1.32 376	9.99 951	17
9840	44	8.67 841	263	5.31 459	5.31 410	8.67 890	264	1.32 110	9.99 951	16
9900	45	8.68 104	263	5.31 459	5.31 409	8.68 154	263	1.31 846	9.99 950	15
9960	46	8.68 367	260	5.31 459	5.31 409	8.68 417	261	1.31 583	9.99 949	14
10020	47	8.68 627	259	5.31 460	5.31 408	8.68 678	260	1.31 322	9.99 949	13
10080	48	8.68 886	258	5.31 460	5.31 408	8.68 938	258	1.31 062	9.99 948	12
10140	49	8.69 144	256	5.31 460	5.31 408	8.69 196	257	1.30 804	9.99 948	11
10200	50	8.69 400	254	5.31 460	5.31 407	8.69 453	255	1.30 547	9.99 947	10
10260	51	8.69 654	253	5.31 460	5.31 407	8.69 708	254	1.30 292	9.99 946	9
10320	52	8.69 907	252	5.31 461	5.31 406	8.69 962	252	1.30 038	9.99 946	8
10380	53	8.70 159	250	5.31 461	5.31 406	8.70 214	251	1.29 786	9.99 945	7
10440	54	8.70 409	249	5.31 461	5.31 405	8.70 465	249	1.29 535	9.99 944	6
10500	55	8.70 658	247	5.31 461	5.31 405	8.70 714	248	1.29 286	9.99 944	5
10560	56	8.70 905	246	5.31 461	5.31 405	8.70 962	246	1.29 038	9.99 943	4
10620	57	8.71 151	244	5.31 462	5.31 404	8.71 208	245	1.28 792	9.99 942	3
10680	58	8.71 395	243	5.31 462	5.31 404	8.71 453	244	1.28 547	9.99 942	2
10740	59	8.71 638	242	5.31 462	5.31 403	8.71 697	243	1.28 303	9.99 941	1
10800	60	8.71 880		5.31 462	5.31 403	8.71 940		1.28 060	9.99 940	0
"	′	L. Cos.	d.	C. S.	C. T.	L. Cot.	c.d.	L. Tan.	L. Sin.	

92° (272°)   **(267°) 87**

* Interpolation in this section of the table is not accurate.

COMMON LOGARITHMS OF THE TRIGONOMETRIC
FUNCTIONS (Continued)

3° (183°)   **(356°) 176°**

′	L. Sin.	*d.	L. Tan.	*c.d.	L. Cot.	L. Cos.	′		P. P.			
0	8.71 880		8.71 940		1.28 060	9.99 940	**60**	″	**241**	**239**	**237**	**235**	**234**
1	8.72 120	240	8.72 181	241	1.27 819	9.99 940	59	1	4.0	4.0	4.0	3.9	3.9
2	8.72 359	239	8.72 420	239	1.27 580	9.99 939	58	2	8.0	8.0	7.9	7.8	7.8
3	8.72 597	238	8.72 659	239	1.27 341	9.99 938	57	3	12.0	12.0	11.8	11.8	11.7
4	8.72 834	237	8.72 896	237	1.27 104	9.99 938	56	4	16.1	15.9	15.8	15.7	15.6
		235		236									
5	8.73 069		8.73 132		1.26 868	9.99 937	55	5	20.1	19.9	19.8	19.6	19.5
6	8.73 303	234	8.73 366	234	1.26 634	9.99 936	54	6	24.1	23.9	23.7	23.5	23.4
7	8.73 535	232	8.73 600	234	1.26 400	9.99 936	53	7	28.1	27.9	27.6	27.4	27.3
8	8.73 767	232	8.73 832	232	1.26 168	9.99 935	52	8	32.1	31.9	31.6	31.3	31.2
9	8.73 997	230	8.74 063	231	1.25 937	9.99 934	51	9	36.2	35.8	35.6	35.2	35.1
		229		229									
10	8.74 226		8.74 292		1.25 708	9.99 934	**50**	″	**232**	**229**	**227**	**225**	**223**
11	8.74 454	228	8.74 521	229	1.25 479	9.99 933	49	1	3.9	3.8	3.8	3.8	3.7
12	8.74 680	226	8.74 748	227	1.25 252	9.99 932	48	2	7.7	7.6	7.6	7.5	7.4
13	8.74 906	226	8.74 974	226	1.25 026	9.99 932	47	3	11.6	11.4	11.4	11.2	11.2
14	8.75 130	224	8.75 199	225	1.24 801	9.99 931	46	4	15.5	15.3	15.1	15.0	14.9
		223		224									
15	8.75 353		8.75 423		1.24 577	9.99 930	45	5	19.3	19.1	18.9	18.8	18.6
16	8.75 575	222	8.75 645	222	1.24 355	9.99 929	44	6	23.2	22.9	22.7	22.5	22.3
17	8.75 795	220	8.75 867	222	1.24 133	9.99 929	43	7	27.1	26.7	26.5	26.2	26.0
18	8.76 015	220	8.76 087	220	1.23 913	9.99 928	42	8	30.9	30.5	30.3	30.0	29.7
19	8.76 234	219	8.76 306	219	1.23 694	9.99 927	41	9	34.8	34.4	34.0	33.8	33.4
		217		219									
20	8.76 451		8.76 525		1.23 475	9.99 926	**40**	″	**222**	**220**	**217**	**215**	**213**
21	8.76 667	216	8.76 742	217	1.23 258	9.99 926	39	1	3.7	3.7	3.6	3.6	3.6
22	8.76 883	216	8.76 958	216	1.23 042	9.99 925	38	2	7.4	7.3	7.2	7.2	7.1
23	8.77 097	214	8.77 173	215	1.22 827	9.99 924	37	3	11.1	11.0	10.8	10.8	10.6
24	8.77 310	213	8.77 387	214	1.22 613	9.99 923	36	4	14.8	14.7	14.5	14.3	14.2
		212		213									
25	8.77 522		8.77 600		1.22 400	9.99 923	35	5	18.5	18.3	18.1	17.9	17.8
26	8.77 733	211	8.77 811	211	1.22 189	9.99 922	34	6	22.2	22.0	21.7	21.5	21.3
27	8.77 943	210	8.78 022	211	1.21 978	9.99 921	33	7	25.9	25.7	25.3	25.1	24.8
28	8.78 152	209	8.78 232	210	1.21 768	9.99 920	32	8	29.6	29.3	28.9	28.7	28.4
29	8.78 360	208	8.78 441	209	1.21 559	9.99 920	31	9	33.3	33.0	32.6	32.2	32.0
		208		208									
30	8.78 568		8.78 649		1.21 351	9.99 919	**30**	″	**211**	**208**	**206**	**203**	**201**
31	8.78 774	206	8.78 855	206	1.21 145	9.99 918	29	1	3.5	3.5	3.4	3.4	3.4
32	8.78 979	205	8.79 061	206	1.20 939	9.99 917	28	2	7.0	6.9	6.9	6.8	6.7
33	8.79 183	204	8.79 266	205	1.20 734	9.99 917	27	3	10.6	10.4	10.3	10.2	10.0
34	8.79 386	203	8.79 470	204	1.20 530	9.99 916	26	4	14.1	13.9	13.7	13.5	13.4
		202		203									
35	8.79 588		8.79 673		1.20 327	9.99 915	25	5	17.6	17.3	17.2	16.9	16.8
36	8.79 789	201	8.79 875	202	1.20 125	9.99 914	24	6	21.1	20.8	20.6	20.3	20.1
37	8.79 990	201	8.80 076	201	1.19 924	9.99 913	23	7	24.6	24.3	24.0	23.7	23.4
38	8.80 189	199	8.80 277	201	1.19 723	9.99 913	22	8	28.1	27.7	27.5	27.1	26.8
39	8.80 388	199	8.80 476	199	1.19 524	9.99 912	21	9	31.6	31.2	30.9	30.4	30.2
		197		198									
40	8.80 585		8.80 674		1.19 326	9.99 911	**20**	″	**199**	**197**	**195**	**193**	**192**
41	8.80 782	197	8.80 872	198	1.19 128	9.99 910	19	1	3.3	3.3	3.2	3.2	3.2
42	8.80 978	196	8.81 068	196	1.18 932	9.99 909	18	2	6.6	6.6	6.5	6.4	6.4
43	8.81 173	195	8.81 264	196	1.18 736	9.99 909	17	3	10.0	9.8	9.8	9.6	9.6
44	8.81 367	194	8.81 459	195	1.18 541	9.99 908	16	4	13.3	13.1	13.0	12.9	12.8
		193		194									
45	8.81 560		8.81 653		1.18 347	9.99 907	15	5	16.6	16.4	16.2	16.1	16.0
46	8.81 752	192	8.81 846	193	1.18 154	9.99 906	14	6	19.9	19.7	19.5	19.3	19.2
47	8.81 944	192	8.82 038	192	1.17 962	9.99 905	13	7	23.2	23.0	22.8	22.5	22.4
48	8.82 134	190	8.82 230	192	1.17 770	9.99 904	12	8	26.5	26.3	26.0	25.7	25.6
49	8.82 324	190	8.82 420	190	1.17 580	9.99 904	11	9	29.8	29.6	29.2	29.0	28.8
		189		190									
50	8.82 513		8.82 610		1.17 390	9.99 903	**10**	″	**189**	**187**	**185**	**183**	**181**
51	8.82 701	188	8.82 799	189	1.17 201	9.99 902	9	1	3.2	3.1	3.1	3.0	3.0
52	8.82 888	187	8.82 987	188	1.17 013	9.99 901	8	2	6.3	6.2	6.2	6.1	6.0
53	8.83 075	187	8.83 175	188	1.16 825	9.99 900	7	3	9.4	9.4	9.2	9.2	9.0
54	8.83 261	186	8.83 361	186	1.16 639	9.99 899	6	4	12.6	12.5	12.3	12.2	12.1
		185		186									
55	8.83 446		8.83 547		1.16 453	9.99 898	5	5	15.8	15.6	15.4	15.2	15.1
56	8.83 630	184	8.83 732	185	1.16 268	9.99 898	4	6	18.9	18.7	18.5	18.3	18.1
57	8.83 813	183	8.83 916	184	1.16 084	9.99 897	3	7	22.0	21.8	21.6	21.4	21.1
58	8.83 996	183	8.84 100	184	1.15 900	9.99 896	2	8	25.2	24.9	24.7	24.4	24.1
59	8.84 177	181	8.84 282	182	1.15 718	9.99 895	1	9	28.4	28.0	27.8	27.4	27.2
		181		182									
60	8.84 358		8.84 464		1.15 536	9.99 894	**0**	10	31.5	31.2	30.8	30.5	30.2
′	L. Cos.	d.	L. Cot.	c.d	L. Tan.	L. Sin.	′		P. P.				

93° (273°)   **(266°) 86°**

* Interpolation in this section of the table is not accurate.

COMMON LOGARITHMS OF THE TRIGONOMETRIC FUNCTIONS (Continued)

4° (184°)   (355°) 175°

′	L. Sin.	*d.	L. Tan.	*c.d.	L. Cot.	L. Cos.	′
0	8.84 358	181	8.84 464	182	1.15 536	9.99 894	60
1	8.84 539	179	8.84 646	180	1.15 354	9.99 893	59
2	8.84 718	179	8.84 826	180	1.15 174	9.99 892	58
3	8.84 897	178	8.85 006	179	1.14 994	9.99 891	57
4	8.85 075	177	8.85 185	178	1.14 815	9.99 891	56
5	8.85 252	177	8.85 363	177	1.14 637	9.99 890	55
6	8.85 429	176	8.85 540	177	1.14 460	9.99 889	54
7	8.85 605	175	8.85 717	176	1.14 283	9.99 888	53
8	8.85 780	175	8.85 893	176	1.14 107	9.99 887	52
9	8.85 955	173	8.86 069	174	1.13 931	9.99 886	51
10	8.86 128	173	8.86 243	174	1.13 757	9.99 885	50
11	8.86 301	173	8.86 417	174	1.13 583	9.99 884	49
12	8.86 474	171	8.86 591	172	1.13 409	9.99 883	48
13	8.86 645	171	8.86 763	172	1.13 237	9.99 882	47
14	8.86 816	171	8.86 935	171	1.13 065	9.99 881	46
15	8.86 987	169	8.87 106	171	1.12 894	9.99 880	45
16	8.87 156	169	8.87 277	170	1.12 723	9.99 879	44
17	8.87 325	169	8.87 447	169	1.12 553	9.99 879	43
18	8.87 494	167	8.87 616	169	1.12 384	9.99 878	42
19	8.87 661	168	8.87 785	168	1.12 215	9.99 877	41
20	8.87 829	166	8.87 953	167	1.12 047	9.99 876	40
21	8.87 995	166	8.88 120	167	1.11 880	9.99 875	39
22	8.88 161	165	8.88 287	166	1.11 713	9.99 874	38
23	8.88 326	164	8.88 453	165	1.11 547	9.99 873	37
24	8.88 490	164	8.88 618	165	1.11 382	9.99 872	36
25	8.88 654	163	8.88 783	165	1.11 217	9.99 871	35
26	8.88 817	163	8.88 948	163	1.11 052	9.99 870	34
27	8.88 980	162	8.89 111	163	1.10 889	9.99 869	33
28	8.89 142	162	8.89 274	163	1.10 726	9.99 868	32
29	8.89 304	160	8.89 437	161	1.10 563	9.99 867	31
30	8.89 464	161	8.89 598	162	1.10 402	9.99 866	30
31	8.89 625	159	8.89 760	160	1.10 240	9.99 865	29
32	8.89 784	159	8.89 920	160	1.10 080	9.99 864	28
33	8.89 943	159	8.90 080	160	1.09 920	9.99 863	27
34	8.90 102	158	8.90 240	159	1.09 760	9.99 862	26
35	8.90 260	157	8.90 399	158	1.09 601	9.99 861	25
36	8.90 417	157	8.90 557	158	1.09 443	9.99 860	24
37	8.90 574	156	8.90 715	157	1.09 285	9.99 859	23
38	8.90 730	155	8.90 872	157	1.09 128	9.99 858	22
39	8.90 885	155	8.91 029	156	1.08 971	9.99 857	21
40	8.91 040	155	8.91 185	155	1.08 815	9.99 856	20
41	8.91 195	154	8.91 340	155	1.08 660	9.99 855	19
42	8.91 349	153	8.91 495	155	1.08 505	9.99 854	18
43	8.91 502	153	8.91 650	153	1.08 350	9.99 853	17
44	8.91 655	152	8.91 803	154	1.08 197	9.99 852	16
45	8.91 807	152	8.91 957	153	1.08 043	9.99 851	15
46	8.91 959	151	8.92 110	152	1.07 890	9.99 850	14
47	8.92 110	151	8.92 262	152	1.07 738	9.99 848	13
48	8.92 261	150	8.92 414	151	1.07 586	9.99 847	12
49	8.92 411	150	8.92 565	151	1.07 435	9.99 846	11
50	8.92 561	149	8.92 716	150	1.07 284	9.99 845	10
51	8.92 710	149	8.92 866	150	1.07 134	9.99 844	9
52	8.92 859	148	8.93 016	149	1.06 984	9.99 843	8
53	8.93 007	147	8.93 165	148	1.06 835	9.99 842	7
54	8.93 154	147	8.93 313	149	1.06 687	9.99 841	6
55	8.93 301	147	8.93 462	147	1.06 538	9.99 840	5
56	8.93 448	146	8.93 609	147	1.06 391	9.99 839	4
57	8.93 594	146	8.93 756	147	1.06 244	9.99 838	3
58	8.93 740	145	8.93 903	146	1.06 097	9.99 837	2
59	8.93 885	145	8.94 049	146	1.05 951	9.99 836	1
60	8.94 030		8.94 195		1.05 805	9.99 834	0

P. P.

″	182	181	179	178	177
1	3.0	3.0	3.0	3.0	3.0
2	6.1	6.0	6.0	5.9	5.9
3	9.1	9.0	9.0	8.9	8.8
4	12.1	12.1	11.9	11.9	11.8
5	15.2	15.1	14.9	14.8	14.8
6	18.2	18.1	17.9	17.8	17.7
7	21.2	21.1	20.9	20.8	20.6
8	24.3	24.1	23.9	23.7	23.6
9	27.3	27.2	26.8	26.7	26.6

″	176	175	174	173	172
1	2.9	2.9	2.9	2.9	2.9
2	5.9	5.8	5.8	5.8	5.7
3	8.8	8.8	8.7	8.6	8.6
4	11.7	11.7	11.6	11.5	11.3
5	14.7	14.6	14.5	14.4	14.3
6	17.6	17.5	17.4	17.3	17.2
7	20.5	20.4	20.3	20.2	20.1
8	23.5	23.3	23.2	23.1	22.9
9	26.4	26.2	26.1	26.0	25.8

″	171	170	169	168	167
1	2.8	2.8	2.8	2.8	2.8
2	5.7	5.7	5.6	5.6	5.6
3	8.6	8.5	8.4	8.4	8.4
4	11.4	11.3	11.3	11.2	11.1
5	14.2	14.2	14.1	14.0	13.9
6	17.1	17.0	16.9	16.8	16.7
7	20.0	19.8	19.7	19.6	19.5
8	22.8	22.7	22.5	22.4	22.3
9	25.6	25.5	25.4	25.2	25.0

″	166	165	164	163	162
1	2.8	2.8	2.7	2.7	2.7
2	5.5	5.5	5.5	5.4	5.4
3	8.3	8.2	8.2	8.2	8.1
4	11.1	11.0	10.9	10.9	10.8
5	13.8	13.8	13.7	13.6	13.5
6	16.6	16.5	16.4	16.3	16.2
7	19.4	19.2	19.1	19.0	18.9
8	22.1	22.0	21.9	21.7	21.6
9	24.9	24.8	24.6	24.4	24.3

″	161	160	159	158	157
1	2.7	2.7	2.6	2.6	2.6
2	5.4	5.3	5.3	5.3	5.2
3	8.0	8.0	8.0	7.9	7.8
4	10.7	10.7	10.6	10.5	10.3
5	13.4	13.3	13.2	13.2	13.1
6	16.1	16.0	15.9	15.8	15.7
7	18.8	18.7	18.6	18.4	18.3
8	21.5	21.3	21.2	21.1	20.9
9	24.2	24.0	23.8	23.7	23.6

″	156	155	154	153	152
1	2.6	2.6	2.6	2.6	2.5
2	5.2	5.2	5.1	5.1	5.1
3	7.8	7.8	7.7	7.6	7.6
4	10.4	10.3	10.3	10.2	10.1
5	13.0	12.9	12.8	12.8	12.7
6	15.6	15.5	15.4	15.3	15.2
7	18.2	18.1	18.0	17.8	17.7
8	20.8	20.7	20.5	20.4	20.3
9	23.4	23.2	23.1	23.0	22.8
10	26.0	25.8	25.7	25.5	25.3

′	L. Cos.	d.	L. Cot.	c.d.	L. Tan.	L. Sin.	′

94° (274°)   (265°) 85°

* Interpolation in this section of the table is not accurate.

COMMON LOGARITHMS OF THE TRIGONOMETRIC
FUNCTIONS (Continued)

5° (185°)   **(354°) 174°**

'	L. Sin.	d.	L. Tan.	c.d.	L. Cot.	L. Cos.	'		P. P.				
0	8.94 030	144	8.94 195	145	1.05 805	9.99 834	60	''	151	149	148	147	146
1	8.94 174	143	8.94 340	145	1.05 660	9.99 833	59	1	2.5	2.5	2.5	2.4	2.4
2	8.94 317	144	8.94 485	145	1.05 515	9.99 832	58	2	5.0	5.0	4.9	4.9	4.9
3	8.94 461	142	8.94 630	143	1.05 370	9.99 831	57	3	7.6	7.4	7.4	7.4	7.3
4	8.94 603	143	8.94 773	144	1.05 227	9.99 830	56	4	10.1	9.9	9.9	9.8	9.7
5	8.94 746	141	8.94 917	143	1.05 083	9.99 829	55	5	12.6	12.4	12.3	12.2	12.2
6	8.94 887	142	8.95 060	142	1.04 940	9.99 828	54	6	15.1	14.9	14.8	14.7	14.6
7	8.95 029	141	8.95 202	142	1.04 798	9.99 827	53	7	17.6	17.4	17.3	17.2	17.0
8	8.95 170	140	8.95 344	142	1.04 656	9.99 825	52	8	20.1	19.9	19.7	19.6	19.5
9	8.95 310	140	8.95 486	141	1.04 514	9.99 824	51	9	22.6	22.4	22.2	22.0	21.9
10	8.95 450	139	8.95 627	140	1.04 373	9.99 823	50	''	145	144	143	142	141
11	8.95 589	139	8.95 767	141	1.04 233	9.99 822	49	1	2.4	2.4	2.4	2.4	2.4
12	8.95 728	139	8.95 908	139	1.04 092	9.99 821	48	2	4.8	4.8	4.8	4.7	4.7
13	8.95 867	138	8.96 047	140	1.03 953	9.99 820	47	3	7.2	7.2	7.2	7.1	7.0
14	8.96 005	138	8.96 187	138	1.03 813	9.99 819	46	4	9.7	9.6	9.5	9.5	9.4
15	8.96 143	137	8.96 325	139	1.03 675	9.99 817	45	5	12.1	12.0	11.9	11.8	11.8
16	8.96 280	137	8.96 464	138	1.03 536	9.99 816	44	6	14.5	14.4	14.3	14.2	14.1
17	8.96 417	136	8.96 602	137	1.03 398	9.99 815	43	7	16.9	16.8	16.7	16.6	16.4
18	8.96 553	136	8.96 739	138	1.03 261	9.99 814	42	8	19.3	19.2	19.1	18.9	18.8
19	8.96 689	136	8.96 877	136	1.03 123	9.99 813	41	9	21.8	21.6	21.4	21.3	21.2
20	8.96 825	135	8.97 013	137	1.02 987	9.99 812	40	''	140	139	138	137	136
21	8.96 960	135	8.97 150	135	1.02 850	9.99 810	39	1	2.3	2.3	2.3	2.3	2.3
22	8.97 095	134	8.97 285	136	1.02 715	9.99 809	38	2	4.7	4.6	4.6	4.6	4.5
23	8.97 229	134	8.97 421	135	1.02 579	9.99 808	37	3	7.0	7.0	6.9	6.8	6.8
24	8.97 363	133	8.97 556	135	1.02 444	9.99 807	36	4	9.3	9.3	9.2	9.1	9.1
25	8.97 496	133	8.97 691	134	1.02 309	9.99 806	35	5	11.7	11.6	11.5	11.4	11.3
26	8.97 629	133	8.97 825	134	1.02 175	9.99 804	34	6	14.0	13.9	13.8	13.7	13.6
27	8.97 762	132	8.97 959	133	1.02 041	9.99 803	33	7	16.3	16.2	16.1	16.0	15.9
28	8.97 894	132	8.98 092	133	1.01 908	9.99 802	32	8	18.7	18.5	18.4	18.3	18.1
29	8.98 026	131	8.98 225	133	1.01 775	9.99 801	31	9	21.0	20.8	20.7	20.6	20.4
30	8.98 157	131	8.98 358	132	1.01 642	9.99 800	30	''	135	134	133	132	131
31	8.98 288	131	8.98 490	132	1.01 510	9.99 798	29	1	2.2	2.2	2.2	2.2	2.2
32	8.98 419	130	8.98 622	131	1.01 378	9.99 797	28	2	4.5	4.5	4.4	4.4	4.4
33	8.98 549	130	8.98 753	131	1.01 247	9.99 796	27	3	6.8	6.7	6.6	6.6	6.6
34	8.98 679	129	8.98 884	131	1.01 116	9.99 795	26	4	9.0	8.9	8.9	8.8	8.7
35	8.98 808	129	8.99 015	130	1.00 985	9.99 793	25	5	11.2	11.2	11.1	11.0	10.9
36	8.98 937	129	8.99 145	130	1.00 855	9.99 792	24	6	13.5	13.4	13.3	13.2	13.1
37	8.99 066	128	8.99 275	130	1.00 725	9.99 791	23	7	15.8	15.6	15.5	15.4	15.3
38	8.99 194	128	8.99 405	129	1.00 595	9.99 790	22	8	18.0	17.9	17.7	17.6	17.5
39	8.99 322	128	8.99 534	128	1.00 466	9.99 788	21	9	20.2	20.1	20.0	19.8	19.6
40	8.99 450	127	8.99 662	129	1.00 338	9.99 787	20	''	130	129	128	127	126
41	8.99 577	127	8.99 791	128	1.00 209	9.99 786	19	1	2.2	2.2	2.1	2.1	2.1
42	8.99 704	126	8.99 919	127	1.00 081	9.99 785	18	2	4.3	4.3	4.3	4.2	4.2
43	8.99 830	126	9.00 046	128	0.99 954	9.99 783	17	3	6.5	6.4	6.4	6.4	6.3
44	8.99 956	126	9.00 174	127	0.99 826	9.99 782	16	4	8.7	8.6	8.5	8.5	8.4
45	9.00 082	125	9.00 301	126	0.99 699	9.99 781	15	5	10.8	10.8	10.7	10.6	10.5
46	9.00 207	125	9.00 427	126	0.99 573	9.99 780	14	6	13.0	12.9	12.8	12.7	12.6
47	9.00 332	124	9.00 553	126	0.99 447	9.99 778	13	7	15.2	15.0	14.9	14.8	14.7
48	9.00 456	125	9.00 679	126	0.99 321	9.99 777	12	8	17.3	17.2	17.1	16.9	16.8
49	9.00 581	123	9.00 805	125	0.99 195	9.99 776	11	9	19.5	19.4	19.2	19.0	18.9
50	9.00 704	124	9.00 930	125	0.99 070	9.99 775	10	''	125	124	123	122	121
51	9.00 828	123	9.01 055	124	0.98 945	9.99 773	9	1	2.1	2.1	2.0	2.0	2.0
52	9.00 951	123	9.01 179	124	0.98 821	9.99 772	8	2	4.2	4.1	4.1	4.1	4.0
53	9.01 074	122	9.01 303	124	0.98 697	9.99 771	7	3	6.2	6.2	6.2	6.1	6.0
54	9.01 196	122	9.01 427	123	0.98 573	9.99 769	6	4	8.3	8.3	8.2	8.1	8.1
55	9.01 318	122	9.01 550	123	0.98 450	9.99 768	5	5	10.4	10.3	10.2	10.2	10.1
56	9.01 440	121	9.01 673	123	0.98 327	9.99 767	4	6	12.5	12.4	12.3	12.2	12.1
57	9.01 561	121	9.01 796	122	0.98 204	9.99 765	3	7	14.6	14.5	14.4	14.2	14.1
58	9.01 682	121	9.01 918	122	0.98 082	9.99 764	2	8	16.7	16.5	16.4	16.3	16.1
59	9.01 803	120	9.02 040	122	0.97 960	9.99 763	1	9	18.8	18.6	18.4	18.3	18.2
60	9.01 923		9.02 162		0.97 838	9.99 761	0	10	20.8	20.7	20.5	20.3	20.2
'	L. Cos.	d.	L. Cot.	c.d.	L. Tan.	L. Sin.	'		P. P.				

COMMON LOGARITHMS OF THE TRIGONOMETRIC FUNCTIONS (Continued)

6° (186°)   (353°) **173°**

′	L. Sin.	d.	L. Tan.	c.d.	L. Cot.	L. Cos.	′
0	9.01 923	120	9.02 162	121	0.97 838	9.99 761	60
1	9.02 043	120	9.02 283	121	0.97 717	9.99 760	59
2	9.02 163	120	9.02 404	121	0.97 596	9.99 759	58
3	9.02 283	119	9.02 525	120	0.97 475	9.99 757	57
4	9.02 402	118	9.02 645	121	0.97 355	9.99 756	56
5	9.02 520	119	9.02 766	119	0.97 234	9.99 755	55
6	9.02 639	118	9.02 885	120	0.97 115	9.99 753	54
7	9.02 757	117	9.03 005	119	0.96 995	9.99 752	53
8	9.02 874	118	9.03 124	118	0.96 876	9.99 751	52
9	9.02 992	117	9.03 242	119	0.96 758	9.99 749	51
10	9.03 109	117	9.03 361	118	0.96 639	9.99 748	50
11	9.03 226	116	9.03 479	118	0.96 521	9.99 747	49
12	9.03 342	116	9.03 597	117	0.96 403	9.99 745	48
13	9.03 458	116	9.03 714	118	0.96 286	9.99 744	47
14	9.03 574	116	9.03 832	116	0.96 168	9.99 742	46
15	9.03 690	115	9.03 948	117	0.96 052	9.99 741	45
16	9.03 805	115	9.04 065	116	0.95 935	9.99 740	44
17	9.03 920	114	9.04 181	116	0.95 819	9.99 738	43
18	9.04 034	115	9.04 297	116	0.95 703	9.99 737	42
19	9.04 149	113	9.04 413	115	0.95 587	9.99 736	41
20	9.04 262	114	9.04 528	115	0.95 472	9.99 734	40
21	9.04 376	114	9.04 643	115	0.95 357	9.99 733	39
22	9.04 490	113	9.04 758	115	0.95 242	9.99 731	38
23	9.04 603	112	9.04 873	114	0.95 127	9.99 730	37
24	9.04 715	113	9.04 987	114	0.95 013	9.99 728	36
25	9.04 828	112	9.05 101	113	0.94 899	9.99 727	35
26	9.04 940	112	9.05 214	114	0.94 786	9.99 726	34
27	9.05 052	112	9.05 328	113	0.94 672	9.99 724	33
28	9.05 164	111	9.05 441	112	0.94 559	9.99 723	32
29	9.05 275	111	9.05 553	113	0.94 447	9.99 721	31
30	9.05 386	111	9.05 666	112	0.94 334	9.99 720	30
31	9.05 497	110	9.05 778	112	0.94 222	9.99 718	29
32	9.05 607	110	9.05 890	112	0.94 110	9.99 717	28
33	9.05 717	110	9.06 002	111	0.93 998	9.99 716	27
34	9.05 827	110	9.06 113	111	0.93 887	9.99 714	26
35	9.05 937	109	9.06 224	111	0.93 776	9.99 713	25
36	9.06 046	109	9.06 335	110	0.93 665	9.99 711	24
37	9.06 155	109	9.06 445	111	0.93 555	9.99 710	23
38	9.06 264	108	9.06 556	110	0.93 444	9.99 708	22
39	9.06 372	109	9.06 666	109	0.93 334	9.99 707	21
40	9.06 481	108	9.06 775	110	0.93 225	9.99 705	20
41	9.06 589	107	9.06 885	109	0.93 115	9.99 704	19
42	9.06 696	108	9.06 994	109	0.93 006	9.99 702	18
43	9.06 804	107	9.07 103	108	0.92 897	9.99 701	17
44	9.06 911	107	9.07 211	109	0.92 789	9.99 699	16
45	9.07 018	106	9.07 320	108	0.92 680	9.99 698	15
46	9.07 124	107	9.07 428	108	0.92 572	9.99 696	14
47	9.07 231	106	9.07 536	107	0.92 464	9.99 695	13
48	9.07 337	105	9.07 643	108	0.92 357	9.99 693	12
49	9.07 442	106	9.07 751	107	0.92 249	9.99 692	11
50	9.07 548	105	9.07 858	106	0.92 142	9.99 690	10
51	9.07 653	105	9.07 964	107	0.92 036	9.99 689	9
52	9.07 758	105	9.08 071	106	0.91 929	9.99 687	8
53	9.07 863	105	9.08 177	106	0.91 823	9.99 686	7
54	9.07 968	104	9.08 283	106	0.91 717	9.99 684	6
55	9.08 072	104	9.08 389	106	0.91 611	9.99 683	5
56	9.08 176	104	9.08 495	105	0.91 505	9.99 681	4
57	9.08 280	103	9.08 600	105	0.91 400	9.99 680	3
58	9.08 383	103	9.08 705	105	0.91 295	9.99 678	2
59	9.08 486	103	9.08 810	104	0.91 190	9.99 677	1
60	9.08 589		9.08 914		0.91 086	9.99 675	0

′	L. Cos.	d.	L. Cot.	c.d.	L. Tan.	L. Sin.	′

96° (276°)   (263°) **83°**

P. P.

	121	120	119	118
1	2.0	2.0	2.0	2.0
2	4.0	4.0	4.0	5.9
3	6.0	6.0	6.0	5.9
4	8.1	8.0	7.9	7.9
5	10.1	10.0	9.9	9.8
6	12.1	12.0	11.9	11.8
7	14.1	14.0	13.9	13.8
8	16.1	16.0	15.9	15.7
9	18.2	18.0	17.8	17.7
10	20.2	20.0	19.8	19.7
20	40.3	40.0	39.7	39.3
30	60.5	60.0	59.5	59.0
40	80.7	80.0	79.3	78.7
50	100.8	100.0	99.2	98.3

	117	116	115	114
1	2.0	1.9	1.9	1.9
2	3.9	3.9	3.8	3.8
3	5.8	5.8	5.8	5.7
4	7.8	7.7	7.7	7.6
5	9.8	9.7	9.6	9.5
6	11.7	11.6	11.5	11.4
7	13.6	13.5	13.4	13.3
8	15.6	15.5	15.3	15.2
9	17.6	17.4	17.2	17.1
10	19.5	19.3	19.2	19.0
20	39.0	38.7	38.3	38.0
30	58.5	58.0	57.5	57.0
40	78.0	77.3	76.7	76.0
50	97.5	96.7	95.8	95.0

	113	112	111	110
1	1.9	1.9	1.8	1.8
2	3.8	3.7	3.7	3.7
3	5.6	5.6	5.6	5.5
4	7.5	7.5	7.4	7.3
5	9.4	9.3	9.2	9.2
6	11.3	11.2	11.1	11.0
7	13.2	13.1	13.0	12.8
8	15.1	14.9	14.8	14.7
9	17.0	16.8	16.6	16.5
10	18.8	18.7	18.5	18.3
20	37.7	37.3	37.0	36.7
30	56.5	56.0	55.5	55.0
40	75.3	74.7	74.0	73.3
50	94.2	93.3	92.5	91.7

	109	108	107	106
1	1.8	1.8	1.8	1.8
2	3.6	3.6	3.6	3.5
3	5.4	5.4	5.4	5.3
4	7.3	7.2	7.1	7.1
5	9.1	9.0	8.9	8.8
6	10.9	10.8	10.7	10.6
7	12.7	12.6	12.5	12.4
8	14.5	14.4	14.3	14.1
9	16.4	16.2	16.0	15.9
10	18.2	18.0	17.8	17.7
20	36.3	36.0	35.7	35.3
30	54.5	54.0	53.5	53.0
40	72.7	72.0	71.3	70.7
50	90.8	90.0	89.2	88.3

COMMON LOGARITHMS OF THE TRIGONOMETRIC
FUNCTIONS (Continued)

7° (187°)   **(352°) 172°**

′	L. Sin.	d.	L. Tan.	c.d.	L. Cot.	L. Cos.	′		P. P.			
0	9.08 589	103	9.08 914	105	0.91 086	9.99 675	60	″	**105**	**104**	**103**	**102**
1	9.08 692	103	9.09 019	104	0.90 981	9.99 674	59	1	1.8	1.7	1.7	1.7
2	9.08 795	102	9.09 123	104	0.90 877	9.99 672	58	2	3.5	3.5	3.4	3.4
3	9.08 897	102	9.09 227	103	0.90 773	9.99 670	57	3	5.2	5.2	5.2	5.1
4	9.08 999	102	9.09 330	104	0.90 670	9.99 669	56	4	7.0	6.9	6.9	6.8
5	9.09 101	101	9.09 434	103	0.90 566	9.99 667	55	5	8.8	8.7	8.6	8.5
6	9.09 202	102	9.09 537	103	0.90 463	9.99 666	54	6	10.5	10.4	10.3	10.2
7	9.09 304	101	9.09 640	102	0.90 360	9.99 664	53	7	12.2	12.1	12.0	11.9
8	9.09 405	101	9.09 742	103	0.90 258	9.99 663	52	8	14.0	13.9	13.7	13.6
9	9.09 506	100	9.09 845	102	0.90 155	9.99 661	51	9	15.8	15.6	15.4	15.3
10	9.09 606	101	9.09 947	102	0.90 053	9.99 659	50	10	17.5	17.3	17.2	17.0
11	9.09 707	100	9.10 049	101	0.89 951	9.99 658	49	20	35.0	34.7	34.3	34.0
12	9.09 807	100	9.10 150	102	0.89 850	9.99 656	48	30	52.5	52.0	51.5	51.0
13	9.09 907	99	9.10 252	101	0.89 748	9.99 655	47	40	70.0	69.3	68.7	68.0
14	9.10 006	100	9.10 353	101	0.89 647	9.99 653	46	50	87.5	86.7	85.8	85.0
15	9.10 106	99	9.10 454	101	0.89 546	9.99 651	45	″	**101**	**100**	**99**	**98**
16	9.10 205	99	9.10 555	101	0.89 445	9.99 650	44	1	1.7	1.7	1.6	1.6
17	9.10 304	98	9.10 656	100	0.89 344	9.99 648	43	2	3.4	3.3	3.3	3.3
18	9.10 402	99	9.10 756	100	0.89 244	9.99 647	42	3	5.0	5.0	5.0	4.9
19	9.10 501	98	9.10 856	100	0.89 144	9.99 645	41	4	6.7	6.7	6.6	6.5
20	9.10 599	98	9.10 956	100	0.89 044	9.99 643	40	5	8.4	8.3	8.2	8.2
21	9.10 697	98	9.11 056	99	0.88 944	9.99 642	39	6	10.1	10.0	9.9	9.8
22	9.10 795	98	9.11 155	99	0.88 845	9.99 640	38	7	11.8	11.7	11.6	11.4
23	9.10 893	97	9.11 254	99	0.88 746	9.99 638	37	8	13.5	13.3	13.2	13.1
24	9.10 990	97	9.11 353	99	0.88 647	9.99 637	36	9	15.2	15.0	14.8	14.7
25	9.11 087	97	9.11 452	99	0.88 548	9.99 635	35	10	16.8	16.7	16.5	16.3
26	9.11 184	97	9.11 551	98	0.88 449	9.99 633	34	20	33.7	33.3	33.0	32.7
27	9.11 281	96	9.11 649	98	0.88 351	9.99 632	33	30	50.5	50.0	49.5	49.0
28	9.11 377	97	9.11 747	98	0.88 253	9.99 630	32	40	67.3	66.7	66.0	65.3
29	9.11 474	96	9.11 845	98	0.88 155	9.99 629	31	50	84.2	83.3	82.5	81.7
30	9.11 570	96	9.11 943	97	0.88 057	9.99 627	30	″	**97**	**96**	**95**	**94**
31	9.11 666	95	9.12 040	98	0.87 960	9.99 625	29	1	1.6	1.6	1.6	1.6
32	9.11 761	96	9.12 138	97	0.87 862	9.99 624	28	2	3.2	3.2	3.2	3.1
33	9.11 857	95	9.12 235	97	0.87 765	9.99 622	27	3	4.8	4.8	4.8	4.7
34	9.11 952	95	9.12 332	96	0.87 668	9.99 620	26	4	6.5	6.4	6.3	6.3
35	9.12 047	95	9.12 428	97	0.87 572	9.99 618	25	5	8.1	8.0	7.9	7.8
36	9.12 142	94	9.12 525	96	0.87 475	9.99 617	24	6	9.7	9.6	9.5	9.4
37	9.12 236	95	9.12 621	96	0.87 379	9.99 615	23	7	11.3	11.2	11.1	11.0
38	9.12 331	94	9.12 717	96	0.87 283	9.99 613	22	8	12.9	12.8	12.7	12.5
39	9.12 425	94	9.12 813	96	0.87 187	9.99 612	21	9	14.6	14.4	14.2	14.1
40	9.12 519	93	9.12 909	95	0.87 091	9.99 610	20	10	16.2	16.0	15.8	15.7
41	9.12 612	94	9.13 004	95	0.86 996	9.99 608	19	20	32.3	32.0	31.7	31.3
42	9.12 706	93	9.13 099	95	0.86 901	9.99 607	18	30	48.5	48.0	47.5	47.0
43	9.12 799	93	9.13 194	95	0.86 806	9.99 605	17	40	64.7	64.0	63.3	62.7
44	9.12 892	93	9.13 289	95	0.86 711	9.99 603	16	50	80.8	80.0	79.2	78.3
45	9.12 985	93	9.13 384	94	0.86 616	9.99 601	15	″	**93**	**92**	**91**	**90**
46	9.13 078	93	9.13 478	95	0.86 522	9.99 600	14	1	1.6	1.5	1.5	1.5
47	9.13 171	92	9.13 573	94	0.86 427	9.99 598	13	2	3.1	3.1	3.0	3.0
48	9.13 263	92	9.13 667	94	0.86 333	9.99 596	12	3	4.6	4.6	4.6	4.5
49	9.13 355	92	9.13 761	93	0.86 239	9.99 595	11	4	6.2	6.1	6.1	6.0
50	9.13 447	92	9.13 854	94	0.86 146	9.99 593	10	5	7.8	7.7	7.6	7.5
51	9.13 539	91	9.13 948	93	0.86 052	9.99 591	9	6	9.3	9.2	9.1	9.0
52	9.13 630	92	9.14 041	93	0.85 959	9.99 589	8	7	10.8	10.7	10.6	10.5
53	9.13 722	91	9.14 134	93	0.85 866	9.99 588	7	8	12.4	12.3	12.1	12.0
54	9.13 813	91	9.14 227	93	0.85 773	9.99 586	6	9	14.0	13.8	13.6	13.5
55	9.13 904	90	9.14 320	92	0.85 680	9.99 584	5	10	15.5	15.3	15.2	15.0
56	9.13 994	91	9.14 412	92	0.85 588	9.99 582	4	20	31.0	30.7	30.3	30.0
57	9.14 085	90	9.14 504	93	0.85 496	9.99 581	3	30	46.5	46.0	45.5	45.0
58	9.14 175	91	9.14 597	91	0.85 403	9.99 579	2	40	62.0	61.3	60.7	60.0
59	9.14 266	90	9.14 688	92	0.85 312	9.99 577	1	50	77.5	76.7	75.8	75.0
60	9.14 356		9.14 780		0.85 220	9.99 575	0					
′	L. Cos.	d.	L. Cot.	c.d.	L. Tan.	L. Sin.	′		P. P.			

97° (277°)   **(262°) 82°**

COMMON LOGARITHMS OF THE TRIGONOMETRIC
FUNCTIONS (Continued)

8° (188°)   (351°) **171°**

′	L. Sin.	d.	L. Tan.	c.d.	L. Cot.	L. Cos.	′		P. P.		
0	9.14 356	89	9.14 780	92	0.85 220	9.99 575	60	″	**92**	**91**	**90**
1	9.14 445	90	9.14 872	91	0.85 128	9.99 574	59	1	1.5	1.5	1.5
2	9.14 535	89	9.14 963	91	0.85 037	9.99 572	58	2	3.1	3.0	3.0
3	9.14 624	90	9.15 054	91	0.84 946	9.99 570	57	3	4.6	4.6	4.5
4	9.14 714	89	9.15 145	91	0.84 855	9.99 568	56	4	6.1	6.1	6.0
5	9.14 803	88	9.15 236	91	0.84 764	9.99 566	55	5	7.7	7.6	7.5
6	9.14 891	89	9.15 327	90	0.84 673	9.99 565	54	6	9.2	9.1	9.0
7	9.14 980	89	9.15 417	91	0.84 583	9.99 563	53	7	10.7	10.6	10.5
8	9.15 069	88	9.15 508	90	0.84 492	9.99 561	52	8	12.3	12.1	12.0
9	9.15 157	88	9.15 598	90	0.84 402	9.99 559	51	9	13.8	13.6	13.5
10	9.15 245	88	9.15 688	89	0.84 312	9.99 557	50	10	15.3	15.2	15.0
11	9.15 333	88	9.15 777	90	0.84 223	9.99 556	49	20	30.7	30.3	30.0
12	9.15 421	87	9.15 867	89	0.84 133	9.99 554	48	30	46.0	45.5	45.0
13	9.15 508	88	9.15 956	90	0.84 044	9.99 552	47	40	61.3	60.7	60.0
14	9.15 596	87	9.16 046	89	0.83 954	9.99 550	46	50	76.7	75.8	75.0
15	9.15 683	87	9.16 135	89	0.83 865	9.99 548	45	″	**89**	**88**	**87**
16	9.15 770	87	9.16 224	88	0.83 776	9.99 546	44	1	1.5	1.5	1.4
17	9.15 857	87	9.16 312	89	0.83 688	9.99 545	43	2	3.0	2.9	2.9
18	9.15 944	86	9.16 401	88	0.83 599	9.99 543	42	3	4.4	4.4	4.4
19	9.16 030	86	9.16 489	88	0.83 511	9.99 541	41	4	5.9	5.9	5.8
20	9.16 116	87	9.16 577	88	0.83 423	9.99 539	40	5	7.4	7.3	7.2
21	9.16 203	86	9.16 665	88	0.83 335	9.99 537	39	6	8.9	8.8	8.7
22	9.16 289	85	9.16 753	88	0.83 247	9.99 535	38	7	10.4	10.3	10.2
23	9.16 374	86	9.16 841	87	0.83 159	9.99 533	37	8	11.9	11.7	11.6
24	9.16 460	85	9.16 928	88	0.83 072	9.99 532	36	9	13.4	13.2	13.0
25	9.16 545	86	9.17 016	87	0.82 984	9.99 530	35	10	14.8	14.7	14.5
26	9.16 631	85	9.17 103	87	0.82 897	9.99 528	34	20	29.7	29.3	29.0
27	9.16 716	85	9.17 190	87	0.82 810	9.99 526	33	30	44.5	44.0	43.5
28	9.16 801	85	9.17 277	86	0.82 723	9.99 524	32	40	59.3	58.7	58.0
29	9.16 886	84	9.17 363	87	0.82 637	9.99 522	31	50	74.2	73.3	72.5
30	9.16 970	85	9.17 450	86	0.82 550	9.99 520	30	″	**86**	**85**	**84**
31	9.17 055	84	9.17 536	86	0.82 464	9.99 518	29	1	1.4	1.4	1.4
32	9.17 139	84	9.17 622	86	0.82 378	9.99 517	28	2	2.9	2.8	2.8
33	9.17 223	84	9.17 708	86	0.82 292	9.99 515	27	3	4.3	4.2	4.2
34	9.17 307	84	9.17 794	86	0.82 206	9.99 513	26	4	5.7	5.7	5.6
35	9.17 391	83	9.17 880	85	0.82 120	9.99 511	25	5	7.2	7.1	7.0
36	9.17 474	84	9.17 965	86	0.82 035	9.99 509	24	6	8.6	8.5	8.4
37	9.17 558	83	9.18 051	85	0.81 949	9.99 507	23	7	10.0	9.9	9.8
38	9.17 641	83	9.18 136	85	0.81 864	9.99 506	22	8	11.5	11.3	11.2
39	9.17 724	83	9.18 221	85	0.81 779	9.99 503	21	9	12.9	12.8	12.6
40	9.17 807	83	9.18 306	85	0.81 694	9.99 501	20	10	14.3	14.2	14.0
41	9.17 890	83	9.18 391	84	0.81 609	9.99 499	19	20	28.7	28.3	28.0
42	9.17 973	82	9.18 475	85	0.81 525	9.99 497	18	30	43.0	42.5	42.0
43	9.18 055	82	9.18 560	84	0.81 440	9.99 496	17	40	57.3	56.7	56.0
44	9.18 137	83	9.18 644	84	0.81 356	9.99 494	16	50	71.7	70.8	70.0
45	9.18 220	82	9.18 728	84	0.81 272	9.99 492	15	″	**83**	**82**	**81**
46	9.18 302	81	9.18 812	84	0.81 188	9.99 490	14	1	1.4	1.4	1.4
47	9.18 383	82	9.18 896	83	0.81 104	9.99 488	13	2	2.8	2.7	2.7
48	9.18 465	82	9.18 979	84	0.81 021	9.99 486	12	3	4.2	4.1	4.0
49	9.18 547	81	9.19 063	83	0.80 937	9.99 484	11	4	5.5	5.5	5.4
50	9.18 628	81	9.19 146	83	0.80 854	9.99 482	10	5	6.9	6.8	6.8
51	9.18 709	81	9.19 229	83	0.80 771	9.99 480	9	6	8.3	8.2	8.1
52	9.18 790	81	9.19 312	83	0.80 688	9.99 478	8	7	9.7	9.6	9.4
53	9.18 871	81	9.19 395	83	0.80 605	9.99 476	7	8	11.1	10.9	10.8
54	9.18 952	81	9.19 478	83	0.80 522	9.99 474	6	9	12.4	12.3	12.2
55	9.19 033	80	9.19 561	82	0.80 439	9.99 472	5	10	13.8	13.7	13.5
56	9.19 113	80	9.19 643	82	0.80 357	9.99 470	4	20	27.7	27.3	27.0
57	9.19 193	80	9.19 725	82	0.80 275	9.99 468	3	30	41.5	41.0	40.5
58	9.19 273	80	9.19 807	82	0.80 193	9.99 466	2	40	55.3	54.7	54.0
59	9.19 353	80	9.19 889	82	0.80 111	9.99 464	1	50	69.2	68.3	67.5
60	9.19 433		9.19 971		0.80 029	9.99 462	0				
′	L. Cos.	d.	L. Cot.	c.d.	L. Tan.	L. Sin.	′		P. P.		

COMMON LOGARITHMS OF THE TRIGONOMETRIC FUNCTIONS (Continued)

9° (189°)   **(350°) 170°**

'	L. Sin.	d.	L. Tan.	c.d.	L. Cot.	L. Cos.	'
0	9.19 433	80	9.19 971	82	0.80 029	9.99 462	60
1	9.19 513	79	9.20 053	81	0.79 947	9.99 460	59
2	9.19 592	80	9.20 134	82	0.79 866	9.99 458	58
3	9.19 672	79	9.20 216	81	0.79 784	9.99 456	57
4	9.19 751	79	9.20 297	81	0.79 703	9.99 454	56
5	9.19 830	79	9.20 378	81	0.79 622	9.99 452	55
6	9.19 909	79	9.20 459	81	0.79 541	9.99 450	54
7	9.19 988	79	9.20 540	81	0.79 460	9.99 448	53
8	9.20 067	78	9.20 621	80	0.79 379	9.99 446	52
9	9.20 145	78	9.20 701	81	0.79 299	9.99 444	51
10	9.20 223	79	9.20 782	80	0.79 218	9.99 442	50
11	9.20 302	78	9.20 862	80	0.79 138	9.99 440	49
12	9.20 380	78	9.20 942	80	0.79 058	9.99 438	48
13	9.20 458	77	9.21 022	80	0.78 978	9.99 436	47
14	9.20 535	78	9.21 102	80	0.78 898	9.99 434	46
15	9.20 613	78	9.21 182	79	0.78 818	9.99 432	45
16	9.20 691	77	9.21 261	80	0.78 739	9.99 429	44
17	9.20 768	77	9.21 341	79	0.78 659	9.99 427	43
18	9.20 845	77	9.21 420	79	0.78 580	9.99 425	42
19	9.20 922	77	9.21 499	79	0.78 501	9.99 423	41
20	9.20 999	77	9.21 578	79	0.78 422	9.99 421	40
21	9.21 076	77	9.21 657	79	0.78 343	9.99 419	39
22	9.21 153	76	9.21 736	78	0.78 264	9.99 417	38
23	9.21 229	77	9.21 814	79	0.78 186	9.99 415	37
24	9.21 306	76	9.21 893	78	0.78 107	9.99 413	36
25	9 21 382	76	9.21 971	78	0.78 029	9.99 411	35
26	9.21 458	76	9.22 049	78	0.77 951	9.99 409	34
27	9.21 534	76	9.22 127	78	0.77 873	9.99 407	33
28	9.21 610	75	9.22 205	78	0.77 795	9.99 404	32
29	9.21 685	76	9.22 283	78	0.77 717	9.99 402	31
30	9.21 761	75	9.22 361	77	0.77 639	9.99 400	30
31	9.21 836	76	9.22 438	78	0.77 562	9.99 398	29
32	9.21 912	75	9.22 516	77	0.77 484	9.99 396	28
33	9.21 987	75	9.22 593	77	0.77 407	9.99 394	27
34	9.22 062	75	9.22 670	77	0.77 330	9.99 392	26
35	9.22 137	74	9.22 747	77	0.77 253	9.99 390	25
36	9.22 211	75	9.22 824	77	0.77 176	9.99 388	24
37	9.22 286	75	9.22 901	76	0.77 099	9.99 385	23
38	9.22 361	74	9.22 977	77	0.77 023	9.99 383	22
39	9.22 435	74	9.23 054	76	0.76 946	9.99 381	21
40	9.22 509	74	9.23 130	76	0.76 870	9.99 379	20
41	9.22 583	74	9.23 206	77	0.76 794	9.99 377	19
42	9.22 657	74	9.23 283	76	0.76 717	9.99 375	18
43	9.22 731	74	9.23 359	76	0.76 641	9.99 372	17
44	9.22 805	73	9.23 435	75	0.76 565	9.99 370	16
45	9.22 878	74	9.23 510	76	0.76 490	9.99 368	15
46	9.22 952	73	9.23 586	75	0.76 414	9.99 366	14
47	9.23 025	73	9.23 661	76	0.76 339	9.99 364	13
48	9.23 098	73	9.23 737	75	0.76 263	9.99 362	12
49	9.23 171	73	9.23 812	75	0.76 188	9.99 359	11
50	9.23 244	73	9.23 887	75	0.76 113	9.99 357	10
51	9.23 317	73	9.23 962	75	0.76 038	9.99 355	9
52	9.23 390	72	9.24 037	75	0.75 963	9.99 353	8
53	9.23 462	73	9.24 112	74	0.75 888	9.99 351	7
54	9.23 535	72	9.24 186	75	0.75 814	9.99 348	6
55	9.23 607	72	9.24 261	74	0.75 739	9.99 346	5
56	9.23 679	73	9.24 335	75	0.75 665	9.99 344	4
57	9.23 752	71	9.24 410	74	0.75 590	9.99 342	3
58	9.23 823	72	9.24 484	74	0.75 516	9.99 340	2
59	9.23 895	72	9.24 558	74	0.75 442	9.99 337	1
60	9.23 967		9.24 632		0.75 368	9.99 335	0

'	L. Cos.	d.	L. Cot.	c.d.	L. Tan.	L. Sin.	'

P. P.

''	80	79	78	77
1	1.3	1.3	1.3	1.3
2	2.7	2.6	2.6	2.6
3	4.0	4.0	3.9	3.8
4	5.3	5.3	5.2	5.1
5	6.7	6.6	6.5	6.4
6	8.0	7.9	7.8	7.7
7	9.3	9.2	9.1	9.0
8	10.7	10.5	10.4	10.3
9	12.0	11.8	11.7	11.6
10	13.3	13.2	13.0	12.8
20	26.7	26.3	26.0	25.7
30	40.0	39.5	39.0	38.5
40	53.3	52.7	52.0	51.3
50	66.7	65.8	65.0	64.2

''	76	75	74	73
1	1.3	1.2	1.2	1.2
2	2.5	2.5	2.5	2.4
3	3.8	3.8	3.7	3.6
4	5.1	5.0	4.9	4.9
5	6.3	6.2	6.2	6.1
6	7.6	7.5	7.4	7.3
7	8.9	8.8	8.6	8.5
8	10.1	10.0	9.9	9.7
9	11.4	11.2	11.1	11.0
10	12.7	12.5	12.3	12.2
20	25.3	25.0	24.7	24.3
30	38.0	37.5	37.0	36.5
40	50.7	50.0	49.3	48.7
50	63.3	62.5	61.7	60.8

''	72	71	3	2
1	1.2	1.2	0.0	0.0
2	2.4	2.4	0.1	0.1
3	3.6	3.6	0.2	0.1
4	4.8	4.7	0.2	0.1
5	6.0	5.9	0.2	0.2
6	7.2	7.1	0.3	0.2
7	8.4	8.3	0.4	0.2
8	9.6	9.5	0.4	0.3
9	10.8	10.6	0.4	0.3
10	12.0	11.8	0.5	0.3
20	24.0	23.7	1.0	0.7
30	36.0	35.5	1.5	1.0
40	48.0	47.3	2.0	1.3
50	60.0	59.2	2.5	1.7

	3	3	3
	79	78	77
0	13.2	13.0	12.8
1	39.5	39.0	38.5
2, 3	65.8	65.0	64.2

	3	3	3
	76	75	74
0, 1	12.7	12.5	12.3
2	38.0	37.5	37.0
3	63.3	62.5	61.7

99° (279°)   **(260°) 80°**

Tables for Use in Trigonometry

COMMON LOGARITHMS OF THE TRIGONOMETRIC FUNCTIONS (Continued)

10° (190°) (349°) **169°**

'	L. Sin.	d.	L. Tan.	c.d.	L. Cot.	L. Cos.	d.	'
0	9.23 967	72	9.24 632	74	0.75 368	9.99 335	2	60
1	9.24 039	71	9.24 706	73	0.75 294	9.99 333	2	59
2	9.24 110	71	9.24 779	74	0.75 221	9.99 331	2	58
3	9.24 181	72	9.24 853	73	0.75 147	9.99 328	3	57
4	9.24 253	71	9.24 926	74	0.75 074	9.99 326	2	56
5	9.24 324	71	9.25 000	73	0.75 000	9.99 324	2	55
6	9.24 395	71	9.25 073	73	0.74 927	9.99 322	3	54
7	9.24 466	70	9.25 146	73	0.74 854	9.99 319	2	53
8	9.24 536	71	9.25 219	73	0.74 781	9.99 317	2	52
9	9.24 607	70	9.25 292	73	0.74 708	9.99 315	2	51
10	9.24 677	71	9.25 365	72	0.74 635	9.99 313	3	50
11	9.24 748	70	9.25 437	73	0.74 563	9.99 310	2	49
12	9.24 818	70	9.25 510	72	0.74 490	9.99 308	2	48
13	9.24 888	70	9.25 582	73	0.74 418	9.99 306	2	47
14	9.24 958	70	9.25 655	72	0.74 345	9.99 304	3	46
15	9.25 028	70	9.25 727	72	0.74 273	9.99 301	2	45
16	9.25 098	70	9.25 799	72	0.74 201	9.99 299	2	44
17	9.25 168	69	9.25 871	72	0.74 129	9.99 297	3	43
18	9.25 237	70	9.25 943	72	0.74 057	9.99 294	2	42
19	9.25 307	69	9.26 015	71	0.73 985	9.99 292	2	41
20	9.25 376	69	9.26 086	72	0.73 914	9.99 290	2	40
21	9.25 445	69	9.26 158	71	0.73 842	9.99 288	3	39
22	9.25 514	69	9.26 229	72	0.73 771	9.99 285	2	38
23	9.25 583	69	9.26 301	71	0.73 699	9.99 283	2	37
24	9.25 652	69	9.26 372	71	0.73 628	9.99 281	2	36
25	9.25 721	69	9.26 443	71	0.73 557	9.99 278	2	35
26	9.25 790	68	9.26 514	71	0.73 486	9.99 276	2	34
27	9.25 858	69	9.26 585	70	0.73 415	9.99 274	3	33
28	9.25 927	68	9.26 655	71	0.73 345	9.99 271	2	32
29	9.25 995	68	9.26 726	71	0.73 274	9.99 269	2	31
30	9.26 063	68	9.26 797	70	0.73 203	9.99 267	3	30
31	9.26 131	68	9.26 867	70	0.73 133	9.99 264	2	29
32	9.26 199	68	9.26 937	71	0.73 063	9.99 262	2	28
33	9.26 267	68	9.27 008	70	0.72 992	9.99 260	3	27
34	9.26 335	68	9.27 078	70	0.72 922	9.99 257	2	26
35	9.26 403	67	9.27 148	70	0.72 852	9.99 255	3	25
36	9.26 470	68	9.27 218	70	0.72 782	9.99 252	2	24
37	9.26 538	67	9.27 288	69	0.72 712	9.99 250	2	23
38	9.26 605	67	9.27 357	70	0.72 643	9.99 248	3	22
39	9.26 672	67	9.27 427	69	0.72 573	9.99 245	2	21
40	9.26 739	67	9.27 496	70	0.72 504	9.99 243	2	20
41	9.26 806	67	9.27 566	69	0.72 434	9.99 241	3	19
42	9.26 873	67	9.27 635	69	0.72 365	9.99 238	2	18
43	9.26 940	67	9.27 704	69	0.72 296	9.99 236	3	17
44	9.27 007	66	9.27 773	69	0.72 227	9.99 233	2	16
45	9.27 073	67	9.27 842	69	0.72 158	9.99 231	2	15
46	9.27 140	66	9.27 911	69	0.72 089	9.99 229	3	14
47	9.27 206	67	9.27 980	69	0.72 020	9.99 226	2	13
48	9.27 273	66	9.28 049	68	0.71 951	9.99 224	3	12
49	9.27 339	66	9.28 117	69	0.71 883	9.99 221	2	11
50	9.27 405	66	9.28 186	68	0.71 814	9.99 219	2	10
51	9.27 471	66	9.28 254	69	0.71 746	9.99 217	3	9
52	9.27 537	65	9.28 323	68	0.71 677	9.99 214	2	8
53	9.27 602	66	9.28 391	68	0.71 609	9.99 212	3	7
54	9.27 668	66	9.28 459	68	0.71 541	9.99 209	2	6
55	9.27 734	65	9.28 527	68	0.71 473	9.99 207	3	5
56	9.27 799	65	9.28 595	67	0.71 405	9.99 204	2	4
57	9.27 864	66	9.28 662	68	0.71 338	9.99 202	2	3
58	9.27 930	65	9.28 730	68	0.71 270	9.99 200	3	2
59	9.27 995	65	9.28 798	67	0.71 202	9.99 197	2	1
60	9.28 060		9.28 865		0.71 135	9.99 195		0

| ' | L. Cos. | d. | L. Cot. | c.d. | L. Tan. | L. Sin. | d. | ' |

100° (280°) (259°) **79°**

P. P.

"	74	73	72
1	1.2	1.2	1.2
2	2.5	2.4	2.4
3	3.7	3.6	3.6
4	4.9	4.9	4.8
5	6.2	6.1	6.0
6	7.4	7.3	7.2
7	8.6	8.5	8.4
8	9.9	9.7	9.6
9	11.1	11.0	10.8
10	12.3	12.2	12.0
20	24.7	24.3	24.0
30	37.0	36.5	36.0
40	49.3	48.7	48.0
50	61.7	60.8	60.0

"	71	70	69
1	1.2	1.2	1.2
2	2.4	2.3	2.3
3	3.6	3.5	3.4
4	4.7	4.7	4.6
5	5.9	5.8	5.8
6	7.1	7.0	6.9
7	8.3	8.2	8.0
8	9.5	9.3	9.2
9	10.6	10.5	10.4
10	11.8	11.7	11.5
20	23.7	23.3	23.0
30	35.5	35.0	34.5
40	47.3	46.7	46.0
50	59.2	58.3	57.5

"	68	67	66
1	1.1	1.1	1.1
2	2.3	2.2	2.2
3	3.4	3.4	3.3
4	4.5	4.5	4.4
5	5.7	5.6	5.5
6	6.8	6.7	6.6
7	7.9	7.8	7.7
8	9.1	8.9	8.8
9	10.2	10.0	9.9
10	11.3	11.2	11.0
20	22.7	22.3	22.0
30	34.0	33.5	33.0
40	45.3	44.7	44.0
50	56.7	55.8	55.0

	3	3	3
	74	73	72
1	12.3	12.2	12.0
2	37.0	36.5	36.0
3	61.7	60.8	60.0

	3	3	3	3
	71	70	69	68
1	11.8	11.7	11.5	11.3
2	35.5	35.0	34.5	34.0
3	59.2	58.3	57.5	56.7

COMMON LOGARITHMS OF THE TRIGONOMETRIC FUNCTIONS (Continued)

11° (191°)   **(348°) 168°**

'	L. Sin.	d.	L. Tan.	c.d.	L. Cot.	L. Cos.	d.	'
0	9.28 060	65	9.28 865	68	0.71 135	9.99 195	3	60
1	9.28 125	65	9.28 933	67	0.71 067	9.99 192	2	59
2	9.28 190	64	9.29 000	67	0.71 000	9.99 190	2	58
3	9.28 254	65	9.29 067	67	0.70 933	9.99 187	2	57
4	9.28 319	65	9.29 134	67	0.70 866	9.99 185	3	56
5	9.28 384	64	9.29 201	67	0.70 799	9.99 182	2	55
6	9.28 448	64	9.29 268	67	0.70 732	9.99 180	3	54
7	9.28 512	65	9.29 335	67	0.70 665	9.99 177	2	53
8	9.28 577	64	9.29 402	66	0.70 598	9.99 175	3	52
9	9.28 641	64	9.29 468	67	0.70 532	9.99 172	2	51
10	9.28 705	64	9.29 535	66	0.70 465	9.99 170	3	50
11	9.28 769	64	9.29 601	67	0.70 399	9.99 167	3	49
12	9.28 833	63	9.29 668	66	0.70 332	9.99 165	3	48
13	9.28 896	64	9.29 734	66	0.70 266	9.99 162	2	47
14	9.28 960	64	9.29 800	66	0.70 200	9.99 160	3	46
15	9.29 024	63	9.29 866	66	0.70 134	9.99 157	2	45
16	9.29 087	63	9.29 932	66	0.70 068	9.99 155	3	44
17	9.29 150	64	9.29 998	66	0.70 002	9.99 152	2	43
18	9.29 214	63	9.30 064	66	0.69 936	9.99 150	3	42
19	9.29 277	63	9.30 130	65	0.69 870	9.99 147	2	41
20	9.29 340	63	9.30 195	66	0.69 805	9.99 145	3	40
21	9.29 403	63	9.30 261	65	0.69 739	9.99 142	2	39
22	9.29 466	63	9.30 326	65	0.69 674	9.99 140	3	38
23	9.29 529	62	9.30 391	66	0.69 609	9.99 137	2	37
24	9.29 591	63	9.30 457	65	0.69 543	9.99 135	3	36
25	9.29 654	62	9.30 522	65	0.69 478	9.99 132	2	35
26	9.29 716	63	9.30 587	65	0.69 413	9.99 130	3	34
27	9.29 779	62	9.30 652	65	0.69 348	9.99 127	3	33
28	9.29 841	62	9.30 717	65	0.69 283	9.99 124	2	32
29	9.29 903	63	9.30 782	64	0.69 218	9.99 122	3	31
30	9.29 966	62	9.30 846	65	0.69 154	9.99 119	2	30
31	9.30 028	62	9.30 911	64	0.69 089	9.99 117	3	29
32	9.30 090	61	9.30 975	65	0.69 025	9.99 114	2	28
33	9.30 151	62	9.31 040	64	0.68 960	9.99 112	3	27
34	9.30 213	62	9.31 104	64	0.68 896	9.99 109	3	26
35	9.30 275	61	9.31 168	65	0.68 832	9.99 106	2	25
36	9.30 336	62	9.31 233	64	0.68 767	9.99 104	3	24
37	9.30 398	61	9.31 297	64	0.68 703	9.99 101	2	23
38	9.30 459	62	9.31 361	64	0.68 639	9.99 099	3	22
39	9.30 521	61	9.31 425	64	0.68 575	9.99 096	3	21
40	9.30 582	61	9.31 489	63	0.68 511	9.99 093	2	20
41	9.30 643	61	9.31 552	64	0.68 448	9.99 091	3	19
42	9.30 704	61	9.31 616	63	0.68 384	9.99 088	2	18
43	9.30 765	61	9.31 679	64	0.68 321	9.99 086	3	17
44	9.30 826	61	9.31 743	63	0.68 257	9.99 083	3	16
45	9.30 887	60	9.31 806	64	0.68 194	9.99 080	2	15
46	9.30 947	61	9.31 870	63	0.68 130	9.99 078	3	14
47	9.31 008	60	9.31 933	63	0.68 067	9.99 075	3	13
48	9.31 068	61	9.31 996	63	0.68 004	9.99 072	2	12
49	9.31 129	60	9.32 059	63	0.67 941	9.99 070	3	11
50	9.31 189	61	9.32 122	63	0.67 878	9.99 067	3	10
51	9.31 250	60	9.32 185	63	0.67 815	9.99 064	2	9
52	9.31 310	60	9.32 248	63	0.67 752	9.99 062	3	8
53	9.31 370	60	9.32 311	62	0.67 689	9.99 059	3	7
54	9.31 430	60	9.32 373	63	0.67 627	9.99 056	2	6
55	9.31 490	59	9.32 436	62	0.67 564	9.99 054	3	5
56	9.31 549	60	9.32 498	63	0.67 502	9.99 051	3	4
57	9.31 609	60	9.32 561	62	0.67 439	9.99 048	2	3
58	9.31 669	59	9.32 623	62	0.67 377	9.99 046	3	2
59	9.31 728	60	9.32 685	62	0.67 315	9.99 043	3	1
60	9.31 788		9.32 747		0.67 253	9.99 040		0

| | L. Cos. | d. | L. Cot. | c.d. | L. Tan. | L. Sin. | d. | ' |

101° (281°)   **(258°) 78°**

P. P.

"	65	64	63
1	1.1	1.1	1.0
2	2.2	2.1	2.1
3	3.2	3.2	3.2
4	4.3	4.3	4.2
5	5.4	5.3	5.2
6	6.5	6.4	6.3
7	7.6	7.5	7.4
8	8.7	8.5	8.4
9	9.8	9.6	9.4
10	10.8	10.7	10.5
20	21.7	21.3	21.0
30	32.5	32.0	31.5
40	43.3	42.7	42.0
50	54.2	53.3	52.5

"	62	61	60
1	1.0	1.0	1.0
2	2.1	2.0	2.0
3	3.1	3.0	3.0
4	4.1	4.1	4.0
5	5.2	5.1	5.0
6	6.2	6.1	6.0
7	7.2	7.1	7.0
8	8.3	8.1	8.0
9	9.3	9.2	9.0
10	10.3	10.2	10.0
20	20.7	20.3	20.0
30	31.0	30.5	30.0
40	41.3	40.7	40.0
50	51.7	50.8	50.0

"	59	3	2
1	1.0	0.0	0.0
2	2.0	0.1	0.1
3	3.0	0.2	0.1
4	3.9	0.2	0.1
5	4.9	0.2	0.2
6	5.9	0.3	0.2
7	6.9	0.4	0.2
8	7.9	0.4	0.3
9	8.8	0.4	0.3
10	9.8	0.5	0.3
20	19.7	1.0	0.7
30	29.5	1.5	1.0
40	39.3	2.0	1.3
50	49.2	2.5	1.7

	3	3	3
	67	66	65
0	11.2	11.0	10.8
1	33.5	33.0	32.5
2	55.8	55.0	54.2

	3	3	3
	64	63	62
0	10.7	10.5	10.3
1	32.0	31.5	31.0
2	53.3	52.5	51.7

COMMON LOGARITHMS OF THE TRIGONOMETRIC FUNCTIONS (Continued)

12° (192°)   **(347°) 167°**

'	L. Sin.	d.	L. Tan.	c.d.	L. Cot.	L. Cos.	d.	'
0	9.31 788	59	9.32 747	63	0.67 253	9.99 040	2	60
1	9.31 847	60	9.32 810	62	0.67 190	9.99 038	3	59
2	9.31 907	59	9.32 872	61	0.67 128	9.99 035	3	58
3	9.31 966	59	9.32 933	62	0.67 067	9.99 032	2	57
4	9.32 025	59	9.32 995	62	0.67 005	9.99 030	3	56
5	9.32 084	59	9.33 057	62	0.66 943	9.99 027		55
6	9.32 143	59	9.33 119	61	0.66 881	9.99 024	2	54
7	9.32 202	59	9.33 180	62	0.66 820	9.99 022	3	53
8	9.32 261	58	9.33 242	61	0.66 758	9.99 019	3	52
9	9.32 319	59	9.33 303	62	0.66 697	9.99 016	3	51
10	9.32 378	59	9.33 365	61	0.66 635	9.99 013	2	50
11	9.32 437	58	9.33 426	61	0.66 574	9.99 011	3	49
12	9.32 495	58	9.33 487	61	0.66 513	9.99 008	3	48
13	9.32 553	59	9.33 548	61	0.66 452	9.99 005	3	47
14	9.32 612	58	9.33 609	61	0.66 391	9.99 002	2	46
15	9.32 670	58	9.33 670	61	0.66 330	9.99 000	3	45
16	9.32 728	58	9.33 731	61	0.66 269	9.98 997	3	44
17	9.32 786	58	9.33 792	61	0.66 208	9.98 994	3	43
18	9.32 844	58	9.33 853	60	0.66 147	9.98 991	2	42
19	9.32 902	58	9.33 913	61	0.66 087	9.98 989	3	41
20	9.32 960	58	9.33 974	60	0.66 026	9.98 986	3	40
21	9.33 018	57	9.34 034	61	0.65 966	9.98 983	3	39
22	9.33 075	58	9.34 095	60	0.65 905	9.98 980	2	38
23	9.33 133	57	9.34 155	60	0.65 845	9.98 978	3	37
24	9.33 190	58	9.34 215	61	0.65 785	9.98 975	3	36
25	9.33 248	57	9.34 276	60	0.65 724	9.98 972	3	35
26	9.33 305	57	9.34 336	60	0.65 664	9.98 969	2	34
27	9.33 362	58	9.34 396	60	0.65 604	9.98 967	3	33
28	9.33 420	57	9.34 456	60	0.65 544	9.98 964	3	32
29	9.33 477	57	9.34 516	60	0.65 484	9.98 961	3	31
30	9.33 534	57	9.34 576	59	0.65 424	9.98 958	3	30
31	9.33 591	56	9.34 635	60	0.65 365	9.98 955	2	29
32	9.33 647	57	9.34 695	60	0.65 305	9.98 953	3	28
33	9.33 704	57	9.34 755	59	0.65 245	9.98 950	3	27
34	9.33 761	57	9.34 814	60	0.65 186	9.98 947	3	26
35	9.33 818	56	9.34 874	59	0.65 126	9.98 944	3	25
36	9.33 874	57	9.34 933	59	0.65 067	9.98 941	3	24
37	9.33 931	56	9.34 992	59	0.65 008	9.98 938	2	23
38	9.33 987	56	9.35 051	60	0.64 949	9.98 936	3	22
39	9.34 043	57	9.35 111	59	0.64 889	9.98 933	3	21
40	9.34 100	56	9.35 170	59	0.64 830	9.98 930	3	20
41	9.34 156	56	9.35 229	59	0.64 771	9.98 927	3	19
42	9.34 212	56	9.35 288	59	0.64 712	9.98 924	3	18
43	9.34 268	56	9.35 347	58	0.64 653	9.98 921	2	17
44	9.34 324	56	9.35 405	59	0.64 595	9.98 919	3	16
45	9.34 380	56	9.35 464	59	0.64 536	9.98 916	3	15
46	9.34 436	55	9.35 523	58	0.64 477	9.98 913	3	14
47	9.34 491	56	9.35 581	59	0.64 419	9.98 910	3	13
48	9.34 547	55	9.35 640	58	0.64 360	9.98 907	3	12
49	9.34 602	56	9.35 698	59	0.64 302	9.98 904	3	11
50	9.34 658	55	9.35 757	58	0.64 243	9.98 901	3	10
51	9.34 713	56	9.35 815	58	0.64 185	9.98 898	2	9
52	9.34 769	55	9.35 873	58	0.64 127	9.98 896	3	8
53	9.34 824	55	9.35 931	58	0.64 069	9.98 893	3	7
54	9.34 879	55	9.35 989	58	0.64 011	9.98 890	3	6
55	9.34 934	55	9.36 047	58	0.63 953	9.98 887	3	5
56	9.34 989	55	9.36 105	58	0.63 895	9.98 884	3	4
57	9.35 044	55	9.36 163	58	0.63 837	9.98 881	3	3
58	9.35 099	55	9.36 221	58	0.63 779	9.98 878	3	2
59	9.35 154	55	9.36 279	57	0.63 721	9.98 875	3	1
60	9.35 209		9.36 336		0.63 664	9.98 872		0

P. P.

	63	62	61
1	1.0	1.0	1.0
2	2.1	2.1	2.0
3	3.2	3.1	3.0
4	4.2	4.1	4.1
5	5.2	5.2	5.1
6	6.3	6.2	6.1
7	7.4	7.2	7.1
8	8.4	8.3	8.1
9	9.4	9.3	9.2
10	10.5	10.3	10.2
20	21.0	20.7	20.3
30	31.5	31.0	30.5
40	42.0	41.3	40.7
50	52.5	51.7	50.8

	60	59	58
1	1.0	1.0	1.0
2	2.0	2.0	1.9
3	3.0	3.0	2.9
4	4.0	3.9	3.8
5	5.0	4.9	4.8
6	6.0	5.9	5.8
7	7.0	6.9	6.8
8	8.0	7.9	7.7
9	9.0	8.8	8.7
10	10.0	9.8	9.7
20	20.0	19.7	19.3
30	30.0	29.5	29.0
40	40.0	39.3	38.7
50	50.0	49.2	48.3

	57	56	55
1	1.0	0.9	0.9
2	1.9	1.9	1.8
3	2.8	2.8	2.8
4	3.8	3.7	3.7
5	4.8	4.7	4.6
6	5.7	5.6	5.5
7	6.6	6.5	6.4
8	7.6	7.5	7.3
9	8.6	8.4	8.2
10	9.5	9.3	9.2
20	19.0	18.7	18.3
30	28.5	28.0	27.5
40	38.0	37.3	36.7
50	47.5	46.7	45.8

	3 / 62	3 / 61	3 / 60
0	10.3	10.2	10.0
1	31.0	30.5	30.0
2	51.7	50.8	50.0
3			

	3 / 59	3 / 58	3 / 57
0	9.8	9.7	9.5
1	29.5	29.0	28.5
2	49.2	48.3	47.5
3			

'	L. Cos.	d.	L. Cot.	c.d.	L. Tan.	L. Sin.	d.	'	P. P.

102° (282°)   **(257°) 77°**

COMMON LOGARITHMS OF THE TRIGONOMETRIC FUNCTIONS (Continued)

13° (193°)   **(346°) 166°**

′	L. Sin.	d.	L. Tan.	c.d.	L. Cot.	L. Cos.	d.	′
0	9.35 209	34	9.36 336	58	0.63 664	9.98 872	3	60
1	9.35 263	55	9.36 394	58	0.63 606	9.98 869	2	59
2	9.35 318	55	9.36 452	57	0.63 548	9.98 867	3	58
3	9.35 373	54	9.36 509	57	0.63 491	9.98 864	3	57
4	9.35 427	54	9.36 566	58	0.63 434	9.98 861	3	56
5	9.35 481	55	9.36 624	57	0.63 376	9.98 858	3	55
6	9.35 536	54	9.36 681	57	0.63 319	9.98 855	3	54
7	9.35 590	54	9.36 738	57	0.63 262	9.98 852	3	53
8	9.35 644	54	9.36 795	57	0.63 205	9.98 849	3	52
9	9.35 698	54	9.36 852	57	0.63 148	9.98 846	3	51
10	9.35 752	54	9.36 909	57	0.63 091	9.98 843	3	50
11	9.35 806	54	9.36 966	57	0.63 034	9.98 840	3	49
12	9.35 860	54	9.37 023	57	0.62 977	9.98 837	3	48
13	9.35 914	54	9.37 080	57	0.62 920	9.98 834	3	47
14	9.35 968	54	9.37 137	56	0.62 863	9.98 831	3	46
15	9.36 022	53	9.37 193	57	0.62 807	9.98 828	3	45
16	9.36 075	54	9.37 250	56	0.62 750	9.98 825	3	44
17	9.36 129	53	9.37 306	57	0.62 694	9.98 822	3	43
18	9.36 182	54	9.37 363	56	0.62 637	9.98 819	3	42
19	9.36 236	53	9.37 419	57	0.62 581	9.98 816	3	41
20	9.36 289	53	9.37 476	56	0.62 524	9.98 813	3	40
21	9.36 342	53	9.37 532	56	0.62 468	9.98 810	3	39
22	9.36 395	54	9.37 588	56	0.62 412	9.98 807	3	38
23	9.36 449	53	9.37 644	56	0.62 356	9.98 804	3	37
24	9.36 502	53	9.37 700	56	0.62 300	9.98 801	3	36
25	9.36 555	53	9.37 756	56	0.62 244	9.98 798	3	35
26	9.36 608	52	9.37 812	56	0.62 188	9.98 795	3	34
27	9.36 660	53	9.37 868	56	0.62 132	9.98 792	3	33
28	9.36 713	53	9.37 924	56	0.62 076	9.98 789	3	32
29	9.36 766	53	9.37 980	55	0.62 020	9.98 786	3	31
30	9.36 819	52	9.38 035	56	0.61 965	9.98 783	3	30
31	9.36 871	53	9.38 091	56	0.61 909	9.98 780	3	29
32	9.36 924	52	9.38 147	55	0.61 853	9.98 777	3	28
33	9.36 976	52	9.38 202	55	0.61 798	9.98 774	3	27
34	9.37 028	53	9.38 257	56	0.61 743	9.98 771	3	26
35	9.37 081	52	9.38 313	55	0.61 687	9.98 768	3	25
36	9.37 133	52	9.38 368	55	0.61 632	9.98 765	3	24
37	9.37 185	52	9.38 423	55	0.61 577	9.98 762	3	23
38	9.37 237	52	9.38 478	56	0.61 521	9.98 759	3	22
39	9.37 289	52	9.38 534	55	0.61 466	9.98 756	3	21
40	9.37 341	52	9.38 589	55	0.61 411	9.98 753	3	20
41	9.37 393	52	9.38 644	55	0.61 356	9.98 750	4	19
42	9.37 445	52	9.38 699	55	0.61 301	9.98 746	3	18
43	9.37 497	52	9.38 754	55	0.61 246	9.98 743	3	17
44	9.37 549	51	9.38 808	55	0.61 192	9.98 740	3	16
45	9.37 600	52	9.38 863	55	0.61 137	9.98 737	3	15
46	9.37 652	51	9.38 918	54	0.61 082	9.98 734	3	14
47	9.37 703	52	9.38 972	55	0.61 028	9.98 731	3	13
48	9.37 755	51	9.39 027	55	0.60 973	9.98 728	3	12
49	9.37 806	52	9.39 082	54	0.60 918	9.98 725	3	11
50	9.37 858	51	9.39 136	54	0.60 864	9.98 722	3	10
51	9.37 909	51	9.39 190	55	0.60 810	9.98 719	4	9
52	9.37 960	51	9.39 245	54	0.60 755	9.98 715	3	8
53	9.38 011	51	9.39 299	54	0.60 701	9.98 712	3	7
54	9.38 062	51	9.39 353	54	0.60 647	9.98 709	3	6
55	9.38 113	51	9.39 407	54	0.60 593	9.98 706	3	5
56	9.38 164	51	9.39 461	54	0.60 539	9.98 703	3	4
57	9.38 215	51	9.39 515	54	0.60 485	9.98 700	3	3
58	9.38 266	51	9.39 569	54	0.60 431	9.98 697	3	2
59	9.38 317	51	9.39 623	54	0.60 377	9.98 694	4	1
60	9.38 368		9.39 677		0.60 323	9.98 690		0

′	L. Cos.	d.	L. Cot.	c.d.	L. Tan.	L. Sin.	d.	′

103° (283°)   **(256°) 76°**

P. P.

″	57	56	55
1	1.0	0.9	0.9
2	1.9	1.9	1.8
3	2.8	2.8	2.8
4	3.8	3.7	3.7
5	4.8	4.7	4.6
6	5.7	5.6	5.5
7	6.6	6.5	6.4
8	7.6	7.5	7.3
9	8.6	8.4	8.2
10	9.5	9.3	9.2
20	19.0	18.7	18.3
30	28.5	28.0	27.5
40	38.0	37.3	36.7
50	47.5	46.7	45.8

″	54	53	52
1	0.0	0.9	0.9
2	1.8	1.8	1.7
3	2.7	2.6	2.6
4	3.6	3.5	3.5
5	4.5	4.4	4.3
6	5.4	5.3	5.2
7	6.3	6.2	6.1
8	7.2	7.1	6.9
9	8.1	8.0	7.8
10	9.0	8.8	8.7
20	18.0	17.7	17.3
30	27.0	26.5	26.0
40	36.0	35.3	34.7
50	45.0	44.2	43.3

″	51	4	3	2
1	0.8	0.1	0.0	0.0
2	1.7	0.1	0.1	0.1
3	2.6	0.2	0.2	0.1
4	3.4	0.3	0.2	0.1
5	4.2	0.3	0.2	0.2
6	5.1	0.4	0.3	0.2
7	6.0	0.5	0.4	0.2
8	6.8	0.5	0.4	0.3
9	7.6	0.6	0.4	0.3
10	8.5	0.7	0.5	0.3
20	17.0	1.3	1.0	0.7
30	25.5	2.0	1.5	1.0
40	34.0	2.7	2.0	1.3
50	42.5	3.3	2.5	1.7

	4	4	3	3
	55	54	58	57
0	6.9	6.8	9.7	9.5
1	20.6	20.2	29.0	28.5
2	34.4	33.8	48.3	47.5
3	48.1	47.2	—	—

	3	3	3
	56	55	54
0	9.3	9.2	9.3
1	28.0	27.5	27.0
2	46.7	45.8	45.0

COMMON LOGARITHMS OF THE TRIGONOMETRIC FUNCTIONS (Continued)

14° (194°)　　　　　　　　　　　　　　　　**(345°) 165°**

'	L. Sin.	d.	L. Tan.	c.d.	L. Cot.	L. Cos.	d.	'
0	9.38 368	50	9.39 677	54	0.60 323	9.98 690	3	60
1	9.38 418	51	9.39 731	54	0.60 269	9.98 687	3	59
2	9.38 469	50	9.39 785	53	0.60 215	9.98 684	3	58
3	9.38 519	51	9.39 838	54	0.60 162	9.98 681	3	57
4	9.38 570	50	9.39 892	53	0.60 108	9.98 678	3	56
5	9.38 620	50	9.39 945	54	0.60 055	9.98 675	4	55
6	9.38 670	51	9.39 999	53	0.60 001	9.98 671	3	54
7	9.38 721	50	9.40 052	54	0 59 948	9.98 668	3	53
8	9.38 771	50	9.40 106	53	0.59 894	9.98 665	3	52
9	9.38 821	50	9.40 159	53	0.59 841	9.98 662	3	51
10	9.38 871	50	9.40 212	54	0.59 788	9.98 659	3	50
11	9.38 921	50	9.40 266	53	0.59 734	9.98 656	4	49
12	9.38 971	50	9.40 319	53	0.59 681	9.98 652	3	48
13	9.39 021	50	9.40 372	53	0.59 628	9.98 649	3	47
14	9.39 071	50	9.40 425	53	0.59 575	9.98 646	3	46
15	9.39 121	49	9.40 478	53	0.59 522	9.98 643	3	45
16	9.39 170	50	9.40 531	53	0.59 469	9.98 640	4	44
17	9.39 220	50	9.40 584	52	0.59 416	9.98 636	3	43
18	9.39 270	49	9.40 636	53	0.59 364	9.98 633	3	42
19	9.39 319	50	9.40 689	53	0.59 311	9.98 630	3	41
20	9.39 369	49	9.40 742	53	0.59 258	9.98 627	4	40
21	9.39 418	49	9.40 795	52	0.59 205	9.98 623	3	39
22	9.39 467	50	9.40 847	53	0.59 153	9.98 620	3	38
23	9.39 517	49	9.40 900	52	0.59 100	9.98 617	3	37
24	9.39 566	49	9.40 952	53	0.59 048	9.98 614	4	36
25	9.39 615	49	9.41 005	52	0.58 995	9.98 610	3	35
26	9.39 664	49	9.41 057	52	0.58 943	9.98 607	3	34
27	9.39 713	49	9.41 109	52	0.58 891	9.98 604	3	33
28	9.39 762	49	9.41 161	53	0.58 839	9.98 601	4	32
29	9.39 811	49	9.41 214	52	0.58 786	9.98 597	3	31
30	9.39 860	49	9.41 266	52	0.58 734	9.98 594	3	30
31	9.39 909	49	9.41 318	52	0.58 682	9.98 591	3	29
32	9.39 958	48	9.41 370	52	0.58 630	9.98 588	4	28
33	9.40 006	49	9.41 422	52	0.58 578	9.98 584	3	27
34	9.40 055	48	9.41 474	52	0.58 526	9.98 581	3	26
35	9.40 103	49	9.41 526	52	0.58 474	9.98 578	4	25
36	9.40 152	48	9.41 578	51	0.58 422	9.98 574	3	24
37	9.40 200	49	9.41 629	52	0.58 371	9.98 571	3	23
38	9.40 249	48	9.41 681	52	0.58 319	9.98 568	3	22
39	9.40 297	49	9.41 733	51	0.58 267	9.98 565	4	21
40	9.40 346	48	9.41 784	52	0.58 216	9.98 561	3	20
41	9.40 394	48	9.41 836	51	0.58 164	9.98 558	3	19
42	9.40 442	48	9.41 887	52	0.58 113	9.98 555	4	18
43	9.40 490	48	9.41 939	51	0.58 061	9.98 551	3	17
44	9.40 538	48	9.41 990	51	0.58 010	9.98 548	3	16
45	9.40 586	48	9.42 041	52	0.57 959	9.98 543	4	15
46	9.40 634	48	9.42 093	51	0.57 907	9.98 541	3	14
47	9.40 682	48	9.42 144	51	0.57 856	9.98 538	3	13
48	9.40 730	48	9.42 195	51	0.57 805	9.98 535	4	12
49	9.40 778	47	9.42 246	51	0.57 754	9.98 531	3	11
50	9.40 825	48	9.42 297	51	0.57 703	9.98 528	3	10
51	9.40 873	48	9.42 348	51	0.57 652	9.98 525	4	9
52	9.40 921	47	9.42 399	51	0.57 601	9.98 521	3	8
53	9.40 968	48	9.42 450	51	0.57 550	9.98 518	3	7
54	9.41 016	47	9.42 501	51	0.57 499	9.98 515	4	6
55	9.41 063	48	9.42 552	51	0.57 448	9.98 511	3	5
56	9.41 111	47	9.42 603	50	0.57 397	9.98 508	3	4
57	9.41 158	47	9.42 653	51	0.57 347	9.98 505	4	3
58	9.41 205	47	9.42 704	51	0.57 296	9.98 501	3	2
59	9.41 252	48	9.42 755	50	0.57 245	9.98 498	4	1
60	9.41 300		9.42 805		0.57 195	9.98 494		0

'	L. Cos.	d.	L. Cot.	c.d.	L. Tan.	L. Sin.	d.	'

104° (284°)　　　　　　　　　　　　　　　　**(255°) 75°**

P. P.

''	54	53	52
1	0.9	0.9	0.9
2	1.8	1.8	1.7
3	2.7	2.6	2.6
4	3.6	3.5	3.5
5	4.5	4.4	4.3
6	5.4	5.3	5.2
7	6.3	6.2	6.1
8	7.2	7.1	6.9
9	8.1	8.0	7.8
10	9.0	8.8	8.7
20	18.0	17.7	17.3
30	27.0	26.5	26.0
40	36.0	35.3	34.7
50	45.0	44.2	43.3

''	51	50	49
1	0.8	0.8	0.8
2	1.7	1.7	1.6
3	2.6	2.5	2.4
4	3.4	3.3	3.3
5	4.2	4.2	4.1
6	5.1	5.0	4.9
7	6.0	5.8	5.7
8	6.8	6.7	6.5
9	7.6	7.5	7.4
10	8.5	8.3	8.2
20	17.0	16.7	16.3
30	25.5	25.0	24.5
40	34.0	33.3	32.7
50	42.5	41.7	40.8

''	48	47	4	3
1	0.8	0.8	0.1	0.0
2	1.6	1.6	0.1	0.1
3	2.4	2.4	0.2	0.2
4	3.2	3.1	0.3	0.2
5	4.0	3.9	0.3	0.2
6	4.8	4.7	0.4	0.3
7	5.6	5.5	0.5	0.4
8	6.4	6.3	0.5	0.4
9	7.2	7.0	0.6	0.4
10	8.0	7.8	0.7	0.5
20	16.0	15.7	1.3	1.0
30	24.0	23.5	2.0	1.5
40	32.0	31.3	2.7	2.0
50	40.0	39.2	3.3	2.5

	4	4	4	4
	54	53	52	51
0	6.8	6.6	6.5	6.4
1	20.2	19.9	19.5	19.1
2	33.8	33.1	32.5	31.9
3	47.2	46.4	45.5	44.6
4				

	3	3	3	3
	54	53	52	51
0	9.0	8.8	8.7	8.5
1	27.0	26.5	26.0	25.5
2	45.0	44.2	43.3	42.5
3				

COMMON LOGARITHMS OF THE TRIGONOMETRIC FUNCTIONS (Continued)

15° (195°)　　　　　　　　　　　　　　　　　**(344°) 164°**

′	L. Sin.	d.	L. Tan.	c.d.	L.Cot.	L. Cos.	d.	′
0	9.41 300	47	9.42 805	51	0.57 195	9.98 494	3	60
1	9.41 347	47	9.42 856	50	0.57 144	9.98 491	3	59
2	9.41 394	47	9.42 906	51	0.57 094	9.98 488	4	58
3	9.41 441	47	9.42 957	50	0.57 043	9.98 484	3	57
4	9.41 488	47	9.43 007	50	0.56 993	9.98 481	4	56
5	9.41 535	47	9.43 057	51	0.56 943	9.98 477	3	55
6	9.41 582	46	9.43 108	50	0.56 892	9.98 474	3	54
7	9.41 628	47	9.43 158	50	0.56 842	9.98 471	3	53
8	9.41 675	47	9.43 208	50	0.56 792	9.98 467	3	52
9	9.41 722	46	9.43 258	50	0.56 742	9.98 464	3	51
10	9.41 768	47	9.43 308	50	0.56 692	9.98 460	3	50
11	9.41 815	46	9.43 358	50	0.56 642	9.98 457	4	49
12	9.41 861	47	9.43 408	50	0.56 592	9.98 453	3	48
13	9.41 908	46	9.43 458	50	0.56 542	9.98 450	3	47
14	9.41 954	47	9.43 508	50	0.56 492	9.98 447	4	46
15	9.42 001	46	9.43 558	49	0.56 442	9.98 443	3	45
16	9.42 047	46	9.43 607	50	0.56 393	9.98 440	4	44
17	9.42 093	47	9.43 657	50	0.56 343	9.98 436	3	43
18	9.42 140	46	9.43 707	49	0.56 293	9.98 433	4	42
19	9.42 186	46	9.43 756	50	0.56 244	9.98 429	3	41
20	9.42 232	46	9.43 806	49	0.56 194	9.98 426	4	40
21	9.42 278	46	9.43 855	50	0.56 145	9.98 422	3	39
22	9.42 324	46	9.43 905	49	0.56 095	9.98 419	4	38
23	9.42 370	46	9.43 954	50	0.56 046	9.98 415	3	37
24	9.42 416	45	9.44 004	49	0.55 996	9.98 412	4	36
25	9.42 461	46	9.44 053	49	0.55 947	9.98 409	4	35
26	9.42 507	46	9.44 102	49	0.55 898	9.98 405	4	34
27	9.42 553	46	9.44 151	50	0.55 849	9.98 402	4	33
28	9.42 599	45	9.44 201	49	0.55 799	9.98 398	3	32
29	9.42 644	46	9.44 250	49	0.55 750	9.98 395	4	31
30	9.42 690	45	9.44 299	49	0.55 701	9.98 391	3	30
31	9.42 735	46	9.44 348	49	0.55 652	9.98 388	4	29
32	9.42 781	45	9.44 397	49	0.55 603	9.98 384	3	28
33	9.42 826	46	9.44 446	49	0.55 554	9.98 381	4	27
34	9.42 872	45	9.44 495	49	0.55 505	9.98 377	4	26
35	9.42 917	45	9.44 544	48	0.55 456	9.98 373	3	25
36	9.42 962	46	9.44 592	49	0.55 408	9.98 370	4	24
37	9.43 008	45	9.44 641	49	0.55 359	9.98 366	3	23
38	9.43 053	45	9.44 690	48	0.55 310	9.98 363	4	22
39	9.43 098	45	9.44 738	49	0.55 262	9.98 359	3	21
40	9.43 143	45	9.44 787	49	0.55 213	9.98 356	4	20
41	9.43 188	45	9.44 836	48	0.55 164	9.98 352	3	19
42	9.43 233	45	9.44 884	49	0.55 116	9.98 349	4	18
43	9.43 278	45	9.44 933	48	0.55 067	9.98 345	4	17
44	9.43 323	44	9.44 981	48	0.55 019	9.98 342	3	16
45	9.43 367	45	9.45 029	49	0.54 971	9.98 338	4	15
46	9.43 412	45	9.45 078	48	0.54 922	9.98 334	3	14
47	9.43 457	45	9.45 126	48	0.54 874	9.98 331	4	13
48	9.43 502	44	9.45 174	48	0.54 826	9.98 327	3	12
49	9.43 546	45	9.45 222	49	0.54 778	9.98 324	4	11
50	9.43 591	44	9.45 271	48	0.54 729	9.98 320	3	10
51	9.43 635	45	9.45 319	48	0.54 681	9.98 317	4	9
52	9.43 680	44	9.45 367	48	0.54 633	9.98 313	4	8
53	9.43 724	45	9.45 415	48	0.54 585	9.98 309	3	7
54	9.43 769	44	9.45 463	48	0.54 537	9.98 306	4	6
55	9.43 813	44	9.45 511	48	0.54 489	9.98 302	3	5
56	9.43 857	44	9 45 559	47	0.54 441	9.98 299	4	4
57	9.43 901	45	9.45 606	48	0.54 394	9.98 295	4	3
58	9.43 946	44	9.45 654	48	0.54 346	9.98 291	3	2
59	9.43 990	44	9.45 702	48	0.54 298	9.98 288	4	1
60	9.44 034		9.45 750		0.54 250	9.98 284		0

′	L. Cos.	d.	L. Cot.	c.d.	L. Tan.	L. Sin.	d.	′

105° (285°)　　　　　　　　　　　　　　　　　**(254°) 74°**

P. P.

″	51	50	49
1	0.8	0.8	0.8
2	1.7	1.7	1.6
3	2.6	2.5	2.4
4	3.4	3.3	3.3
5	4.2	4.2	4.1
6	5.1	5.0	4.9
7	6.0	5.8	5.7
8	6.8	6.7	6.5
9	7.6	7.5	7.4
10	8.5	8.3	8.2
20	17.0	16.7	16.3
30	25.5	25.0	24.5
40	34.0	33.3	32.7
50	42.5	41.7	40.8

″	48	47	46
1	0.8	0.8	0.8
2	1.6	1.6	1.5
3	2.4	2.4	2.3
4	3.2	3.1	3.1
5	4.0	3.9	3.8
6	4.8	4.7	4.6
7	5.6	5.5	5.4
8	6.4	6.3	6.1
9	7.2	7.0	6.9
10	8.0	7.8	7.7
20	16.0	15.7	15.3
30	24.0	23.5	23.0
40	32.0	31.3	30.7
50	40.0	39.2	38.3

″	45	44	4	3
1	0.8	0.7	0.1	0.0
2	1.5	1.5	0.1	0.1
3	2.2	2.2	0.2	0.2
4	3.0	2.9	0.3	0.2
5	3.8	3.7	0.3	0.2
6	4.5	4.4	0.4	0.3
7	5.2	5.1	0.5	0.4
8	6.0	5.9	0.5	0.4
9	6.8	6.6	0.6	0.4
10	7.5	7.3	0.7	0.5
20	15.0	14.7	1.3	1.0
30	22.5	22.0	2.0	1.5
40	30.0	29.3	2.7	2.0
50	37.5	36.7	3.3	2.5

	4	4	4	4
	50	49	48	47
0				
1	6.2	6.1	6.0	5.9
2	18.8	18.4	18.0	17.6
3	31.2	30.6	30.0	29.4
4	43.8	42.9	42.0	41.1

	3	3	3	3
	51	50	49	48
0				
1	8.5	8.3	8.2	8.0
2	25.5	25.0	24.5	24.0
3	42.5	41.7	40.8	40.0

COMMON LOGARITHMS OF THE TRIGONOMETRIC FUNCTIONS (Continued)

16° (196°)   **(343°) 163°**

'	L. Sin.	d.	L. Tan.	c.d.	L. Cot.	L. Cos.	d.	'
0	9.44 034	44	9.45 750	47	0.54 250	9.98 284	3	60
1	9.44 078	44	9.45 797	48	0.54 203	9.98 281	4	59
2	9.44 122	44	9.45 845	47	0.54 155	9.98 277	4	58
3	9.44 166	44	9.45 892	48	0.54 108	9.98 273	3	57
4	9.44 210	43	9.45 940	47	0.54 060	9.98 270	4	56
5	9.44 253	44	9.45 987	48	0.54 013	9.98 266	4	55
6	9.44 297	44	9.46 035	47	0.53 965	9.98 262	3	54
7	9.44 341	44	9.46 082	48	0.53 918	9.98 259	3	53
8	9.44 385	43	9.46 130	47	0.53 870	9.98 255	4	52
9	9.44 428	44	9.46 177	47	0.53 823	9.98 251	3	51
10	9.44 472	44	9.46 224	47	0.53 776	9.98 248	4	50
11	9.44 516	43	9.46 271	48	0.53 729	9.98 244	4	49
12	9.44 559	43	9.46 319	47	0.53 681	9.98 240	4	48
13	9.44 602	44	9.46 366	47	0.53 634	9.98 237	4	47
14	9.44 646	43	9.46 413	47	0.53 587	9.98 233	4	46
15	9.44 689	44	9.46 460	47	0.53 540	9.98 229	3	45
16	9.44 733	43	9.46 507	47	0.53 493	9.98 226	4	44
17	9.44 776	43	9.46 554	47	0.53 446	9.98 222	4	43
18	9.44 819	43	9.46 601	47	0.53 399	9.98 218	4	42
19	9.44 862	43	9.46 648	46	0.53 352	9.98 215	4	41
20	9.44 905	43	9.46 694	47	0.53 306	9.98 211	4	40
21	9.44 948	44	9.46 741	47	0.53 259	9.98 207	4	39
22	9.44 992	43	9.46 788	47	0.53 212	9.98 204	3	38
23	9.45 035	42	9.46 835	46	0.53 165	9.98 200	4	37
24	9.45 077	43	9.46 881	47	0.53 119	9.98 196	4	36
25	9.45 120	43	9.46 928	47	0.53 072	9.98 192	3	35
26	9.45 163	43	9.46 975	46	0.53 025	9.98 189	4	34
27	9.45 206	43	9.47 021	47	0.52 979	9.98 185	4	33
28	9.45 249	43	9.47 068	46	0.52 932	9.98 181	4	32
29	9.45 292	42	9.47 114	46	0.52 886	9.98 177	3	31
30	9.45 334	43	9.47 160	47	0.52 840	9.98 174	4	30
31	9.45 377	42	9.47 207	46	0.52 793	9.98 170	4	29
32	9.45 419	43	9.47 253	46	0.52 747	9.98 166	4	28
33	9.45 462	42	9.47 299	47	0.52 701	9.98 162	3	27
34	9.45 504	43	9.47 346	46	0.52 654	9.98 159	4	26
35	9.45 547	42	9.47 392	46	0.52 608	9.98 155	4	25
36	9.45 589	43	9.47 438	46	0.52 562	9.98 151	4	24
37	9.45 632	42	9.47 484	46	0.52 516	9.98 147	3	23
38	9.45 674	42	9.47 530	46	0.52 470	9.98 144	4	22
39	9.45 716	42	9.47 576	46	0.52 424	9.98 140	4	21
40	9.45 758	43	9.47 622	46	0.52 378	9.98 136	4	20
41	9.45 801	42	9.47 668	46	0.52 332	9.98 132	3	19
42	9.45 843	42	9.47 714	46	0.52 286	9.98 129	4	18
43	9.45 885	42	9.47 760	46	0.52 240	9.98 125	4	17
44	9.45 927	42	9.47 806	46	0.52 194	9.98 121	4	16
45	9.45 969	42	9.47 852	45	0.52 148	9.98 117	4	15
46	9.46 011	42	9.47 897	46	0.52 103	9.98 113	3	14
47	9.46 053	42	9.47 943	46	0.52 057	9.98 110	4	13
48	9.46 095	41	9.47 989	46	0.52 011	9.98 106	4	12
49	9.46 136	42	9.48 035	45	0.51 965	9.98 102	4	11
50	9.46 178	42	9.48 080	46	0.51 920	9.98 098	4	10
51	9.46 220	42	9.48 126	45	0.51 874	9.98 094	4	9
52	9.46 262	41	9.48 171	46	0.51 829	9.98 090	3	8
53	9.46 303	42	9.48 217	45	0.51 783	9.98 087	4	7
54	9.46 345	41	9.48 262	45	0.51 738	9.98 083	4	6
55	9.46 386	42	9.48 307	46	0.51 693	9.98 079	4	5
56	9.46 428	41	9.48 353	45	0.51 647	9.98 075	4	4
57	9.46 469	42	9.48 398	45	0.51 602	9.98 071	4	3
58	9.46 511	41	9.48 443	46	0.51 557	9.98 067	4	2
59	9.46 552	42	9.48 489	45	0.51 511	9.98 063	3	1
60	9.46 594		9.48 534		0.51 466	9.98 060		0

| ' | L. Cos. | d. | L. Cot. | c.d. | L. Tan. | L. Sin. | d. | ' |

106° (286°)   **(253°) 73°**

P. P.

"	48	47	46
1	0.8	0.8	0.8
2	1.6	1.6	1.5
3	2.4	2.4	2.3
4	3.2	3.1	3.1
5	4.0	3.9	3.8
6	4.8	4.7	4.6
7	5.6	5.5	5.4
8	6.4	6.3	6.1
9	7.2	7.0	6.9
10	8.0	7.8	7.7
20	16.0	15.7	15.3
30	24.0	23.5	23.0
40	32.0	31.3	30.7
50	40.0	39.2	38.3

"	45	44	43
1	0.8	0.7	0.7
2	1.5	1.5	1.4
3	2.2	2.2	2.2
4	3.0	2.9	2.9
5	3.8	3.7	3.6
6	4.5	4.4	4.3
7	5.2	5.1	5.0
8	6.0	5.9	5.7
9	6.8	6.6	6.4
10	7.5	7.3	7.2
20	15.0	14.7	14.3
30	22.5	22.0	21.5
40	30.0	29.3	28.7
50	37.5	36.7	35.8

"	42	41	4	3
1	0.7	0.7	0.1	0.0
2	1.4	1.4	0.1	0.1
3	2.1	2.0	0.2	0.2
4	2.8	2.7	0.3	0.2
5	3.5	3.4	0.3	0.2
6	4.2	4.1	0.4	0.3
7	4.9	4.8	0.5	0.4
8	5.6	5.5	0.5	0.4
9	6.3	6.2	0.6	0.4
10	7.0	6.8	0.7	0.5
20	14.0	13.7	1.3	1.0
30	21.0	20.5	2.0	1.5
40	28.0	27.3	2.7	2.0
50	35.0	34.2	3.3	2.5

	4	4	4	4
	48	47	46	45
0	6.0	5.9	5.8	5.6
1	18.0	17.6	17.2	16.9
2	30.0	29.4	28.8	28.1
3	42.0	41.1	40.2	39.4

	3	3	3	3
	48	47	46	45
0	8.0	7.8	7.7	7.5
1	24.0	23.5	23.0	22.5
2	40.0	39.2	38.3	37.5
3				

COMMON LOGARITHMS OF THE TRIGONOMETRIC
FUNCTIONS (Continued)

17° (197°) (342°) **162°**

'	L. Sin.	d.	L. Tan.	c.d.	L. Cot.	L. Cos.	d.	'	P. P.		
0	9.46 594	41	9.48 534	45	0.51 466	9.98 060	4	60	"	45	44	43
1	9.46 635	41	9.48 579	45	0.51 421	9.98 056	4	59	1	0.8	0.7	0.7
2	9.46 676	41	9.48 624	45	0.51 376	9.98 052	4	58	2	1.5	1.3	1.4
3	9.46 717	41	9.48 669	45	0.51 331	9.98 048	4	57	3	2.2	2.2	2.2
4	9.46 758	42	9.48 714	45	0.51 286	9.98 044	4	56	4	3.0	2.9	2.9
5	9.46 800	41	9.48 759	45	0.51 241	9.98 040	4	55	5	3.8	3.7	3.6
6	9.46 841	41	9.48 804	45	0.51 196	9.98 036	4	54	6	4.5	4.4	4.3
7	9.46 882	41	9.48 849	45	0.51 151	9.98 032	3	53	7	5.2	5.1	5.0
8	9.46 923	41	9.48 894	45	0.51 106	9.98 029	4	52	8	6.0	5.9	5.7
9	9.46 964	41	9.48 939	45	0.51 061	9.98 025	4	51	9	6.8	6.6	6.4
10	9.47 005	40	9.48 984	45	0.51 016	9.98 021	4	50	10	7.5	7.3	7.2
11	9.47 045	41	9.49 029	44	0.50 971	9.98 017	4	49	20	15.0	14.7	14.3
12	9.47 086	41	9.49 073	45	0.50 927	9.98 013	4	48	30	22.5	22.0	21.5
13	9.47 127	41	9.49 118	45	0.50 882	9.98 009	4	47	40	30.0	29.3	28.7
14	9.47 168	41	9.49 163	44	0.50 837	9.98 005	4	46	50	37.5	36.7	35.8
15	9.47 209	40	9.49 207	45	0.50 793	9.98 001	4	45	"	42	41	40
16	9.47 249	41	9.49 252	44	0.50 748	9.97 997	4	44	1	0.7	0.7	0.7
17	9.47 290	40	9.49 296	45	0.50 704	9.97 993	4	43	2	1.4	1.4	1.3
18	9.47 330	41	9.49 341	44	0.50 659	9.97 989	3	42	3	2.1	2.0	2.0
19	9.47 371	40	9.49 385	45	0.50 615	9.97 986	4	41	4	2.8	2.7	2.7
20	9.47 411	41	9.49 430	44	0.50 570	9.97 982	4	40	5	3.5	3.4	3.3
21	9.47 452	40	9.49 474	45	0.50 526	9.97 978	4	39	6	4.2	4.1	4.0
22	9.47 492	41	9.49 519	44	0.50 481	9.97 974	4	38	7	4.9	4.8	4.7
23	9.47 533	40	9.49 563	44	0.50 437	9.97 970	4	37	8	5.6	5.5	5.3
24	9.47 573	40	9.49 607	45	0.50 393	9.97 966	4	36	9	6.3	6.2	6.0
25	9.47 613	41	9.49 652	44	0.50 348	9.97 962	4	35	10	7.0	6.8	6.7
26	9.47 654	40	9.49 696	44	0.50 304	9.97 958	4	34	20	14.0	13.7	13.3
27	9.47 694	40	9.49 740	44	0.50 260	9.97 954	4	33	30	21.0	20.5	20.0
28	9.47 734	40	9.49 784	44	0.50 216	9.97 950	4	32	40	28.0	27.3	26.7
29	9.47 774	40	9.49 828	44	0.50 172	9.97 946	4	31	50	35.0	34.2	33.3
30	9.47 814	40	9.49 872	44	0.50 128	9.97 942	4	30	"	39	5	4	3
31	9.47 854	40	9.49 916	44	0.50 084	9.97 938	4	29	1	0.6	0.1	0.1	0.0
32	9.47 894	40	9.49 960	44	0.50 040	9.97 934	4	28	2	1.3	0.2	0.1	0.1
33	9.47 934	40	9.50 004	44	0.49 996	9.97 930	4	27	3	2.0	0.2	0.2	0.2
34	9.47 974	40	9.50 048	44	0.49 952	9.97 926	4	26	4	2.6	0.3	0.3	0.2
35	9.48 014	40	9.50 092	44	0.49 908	9.97 922	4	25	5	3.2	0.4	0.3	0.2
36	9.48 054	40	9.50 136	44	0.49 864	9.97 918	4	24	6	3.9	0.5	0.4	0.3
37	9.48 094	39	9.50 180	43	0.49 820	9.97 914	4	23	7	4.6	0.6	0.5	0.4
38	9.48 133	40	9.50 223	44	0.49 777	9.97 910	4	22	8	5.2	0.7	0.5	0.4
39	9.48 173	40	9.50 267	44	0.49 733	9.97 906	4	21	9	5.8	0.8	0.6	0.4
40	9.48 213	39	9.50 311	44	0.49 689	9.97 902	4	20	10	6.5	0.8	0.7	0.5
41	9.48 252	40	9.50 355	43	0.49 645	9.97 898	4	19	20	13.0	1.7	1.3	1.0
42	9.48 292	40	9.50 398	44	0.49 602	9.97 894	4	18	30	19.5	2.5	2.0	1.5
43	9.48 332	39	9.50 442	43	0.49 558	9.97 890	4	17	40	26.0	3.3	2.7	2.0
44	9.48 371	40	9.50 485	44	0.49 515	9.97 886	4	16	50	32.5	4.2	3.3	2.5
45	9.48 411	39	9.50 529	43	0.49 471	9.97 882	4	15		5	4	4
46	9.48 450	40	9.50 572	44	0.49 428	9.97 878	4	14				
47	9.48 490	39	9.50 616	43	0.49 384	9.97 874	4	13		43	45	44
48	9.48 529	39	9.50 659	44	0.49 341	9.97 870	4	12				
49	9.48 568	39	9.50 703	43	0.49 297	9.97 866	5	11	0	4.3	5.6	5.5
									1	12.9	16.9	16.5
50	9.48 607	40	9.50 746	43	0.49 254	9.97 861	4	10	2	21.5	28.1	27.5
51	9.48 647	39	9.50 789	44	0.49 211	9.97 857	4	9	3	30.1	39.4	38.5
52	9.48 686	39	9.50 833	43	0.49 167	9.97 853	4	8	4	38.7	—	—
53	9.48 725	39	9.50 876	43	0.49 124	9.97 849	4	7	5			
54	9.48 764	39	9.50 919	43	0.49 081	9.97 845	4	6		4	3	3
55	9.48 803	39	9.50 962	43	0.49 038	9.97 841	4	5		43	45	44
56	9.48 842	39	9.51 005	43	0.48 995	9.97 837	4	4				
57	9.48 881	39	9.51 048	44	0.48 952	9.97 833	4	3	0	5.4	7.5	7.3
58	9.48 920	39	9.51 092	43	0.48 908	9.97 829	4	2	1	16.1	22.5	22.0
59	9.48 959	39	9.51 135	43	0.48 865	9.97 825	4	1	2	26.9	37.5	36.7
									3	37.6	—	—
60	9.48 998		9.51 178		0.48 822	9.97 821		0	4			

'	L. Cos.	d.	L. Cot.	c.d.	L. Tan.	L. Sin.	d.	'	P. P.		

COMMON LOGARITHMS OF THE TRIGONOMETRIC FUNCTIONS (Continued)

18° (198°)　　　　　　　　　　　　　　　　**(341°) 161°**

′	L. Sin.	d.	L. Tan.	c.d.	L. Cot.	L. Cos.	d.	′
0	9.48 998	39	9.51 178	43	0.48 822	9.97 821	4	60
1	9.49 037	39	9.51 221	43	0.48 779	9.97 817	5	59
2	9.49 076	39	9.51 264	42	0.48 736	9.97 812	4	58
3	9.49 115	38	9.51 306	43	0.48 694	9.97 808	4	57
4	9.49 153	39	9.51 349	43	0.48 651	9.97 804	4	56
5	9.49 192	39	9.51 392	43	0.48 608	9.97 800	4	55
6	9.49 231	38	9.51 435	43	0.48 565	9.97 796	4	54
7	9.49 269	39	9.51 478	42	0.48 522	9.97 792	4	53
8	9.49 308	39	9.51 520	43	0.48 480	9.97 788	4	52
9	9.49 347	38	9.51 563	43	0.48 437	9.97 784	5	51
10	9.49 385	39	9.51 606	42	0.48 394	9.97 779	4	50
11	9.49 424	38	9.51 648	43	0.48 352	9.97 775	4	49
12	9.49 462	38	9.51 691	43	0.48 309	9.97 771	4	48
13	9.49 500	39	9.51 734	42	0.48 266	9.97 767	4	47
14	9.49 539	38	9.51 776	43	0.48 224	9.97 763	4	46
15	9.49 577	38	9.51 819	42	0.48 181	9.97 759	5	45
16	9.49 615	39	9.51 861	42	0.48 139	9.97 754	4	44
17	9.49 654	38	9.51 903	43	0.48 097	9.97 750	4	43
18	9.49 692	38	9.51 946	42	0.48 054	9.97 746	4	42
19	9.49 730	38	9.51 988	43	0.48 012	9.97 742	4	41
20	9.49 768	38	9.52 031	42	0.47 969	9.97 738	4	40
21	9.49 806	38	9.52 073	42	0.47 927	9.97 734	5	39
22	9.49 844	38	9.52 115	42	0.47 885	9.97 729	4	38
23	9.49 882	38	9.52 157	43	0.47 843	9.97 725	4	37
24	9.49 920	38	9.52 200	42	0.47 800	9.97 721	4	36
25	9.49 958	38	9.52 242	42	0.47 758	9.97 717	4	35
26	9.49 996	38	9.52 284	42	0.47 716	9.97 713	5	34
27	9.50 034	38	9.52 326	42	0.47 674	9.97 708	4	33
28	9.50 072	38	9.52 368	42	0.47 632	9.97 704	4	32
29	9.50 110	38	9.52 410	42	0.47 590	9.97 700	4	31
30	9.50 148	37	9.52 452	42	0.47 548	9.97 696	5	30
31	9.50 185	38	9.52 494	42	0.47 506	9.97 691	4	29
32	9.50 223	38	9.52 536	42	0.47 464	9.97 687	4	28
33	9.50 261	37	9.52 578	42	0.47 422	9.97 683	4	27
34	9.50 298	38	9.52 620	41	0.47 380	9.97 679	5	26
35	9.50 336	38	9.52 661	42	0.47 339	9.97 674	4	25
36	9.50 374	37	9.52 703	42	0.47 297	9.97 670	4	24
37	9.50 411	38	9.52 745	42	0.47 255	9.97 666	4	23
38	9.50 449	37	9.52 787	42	0.47 213	9.97 662	5	22
39	9.50 486	37	9.52 829	41	0.47 171	9.97 657	4	21
40	9.50 523	38	9.52 870	42	0.47 130	9.97 653	4	20
41	9.50 561	37	9.52 912	41	0.47 088	9.97 649	4	19
42	9.50 598	37	9.52 953	42	0.47 047	9.97 645	5	18
43	9.50 635	38	9.52 995	42	0.47 005	9.97 640	4	17
44	9.50 673	37	9.53 037	41	0.46 963	9.97 636	4	16
45	9.50 710	37	9.53 078	42	0.46 922	9.97 632	4	15
46	9.50 747	37	9.53 120	41	0.46 880	9.97 628	5	14
47	9.50 784	37	9.53 161	41	0.46 839	9.97 623	4	13
48	9.50 821	37	9.53 202	42	0.46 798	9.97 619	4	12
49	9.50 858	38	9.53 244	41	0.46 756	9.97 615	5	11
50	9.50 896	37	9.53 285	42	0.46 715	9.97 610	4	10
51	9.50 933	37	9.53 327	41	0.46 673	9.97 606	4	9
52	9.50 970	37	9.53 368	41	0.46 632	9.97 602	5	8
53	9.51 007	36	9.53 409	41	0.46 591	9.97 597	4	7
54	9.51 043	37	9.53 450	42	0.46 550	9.97 593	4	6
55	9.51 080	37	9.53 492	41	0.46 508	9.97 589	5	5
56	9.51 117	37	9.53 533	41	0.46 467	9.97 584	4	4
57	9.51 154	37	9.53 574	41	0.46 426	9.97 580	4	3
58	9.51 191	36	9.53 615	41	0.46 385	9.97 576	4	2
59	9.51 227	37	9.53 656	41	0.46 344	9.97 571	5	1
60	9.51 264		9.53 697		0.46 303	9.97 567		0

′	L. Cos.	d.	L. Cot.	c.d.	L. Tan.	L. Sin.	d.	′

108° (288°)　　　　　　　　　　　　　　　　**(251°) 71°**

P. P.

″	43	42	41
1	0.7	0.7	0.7
2	1.4	1.4	1.4
3	2.2	2.1	2.0
4	2.9	2.8	2.7
5	3.6	3.5	3.4
6	4.3	4.2	4.1
7	5.0	4.9	4.8
8	5.7	5.6	5.5
9	6.4	6.3	6.2
10	7.2	7.0	6.8
20	14.3	14.0	13.7
30	21.5	21.0	20.5
40	28.7	28.0	27.3
50	35.8	35.0	34.2

″	39	38	37
1	0.6	0.6	0.6
2	1.3	1.3	1.2
3	2.0	1.9	1.8
4	2.6	2.5	2.5
5	3.2	3.2	3.1
6	3.9	3.8	3.7
7	4.6	4.4	4.3
8	5.2	5.1	4.9
9	5.8	5.7	5.6
10	6.5	6.3	6.2
20	13.0	12.7	12.3
30	19.5	19.0	18.5
40	26.0	25.3	24.7
50	32.5	31.7	30.8

″	36	5	4
1	0.6	0.1	0.1
2	1.2	0.2	0.1
3	1.8	0.2	0.2
4	2.4	0.3	0.3
5	3.0	0.4	0.3
6	3.6	0.5	0.4
7	4.2	0.6	0.5
8	4.8	0.7	0.5
9	5.4	0.8	0.6
10	6.0	0.8	0.7
20	12.0	1.7	1.3
30	18.0	2.5	2.0
40	24.0	3.3	2.7
50	30.0	4.2	3.3

	5	5	5
	43	42	41
0			
1	4.3	4.2	4.1
2	12.9	12.6	12.3
3	21.5	21.0	20.5
4	30.1	29.4	28.7
5	38.7	37.8	36.9

	4	4	4
	43	42	41
0			
1	5.4	5.2	5.1
2	16.1	15.8	15.4
3	26.9	26.2	25.6
4	37.6	36.8	35.9

P. P.

COMMON LOGARITHMS OF THE TRIGONOMETRIC FUNCTIONS (Continued)

19° (199°) (340°) **160°**

′	L. Sin.	d.	L. Tan.	c.d.	L. Cot.	L. Cos.	d.	′
0	9.51 264	37	9.53 697	41	0.46 303	9.97 567	4	60
1	9.51 301	37	9.53 738	41	0.46 262	9.97 563	5	59
2	9.51 338	36	9.53 779	41	0.46 221	9.97 558	4	58
3	9.51 374	37	9.53 820	41	0.46 180	9.97 554	4	57
4	9.51 411	36	9.53 861	41	0.46 139	9.97 550	5	56
5	9.51 447	37	9.53 902	41	0.46 098	9.97 545	4	55
6	9.51 484	36	9.53 943	41	0.46 057	9.97 541	5	54
7	9.51 520	37	9.53 984	41	0.46 016	9.97 536	4	53
8	9.51 557	36	9.54 025	40	0.45 975	9.97 532	4	52
9	9.51 593	36	9.54 065	41	0.45 935	9.97 528	5	51
10	9.51 629	37	9.54 106	41	0.45 894	9.97 523	4	50
11	9.51 666	36	9.54 147	40	0.45 853	9.97 519	4	49
12	9.51 702	36	9.54 187	41	0.45 813	9.97 515	5	48
13	9.51 738	36	9.54 228	41	0.45 772	9.97 510	4	47
14	9.51 774	37	9.54 269	40	0.45 731	9.97 506	5	46
15	9.51 811	36	9.54 309	41	0.45 691	9.97 501	4	45
16	9.51 847	36	9.54 350	40	0.45 650	9.97 497	5	44
17	9.51 883	36	9.54 390	41	0.45 610	9.97 492	4	43
18	9.51 919	36	9.54 431	40	0.45 569	9.97 488	4	42
19	9.51 955	36	9.54 471	41	0.45 529	9.97 484	5	41
20	9.51 991	36	9.54 512	40	0.45 488	9.97 479	4	40
21	9.52 027	36	9.54 552	41	0.45 448	9.97 475	5	39
22	9.52 063	36	9.54 593	40	0.45 407	9.97 470	4	38
23	9.52 099	36	9.54 633	40	0.45 367	9.97 466	5	37
24	9.52 135	36	9.54 673	41	0.45 327	9.97 461	4	36
25	9.52 171	36	9.54 714	40	0.45 286	9.97 457	4	35
26	9.52 207	35	9.54 754	40	0.45 246	9.97 453	5	34
27	9.52 242	36	9.54 794	41	0.45 206	9.97 448	4	33
28	9.52 278	36	9.54 835	40	0.45 165	9.97 444	5	32
29	9.52 314	36	9.54 875	40	0.45 125	9.97 439	4	31
30	9.52 350	35	9.54 915	40	0.45 085	9.97 435	5	30
31	9.52 385	36	9.54 955	40	0.45 045	9.97 430	4	29
32	9.52 421	35	9.54 995	40	0.45 005	9.97 426	5	28
33	9.52 456	36	9.55 035	40	0.44 965	9.97 421	5	27
34	9.52 492	35	9.55 075	40	0.44 925	9.97 417	5	26
35	9.52 527	36	9.55 115	40	0.44 885	9.97 412	4	25
36	9.52 563	35	9.55 155	40	0.44 845	9.97 408	5	24
37	9.52 598	36	9.55 195	40	0.44 805	9.97 403	4	23
38	9.52 634	35	9.55 235	40	0.44 765	9.97 399	5	22
39	9.52 669	36	9.55 275	40	0.44 725	9.97 394	5	21
40	9.52 705	35	9.55 315	40	0.44 685	9.97 390	5	20
41	9.52 740	35	9.55 355	40	0.44 645	9.97 385	4	19
42	9.52 775	36	9.55 395	39	0.44 605	9.97 381	5	18
43	9.52 811	35	9.55 434	40	0.44 566	9.97 376	5	17
44	9.52 846	35	9.55 474	40	0.44 526	9.97 372	5	16
45	9.52 881	35	9.55 514	40	0.44 485	9.97 367	4	15
46	9.52 916	35	9.55 554	39	0.44 446	9.97 363	5	14
47	9.52 951	35	9.55 593	40	0.44 407	9.97 358	5	13
48	9.52 986	35	9.55 633	40	0.44 367	9.97 353	4	12
49	9.53 021	35	9.55 673	39	0.44 327	9.97 349	5	11
50	9.53 056	36	9.55 712	40	0.44 288	9.97 344	4	10
51	9.53 092	34	9.55 752	39	0.44 248	9.97 340	5	9
52	9.53 126	35	9.55 791	40	0.44 209	9.97 335	4	8
53	9.53 161	35	9.55 831	39	0.44 169	9.97 331	5	7
54	9.53 196	35	9.55 870	40	0.44 130	9.97 326	4	6
55	9.53 231	35	9.55 910	39	0.44 090	9.97 322	5	5
56	9.53 266	35	9.55 949	40	0.44 051	9.97 317	5	4
57	9.53 301	35	9.55 989	39	0.44 011	9.97 312	4	3
58	9.53 336	34	9.56 028	39	0.43 972	9.97 308	3	2
59	9.53 370	35	9.56 067	40	0.43 933	9.97 303	4	1
60	9.53 405		9.56 107		0.43 893	9.97 299		0

′	L. Cos.	d.	L. Cot.	c.d.	L. Tan.	L. Sin.	d.	′

109° (289°) (250°) **70°**

P. P.

	41	40	39
1	0.7	0.7	0.6
2	1.4	1.3	1.3
3	2.0	2.0	2.0
4	2.7	2.7	2.6
5	3.4	3.3	3.2
6	4.1	4.0	3.9
7	4.8	4.7	4.6
8	5.5	5.3	5.2
9	6.2	6.0	5.8
10	6.8	6.7	6.5
20	13.7	13.3	13.0
30	20.5	20.0	19.5
40	27.3	26.7	26.0
50	34.2	33.3	32.5

	37	36	35
1	0.6	0.6	0.6
2	1.2	1.2	1.2
3	1.8	1.8	1.8
4	2.5	2.4	2.3
5	3.1	3.0	2.9
6	3.7	3.6	3.5
7	4.3	4.2	4.1
8	4.9	4.8	4.7
9	5.6	5.4	5.2
10	6.2	6.0	5.8
20	12.3	12.0	11.7
30	18.5	18.0	17.5
40	24.7	24.0	23.3
50	30.8	30.0	29.2

	34	5	4
1	0.6	0.1	0.1
2	1.1	0.2	0.1
3	1.7	0.2	0.2
4	2.3	0.3	0.3
5	2.8	0.4	0.3
6	3.4	0.5	0.4
7	4.0	0.6	0.5
8	4.5	0.7	0.5
9	5.1	0.8	0.6
10	5.7	0.8	0.7
20	11.3	1.7	1.3
30	17.0	2.5	2.0
40	22.7	3.3	2.7
50	28.3	4.2	3.3

	5	5	5
	41	40	39
1	4.1	4.0	3.9
2	12.3	12.0	11.7
3	20.5	20.0	19.5
4	28.7	28.0	27.3
5	36.9	36.0	35.1

	4	4	4
	41	40	39
1	5.1	5.0	4.9
2	15.4	15.0	14.6
3	25.6	25.0	24.4
4	35.9	35.0	34.1

COMMON LOGARITHMS OF THE TRIGONOMETRIC FUNCTIONS (Continued)

20° (200°)   **(339°) 159°**

′	L. Sin.	d.	L. Tan.	c.d.	L. Cot.	L. Cos.	d.	′
0	9.53 405	35	9.56 107	39	0.43 893	9.97 299	5	60
1	9.53 440	35	9.56 146	39	0.43 854	9.97 294	5	59
2	9.53 475	34	9.56 185	39	0.43 815	9.97 289	4	58
3	9.53 509	35	9.56 224	40	0.43 776	9.97 285	5	57
4	9.53 544	34	9.56 264	39	0.43 736	9.97 280	4	56
5	9.53 578	35	9.56 303	39	0.43 697	9.97 276	5	55
6	9.53 613	34	9.56 342	39	0.43 658	9.97 271	5	54
7	9.53 647	35	9.56 381	39	0.43 619	9.97 266	4	53
8	9.53 682	34	9.56 420	39	0.43 580	9.97 262	5	52
9	9.53 716	35	9.56 459	39	0.43 541	9.97 257	5	51
10	9.53 751	34	9.56 498	39	0.43 502	9.97 252	4	50
11	9.53 785	34	9.56 537	39	0.43 463	9.97 248	5	49
12	9.53 819	35	9.56 576	39	0.43 424	9.97 243	5	48
13	9.53 854	34	9.56 615	39	0.43 385	9.97 238	4	47
14	9.53 888	34	9.56 654	39	0.43 346	9.97 234	5	46
15	9.53 922	35	9.56 693	39	0.43 307	9.97 229	5	45
16	9.53 957	34	9.56 732	39	0.43 268	9.97 224	4	44
17	9.53 991	34	9.56 771	39	0.43 229	9.97 220	5	43
18	9.54 025	34	9.56 810	39	0.43 190	9.97 215	5	42
19	9.54 059	34	9.56 849	38	0.43 151	9.97 210	4	41
20	9.54 093	34	9.56 887	39	0.43 113	9.97 206	5	40
21	9.54 127	34	9.56 926	39	0.43 074	9.97 201	5	39
22	9.54 161	34	9.56 965	39	0.43 035	9.97 196	4	38
23	9.54 195	34	9.57 004	38	0.42 996	9.97 192	5	37
24	9.54 229	34	9.57 042	39	0.42 958	9.97 187	5	36
25	9.54 263	34	9.57 081	39	0.42 919	9.97 182	4	35
26	9.54 297	34	9.57 120	38	0.42 880	9.97 178	5	34
27	9.54 331	34	9.57 158	39	0.42 842	9.97 173	5	33
28	9.54 365	34	9.57 197	38	0.42 803	9.97 168	5	32
29	9.54 399	34	9.57 235	39	0.42 765	9.97 163	4	31
30	9.54 433	33	9.57 274	38	0.42 726	9.97 159	5	30
31	9.54 466	34	9.57 312	39	0.42 688	9.97 154	5	29
32	9.54 500	34	9.57 351	38	0.42 649	9.97 149	4	28
33	9.54 534	33	9.57 389	39	0.42 611	9.97 145	5	27
34	9.54 567	34	9.57 428	38	0.42 572	9.97 140	5	26
35	9.54 601	34	9.57 466	38	0.42 534	9.97 135	5	25
36	9.54 635	33	9.57 504	39	0.42 496	9.97 130	4	24
37	9.54 668	34	9.57 543	38	0.42 457	9.97 126	5	23
38	9.54 702	33	9.57 581	38	0.42 419	9.97 121	5	22
39	9.54 735	34	9.57 619	39	0.42 381	9.97 116	5	21
40	9.54 769	33	9.57 658	38	0.42 342	9.97 111	4	20
41	9.54 802	34	9.57 696	38	0.42 304	9.97 107	5	19
42	9.54 836	33	9.57 734	38	0.42 266	9.97 102	5	18
43	9.54 869	34	9.57 772	38	0.42 228	9.97 097	5	17
44	9.54 903	33	9.57 810	39	0.42 190	9.97 092	5	16
45	9.54 936	33	9.57 849	38	0.42 151	9.97 087	4	15
46	9.54 969	34	9.57 887	38	0.42 113	9.97 083	5	14
47	9.55 003	33	9.57 925	38	0.42 075	9.97 078	5	13
48	9.55 036	33	9.57 963	38	0.42 037	9.97 073	5	12
49	9.55 069	33	9.58 001	38	0.41 999	9.97 068	5	11
50	9.55 102	34	9.58 039	38	0.41 961	9.97 063	4	10
51	9.55 136	33	9.58 077	38	0.41 923	9.97 059	5	9
52	9.55 169	33	9.58 115	38	0.41 885	9.97 054	5	8
53	9.55 202	33	9.58 153	38	0.41 847	9.97 049	5	7
54	9.55 235	33	9.58 191	38	0.41 809	9.97 044	5	6
55	9.55 268	33	9.58 229	38	0.41 771	9.97 039	4	5
56	9.55 301	33	9.58 267	37	0.41 733	9.97 035	5	4
57	9.55 334	33	9.58 304	38	0.41 696	9.97 030	5	3
58	9.55 367	33	9.58 342	38	0.41 658	9.97 025	5	2
59	9.55 400	33	9.58 380	38	0.41 620	9.97 020	5	1
60	9.55 433		9.58 418		0.41 582	9.97 015		0

P. P.

″	40	39	38
1	0.7	0.6	0.6
2	1.3	1.3	1.3
3	2.0	2.0	1.9
4	2.7	2.6	2.5
5	3.3	3.2	3.2
6	4.0	3.9	3.8
7	4.7	4.6	4.4
8	5.3	5.2	5.1
9	6.0	5.8	5.7
10	6.7	6.5	6.3
20	13.3	13.0	12.7
30	20.0	19.5	19.0
40	26.7	26.0	25.3
50	33.3	32.5	31.7

″	37	35	34
1	0.6	0.6	0.6
2	1.2	1.2	1.1
3	1.8	1.8	1.7
4	2.5	2.3	2.3
5	3.1	2.9	2.8
6	3.7	3.5	3.4
7	4.3	4.1	4.0
8	4.9	4.7	4.5
9	5.6	5.2	5.1
10	6.2	5.8	5.7
20	12.3	11.7	11.3
30	18.5	17.5	17.0
40	24.7	23.3	22.7
50	30.8	29.2	28.3

″	33	5	4
1	0.6	0.1	0.1
2	1.1	0.2	0.1
3	1.6	0.2	0.2
4	2.2	0.3	0.3
5	2.8	0.4	0.3
6	3.3	0.5	0.4
7	3.8	0.6	0.5
8	4.4	0.7	0.5
9	5.0	0.8	0.6
10	5.5	0.8	0.7
20	11.0	1.7	1.3
30	16.5	2.5	2.0
40	22.0	3.3	2.7
50	27.5	4.2	3.3

	5	5	5
	40	39	38
1	4.0	3.9	3.8
2	12.0	11.7	11.4
3	20.0	19.5	19.0
4	28.0	27.3	26.6
5	36.0	35.1	34.2

	5	4	4
	37	39	38
1	3.7	4.9	4.8
2	11.1	14.6	14.2
3	18.5	24.4	23.8
4	25.9	34.1	33.2
5	33.3	—	

′	L. Cos.	d.	L. Cot.	c.d.	L. Tan.	L. Sin.	d.	′	P. P.

COMMON LOGARITHMS OF THE TRIGONOMETRIC FUNCTIONS (Continued)

21° (201°) (338°)**158°**

	L. Sin.	d.	L. Tan.	c.d.	L. Cot.	L. Cos.	d.	'
0	9.55 433	33	9.58 418	37	0.41 582	9.97 015	5	60
1	9.55 466	33	9.58 455	38	0.41 545	9.97 010	5	59
2	9.55 499	33	9.58 493	38	0.41 507	9.97 005	4	58
3	9.55 532	32	9.58 531	38	0.41 469	9.97 001	5	57
4	9.55 564	33	9.58 569	37	0.41 431	9.96 996	5	56
5	9.55 597	33	9.58 606	38	0.41 394	9.96 991	5	55
6	9.55 630	33	9.58 644	37	0.41 356	9.96 986	5	54
7	9.55 663	32	9.58 681	38	0.41 319	9.96 981	5	53
8	9.55 695	33	9.58 719	38	0.41 281	9.96 976	5	52
9	9.55 728	33	9.58 757	37	0.41 243	9.96 971	5	51
10	9.55 761	32	9.58 794	38	0.41 206	9.96 966	4	50
11	9.55 793	33	9.58 832	37	0.41 168	9.96 962	5	49
12	9.55 826	32	9.58 869	38	0.41 131	9.96 957	5	48
13	9.55 858	33	9.58 907	37	0.41 093	9.96 952	5	47
14	9.55 891	32	9.58 944	37	0.41 056	9.96 947	5	46
15	9.55 923	33	9.58 981	38	0.41 019	9.96 942	5	45
16	9.55 956	32	9.59 019	37	0.40 981	9.96 937	5	44
17	9.55 988	33	9.59 056	38	0.40 944	9.96 932	5	43
18	9.56 021	32	9.59 094	37	0.40 906	9.96 927	5	42
19	9.56 053	32	9.59 131	37	0.40 869	9.96 922	5	41
20	9.56 085	33	9.59 168	37	0.40 832	9.96 917	5	40
21	9.56 118	32	9.59 205	38	0.40 795	9.96 912	5	39
22	9.56 150	32	9.59 243	37	0.40 757	9.96 907	4	38
23	9.56 182	33	9.59 280	37	0.40 720	9.96 903	5	37
24	9.56 215	32	9.59 317	37	0.40 683	9.96 898	5	36
25	9.56 247	32	9.59 354	37	0.40 646	9.96 893	5	35
26	9.56 279	32	9.59 391	38	0.40 609	9.96 888	5	34
27	9.56 311	32	9.59 429	37	0.40 571	9.96 883	5	33
28	9.56 343	32	9.59 466	37	0.40 534	9.96 878	5	32
29	9.56 375	33	9.59 503	37	0.40 497	9.96 873	5	31
30	9.56 408	32	9.59 540	37	0.40 460	9.96 868	5	30
31	9.56 440	32	9.59 577	37	0.40 423	9.96 863	5	29
32	9.56 472	32	9.59 614	37	0.40 386	9.96 858	5	28
33	9.56 504	32	9.59 651	37	0.40 349	9.96 853	5	27
34	9.56 536	32	9.59 688	37	0.40 312	9.96 848	5	26
35	9.56 568	31	9.59 725	37	0.40 275	9.96 843	5	25
36	9.56 599	32	9.59 762	37	0.40 238	9.96 838	5	24
37	9.56 631	32	9.59 799	36	0.40 201	9.96 833	5	23
38	9.56 663	32	9.59 835	37	0.40 165	9.96 828	5	22
39	9.56 695	32	9.59 872	37	0.40 128	9.96 823	5	21
40	9.56 727	32	9.59 909	37	0.40 091	9.96 818	5	20
41	9.56 759	31	9.59 946	37	0.40 054	9.96 813	5	19
42	9.56 790	32	9.59 983	36	0.40 017	9.96 808	5	18
43	9.56 822	32	9.60 019	37	0.39 981	9.96 803	5	17
44	9.56 854	32	9.60 056	37	0.39 944	9.96 798	5	16
45	9.56 886	31	9.60 093	37	0.39 907	9.96 793	5	15
46	9.56 917	32	9.60 130	36	0.39 870	9.96 788	5	14
47	9.56 949	31	9.60 166	37	0.39 834	9.96 783	5	13
48	9.56 980	32	9.60 203	37	0.39 797	9.96 778	6	12
49	9.57 012	32	9.60 240	36	0.39 760	9.96 772	5	11
50	9.57 044	31	9.60 276	37	0.39 724	9.96 767	5	10
51	9.57 075	32	9.60 313	36	0.39 687	9.96 762	5	9
52	9.57 107	31	9.60 349	37	0.39 651	9.96 757	5	8
53	9.57 138	31	9.60 386	36	0.39 614	9.96 752	5	7
54	9.57 169	32	9.60 422	37	0.39 578	9.96 747	5	6
55	9.57 201	31	9.60 459	36	0.39 541	9.96 742	5	5
56	9.57 232	32	9.60 495	37	0.39 505	9.96 737	5	4
57	9.57 264	31	9.60 532	36	0.39 468	9.96 732	5	3
58	9.57 295	31	9.60 568	37	0.39 432	9.96 727	5	2
59	9.57 326	32	9.60 605	36	0.39 395	9.96 722	5	1
60	9.57 358		9.60 641		0.39 359	9.96 717		0

'	L. Cos.	d.	L. Cot.	c.d.	L. Tan.	L. Sin.	d.	'	P. P.

P. P.

"	38	37	36
1	0.6	0.6	0.6
2	1.3	1.2	1.2
3	1.9	1.8	1.8
4	2.5	2.3	2.4
5	3.2	3.1	3.0
6	3.8	3.7	3.6
7	4.4	4.3	4.2
8	5.1	4.9	4.8
9	5.7	5.6	5.4
10	6.3	6.2	6.0
20	12.7	12.3	12.0
30	19.0	18.5	18.0
40	25.3	24.7	24.0
50	31.7	30.8	30.0

"	33	32	31
1	0.6	0.5	0.5
2	1.1	1.1	1.0
3	1.6	1.6	1.6
4	2.2	2.1	2.1
5	2.8	2.7	2.6
6	3.3	3.2	3.1
7	3.8	3.7	3.6
8	4.4	4.3	4.1
9	5.0	4.8	4.6
10	5.5	5.3	5.2
20	11.0	10.7	10.3
30	16.5	16.0	15.5
40	22.0	21.3	20.7
50	27.5	26.7	25.8

"	6	5	4
1	0.1	0.1	0.1
2	0.2	0.2	0.1
3	0.3	0.2	0.2
4	0.4	0.3	0.3
5	0.5	0.4	0.3
6	0.6	0.5	0.4
7	0.7	0.6	0.5
8	0.8	0.7	0.5
9	0.9	0.8	0.6
10	1.0	0.8	0.7
20	2.0	1.7	1.3
30	3.0	2.5	2.0
40	4.0	3.3	2.7
50	5.0	4.2	3.3

	6	5	5
	37	38	37
0	3.1	3.8	3.7
1	9.2	11.4	11.1
2	15.4	19.0	18.5
3	21.6	26.6	25.9
4	27.8	34.2	33.3
5	33.9	—	—
6			

	5	4	4
	36	38	37
0	3.6	4.8	4.6
1	10.8	14.2	13.9
2	18.0	23.8	23.1
3	25.2	33.2	32.4
4	32.4	—	—
5			

COMMON LOGARITHMS OF THE TRIGONOMETRIC FUNCTIONS (Continued)

22° (202°)   **(337°) 157°**

'	L. Sin.	d.	L. Tan.	c.d.	L. Cot.	L. Cos.	d.	'
0	9.57 358	31	9.60 641	36	0.39 359	9.96 717	6	60
1	9.57 389	31	9.60 677	37	0.39 323	9.96 711	6	59
2	9.57 420	31	9.60 714	36	0.39 286	9.96 706	5	58
3	9.57 451	31	9.60 750	36	0.39 250	9.96 701	5	57
4	9.57 482	32	9.60 786	37	0.39 214	9.96 696	5	56
5	9.57 514	31	9.60 823	36	0.39 177	9.96 691	5	55
6	9.57 545	31	9.60 859	36	0.39 141	9.96 686	5	54
7	9.57 576	31	9.60 895	36	0.39 105	9.96 681	5	53
8	9.57 607	31	9.60 931	36	0.39 069	9.96 676	6	52
9	9.57 638	31	9.60 967	37	0.39 033	9.96 670	5	51
10	9.57 669	31	9.61 004	36	0.38 996	9.96 665	5	50
11	9.57 700	31	9.61 040	36	0.38 960	9.96 660	5	49
12	9.57 731	31	9.61 076	36	0.38 924	9.96 655	5	48
13	9.57 762	31	9.61 112	36	0.38 888	9.96 650	5	47
14	9.57 793	31	9.61 148	36	0.38 852	9.96 645	5	46
15	9.57 824	31	9.61 184	36	0.38 816	9.96 640	6	45
16	9.57 855	30	9.61 220	36	0.38 780	9.96 634	5	44
17	9.57 885	31	9.61 256	36	0.38 744	9.96 629	5	43
18	9.57 916	31	9.61 292	36	0.38 708	9.96 624	5	42
19	9.57 947	31	9.61 328	36	0.38 672	9.96 619	5	41
20	9.57 978	30	9.61 364	36	0.38 636	9.96 614	6	40
21	9.58 008	31	9.61 400	36	0.38 600	9.96 608	5	39
22	9.58 039	31	9.61 436	36	0.38 564	9.96 603	5	38
23	9.58 070	31	9.61 472	36	0.38 528	9.96 598	5	37
24	9.58 101	30	9.61 508	36	0.38 492	9.96 593	5	36
25	9.58 131	31	9.61 544	35	0.38 456	9.96 588	6	35
26	9.58 162	30	9.61 579	36	0.38 421	9.96 582	5	34
27	9.58 192	31	9.61 615	36	0.38 385	9.96 577	5	33
28	9.58 223	30	9.61 651	36	0.38 349	9.96 572	5	32
29	9.58 253	31	9.61 687	35	0.38 313	9.96 567	5	31
30	9.58 284	30	9.61 722	36	0.38 278	9.96 562	6	30
31	9.58 314	31	9.61 758	36	0.38 242	9.96 556	5	29
32	9.58 345	30	9.61 794	36	0.38 206	9.96 551	5	28
33	9.58 375	31	9.61 830	35	0.38 170	9.96 546	5	27
34	9.58 406	30	9.61 865	36	0.38 135	9.96 541	6	26
35	9.58 436	31	9.61 901	35	0.38 099	9.96 535	5	25
36	9.58 467	30	9.61 936	36	0.38 064	9.96 530	5	24
37	9.58 497	30	9.61 972	36	0.38 028	9.96 525	5	23
38	9.58 527	30	9.62 008	35	0.37 992	9.96 520	6	22
39	9.58 557	31	9.62 043	36	0.37 957	9.96 514	5	21
40	9.58 588	30	9.62 079	35	0.37 921	9.96 509	5	20
41	9.58 618	30	9.62 114	36	0.37 886	9.96 504	6	19
42	9.58 648	30	9.62 150	35	0.37 850	9.96 498	5	18
43	9.58 678	31	9.62 185	36	0.37 815	9.96 493	5	17
44	9.58 709	30	9.62 221	35	0.37 779	9.96 488	5	16
45	9.58 739	30	9.62 256	36	0.37 744	9.96 483	6	15
46	9.58 769	30	9.62 292	35	0.37 708	9.96 477	5	14
47	9.58 799	30	9.62 327	35	0.37 673	9.96 472	5	13
48	9.58 829	30	9.62 362	36	0.37 638	9.96 467	5	12
49	9.58 859	30	9.62 398	35	0.37 602	9.96 461	6	11
50	9.58 889	30	9.62 433	35	0.37 567	9.96 456	5	10
51	9.58 919	30	9.62 468	36	0.37 532	9.96 451	6	9
52	9.58 949	30	9.62 504	35	0.37 496	9.96 445	5	8
53	9.58 979	30	9.62 539	35	0.37 461	9.96 440	5	7
54	9.59 009	30	9.62 574	35	0.37 426	9.96 435	6	6
55	9.59 039	30	9.62 609	36	0.37 391	9.96 429	5	5
56	9.59 069	29	9.62 645	35	0.37 355	9.96 424	5	4
57	9.59 098	30	9.62 680	35	0.37 320	9.96 419	6	3
58	9.59 128	30	9.62 715	35	0.37 285	9.96 413	5	2
59	9.59 158	30	9.62 750	35	0.37 250	9.96 408	5	1
60	9.59 188		9.62 785		0.37 215	9.96 403		0
'	L. Cos.	d.	L. Cot.	c.d.	L. Tan.	L. Sin.	d.	'

112° (292°)   **(247°) 67°**

P. P.

"	37	36	35
1	0.6	0.6	0.6
2	1.2	1.2	1.2
3	1.8	1.8	1.8
4	2.5	2.4	2.3
5	3.1	3.0	2.9
6	3.7	3.6	3.5
7	4.3	4.2	4.1
8	4.9	4.8	4.7
9	5.6	5.4	5.2
10	6.2	6.0	5.8
20	12.3	12.0	11.7
30	18.5	18.0	17.5
40	24.7	24.0	23.3
50	30.8	30.0	29.2

"	32	31	30
1	0.5	0.5	0.5
2	1.1	1.0	1.0
3	1.6	1.6	1.5
4	2.1	2.1	2.0
5	2.7	2.6	2.5
6	3.2	3.1	3.0
7	3.7	3.6	3.5
8	4.3	4.1	4.0
9	4.8	4.6	4.5
10	5.3	5.2	5.0
20	10.7	10.3	10.0
30	16.0	15.5	15.0
40	21.3	20.7	20.0
50	26.7	25.8	25.0

"	29	6	5
1	0.5	0.1	0.1
2	1.0	0.2	0.2
3	1.4	0.3	0.2
4	1.9	0.4	0.3
5	2.4	0.5	0.4
6	2.9	0.6	0.5
7	3.4	0.7	0.6
8	3.9	0.8	0.7
9	4.4	0.9	0.8
10	4.8	1.0	0.8
20	9.7	2.0	1.7
30	14.5	3.0	2.5
40	19.3	4.0	3.3
50	24.2	5.0	4.2

	6	6
	36	35
0		
1	3.0	2.9
2	9.0	8.8
3	15.0	14.6
4	21.0	20.4
5	27.0	26.2
6	33.0	32.1

	5	5	5
	37	36	35
0			
1	3.7	3.6	3.5
2	11.1	10.8	10.5
3	18.5	18.0	17.5
4	25.9	25.2	24.5
5	33.3	32.4	31.5

COMMON LOGARITHMS OF THE TRIGONOMETRIC
FUNCTIONS (Continued)

23° (203°)   **(336°) 156°**

′	L. Sin.	d.	L. Tan.	c.d.	L. Cot.	L. Cos.	d.	′		P. P.		
0	9.59 188	30	9.62 785	35	0.37 215	9.96 403	6	60	″	**36**	**35**	**34**
1	9.59 218	29	9.62 820	35	0.37 180	9.96 397	5	59	1	0.6	0.6	0.6
2	9.59 247	30	9.62 855	35	0.37 145	9.96 392	5	58	2	1.2	1.2	1.1
3	9.59 277	30	9.62 890	36	0.37 110	9.96 387	6	57	3	1.8	1.8	1.7
4	9.59 307	29	9.62 926	35	0.37 074	9.96 381	5	56	4	2.4	2.3	2.3
									5	3.0	2.9	2.8
5	9.59 336	30	9.62 961	35	0.37 039	9.96 376	6	55				
6	9.59 366	30	9.62 996	35	0.37 004	9.96 370	5	54	6	3.6	3.5	3.4
7	9.59 396	30	9.63 031	35	0.36 969	9.96 365	5	53	7	4.2	4.1	4.0
8	9.59 425	30	9.63 066	35	0.36 934	9.96 360	6	52	8	4.8	4.7	4.5
9	9.59 455	29	9.63 101	34	0.36 899	9.96 354	5	51	9	5.4	5.2	5.1
10	9.59 484	30	9.63 135	35	0.36 865	9.96 349	6	50	10	6.0	5.8	5.7
11	9.59 514	29	9.63 170	35	0.36 830	9.96 343	5	49	20	12.0	11.7	11.3
12	9.59 543	30	9.63 205	35	0.36 795	9.96 338	5	48	30	18.0	17.5	17.0
13	9.59 573	29	9.63 240	35	0.36 760	9.96 333	6	47	40	24.0	23.3	22.7
14	9.59 602	30	9.63 275	35	0.36 725	9.96 327	5	46	50	30.0	29.2	28.3
									″	30	29	28
15	9.59 632	29	9.63 310	35	0.36 690	9.96 322	6	45	1	0.5	0.5	0.5
16	9.59 661	29	9.63 345	34	0.36 655	9.96 316	5	44	2	1.0	1.0	0.9
17	9.59 690	30	9.63 379	35	0.36 621	9.96 311	6	43	3	1.5	1.4	1.4
18	9.59 720	29	9.63 414	35	0.36 586	9.96 305	5	42	4	2.0	1.9	1.9
19	9.59 749	29	9.63 449	35	0.36 551	9.96 300	6	41				
									5	2.5	2.4	2.3
20	9.59 778	30	9.63 484	35	0.36 516	9.96 294	5	40	6	3.0	2.9	2.8
21	9.59 808	29	9.63 519	34	0.36 481	9.96 289	5	39	7	3.5	3.4	3.3
22	9.59 837	29	9.63 553	35	0.36 447	9.96 284	5	38	8	4.0	3.9	3.7
23	9.59 866	29	9.63 588	35	0.36 412	9.96 278	5	37	9	4.5	4.4	4.2
24	9.59 895	29	9.63 623	34	0.36 377	9.96 273	6	36				
									10	5.0	4.8	4.7
25	9.59 924	30	9.63 657	35	0.36 343	9.96 267	5	35	20	10.0	9.7	9.3
26	9.59 954	29	9.63 692	34	0.36 308	9.96 262	6	34	30	15.0	14.5	14.0
27	9.59 983	29	9.63 726	35	0.36 274	9.96 256	5	33	40	20.0	19.3	18.7
28	9.60 012	29	9.63 761	35	0.36 239	9.96 251	6	32	50	25.0	24.2	23.3
29	9.60 041	29	9.63 796	34	0.36 204	9.96 245	5	31	″		6	5
30	9.60 070	29	9.63 830	35	0.36 170	9.96 240	6	30	1	0.1	0.1	
31	9.60 099	29	9.63 865	34	0.36 135	9.96 234	5	29	2	0.2	0.2	
32	9.60 128	29	9.63 899	35	0.36 101	9.96 229	5	28	3	0.3	0.2	
33	9.60 157	29	9.63 934	34	0.36 066	9.96 223	6	27	4	0.4	0.3	
34	9.60 186	29	9.63 968	35	0.36 032	9.96 218	6	26				
									5	0.5	0.4	
35	9.60 215	29	9.64 003	34	0.35 997	9.96 212	6	25	6	0.6	0.5	
36	9.60 244	29	9.64 037	35	0.35 963	9.96 207	5	24	7	0.7	0.6	
37	9.60 273	29	9.64 072	34	0.35 928	9.96 201	6	23	8	0.8	0.7	
38	9.60 302	29	9.64 106	34	0.35 894	9.96 196	5	22	9	0.9	0.8	
39	9.60 331	28	9.64 140	35	0.35 860	9.96 190	5	21				
									10	1.0	0.8	
40	9.60 359	29	9.64 175	34	0.35 825	9.96 185	6	20	20	2.0	1.7	
41	9.60 388	29	9.64 209	34	0.35 791	9.96 179	5	19	30	3.0	2.5	
42	9.60 417	29	9.64 243	35	0.35 757	9.96 174	6	18	40	4.0	3.3	
43	9.60 446	28	9.64 278	34	0.35 722	9.96 168	6	17	50	5.0	4.2	
44	9.60 474	29	9.64 312	34	0.35 688	9.96 162	5	16				
										6	6	6
45	9.60 503	29	9.64 346	35	0.35 654	9.96 157	6	15		36	35	34
46	9.60 532	29	9.64 381	34	0.35 619	9.96 151	5	14				
47	9.60 561	28	9.64 415	34	0.35 585	9.96 146	6	13	0	3.0	2.9	2.8
48	9.60 589	29	9.64 449	34	0.35 551	9.96 140	5	12	1	9.0	8.8	8.5
49	9.60 618	28	9.64 483	34	0.35 517	9.96 135	6	11	2	15.0	14.6	14.2
									3	21.0	20.4	19.8
50	9.60 646	29	9.64 517	35	0.35 483	9.96 129	6	10	4	27.0	26.2	25.5
51	9.60 675	29	9.64 552	34	0.35 448	9.96 123	5	9	5	33.0	32.1	31.2
52	9.60 704	28	9.64 586	34	0.35 414	9.96 118	6	8	6			
53	9.60 732	29	9.64 620	34	0.35 380	9.96 112	5	7		5	5	
54	9.60 761	28	9.64 654	34	0.35 346	9.96 107	6	6		35	34	
55	9.60 789	29	9.64 688	34	0.35 312	9.96 101	6	5				
56	9.60 818	28	9.64 722	34	0.35 278	9.96 095	5	4	0	3.5	3.4	
57	9.60 846	29	9.64 756	34	0.35 244	9.96 090	6	3	1	10.5	10.2	
58	9.60 875	28	9.64 790	34	0.35 210	9.96 084	5	2	2	17.5	17.0	
59	9.60 903	28	9.64 824	34	0.35 176	9.96 079	6	1	3	24.5	23.8	
									4	31.5	30.6	
									5			
60	9.60 931		9.64 858		0.35 142	9.96 073		0				
′	L. Cos.	d.	L. Cot.	c.d.	L. Tan.	L. Sin.	d.	′		P. P.		

113° (293°)   **(246°) 66°**

COMMON LOGARITHMS OF THE TRIGONOMETRIC FUNCTIONS (Continued)

24° (204°)   **(335°) 155°**

′	L. Sin.	d.	L. Tan.	c.d.	L. Cot.	L. Cos.	d.	′
0	9.60 931	29	9.64 858	34	0.35 142	9.96 073	6	60
1	9.60 960	28	9.64 892	34	0.35 108	9.96 067	5	59
2	9.60 988	28	9.64 926	34	0.35 074	9.96 062	6	58
3	9.61 016	29	9.64 960	34	0.35 040	9.96 056	6	57
4	9.61 045	28	9.64 994	34	0.35 006	9.96 050	5	56
5	9.61 073	28	9.65 028	34	0.34 972	9.96 045	6	55
6	9.61 101	28	9.65 062	34	0.34 938	9.96 039	5	54
7	9.61 129	29	9.65 096	34	0.34 904	9.96 034	6	53
8	9.61 158	28	9.65 130	34	0.34 870	9.96 028	6	52
9	9.61 186	28	9.65 164	33	0.34 836	9.96 022	5	51
10	9.61 214	28	9.65 197	34	0.34 803	9.96 017	6	50
11	9.61 242	28	9.65 231	34	0.34 769	9.96 011	6	49
12	9.61 270	28	9.65 265	34	0.34 735	9.96 005	5	48
13	9.61 298	28	9.65 299	34	0.34 701	9.96 000	6	47
14	9.61 326	28	9.65 333	33	0.34 667	9.95 994	6	46
15	9.61 354	28	9.65 366	34	0.34 634	9.95 988	6	45
16	9.61 382	29	9.65 400	34	0.34 600	9.95 982	5	44
17	9.61 411	27	9.65 434	33	0.34 566	9.95 977	6	43
18	9.61 438	28	9.65 467	34	0.34 533	9.95 971	6	42
19	9.61 466	28	9.65 501	34	0.34 499	9.95 965	5	41
20	9.61 494	28	9.65 535	33	0.34 465	9.95 960	6	40
21	9.61 522	28	9.65 568	34	0.34 432	9.95 954	6	39
22	9.61 550	28	9.65 602	34	0.34 398	9.95 948	6	38
23	9.61 578	28	9.65 636	33	0.34 364	9.95 942	5	37
24	9.61 606	28	9.65 669	34	0.34 331	9.95 937	6	36
25	9.61 634	28	9.65 703	33	0.34 297	9.95 931	6	35
26	9.61 662	27	9.65 736	34	0.34 264	9.95 925	5	34
27	9.61 689	28	9.65 770	33	0.34 230	9.95 920	6	33
28	9.61 717	28	9.65 803	34	0.34 197	9.95 914	6	32
29	9.61 745	28	9.65 837	33	0.34 163	9.95 908	6	31
30	9.61 773	27	9.65 870	34	0.34 130	9.95 902	5	30
31	9.61 800	28	9.65 904	33	0.34 096	9.95 897	6	29
32	9.61 828	28	9.65 937	34	0.34 063	9.95 891	6	28
33	9.61 856	27	9.65 971	33	0.34 029	9.95 885	6	27
34	9.61 883	28	9.66 004	34	0.33 996	9.95 879	6	26
35	9.61 911	28	9.66 038	33	0.33 962	9.95 873	5	25
36	9.61 939	27	9.66 071	33	0.33 929	9.95 868	6	24
37	9.61 966	28	9.66 104	34	0.33 896	9.95 862	6	23
38	9.61 994	27	9.66 138	33	0.33 862	9.95 856	6	22
39	9.62 021	28	9.66 171	33	0.33 829	9.95 850	6	21
40	9.62 049	27	9.66 204	34	0.33 796	9.95 844	5	20
41	9.62 076	28	9.66 238	33	0.33 762	9.95 839	6	19
42	9.62 104	27	9.66 271	33	0.33 729	9.95 833	6	18
43	9.62 131	28	9.66 304	33	0.33 696	9.95 827	6	17
44	9.62 159	27	9.66 337	34	0.33 663	9.95 821	6	16
45	9.62 186	28	9.66 371	33	0.33 629	9.95 815	5	15
46	9.62 214	27	9.66 404	33	0.33 596	9.95 810	6	14
47	9.62 241	27	9.66 437	33	0.33 563	9.95 804	6	13
48	9.62 268	28	9.66 470	33	0.33 530	9.95 798	6	12
49	9.62 296	27	9.66 503	34	0.33 497	9.95 792	6	11
50	9.62 323	27	9.66 537	33	0.33 463	9.95 786	6	10
51	9.62 350	27	9.66 570	33	0.33 430	9.95 780	5	9
52	9.62 377	28	9.66 603	33	0.33 397	9.95 775	6	8
53	9.62 405	27	9.66 636	33	0.33 364	9.95 769	6	7
54	9.62 432	27	9.66 669	33	0.33 331	9.95 763	6	6
55	9.62 459	27	9.66 702	33	0.33 298	9.95 757	6	5
56	9.62 486	27	9.66 735	33	0.33 265	9.95 751	6	4
57	9.62 513	28	9.66 768	33	0.33 232	9.95 745	6	3
58	9.62 541	27	9.66 801	33	0.33 199	9.95 739	6	2
59	9.62 568	27	9.66 834	33	0.33 166	9.95 733	5	1
60	9.62 595		9.66 867		0.33 133	9.95 728		0
′	L. Cos.	d.	L. Cot.	c.d.	L. Tan.	L. Sin.	d.	′

P. P.

```
      ″        34    33
      1       0.6   0.6
      2       1.1   1.1
      3       1.7   1.6
      4       2.3   2.2
      5       2.8   2.8
      6       3.4   3.3
      7       4.0   3.8
      8       4.5   4.4
      9       5.1   5.0
     10       5.7   5.5
     20      11.3  11.0
     30      17.0  16.5
     40      22.7  22.0
     50      28.3  27.5

      ″        29    28    27
      1       0.5   0.5   0.4
      2       1.0   0.9   0.9
      3       1.4   1.4   1.4
      4       1.9   1.9   1.8
      5       2.4   2.3   2.2
      6       2.9   2.8   2.7
      7       3.4   3.3   3.2
      8       3.9   3.7   3.6
      9       4.4   4.2   4.0
     10       4.8   4.7   4.5
     20       9.7   9.3   9.0
     30      14.5  14.0  13.5
     40      19.3  18.7  18.0
     50      24.2  23.3  22.5

      ″         6     5
      1       0.1   0.1
      2       0.2   0.2
      3       0.3   0.2
      4       0.4   0.3
      5       0.5   0.4
      6       0.6   0.5
      7       0.7   0.6
      8       0.8   0.7
      9       0.9   0.8
     10       1.0   0.8
     20       2.0   1.7
     30       3.0   2.5
     40       4.0   3.3
     50       5.0   4.2

               6     6     5
              34    33    34
   0
   1         2.8   2.8   3.4
   2         8.5   8.2  10.2
   3        14.2  13.8  17.0
   4        19.8  19.2  23.8
   5        25.5  24.8  30.6
   6        31.2  30.2
```

114° (294°)   **(245°) 65°**

COMMON LOGARITHMS OF THE TRIGONOMETRIC
FUNCTIONS (Continued)

25° (205°)　　　　　　　　　　　　　　　　**(334°) 154°**

'	L. Sin.	d.	L. Tan.	c.d.	L. Cot.	L. Cos.	d	'
0	9.62 595	27	9.66 867	33	0.33 133	9.95 728	6	60
1	5.62 622	27	9.66 900	33	0.33 100	9.95 722	6	59
2	9.62 649	27	9.66 933	33	0.33 067	9.95 716	6	58
3	9.62 676	27	9.66 966	33	0.33 034	9.95 710	6	57
4	9.62 703	27	9.66 999	33	0.33 001	9.95 704	6	56
5	9.62 730	27	9.67 032	33	0.32 968	9.95 698	6	55
6	9.62 757	27	9.67 065	33	0.32 935	9.95 692	6	54
7	9.62 784	27	9.67 098	33	0.32 902	9.95 686	6	53
8	9.62 811	27	9.67 131	32	0.32 869	9.95 680	6	52
9	9.62 838	27	9.67 163	33	0.32 837	9.95 674	6	51
10	9.62 865	27	9.67 196	33	0.32 804	9.95 668	5	50
11	9.62 892	26	9.67 229	33	0.32 771	9.95 663	6	49
12	9.62 918	27	9.67 262	33	0.32 738	9.95 657	6	48
13	9.62 945	27	9.67 295	33	0.32 705	9.95 651	6	47
14	9.62 972	27	9.67 327	33	0.32 673	9.95 645	6	46
15	9.62 999	27	9.67 360	33	0.32 640	9.95 639	6	45
16	9.63 026	26	9.67 393	33	0.32 607	9.95 633	6	44
17	9.63 052	27	9.67 426	32	0.32 574	9.95 627	6	43
18	9.63 079	27	9.67 458	33	0.32 542	9.95 621	6	42
19	9.63 106	27	9.67 491	33	0.32 509	9.95 615	6	41
20	9.63 133	26	9.67 524	32	0.32 476	9.95 609	6	40
21	9.63 159	27	9.67 556	33	0.32 444	9.95 603	6	39
22	9.63 186	27	9.67 589	33	0.32 411	9.95 597	6	38
23	9.63 213	26	9.67 622	32	0.32 378	9.95 591	6	37
24	9.63 239	27	9.67 654	33	0.32 346	9.95 585	6	36
25	9.63 266	26	9.67 687	32	0.32 313	9.95 579	6	35
26	9.63 292	27	9.67 719	33	0.32 281	9.95 573	6	34
27	9.63 319	26	9.67 752	33	0.32 248	9.95 567	6	33
28	9.63 345	27	9.67 785	32	0.32 215	9.95 561	6	32
29	9.63 372	26	9.67 817	33	0.32 183	9.95 555	6	31
30	9.63 398	27	9.67 850	32	0.32 150	9.95 549	6	30
31	9.63 425	26	9.67 882	33	0.32 118	9.95 543	6	29
32	9.63 451	27	9.67 915	32	0.32 085	9.95 537	6	28
33	9.63 478	26	9.67 947	33	0.32 053	9.95 531	6	27
34	9.63 504	27	9.67 980	32	0.32 020	9.95 525	6	26
35	9.63 531	26	9.68 012	32	0.31 988	9.95 519	6	25
36	9.63 557	26	9.68 044	33	0.31 956	9.95 513	6	24
37	9.63 583	27	9.68 077	32	0.31 923	9.95 507	7	23
38	9.63 610	26	9.68 109	33	0.31 891	9.95 500	6	22
39	9.63 636	26	9.68 142	32	0.31 858	9.95 494	6	21
40	9.63 662	27	9.68 174	32	0.31 826	9.95 488	6	20
41	9.63 689	26	9.68 206	33	0.31 794	9.95 482	6	19
42	9.63 715	26	9.68 239	32	0.31 761	9.95 476	6	18
43	9.63 741	26	9.68 271	32	0.31 729	9.95 470	6	17
44	9.63 767	27	9.68 303	33	0.31 697	9.95 464	6	16
45	9.63 794	26	9.68 336	32	0.31 664	9.95 458	6	15
46	9.63 820	26	9.68 368	32	0.31 632	9.95 452	6	14
47	9.63 846	26	9.68 400	32	0.31 600	9.95 446	6	13
48	9.63 872	26	9.68 432	33	0.31 568	9.95 440	6	12
49	9.63 898	26	9.68 465	32	0.31 535	9.95 434	7	11
50	9.63 924	26	9.68 497	32	0.31 503	9.95 427	6	10
51	9.63 950	26	9.68 529	32	0.31 471	9.95 421	6	9
52	9.63 976	26	9.68 561	32	0.31 439	9.95 415	6	8
53	9.64 002	26	9.68 593	33	0.31 407	9.95 409	6	7
54	9.64 028	26	9.68 626	32	0.31 374	9.95 403	6	6
55	9.64 054	26	9.68 658	32	0.31 342	9.95 397	6	5
56	9.64 080	26	9.68 690	32	0.31 310	9.95 391	7	4
57	9.64 106	26	9.68 722	32	0.31 278	9.95 384	6	3
58	9.64 132	26	9.68 754	32	0.31 246	9.95 378	6	2
59	9.64 158	26	9.68 786	32	0.31 214	9.95 372	6	1
60	9.64 184		9.68 818		0.31 182	9.95 366		0

'	L. Cos.	d.	L. Cot.	c.d.	L. Tan.	L. Sin.	d.	'

P. P.

"	33	32
1	0.6	0.5
2	1.1	1.1
3	1.6	1.6
4	2.2	2.1
5	2.8	2.7
6	3.3	3.2
7	3.8	3.7
8	4.4	4.3
9	5.0	4.8
10	5.5	5.3
20	11.0	10.7
30	16.5	16.0
40	22.0	21.3
50	27.5	26.7

"	27	26
1	0.4	0.4
2	0.9	0.9
3	1.4	1.3
4	1.8	1.7
5	2.2	2.2
6	2.7	2.6
7	3.2	3.0
8	3.6	3.5
9	4.0	3.9
10	4.5	4.3
20	9.0	8.7
30	13.5	13.0
40	18.0	17.3
50	22.5	21.7

"	7	6	5
1	0.1	0.1	0.1
2	0.2	0.2	0.2
3	0.4	0.3	0.2
4	0.5	0.4	0.3
5	0.6	0.5	0.4
6	0.7	0.6	0.5
7	0.8	0.7	0.6
8	0.9	0.8	0.7
9	1.0	0.9	0.8
10	1.2	1.0	0.8
20	2.3	2.0	1.7
30	3.5	3.0	2.5
40	4.7	4.0	3.3
50	5.8	5.0	4.2

	7	6	5
	32	32	33
0			
1	2.3	2.7	3.3
2	6.9	8.0	9.9
3	11.4	13.3	16.5
4	16.0	18.7	23.1
5	20.6	24.0	29.7
6	25.1	29.3	—
7	29.7	—	—

115° (295°)　　　　　　　　　　　　　　　　**(244°) 64°**

COMMON LOGARITHMS OF THE TRIGONOMETRIC FUNCTIONS (Continued)

26° (206°)   **(333°) 153°**

′	L. Sin.	d.	L. Tan.	c.d.	L. Cot.	L. Cos.	d.	′
0	9.64 184	26	9.68 818	32	0.31 182	9.95 366	6	60
1	9.64 210	26	9.68 850	32	0.31 150	9.95 360	6	59
2	9.64 236	26	9.68 882	32	0.31 118	9.95 354	6	58
3	9.64 262	26	9.68 914	32	0.31 086	9.95 348	7	57
4	9.64 288	25	9.68 946	32	0.31 054	9.95 341	6	56
5	9.64 313	26	9.68 978	32	0.31 022	9.95 335	6	55
6	9.64 339	26	9.69 010	32	0.30 990	9.95 329	6	54
7	9.64 365	26	9.69 042	32	0.30 958	9.95 323	6	53
8	9.64 391	26	9.69 074	32	0.30 926	9.95 317	7	52
9	9.64 417	25	9.69 106	32	0.30 894	9.95 310	6	51
10	9.64 442	26	9.69 138	32	0.30 862	9.95 304	6	50
11	9.64 468	26	9.69 170	32	0.30 830	9.95 298	6	49
12	9.64 494	25	9.69 202	32	0.30 798	9.95 292	6	48
13	9.64 519	26	9.69 234	32	0.30 766	9.95 286	7	47
14	9.64 545	26	9.69 266	32	0.30 734	9.95 279	6	46
15	9.64 571	25	9.69 298	31	0.30 702	9.95 273	6	45
16	9.64 596	26	9.69 329	32	0.30 671	9.95 267	6	44
17	9.64 622	25	9.69 361	32	0.30 639	9.95 261	7	43
18	9.64 647	26	9.69 393	32	0.30 607	9.95 254	6	42
19	9.64 673	25	9.69 425	32	0.30 575	9.95 248	6	41
20	9.64 698	26	9.69 457	31	0.30 543	9.95 242	6	40
21	9.64 724	25	9.69 488	32	0.30 512	9.95 236	7	39
22	9.64 749	26	9.69 520	32	0.30 480	9.95 229	6	38
23	9.64 775	25	9.69 552	32	0.30 448	9.95 223	6	37
24	9.64 800	26	9.69 584	31	0.30 416	9.95 217	6	36
25	9.64 826	25	9.69 615	32	0.30 385	9.95 211	7	35
26	9.64 851	26	9.69 647	32	0.30 353	9.95 204	6	34
27	9.64 877	25	9.69 679	31	0.30 321	9.95 198	6	33
28	9.64 902	25	9.69 710	32	0.30 290	9.95 192	7	32
29	9.64 927	26	9.69 742	32	0.30 258	9.95 185	6	31
30	9.64 953	25	9.69 774	31	0.30 226	9.95 179	6	30
31	9.64 978	25	9.69 805	32	0.30 195	9.95 173	7	29
32	9.65 003	26	9.69 837	31	0.30 163	9.95 167	6	28
33	9.65 029	25	9.69 868	32	0.30 132	9.95 160	6	27
34	9.65 054	25	9.69 900	32	0.30 100	9.95 154	7	26
35	9.65 079	25	9.69 932	31	0.30 068	9.95 148	6	25
36	9.65 104	26	9.69 963	32	0.30 037	9.95 141	6	24
37	9.65 130	25	9.69 995	31	0.30 005	9.95 135	7	23
38	9.65 155	25	9.70 026	32	0.29 974	9.95 129	6	22
39	9.65 180	25	9.70 058	31	0.29 942	9.95 122	7	21
40	9.65 205	25	9.70 089	32	0.29 911	9.95 116	6	20
41	9.65 230	25	9.70 121	31	0.29 879	9.95 110	7	19
42	9.65 255	26	9.70 152	32	0.29 848	9.95 103	6	18
43	9.65 281	25	9.70 184	31	0.29 816	9.95 097	7	17
44	9.65 306	25	9.70 215	32	0.29 785	9.95 090	6	16
45	9.65 331	25	9.70 247	31	0.29 753	9.95 084	6	15
46	9.65 356	25	9.70 278	31	0.29 722	9.95 078	7	14
47	9.65 381	25	9.70 309	32	0.29 691	9.95 071	6	13
48	9.65 406	25	9.70 341	31	0.29 659	9.95 065	7	12
49	9.65 431	25	9.70 372	32	0.29 628	9.95 059	7	11
50	9.65 456	25	9.70 404	31	0.29 596	9.95 052	6	10
51	9.65 481	25	9.70 435	31	0.29 565	9.95 046	7	9
52	9.65 506	25	9.70 466	32	0.29 534	9.95 039	6	8
53	9.65 531	25	9.70 498	31	0.29 502	9.95 033	7	7
54	9.65 556	24	9.70 529	31	0.29 471	9.95 027	7	6
55	9.65 580	25	9.70 560	32	0.29 440	9.95 020	6	5
56	9.65 605	25	9.70 592	31	0.29 408	9.95 014	7	4
57	9.65 630	25	9.70 623	31	0.29 377	9.95 007	6	3
58	9.65 655	25	9.70 654	31	0.29 346	9.95 001	7	2
59	9.65 680	25	9.70 685	32	0.29 315	9.94 995	7	1
60	9.65 705		9.70 717		0.29 283	9.94 988		0

P. P.

″	32	31
1	0.5	0.5
2	1.1	1.0
3	1.6	1.6
4	2.1	2.1
5	2.7	2.6
6	3.2	3.1
7	3.7	3.6
8	4.3	4.1
9	4.8	4.6
10	5.3	5.2
20	10.7	10.3
30	16.0	15.5
40	21.3	20.7
50	26.7	25.8

″	26	25	24
1	0.4	0.4	0.4
2	0.9	0.8	0.8
3	1.3	1.2	1.2
4	1.7	1.7	1.6
5	2.2	2.1	2.0
6	2.6	2.5	2.4
7	3.0	2.9	2.8
8	3.5	3.3	3.2
9	3.9	3.8	3.6
10	4.3	4.2	4.0
20	8.7	8.3	8.0
30	13.0	12.5	12.0
40	17.3	16.7	16.0
50	21.7	20.8	20.0

″	7	6
1	0.1	0.1
2	0.2	0.2
3	0.4	0.3
4	0.5	0.4
5	0.6	0.5
6	0.7	0.6
7	0.8	0.7
8	0.9	0.8
9	1.0	0.9
10	1.2	1.0
20	2.3	2.0
30	3.5	3.0
40	4.7	4.0
50	5.8	5.0

	$\frac{7}{32}$	$\frac{7}{31}$	$\frac{6}{32}$
0			
1	2.3	2.2	2.7
2	6.9	6.6	8.0
3	11.4	11.1	13.3
4	16.0	15.5	18.7
5	20.6	19.9	24.0
6	25.1	24.4	29.3
7	29.7	28.8	—

′	L. Cos.	d.	L. Cot.	c.d.	L. Tan.	L. Sin.	d.	′	P.P.

116° (296°)   **(243°) 63°**

COMMON LOGARITHMS OF THE TRIGONOMETRIC
FUNCTIONS (Continued)

27° (207°)　　　　　　　　　　　　　　　　　(332°) **152°**

'	L. Sin.	d.	L. Tan.	c.d.	L. Cot.	L. Cos.	d.	'
0	9.65 705	24	9.70 717	31	0.29 283	9.94 988	6	60
1	9.65 729	25	9.70 748	31	0.29 252	9.94 982	7	59
2	9.65 754	25	9.70 779	31	0.29 221	9.94 975	6	58
3	9.65 779	25	9.70 810	31	0.29 190	9.94 969	7	57
4	9.65 804	24	9.70 841	32	0.29 159	9.94 962	6	56
5	9.65 828	25	9.70 873	31	0.29 127	9.94 956	7	55
6	9.65 853	25	9.70 904	31	0.29 096	9.94 949	6	54
7	9.65 878	24	9.70 935	31	0.29 065	9.94 943	7	53
8	9.65 902	25	9.70 966	31	0.29 034	9.94 936	6	52
9	9.65 927	25	9.70 997	31	0.29 003	9.94 930	7	51
10	9.65 952	24	9.71 028	31	0.28 972	9.94 923	6	50
11	9.65 976	25	9.71 059	31	0.28 941	9.94 917	6	49
12	9.66 001	24	9.71 090	31	0.28 910	9.94 911	7	48
13	9.66 025	25	9.71 121	32	0.28 879	9.94 904	6	47
14	9.66 050	25	9.71 153	31	0.28 847	9.94 898	7	46
15	9.66 075	24	9.71 184	31	0.28 816	9.94 891	6	45
16	9.66 099	25	9.71 215	31	0.28 785	9.94 885	7	44
17	9.66 124	24	9.71 246	31	0.28 754	9.94 878	7	43
18	9.66 148	25	9.71 277	31	0.28 723	9.94 871	7	42
19	9.66 173	24	9.71 308	31	0.28 692	9.94 865	6	41
20	9.66 197	24	9.71 339	31	0.28 661	9.94 858	6	40
21	9.66 221	25	9.71 370	31	0.28 630	9.94 852	7	39
22	9.66 246	24	9.71 401	30	0.28 599	9.94 845	6	38
23	9.66 270	25	9.71 431	31	0.28 569	9.94 839	7	37
24	9.66 295	24	9.71 462	31	0.28 538	9.94 832	6	36
25	9.66 319	24	9.71 493	31	0.28 507	9.94 826	7	35
26	9.66 343	25	9.71 524	31	0.28 476	9.94 819	6	34
27	9.66 368	24	9.71 555	31	0.28 445	9.94 813	7	33
28	9.66 392	24	9.71 586	31	0.28 414	9.94 806	7	32
29	9.66 416	25	9.71 617	31	0.28 383	9.94 799	6	31
30	9.66 441	24	9.71 648	31	0.28 352	9.94 793	7	30
31	9.66 465	24	9.71 679	30	0.28 321	9.94 786	6	29
32	9.66 489	24	9.71 709	31	0.28 291	9.94 780	7	28
33	9.66 513	24	9.71 740	31	0.28 260	9.94 773	7	27
34	9.66 537	25	9.71 771	31	0.28 229	9.94 767	7	26
35	9.66 562	24	9.71 802	31	0.28 198	9.94 760	7	25
36	9.66 586	24	9.71 833	30	0.28 167	9.94 753	6	24
37	9.66 610	24	9.71 863	31	0.28 137	9.94 747	7	23
38	9.66 634	24	9.71 894	31	0.28 106	9.94 740	6	22
39	9.66 658	24	9.71 925	30	0.28 075	9.94 734	7	21
40	9.66 682	24	9.71 955	31	0.28 045	9.94 727	7	20
41	9.66 706	24	9.71 986	31	0.28 014	9.94 720	6	19
42	9.66 731	24	9.72 017	31	0.27 983	9.94 714	7	18
43	9.66 755	24	9.72 048	30	0.27 952	9.94 707	7	17
44	9.66 779	24	9.72 078	31	0.27 922	9.94 700	6	16
45	9.66 803	24	9.72 109	31	0.27 891	9.94 694	7	15
46	9.66 827	24	9.72 140	30	0.27 860	9.94 687	7	14
47	9.66 851	24	9.72 170	31	0.27 830	9.94 680	6	13
48	9.66 875	24	9.72 201	30	0.27 799	9.94 674	7	12
49	9.66 899	23	9.72 231	31	0.27 769	9.94 667	7	11
50	9.66 922	24	9.72 262	31	0.27 738	9.94 660	6	10
51	9.66 946	24	9.72 293	30	0.27 707	9.94 654	7	9
52	9.66 970	24	9.72 323	31	0.27 677	9.94 647	7	8
53	9.66 994	24	9.72 354	30	0.27 646	9.94 640	6	7
54	9.67 018	24	9.72 384	31	0.27 616	9.94 634	7	6
55	9.67 042	24	9.72 415	30	0.27 585	9.94 627	7	5
56	9.67 066	24	9.72 445	31	0.27 555	9.94 620	6	4
57	9.67 090	23	9.72 476	30	0.27 524	9.94 614	7	3
58	9.67 113	24	9.72 506	31	0.27 494	9.94 607	7	2
59	9.67 137	24	9.72 537	30	0.27 463	9.94 600	7	1
60	9.67 161		9.72 567		0.27 433	9.94 593		0
'	L. Cos.	d.	L. Cot.	c.d.	L. Tan.	L. Sin.	d.	'

117° (297°)　　　　　　　　　　　　　　　　(242°) **62°**

P. P.

"	32	31	30
1	0.5	0.5	0.5
2	1.1	1.0	1.0
3	1.6	1.6	1.5
4	2.1	2.1	2.0
5	2.7	2.6	2.5
6	3.2	3.1	3.0
7	3.7	3.6	3.5
8	4.3	4.1	4.0
9	4.8	4.6	4.5
10	5.3	5.2	5.0
20	10.7	10.3	10.0
30	16.0	15.5	15.0
40	21.3	20.7	20.0
50	26.7	25.8	25.0

"	25	24	23
1	0.4	0.4	0.4
2	0.8	0.8	0.8
3	1.2	1.2	1.2
4	1.7	1.6	1.5
5	2.1	2.0	1.9
6	2.5	2.4	2.3
7	2.9	2.8	2.7
8	3.3	3.2	3.1
9	3.8	3.6	3.4
10	4.2	4.0	3.8
20	8.3	8.0	7.7
30	12.5	12.0	11.5
40	16.7	16.0	15.3
50	20.8	20.0	19.2

"	7	6
1	0.1	0.1
2	0.2	0.2
3	0.4	0.3
4	0.5	0.4
5	0.6	0.5
6	0.7	0.6
7	0.8	0.7
8	0.9	0.8
9	1.0	0.9
10	1.2	1.0
20	2.3	2.0
30	3.5	3.0
40	4.7	4.0
50	5.8	5.0

	7	6	6
	30	31	30
0			
1	2.1	2.6	2.5
2	6.4	7.8	7.5
3	10.7	12.9	12.5
4	15.0	18.1	17.5
5	19.3	23.2	22.5
6	23.6	28.4	27.5
7	27.9	—	—

COMMON LOGARITHMS OF THE TRIGONOMETRIC FUNCTIONS (Continued)

28° (208°)   **(331°) 151°**

′	L. Sin.	d.	L. Tan.	c.d.	L. Cot.	L. Cos.	d.	′
0	9.67 161	24	9.72 567	31	0.27 433	9.94 593	6	60
1	9.67 185	23	9.72 598	30	0.27 402	9.94 587	7	59
2	9.67 208	24	9.72 628	31	0.27 372	9.94 580	7	58
3	9.67 232	24	9.72 659	30	0.27 341	9.94 573	6	57
4	9.67 256	24	9.72 689	31	0.27 311	9.94 567	7	56
5	9.67 280	23	9.72 720	30	0.27 280	9.94 560	7	55
6	9.67 303	24	9.72 750	30	0.27 250	9.94 553	7	54
7	9.67 327	23	9.72 780	31	0.27 220	9.94 546	6	53
8	9.67 350	24	9.72 811	30	0.27 189	9.94 540	7	52
9	9.67 374	24	9.72 841	31	0.27 159	9.94 533	7	51
10	9.67 398	23	9.72 872	30	0.27 128	9.94 526	7	50
11	9.67 421	24	9.72 902	30	0.27 098	9.94 519	6	49
12	9.67 445	23	9.72 932	31	0.27 068	9.94 513	7	48
13	9.67 468	23	9.72 963	30	0.27 037	9.94 506	7	47
14	9.67 492	23	9.72 993	30	0.27 007	9.94 499	7	46
15	9.67 515	24	9.73 023	31	0.26 977	9.94 492	7	45
16	9.67 539	23	9.73 054	30	0.26 946	9.94 485	6	44
17	9.67 562	24	9.73 084	30	0.26 916	9.94 479	7	43
18	9.67 586	23	9.73 114	30	0.26 886	9.94 472	7	42
19	9.67 609	24	9.73 144	31	0.26 856	9.94 465	7	41
20	9.67 633	23	9.73 175	30	0.26 825	9.94 458	7	40
21	9.67 656	24	9.73 205	30	0.26 795	9.94 451	6	39
22	9.67 680	23	9.73 235	30	0.26 765	9.94 445	7	38
23	9.67 703	23	9.73 265	30	0.26 735	9.94 438	7	37
24	9.67 726	24	9.73 295	31	0.26 705	9.94 431	7	36
25	9.67 750	23	9.73 326	30	0.26 674	9.94 424	7	35
26	9.67 773	23	9.73 356	30	0.26 644	9.94 417	7	34
27	9.67 796	24	9.73 386	30	0.26 614	9.94 410	6	33
28	9.67 820	23	9.73 416	30	0.26 584	9.94 404	7	32
29	9.67 843	23	9.73 446	30	0.26 554	9.94 397	7	31
30	9.67 866	24	9.73 476	31	0.26 524	9.94 390	7	30
31	9.67 890	23	9.73 507	30	0.26 493	9.94 383	7	29
32	9.67 913	23	9.73 537	30	0.26 463	9.94 376	7	28
33	9.67 936	23	9.73 567	30	0.26 433	9.94 369	7	27
34	9.67 959	23	9.73 597	30	0.26 403	9.94 362	7	26
35	9.67 982	24	9.73 627	30	0.26 373	9.94 355	6	25
36	9.68 006	23	9.73 657	30	0.26 343	9.94 349	7	24
37	9.68 029	23	9.73 687	30	0.26 313	9.94 342	7	23
38	9.68 052	23	9.73 717	30	0.26 283	9.94 335	7	22
39	9.68 075	23	9.73 747	30	0.26 253	9.94 328	7	21
40	9.68 098	23	9.73 777	30	0.26 223	9.94 321	7	20
41	9.68 121	23	9.73 807	30	0.26 193	9.94 314	7	19
42	9.68 144	23	9.73 837	30	0.26 163	9.94 307	7	18
43	9.68 167	23	9.73 867	30	0.26 133	9.94 300	7	17
44	9.68 190	23	9.73 897	30	0.26 103	9.94 293	7	16
45	9.68 213	24	9.73 927	30	0.26 073	9.94 286	7	15
46	9.68 237	23	9.73 957	30	0.26 043	9.94 279	6	14
47	9.68 260	23	9.73 987	30	0.26 013	9.94 273	7	13
48	9.68 283	22	9.74 017	30	0.25 983	9.94 266	7	12
49	9.68 305	23	9.74 047	30	0.25 953	9.94 259	7	11
50	9.68 328	23	9.74 077	30	0.25 923	9.94 252	7	10
51	9.68 351	23	9.74 107	30	0.25 893	9.94 245	7	9
52	9.68 374	23	9.74 137	29	0.25 863	9.94 238	7	8
53	9.68 397	23	9.74 166	30	0.25 834	9.94 231	7	7
54	9.68 420	23	9.74 196	30	0.25 804	9.94 224	7	6
55	9.68 443	23	9.74 226	30	0.25 774	9.94 217	7	5
56	9.68 466	23	9.74 256	30	0.25 744	9.94 210	7	4
57	9.68 489	23	9.74 286	30	0.25 714	9.94 203	7	3
58	9.68 512	22	9.74 316	29	0.25 684	9.94 196	7	2
59	9.68 534	23	9.74 345	30	0.25 655	9.94 189	7	1
60	9.68 557		9.74 375		0.25 625	9.94 182		0
′	L. Cos.	d.	L. Cot.	c.d.	L. Tan.	L. Sin.	d.	′

P. P.

″	31	30	29
1	0.5	0.5	0.5
2	1.0	1.0	1.0
3	1.6	1.5	1.4
4	2.1	2.0	1.9
5	2.6	2.5	2.4
6	3.1	3.0	2.9
7	3.6	3.5	3.4
8	4.1	4.0	3.9
9	4.6	4.5	4.4
10	5.2	5.0	4.8
20	10.3	10.0	9.7
30	15.5	15.0	14.5
40	20.7	20.0	19.3
50	25.8	25.0	24.2

″	24	23	22
1	0.4	0.4	0.4
2	0.8	0.8	0.7
3	1.2	1.2	1.1
4	1.6	1.5	1.5
5	2.0	1.9	1.8
6	2.4	2.3	2.2
7	2.8	2.7	2.6
8	3.2	3.1	2.9
9	3.6	3.4	3.3
10	4.0	3.8	3.7
20	8.0	7.7	7.3
30	12.0	11.5	11.0
40	16.0	15.3	14.7
50	20.0	19.2	18.3

″	7	6
1	0.1	0.1
2	0.2	0.2
3	0.4	0.3
4	0.5	0.4
5	0.6	0.5
6	0.7	0.6
7	0.8	0.7
8	0.9	0.8
9	1.0	0.9
10	1.2	1.0
20	2.3	2.0
30	3.5	3.0
40	4.7	4.0
50	5.8	5.0

	7	6	6
	31	31	30
0			
1	2.2	2.6	2.5
2	6.6	7.8	7.5
3	11.1	12.9	12.5
4	15.5	18.1	17.5
5	19.9	23.2	22.5
6	24.4	28.4	27.5
7	28.8	—	—

COMMON LOGARITHMS OF THE TRIGONOMETRIC FUNCTIONS (Continued)

29° (209°)   **(330°) 150°**

'	L. Sin.	d.	L. Tan.	c.d.	L. Cot.	L. Cos.	d.	'
0	9.68 557	23	9.74 375	30	0.25 625	9.94 182	7	60
1	9.68 580	23	9.74 405	30	0.25 595	9.94 175	7	59
2	9.68 603	22	9.74 435	30	0.25 565	9.94 168	7	58
3	9.68 625	23	9.74 465	29	0.25 535	9.94 161	7	57
4	9.68 648	23	9.74 494	30	0.25 506	9.94 154	7	56
5	9.68 671	23	9.74 524	30	0.25 476	9.94 147	7	55
6	9.68 694	22	9.74 554	29	0.25 446	9.94 140	7	54
7	9.68 716	23	9.74 583	30	0.25 417	9.94 133	7	53
8	9.68 739	23	9.74 613	30	0.25 387	9.94 126	7	52
9	9.68 762	22	9.74 643	30	0.25 357	9.94 119	7	51
10	9.68 784	23	9.74 673	29	0.25 327	9.94 112	7	50
11	9.68 807	22	9.74 702	30	0.25 298	9.94 105	7	49
12	9.68 829	23	9.74 732	30	0.25 268	9.94 098	8	48
13	9.68 852	23	9.74 762	29	0.25 238	9.94 090	7	47
14	9.68 875	22	9.74 791	30	0.25 209	9.94 083	7	46
15	9.68 897	23	9.74 821	30	0.25 179	9.94 076	7	45
16	9.68 920	22	9.74 851	29	0.25 149	9.94 069	7	44
17	9.68 942	23	9.74 880	30	0.25 120	9.94 062	7	43
18	9.68 965	22	9.74 910	30	0.25 090	9.94 055	7	42
19	9.68 987	23	9.74 939	30	0.25 061	9.94 048	7	41
20	9.69 010	22	9.74 969	29	0.25 031	9.94 041	7	40
21	9.69 032	23	9.74 998	30	0.25 002	9.94 034	7	39
22	9.69 055	22	9.75 028	30	0.24 972	9.94 027	7	38
23	9.69 077	23	9.75 058	29	0.24 942	9.94 020	8	37
24	9.69 100	22	9.75 087	30	0.24 913	9.94 012	7	36
25	9.69 122	22	9.75 117	29	0.24 883	9.94 005	7	35
26	9.69 144	23	9.75 146	30	0.24 854	9.93 998	7	34
27	9.69 167	22	9.75 176	29	0.24 824	9.93 991	7	33
28	9.69 189	23	9.75 205	30	0.24 795	9.93 984	7	32
29	9.69 212	22	9.75 235	29	0.24 765	9.93 977	7	31
30	9.69 234	22	9.75 264	30	0.24 736	9.93 970	7	30
31	9.69 256	23	9.75 294	29	0.24 706	9.93 963	8	29
32	9.69 279	22	9.75 323	30	0.24 677	9.93 955	7	28
33	9.69 301	22	9.75 353	29	0.24 647	9.93 948	7	27
34	9.69 323	22	9.75 382	29	0.24 618	9.93 941	7	26
35	9.69 345	23	9.75 411	30	0.24 589	9.93 934	7	25
36	9.69 368	22	9.75 441	29	0.24 559	9.93 927	7	24
37	9.69 390	22	9.75 470	30	0.24 530	9.93 920	8	23
38	9.69 412	22	9.75 500	29	0.24 500	9.93 912	7	22
39	9.69 434	22	9.75 529	29	0.24 471	9.93 905	7	21
40	9.69 456	23	9.75 558	30	0.24 442	9.93 898	7	20
41	9.69 479	22	9.75 588	29	0.24 412	9.93 891	7	19
42	9.69 501	22	9.75 617	30	0.24 383	9.93 884	8	18
43	9.69 523	22	9.75 647	29	0.24 353	9.93 876	7	17
44	9.69 545	22	9.75 676	29	0.24 324	9.93 869	7	16
45	9.69 567	22	9.75 705	30	0.24 295	9.93 862	7	15
46	9.69 589	22	9.75 735	29	0.24 265	9.93 855	8	14
47	9.69 611	22	9.75 764	29	0.24 236	9.93 847	7	13
48	9.69 633	22	9.75 793	29	0.24 207	9.93 840	7	12
49	9.69 655	22	9.75 822	30	0.24 178	9.93 833	7	11
50	9.69 677	22	9.75 852	29	0.24 148	9.93 826	7	10
51	9.69 699	22	9.75 881	29	0.24 119	9.93 819	8	9
52	9.69 721	22	9.75 910	29	0.24 090	9.93 811	7	8
53	9.69 743	22	9.75 939	30	0.24 061	9.93 804	7	7
54	9.69 765	22	9.75 969	29	0.24 031	9.93 797	8	6
55	9.69 787	22	9.75 998	29	0.24 002	9.93 789	7	5
56	9.69 809	22	9.76 027	29	0.23 973	9.93 782	7	4
57	9.69 831	22	9.76 056	30	0.23 944	9.93 775	7	3
58	9.69 853	22	9.76 086	29	0.23 914	9.93 768	8	2
59	9.69 875	22	9.76 113	29	0.23 885	9.93 760	7	1
60	9.69 897		9.76 144		0.23 856	9.93 753		0
'	L. Cos.	d.	L. Cot.	c.d.	L. Tan.	L. Sin.	d.	'

119° (299°)   **(240°) 60°**

P. P.

"	30	29	23
1	0.5	0.5	0.4
2	1.0	1.0	0.8
3	1.5	1.4	1.2
4	2.0	1.9	1.5
5	2.5	2.4	1.9
6	3.0	2.9	2.3
7	3.5	3.4	2.7
8	4.0	3.9	3.1
9	4.5	4.4	3.4
10	5.0	4.8	3.8
20	10.0	9.7	7.7
30	15.0	14.5	11.5
40	20.0	19.3	15.3
50	25.0	24.2	19.2

"	22	8	7
1	0.4	0.1	0.1
2	0.7	0.3	0.2
3	1.1	0.4	0.4
4	1.5	0.5	0.5
5	1.8	0.7	0.6
6	2.2	0.8	0.7
7	2.6	0.9	0.8
8	2.9	1.1	0.9
9	3.3	1.2	1.0
10	3.7	1.3	1.2
20	7.3	2.7	2.3
30	11.0	4.0	3.5
40	14.7	5.3	4.7
50	18.3	6.7	5.8

	8 / 30	8 / 29
0	1.9	1.8
1	5.6	5.4
2	9.4	9.1
3	13.1	12.7
4	16.9	16.3
5	20.6	19.9
6	24.4	23.6
7	28.1	27.2
8		

	7 / 30	7 / 29
0	2.1	2.1
1	6.4	6.2
2	10.7	10.4
3	15.0	14.5
4	19.3	18.6
5	23.6	22.8
6	27.9	26.9
7		

COMMON LOGARITHMS OF THE TRIGONOMETRIC FUNCTIONS (Continued)

30° (210°)   **(329°) 149°**

'	L. Sin.	d.	L. Tan.	c.d.	L. Cot.	L. Cos.	d.	'
0	9.69 897	22	9.76 144	29	0.23 856	9.93 753	7	60
1	9.69 919	22	9.76 173	29	0.23 827	9.93 746	8	59
2	9.69 941	22	9.76 202	29	0.23 798	9.93 738	7	58
3	9.69 963	21	9.76 231	30	0.23 769	9.93 731	7	57
4	9.69 984	22	9.76 261	29	0.23 739	9.93 724	7	56
5	9.70 006	22	9.76 290	29	0.23 710	9.93 717	8	55
6	9.70 028	22	9.76 319	29	0.23 681	9.93 709	7	54
7	9.70 050	22	9.76 348	29	0.23 652	9.93 702	7	53
8	9.70 072	21	9.76 377	29	0.23 623	9.93 695	8	52
9	9.70 093	22	9.76 406	29	0.23 594	9.93 687	7	51
10	9.70 115	22	9.76 435	29	0.23 565	9.93 680	7	50
11	9.70 137	22	9.76 464	29	0.23 536	9.93 673	8	49
12	9.70 159	21	9.76 493	29	0.23 507	9.93 665	7	48
13	9.70 180	22	9.76 522	29	0.23 478	9.93 658	8	47
14	9.70 202	22	9.76 551	29	0.23 449	9.93 650	7	46
15	9.70 224	21	9.76 580	29	0.23 420	9.93 643	7	45
16	9.70 245	22	9.76 609	30	0.23 391	9.93 636	8	44
17	9.70 267	21	9.76 639	29	0.23 361	9.93 628	7	43
18	9.70 288	22	9.76 668	29	0.23 332	9.93 621	7	42
19	9.70 310	22	9.76 697	28	0.23 303	9.93 614	8	41
20	9.70 332	21	9.76 725	29	0.23 275	9.93 606	7	40
21	9.70 353	22	9.76 754	29	0.23 246	9.93 599	8	39
22	9.70 375	21	9.76 783	29	0.23 217	9.93 591	7	38
23	9.70 396	22	9.76 812	29	0.23 188	9.93 584	7	37
24	9.70 418	21	9.76 841	29	0.23 159	9.93 577	8	36
25	9.70 439	22	9.76 870	29	0.23 130	9.93 569	7	35
26	9.70 461	21	9.76 899	29	0.23 101	9.93 562	8	34
27	9.70 482	22	9.76 928	29	0.23 072	9.93 554	7	33
28	9.70 504	21	9.76 957	29	0.23 043	9.93 547	8	32
29	9.70 525	22	9.76 986	29	0.23 014	9.93 539	7	31
30	9.70 547	21	9.77 015	29	0.22 985	9.93 532	7	30
31	9.70 568	22	9.77 044	29	0.22 956	9.93 525	8	29
32	9.70 590	21	9.77 073	28	0.22 927	9.93 517	7	28
33	9.70 611	22	9.77 101	29	0.22 899	9.93 510	8	27
34	9.70 633	21	9.77 130	29	0.22 870	9.93 502	7	26
35	9.70 654	21	9.77 159	29	0.22 841	9.93 495	8	25
36	9.70 675	22	9.77 188	29	0.22 812	9.93 487	8	24
37	9.70 697	21	9.77 217	29	0.22 783	9.93 480	8	23
38	9.70 718	21	9.77 246	28	0.22 754	9.93 472	8	22
39	9.70 739	22	9.77 274	29	0.22 726	9.93 465	8	21
40	9.70 761	21	9.77 303	29	0.22 697	9.93 457	7	20
41	9.70 782	21	9.77 332	29	0.22 668	9.93 450	8	19
42	9.70 803	21	9.77 361	29	0.22 639	9.93 442	7	18
43	9.70 824	22	9.77 390	28	0.22 610	9.93 435	8	17
44	9.70 846	21	9.77 418	29	0.22 582	9.93 427	7	16
45	9.70 867	21	9.77 447	29	0.22 553	9.93 420	8	15
46	9.70 888	21	9.77 476	29	0.22 524	9.93 412	8	14
47	9.70 909	22	9.77 505	28	0.22 495	9.93 405	8	13
48	9.70 931	21	9.77 533	29	0.22 467	9.93 397	8	12
49	9.70 952	21	9.77 562	29	0.22 438	9.93 390	8	11
50	9.70 973	21	9.77 591	28	0.22 409	9.93 382	7	10
51	9.70 994	21	9.77 619	29	0.22 381	9.93 375	8	9
52	9.71 015	21	9.77 648	29	0.22 352	9.93 367	7	8
53	9.71 036	22	9.77 677	29	0.22 323	9.93 360	8	7
54	9.71 058	21	9.77 706	28	0.22 294	9.93 352	8	6
55	9.71 079	21	9.77 734	29	0.22 266	9.93 344	7	5
56	9.71 100	21	9.77 763	28	0.22 237	9.93 337	8	4
57	9.71 121	21	9.77 791	29	0.22 209	9.93 329	7	3
58	9.71 142	21	9.77 820	29	0.22 180	9.93 322	8	2
59	9.71 163	21	9.77 849	28	0.22 151	9.93 314	7	1
60	9.71 184		9.77 877		0.22 123	9.93 307		0

'	L. Cos.	d.	L. Cot.	c.d.	L. Tan.	L. Sin.	d.	'

120° (300°)   **(239°) 59°**

P. P.

''	30	29	28
1	0.5	0.5	0.5
2	1.0	1.0	0.9
3	1.5	1.4	1.4
4	2.0	1.9	1.9
5	2.5	2.4	2.3
6	3.0	2.9	2.8
7	3.5	3.4	3.3
8	4.0	3.9	3.7
9	4.5	4.4	4.2
10	5.0	4.8	4.7
20	10.0	9.7	9.3
30	15.0	14.5	14.0
40	20.0	19.3	18.7
50	25.0	24.2	23.3

''	22	21
1	0.4	0.4
2	0.7	0.7
3	1.1	1.0
4	1.5	1.4
5	1.8	1.8
6	2.2	2.1
7	2.6	2.4
8	2.9	2.8
9	3.3	3.2
10	3.7	3.5
20	7.3	7.0
30	11.0	10.5
40	14.7	14.0
50	18.3	17.5

''	8	7
1	0.1	0.1
2	0.3	0.2
3	0.4	0.4
4	0.5	0.5
5	0.7	0.6
6	0.8	0.7
7	0.9	0.8
8	1.1	0.9
9	1.2	1.0
10	1.3	1.2
20	2.7	2.3
30	4.0	3.5
40	5.3	4.7
50	6.7	5.8

	7	7	7
	30	29	28
0			
1	2.1	2.1	2.0
2	6.4	6.2	6.0
3	10.7	10.4	10.0
4	15.0	14.5	14.0
5	19.3	18.6	18.0
6	23.6	22.8	22.0
7	27.9	26.9	26.0

P. P.

COMMON LOGARITHMS OF THE TRIGONOMETRIC FUNCTIONS (Continued)

31° (211°)   (328°) **148°**

'	L. Sin.	d.	L. Tan.	c.d.	L. Cot.	L. Cos.	d.	'
0	9.71 184	21	9.77 877	29	0.22 123	9.93 307	8	60
1	9.71 205	21	9.77 906	29	0.22 094	9.93 299	8	59
2	9.71 226	21	9.77 935	28	0.22 065	9.93 291	7	58
3	9.71 247	21	9.77 963	29	0.22 037	9.93 284	8	57
4	9.71 268	21	9.77 992	28	0.22 008	9.93 276	7	56
5	9.71 289	21	9.78 020	29	0.21 980	9.93 269	8	55
6	9.71 310	21	9.78 049	28	0.21 951	9.93 261	8	54
7	9.71 331	21	9.78 077	29	0.21 923	9.93 253	7	53
8	9.71 352	21	9.78 106	28	0.21 894	9.93 246	8	52
9	9.71 373	20	9.78 135	28	0.21 865	9.93 238	8	51
10	9.71 393	21	9.78 163	29	0.21 837	9.93 230	7	50
11	9.71 414	21	9.78 192	28	0.21 808	9.93 223	8	49
12	9.71 435	21	9.78 220	29	0.21 780	9.93 215	8	48
13	9.71 456	21	9.78 249	28	0.21 751	9.93 207	7	47
14	9.71 477	21	9.78 277	29	0.21 723	9.93 200	8	46
15	9.71 498	21	9.78 306	28	0.21 694	9.93 192	8	45
16	9.71 519	20	9.78 334	29	0.21 666	9.93 184	7	44
17	9.71 539	21	9.78 363	28	0.21 637	9.93 177	8	43
18	9.71 560	21	9.78 391	28	0.21 609	9.93 169	8	42
19	9.71 581	21	9.78 419	29	0.21 581	9.93 161	7	41
20	9.71 602	20	9.78 448	28	0.21 552	9.93 154	8	40
21	9.71 622	21	9.78 476	29	0.21 524	9.93 146	8	39
22	9.71 643	21	9.78 505	28	0.21 495	9.93 138	7	38
23	9.71 664	21	9.78 533	29	0.21 467	9.93 131	8	37
24	9.71 685	20	9.78 562	28	0.21 438	9.93 123	8	36
25	9.71 705	21	9.78 590	28	0.21 410	9.93 115	7	35
26	9.71 726	21	9.78 618	29	0.21 382	9.93 108	8	34
27	9.71 747	21	9.78 647	28	0.21 353	9.93 100	8	33
28	9.71 767	21	9.78 675	29	0.21 325	9.93 092	8	32
29	9.71 788	21	9.78 704	28	0.21 296	9.93 084	7	31
30	9.71 809	20	9.78 732	28	0.21 268	9.93 077	8	30
31	9.71 829	21	9.78 760	29	0.21 240	9.93 069	8	29
32	9.71 850	20	9.78 789	28	0.21 211	9.93 061	8	28
33	9.71 870	21	9.78 817	28	0.21 183	9.93 053	7	27
34	9.71 891	20	9.78 845	29	0.21 155	9.93 046	8	26
35	9.71 911	21	9.78 874	28	0.21 126	9.93 038	8	25
36	9.71 932	20	9.78 902	28	0.21 098	9.93 030	8	24
37	9.71 952	21	9.78 930	29	0.21 070	9.93 022	8	23
38	9.71 973	21	9.78 959	28	0.21 041	9.93 014	7	22
39	9.71 994	20	9.78 987	28	0.21 013	9.93 007	8	21
40	9.72 014	20	9.79 015	28	0.20 985	9.92 999	8	20
41	9.72 034	20	9.79 043	29	0.20 957	9.92 991	8	19
42	9.72 053	20	9.79 072	28	0.20 928	9.92 983	7	18
43	9.72 075	21	9.79 100	28	0.20 900	9.92 976	8	17
44	9.72 096	20	9.79 128	28	0.20 872	9.92 968	8	16
45	9.72 116	21	9.79 156	29	0.20 844	9.92 960	8	15
46	9.72 137	20	9.79 185	28	0.20 815	9.92 952	8	14
47	9.72 157	20	9.79 213	28	0.20 787	9.92 944	8	13
48	9.72 177	21	9.79 241	28	0.20 759	9.92 936	7	12
49	9.72 198	20	9.79 269	28	0.20 731	9.92 929	8	11
50	9.72 218	20	9.79 297	29	0.20 703	9.92 921	8	10
51	9.72 238	21	9.79 326	28	0.20 674	9.92 913	8	9
52	9.72 259	20	9.79 354	28	0.20 646	9.92 905	8	8
53	9.72 279	20	9.79 382	28	0.20 618	9.92 897	8	7
54	9.72 299	21	9.79 410	28	0.20 590	9.92 889	8	6
55	9.72 320	20	9.79 438	28	0.20 562	9.92 881	7	5
56	9.72 340	20	9.79 466	29	0.20 534	9.92 874	8	4
57	9.72 360	21	9.79 495	28	0.20 505	9.92 866	8	3
58	9.72 381	20	9.79 523	28	0.20 477	9.92 858	8	2
59	9.72 401	20	9.79 551	28	0.20 449	9.92 850	8	1
60	9.72 421		9.79 579		0.20 421	9.92 842		0

'	L. Cos.	d.	L. Cot.	c.d.	L. Tan.	L.Sin.	d.	'

121° (301°)   (238°) **58°**

P. P.

"	29	28
1	0.5	0.5
2	1.0	0.9
3	1.4	1.4
4	1.9	1.9
5	2.4	2.3
6	2.9	2.8
7	3.4	3.3
8	3.9	3.7
9	4.4	4.2
10	4.8	4.7
20	9.7	9.3
30	14.5	14.0
40	19.3	18.7
50	24.2	23.3

"	21	20
1	0.4	0.3
2	0.7	0.7
3	1.0	1.0
4	1.4	1.3
5	1.8	1.7
6	2.1	2.0
7	2.4	2.3
8	2.8	2.7
9	3.2	3.0
10	3.5	3.3
20	7.0	6.7
30	10.5	10.0
40	14.0	13.3
50	17.5	16.7

"	8	7
1	0.1	0.1
2	0.3	0.2
3	0.4	0.4
4	0.5	0.5
5	0.7	0.6
6	0.8	0.7
7	0.9	0.8
8	1.1	0.9
9	1.2	1.0
10	1.3	1.2
20	2.7	2.3
30	4.0	3.5
40	5.3	4.7
50	6.7	5.8

	8 / 30	8 / 29	8 / 28
0			
1	1.9	1.8	1.8
2	5.6	5.4	5.2
3	9.4	9.1	8.8
4	13.1	12.7	12.2
5	16.9	16.3	15.8
6	20.6	19.9	19.2
7	24.4	23.6	22.8
8	28.1	27.2	26.2

COMMON LOGARITHMS OF THE TRIGONOMETRIC
FUNCTIONS (Continued)

32° (212°)   **(327°) 147°**

′	L. Sin.	d.	L. Tan.	c.d.	L. Cot.	L. Cos.	d.	′	P. P.		
0	9.72 421	20	9.79 579	28	0.20 421	9.92 842	8	60				
1	9.72 441	20	9.79 607	28	0.20 393	9.92 834	8	59	″	**29**	**28**	**27**
2	9.72 461	21	9.79 635	28	0.20 365	9.92 826	8	58	1	0.5	0.5	0.4
3	9.72 482	20	9.79 663	28	0.20 337	9.92 818	8	57	2	1.0	0.9	0.9
4	9.72 502	20	9.79 691	28	0.20 309	9.92 810	7	56	3	1.4	1.4	1.4
									4	1.9	1.9	1.8
5	9.72 522	20	9.79 719	28	0.20 281	9.92 803	8	55				
6	9.72 542	20	9.79 747	29	0.20 253	9.92 795	8	54	5	2.4	2.3	2.2
7	9.72 562	20	9.79 776	28	0.20 224	9.92 787	8	53	6	2.9	2.8	2.7
8	9.72 582	20	9.79 804	28	0.20 196	9.92 779	8	52	7	3.4	3.3	3.2
9	9.72 602	20	9.79 832	28	0.20 168	9.92 771	8	51	8	3.9	3.7	3.6
									9	4.4	4.2	4.0
10	9.72 622	21	9.79 860	28	0.20 140	9.92 763	8	50				
11	9.72 643	20	9.79 888	28	0.20 112	9.92 755	8	49	10	4.8	4.7	4.5
12	9.72 663	20	9.79 916	28	0.20 084	9.92 747	8	48	20	9.7	9.3	9.0
13	9.72 683	20	9.79 944	28	0.20 056	9.92 739	8	47	30	14.5	14.0	13.5
14	9.72 703	20	9.79 972	28	0.20 028	9.92 731	8	46	40	19.3	18.7	18.0
									50	24.2	23.3	22.5
15	9.72 723	20	9.80 000	28	0.20 000	9.92 723	8	45				
16	9.72 743	20	9.80 028	28	0.19 972	9.92 715	8	44	″	**21**	**20**	**19**
17	9.72 763	20	9.80 056	28	0.19 944	9.92 707	8	43	1	0.4	0.3	0.3
18	9.72 783	20	9.80 084	28	0.19 916	9.92 699	8	42	2	0.7	0.7	0.6
19	9.72 803	20	9.80 112	28	0.19 888	9.92 691	8	41	3	1.0	1.0	1.0
									4	1.4	1.3	1.3
20	9.72 823	20	9.80 140	28	0.19 860	9.92 683	8	40				
21	9.72 843	20	9.80 168	27	0.19 832	9.92 675	8	39	5	1.8	1.7	1.6
22	9.72 863	20	9.80 195	28	0.19 805	9.92 667	8	38	6	2.1	2.0	1.9
23	9.72 883	19	9.80 223	28	0.19 777	9.92 659	8	37	7	2.4	2.3	2.2
24	9.72 902	20	9.80 251	28	0.19 749	9.92 651	8	36	8	2.8	2.7	2.5
									9	3.2	3.0	2.8
25	9.72 922	20	9.80 279	28	0.19 721	9.92 643	8	35				
26	9.72 942	20	9.80 307	28	0.19 693	9.92 635	8	34	10	3.5	3.3	3.2
27	9.72 962	20	9.80 335	28	0.19 665	9.92 627	8	33	20	7.0	6.7	6.3
28	9.72 982	20	9.80 363	28	0.19 637	9.92 619	8	32	30	10.5	10.0	9.5
29	9.73 002	20	9.80 391	28	0.19 609	9.92 611	8	31	40	14.0	13.3	12.7
									50	17.5	16.7	15.8
30	9.73 022	19	9.80 419	28	0.19 581	9.92 603	8	30				
31	9.73 041	20	9.80 447	27	0.19 553	9.92 595	8	29	″	**9**	**8**	**7**
32	9.73 061	20	9.80 474	28	0.19 526	9.92 587	8	28	1	0.2	0.1	0.1
33	9.73 081	20	9.80 502	28	0.19 498	9.92 579	8	27	2	0.3	0.3	0.2
34	9.73 101	20	9.80 530	28	0.19 470	9.92 571	8	26	3	0.4	0.4	0.4
									4	0.6	0.5	0.5
35	9.73 121	19	9.80 558	28	0.19 442	9.92 563	8	25				
36	9.73 140	20	9.80 586	28	0.19 414	9.92 555	9	24	5	0.8	0.7	0.6
37	9.73 160	20	9.80 614	28	0.19 386	9.92 546	8	23	6	0.9	0.8	0.7
38	9.73 180	20	9.80 642	27	0.19 358	9.92 538	8	22	7	1.0	0.9	0.8
39	9.73 200	19	9.80 669	28	0.19 331	9.92 530	8	21	8	1.2	1.1	0.9
									9	1.4	1.2	1.0
40	9.73 219	20	9.80 697	28	0.19 303	9.92 522	8	20				
41	9.73 239	20	9.80 725	28	0.19 275	9.92 514	8	19	10	1.5	1.3	1.2
42	9.73 259	19	9.80 753	28	0.19 247	9.92 506	8	18	20	3.0	2.7	2.3
43	9.73 278	20	9.80 781	27	0.19 219	9.92 498	8	17	30	4.5	4.0	3.5
44	9.73 298	20	9.80 808	28	0.19 192	9.92 490	8	16	40	6.0	5.3	4.7
									50	7.5	6.7	5.8
45	9.73 318	19	9.80 836	28	0.19 164	9.92 482	9	15				
46	9.73 337	20	9.80 864	28	0.19 136	9.92 473	8	14				
47	9.73 357	20	9.80 892	27	0.19 108	9.92 465	8	13				
48	9.73 377	19	9.80 919	28	0.19 081	9.92 457	8	12		**8**	**8**	**7**
49	9.73 396	20	9.80 947	28	0.19 053	9.92 449	8	11		**29**	**28**	**28**
50	9.73 416	19	9.80 975	28	0.19 025	9.92 441	8	10				
51	9.73 435	20	9.81 003	27	0.18 997	9.92 433	8	9	0			
52	9.73 455	19	9.81 030	28	0.18 970	9.92 425	9	8	1	1.8	1.8	2.0
53	9.73 474	20	9.81 058	28	0.18 942	9.92 416	8	7	2	5.4	5.2	6.0
54	9.73 494	19	9.81 086	27	0.18 914	9.92 408	8	6	3	9.1	8.8	10.0
									4	12.7	12.2	14.0
55	9.73 513	20	9.81 113	28	0.18 887	9.92 400	8	5	5	16.3	15.8	18.0
56	9.73 533	19	9.81 141	28	0.18 859	9.92 392	8	4	6	19.9	19.2	22.0
57	9.73 552	20	9.81 169	27	0.18 831	9.92 384	8	3	7	23.6	22.8	26.0
58	9.73 572	19	9.81 196	28	0.18 804	9.92 376	9	2	8	27.2	26.2	—
59	9.73 591	20	9.81 224	28	0.18 776	9.92 367	8	1				
60	9.73 611		9.81 252		0.18 748	9.92 359		0				
′	L. Cos.	d.	L. Cot.	c.d.	L. Tan.	L. Sin.	d.	′	P. P.		

122° (302°)   **(237°) 57°**

COMMON LOGARITHMS OF THE TRIGONOMETRIC
FUNCTIONS (Continued)

33° (213°)   **(326°) 146°**

′	L. Sin.	d.	L. Tan.	c.d.	L. Cot.	L. Cos.	d.	′		P. P.	
0	9.73 611	19	9.81 252	27	0.18 748	9.92 359	8	60			
1	9.73 630	20	9.81 279	28	0.18 721	9.92 351	8	59	″	**28**	**27**
2	9.73 650	19	9.81 307	28	0.18 693	9.92 343	8	58	1	0.5	0.4
3	9.73 669	20	9.81 335	27	0.18 665	9.92 335	9	57	2	0.9	0.9
4	9.73 689	19	9.81 362	28	0.18 638	9.92 326	8	56	3	1.4	1.4
									4	1.9	1.8
5	9.73 708	19	9.81 390	28	0.18 610	9.92 318	8	55			
6	9.73 727	20	9.81 418	27	0.18 582	9.92 310	8	54	5	2.3	2.2
7	9.73 747	19	9.81 445	28	0.18 555	9.92 302	9	53	6	2.8	2.7
8	9.73 766	19	9.81 473	27	0.18 527	9.92 293	8	52	7	3.3	3.2
9	9.73 785	20	9.81 500	28	0.18 500	9.92 285	8	51	8	3.7	3.6
									9	4.2	4.0
10	9.73 805	19	9.81 528	28	0.18 472	9.92 277	8	50			
11	9.73 824	19	9.81 556	27	0.18 444	9.92 269	9	49	10	4.7	4.5
12	9.73 843	20	9.81 583	28	0.18 417	9.92 260	8	48	20	9.3	9.0
13	9.73 863	19	9.81 611	27	0.18 389	9.92 252	8	47	30	14.0	13.5
14	9.73 882	19	9.81 638	28	0.18 362	9.92 244	9	46	40	18.7	18.0
									50	23.3	22.5
15	9.73 901	20	9.81 666	27	0.18 334	9.92 235	8	45			
16	9.73 921	19	9.81 693	28	0.18 307	9.92 227	8	44	″	**20**	**19** **18**
17	9.73 940	19	9.81 721	27	0.18 279	9.92 219	8	43	1	0.3	0.3 0.3
18	9.73 959	19	9.81 748	28	0.18 252	9.92 211	9	42	2	0.7	0.6 0.6
19	9.73 978	19	9.81 776	27	0.18 224	9.92 202	8	41	3	1.0	1.0 0.9
									4	1.3	1.3 1.2
20	9.73 997	20	9.81 803	28	0.18 197	9.92 194	8	40			
21	9.74 017	19	9.81 831	27	0.18 169	9.92 186	9	39	5	1.7	1.6 1.5
22	9.74 036	19	9.81 858	28	0.18 142	9.92 177	8	38	6	2.0	1.9 1.8
23	9.74 055	19	9.81 886	27	0.18 114	9.92 169	8	37	7	2.3	2.2 2.1
24	9.74 074	19	9.81 913	28	0.18 087	9.92 161	9	36	8	2.7	2.5 2.4
									9	3.0	2.8 2.7
25	9.74 093	20	9.81 941	27	0.18 059	9.92 152	8	35			
26	9.74 113	19	9.81 968	28	0.18 032	9.92 144	8	34	10	3.3	3.2 3.0
27	9.74 132	19	9.81 996	27	0.18 004	9.92 136	9	33	20	6.7	6.3 6.0
28	9.74 151	19	9.82 023	28	0.17 977	9.92 127	8	32	30	10.0	9.5 9.0
29	9.74 170	19	9.82 051	27	0.17 949	9.92 119	8	31	40	13.3	12.7 12.0
									50	16.7	15.8 15.0
30	9.74 189	19	9.82 078	28	0.17 922	9.92 111	9	30			
31	9.74 208	19	9.82 106	27	0.17 894	9.92 102	8	29	″	**9**	**8**
32	9.74 227	19	9.82 133	28	0.17 867	9.92 094	8	28	1	0.2	0.1
33	9.74 246	19	9.82 161	27	0.17 839	9.92 086	9	27	2	0.3	0.3
34	9.74 265	19	9.82 188	27	0.17 812	9.92 077	8	26	3	0.4	0.4
									4	0.6	0.5
35	9.74 284	19	9.82 215	28	0.17 785	9.92 069	9	25			
36	9.74 303	19	9.82 243	27	0.17 757	9.92 060	8	24	5	0.8	0.7
37	9.74 322	19	9.82 270	28	0.17 730	9.92 052	8	23	6	0.9	0.8
38	9.74 341	19	9.82 298	27	0.17 702	9.92 044	9	22	7	1.0	0.9
39	9.74 360	19	9.82 325	27	0.17 675	9.92 035	8	21	8	1.2	1.1
									9	1.4	1.2
40	9.74 379	19	9.82 352	28	0.17 648	9.92 027	9	20			
41	9.74 398	19	9.82 380	27	0.17 620	9.92 018	8	19	10	1.5	1.3
42	9.74 417	19	9.82 407	28	0.17 593	9.92 010	8	18	20	3.0	2.7
43	9.74 436	19	9.82 435	27	0.17 565	9.92 002	9	17	30	4.5	4.0
44	9.74 455	19	9.82 462	27	0.17 538	9.91 993	8	16	40	6.0	5.3
									50	7.5	6.7
45	9.74 474	19	9.82 489	28	0.17 511	9.91 985	9	15			
46	9.74 493	19	9.82 517	27	0.17 483	9.91 976	9	14			
47	9.74 512	19	9.82 544	27	0.17 456	9.91 968	9	13			
48	9.74 531	18	9.82 571	28	0.17 429	9.91 959	8	12		**9**	**9** **8**
49	9.74 549	19	9.82 599	27	0.17 401	9.91 951	9	11		28	27 27
50	9.74 568	19	9.82 626	27	C.17 374	9.91 942	8	10	0		
51	9.74 587	19	9.82 653	28	0.17 347	9.91 934	9	9	1	1.6	1.5 1.7
52	9.74 606	19	9.82 681	27	0.17 319	9.91 925	9	8	2	4.7	4.5 5.1
53	9.74 625	19	9.82 708	27	0.17 292	9.91 917	9	7	3	7.8	7.5 8.4
54	9.74 644	18	9.82 735	27	0.17 265	9.91 908	8	6	4	10.9	10.5 11.8
									5	14.0	13.5 15.2
55	9.74 662	19	9.82 762	28	0.17 238	9.91 900	9	5	6	17.1	16.5 18.6
56	9.74 681	19	9.82 790	27	0.17 210	9.91 891	8	4	7	20.2	19.5 21.9
57	9.74 700	19	9.82 817	27	0.17 183	9.91 883	9	3	8	23.3	22.5 25.3
58	9.74 719	18	9.82 844	27	0.17 156	9.91 874	8	2	9	26.4	25.5 —
59	9.74 737	19	9.82 871	28	0.17 129	9.91 866	9	1			
60	9.74 756		9.82 899		0.17 101	9.91 857		0			
′	L. Cos.	d.	L. Cot.	c.d.	L. Tan.	L. Sin.	d.	′		P. P.	

123° (303°)   **(236°) 56°**

COMMON LOGARITHMS OF THE TRIGONOMETRIC FUNCTIONS (Continued)

34° (214°)   **(325°) 145°**

'	L. Sin.	d.	L. Tan.	c.d.	L. Cot.	L. Cos.	d.	'
0	9.74 756	19	9.82 899	27	0.17 101	9.91 857	8	60
1	9.74 775	19	9.82 926	27	0.17 074	9.91 849	9	59
2	9.74 794	18	9.82 953	27	0.17 047	9.91 840	8	58
3	9.74 812	19	9.82 980	28	0.17 020	9.91 832	9	57
4	9.74 831	19	9.83 008	27	0.16 992	9.91 823	8	56
5	9.74 850	18	9.83 035	27	0.16 965	9.91 815	9	55
6	9.74 868	19	9.83 062	27	0.16 938	9.91 806	9	54
7	9.74 887	19	9.83 089	28	0.16 911	9.91 798	9	53
8	9.74 906	18	9.83 117	27	0.16 883	9.91 789	8	52
9	9.74 924	19	9.83 144	27	0.16 856	9.91 781	9	51
10	9.74 943	18	9.83 171	27	0.16 829	9.91 772	9	50
11	9.74 961	19	9.83 198	27	0.16 802	9.91 763	8	49
12	9.74 980	19	9.83 225	27	0.16 775	9.91 755	9	48
13	9.74 999	18	9.83 252	28	0.16 748	9.91 746	8	47
14	9.75 017	19	9.83 280	27	0.16 720	9.91 738	8	46
15	9.75 036	18	9.83 307	27	0.16 693	9.91 729	9	45
16	9.75 054	19	9.83 334	27	0.16 666	9.91 720	8	44
17	9.75 073	18	9.83 361	27	0.16 639	9.91 712	9	43
18	9.75 091	19	9.83 388	27	0.16 612	9.91 703	8	42
19	9.75 110	18	9.83 415	27	0.16 585	9.91 695	9	41
20	9.75 128	19	9.83 442	28	0.16 558	9.91 686	9	40
21	9.75 147	18	9.83 470	27	0.16 530	9.91 677	8	39
22	9.75 165	19	9.83 497	27	0.16 503	9.91 669	9	38
23	9.75 184	18	9.83 524	27	0.16 476	9.91 660	9	37
24	9.75 202	19	9.83 551	27	0.16 449	9.91 651	8	36
25	9.75 221	18	9.83 578	27	0.16 422	9.91 643	9	35
26	9.75 239	19	9.83 605	27	0.16 395	9.91 634	9	34
27	9.75 258	18	9.83 632	27	0.16 368	9.91 625	8	33
28	9.75 276	18	9.83 659	27	0.16 341	9.91 617	9	32
29	9.75 294	19	9.83 686	27	0.16 314	9.91 608	8	31
30	9.75 313	18	9.83 713	27	0.16 287	9.91 599	8	30
31	9.75 331	19	9.83 740	28	0.16 260	9.91 591	9	29
32	9.75 350	18	9.83 768	27	0.16 232	9.91 582	9	28
33	9.75 368	18	9.83 795	27	0.16 205	9.91 573	8	27
34	9.75 386	19	9.83 822	27	0.16 178	9.91 565	9	26
35	9.75 405	18	9.83 849	27	0.16 151	9.91 556	9	25
36	9.75 423	18	9.83 876	27	0.16 124	9.91 547	9	24
37	9.75 441	18	9.83 903	27	0.16 097	9.91 538	8	23
38	9.75 459	19	9.83 930	27	0.16 070	9.91 530	9	22
39	9.75 478	18	9.83 957	27	0.16 043	9.91 521	9	21
40	9.75 496	18	9.83 984	27	0.16 016	9.91 512	8	20
41	9.75 514	19	9.84 011	27	0.15 989	9.91 504	9	19
42	9.75 533	18	9.84 038	27	0.15 962	9.91 495	9	18
43	9.75 551	18	9.84 065	27	0.15 935	9.91 486	9	17
44	9.75 569	18	9.84 092	27	0.15 908	9.91 477	8	16
45	9.75 587	18	9.84 119	27	0.15 881	9.91 469	9	15
46	9.75 605	19	9.84 146	27	0.15 854	9.91 460	9	14
47	9.75 624	18	9.84 173	27	0.15 827	9.91 451	9	13
48	9.75 642	18	9.84 200	27	0.15 800	9.91 442	9	12
49	9.75 660	18	9.84 227	27	0.15 773	9.91 433	8	11
50	9.75 678	18	9.84 254	26	0.15 746	9.91 425	9	10
51	9.75 696	18	9.84 280	27	0.15 720	9.91 416	9	9
52	9.75 714	19	9.84 307	27	0.15 693	9.91 407	9	8
53	9.75 733	18	9.84 334	27	0.15 666	9.91 398	8	7
54	9.75 751	18	9.84 361	27	0.15 639	9.91 389	9	6
55	9.75 769	18	9.84 388	27	0.15 612	9.91 381	9	5
56	9.75 787	18	9.84 415	27	0.15 585	9.91 372	9	4
57	9.75 805	18	9.84 442	27	0.15 558	9.91 363	9	3
58	9.75 823	18	9.84 469	27	0.15 531	9.91 354	9	2
59	9.75 841	18	9.84 496	27	0.15 504	9.91 345	9	1
60	9.75 859		9.84 523		0.15 477	9.91 336		0
'	L. Cos.	d.	L. Cot.	c.d.	L. Tan.	L. Sin.	d.	'

P. P.

"	28	27	26
1	0.5	0.4	0.4
2	0.9	0.9	0.9
3	1.4	1.4	1.3
4	1.9	1.8	1.7
5	2.3	2.2	2.2
6	2.8	2.7	2.6
7	3.3	3.2	3.0
8	3.7	3.6	3.5
9	4.2	4.0	3.9
10	4.7	4.5	4.3
20	9.3	9.0	8.7
30	14.0	13.5	13.0
40	18.7	18.0	17.3
50	23.3	22.5	21.7

"	19	18
1	0.3	0.3
2	0.6	0.6
3	1.0	0.9
4	1.3	1.2
5	1.6	1.5
6	1.9	1.8
7	2.2	2.1
8	2.5	2.4
9	2.8	2.7
10	3.2	3.0
20	6.3	6.0
30	9.5	9.0
40	12.7	12.0
50	15.8	15.0

"	9	8
1	0.2	0.1
2	0.3	0.3
3	0.4	0.4
4	0.6	0.5
5	0.8	0.7
6	0.9	0.8
7	1.0	0.9
8	1.2	1.1
9	1.4	1.2
10	1.5	1.3
20	3.0	2.7
30	4.5	4.0
40	6.0	5.3
50	7.5	6.7

	9	8	8
	28	28	27
0	1.6	1.8	1.7
1	4.7	5.2	5.1
2	7.8	8.8	8.4
3	10.9	12.2	11.8
4	14.0	15.8	15.2
5	17.1	19.2	18.6
6	20.2	22.8	21.9
7	23.3	26.2	25.3
8	26.4	—	—
9			

P. P.

COMMON LOGARITHMS OF THE TRIGONOMETRIC FUNCTIONS (Continued)

35° (215°)   **(324°) 144°**

'	L. Sin.	d.	L. Tan.	c.d.	L. Cot.	L. Cos.	d.	'
0	9.75 859	18	9.84 523	27	0.15 477	9.91 336	8	60
1	9.75 877	18	9.84 550	26	0.15 450	9.91 328	9	59
2	9.75 895	18	9.84 576	27	0.15 424	9.91 319	9	58
3	9.75 913	18	9.84 603	27	0.15 397	9.91 310	9	57
4	9.75 931	18	9.84 630	27	0.15 370	9.91 301	9	56
5	9.75 949	18	9.84 657	27	0.15 343	9.91 292	9	55
6	9.75 967	18	9.84 684	27	0.15 316	9.91 283	9	54
7	9.75 985	18	9.84 711	27	0.15 289	9.91 274	8	53
8	9.76 003	18	9.84 738	26	0.15 262	9.91 266	9	52
9	9.76 021	18	9.84 764	27	0.15 236	9.91 257	9	51
10	9.76 039	18	9.84 791	27	0.15 209	9.91 248	9	50
11	9.76 057	18	9.84 818	27	0.15 182	9.91 239	9	49
12	9.76 075	18	9.84 845	27	0.15 155	9.91 230	9	48
13	9.76 093	18	9.84 872	27	0.15 128	9.91 221	9	47
14	9.76 111	18	9.84 899	26	0.15 101	9.91 212	9	46
15	9.76 129	17	9.84 925	27	0.15 075	9.91 203	9	45
16	9.76 146	18	9.84 952	27	0.15 048	9.91 194	9	44
17	9.76 164	18	9.84 979	27	0.15 021	9.91 185	9	43
18	9.76 182	18	9.85 006	27	0.14 994	9.91 176	9	42
19	9.76 200	18	9.85 033	26	0.14 967	9.91 167	9	41
20	9.76 218	18	9.85 059	27	0.14 941	9.91 158	9	40
21	9.76 236	17	9.85 086	27	0.14 914	9.91 149	8	39
22	9.76 253	18	9.85 113	27	0.14 887	9.91 141	9	38
23	9.76 271	18	9.85 140	26	0.14 860	9.91 132	9	37
24	9.76 289	18	9.85 166	27	0.14 834	9.91 123	9	36
25	9.76 307	17	9.85 193	27	0.14 807	9.91 114	9	35
26	9.76 324	18	9.85 220	27	0.14 780	9.91 105	9	34
27	9.76 342	18	9.85 247	26	0.14 753	9.91 096	9	33
28	9.76 360	18	9.85 273	27	0.14 727	9.91 087	9	32
29	9.76 378	17	9.85 300	27	0.14 700	9.91 078	9	31
30	9.76 395	18	9.85 327	27	0.14 673	9.91 069	9	30
31	9.76 413	18	9.85 354	26	0.14 646	9.91 060	9	29
32	9.76 431	17	9.85 380	27	0.14 620	9.91 051	9	28
33	9.76 448	18	9.85 407	27	0.14 593	9.91 042	9	27
34	9.76 466	18	9.85 434	26	0.14 566	9.91 033	10	26
35	9.76 484	17	9.85 460	27	0.14 540	9.91 023	9	25
36	9.76 501	18	9.85 487	27	0.14 513	9.91 014	9	24
37	9.76 519	18	9.85 514	26	0.14 486	9.91 005	9	23
38	9.76 537	17	9.85 540	27	0.14 460	9.90 996	9	22
39	9.76 554	18	9.85 567	27	0.14 433	9.90 987	9	21
40	9.76 572	18	9.85 594	26	0.14 406	9.90 978	9	20
41	9.76 590	17	9.85 620	27	0.14 380	9.90 969	9	19
42	9.76 607	18	9.85 647	27	0.14 353	9.90 960	9	18
43	9.76 625	17	9.85 674	26	0.14 326	9.90 951	9	17
44	9.76 642	18	9.85 700	27	0.14 300	9.90 942	9	16
45	9.76 660	17	9.85 727	27	0.14 273	9.90 933	9	15
46	9.76 677	18	9.85 754	26	0.14 246	9.90 924	9	14
47	9.76 695	17	9.85 780	27	0.14 220	9.90 915	9	13
48	9.76 712	18	9.85 807	27	0.14 193	9.90 906	10	12
49	9.76 730	17	9.85 834	26	0.14 166	9.90 896	9	11
50	9.76 747	18	9.85 860	27	0.14 140	9.90 887	9	10
51	9.76 765	17	9.85 887	27	0.14 113	9.90 878	9	9
52	9.76 782	18	9.85 913	27	0.14 087	9.90 869	9	8
53	9.76 800	17	9.85 940	27	0.14 060	9.90 860	9	7
54	9.76 817	18	9.85 967	26	0.14 033	9.90 851	9	6
55	9.76 835	17	9.85 993	27	0.14 007	9.90 842	10	5
56	9.76 852	18	9.86 020	26	0.13 980	9.90 832	9	4
57	9.76 870	17	9.86 046	27	0.13 954	9.90 823	9	3
58	9.76 887	17	9.86 073	27	0.13 927	9.90 814	9	2
59	9.76 904	18	9.86 100	26	0.13 900	9.90 805	9	1
60	9.76 922		9.86 126		0.13 874	9.90 796		0

'	L. Cos.	d.	L. Cot.	c.d.	L. Tan.	L. Sin.	d.	'

125° (305°)   **(234°) 54°**

P. P.

"	27	26	18
1	0.4	0.4	0.3
2	0.9	0.9	0.6
3	1.4	1.3	0.9
4	1.8	1.7	1.2
5	2.2	2.2	1.5
6	2.7	2.6	1.8
7	3.2	3.0	2.1
8	3.6	3.5	2.4
9	4.0	3.9	2.7
10	4.5	4.3	3.0
20	9.0	8.7	6.0
30	13.5	13.0	9.0
40	18.0	17.3	12.0
50	22.5	21.7	15.0

"	17	10	9	8
1	0.3	0.2	0.2	0.1
2	0.6	0.3	0.3	0.3
3	0.8	0.5	0.4	0.4
4	1.1	0.7	0.6	0.5
5	1.4	0.8	0.8	0.7
6	1.7	1.0	0.9	0.8
7	2.0	1.2	1.0	0.9
8	2.3	1.3	1.2	1.1
9	2.6	1.5	1.4	1.2
10	2.8	1.7	1.5	1.3
20	5.7	3.3	3.0	2.7
30	8.5	5.0	4.5	4.0
40	11.3	6.7	6.0	5.3
50	14.2	8.3	7.5	6.7

	10	10
	27	26
0		
1	1.4	1.3
2	4.1	3.9
3	6.8	6.5
4	9.4	9.1
5	12.2	11.7
6	14.8	14.3
7	17.6	16.9
8	20.2	19.5
9	22.9	22.1
10	25.6	24.7

	9	9
	27	26
0		
1	1.5	1.4
2	4.5	4.3
3	7.5	7.2
4	10.5	10.1
5	13.5	13.0
6	16.5	15.9
7	19.5	18.8
8	22.5	21.7
9	25.5	24.6

COMMON LOGARITHMS OF THE TRIGONOMETRIC FUNCTIONS (Continued)

36° (216°)　　　　　　　　　　　　　　　　　　　　　**(323°) 143°**

'	L. Sin.	d.	L. Tan.	c.d.	L. Cot	L. Cos.	d.	'
0	9.76 922	17	9.86 126	27	0.13 874	9.90 796	9	60
1	9.76 939	18	9.86 153	26	0.13 847	9.90 787	10	59
2	9.76 957	17	9.86 179	27	0.13 821	9.90 777	9	58
3	9.76 974	17	9.86 206	26	0.13 794	9.90 768	9	57
4	9.76 991	18	9.86 232	27	0.13 768	9.90 759	9	56
5	9.77 009	17	9.86 259	26	0.13 741	9.90 750	10	55
6	9.77 026	17	9.86 285	27	0.13 715	9.90 741	10	54
7	9.77 043	18	9.86 312	26	0.13 688	9.90 731	9	53
8	9.77 061	17	9.86 338	27	0.13 662	9.90 722	9	52
9	9.77 078	17	9.86 365	27	0.13 635	9.90 713	9	51
10	9.77 095	17	9.86 392	26	0.13 608	9.90 704	10	50
11	9.77 112	18	9.86 418	27	0.13 582	9.90 694	9	49
12	9.77 130	17	9.86 445	26	0.13 555	9.90 685	9	48
13	9.77 147	17	9.86 471	27	0.13 529	9.90 676	9	47
14	9.77 164	17	9.86 498	26	0.13 502	9.90 667	10	46
15	9.77 181	18	9.86 524	27	0.13 476	9.90 657	9	45
16	9.77 199	17	9.86 551	26	0.13 449	9.90 648	9	44
17	9.77 216	17	9.86 577	26	0.13 423	9.90 639	9	43
18	9.77 233	17	9.86 603	27	0.13 397	9.90 630	10	42
19	9.77 250	18	9.86 630	26	0.13 370	9.90 620	9	41
20	9.77 268	17	9.86 656	27	0.13 344	9.90 611	9	40
21	9.77 285	17	9.86 683	26	0.13 317	9.90 602	10	39
22	9.77 302	17	9.86 709	27	0.13 291	9.90 592	9	38
23	9.77 319	17	9.86 736	26	0.13 264	9.90 583	9	37
24	9.77 336	17	9.86 762	27	0.13 238	9.90 574	9	36
25	9.77 353	17	9.86 789	26	0.13 211	9.90 565	10	35
26	9.77 370	17	9.86 815	27	0.13 185	9.90 555	9	34
27	9.77 387	18	9.86 842	26	0.13 158	9.90 546	9	33
28	9.77 405	17	9.86 868	26	0.13 132	9.90 537	10	32
29	9.77 422	17	9.86 894	27	0.13 106	9.90 527	9	31
30	9.77 439	17	9.86 921	26	0.13 079	9.90 518	9	30
31	9.77 456	17	9.86 947	27	0.13 053	9.90 509	10	29
32	9.77 473	17	9.86 974	26	0.13 026	9.90 499	9	28
33	9.77 490	17	9.87 000	27	0.13 000	9.90 490	10	27
34	9.77 507	17	9.87 027	26	0.12 973	9.90 480	9	26
35	9.77 524	17	9.87 053	26	0.12 947	9.90 471	9	25
36	9.77 541	17	9.87 079	27	0.12 921	9.90 462	10	24
37	9.77 558	17	9.87 106	26	0.12 894	9.90 452	9	23
38	9.77 575	17	9.87 132	26	0.12 868	9.90 443	9	22
39	9.77 592	17	9.87 158	27	0.12 842	9.90 434	10	21
40	9.77 609	17	9.87 185	26	0.12 815	9.90 424	9	20
41	9.77 626	17	9.87 211	27	0.12 789	9.90 415	10	19
42	9.77 643	17	9.87 238	26	0.12 762	9.90 405	9	18
43	9.77 660	17	9.87 264	26	0.12 736	9.90 396	10	17
44	9.77 677	17	9.87 290	27	0.12 710	9.90 386	9	16
45	9.77 694	17	9.87 317	26	0.12 683	9.90 377	9	15
46	9.77 711	17	9.87 343	26	0.12 657	9.90 368	10	14
47	9.77 728	16	9.87 369	27	0.12 631	9.90 358	9	13
48	9.77 744	17	9.87 396	26	0.12 604	9.90 349	9	12
49	9.77 761	17	9.87 422	26	0.12 578	9.90 339	10	11
50	9.77 778	17	9.87 448	27	0.12 552	9.90 330	10	10
51	9.77 795	17	9.87 475	26	0.12 525	9.90 320	9	9
52	9.77 812	17	9.87 501	26	0.12 499	9.90 311	10	8
53	9.77 829	17	9.87 527	27	0.12 473	9.90 301	9	7
54	9.77 846	16	9.87 554	26	0.12 446	9.90 292	10	6
55	9.77 862	17	9.87 580	26	0.12 420	9.90 282	9	5
56	9.77 879	17	9.87 606	27	0.12 394	9.90 273	10	4
57	9.77 896	17	9.87 633	26	0.12 367	9.90 263	9	3
58	9.77 913	17	9.87 659	26	0.12 341	9.90 254	10	2
59	9.77 930	16	9.87 685	26	0.12 315	9.90 244	9	1
60	9.77 946		9.87 711		0.12 289	9.90 235		0
'	L. Cos.	d.	L. Cot.	c.d.	L. Tan.	L. Sin.	d.	'

126° (306°)　　　　　　　　　　　　　　　　　　　　　**(233°) 53°**

P. P.

"	27	26
1	0.4	0.4
2	0.9	0.9
3	1.4	1.3
4	1.8	1.7
5	2.2	2.2
6	2.7	2.6
7	3.2	3.0
8	3.6	3.5
9	4.0	3.9
10	4.5	4.3
20	9.0	8.7
30	13.5	13.0
40	18.0	17.3
50	22.5	21.7

"	18	17	16
1	0.3	0.3	0.3
2	0.6	0.6	0.5
3	0.9	0.8	0.8
4	1.2	1.1	1.1
5	1.5	1.4	1.3
6	1.8	1.7	1.6
7	2.1	2.0	1.9
8	2.4	2.3	2.1
9	2.7	2.6	2.4
10	3.0	2.8	2.7
20	6.0	5.7	5.3
30	9.0	8.5	8.0
40	12.0	11.3	10.7
50	15.0	14.2	13.3

"	10	9
1	0.2	0.2
2	0.3	0.3
3	0.5	0.4
4	0.7	0.6
5	0.8	0.8
6	1.0	0.9
7	1.2	1.0
8	1.3	1.2
9	1.5	1.4
10	1.7	1.5
20	3.3	3.0
30	5.0	4.5
40	6.7	6.0
50	8.3	7.5

	9/27	9/26
0		
1	1.5	1.4
2	4.5	4.3
3	7.5	7.2
4	10.5	10.1
5	13.5	13.0
6	16.5	15.9
7	19.5	18.8
8	22.5	21.7
9	25.5	24.6

COMMON LOGARITHMS OF THE TRIGONOMETRIC FUNCTIONS (Continued)

37° (217°)   **(322°) 142°**

′	L. Sin.	d.	L. Tan.	c.d.	L. Cot.	L. Cos.	d.	′
0	9.77 946	17	9.87 711	27	0.12 289	9.90 235	10	60
1	9.77 963	17	9.87 738	26	0.12 262	9.90 225	9	59
2	9.77 980	17	9.87 764	26	0.12 236	9.90 216	10	58
3	9.77 997	16	9.87 790	27	0.12 210	9.90 206	9	57
4	9.78 013	17	9.87 817	26	0.12 183	9.90 197	10	56
5	9.78 030	17	9.87 843	26	0.12 157	9.90 187	9	55
6	9.78 047	16	9.87 869	26	0.12 131	9.90 178	10	54
7	9.78 063	17	9.87 895	27	0.12 105	9.90 168	9	53
8	9.78 080	17	9.87 922	26	0.12 078	9.90 159	10	52
9	9.78 097	16	9.87 948	26	0.12 052	9.90 149	10	51
10	9.78 113	17	9.87 974	26	0.12 026	9.90 139	9	50
11	9.78 130	17	9.88 000	27	0.12 000	9.90 130	10	49
12	9.78 147	16	9.88 027	26	0.11 973	9.90 120	9	48
13	9.78 163	17	9.88 053	26	0.11 947	9.90 111	10	47
14	9.78 180	17	9.88 079	26	0.11 921	9.90 101	10	46
15	9.78 197	16	9.88 105	26	0.11 895	9.90 091	9	45
16	9.78 213	17	9.88 131	27	0.11 869	9.90 082	10	44
17	9.78 230	16	9.88 158	26	0.11 842	9.90 072	9	43
18	9.78 246	17	9.88 184	26	0.11 816	9.90 063	10	42
19	9.78 263	17	9.88 210	26	0.11 790	9.90 053	10	41
20	9.78 280	16	9.88 236	26	0.11 764	9.90 043	9	40
21	9.78 296	17	9.88 262	27	0.11 738	9.90 034	10	39
22	9.78 313	16	9.88 289	26	0.11 711	9.90 024	10	38
23	9.78 329	17	9.88 315	26	0.11 685	9.90 014	9	37
24	9.78 346	16	9.88 341	26	0.11 659	9.90 005	10	36
25	9.78 362	17	9.88 367	26	0.11 633	9.89 995	10	35
26	9.78 379	16	9.88 393	27	0.11 607	9.89 985	9	34
27	9.78 395	17	9.88 420	25	0.11 580	9.89 976	10	33
28	9.78 412	16	9.88 446	26	0.11 554	9.89 966	10	32
29	9.78 428	17	9.88 472	26	0.11 528	9.89 956	9	31
30	9.78 445	16	9.88 498	26	0.11 502	9.89 947	10	30
31	9.78 461	17	9.88 524	25	0.11 476	9.89 937	10	29
32	9.78 478	16	9.88 550	27	0.11 450	9.89 927	9	28
33	9.78 494	16	9.88 577	26	0.11 423	9.89 918	10	27
34	9.78 510	17	9.88 603	26	0.11 397	9.89 908	10	26
35	9.78 527	16	9.88 629	26	0.11 371	9.89 898	10	25
36	9.78 543	17	9.88 655	26	0.11 345	9.89 888	9	24
37	9.78 560	16	9.88 681	26	0.11 319	9.89 879	10	23
38	9.78 576	16	9.88 707	26	0.11 293	9.89 869	10	22
39	9.78 592	17	9.88 733	26	0.11 267	9.89 859	10	21
40	9.78 609	16	9.88 759	27	0.11 241	9.89 849	9	20
41	9.78 625	17	9.88 786	26	0.11 214	9.89 840	10	19
42	9.78 642	16	9.88 812	26	0.11 188	9.89 830	10	18
43	9.78 658	16	9.88 838	26	0.11 162	9.89 820	10	17
44	9.78 674	17	9.88 864	26	0.11 136	9.89 810	9	16
45	9.78 691	16	9.88 890	26	0.11 110	9.89 801	10	15
46	9.78 707	16	9.88 916	26	0.11 084	9.89 791	10	14
47	9.78 723	16	9.88 942	26	0.11 058	9.89 781	10	13
48	9.78 739	17	9.88 968	26	0.11 032	9.89 771	10	12
49	9.78 756	16	9.88 994	26	0.11 006	9.89 761	9	11
50	9.78 772	16	9.89 020	26	0.10 980	9.89 752	10	10
51	9.78 788	17	9.89 046	27	0.10 954	9.89 742	10	9
52	9.78 805	16	9.89 073	26	0.10 927	9.89 732	10	8
53	9.78 821	16	9.89 099	26	0.10 901	9.89 722	10	7
54	9.78 837	16	9.89 125	26	0.10 875	9.89 712	10	6
55	9.78 853	16	9.89 151	26	0.10 849	9.89 702	9	5
56	9.78 869	17	9.89 177	26	0.10 823	9.89 693	10	4
57	9.78 886	16	9.89 203	26	0.10 797	9.89 683	10	3
58	9.78 902	16	9.89 229	26	0.10 771	9.89 673	10	2
59	9.78 918	16	9.89 255	26	0.10 745	9.89 663	10	1
60	9.78 934		9.89 281		0.10 719	9.89 653		0
′	L. Cos.	d.	L. Cot.	c.d.	L. Tan.	L. Sin.	d.	′

P. P.

″	27	26
1	0.4	0.4
2	0.9	0.9
3	1.4	1.3
4	1.8	1.7
5	2.2	2.2
6	2.7	2.6
7	3.2	3.0
8	3.6	3.5
9	4.0	3.9
10	4.5	4.3
20	9.0	8.7
30	13.5	13.0
40	18.0	17.3
50	22.5	21.7

″	17	16
1	0.3	0.3
2	0.6	0.5
3	0.8	0.8
4	1.1	1.1
5	1.4	1.3
6	1.7	1.6
7	2.0	1.9
8	2.3	2.1
9	2.6	2.4
10	2.8	2.7
20	5.7	5.3
30	8.5	8.0
40	11.3	10.7
50	14.2	13.3

″	10	9
1	0.2	0.2
2	0.3	0.3
3	0.5	0.4
4	0.7	0.6
5	0.8	0.8
6	1.0	0.9
7	1.2	1.0
8	1.3	1.2
9	1.5	1.4
10	1.7	1.5
20	3.3	3.0
30	5.0	4.5
40	6.7	6.0
50	8.3	7.5

	10	10
	27	26
0		
1	1.4	1.3
2	4.1	3.9
3	6.8	6.5
4	9.4	9.1
5	12.2	11.7
6	14.8	14.3
7	17.6	16.9
8	20.2	19.5
9	22.9	22.1
10	25.6	24.7

COMMON LOGARITHMS OF THE TRIGONOMETRIC FUNCTIONS (Continued)

38° (218°)   **(321°) 141°**

'	L. Sin.	d.	L. Tan.	c.d.	L. Cot.	L. Cos.	d.	'
0	9.78 934	16	9.89 281	26	0.10 719	9.89 653	10	60
1	9.78 950	17	9.89 307	26	0.10 693	9.89 643	10	59
2	9.78 967	16	9.89 333	26	0.10 667	9.89 633	9	58
3	9.78 983	16	9.89 359	26	0.10 641	9.89 624	10	57
4	9.78 999	16	9.89 385	26	0.10 615	9.89 614	10	56
5	9.79 015	16	9.89 411	26	0.10 589	9.89 604	10	55
6	9.79 031	16	9.89 437	26	0.10 563	9.89 594	10	54
7	9.79 047	16	9.89 463	26	0.10 537	9.89 584	10	53
8	9.79 063	16	9.89 489	26	0.10 511	9.89 574	10	52
9	9.79 079	16	9.89 515	26	0.10 485	9.89 564	10	51
10	9.79 095	16	9.89 541	26	0.10 459	9.89 554	10	50
11	9.79 111	17	9.89 567	26	0.10 433	9.89 544	10	49
12	9.79 128	16	9.89 593	26	0.10 407	9.89 534	10	48
13	9.79 144	16	9.89 619	26	0.10 381	9.89 524	10	47
14	9.79 160	16	9.89 645	26	0.10 355	9.89 514	10	46
15	9.79 176	16	9.89 671	26	0.10 329	9.89 504	9	45
16	9.79 192	16	9.89 697	26	0.10 303	9.89 495	10	44
17	9.79 208	16	9.89 723	26	0.10 277	9.89 485	10	43
18	9.79 224	16	9.89 749	26	0.10 251	9.89 475	10	42
19	9.79 240	16	9.89 775	26	0.10 225	9.89 465	10	41
20	9.79 256	16	9.89 801	26	0.10 199	9.89 455	10	40
21	9.79 272	16	9.89 827	26	0.10 173	9.89 445	10	39
22	9.79 288	16	9.89 853	26	0.10 147	9.89 435	10	38
23	9.79 304	15	9.89 879	26	0.10 121	9.89 425	10	37
24	9.79 319	16	9.89 905	26	0.10 095	9.89 415	10	36
25	9.79 335	16	9.89 931	26	0.10 069	9.89 405	10	35
26	9.79 351	16	9.89 957	26	0.10 043	9.89 395	10	34
27	9.79 367	16	9.89 983	26	0.10 017	9.89 385	10	33
28	9.79 383	16	9.90 009	26	0.09 991	9.89 375	11	32
29	9.79 399	16	9.90 035	26	0.09 965	9.89 364	10	31
30	9.79 415	16	9.90 061	25	0.09 939	9.89 354	10	30
31	9.79 431	16	9.90 086	26	0.09 914	9.89 344	10	29
32	9.79 447	16	9.90 112	26	0.09 888	9.89 334	10	28
33	9.79 463	15	9.90 138	26	0.09 862	9.89 324	10	27
34	9.79 478	16	9.90 164	26	0.09 836	9.89 314	10	26
35	9.79 494	16	9.90 190	26	0.09 810	9.89 304	10	25
36	9.79 510	16	9.90 216	26	0.09 784	9.89 294	10	24
37	9.79 526	16	9.90 242	26	0.09 758	9.89 284	10	23
38	9.79 542	16	9.90 268	26	0.09 732	9.89 274	10	22
39	9.79 558	15	9.90 294	26	0.09 706	9.89 264	10	21
40	9.79 573	16	9.90 320	26	0.09 680	9.89 254	10	20
41	9.79 589	16	9.90 346	25	0.09 654	9.89 244	11	19
42	9.79 605	16	9.90 371	26	0.09 629	9.89 233	10	18
43	9.79 621	15	9.90 397	26	0.09 603	9.89 223	10	17
44	9.79 636	16	9.90 423	26	0.09 577	9.89 213	10	16
45	9.79 652	16	9.90 449	26	0.09 551	9.89 203	10	15
46	9.79 668	16	9.90 475	26	0.09 525	9.89 193	10	14
47	9.79 684	15	9.90 501	26	0.09 499	9.89 183	10	13
48	9.79 699	16	9.90 527	26	0.09 473	9.89 173	11	12
49	9.79 715	16	9.90 553	25	0.09 447	9.89 162	10	11
50	9.79 731	15	9.90 578	26	0.09 422	9.89 152	10	10
51	9.79 746	16	9.90 604	26	0.09 396	9.89 142	10	9
52	9.79 762	16	9.90 630	26	0.09 370	9.89 132	10	8
53	9.79 778	15	9.90 656	26	0.09 344	9.89 122	10	7
54	9.79 793	16	9.90 682	26	0.09 318	9.89 112	11	6
55	9.79 809	16	9.90 708	26	0.09 292	9.89 101	10	5
56	9.79 825	15	9.90 734	25	0.09 266	9.89 091	10	4
57	9.79 840	16	9.90 759	26	0.09 241	9.89 081	10	3
58	9.79 856	16	9.90 785	26	0.09 215	9.89 071	11	2
59	9.79 872	15	9.90 811	26	0.09 189	9.89 060	10	1
60	9.79 887		9.90 837		0.09 163	9.89 050		0

'	L. Cos.	d.	L. Cot.	c.d.	L. Tan.	L. Sin.	d.	'

P. P.

	26	25
1	0.4	0.4
2	0.9	0.8
3	1.3	1.2
4	1.7	1.7
5	2.2	2.1
6	2.6	2.5
7	3.0	2.9
8	3.5	3.3
9	3.9	3.8
10	4.3	4.2
20	8.7	8.3
30	13.0	12.5
40	17.3	16.7
50	21.7	20.8

	17	16	15
1	0.3	0.3	0.2
2	0.6	0.5	0.5
3	0.8	0.8	0.8
4	1.1	1.1	1.0
5	1.4	1.3	1.2
6	1.7	1.6	1.5
7	2.0	1.9	1.8
8	2.3	2.1	2.0
9	2.6	2.4	2.2
10	2.8	2.7	2.5
20	5.7	5.3	5.0
30	8.5	8.0	7.5
40	11.3	10.7	10.0
50	14.2	13.3	12.5

	11	10	9
1	0.2	0.2	0.2
2	0.4	0.3	0.3
3	0.6	0.5	0.4
4	0.7	0.7	0.6
5	0.9	0.8	0.8
6	1.1	1.0	0.9
7	1.3	1.2	1.0
8	1.5	1.3	1.2
9	1.6	1.5	1.4
10	1.8	1.7	1.5
20	3.7	3.3	3.0
30	5.5	5.0	4.5
40	7.3	6.7	6.0
50	9.2	8.3	7.5

	10/26	10/25	9/26
0			
1	1.3	1.2	1.4
2	3.9	3.8	4.3
3	6.5	6.2	7.2
4	9.1	8.8	10.1
5	11.7	11.2	13.0
6	14.3	13.8	15.9
7	16.9	16.2	18.8
8	19.5	18.8	21.7
9	22.1	21.2	24.6
10	24.7	23.8	

COMMON LOGARITHMS OF THE TRIGONOMETRIC FUNCTIONS (Continued)

39° (219°)   **(320°) 140°**

'	L. Sin.	d.	L. Tan.	c.d.	L. Cot.	L. Cos.	d.	'
0	9.79 887	16	9.90 837	26	0.09 163	9.89 050	10	60
1	9.79 903	15	9.90 863	26	0.09 137	9.89 040	10	59
2	9.79 918	16	9.90 889	25	0.09 111	9.89 030	10	58
3	9.79 934	16	9.90 914	26	0.09 086	9.89 020	11	57
4	9.79 950	15	9.90 940	26	0.09 060	9.89 009	10	56
5	9.79 965	16	9.90 966	26	0.09 034	9.88 999	10	55
6	9.79 981	15	9.90 992	26	0.09 008	9.88 989	11	54
7	9.79 996	16	9.91 018	25	0.08 982	9.88 978	10	53
8	9.80 012	15	9.91 043	26	0.08 957	9.88 968	10	52
9	9.80 027	16	9.91 069	26	0.08 931	9.88 958	10	51
10	9.80 043	15	9.91 095	26	0.08 905	9.88 948	11	50
11	9.80 058	16	9.91 121	26	0.08 879	9.88 937	10	49
12	9.80 074	15	9.91 147	25	0.08 853	9.88 927	10	48
13	9.80 089	16	9.91 172	26	0.08 828	9.88 917	11	47
14	9.80 105	15	9.91 198	26	0.08 802	9.88 906	10	46
15	9.80 120	16	9.91 224	26	0.08 776	9.88 896	10	45
16	9.80 136	15	9.91 250	26	0.08 750	9.88 886	10	44
17	9.80 151	15	9.91 276	25	0.08 724	9.88 875	11	43
18	9.80 166	16	9.91 301	26	0.08 699	9.88 865	10	42
19	9.80 182	15	9.91 327	26	0.08 673	9.88 855	11	41
20	9.80 197	16	9.91 353	26	0.08 647	9.88 844	10	40
21	9.80 213	15	9.91 379	25	0.08 621	9.88 834	10	39
22	9.80 228	16	9.91 404	26	0.08 596	9.88 824	11	38
23	9.80 244	15	9.91 430	26	0.08 570	9.88 813	10	37
24	9.80 259	15	9.91 456	26	0.08 544	9.88 803	10	36
25	9.80 274	16	9.91 482	25	0.08 518	9.88 793	11	35
26	9.80 290	15	9.91 507	26	0.08 493	9.88 782	11	34
27	9.80 305	15	9.91 533	26	0.08 467	9.88 772	11	33
28	9.80 320	16	9.91 559	26	0.08 441	9.88 761	10	32
29	9.80 336	15	9.91 585	25	0.08 415	9.88 751	10	31
30	9.80 351	15	9.91 610	26	0.08 390	9.88 741	11	30
31	9.80 366	16	9.91 636	26	0.08 364	9.88 730	10	29
32	9.80 382	15	9.91 662	26	0.08 338	9.88 720	11	28
33	9.80 397	15	9.91 688	25	0.08 312	9.88 709	10	27
34	9.80 412	16	9.91 713	26	0.08 287	9.88 699	11	26
35	9.80 428	15	9.91 739	26	0.08 261	9.88 688	10	25
36	9.80 443	15	9.91 765	26	0.08 235	9.88 678	10	24
37	9.80 458	15	9.91 791	25	0.08 209	9.88 668	11	23
38	9.80 473	16	9.91 816	26	0.08 184	9.88 657	10	22
39	9.80 489	15	9.91 842	26	0.08 158	9.88 647	11	21
40	9.80 504	15	9.91 868	25	0.08 132	9.88 636	10	20
41	9.80 519	15	9.91 893	26	0.08 107	9.88 626	11	19
42	9.80 534	16	9.91 919	26	0.08 081	9.88 615	10	18
43	9.80 550	15	9.91 945	26	0.08 055	9.88 605	11	17
44	9.80 565	15	9.91 971	25	0.08 029	9.88 594	10	16
45	9.80 580	15	9.91 996	26	0.08 004	9.88 584	11	15
46	9.80 595	15	9.92 022	26	0.07 978	9.88 573	10	14
47	9.80 610	15	9.92 048	25	0.07 952	9.88 563	11	13
48	9.80 625	16	9.92 073	26	0.07 927	9.88 552	10	12
49	9.80 641	15	9.92 099	26	0.07 901	9.88 542	11	11
50	9.80 656	15	9.92 125	25	0.07 875	9.88 531	10	10
51	9.80 671	15	9.92 150	26	0.07 850	9.88 521	11	9
52	9.80 686	15	9.92 176	26	0.07 824	9.88 510	11	8
53	9.80 701	15	9.92 202	25	0.07 798	9.88 499	11	7
54	9.80 716	15	9.92 227	26	0.07 773	9.88 489	10	6
55	9.80 731	15	9.92 253	26	0.07 747	9.88 478	11	5
56	9.80 746	16	9.92 279	25	0.07 721	9.88 468	11	4
57	9.80 762	15	9.92 304	26	0.07 696	9.88 457	10	3
58	9.80 777	15	9.92 330	26	0.07 670	9.88 447	11	2
59	9.80 792	15	9.92 356	25	0.07 644	9.88 436	11	1
60	9.80 807		9.92 381		0.07 619	9.88 425		0

'	L. Cos.	d.	L. Cot.	c.d.	L. Tan.	L. Sin.	d.	'

129° (309°)   **(230°) 50°**

P. P.

''	26	25
1	0.4	0.4
2	0.9	0.8
3	1.3	1.2
4	1.7	1.7
5	2.2	2.1
6	2.6	2.5
7	3.0	2.9
8	3.5	3.3
9	3.9	3.8
10	4.3	4.2
20	8.7	8.3
30	13.0	12.5
40	17.3	16.7
50	21.7	20.8

''	16	15
1	0.3	0.2
2	0.5	0.5
3	0.8	0.8
4	1.1	1.0
5	1.3	1.2
6	1.6	1.5
7	1.9	1.8
8	2.1	2.0
9	2.4	2.2
10	2.7	2.5
20	5.3	5.0
30	8.0	7.5
40	10.7	10.0
50	13.3	12.5

''	11	10
1	0.2	0.2
2	0.4	0.3
3	0.6	0.5
4	0.7	0.7
5	0.9	0.8
6	1.1	1.0
7	1.3	1.2
8	1.5	1.3
9	1.6	1.5
10	1.8	1.7
20	3.7	3.3
30	5.5	5.0
40	7.3	6.7
50	9.2	8.3

	11	11
	26	25
0	1.2	1.1
1	3.5	3.4
2	5.9	5.7
3	8.3	7.9
4	10.6	10.2
5	13.0	12.5
6	15.4	14.8
7	17.7	17.1
8	20.1	19.3
9	22.5	21.6
10	24.8	23.9
11		

COMMON LOGARITHMS OF THE TRIGONOMETRIC FUNCTIONS (Continued)

40° (220°) (319°) **139°**

'	L. Sin.	d.	L. Tan.	c.d.	L. Cot.	L. Cos.	d.	'
0	9.80 807	15	9.92 381	26	0.07 619	9.88 425	10	60
1	9.80 822	15	9.92 407	26	0.07 593	9.88 415	11	59
2	9.80 837	15	9.92 433	25	0.07 567	9.88 404	11	58
3	9.80 852	15	9.92 458	26	0.07 542	9.88 394	11	57
4	9.80 867	15	9.92 484	26	0.07 516	9.88 383	11	56
5	9.80 882	15	9.92 510	25	0.07 490	9.88 372	10	55
6	9.80 897	15	9.92 535	26	0.07 465	9.88 362	11	54
7	9.80 912	15	9.92 561	26	0.07 439	9.88 351	11	53
8	9.80 927	15	9.92 587	25	0.07 413	9.88 340	10	52
9	9.80 942	15	9.92 612	26	0.07 388	9.88 330	11	51
10	9.80 957	15	9.92 638	25	0.07 362	9.88 319	11	50
11	9.80 972	15	9.92 663	26	0.07 337	9.88 308	10	49
12	9.80 987	15	9.92 689	26	0.07 311	9.88 298	11	48
13	9.81 002	15	9.92 715	25	0.07 285	9.88 287	11	47
14	9.81 017	15	9.92 740	26	0.07 260	9.88 276	10	46
15	9.81 032	15	9.92 766	26	0.07 234	9.88 266	11	45
16	9.81 047	14	9.92 792	25	0.07 208	9.88 255	11	44
17	9.81 061	15	9.92 817	26	0.07 183	9.88 244	10	43
18	9.81 076	15	9.92 843	25	0.07 157	9.88 234	11	42
19	9.81 091	15	9.92 868	26	0.07 132	9.88 223	11	41
20	9.81 106	15	9.92 894	26	0.07 106	9.88 212	11	40
21	9.81 121	15	9.92 920	25	0.07 080	9.88 201	10	39
22	9.81 136	15	9.92 945	26	0.07 055	9.88 191	11	38
23	9.81 151	15	9.92 971	26	0.07 029	9.88 180	11	37
24	9.81 166	14	9.92 996	26	0.07 004	9.88 169	11	36
25	9.81 180	15	9.93 022	26	0.06 978	9.88 158	10	35
26	9.81 195	15	9.93 048	25	0.06 952	9.88 148	11	34
27	9.81 210	15	9.93 073	26	0.06 927	9.88 137	11	33
28	9.81 225	15	9.93 099	25	0.06 901	9.88 126	11	32
29	9.81 240	14	9.93 124	26	0.06 876	9.88 115	10	31
30	9.81 254	15	9.93 150	25	0.06 850	9.88 105	11	30
31	9.81 269	15	9.93 175	26	0.06 825	9.88 094	11	29
32	9.81 284	15	9.93 201	26	0.06 799	9.88 083	11	28
33	9.81 299	15	9.93 227	25	0.06 773	9.88 072	11	27
34	9.81 314	14	9.93 252	26	0.06 748	9.88 061	10	26
35	9.81 328	15	9.93 278	25	0.06 722	9.88 051	11	25
36	9.81 343	15	9.93 303	26	0.06 697	9.88 040	11	24
37	9.81 358	14	9.93 329	25	0.06 671	9.88 029	11	23
38	9.81 372	15	9.93 354	26	0.06 646	9.88 018	11	22
39	9.81 387	15	9.93 380	26	0.06 620	9.88 007	11	21
40	9.81 402	15	9.93 406	25	0.06 594	9.87 996	11	20
41	9.81 417	14	9.93 431	26	0.06 569	9.87 985	11	19
42	9.81 431	15	9.93 457	25	0.06 543	9.87 975	11	18
43	9.81 446	15	9.93 482	26	0.06 518	9.87 964	11	17
44	9.81 461	14	9.93 508	25	0.06 492	9.87 953	11	16
45	9.81 475	15	9.93 533	26	0.06 467	9.87 942	11	15
46	9.81 490	15	9.93 559	25	0.06 441	9.87 931	11	14
47	9.81 505	14	9.93 584	26	0.06 416	9.87 920	11	13
48	9.81 519	15	9.93 610	26	0.06 390	9.87 909	11	12
49	9.81 534	15	9.93 636	25	0.06 364	9.87 898	11	11
50	9.81 549	14	9.93 661	26	0.06 339	9.87 887	10	10
51	9.81 563	15	9.93 687	25	0.06 313	9.87 877	11	9
52	9.81 578	14	9.93 712	26	0.06 288	9.87 866	11	8
53	9.81 592	15	9.93 738	25	0.06 262	9.87 855	11	7
54	9.81 607	15	9.93 763	26	0.06 237	9.87 844	11	6
55	9.81 622	14	9.93 789	25	0.06 211	9.87 833	11	5
56	9.81 636	15	9.93 814	26	0.06 186	9.87 822	11	4
57	9.81 651	14	9.93 840	25	0.06 160	9.87 811	11	3
58	9.81 665	15	9.93 865	26	0.06 135	9.87 800	11	2
59	9.81 680	14	9.93 891	25	0.06 109	9.87 789	11	1
60	9.81 694		9.93 916		0.06 084	9.87 778		0
'	L. Cos.	d.	L. Cot.	c.d.	L. Tan.	L. Sin.	d.	'

130° (310°) (229°) **49°**

P. P.

	26	25
1	0.4	0.4
2	0.9	0.8
3	1.3	1.2
4	1.7	1.7
5	2.2	2.1
6	2.6	2.5
7	3.0	2.9
8	3.5	3.3
9	3.9	3.8
10	4.3	4.2
20	8.7	8.3
30	13.0	12.5
40	17.3	16.7
50	21.7	20.8

	15	14
1	0.2	0.2
2	0.5	0.5
3	0.8	0.7
4	1.0	0.9
5	1.2	1.2
6	1.5	1.4
7	1.8	1.6
8	2.0	1.9
9	2.2	2.1
10	2.5	2.3
20	5.0	4.7
30	7.5	7.0
40	10.0	9.3
50	12.5	11.7

	11	10
1	0.2	0.2
2	0.4	0.3
3	0.6	0.5
4	0.7	0.7
5	0.9	0.8
6	1.1	1.0
7	1.3	1.2
8	1.5	1.3
9	1.6	1.5
10	1.8	1.7
20	3.7	3.3
30	5.5	5.0
40	7.3	6.7
50	9.2	8.3

	11	10	10
	26	26	25
0	1.2	1.3	1.2
1	3.5	3.9	3.8
2	5.9	6.5	6.2
3	8.3	9.1	8.8
4	10.6	11.7	11.2
5	13.0	14.3	13.8
6	15.4	16.9	16.2
7	17.7	19.5	18.8
8	20.1	22.1	21.2
9	22.5	24.7	23.8
10	24.8	—	—
11			

COMMON LOGARITHMS OF THE TRIGONOMETRIC FUNCTIONS (Continued)

41° (221°)   **(318°) 138°**

'	L. Sin.	d.	L. Tan.	c.d.	L. Cot.	L. Cos.	d.	'
0	9.81 694	15	9.93 916	26	0.06 084	9.87 778	11	60
1	9.81 709	14	9.93 942	25	0.06 058	9.87 767	11	59
2	9.81 723	15	9.93 967	26	0.06 033	9.87 756	11	58
3	9.81 738	14	9.93 993	25	0.06 007	9.87 745	11	57
4	9.81 752	15	9.94 018	26	0.05 982	9.87 734	11	56
5	9.81 767	14	9.94 044	25	0.05 956	9.87 723	11	55
6	9.81 781	15	9.94 069	26	0.05 931	9.87 712	11	54
7	9.81 796	14	9.94 095	25	0.05 905	9.87 701	11	53
8	9.81 810	15	9.94 120	26	0.05 880	9.87 690	11	52
9	9.81 825	14	9.94 146	25	0.05 854	9.87 679	11	51
10	9.81 839	15	9.94 171	26	0.05 829	9.87 668	11	50
11	9.81 854	14	9.94 197	25	0.05 803	9.87 657	11	49
12	9.81 868	14	9.94 222	26	0.05 778	9.87 646	11	48
13	9.81 882	15	9.94 248	25	0.05 752	9.87 635	11	47
14	9.81 897	14	9.94 273	26	0.05 727	9.87 624	11	46
15	9.81 911	15	9.94 299	25	0.05 701	9.87 613	12	45
16	9.81 926	14	9.94 324	26	0.05 676	9.87 601	11	44
17	9.81 940	15	9.94 350	25	0.05 650	9.87 590	11	43
18	9.81 955	14	9.94 375	26	0.05 625	9.87 579	11	42
19	9.81 969	14	9.94 401	25	0.05 599	9.87 568	11	41
20	9.81 983	15	9.94 426	26	0.05 574	9.87 557	11	40
21	9.81 998	14	9.94 452	25	0.05 548	9.87 546	11	39
22	9.82 012	14	9.94 477	26	0.05 523	9.87 535	11	38
23	9.82 026	15	9.94 503	25	0.05 497	9.87 524	11	37
24	9.82 041	14	9.94 528	26	0.05 472	9.87 513	12	36
25	9.82 055	14	9.94 554	25	0.05 446	9.87 501	11	35
26	9.82 069	15	9.94 579	25	0.05 421	9.87 490	11	34
27	9.82 084	14	9.94 604	26	0.05 396	9.87 479	11	33
28	9.82 098	14	9.94 630	25	0.05 370	9.87 468	11	32
29	9.82 112	14	9.94 655	26	0.05 345	9.87 457	11	31
30	9.82 126	15	9.94 681	25	0.05 319	9.87 446	12	30
31	9.82 141	14	9.94 706	26	0.05 294	9.87 434	11	29
32	9.82 155	14	9.94 732	25	0.05 268	9.87 423	11	28
33	9.82 169	15	9.94 757	26	0.05 243	9.87 412	11	27
34	9.82 184	14	9.94 783	25	0.05 217	9.87 401	11	26
35	9.82 198	14	9.94 808	26	0.05 192	9.87 390	12	25
36	9.82 212	14	9.94 834	25	0.05 166	9.87 378	11	24
37	9.82 226	14	9.94 859	25	0.05 141	9.87 367	11	23
38	9.82 240	15	9.94 884	26	0.05 116	9.87 356	11	22
39	9.82 255	14	9.94 910	25	0.05 090	9.87 345	11	21
40	9.82 269	14	9.94 935	26	0.05 065	9.87 334	12	20
41	9.82 283	14	9.94 961	25	0.05 039	9.87 322	11	19
42	9.82 297	14	9.94 986	26	0.05 014	9.87 311	11	18
43	9.82 311	15	9.95 012	25	0.04 988	9.87 300	12	17
44	9.82 326	14	9.95 037	25	0.04 963	9.87 288	11	16
45	9.82 340	14	9.95 062	26	0.04 938	9.87 277	11	15
46	9.82 354	14	9.95 088	25	0.04 912	9.87 266	11	14
47	9.82 368	14	9.95 113	26	0.04 887	9.87 255	12	13
48	9.82 382	14	9.95 139	25	0.04 861	9.87 243	11	12
49	9.82 396	14	9.95 164	26	0.04 836	9.87 232	11	11
50	9.82 410	14	9.95 190	25	0.04 810	9.87 221	12	10
51	9.82 424	15	9.95 215	25	0.04 785	9.87 209	11	9
52	9.82 439	14	9.95 240	26	0.04 760	9.87 198	11	8
53	9.82 453	14	9.95 266	25	0.04 734	9.87 187	12	7
54	9.82 467	14	9.95 291	26	0.04 709	9.87 175	11	6
55	9.82 481	14	9.95 317	25	0.04 683	9.87 164	11	5
56	9.82 495	14	9.95 342	26	0.04 658	9.87 153	12	4
57	9.82 509	14	9.95 368	25	0.04 632	9.87 141	11	3
58	9.82 523	14	9.95 393	25	0.04 607	9.87 130	11	2
59	9.82 537	14	9.95 418	26	0.04 582	9.87 119	12	1
60	9.82 551		9.95 444		0.04 556	9.87 107		0

'	L. Cos.	d.	L. Cot.	c.d.	L. Tan.	L. Sin.	d.	'

131° (311°)   **(228°) 48°**

P. P.

"	26	25
1	0.4	0.4
2	0.9	0.8
3	1.3	1.2
4	1.7	1.7
5	2.2	2.1
6	2.6	2.5
7	3.0	2.9
8	3.5	3.3
9	3.9	3.8
10	4.3	4.2
20	8.7	8.3
30	13.0	12.5
40	17.3	16.7
50	21.7	20.8

"	15	14
1	0.2	0.2
2	0.5	0.5
3	0.8	0.7
4	1.0	0.9
5	1.2	1.2
6	1.5	1.4
7	1.8	1.6
8	2.0	1.9
9	2.2	2.1
10	2.5	2.3
20	5.0	4.7
30	7.5	7.0
40	10.0	9.3
50	12.5	11.7

"	12	11
1	0.2	0.2
2	0.4	0.4
3	0.6	0.6
4	0.8	0.7
5	1.0	0.9
6	1.2	1.1
7	1.4	1.3
8	1.6	1.5
9	1.8	1.6
10	2.0	1.8
20	4.0	3.7
30	6.0	5.5
40	8.0	7.3
50	10.0	9.2

	12	12	11
	26	25	25
0	1.1	1.1	1.1
1	3.2	3.1	3.4
2	5.4	5.2	5.7
3	7.6	7.3	7.9
4	9.8	9.4	10.2
5	11.9	11.5	12.5
6	14.1	13.5	14.8
7	16.2	15.6	17.1
8	18.4	17.7	19.3
9	20.6	19.8	21.6
10	22.8	21.9	23.9
11	24.9	23.9	—
12			

COMMON LOGARITHMS OF THE TRIGONOMETRIC FUNCTIONS (Continued)

42° (222°)   **(317°) 137°**

'	L. Sin.	d.	L. Tan.	c.d.	L. Cot.	L. Cos.	d.	'
0	9.82 551	14	9.95 444	25	0.04 556	9.87 107	11	60
1	9.82 565	14	9.95 469	26	0.04 531	9.87 096	11	59
2	9.82 579	14	9.95 495	25	0.04 505	9.87 085	12	58
3	9.82 593	14	9.95 520	25	0.04 480	9.87 073	11	57
4	9.82 607	14	9.95 545	26	0.04 455	9.87 062	12	56
5	9.82 621	14	9.95 571	25	0.04 429	9.87 050	11	55
6	9.82 635	14	9.95 596	26	0.04 404	9.87 039	11	54
7	9.82 649	14	9.95 622	25	0.04 378	9.87 028	11	53
8	9.82 663	14	9.95 647	25	0.04 353	9.87 016	11	52
9	9.82 677	14	9.95 672	26	0.04 328	9.87 005	12	51
10	9.82 691	14	9.95 698	25	0.04 302	9.86 993	11	50
11	9.82 705	14	9.95 723	25	0.04 277	9.86 982	12	49
12	9.82 719	14	9.95 748	26	0.04 252	9.86 970	11	48
13	9.82 733	14	9.95 774	25	0.04 226	9.86 959	12	47
14	9.82 747	14	9.95 799	26	0.04 201	9.86 947	11	46
15	9.82 761	14	9.95 825	25	0.04 175	9.86 936	12	45
16	9.82 775	13	9.95 850	25	0.04 150	9.86 924	11	44
17	9.82 788	14	9.95 875	26	0.04 125	9.86 913	11	43
18	9.82 802	14	9.95 901	25	0.04 099	9.86 902	12	42
19	9.82 816	14	9.95 926	26	0.04 074	9.86 890	11	41
20	9.82 830	14	9.95 952	25	0.04 048	9.86 879	12	40
21	9.82 844	14	9.95 977	25	0.04 023	9.86 867	12	39
22	9.82 858	14	9.96 002	26	0.03 998	9.86 855	11	38
23	9.82 872	13	9.96 028	25	0.03 972	9.86 844	12	37
24	9.82 885	14	9.96 053	25	0.03 947	9.86 832	11	36
25	9.82 899	14	9.96 078	26	0.03 922	9.86 821	12	35
26	9.82 913	14	9.96 104	25	0.03 896	9.86 809	11	34
27	9.82 927	14	9.96 129	26	0.03 871	9.86 798	12	33
28	9.82 941	14	9.96 155	25	0.03 845	9.86 786	11	32
29	9.82 955	13	9.96 180	25	0.03 820	9.86 775	12	31
30	9.82 968	14	9.96 205	26	0.03 795	9.86 763	11	30
31	9.82 982	14	9.96 231	25	0.03 769	9.86 752	12	29
32	9.82 996	14	9.96 256	25	0.03 744	9.86 740	12	28
33	9.83 010	13	9.96 281	26	0.03 719	9.86 728	11	27
34	9.83 023	14	9.96 307	25	0.03 693	9.86 717	12	26
35	9.83 037	14	9.96 332	25	0.03 668	9.86 705	11	25
36	9.83 051	14	9.96 357	26	0.03 643	9.86 694	12	24
37	9.83 065	13	9.96 383	25	0.03 617	9.86 682	12	23
38	9.83 078	14	9.96 408	25	0.03 592	9.86 670	11	22
39	9.83 092	14	9.96 433	26	0.03 567	9.86 659	12	21
40	9.83 106	14	9.96 459	25	0.03 541	9.86 647	12	20
41	9.83 120	13	9.96 484	26	0.03 516	9.86 635	11	19
42	9.83 133	14	9.96 510	25	0.03 490	9.86 624	12	18
43	9.83 147	14	9.96 535	25	0.03 465	9.86 612	12	17
44	9.83 161	13	9.96 560	26	0.03 440	9.86 600	11	16
45	9.83 174	14	9.96 586	25	0.03 414	9.86 589	12	15
46	9.83 188	14	9.96 611	25	0.03 389	9.86 577	12	14
47	9.83 202	13	9.96 636	26	0.03 364	9.86 565	12	13
48	9.83 215	14	9.96 662	25	0.03 338	9.86 554	12	12
49	9.83 229	13	9.96 687	25	0.03 313	9.86 542	12	11
50	9.83 242	14	9.96 712	26	0.03 288	9.86 530	12	10
51	9.83 256	14	9.96 738	25	0.03 262	9.86 518	11	9
52	9.83 270	13	9.96 763	25	0.03 237	9.86 507	12	8
53	9.83 283	14	9.96 788	26	0.03 212	9.86 495	12	7
54	9.83 297	13	9.96 814	25	0.03 186	9.86 483	11	6
55	9.83 310	14	9.96 839	25	0.03 161	9.86 472	12	5
56	9.83 324	14	9.96 864	26	0.03 136	9.86 460	12	4
57	9.83 338	13	9.96 890	25	0.03 110	9.86 448	12	3
58	9.83 351	14	9.96 915	25	0.03 085	9.86 436	11	2
59	9.83 365	13	9.96 940	26	0.03 060	9.86 423	12	1
60	9.83 378		9.96 966		0.03 034	9.86 413		0

'	L. Cos.	d.	L. Cot.	c.d.	L. Tan.	L. Sin.	d.	'

132° (312°)   **(227°) 47°**

P. P.

"	26	25
1	0.4	0.4
2	0.9	0.8
3	1.3	1.2
4	1.7	1.7
5	2.2	2.1
6	2.6	2.5
7	3.0	2.9
8	3.5	3.3
9	3.9	3.8
10	4.3	4.2
20	8.7	8.3
30	13.0	12.5
40	17.3	16.7
50	21.7	20.8

"	14	13
1	0.2	0.2
2	0.5	0.4
3	0.7	0.6
4	0.9	0.9
5	1.2	1.1
6	1.4	1.3
7	1.6	1.5
8	1.9	1.7
9	2.1	2.0
10	2.3	2.2
20	4.7	4.3
30	7.0	6.5
40	9.3	8.7
50	11.7	10.8

"	12	11
1	0.2	0.2
2	0.4	0.4
3	0.6	0.6
4	0.8	0.7
5	1.0	0.9
6	1.2	1.1
7	1.4	1.3
8	1.6	1.5
9	1.8	1.6
10	2.0	1.8
20	4.0	3.7
30	6.0	5.5
40	8.0	7.3
50	10.0	9.2

	12	11	11
	26	26	25
0	1.1	1.2	1.1
1	3.2	3.5	3.4
2	5.4	5.9	5.7
3	7.6	8.3	7.9
4	9.8	10.6	10.2
5	11.9	13.0	12.5
6	14.1	15.4	14.8
7	16.2	17.7	17.1
8	18.4	20.1	19.3
9	20.6	22.5	21.6
10	22.8	24.8	23.9
11	24.9	—	—
12			

COMMON LOGARITHMS OF THE TRIGONOMETRIC
FUNCTIONS (Continued)

43° (223°)   **(316°) 136°**

′	L. Sin.	d.	L. Tan.	c.d.	L. Cot.	L. Cos.	d.	′	P. P.		
0	9.83 378	14	9.96 966	25	0.03 034	9.86 413	12	60			
1	9.83 392	13	9.96 991	25	0.03 009	9.86 401	12	59	″	**26**	**25**
2	9.83 405	14	9.97 016	25	0.02 984	9.86 389	12	58	1	0.4	0.4
3	9.83 419	13	9.97 042	25	0.02 958	9.86 377	11	57	2	0.9	0.8
4	9.83 432	14	9.97 067	25	0.02 933	9.86 366	12	56	3	1.3	1.2
									4	1.7	1.7
5	9.83 446	13	9.97 092	26	0.02 908	9.86 354	12	55			
6	9.83 459	14	9.97 118	25	0.02 882	9.86 342	12	54	5	2.2	2.1
7	9.83 473	13	9.97 143	25	0.02 857	9.86 330	12	53	6	2.6	2.5
8	9.83 486	14	9.97 168	25	0.02 832	9.86 318	12	52	7	3.0	2.9
9	9.83 500	13	9.97 193	26	0.02 807	9.86 306	11	51	8	3.5	3.3
									9	3.9	3.8
10	9.83 513	14	9.97 219	25	0.02 781	9.86 295	12	50			
11	9.83 527	13	9.97 244	25	0.02 756	9.86 283	12	49	10	4.3	4.2
12	9.83 540	14	9.97 269	26	0.02 731	9.86 271	12	48	20	8.7	8.3
13	9.83 554	13	9.97 295	25	0.02 705	9.86 259	12	47	30	13.0	12.5
14	9.83 567	14	9.97 320	25	0.02 680	9.86 247	12	46	40	17.3	16.7
									50	21.7	20.8
15	9.83 581	13	9.97 345	26	0.02 655	9.86 235	12	45			
16	9.83 594	14	9.97 371	25	0.02 629	9.86 223	12	44	″	**14**	**13**
17	9.83 608	13	9.97 396	25	0.02 604	9.86 211	11	43	1	0.2	0.2
18	9.83 621	13	9.97 421	26	0.02 579	9.86 200	12	42	2	0.5	0.4
19	9.83 634	14	9.97 447	25	0.02 553	9.86 188	12	41	3	0.7	0.6
									4	0.9	0.9
20	9.83 648	13	9.97 472	25	0.02 528	9.86 176	12	40			
21	9.83 661	13	9.97 497	26	0.02 503	9.86 164	12	39	5	1.2	1.1
22	9.83 674	14	9.97 523	25	0.02 477	9.86 152	12	38	6	1.4	1.3
23	9.83 688	13	9.97 548	25	0.02 452	9.86 140	12	37	7	1.6	1.5
24	9.83 701	14	9.97 573	25	0.02 427	9.86 128	12	36	8	1.9	1.7
									9	2.1	2.0
25	9.83 715	13	9.97 598	26	0.02 402	9.86 116	12	35			
26	9.83 728	13	9.97 624	25	0.02 376	9.86 104	12	34	10	2.3	2.2
27	9.83 741	14	9.97 649	25	0.02 351	9.86 092	12	33	20	4.7	4.3
28	9.83 755	13	9.97 674	26	0.02 326	9.86 080	12	32	30	7.0	6.5
29	9.83 768	13	9.97 700	25	0.02 300	9.86 068	12	31	40	9.3	8.7
									50	11.7	10.8
30	9.83 781	14	9.97 725	25	0.02 275	9.86 056	12	30			
31	9.83 795	13	9.97 750	26	0.02 250	9.86 044	12	29	″	**12**	**11**
32	9.83 808	13	9.97 776	25	0.02 224	9.86 032	12	28	1	0.2	0.2
33	9.83 821	13	9.97 801	25	0.02 199	9.86 020	12	27	2	0.4	0.4
34	9.83 834	14	9.97 826	25	0.02 174	9.86 008	12	26	3	0.6	0.6
									4	0.8	0.7
35	9.83 848	13	9.97 851	26	0.02 149	9.85 996	12	25			
36	9.83 861	13	9.97 877	25	0.02 123	9.85 984	12	24	5	1.0	0.9
37	9.83 874	13	9.97 902	25	0.02 098	9.85 972	12	23	6	1.2	1.1
38	9.83 887	14	9.97 927	26	0.02 073	9.85 960	12	22	7	1.4	1.3
39	9.83 901	13	9.97 953	25	0.02 047	9.85 948	12	21	8	1.6	1.5
									9	1.8	1.6
40	9.83 914	13	9.97 978	25	0.02 022	9.85 936	12	20			
41	9.83 927	13	9.98 003	26	0.01 997	9.85 924	12	19	10	2.0	1.8
42	9.83 940	14	9.98 029	25	0.01 971	9.85 912	12	18	20	4.0	3.7
43	9.83 954	13	9.98 054	25	0.01 946	9.85 900	12	17	30	6.0	5.5
44	9.83 967	13	9.98 079	25	0.01 921	9.85 888	12	16	40	8.0	7.3
									50	10.0	9.2
45	9.83 980	13	9.98 104	26	0.01 896	9.85 876	12	15			
46	9.83 993	13	9.98 130	25	0.01 870	9.85 864	13	14		**13**	**13**	**12**
47	9.84 006	14	9.98 155	25	0.01 845	9.85 851	12	13			
48	9.84 020	13	9.98 180	26	0.01 820	9.85 839	12	12		**26**	**25**	**25**
49	9.84 033	13	9.98 206	25	0.01 794	9.85 827	12	11	0	1.0	0.9	1.1
									1	3.0	2.9	3.1
50	9.84 046	13	9.98 231	25	0.01 769	9.85 815	12	10	2	5.0	4.8	5.2
51	9.84 059	13	9.98 256	25	0.01 744	9.85 803	12	9	3	7.0	6.7	7.3
52	9.84 072	13	9.98 281	26	0.01 719	9.85 791	12	8	4	9.0	8.7	9.4
53	9.84 085	13	9.98 307	25	0.01 693	9.85 779	13	7	5	11.0	10.6	11.5
54	9.84 098	14	9.98 332	25	0.01 668	9.85 766	12	6	6	13.0	12.5	13.5
									7	15.0	14.4	15.6
55	9.84 112	13	9.98 357	26	0.01 643	9.85 754	12	5	8	17.0	16.3	17.7
56	9.84 125	13	9.98 383	25	0.01 617	9.85 742	12	4	9	19.0	18.3	19.8
57	9.84 138	13	9.98 408	25	0.01 592	9.85 730	12	3	10	21.0	20.2	21.9
58	9.84 151	13	9.98 433	25	0.01 567	9.85 718	12	2	11	23.0	22.1	23.9
59	9.84 164	13	9.98 458	26	0.01 542	9.85 706	13	1	12	25.0	24.1	—
									13			
60	9.84 177		9.98 484		0.01 516	9.85 693		0			
′	L. Cos.	d.	L. Cot.	c.d.	L. Tan.	L. Sin.	d.	′	P. P.		

133° (313°)   **(226°) 46°**

COMMON LOGARITHMS OF THE TRIGONOMETRIC FUNCTIONS (Continued)

44° (224°)   **(315°) 135°**

'	L. Sin.	d.	L. Tan.	c.d.	L. Cot.	L. Cos.	d.	'
0	9.84 177	13	9.98 484	25	0.01 516	9.85 693	12	60
1	9.84 190	13	9.98 509	25	0.01 491	9.85 681	12	59
2	9.84 203	13	9.98 534	26	0.01 466	9.85 669	12	58
3	9.84 216	13	9.98 560	25	0.01 440	9.85 657	12	57
4	9.84 229	13	9.98 585	25	0.01 415	9.85 645	13	56
5	9.84 242	13	9.98 610	25	0.01 390	9.85 632	12	55
6	9.84 255	14	9.98 635	26	0.01 365	9.85 620	12	54
7	9.84 269	13	9.98 661	25	0.01 339	9.85 608	12	53
8	9.84 282	13	9.98 686	25	0.01 314	9.85 596	13	52
9	9.84 295	13	9.98 711	26	0.01 289	9.85 583	12	51
10	9.84 308	13	9.98 737	25	0.01 263	9.85 571	12	50
11	9.84 321	13	9.98 762	25	0.01 238	9.85 559	12	49
12	9.84 334	13	9.98 787	25	0.01 213	9.85 547	13	48
13	9.84 347	13	9.98 812	26	0.01 188	9.85 534	12	47
14	9.84 360	13	9.98 838	25	0.01 162	9.85 522	12	46
15	9.84 373	12	9.98 863	25	0.01 137	9.85 510	13	45
16	9.84 385	13	9.98 888	25	0.01 112	9.85 497	12	44
17	9.84 398	13	9.98 913	26	0.01 087	9.85 485	12	43
18	9.84 411	13	9.98 939	25	0.01 061	9.85 473	13	42
19	9.84 424	13	9.98 964	25	0.01 036	9.85 460	12	41
20	9.84 437	13	9.98 989	26	0.01 011	9.85 448	12	40
21	9.84 450	13	9.99 015	25	0.00 985	9.85 436	12	39
22	9.84 463	13	9.99 040	25	0.00 960	9.85 423	12	38
23	9.84 476	13	9.99 065	25	0.00 935	9.85 411	12	37
24	9.84 489	13	9.99 090	26	0.00 910	9.85 399	13	36
25	9.84 502	13	9.99 116	25	0.00 884	9.85 386	12	35
26	9.84 515	13	9.99 141	25	0.00 859	9.85 374	13	34
27	9.84 528	13	9.99 166	25	0.00 834	9.85 361	12	33
28	9.84 540	13	9.99 191	26	0.00 809	9.85 349	12	32
29	9.84 553	13	9.99 217	25	0.00 783	9.85 337	13	31
30	9.84 566	13	9.99 242	25	0.00 758	9.85 324	12	30
31	9.84 579	13	9.99 267	26	0.00 733	9.85 312	13	29
32	9.84 592	13	9.99 293	25	0.00 707	9.85 299	13	28
33	9.84 605	13	9.99 318	25	0.00 682	9.85 287	13	27
34	9.84 618	12	9.99 343	25	0.00 657	9.85 274	12	26
35	9.84 630	13	9.99 368	26	0.00 632	9.85 262	12	25
36	9.84 643	13	9.99 394	25	0.00 606	9.85 250	13	24
37	9.84 656	13	9.99 419	25	0.00 581	9.85 237	12	23
38	9.84 669	13	9.99 444	25	0.00 556	9.85 225	13	22
39	9.84 682	12	9.99 469	26	0.00 531	9.85 212	12	21
40	9.84 694	13	9.99 495	25	0.00 505	9.85 200	13	20
41	9.84 707	13	9.99 520	25	0.00 480	9.85 187	12	19
42	9.84 720	13	9.99 545	25	0.00 455	9.85 175	13	18
43	9.84 733	12	9.99 570	26	0.00 430	9.85 162	12	17
44	9.84 745	13	9.99 596	25	0.00 404	9.85 150	13	16
45	9.84 758	13	9.99 621	25	0.00 379	9.85 137	12	15
46	9.84 771	13	9.99 646	26	0.00 354	9.85 125	13	14
47	9.84 784	12	9.99 672	25	0.00 328	9.85 112	12	13
48	9.84 796	13	9.99 697	25	0.00 303	9.85 100	13	12
49	9.84 809	13	9.99 722	25	0.00 278	9.85 087	13	11
50	9.84 822	13	9.99 747	26	0.00 253	9.85 074	12	10
51	9.84 835	12	9.99 773	25	0.00 227	9.85 062	13	9
52	9.84 847	13	9.99 798	25	0.00 202	9.85 049	13	8
53	9.84 860	13	9.99 823	25	0.00 177	9.85 037	13	7
54	9.84 873	12	9.99 848	26	0.00 152	9.85 024	12	6
55	9.84 885	13	9.99 874	25	0.00 126	9.85 012	13	5
56	9.84 898	13	9.99 899	25	0.00 101	9.84 999	13	4
57	9.84 911	12	9.99 924	25	0.00 076	9.84 986	12	3
58	9.84 923	13	9.99 949	26	0.00 051	9.84 974	13	2
59	9.84 936	13	9.99 975	25	0.00 025	9.84 961	13	1
60	9.84 949		0.00 000		0.00 000	9.84 949		0

'	L. Cos.	d.	L. Cot.	c.d.	L. Tan.	L. Sin.	d.	'

P. P.

"	26	25
1	0.4	0.4
2	0.9	0.8
3	1.3	1.2
4	1.7	1.7
5	2.2	2.1
6	2.6	2.5
7	3.0	2.9
8	3.5	3.3
9	3.9	3.8
10	4.3	4.2
20	8.7	8.3
30	13.0	12.5
40	17.3	16.7
50	21.7	20.8

"	14	13	12
1	0.2	0.2	0.2
2	0.5	0.4	0.4
3	0.7	0.6	0.6
4	0.9	0.9	0.8
5	1.2	1.1	1.0
6	1.4	1.3	1.2
7	1.6	1.5	1.4
8	1.9	1.7	1.6
9	2.1	2.0	1.8
10	2.3	2.2	2.0
20	4.7	4.3	4.0
30	7.0	6.5	6.0
40	9.3	8.7	8.0
50	11.7	10.8	10.0

	13	13
	26	25
0	1.0	0.9
1	3.0	2.9
2	5.0	4.8
3	7.0	6.7
4	9.0	8.7
5	11.0	10.6
6	13.0	12.5
7	15.0	14.4
8	17.0	16.3
9	19.0	18.3
10	21.0	20.2
11	23.0	22.1
12	25.0	24.1
13		

	12	12
	26	25
0	1.1	1.1
1	3.2	3.1
2	5.4	5.2
3	7.6	7.3
4	9.8	9.4
5	11.9	11.5
6	14.1	13.5
7	16.2	15.6
8	18.4	17.7
9	20.6	19.8
10	22.8	21.9
11	24.9	23.9
12		

COMMON LOGARITHMS OF THE TRIGONOMETRIC FUNCTIONS FOR ANGLES IN DEGREES AND DECIMALS

The table that follows gives the common logarithms of the functions sine, cosine, tangent and cotangent for each tenth of a degree from 0° to 90°. Linear interpolation may be used to obtain functional values for angles expressed in hundredths of a degree, except where the values of the functions are rapidly changing.

For argument values found in the left column, use the column headings at the top of the columns. For argument values found in the right column, use the column headings at the bottom of the columns.

The quantity − 10 is to be appended to the logarithm of all sines and cosines, and to logarithms of tangents from 0° to 45°, and cotangents from 45° to 90°.

COMMON LOGARITHMS OF THE TRIGONOMETRIC FUNCTIONS FOR ANGLES IN DEGREES AND DECIMALS

Deg.	L. Sin	*L. Tan	*L. Cot	L. Cos	
0.0	− ∞	− ∞	∞	0.00000	**90.0**
.1	7.24188	7.24188	2.75812	0.00000	89.9
.2	7.54291	7.54291	2.45709	0.00000	.8
.3	7.71900	7.71900	2.28100	9.99999	.7
.4	7.84393	7.84394	2.15606	9.99999	.6
.5	7.94084	7.94086	2.05914	9.99998	.5
.6	8.02002	8.02004	1.97996	9.99998	.4
.7	8.08696	8.08700	1.91300	9.99997	.3
.8	8.14495	8.14500	1.85500	9.99996	.2
.9	8.19610	8.19616	1.80384	9.99995	89.1
1.0	8.24186	8.24192	1.75808	9.99993	**89.0**
.1	8.28324	8.28332	1.71668	9.99992	88.9
.2	8.32103	8.32112	1.67888	9.99990	.8
.3	8.35578	8.35590	1.64410	9.99989	.7
.4	8.38796	8.38809	1.61191	9.99987	.6
.5	8.41792	8.41807	1.58193	9.99985	.5
.6	8.44594	8.44611	1.55389	9.99983	.4
.7	8.47226	8.47245	1.52755	9.99981	.3
.8	8.49708	8.49729	1.50271	9.99979	.2
.9	8.52055	8.52079	1.47921	9.99976	88.1
2.0	8.54282	8.54308	1.45692	9.99974	**88.0**
.1	8.56400	8.56429	1.43571	9.99971	87.9
.2	8.58419	8.58451	1.41549	9.99968	.8
.3	8.60349	8.60384	1.39616	9.99965	.7
.4	8.62196	8.62234	1.37766	9.99962	.6
.5	8.63968	8.64009	1.35991	9.99959	.5
.6	8.65670	8.65715	1.34285	9.99955	.4
.7	8.67308	8.67356	1.32644	9.99952	.3
.8	8.68886	8.68938	1.31062	9.99948	.2
.9	8.70409	8.70465	1.29535	9.99944	87.1
3.0	8.71880	8.71940	1.28060	9.99940	**87.0**
.1	8.73303	8.73366	1.26634	9.99936	86.9
.2	8.74680	8.74748	1.25252	9.99932	.8
.3	8.76015	8.76087	1.23913	9.99928	.7
.4	8.77310	8.77387	1.22613	9.99923	.6
.5	8.78568	8.78649	1.21351	9.99919	.5
.6	8.79789	8.79875	1.20125	9.99914	.4
.7	8.80978	8.81068	1.18932	9.99909	.3
.8	8.82134	8.82230	1.17770	9.99904	.2
.9	8.83261	8.83361	1.16639	9.99899	86.1
4.0	8.84358	8.84464	1.15536	9.99894	**86.0**
.1	8.85429	8.85540	1.14460	9.99889	85.9
.2	8.86474	8.86591	1.13409	9.99883	.8
.3	8.87494	8.87616	1.12384	9.99878	.7
.4	8.88490	8.88618	1.11382	9.99872	.6
.5	8.89464	8.89598	1.10402	9.99866	.5
.6	8.90417	8.90557	1.09443	9.99860	.4
.7	8.91349	8.91495	1.08505	9.99854	.3
.8	8.92261	8.92414	1.07586	9.99847	.2
.9	8.93154	8.93313	1.06687	9.99841	85.1
5.0	8.94030	8.94195	1.05805	9.99834	**85.0**
.1	8.94887	8.95060	1.04940	9.99828	84.9
.2	8.95728	8.95908	1.04092	9.99821	.8
.3	8.96553	8.96739	1.03261	9.99814	.7
.4	8.97363	8.97556	1.02444	9.99807	.6
.5	8.98157	8.98358	1.01642	9.99800	.5
.6	8.98937	8.99145	1.00855	9.99792	.4
.7	8.99704	8.99919	1.00081	9.99785	.3
.8	9.00456	9.00679	0.99321	9.99777	.2
.9	9.01196	9.01427	0.98573	9.99769	84.1
6.0	9.01923	9.02162	0.97838	9.99761	**84.0**
	L. Cos	*L. Cot	*L. Tan	L. Sin	Deg.

Deg.	L. Sin	L. Tan	L. Cot	L. Cos	
6.0	9.01923	9.02162	0.97838	9.99761	**84.0**
.1	9.02639	9.02885	0.97115	9.99753	83.9
.2	9.03342	9.03597	0.96403	9.99745	.8
.3	9.04034	9.04297	0.95703	9.99737	.7
.4	9.04715	9.04987	0.95013	9.99728	.6
.5	9.05386	9.05666	0.94334	9.99720	.5
.6	9.06046	9.06335	0.93665	9.99711	.4
.7	9.06696	9.06994	0.93006	9.99702	.3
.8	9.07337	9.07643	0.92357	9.99693	.2
.9	9.07968	9.08283	0.91717	9.99684	83.1
7.0	9.08589	9.08914	0.91086	9.99675	**83.0**
.1	9.09202	9.09537	0.90463	9.99666	82.9
.2	9.09807	9.10150	0.89850	9.99656	.8
.3	9.10402	9.10756	0.89244	9.99647	.7
.4	9.10990	9.11353	0.88647	9.99637	.6
.5	9.11570	9.11943	0.88057	9.99627	.5
.6	9.12142	9.12525	0.87475	9.99617	.4
.7	9.12706	9.13099	0.86901	9.99607	.3
8	9.13263	9.13667	0.86333	9.99596	.2
.9	9.13813	9.14227	0.85773	9.99586	82.1
8.0	9.14356	9.14780	0.85220	9.99575	**82.0**
.1	9.14891	9.15327	0.84673	9.99565	81.9
2	9.15421	9.15867	0.84133	9.99554	.8
.3	9.15944	9.16401	0.83599	9.99543	.7
.4	9.16460	9.16928	0.83072	9.99532	.6
.5	9.16970	9.17450	0.82550	9.99520	.5
.6	9.17474	9.17965	0.82035	9.99509	.4
.7	9.17973	9.18475	0.81525	9.99497	.3
.8	9.18465	9.18979	0.81021	9.99486	.2
.9	9.18952	9.19478	0.80522	9.99474	81.1
9.0	9.19433	9.19971	0.80029	9.99462	**81.0**
.1	9.19909	9.20459	0.79541	9.99450	80.9
.2	9.20380	9.20942	0.79058	9.99438	.8
.3	9.20845	9.21420	0.78580	9.99425	.7
.4	9.21306	9.21893	0.78107	9.99413	.6
.5	9.21761	9.22361	0.77639	9.99400	.5
6	9.22211	9.22824	0.77176	9.99388	.4
.7	9.22657	9.23283	0.76717	9.99375	.3
.8	9.23098	9.23737	0.76263	9.99362	.2
.9	9.23535	9.24186	0.75814	9.99348	80.1
10.0	9.23967	9.24632	0.75368	9.99335	**80.0**
.1	9.24395	9.25073	0.74927	9.99322	79.9
2	9.24818	9.25510	0.74490	9.99308	.8
3	9.25237	9.25943	0.74057	9.99294	.7
.4	9.25652	9.26372	0.73628	9.99281	.6
.5	9.26063	9.26797	0.73203	9.99267	.5
.6	9.26470	9.27218	0.72782	9.99252	.4
.7	9.26873	9.27635	0.72365	9.99238	.3
.8	9.27273	9.28049	0.71951	9.99224	.2
.9	9.27668	9.28459	0.71541	9.99209	79.1
11.0	9.28060	9.28865	0.71135	9.99195	**79.0**
.1	9.28448	9.29268	0.70732	9.99180	78.9
.2	9.28833	9.29668	0.70332	9.99165	.8
.3	9.29214	9.30064	0.69936	9.99150	.7
.4	9.29591	9.30457	0.69543	9.99135	.6
.5	9.29966	9.30846	0.69154	9.99119	.5
.6	9.30336	9.31233	0.68767	9.99104	.4
.7	9.30704	9.31616	0.68384	9.99088	.3
.8	9.31068	9.31996	0.68004	9.99072	.2
.9	9.31430	9.32373	0.67627	9.99056	78.1
12.0	9.31788	9.32747	0 67253	9.99040	**78.0**
	L. Cos	L. Cot	L. Tan	L. Sin	Deg.

*Linear interpolation in this section of the table is inaccurate.

COMMON LOGARITHMS OF THE TRIGONOMETRIC FUNCTIONS FOR ANGLES IN DEGREES AND DECIMALS (Continued)

Deg.	L. Sin	L. Tan	L. Cot	L. Cos	
12.0	9.31788	9.32747	0.67253	9.99040	**78.0**
.1	9.32143	9.33119	0.66881	9.99024	77.9
.2	9.32495	9.33487	0.66513	9.99008	.8
.3	9.32844	9.33853	0.66147	9.98991	.7
.4	9.33190	9.34215	0.65785	9.98975	.6
.5	9.33534	9.34576	0.65424	9.98958	.5
.6	9.33874	9.34933	0.65067	9.98941	.4
.7	9.34212	9.35288	0.64712	9.98924	.3
.8	9.34547	9.35640	0.64360	9.98907	.2
.9	9.34879	9.35989	0.64011	9.98890	77.1
13.0	9.35209	9.36336	0.63664	9.98872	**77.0**
.1	9.35536	9.36681	0.63319	9.98855	76.9
.2	9.35860	9.37023	0.62977	9.98837	.8
.3	9.36182	9.37363	0.62637	9.98819	.7
.4	9.36502	9.37700	0.62300	9.98801	.6
.5	9.36819	9.38035	0.61965	9.98783	.5
.6	9.37133	9.38368	0.61632	9.98765	.4
.7	9.37445	9.38699	0.61301	9.98746	.3
.8	9.37755	9.39027	0.60973	9.98728	.2
.9	9.38062	9.39353	0.60647	9.98709	76.1
14.0	9.38368	9.39677	0.60323	9.98690	**76.0**
.1	9.38670	9.39999	0.60001	9.98671	75.9
.2	9.38971	9.40319	0.59681	9.98652	.8
.3	9.39270	9.40636	0.59364	9.98633	.7
.4	9.39566	9.40952	0.59048	9.98614	.6
.5	9.39860	9.41266	0.58734	9.98594	.5
.6	9.40152	9.41578	0.58422	9.98574	.4
.7	9.40442	9.41887	0.58113	9.98555	.3
.8	9.40730	9.42195	0.57805	9.98535	.2
.9	9.41016	9.42501	0.57499	9.98515	75.1
15.0	9.41300	9.42805	0.57195	9.98494	**75.0**
.1	9.41582	9.43108	0.56892	9.98474	74.9
.2	9.41861	9.43408	0.56592	9.98453	.8
.3	9.42140	9.43707	0.56293	9.98433	.7
.4	9.42416	9.44004	0.55996	9.98412	.6
.5	9.42690	9.44299	0.55701	9.98391	.5
.6	9.42962	9.44592	0.55408	9.98370	.4
.7	9.43233	9.44884	0.55116	9.98349	.3
.8	9.43502	9.45174	0.54826	9.98327	.2
.9	9.43769	9.45463	0.54537	9.98306	74.1
16.0	9.44034	9.45750	0.54250	9.98284	**74.0**
.1	9.44297	9.46035	0.53965	9.98262	73.9
.2	9.44559	9.46319	0.53681	9.98240	.8
.3	9.44819	9.46601	0.53399	9.98218	.7
.4	9.45077	9.46881	0.53119	9.98196	.6
.5	9.45334	9.47160	0.52840	9.98174	.5
.6	9.45589	9.47438	0.52562	9.98151	.4
.7	9.45843	9.47714	0.52286	9.98129	.3
.8	9.46095	9.47989	0.52011	9.98106	.2
.9	9.46345	9.48262	0.51738	9.98083	73.1
17.0	9.46594	9.48534	0.51466	9.98060	**73.0**
.1	9.46841	9.48804	0.51196	9.98036	72.9
.2	9.47086	9.49073	0.50927	9.98013	.8
.3	9.47330	9.49341	0.50659	9.97989	.7
.4	9.47573	9.49607	0.50393	9.97966	.6
.5	9.47814	9.49872	0.50128	9.97942	.5
.6	9.48054	9.50136	0.49864	9.97918	.4
.7	9.48292	9.50398	0.49602	9.97894	.3
.8	9.48529	9.50659	0.49341	9.97870	.2
.9	9.48764	9.50919	0.49081	9.97845	72.1
18.0	9.48998	9.51178	0.48822	9.97821	**72.0**
	L. Cos	L. Cot	L. Tan	L. Sin	Deg.

Deg.	L. Sin	L. Tan	L. Cot	L. Cos	
18.0	9.48998	9.51178	0.48822	9.97821	**72.0**
.1	9.49231	9.51435	0.48565	9.97796	71.9
.2	9.49462	9.51691	0.48309	9.97771	.8
.3	9.49692	9.51946	0.48054	9.97746	.7
.4	9.49920	9.52200	0.47800	9.97721	.6
.5	9.50148	9.52452	0.47548	9.97696	.5
.6	9.50374	9.52703	0.47297	9.97670	.4
.7	9.50598	9.52953	0.47047	9.97645	.3
.8	9.50821	9.53202	0.46798	9.97619	.2
.9	9.51043	9.53450	0.46550	9.97593	71.1
19.0	9.51264	9.53697	0.46303	9.97567	**71.0**
.1	9.51484	9.53943	0.40057	9.97541	70.9
.2	9.51702	9.54187	0.45813	9.97515	.8
.3	9.51919	9.54431	0.45569	9.97488	.7
.4	9 52135	9.54673	0.45327	9.97461	.6
.5	9.52350	9.54915	0.45085	9.97435	.5
.6	9.52563	9.55155	0.44845	9.97408	.4
.7	9.52775	9.55395	0 44605	9.97381	.3
.8	9.52986	9.55633	0.44367	9.97353	.2
.9	9.53196	9.55870	0.44130	9.97326	70.1
20.0	9.53405	9.56107	0.43893	9.97299	**70.0**
.1	9.53613	9.56342	0.43658	9.97271	69.9
.2	9.53819	9.56576	0.43424	9.97243	.8
.3	9.54025	9.56810	0.43190	9.97215	.7
.4	9.54229	9.57042	0.42958	9.97187	.6
.5	9.54433	9.57274	0.42726	9.97159	.5
.6	9.54635	9.57504	0.42496	9.97130	.4
.7	9.54836	9.57734	0.42266	9.97102	.3
.8	9.55036	9.57963	0.42037	9.97073	.2
.9	9.55235	9.58191	0.41809	9.97044	69.1
21.0	9.55433	9.58418	0.41582	9.97015	**69.0**
.1	9.55630	9.58644	0.41356	9.96986	68.9
.2	9.55826	9.58869	0.41131	9.96957	.8
.3	9.56021	9.59094	0.40906	9.96927	.7
.4	9.56215	9.59317	0.40683	9.96898	.6
.5	9.56408	9.59540	0.40460	9.96868	.5
.6	9.56599	9.59762	0.40238	9.96838	.4
.7	9.56790	9.59983	0.40017	9.96808	.3
.8	9.56980	9.60203	0.39797	9.96778	.2
.9	9.57169	9.60422	0.39578	9.96747	68.1
22.0	9.57358	9.60641	0.39359	9.96717	**68.0**
.1	9.57545	9.60859	0.39141	9.96686	67.9
.2	9.57731	9.61076	0.38924	9.96655	.8
.3	9.57916	9.61292	0.38708	9.96624	.7
.4	9.58101	9.61508	0.38492	9.96593	.6
.5	9.58284	9.61722	0.38278	9.96562	.5
.6	9.58467	9.61936	0.38064	9.96530	.4
.7	9.58648	9.62150	0.37850	9.96498	.3
.8	9.58829	9.62362	0.37638	9.96467	.2
.9	9.59009	9.62574	0.37426	9.96435	67.1
23.0	9.59188	9.62785	0.37215	9.96403	**67.0**
.1	9.59366	9.62996	0.37004	9.96370	66.9
.2	9.59543	9.63205	0.36795	9.96338	.8
.3	9.59720	9.63414	0.36586	9.96305	.7
.4	9.59895	9.63623	0.36377	9.96273	.6
.5	9.60070	9.63830	0.36170	9.96240	.5
.6	9.60244	9.64037	0.35963	9.96207	.4
.7	9.60417	9.64243	0.35757	9.96174	.3
.8	9.60589	9.64449	0.35551	9.96140	.2
.9	9.60761	9.64654	0.35346	9.96107	66.1
24.0	9.60931	9.64858	0.35142	9.96073	**66.0**
	L. Cos	L. Cot	L. Tan	L. Sin	Deg.

COMMON LOGARITHMS OF THE TRIGONOMETRIC FUNCTIONS FOR ANGLES IN DEGREES AND DECIMALS (Continued)

Deg.	L. Sin	L. Tan	L. Cot	L. Cos	
24.0	9.60931	9.64858	0.35142	9\96073	**66.0**
.1	9.61101	9 65062	0 34938	9.96039	65.9
.2	9.61270	9 65265	0.34735	9.96005	.8
.3	9.61438	9.65467	0.34533	9 95971	.7
.4	9.61606	9.65669	0.34331	9 95937	.6
.5	9 61773	9.65870	0.34130	9.95902	.5
.6	9 61939	9.66071	0.33929	9.95868	.4
.7	9.62104	9.66271	0.33729	9 95833	3
.8	9.62268	9.66470	0.33530	9.95798	.2
.9	9.62432	9.66669	0.33331	9.95763	65.1
25.0	9.62595	9.66867	0.33133	9.95728	**65.0**
.1	9.62757	9.67065	0.32935	9.95692	64.9
.2	9 62918	9.67262	0.32738	9.95657	.8
.3	9.63079	9.67458	0 32542	9.95621	.7
.4	9.63239	9.67654	0 32346	9.95585	.6
.5	9.63398	9.67850	0.32150	9.95549	.5
.6	9 63557	9.68044	0.31956	9 95513	.4
.7	9.63715	0.68239	0.31761	9 95476	.3
.8	9.63872	9.68432	0.31568	9.95440	.2
.9	9.64028	9.68626	0.31374	9.95403	64.1
26.0	9.64184	9.68818	0.31182	9 95366	**64.0**
.1	9.64339	9.69010	0.30990	9.95329	63.9
.2	9 64494	9.69202	0 30798	9.95292	.8
.3	9.64647	9.69393	0.30607	9.95254	.7
.4	9.64800	9 69584	0.30416	9.95217	.6
.5	9.64953	9.69774	0.30226	9.95179	.5
.6	9.65104	9.69963	0.30037	9 95141	.4
.7	9.65255	9.70152	0.29848	9 95103	.3
.8	9.65406	9 70341	0 29659	9.95065	.2
.9	9.65556	0.70529	0.29471	9.95027	63.1
27.0	9.65705	9.70717	0.29283	9.94988	**63.0**
.1	9.65853	9.70904	0.29096	9.94949	62.9
.2	9.66001	9.71090	0 28910	9.94911	.8
.3	9.66148	9.71277	0 28723	9.94871	.7
.4	9.66295	9.71462	0.28538	9 94832	.6
.5	9 66441	9.71648	0 28352	9.94793	.5
.6	9.66586	9.71833	0.28167	9 94753	.4
.7	9.66731	9.72017	0.27983	9 94714	.3
.8	9 66875	9.72201	0.27799	9.94674	.2
.9	9.67018	9.72384	0.27616	9.94634	62.1
28.0	9.67161	9.72567	0.27433	9.94593	**62.0**
.1	9.67303	9.72750	0 27250	9.94553	61.9
.2	9.67445	9 72932	0.27068	9.94513	.8
.3	9.67586	9.73114	0.26886	9.94472	.7
.4	9.67726	9 73295	0.26705	9.94431	.6
.5	9.67866	9.73476	0.26524	9.94390	.5
.6	9.68006	9.73657	0.26343	9.94349	.4
.7	9.68144	9.73837	0.26163	9.94307	.3
.8	9.68283	9.74017	0.25983	9.94266	.2
.9	9.68420	9.74196	0.25804	9.94224	61.1
29.0	9.68557	9.74375	0.25625	9.94182	**61.0**
.1	9.68694	9.74554	0.25446	9.94140	60.9
.2	9.68829	9.74732	0.25268	9.94098	.8
.3	9.68965	9.74910	0.25090	9.94055	.7
.4	9.69100	9.75087	0.24913	9.94012	.6
.5	9.69234	9.75264	0.24736	9.93970	.5
.6	9.69368	9.75441	0.24559	9.93927	.4
.7	9.69501	9.75617	0.24383	9 93884	.3
.8	9.69633	9.75793	0.24207	9.93840	.2
.9	9.69765	9.75969	0.24031	9.93797	60.1
30.0	9.69897	9.76144	0.23856	9.93753	**60.0**
	L. Cos	L. Cot	L. Tan	L Sin	Deg.

Deg.	L. Sin	L Tan	L. Cot	L. Cos	
30.0	9.69897	9.76144	0.23856	9.93753	**60.0**
.1	9.70028	9.76319	0.23681	9.93709	59.9
.2	9.70159	9.76493	0.23507	9.93665	.8
.3	9.70288	9.76668	0.23332	9.93621	.7
.4	9.70418	9.76841	0.23159	9.93577	.6
.5	9.70547	9.77015	0.22985	9 93532	.5
.6	9 70675	9.77188	0.22812	9 93487	.4
.7	9.70803	9.77361	0 22639	9.93442	.3
.8	9.70931	9.77533	0.22467	9.93397	.2
.9	9.71058	9.77706	0.22294	9 93352	59.1
31.0	9.71184	9.77877	0.22123	9.93307	**59.0**
.1	9.71310	9.78049	0.21951	9.93261	58.9
.2	9.71435	9.78220	0 21780	9.93215	.8
.3	9.71560	9 78391	0.21609	9.93169	.7
.4	9.71685	9.78562	0.21438	9.93123	.6
.5	9.71809	9.78732	0.21268	9.93077	.5
.6	9.71932	9.78902	0.21098	9.93030	.4
.7	9.72055	9.79072	0 20928	9.92983	.3
.8	9.72177	9.79241	0.20759	9.92936	.2
.9	9.72299	9.79410	0.20590	9.92889	58.1
32.0	9.72421	9.79579	0 20421	9.92842	**58.0**
.1	9.72542	9.79747	0 20253	9.92795	57.9
.2	9.72663	9.79916	0.20084	9.92747	.8
.3	9.72783	9.80084	0 19916	9.92699	.7
.4	9.72902	9.80251	0.19749	9 92651	.6
.5	9 73022	9.80419	0.19581	9 92603	.5
.6	9.73140	9 80586	0 19414	9.92555	.4
.7	9 73259	9 80753	0 19247	9.92506	.3
.8	9.73377	9.80919	0.19081	9 92457	.2
.9	9.73494	9.81086	0.18914	9.92408	57.1
33.0	9.73611	9.81252	0.18748	9.92359	**57.0**
.1	9.73727	9 81418	0 18582	9 92310	56.9
.2	9 73843	9 81583	0 18417	9.92260	.8
.3	9.73959	9 81748	0.18252	9.92211	.7
.4	9.74074	9.81913	0.18087	9 92161	.6
.5	9.74189	9.82078	0.17922	9.92111	.5
.6	9.74303	9.82243	0.17757	9.92060	.4
.7	9 74417	9 82407	0 17593	9.92010	.3
.8	9 74531	9.82571	0.17429	9 91959	.2
.9	9.74644	9.82735	0.17265	9 91908	56.1
34.0	9 74756	9.82899	0.17101	9.91857	**56.0**
.1	9.74868	9.83062	0.16938	9.91806	55.9
.2	9.74980	9 83225	0.16775	9.91755	.8
.3	9.75091	9 83388	0.16612	9.91703	.7
.4	9.75202	9 83551	0.16449	9 91651	.6
.5	9.75313	9 83713	0.16287	9.91599	.5
.6	9 75423	9 83876	0.16124	9.91547	.4
.7	9.75533	9.84038	0 15962	9.91495	.3
.8	9.75642	9.84200	0.15800	9.91442	.2
.9	9.75751	9.84361	0.15639	9.91389	55.1
35.0	9.75859	9.84523	0.15477	9.91336	**55.0**
.1	9.75967	9.84684	0.15316	9.91283	54.9
.2	9.76075	9.84845	0.15155	9.91230	.8
.3	9.76182	9 85006	0.14994	9.91176	.7
.4	9 76289	9.85166	0.14834	9.91123	.6
.5	9.76395	9.85327	0.14673	9.91069	.5
.6	9.76501	9 85487	0.14513	9.91014	.4
.7	9 76607	9 85647	0 14353	9.90960	.3
.8	9.76712	9 85807	0.14193	9.90906	.2
.9	9.76817	9.85967	0.14033	9.90851	54.1
36.0	9.76922	9.86126	0 13874	9.90796	**54.0**
	L. Cos	L. Cot	L. Tan	L. Sin	Deg.

COMMON LOGARITHMS OF THE TRIGONOMETRIC FUNCTIONS FOR ANGLES IN DEGREES AND DECIMALS (Continued)

Deg.	L. Sin	L. Tan	L. Cot	L. Cos	
36.0	9 76922	9.86126	0.13874	9.90796	**54.0**
.1	9.77026	9.86285	0.13715	9.90741	53.9
.2	9.77130	9.86445	0.13555	9.90685	.8
.3	9.77233	9.86603	0.13397	9.90630	.7
.4	9.77336	9.86762	0.13238	9.90574	.6
.5	9.77439	9.86921	0.13079	9.90518	.5
.6	9.77541	9.87079	0.12921	9.90462	.4
.7	9.77643	9.87238	0.12762	9.90405	.3
.8	9.77744	9.87396	0.12604	9.90349	.2
.9	9.77846	9.87554	0.12446	9.90292	53.1
37.0	9.77946	9 87711	0.12289	9.90235	**53.0**
.1	9.78047	9.87869	0.12131	9.90178	52.9
.2	9 78147	9 88027	0.11973	9 90120	.8
.3	9.78246	9 88184	0.11816	9.90063	.7
.4	9.78346	9.88341	0.11659	9.90005	.6
.5	9.78445	9.88498	0.11502	9.89947	.5
.6	9 78543	9.88655	0.11345	9.89888	.4
.7	9 78642	9.88812	0.11188	9 89830	.3
.8	9.78739	9.88968	0.11032	9.89771	.2
.9	9.78837	9.89125	0.10875	9.89712	52.1
38.0	9 78934	9 89281	0.10719	9.89653	**52.0**
.1	9.79031	9.89437	0.10563	9.89594	51.9
.2	9.79128	9 89593	0.10407	9.89534	.8
.3	9.79224	9.89749	0.10251	9.89475	.7
.4	9.79319	9 89905	0.10095	9.89415	.6
.5	9.79415	9.90061	0.09939	9.89354	.5
.6	9.79510	9.90216	0.09784	9.89294	.4
.7	9.79605	9.90371	0.09629	9.89233	.3
.8	9 79699	9.90527	0.09473	9.89173	.2
.9	9.79793	9 90682	0.09318	9.89112	51.1
39.0	9 79887	9 90837	0.09163	9.89050	**51.0**
.1	9 79981	9.90992	0.09008	9.88989	50.9
.2	9.80074	9 91147	0 08853	9.88927	.8
.3	9.80166	9.91301	0.08699	9.88865	.7
.4	9.80259	9.91456	0 08544	9.88803	.6
.5	9.80351	9.91610	0.08390	9.88741	.5
.6	9 80443	9.91765	0 08235	9.88678	.4
.7	9.80534	9 91919	0 08081	9 88615	.3
.8	9 80625	9.92073	0.07927	9.88552	.2
.9	9.80716	9.92227	0.07773	9.88489	50.1
40.0	9 80807	9.92381	0.07619	9 88425	**50.0**
.1	9.80897	9.92535	0.07465	9.88362	49.9
.2	9.80987	9.92689	0.07311	9.88298	.8
.3	9 81076	9.92843	0.07157	9.88234	.7
.4	9.81166	9.92996	0.07004	9 88169	.6
.5	9.81254	9.93150	0.06850	9.88105	.5
.6	9 81343	9.93303	0.06697	9.88040	.4
.7	9.81431	9.93457	0.06543	9 87975	.3
.8	9.81519	9.93610	0.06390	9.87909	.2
.9	9.81607	9.93763	0.06237	9.87844	49.1
41.0	9.81694	9.93916	0.06084	9.87778	**49.0**
	L. Cos	L. Cot	L. Tan	L. Sin	Deg.

Deg.	D Sin	L. Tan	L. Cot	L. Cos	
41.0	9.81694	9.93916	0.06084	9.87778	**49.0**
.1	9.81781	9.94069	0.05931	9.87712	48.9
.2	9 81868	9.94222	0.05778	9.87646	.8
.3	9.81955	9.94375	0.05625	9.87579	.7
.4	9.82041	9.94528	0.05472	9.87513	.6
.5	9 82126	9.94681	0.05319	9.87446	.5
.6	9.82212	9.94834	0 05166	9.87378	.4
.7	9.82297	9.94986	0.05014	9.87311	.3
.8	9.82382	9.95139	0.04861	9.87243	.2
.9	9.82467	9.95291	0.04709	9.87175	48.1
42.0	9 82551	9.95444	0.04556	9.87107	**48.0**
.1	9.82635	9.95596	0.04404	9.87039	47.9
.2	9 82719	9.95748	0.04252	9 86970	.8
.3	9.82802	9 95901	0.04099	9 86902	.7
.4	9.82885	9.96053	0.03947	9 86832	.6
.5	9.82968	9.96205	0 03795	9.86763	.5
.6	9 83051	9.96357	0 03643	9 86694	.4
7	9.83133	9.96510	0 03490	9.86624	.3
.8	9 83215	9.96662	0.03338	9.86554	.2
.9	9.83297	9.96814	0.03186	9.86483	47.1
43.0	9.83378	9.96966	0.03034	9.86413	**47.0**
.1	9 83459	9.97118	0.02882	9 86342	46.9
.2	9.83540	9.97269	0.02731	9.86271	.8
.3	9 83621	9 97421	0.02579	9.86200	7
.4	9.83701	9 97573	0.02427	9 86128	.6
.5	9.83781	9.97725	0.02275	9.86056	.5
.6	9.83861	9 97877	0 02123	9.85984	.4
.7	9.83940	9.98029	0.01971	9.85912	.3
.8	9.84020	9 98180	0.01820	9.85839	.2
.9	9.84098	9.98332	0.01668	9.85766	46.1
44.0	9.84177	9 98484	0.01516	9 85693	**46.0**
.1	9.84255	9.98635	0 01365	9.85620	45.9
.2	9 84334	9.98787	0 01213	9 85547	.8
.3	9 84411	9 98939	0 01061	9.85473	.7
.4	9.84489	9 99090	0 00910	9.85399	.6
.5	9.84566	9.99242	0.00758	9 85324	.5
.6	9 84643	9.99394	0.00606	9.85250	.4
.7	9.84720	9.99545	0.00455	9 85175	.3
.8	9.84796	9.99697	0 00303	9.85100	.2
.9	9.84873	9.99848	0.00152	9.85024	45.1
45.0	9.84949	0.00000	0.00000	9.84949	**45.0**
	L. Cos	L. Cot	L. Tan	L. Sin	Deg.

COMMON LOGARITHMS OF THE TRIGONOMETRIC FUNCTIONS FOR ANGLES IN RADIANS

The table that follows gives the common logarithms of the functions sine, cosine, tangent and cotangent for each hundredth of a radian from 0 to 2.

The quantity -10 is to be appended to all logarithms of the sine and cosine, to logarithms of the tangent from 0 to .78, and of the cotangent from .79 to 2.

Rad.	L. Sin	L. Tan	L. Cot	L. Cos	Rad.	L. Sin	L. Tan	L. Cot	L. Cos
.00	$-\infty$	$-\infty$	∞	0.00000	.50	9.68072	9.73743	0.26257	9.94329
.01	7.99999	8.00001	1.99999	9.99998	.51	9.68858	9.74769	0.25231	9.94089
.02	8.30100	8.30109	1.69891	9.99991	.52	9.69625	9.75782	0.24218	9.93843
.03	8.47706	8.47725	1.52275	9.99980	.53	9.70375	9.76784	0.23216	9.93591
.04	8.60194	8.60229	1.39771	9.99965	.54	9.71108	9.77774	0.22226	9.93334
.05	8.69879	8.69933	1.30067	9.99946	.55	9.71824	9.78754	0.21246	9.93071
.06	8.77789	8.77867	1.22133	9.99922	.56	9.72525	9.79723	0.20277	9.92801
.07	8.84474	8.84581	1.15419	9.99894	.57	9.73210	9.80684	0.19316	9.92526
.08	8.90263	8.90402	1.09598	9.99861	.58	9.73880	9.81635	0.18365	9.92245
.09	8.95366	8.95542	1.04458	9.99824	.59	9.74536	9.82579	0.17421	9.91957
.10	8.99928	9.00145	0.99855	9.99782	.60	9.75177	9.83514	0.16486	9.91663
.11	9.04052	9.04315	0.95685	9.99737	.61	9.75805	9.84443	0.15557	9.91363
.12	9.07814	9.08127	0.91873	9.99687	.62	9.76420	9.85364	0.14636	9.91056
.13	9.11272	9.11640	0.88360	9.99632	.63	9.77022	9.86280	0.13720	9.90743
.14	9.14471	9.14898	0.85102	9.99573	.64	9.77612	9.87189	0.12811	9.90423
.15	9.17446	9.17937	0.82063	9.99510	.65	9.78189	9.88093	0.11907	9.90096
.16	9.20227	9.20785	0.79215	9.99442	.66	9.78754	9.88992	0.11008	9.89762
.17	9.22836	9.23466	0.76534	9.99369	.67	9.79308	9.89886	0.10114	9.89422
.18	9.25292	9.26000	0.74000	9.99293	.68	9.79851	9.90777	0.09223	9.89074
.19	9.27614	9.28402	0.71598	9.99211	.69	9.80382	9.91663	0.08337	9.88719
.20	9.29813	9.30688	0.69312	9.99126	.70	9.80903	9.92546	0.07454	9.88357
.21	9.31902	9.32867	0.67133	9.99035	.71	9.81414	9.93426	0.06574	9.87988
.22	9.33891	9.34951	0.65049	9.98940	.72	9.81914	9.94303	0.05697	9.87611
.23	9.35789	9.36948	0.63052	9.98841	.73	9.82404	9.95178	0.04822	9.87226
.24	9.37603	9.38866	0.61134	9.98737	.74	9.82885	9.96051	0.03949	9.86833
.25	9.39341	9.40712	0.59288	9.98628	.75	9.83355	9.96923	0.03077	9.86433
.26	9.41007	9.42492	0.57508	9.98515	.76	9.83817	9.97793	0.02207	9.86024
.27	9.42607	9.44210	0.55790	9.98397	.77	9.84269	9.98662	0.01338	9.85607
.28	9.44147	9.45872	0.54128	9.98275	.78	9.84713	9.99531	0.00469	9.85182
.29	9.45629	9.47482	0.52518	9.98148	.79	9.85147	0.00400	9.99600	9.84748
.30	9.47059	9.49043	0.50957	9.98016	.80	9.85573	0.01268	9.98732	9.84305
.31	9.48438	9.50559	0.49441	9.97879	.81	9.85991	0.02138	9.97862	9.83853
.32	9.49771	9.52034	0.47966	9.97737	.82	9.86400	0.03008	9.96992	9.83393
.33	9.51060	9.53469	0.46531	9.97591	.83	9.86802	0.03879	9.96121	9.82922
.34	9.52308	9.54868	0.45132	9.97440	.84	9.87195	0.04752	9.95248	9.82443
.35	9.53516	9.56233	0.43767	9.97284	.85	9.87580	0.05627	9.94373	9.81953
.36	9.54688	9.57565	0.42435	9.97123	.86	9.87958	0.06504	9.93496	9.81454
.37	9.55825	9.58868	0.41132	9.96957	.87	9.88328	0.07384	9.92616	9.80944
.38	9.56928	9.60142	0.39858	9.96786	.88	9.88691	0.08266	9.91734	9.80424
.39	9.58000	9.61390	0.38610	9.96610	.89	9.89046	0.09153	9.90847	9.79894
.40	9.59042	9.62613	0.37387	9.96429	.90	9.89394	0.10043	9.89957	9.79352
.41	9.60055	9.63812	0.36188	9.96243	.91	9.89735	0.10937	9.89063	9.78799
.42	9.61041	9.64989	0.35011	9.96051	.92	9.90070	0.11835	9.88165	9.78234
.43	9.62000	9.66145	0.33855	9.95855	.93	9.90397	0.12739	9.87261	9.77658
.44	9.62935	9.67282	0.32718	9.95653	.94	9.90717	0.13648	9.86352	9.77070
.45	9.63845	9.68400	0.31600	9.95446	.95	9.91031	0.14563	9.85437	9.76469
.46	9.64733	9.69500	0.30500	9.95233	.96	9.91339	0.15484	9.84516	9.75855
.47	9.65599	9.70583	0.29417	9.95015	.97	9.91639	0.16412	9.83588	9.75228
.48	9.66443	9.71651	0.28349	9.94792	.98	9.91934	0.17347	9.82653	9.74587
.49	9.67268	9.72704	0.27296	9.94563	.99	9.92222	0.18289	9.81711	9.73933
.50	9.68072	9.73743	0.26257	9.94329	1.00	9.92504	0.19240	9.80760	9.73264
Rad.	L. Sin	L. Tan	L. Cot	L. Cos	Rad.	L. Sin	L. Tan	L. Cot	L. Cos

COMMON LOGARITHMS OF THE
TRIGONOMETRIC FUNCTIONS FOR
ANGLES IN RADIANS (Continued)

Rad.	L. Sin	L. Tan	L. Cot	L. Cos	Rad.	L. Sin	L. Tan	L. Cot	L. Cos
1.00	9.92504	0.19240	9.80760	9.73264	**1.50**	9.99891	1.14926	8.85074	8.84965
1.01	9.92780	0.20200	9.79800	9.72580	1.51	9.99920	1.21559	8.78441	8.78361
1.02	9.93049	0.21169	9.78831	9.71881	1.52	9.99944	1.29379	8.70621	8.70565
1.03	9.93313	0.22148	9.77852	9.71165	1.53	9.99964	1.38914	8.61086	8.61050
1.04	9.93571	0.23137	9.76863	9.70434	1.54	9.99979	1.51136	8.48864	8.48843
1.05	9.93823	0.24138	9.75862	9.69686	1.55	9.99991	1.68195	8.31805	8.31796
1.06	9.94069	0.25150	9.74850	9.68920	1.56	9.99997	1.96671	8.03329	8.03327
1.07	9.94310	0.26175	9.73825	9.68135	1.57	0.00000	3.09891	6.90109	6.90109
1.08	9.94545	0.27212	9.72788	9.67332	1.58	9.99998	2.03603*	7.96397*	7.96396*
1.09	9.94774	0.28264	9.71736	9.66510	1.59	9.99992	1.71656	8.28344	8.28336
1.10	9.94998	0.29331	9.70669	9.65667	**1.60**	9.99981	1.53444	8.46556	8.46538
1.11	9.95216	0.30413	9.69587	9.64803	1.61	9.99967	1.40645	8.59355	8.59322
1.12	9.95429	0.31512	9.68488	9.63917	1.62	9.99947	1.30765	8.69235	8.69182
1.13	9.95637	0.32628	9.67372	9.63008	1.63	9.99924	1.22714	8.77286	8.77209
1.14	9.95839	0.33763	9.66237	9.62075	1.64	9.99896	1.15918	8.84082	8.83978
1.15	9.96036	0.34918	9.65082	9.61118	1.65	9.99864	1.10035	8.89965	8.89829
1.16	9.96228	0.36093	9.63907	9.60134	1.66	9.99827	1.04846	8.95154	8.94981
1.17	9.96414	0.37291	9.62709	9.59123	1.67	9.99786	1.00204	8.99796	8.99582
1.18	9.96596	0.38512	9.61488	9.58084	1.68	9.99741	0.96003	9.03997	9.03737
1.19	9.96772	0.39757	9.60243	9.57015	1.69	9.99691	0.92165	9.07835	9.07526
1.20	9.96943	0.41030	9.58970	9.55914	**1.70**	9.99636	0.88630	9.11370	9.11007
1.21	9.97110	0.42330	9.57670	9.54780	1.71	9.99578	0.85353	9.14647	9.14225
1.22	9.97271	0.43660	9.56340	9.53611	1.72	9.99515	0.82298	9.17702	9.17217
1.23	9.97428	0.45022	9.54978	9.52406	1.73	9.99447	0.79436	9.20564	9.20012
1.24	9.97579	0.46418	9.53582	9.51161	1.74	9.99375	0.76742	9.23258	9.22634
1.25	9.97726	0.47850	9.52150	9.49875	1.75	9.99299	0.74197	9.25803	9.25102
1.26	9.97868	0.49322	9.50678	9.48546	1.76	9.99218	0.71784	9.28216	9.27434
1.27	9.98005	0.50835	9.49165	9.47170	1.77	9.99133	0.69490	9.30510	9.29642
1.28	9.98137	0.52392	9.47608	9.45745	1.78	9.99043	0.67303	9.32697	9.31740
1.29	9.98265	0.53998	9.46002	9.44267	1.79	9.98948	0.65212	9.34788	9.33736
1.30	9.98388	0.55656	9.44344	9.42732	**1.80**	9.98849	0.63208	9.36792	9.35641
1.31	9.98506	0.57369	9.42631	9.41137	1.81	9.98745	0.61284	9.38716	9.37462
1.32	9.98620	0.59144	9.40856	9.39476	1.82	9.98637	0.59432	9.40568	9.39205
1.33	9.98729	0.60984	9.39016	9.37744	1.83	9.98524	0.57648	9.42352	9.40877
1.34	9.98833	0.62896	9.37104	9.35937	1.84	9.98407	0.55925	9.44075	9.42482
1.35	9.98933	0.64887	9.35113	9.34046	1.85	9.98285	0.54258	9.45742	9.44026
1.36	9.99028	0.66964	9.33036	9.32064	1.86	9.98158	0.52645	9.47355	9.45513
1.37	9.99119	0.69135	9.30865	9.29983	1.87	9.98026	0.51080	9.48920	9.46947
1.38	9.99205	0.71411	9.28589	9.27793	1.88	9.97890	0.49560	9.50440	9.48330
1.39	9.99286	0.73804	9.26196	9.25482	1.89	9.97749	0.48082	9.51918	9.49667
1.40	9.99363	0.76327	9.23673	9.23036	**1.90**	9.97603	0.46644	9.53356	9.50959
1.41	9.99436	0.78996	9.21004	9.20440	1.91	9.97452	0.45242	9.54758	9.52210
1.42	9.99504	0.81830	9.18170	9.17674	1.92	9.97296	0.43875	9.56125	9.53422
1.43	9.99568	0.84853	9.15147	9.14716	1.93	9.97136	0.42540	9.57460	9.54596
1.44	9.99627	0.88092	9.11908	9.11536	1.94	9.96970	0.41235	9.58765	9.55735
1.45	9.99682	0.91583	9.08417	9.08100	1.95	9.96800	0.39958	9.60042	9.56841
1.46	9.99733	0.95369	9.04631	9.04364	1.96	9.96624	0.38708	9.61292	9.57916
1.47	9.99779	0.99508	9.00492	9.00271	1.97	9.96443	0.37484	9.62516	9.58960
1.48	9.99821	1.04074	8.95926	8.95747	1.98	9.96258	0.36283	9.63717	9.59975
1.49	9.99858	1.09166	8.90834	8.90692	1.99	9.96067	0.35104	9.64896	9.60963
1.50	9.99891	1.14926	8.85074	8.84965	**2.00**	9.95871	0.33946	9.66054	9.61925
Rad.	L. Sin	L. Tan	L. Cot	L. Cos	Rad.	L. Sin	L. Tan	L. Cot	L. Cos

* Values of the cosine, tangent and cotangent for angles in the table, 1.58 radians and above, are negative. As a consequence the logarithms of the functions involved are for their absolute values. For example log |cos 1.90| = 9.50959 − 10.

SINE AND COSINE FUNCTIONS FOR SPECIAL MULTIPLES OF π RADIANS

k	$\sin\dfrac{2\pi k}{m}$	$\cos\dfrac{2\pi k}{m}$	$\sin\dfrac{2\pi k}{m}$	$\cos\dfrac{2\pi k}{m}$	$\sin\dfrac{2\pi k}{m}$	$\cos\dfrac{2\pi k}{m}$
	$m=3$		$m=4$		$m=5$	
1	0.86603	-0.50000	1.00000	$+0.00000$	0.95106	$+0.30902$
2	0.58779		0.00000	-1.00000	0.58779	-0.80902
	$m=6$		$m=7$		$m=8$	
1	0.86603	$+0.50000$	0.78183	$+0.62349$	0.70711	0.70711
2	0.86603	-0.50000	0.97493	-0.22252	1.00000	$+0.00000$
3	0.00000	-1.00000	0.43388	-0.90097	0.70711	-0.70711
4					0.00000	-1.00000
	$m=9$		$m=10$		$m=11$	
1	0.64279	0.76604	0.58779	0.80902	0.54064	0.84125
2	0.98481	$+0.17365$	0.95106	0.30902	0.90963	$+0.41542$
3	0.86603	-0.50000	0.95106	-0.30902	0.98982	-0.14231
4	0.34202	-0.93969	0.58779	-0.80902	0.75575	-0.65486
5			0.00000	-1.00000	0.28173	-0.95949
	$m=12$		$m=13$		$m=14$	
1	0.50000	0.86603	0.46472	0.88546	0.43388	0.90097
2	0.86603	0.50000	0.82298	0.56806	0.78183	0.62349
3	1.00000	$+0.00000$	0.99271	$+0.12054$	0.97493	$+0.22252$
4	0.86603	-0.50000	0.93502	-0.35460	0.97493	-0.22252
5	0.50000	-0.86603	0.66312	-0.74851	0.78183	-0.62349
6	0.00000	-1.00000	0.23932	-0.97094	0.43388	-0.90097
7					0.00000	-1.00000
	$m=15$		$m=16$		$m=17$	
1	0.40674	0.91355	0.38268	0.92388	0.36124	0.93247
2	0.74314	0.66913	0.70711	0.70711	0.67370	0.73901
3	0.95106	$+0.30902$	0.92388	0.38268	0.89516	0.44574
4	0.99452	-0.10453	1.00000	$+0.00000$	0.99573	$+0.09227$
5	0.86603	-0.50000	0.92388	-0.38268	0.96183	-0.27366
6	0.58779	-0.80902	0.70711	-0.70711	0.79802	-0.60263
7	0.20791	-0.97815	0.38268	-0.92388	0.52643	-0.85022
8			0.00000	-1.00000	0.18375	-0.98297
	$m=18$		$m=19$		$m=20$	
1	0.34202	0.93969	0.32470	0.94582	0.30902	0.95106
2	0.64279	0.76604	0.61421	0.78914	0.58779	0.80902
3	0.86603	0.50000	0.83717	0.54695	0.80902	0.58779
4	0.98481	$+0.17365$	0.96940	$+0.24549$	0.95106	0.30902
5	0.98481	-0.17365	0.99658	-0.08258	1.00000	$+0.00000$
6	0.86603	-0.50000	0.91577	-0.40170	0.95106	-0.30902
7	0.64279	-0.76604	0.73572	-0.67728	0.80902	-0.58779
8	0.34202	-0.93969	0.47595	-0.87947	0.58779	-0.80902
9	0.00000	-1.00000	0.16459	-0.98636	0.30902	-0.95106
10					0.00000	-1.00000
	$m=21$		$m=22$		$m=23$	
1	0.29476	0.95557	0.28173	0.95949	0.26980	0.96292
2	0.56332	0.82624	0.54064	0.84125	0.51958	0.85442
3	0.78183	0.62349	0.75575	0.65486	0.73084	0.68255
4	0.93087	0.36534	0.90963	0.41542	0.88789	0.46007
5	0.99720	$+0.07473$	0.98982	$+0.14231$	0.97908	$+0.20346$
6	0.97493	-0.22252	0.98982	-0.14231	0.99767	-0.06824
7	0.86603	-0.50000	0.90963	-0.41542	0.94226	-0.33488
8	0.68017	-0.73305	0.75575	-0.65486	0.81697	-0.57668
9	0.43388	-0.90097	0.54064	-0.84125	0.63109	-0.77571
10	0.14904	-0.98883	0.28173	-0.95949	0.39840	-0.91721
11			0.00000	-1.00000	0.13617	-0.99069
	$m=24$		$m=25$			
1	0.25882	0.96593	0.24869	0.96858		
2	0.50000	0.86603	0.48175	0.87631		
3	0.70711	0.70711	0.68455	0.72897		
4	0.86603	0.50000	0.84433	0.53583		
5	0.96593	0.25882	0.95106	0.30902		
6	1.00000	$+0.00000$	0.99803	$+0.06279$		
7	0.96593	-0.25882	0.98229	-0.18738		
8	0.86603	-0.50000	0.90483	-0.42578		
9	0.70711	-0.70711	0.77051	-0.63742		
10	0.50000	-0.86603	0.58779	-0.80902		
11	0.25882	-0.96593	0.36812	-0.92978		
12	0.00000	-1.00000	0.12533	-0.99211		

HYPERBOLIC AND RELATED FUNCTIONS

Dr. Madhu S. Gupta

HYPERBOLIC FUNCTIONS

Geometrical Definition

Let O be the center, A the vertex, and P any point with coordinates (x,y) on the branch B′AB of the rectangular hyperbola $X^2 - Y^2 = a^2$. Set OM = x, MP = y and OA = a. The shaded area shown in the figure is given by

$$\text{Area OPAP'} = a^2 \log_e \frac{(x+y)}{a}$$

If the angle POP′ in hyperbolic radians is denoted by u,

$$u = \frac{\text{area OPAP'}}{a^2} \text{ hyperbolic radians.}$$

The hyperbolic functions are defined by

hyperbolic sine of u = sinh u = y/a
hyperbolic cosine of u = cosh u - x/a

The approximate length of the hyperbolic curve is given by

$$\text{arc AP} = \frac{3}{2} y - \frac{1}{2} \tan^{-1} y$$

while the straight line distance is

$$\text{line AP} = \sqrt{\sinh^2 u + (\cosh u - 1)^2}$$

Exponential Definition

hyperbolic sine of $u = \sinh u = 1/2(e^u - e^{-u})$

hyperbolic cosine of $u = \cosh u = 1/2(e^u + e^{-u})$

hyperbolic tangent of $u = \tanh u = \dfrac{\sinh u}{\cosh u} = \dfrac{e^u - e^{-u}}{e^u + e^{-u}}$

$\text{csch } u = \dfrac{1}{\sinh u},$

$\text{sech } u = \dfrac{1}{\cosh u},$

$\coth u = \dfrac{1}{\tanh u},$

Domain and Range for Real Argument

Function	Domain (interval of u)	Range (interval of function)	Remarks
sinh u	$(-\infty, +\infty)$	$(-\infty, +\infty)$	
cosh u	$(-\infty, +\infty)$	$[1, +\infty)$	
tanh u	$(-\infty, +\infty)$	$(-1, +1)$	
cosech u	$(-\infty, 0)$	$(0, -\infty)$	Two branches, pole
	$(0, +\infty)$	$(+\infty, 0)$	at $u = 0$.
sech u	$(-\infty, +\infty)$	$(0, 1]$	
coth u	$(-\infty, 0)$	$(-1, -\infty)$	Two branches, pole
	$(0, +\infty)$	$(+\infty, 1)$	at $u = 0$

Hyperbolic Functions In Terms of One Another

Function	$\sinh x$	$\cosh x$	$\tanh x$
$\sinh x =$	$\sinh x$	$\pm \sqrt{\cosh^2 x - 1}$	$\dfrac{\tanh x}{\sqrt{1 - \tanh^2 x}}$
$\cosh x =$	$\sqrt{1 + \sinh^2 x}$	$\cosh x$	$\dfrac{1}{\sqrt{1 - \tanh^2 x}}$
$\tanh x =$	$\dfrac{\sinh x}{\sqrt{1 + \sinh^2 x}}$	$\pm \dfrac{\sqrt{\cosh^2 x - 1}}{\cosh x}$	$\tanh x$
$\operatorname{cosech} x =$	$\dfrac{1}{\sinh x}$	$\pm \dfrac{1}{\sqrt{\cosh^2 x - 1}}$	$\dfrac{\sqrt{1 - \tanh^2 x}}{\tanh x}$
$\operatorname{sech} x =$	$\dfrac{1}{\sqrt{1 + \sinh^2 x}}$	$\dfrac{1}{\cosh x}$	$\sqrt{1 - \tanh^2 x}$
$\coth x =$	$\dfrac{\sqrt{1 + \sinh^2 x}}{\sinh x}$	$\dfrac{\pm \cosh x}{\sqrt{\cosh^2 x - 1}}$	$\dfrac{1}{\tanh x}$

Function	$\operatorname{cosech} x$	$\operatorname{sech} x$	$\coth x$
$\sinh x =$	$\dfrac{1}{\operatorname{cosech} x}$	$\pm \dfrac{\sqrt{1 - \operatorname{sech}^2 x}}{\operatorname{sech} x}$	$\dfrac{\pm 1}{\sqrt{\coth^2 x - 1}}$
$\cosh x =$	$\pm \dfrac{\sqrt{\operatorname{cosech}^2 x + 1}}{\operatorname{cosech} x}$	$\dfrac{1}{\operatorname{sech} x}$	$\pm \dfrac{\coth x}{\sqrt{\coth^2 x - 1}}$
$\tanh x =$	$\dfrac{1}{\sqrt{\operatorname{cosech}^2 x + 1}}$	$\pm \sqrt{1 - \operatorname{sech}^2 x}$	$\dfrac{1}{\coth x}$
$\operatorname{cosech} x =$	$\operatorname{cosech} x$	$\pm \dfrac{\operatorname{sech} x}{\sqrt{1 - \operatorname{sech}^2 x}}$	$\pm \dfrac{\sqrt{\coth^2 x - 1}}{1}$
$\operatorname{sech} x =$	$\pm \dfrac{\operatorname{cosec} x}{\sqrt{\operatorname{cosech}^2 x + 1}}$	$\operatorname{sech} x$	$\pm \dfrac{\sqrt{\coth^2 x - 1}}{\coth x}$
$\coth x =$	$\sqrt{\operatorname{cosech}^2 x + 1}$	$\pm \dfrac{1}{\sqrt{1 - \operatorname{sech}^2 x}}$	$\coth x$

Whenever two signs are shown, choose $+$ sign if x is positive, $-$ sign if x is negative.

Special Values of Hyperbolic Functions

x	0	$\dfrac{\pi}{2} i$	πi	$\dfrac{3\pi}{2} i$	∞
$\sinh x$	0	i	0	$-i$	∞
$\cosh x$	1	0	-1	0	∞
$\tanh x$	0	∞i	0	$-\infty i$	1
$\operatorname{csch} x$	∞	$-i$	∞	i	0
$\operatorname{sech} x$	1	∞	-1	∞	0
$\coth x$	∞	0	∞	0	1

Symmetry and Periodicity

$$\sinh(-u) = -\sinh u, \qquad \operatorname{csch}(-u) = -\operatorname{csch} u$$
$$\cosh(-u) = \cosh u, \qquad \operatorname{sech}(-u) = \operatorname{sech} u$$
$$\tanh(-u) = -\tanh u, \qquad \coth(-u) = -\coth u$$

$\sinh u$, $\cosh u$, $\operatorname{cosech} u$ and $\operatorname{sech} u$ are periodic with a period $2\pi i$; $\tanh u$ and $\coth u$ are periodic with a period πi.

Fundamental Identities

Reciprocal Relations

$$\operatorname{csch} u = \frac{1}{\sinh u}, \qquad \operatorname{sech} u = \frac{1}{\cosh u}, \qquad \coth u = \frac{1}{\tanh u}$$

Product Relations

$$\sinh u = \tanh u \cosh u \qquad \cosh u = \coth u \sinh u$$
$$\tanh u = \sinh u \operatorname{sech} u \qquad \coth u = \cosh u \operatorname{cosech} u$$
$$\operatorname{sech} u = \operatorname{cosech} u \tanh u \qquad \operatorname{cosech} u = \operatorname{sech} u \coth u$$

Quotient Relations

$$\sinh u = \frac{\tanh u}{\operatorname{sech} u} \qquad \cosh u = \frac{\coth u}{\operatorname{cosech} u} \qquad \tanh u = \frac{\sinh u}{\cosh u}$$

$$\operatorname{cosech} u = \frac{\operatorname{sech} u}{\tanh u} \qquad \operatorname{sech} u = \frac{\operatorname{cosech} u}{\coth u} \qquad \coth u = \frac{\cosh u}{\sinh u}$$

Relations Between Squares of Functions

$$\cosh^2 u - \sinh^2 u = 1, \qquad \tanh^2 u + \operatorname{sech}^2 u = 1$$
$$\coth^2 u - \operatorname{csch}^2 u = 1, \qquad \operatorname{csch}^2 u - \operatorname{sech}^2 u = \operatorname{csch}^2 u \operatorname{sech}^2 u$$

Angle-Sum and Angle-Difference Relations

$$\sinh (u + v) = \sinh u \cosh v + \cosh u \sinh v$$
$$\sinh (u - v) = \sinh u \cosh v - \cosh u \sinh v$$
$$\cosh (u + v) = \cosh u \cosh v + \sinh u \sinh v$$
$$\cosh (u - v) = \cosh u \cosh v - \sinh u \sinh v$$

$$\tanh (u + v) = \frac{\tanh u + \tanh v}{1 + \tanh u \tanh v} = \frac{\sinh 2u + \sinh 2v}{\cosh 2u + \cosh 2v}$$

$$\tanh (u - v) = \frac{\tanh u - \tanh v}{1 - \tanh u \tanh v} = \frac{\sinh 2u - \sinh 2v}{\cosh 2u - \cosh 2v}$$

$$\coth (u + v) = \frac{1 + \coth u \coth v}{\coth u + \coth v} = \frac{\sinh 2u - \sinh 2v}{\cosh 2u - \cosh 2v}$$

$$\coth (u - v) = \frac{1 - \coth u \coth v}{\coth u - \coth v} = \frac{\sinh 2u + \sinh 2v}{\cosh 2u - \cosh 2v}$$

Multiple Angle Relations

$$\sinh 2u = 2 \sinh u \cosh u = \frac{2 \tanh u}{1 - \tanh^2 u}$$

$$\cosh 2u = \cosh^2 u + \sinh^2 u = 2 \cosh^2 u - 1 = 1 + 2 \sinh^2 u = \frac{1 + \tanh^2 u}{1 - \tanh^2 u}$$

$$\tanh 2u = \frac{2 \tanh u}{1 + \tanh^2 u}$$

$$\coth 2u = \frac{\coth^2 u + 1}{2 \coth u}$$

$$\sinh 3u = 3 \sinh u + 4 \sinh^3 u = \sinh u \,(4 \cosh^2 u - 1)$$
$$\cosh 3u = 4 \cosh^3 u - 3 \cosh u = \cosh u \,(1 + 4 \sinh^2 u)$$

$$\tanh 3u = \frac{3 \tanh u + \tanh^3 u}{1 + 3 \tanh^2 u}$$

$$\coth 3u = \frac{3 \coth u + \coth^3 u}{1 + 3 \coth^2 u}$$

$$\sinh 4u = 4 \sinh u \cosh u (2 \cosh^2 u - 1)$$
$$= 4 \sinh u \cosh u (1 + 2 \sinh^2 u)$$
$$= 4 \sinh u \cosh u (\cosh^2 u + \sinh^2 u)$$

$$\cosh 4u = 1 + 8 \cosh^2 u (\cosh^2 u - 1)$$
$$= 1 + 8 \sinh^2 u (\sinh^2 u + 1)$$
$$= \cosh^4 u + 6 \sinh^2 u \cosh^2 u + \sinh^4 u$$

$$\tanh 4u = \frac{4 \tanh u (1 + \tanh^2 u)}{1 + 6 \tanh^2 u + \tanh^4 u}$$

$$\coth 4u = \frac{\coth^4 u + 6 \coth^2 u + 1}{4 \coth u (\coth^2 u + 1)}$$

$$\sinh 5u = \sinh u (16 \sinh^4 u + 20 \sinh^2 u + 5)$$
$$= \sinh u (16 \cosh^4 u - 12 \cosh^2 u + 1)$$

$$\cosh 5u = \cosh u (16 \cosh^4 u - 20 \cosh^2 u + 5)$$
$$= \cosh u (16 \sinh^4 u + 12 \sinh^2 u + 1)$$

$$\sinh 6u = 2 \sinh u \cosh u (16 \cosh^4 u - 16 \cosh^2 u + 3)$$
$$= 2 \sinh u \cosh u (16 \sinh^4 u + 16 \sinh^2 u + 3)$$

$$\cosh 6u = 32 \cosh^6 u - 48 \cosh^4 u + 18 \cosh^2 u - 1$$
$$= 32 \sinh^6 u + 48 \sinh^4 u + 18 \sinh^2 u + 1$$

$$\sinh nu = \sinh u \left[(2 \cosh u)^{n-1} - \frac{(n-2)}{1!} \cdot (2 \cosh u)^{n-3} + \frac{(n-3)(n-4)}{2!} \right.$$
$$\left. \cdot (2 \cosh u)^{n-5} - \frac{(n-4)(n-5)(n-6)}{3!} (2 \cosh u)^{n-7} + \cdots \right].$$

$$\cosh nu = \frac{1}{2} \left[(2 \cosh u)^n - \frac{n}{1!} (2 \cosh u)^{n-2} + \frac{n(n-3)}{2!} (2 \cosh u)^{n-4} \right.$$
$$\left. - \frac{n(n-4)(n-5)}{3!} (2 \cosh u)^{n-6} + \cdots \right].$$

Half Angle Relations

$$\sinh \tfrac{1}{2}u = \pm \sqrt{\tfrac{1}{2}(\cosh u - 1)}$$
$$\cosh \tfrac{1}{2}u = \sqrt{\tfrac{1}{2}(\cosh u + 1)}$$

$$\tanh \frac{u}{2} = \frac{\sinh u}{1 + \cosh u} = \frac{\cosh u - 1}{\sinh u} = \pm \sqrt{\frac{\cosh u - 1}{\cosh u + 1}}$$

$$\coth \frac{u}{2} = \frac{1 + \cosh u}{\sinh u} = \frac{\sinh u}{\cosh u - 1} = \pm \sqrt{\frac{\cosh u + 1}{\cosh u - 1}}$$

Choose $+$ sign if u is positive, otherwise choose the $-$ sign.

Function Sum and Function Difference Relations

$$\sinh u + \sinh v = 2 \sinh \tfrac{1}{2}(u + v) \cosh \tfrac{1}{2}(u - v)$$
$$\sinh u - \sinh v = 2 \cosh \tfrac{1}{2}(u + v) \sinh \tfrac{1}{2}(u - v)$$
$$\cosh u + \cosh v = 2 \cosh \tfrac{1}{2}(u + v) \cosh \tfrac{1}{2}(u - v)$$
$$\cosh u - \cosh v = 2 \sinh \tfrac{1}{2}(u + v) \sinh \tfrac{1}{2}(u - v)$$

$$\tanh u + \tanh v = (1 + \tanh u \tanh v) \tanh (u + v) = \frac{\sinh (u + v)}{\cosh u \cosh v}$$

$$\tanh u - \tanh v = (1 - \tanh u \tanh v) \tanh (u - v) = \frac{\sinh (u - v)}{\cosh u \cosh v}$$

$$\coth u + \coth v = \frac{1 + \coth u \coth v}{\coth (u + v)} = \frac{\sinh (u + v)}{\sinh u \sinh v}$$

$$\coth u - \coth v = \frac{1 - \coth u \coth v}{\coth (u - v)} = \frac{\sinh (u - v)}{\sinh u \sinh v}$$

$$\sinh u + \cosh u = \frac{1 + \tanh \frac{1}{2}u}{1 - \tanh \frac{1}{2}u} = e^{u} \qquad \cosh u - \sinh u = \frac{1 - \tanh \frac{1}{2}u}{1 + \tanh \frac{1}{2}u} = e^{-u}$$

Function Product Relations

$$\sinh u \cosh v = \tfrac{1}{2} \sinh (u + v) + \tfrac{1}{2} \sinh (u - v)$$
$$\cosh u \sinh v = \tfrac{1}{2} \sinh (u + v) - \tfrac{1}{2} \sinh (u - v)$$
$$\cosh u \cosh v = \tfrac{1}{2} \cosh (u + v) + \tfrac{1}{2} \cosh (u - v)$$
$$\sinh u \sinh v = \tfrac{1}{2} \cosh (u + v) - \tfrac{1}{2} \cosh (u - v)$$
$$\sinh (u + v) \sinh (u - v) = \sinh^2 u - \sinh^2 v = \cosh^2 u - \cosh^2 v$$
$$\cosh (u + v) \cosh (u - v) = \sinh^2 u + \cosh^2 v = \cosh^2 u + \sinh^2 v$$

Power Relations

$$\sinh^2 u = \tfrac{1}{2}(\cosh 2u - 1)$$
$$\cosh^2 u = \tfrac{1}{2}(\cosh 2u + 1)$$
$$\sinh^3 u = \tfrac{1}{4}(-3 \sinh u + \sinh 3u)$$
$$\cosh^3 u = \tfrac{1}{4}(3 \cosh u + \cosh 3u)$$
$$\sinh^4 u = \tfrac{1}{8}(3 - 4 \cosh 2u + \cosh 4u)$$
$$\cosh^4 u = \tfrac{1}{8}(3 + 4 \cosh 2u + \cosh 4u)$$
$$\sinh^5 u = \tfrac{1}{16}(10 \sinh u - 5 \sinh 3u + \sinh 5u)$$
$$\cosh^5 u = \tfrac{1}{16}(10 \cosh u + 5 \cosh 3u + \cosh 5u)$$
$$\sinh^6 u = \tfrac{1}{32}(-10 + 15 \cosh 2u - 6 \cosh 4u + \cosh 6u)$$
$$\cosh^6 u = \tfrac{1}{32}(10 + 15 \cosh 2u + 6 \cosh 4u + \cosh 6u)$$
$$(\cosh u \pm \sinh u)^n = \cosh nu \pm \sinh nu$$

Relations with Circular Functions

$$\sinh iu = i \sin u, \qquad \sinh u = -i \sin iu$$
$$\cosh iu = \cos u, \qquad \cosh u = \cos iu$$
$$\tanh iu = i \tan u, \qquad \tanh u = -i \tan iu$$
$$\operatorname{cosech} iu = -i \operatorname{cosec} u \qquad \operatorname{cosech} u = i \operatorname{cosec} iu$$
$$\operatorname{sech} iu = \sec u \qquad \operatorname{sech} u = \sec iu$$
$$\coth iu = -i \cot u \qquad \coth u = i \coth iu$$

Hyperbolic Functions of Complex Argument

$$\sinh (u + iv) = \sinh u \cos v + i \cosh u \sin v$$
$$\sinh (u - iv) = \sinh u \cos v - i \cosh u \sin v$$
$$\cosh (u + iv) = \cosh u \cos v + i \sinh u \sin v$$
$$\cosh (u - iv) = \cosh u \cos v - i \sinh u \sin v$$

$$\tanh (u + iv) = \frac{\sinh 2u + i \sin 2v}{\cosh 2u + \cos 2v}$$

$$\tanh (u - iv) = \frac{\sinh 2u - i \sin 2v}{\cosh 2u + \cos 2v}$$

$$\coth (u + iv) = \frac{\sinh 2u - i \sin 2v}{\cosh 2u - \cos 2v}$$

$$\coth (u - iv) = \frac{\sinh 2u + i \sin 2v}{\cosh 2u - \cos 2v}$$

$$\sinh (u + \tfrac{1}{2}\pi i) = i \cosh u, \qquad \cosh (u + \tfrac{1}{2}\pi i) = i \sinh u$$
$$\sinh (u + \pi i) = -\sinh u, \qquad \cosh (u + \pi i) = -\cosh u$$
$$\sinh (u + 2\pi i) = \sinh u, \qquad \cosh (u + 2\pi i) = \cosh u$$

Series for Hyperbolic Functions

(see series expansions for $\sinh nu$ and $\cosh nu$ under multiple angle relations).

$$\sinh x = x + \frac{x^3}{3!} + \frac{x^5}{5!} + \frac{x^7}{7!} + \cdots + \frac{x^{2n+1}}{(2n+1)!} + \cdots \qquad |x| < \infty$$

$$\sinh ax = \frac{2}{\pi} \sinh \pi a \left[\frac{\sin x}{a^2 + 1^2} - \frac{2 \sin 2x}{a^2 + 2^2} + \frac{3 \sin 3x}{a^2 + 3^2} - + \cdots \right]$$

$$= \frac{2}{\pi} \sinh \pi a \sum_{n=1}^{\infty} (-1)^{n+1} \frac{n \sin nx}{n^2 + a^2}, \qquad |x| < \pi$$

$$\cosh x = 1 + \frac{x^2}{2!} + \frac{x^4}{4!} + \frac{x^6}{6!} + \cdots + \frac{x^{2n}}{(2n)!} + \cdots \qquad |x| < \infty$$

$$\cosh ax = \frac{2a}{\pi} \sinh \pi a \left[\frac{1}{2a^2} - \frac{\cos x}{a^2 + 1^2} + \frac{\cos 2x}{a^2 + 2^2} - \frac{\cos 3x}{a^2 + 3^2} + - \cdots \right]$$

$$= \frac{\sinh \pi a}{a\pi} + \frac{2a}{\pi} \sinh \pi a \sum_{n=1}^{\infty} (-1)^n \frac{\cos nx}{n^2 + a^2}, \qquad |x| < \pi$$

$$\tanh x = x - \frac{1}{3} x^3 + \frac{2}{15} x^5 - \frac{17}{315} x^7 + \frac{62}{2835} x^9 - \cdots$$
$$+ \frac{2^{2n}(2^{2n} - 1) B_{2n} x^{2n-1}}{(2n)!} \pm \cdots \quad (1) \qquad |x| < \frac{\pi}{2}$$

$$\tanh x = 1 - 2e^{-2x} + 2e^{-4x} - 2e^{-6x} + - \cdots$$

$$= 1 + 2 \sum_{n=1}^{\infty} (-1)^n e^{-2nx}, \qquad \mathrm{Re}\,(x) > 0$$

$$\tanh x = 2x \left[\frac{1}{\left(\frac{\pi}{2}\right)^2 + x^2} + \frac{1}{\left(\frac{3\pi}{2}\right)^2 + x^2} + \frac{1}{\left(\frac{5\pi}{2}\right)^2 + x^2} + \cdots \right]$$

$$= 2x \sum_{n=0}^{\infty} \frac{1}{\left(n + \frac{1}{2}\right)^2 \pi^2 + x^2}$$

$$\coth x = \frac{1}{x} + \frac{x}{3} - \frac{x^3}{45} + \frac{2x^5}{945} - \frac{x^7}{4725} + \cdots + \frac{2^{2n}}{(2n)!} B_{2n} x^{2n-1} \pm \cdots \quad (1)$$
$$0 < |x| < \pi$$

$$\coth x = 1 + 2e^{-2x} + 2e^{-4x} + 2e^{-6x} + \cdots$$

$$= 1 + 2 \sum_{n=1}^{\infty} e^{-2nx} \qquad \mathrm{Re}\,(x) > 0$$

$$\coth x = \frac{1}{x} + 2x \left[\frac{1}{\pi^2 + x^2} + \frac{1}{(2\pi)^2 + x^2} + \frac{1}{(3\pi)^2 + x^2} + \cdots \right]$$

$$= \frac{1}{x} + 2x \sum_{n=1}^{\infty} \frac{1}{(n\pi)^2 + x^2}$$

(1) B_{2n} denotes Bernoulli numbers.

$$\text{sech } x = 1 - \frac{1}{2!}\,x^2 + \frac{5}{4!}\,x^4 - \frac{61}{6!}\,x^6 + \frac{1385}{8!}\,x^8 - \cdots + \frac{E_{2n}x^{2n}}{(2n)!} \pm \cdots \text{ (2)}$$

$$|x| < \frac{\pi}{2}$$

$$\text{sech } x = 2e^{-x} - 2e^{-3x} + 2e^{-5x} - 2e^{-7x} + - \cdots$$

$$= 2\sum_{n=0}^{\infty} (-1)^n e^{-(2n+1)x}, \text{ Re }(x) > 0$$

$$\text{sech } x = 4\pi \left[\frac{1}{\pi^2 + 4x^2} - \frac{3}{(3\pi)^2 + 4x^2} + \frac{5}{(5\pi)^2 + 4x^2} - + \cdots \right]$$

$$= 4\pi \sum_{n=0}^{\infty} \frac{(-1)^n(2n+1)}{(2n+1)^2\pi^2 + 4x^2}$$

$$\text{cosech } x = \frac{1}{x} - \frac{x}{6} + \frac{7x^3}{360} - \frac{31x^5}{15{,}120} + \cdots - \frac{2(2^{2n-1} - 1)}{(2n)!}\,B_{2n}x^{2n-1} + \cdots \text{ (1)}$$

$$0 < |x| < \pi$$

$$\text{cosech } x = 2e^{-x} + 2e^{-3x} + 2e^{-5x} + \cdots$$

$$= 2\sum_{n=0}^{\infty} e^{-(2n+1)x}, \text{ Re }(x) > 0$$

$$\text{cosech } x = \frac{1}{x} - \frac{2x}{\pi^2 + x^2} + \frac{2x}{(2\pi)^2 + x^2} - \frac{2x}{(3\pi)^2 + x^2} + - \cdots$$

$$= \frac{1}{x} + 2x \sum_{n=1}^{\infty} \frac{(-1)^n}{(n\pi)^2 + x^2}$$

[1] E_{2n} denotes Euler numbers.

INVERSE HYPERBOLIC FUNCTIONS

Definitions

If $x = \sinh y$, then $y = \sinh^{-1} x$. Other inverse functions are defined similarly.

Domain and Range

Function	Domain	Range	Remarks
$\sinh^{-1} x$	$(-\infty, +\infty)$	$(-\infty, +\infty)$	odd function
$\cosh^{-1} x$	$[1, +\infty)$	$(-\infty, +\infty)$	even function double valued
$\tanh^{-1} x$	$(-1,1)$	$(-\infty, +\infty)$	odd function
$\operatorname{cosech}^{-1} x$	$(-\infty,0), (0,\infty)$	$(0,-\infty), (\infty,0)$	odd function two branches, pole at $x = 0$
$\operatorname{sech}^{-1} x$	$(0,1]$	$(-\infty, +\infty)$	double valued
$\coth^{-1} x$	$(-\infty,-1), (1,\infty)$	$(0,-\infty), (\infty,0)$	odd function two branches

Graph of the Inverse Functions

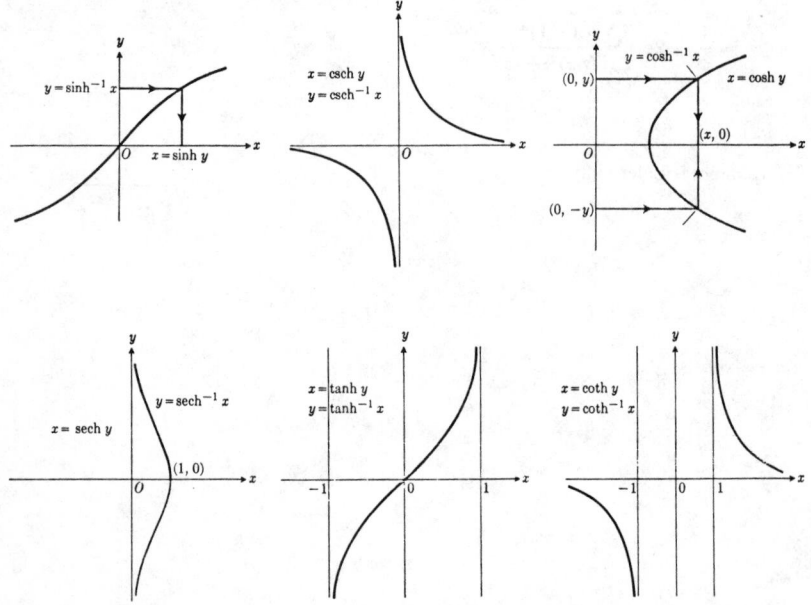

Inverse Hyperbolic Functions In Terms of One Another

Function	$\sinh^{-1} x$	$\cosh^{-1} x$ + if $x > 0$ − if $x < 0$	$\tanh^{-1} x$
$\sinh^{-1} x =$	$\sinh^{-1} x$	$\pm \cosh^{-1} \sqrt{x^2 + 1}$	$\tanh^{-1} \dfrac{x}{\sqrt{1 + x^2}}$
$\cosh^{-1} x =$	$\pm \sinh^{-1} \sqrt{x^2 - 1}$	$\cosh^{-1} x$	$\pm \tanh^{-1} \dfrac{\sqrt{x^2 - 1}}{x}$
$\tanh^{-1} x =$	$\sinh^{-1} \dfrac{x}{\sqrt{1 - x^2}}$	$\pm \cosh^{-1} \dfrac{1}{\sqrt{1 - x^2}}$	$\tanh^{-1} x$
$\text{cosech}^{-1} x =$	$\sinh^{-1} \dfrac{1}{x}$	$\pm \cosh^{-1} \dfrac{\sqrt{x^2 + 1}}{x}$	$\tanh^{-1} \dfrac{1}{\sqrt{1 + x^2}}$
$\text{sech}^{-1} x =$	$\pm \sinh^{-1} \dfrac{\sqrt{1 - x^2}}{x}$	$\cosh^{-1} \dfrac{1}{x}$	$\pm \tanh^{-1} \sqrt{1 - x^2}$
$\coth^{-1} x =$	$\sinh^{-1} \dfrac{1}{\sqrt{x^2 - 1}}$	$\pm \cosh^{-1} \dfrac{x}{\sqrt{x^2 - 1}}$	$\tanh^{-1} \dfrac{1}{x}$

Function	$\text{cosech}^{-1} x$	$\text{sech}^{-1} x$ + if $x > 0$ − if $x < 0$	$\coth^{-1} x$
$\sinh^{-1} x =$	$\text{cosech}^{-1} \dfrac{1}{x}$	$\pm \text{sech}^{-1} \dfrac{1}{\sqrt{1 + x^2}}$	$\coth^{-1} \dfrac{\sqrt{1 + x^2}}{x}$
$\cosh^{-1} x =$	$\pm \text{cosech}^{-1} \dfrac{1}{\sqrt{x^2 - 1}}$	$\text{sech}^{-1} \dfrac{1}{x}$	$\pm \coth^{-1} \dfrac{x}{\sqrt{x^2 - 1}}$
$\tanh^{-1} x =$	$\text{cosech}^{-1} \dfrac{\sqrt{1 - x^2}}{x}$	$\pm \text{sech}^{-1} \sqrt{1 - x^2}$	$\coth^{-1} \dfrac{1}{x}$
$\text{cosech}^{-1} x =$	$\text{cosech}^{-1} x$	$\pm \text{sech}^{-1} \dfrac{x}{\sqrt{x^2 + 1}}$	$\coth^{-1} \sqrt{1 + x^2}$
$\text{sech}^{-1} x =$	$\pm \text{cosech}^{-1} \dfrac{x}{\sqrt{1 - x^2}}$	$\text{sech}^{-1} x$	$\pm \coth^{-1} \dfrac{1}{\sqrt{1 - x^2}}$
$\coth^{-1} x =$	$\text{cosech}^{-1} \sqrt{x^2 - 1}$	$\text{sech}^{-1} \dfrac{\sqrt{x^2 - 1}}{x}$	$\coth^{-1} x$

Fundamental Identities

Relations with Logarithmic Functions

$$\sinh^{-1} x = \log_e (x + \sqrt{x^2 + 1})$$
$$\cosh^{-1} x = \log_e (x \pm \sqrt{x^2 - 1}), \quad x \geqq 1. \quad \text{The plus sign is used for the principal value.}$$

$$\tanh^{-1} x = \tfrac{1}{2} \log_e \left(\frac{1 + x}{1 - x}\right), \quad x^2 < 1$$

$$\operatorname{csch}^{-1} x = \log_e \left(\frac{1 \pm \sqrt{1 + x^2}}{x}\right). \quad \text{The plus sign is used if } x > 0, \text{ the minus sign if } x < 0.$$

$$\operatorname{sech}^{-1} x = \log_e \left(\frac{1 \pm \sqrt{1 - x^2}}{x}\right), \quad 0 < x \leqq 1. \quad \text{The plus sign is used for the principal values.}$$

$$\coth^{-1} x = \tfrac{1}{2} \log_e \left(\frac{x + 1}{x - 1}\right), \quad x^2 > 1$$

Relations with Circular Functions

$$\sinh^{-1} x = -i \sin^{-1} (ix) \qquad \sinh^{-1} (ix) = i \sin^{-1} x$$
$$\cosh^{-1} x = \pm i \cos^{-1} x \qquad \cosh^{-1} (ix) = \pm i \cos^{-1} (ix)$$
$$\tanh^{-1} x = -i \tan^{-1} (ix) \qquad \tanh^{-1} (ix) = i \tan^{-1} x$$
$$\operatorname{cosech}^{-1} x = i \operatorname{cosec}^{-1} (ix) \qquad \operatorname{cosech}^{-1} (ix) = -i \operatorname{cosec}^{-1} x$$
$$\operatorname{sech}^{-1} x = \pm i \sec^{-1} x \qquad \operatorname{sech}^{-1} (ix) = \pm i \sec^{-1} (ix)$$
$$\coth^{-1} x = i \coth^{-1} (ix) \qquad \coth^{-1} (ix) = -i \cot^{-1} (x)$$

Function Sum and Function Difference Relations

$$\sinh^{-1} x + \sinh^{-1} y = \sinh^{-1} (x \sqrt{1 + y^2} + y \sqrt{1 + x^2})$$
$$\sinh^{-1} x - \sinh^{-1} y = \sinh^{-1} (x \sqrt{1 + y^2} - y \sqrt{1 + x^2})$$
$$\cosh^{-1} x + \cosh^{-1} y = \cosh^{-1} (xy + \sqrt{(x^2 - 1)(y^2 - 1)})$$
$$\cosh^{-1} x - \cosh^{-1} y = \cosh^{-1} (xy - \sqrt{(x^2 - 1)(y^2 - 1)})$$
$$\tanh^{-1} x + \tanh^{-1} y = \tanh^{-1} \left(\frac{x + y}{1 + xy}\right)$$
$$\tanh^{-1} x - \tanh^{-1} y = \tanh^{-1} \left(\frac{x - y}{1 - xy}\right)$$
$$\sinh^{-1} x + \cosh^{-1} y = \sinh^{-1} (xy + \sqrt{(1 + x^2)(y^2 - 1)})$$
$$= \cosh^{-1} (y \sqrt{1 + x^2} + x \sqrt{y^2 - 1})$$
$$\sinh^{-1} x - \cosh^{-1} y = \sinh^{-1} (xy - \sqrt{(1 + x^2)(y^2 - 1)})$$
$$= \cosh^{-1} (y \sqrt{1 + x^2} - x \sqrt{y^2 - 1})$$
$$\tanh^{-1} x + \coth^{-1} y = \tanh^{-1} \left(\frac{xy + 1}{y + x}\right)$$
$$= \coth^{-1} \left(\frac{y + x}{xy + 1}\right)$$
$$\tanh^{-1} x - \coth^{-1} y = \tanh^{-1} \left(\frac{xy - 1}{y - x}\right)$$
$$= \coth^{-1} \left(\frac{y - x}{xy - 1}\right)$$

Series Expansions

$$\sinh^{-1} x = x - \frac{1}{2 \cdot 3} x^3 + \frac{1 \cdot 3}{2 \cdot 4 \cdot 5} x^5 - \frac{1 \cdot 3 \cdot 5}{2 \cdot 4 \cdot 6 \cdot 7} x^7 + \cdots$$

$$+ (-1)^n \cdot \frac{1 \cdot 3 \cdot 5 \ldots (2n-1)}{2 \cdot 4 \cdot 6 \ldots 2n(2n+1)} x^{2n+1} \pm \cdots \quad |x| < 1$$

$$\sinh^{-1} x = \ln (2x) + \frac{1}{2} \cdot \frac{1}{2x^2} - \frac{1 \cdot 3}{2 \cdot 4} \cdot \frac{1}{4x^4} + \frac{1 \cdot 3 \cdot 5}{2 \cdot 4 \cdot 6} \cdot \frac{1}{6x^6} - \cdots$$

$$= \ln (2x) + \sum_{n=1}^{\infty} (-1)^{n+1} \frac{(2n)! x^{-2n}}{2^{2n}(n!)^2 2n}, \quad |x| > 1$$

$$\cosh^{-1} x = \pm \left[\ln (2x) - \frac{1}{2 \cdot 2x^2} - \frac{1 \cdot 3}{2 \cdot 4 \cdot 4x^4} - \frac{1 \cdot 3 \cdot 5}{2 \cdot 4 \cdot 6 \cdot 6x^6} - \cdots \right] \quad x > 1$$

$$\operatorname{cosech}^{-1} x = \frac{1}{x} - \frac{1}{2} \cdot \frac{1}{3x^3} + \frac{1 \cdot 3}{2 \cdot 4} \cdot \frac{1}{5x^5} - \frac{1 \cdot 3 \cdot 5}{2 \cdot 4 \cdot 6} \cdot \frac{1}{7x^7} + - \cdots$$

$$= \sum_{n=0}^{\infty} (-1)^n \frac{(2n)! x^{-2n-1}}{2^{2n}(n!)^2 (2n+1)}, \quad |x| > 1$$

$$\operatorname{cosech}^{-1} x = \ln \frac{2}{x} + \frac{1}{2} \cdot \frac{x^2}{2} - \frac{1 \cdot 3}{2 \cdot 4} \cdot \frac{x^4}{4} + \frac{1 \cdot 3 \cdot 5}{2 \cdot 4 \cdot 6} \cdot \frac{x^6}{6} - + \cdots$$

$$= \ln \frac{2}{x} + \sum_{n=1}^{\infty} \frac{(-1)^{n+1}(2n)! x^{2n}}{2^{2n}(n!)^2 2n}, \quad 0 < x < 1$$

$$\operatorname{sech}^{-1} x = \ln \frac{2}{x} - \frac{1}{2} \frac{x^2}{2} - \frac{1 \cdot 3}{2 \cdot 4} \cdot \frac{x^4}{4} - \frac{1 \cdot 3 \cdot 5}{2 \cdot 4 \cdot 6} \cdot \frac{x^6}{6} - - \cdots$$

$$= \ln \frac{2}{x} - \sum_{n=1}^{\infty} \frac{(2n)! x^{2n}}{2^{2n}(n!)^2 2n}, \quad 0 < x < 1$$

$$*\tanh^{-1} x = x + \frac{x^3}{3} + \frac{x^5}{5} + \frac{x^7}{7} + \cdots + \frac{x^{2n+1}}{2n+1} + \cdots \quad |x| < 1$$

$$*\coth^{-1} x = \frac{1}{x} + \frac{1}{3x^3} + \frac{1}{5x^5} + \frac{1}{7x^7} + \cdots + \frac{1}{(2n+1)x^{2n+1}} + \cdots \quad |x| > 1$$

GUDERMANNIAN FUNCTION

This function is useful because it relates circular and hyperbolic functions without the use of functions of imaginary argument.

Definition

$$\gamma = \text{the gudermannian of } x, \text{ written as gd } x$$

$$= 2 \tan^{-1} e^x - \frac{\pi}{2}$$

$$x = \text{gd}^{-1} \gamma$$

$$= \ln \tan \left(\frac{\pi}{4} + \frac{\gamma}{2} \right)$$

$$= \ln (\sec \gamma + \tan \gamma)$$

---

* Can also be written as arg tanh x and arg coth x respectively.

Special Values of Gudermannian Function

$$
\begin{array}{cccc}
x & 0 & \infty & -\infty \\
\mathrm{gd}\, x & 0 & \tfrac{1}{2}\pi & -\tfrac{1}{2}\pi
\end{array}
$$

Relations with Hyperbolic and Circular Functions

$$\sinh x = \tan (\mathrm{gd}\, x) \qquad \operatorname{cosech} x = \cot (\mathrm{gd}\, x)$$
$$\cosh x = \sec (\mathrm{gd}\, x) \qquad \operatorname{sech} (x) = \cos (\mathrm{gd}\, x)$$
$$\tanh x = \sin (\mathrm{gd}\, x) \qquad \coth (x) = \operatorname{cosec} (\mathrm{gd}\, x)$$

Derivatives

$$\frac{d}{dx} (\mathrm{gd}\, x) = \operatorname{sech} x$$

$$\frac{d}{dx} (\mathrm{gd}^{-1}\, \gamma) = \sec \gamma$$

Fundamental Identities

$$\tanh (\tfrac{1}{2}x) = \tan (\tfrac{1}{2}\mathrm{gd}\, x)$$
$$e^x = \cosh x + \sinh x = \sec (\mathrm{gd}\, x) + \tan (\mathrm{gd}\, x)$$
$$= \tan \left(\frac{\pi}{4} + \frac{1}{2}\,\mathrm{gd}\, x \right) = \frac{1 + \sin (\mathrm{gd}\, x)}{\cos (\mathrm{gd}\, x)} = \frac{1 + \tan (\tfrac{1}{2}\mathrm{gd}\, x)}{1 - \tan (\tfrac{1}{2}\mathrm{gd}\, x)}$$
$$\mathrm{gd}\, x = 2 \tan^{-1} \left(\tanh \frac{1}{2}\, x \right) = \int_0^x \frac{dt}{\cosh t}$$
$$\mathrm{gd}^{-1}\, \gamma = \int_0^\gamma \frac{dt}{\cos t}$$
$$i\, \mathrm{gd}^{-1}\, \gamma = \mathrm{gd}\, i\gamma, \text{ where } i = \sqrt{-1}.$$

If

$$\alpha + i\beta = \mathrm{gd}(x + iy)$$

then

$$\tan \alpha = \frac{\sinh x}{\cos y} \qquad \tanh \beta = \frac{\sin y}{\cosh x}$$

$$\tanh x = \frac{\sin \alpha}{\cosh \beta} \qquad \tan y = \frac{\sinh \beta}{\cosh \alpha}$$

Series Expansions

$$\mathrm{gd}\, x = x - \frac{1}{6}\, x^3 + \frac{1}{24}\, x^5 - \frac{61}{5040}\, x^7 + - \cdots$$

$$= \sum_{n=0}^{\infty} \frac{E_{2n}}{(2n+1)!}\, x^{2n+1}, \quad |x| < 1 \qquad \qquad {}^{(1)},$$

$$\mathrm{gd}\, x = \frac{\pi}{2} - \operatorname{sech} x - \frac{1}{2} \frac{\operatorname{sech}^3 x}{3} - \frac{1 \cdot 3}{2 \cdot 4} \frac{\operatorname{sech}^5 x}{5} + - \cdots$$

$$= \frac{\pi}{2} - \sum_{n=0}^{\infty} \frac{(2n)!}{2^{2n}(n!)^2} \frac{\operatorname{sech}^{2n+1} x}{(2n+1)} \qquad x \text{ large}$$

---

[1] E_n denotes Euler numbers.

$$\operatorname{gd} x = \frac{2}{1} \tanh \frac{x}{2} - \frac{2}{3} \tanh^3 \frac{x}{2} + \frac{2}{5} \tanh^5 \frac{x}{2} - \frac{2}{7} \tanh^7 \frac{x}{2} + - \cdots$$

$$= 2 \sum_{n=0}^{\infty} \frac{(-1)^n}{2n+1} \tanh^{2n+1} \frac{x}{2}$$

$$\operatorname{gd}^{-1} \gamma = \gamma + \frac{1}{6} \gamma^3 + \frac{1}{24} \gamma^5 + \frac{61}{5040} \gamma^7 + \cdots$$

$$= \sum_{n=0}^{\infty} \frac{(-1)^n E_{2n} \gamma^{2n+1}}{(2n+1)!}, \qquad |\gamma| < \frac{\pi}{2} \tag{1}$$

$$\operatorname{gd}^{-1} \gamma = \frac{2}{1} \tan \frac{\gamma}{2} + \frac{2}{3} \tan^3 \frac{\gamma}{2} + \frac{2}{5} \tan^5 \frac{\gamma}{2} + \cdots$$

$$= 2 \sum_{n=0}^{\infty} \frac{1}{2n+1} \tan^{2n+1} \frac{\gamma}{2}$$

[1] E_n are Euler's numbers.

References

1. For extensive tables of inverse hyperbolic functions: Tables of Inverse Hyperbolic Functions, Harvard University Computation Laboratory (Cambridge, Harvard University Press, 1949).
2. For tables of hyperbolic functions with complex argument: Tables of Complex Hyperbolic and Circular Functions, A. E. Kennelly (Cambridge, Harvard University Press, 1914).

HYPERBOLIC FUNCTIONS AND THEIR COMMON LOGARITHMS

The logarithms given below show the mantissa only. The proper characteristic must be added.

x	Sinh x Value	$\log_{10}$	Cosh x Value	$\log_{10}$	Tanh x Value	$\log_{10}$	Coth x Value	$\log_{10}$
0.00	0.00000	$-\infty$	1.00000	.00000	0.00000	$-\infty$	∞	∞
0.01	.01000	.00001	1.00005	.00002	.01000	.99999	100.003	.00001
0.02	.02000	.30106	1.00020	.00009	.02000	.30097	50.007	.69903
0.03	.03000	.47719	1.00045	.00020	.02999	.47699	33.343	.52301
0.04	.04001	.60218	1.00080	.00035	.03998	.60183	25.013	.39817
0.05	0.05002	.69915	1.00125	.00054	0.04996	.69861	20.017	.30139
0.06	.06004	.77841	1.00180	.00078	.05993	.77763	16.687	.22237
0.07	.07006	.84545	1.00245	.00106	.06989	.84439	14.309	.15561
0.08	.08009	.90355	1.00320	.00139	.07983	.90216	12.527	.09784
0.09	.09012	.95483	1.00405	.00176	.08976	.95307	11.141	.04693
0.10	0.10017	.00072	1.00500	.00217	0.09967	.99856	10.0333	.00144
0.11	.11022	.04227	1.00606	.00262	.10956	.03965	9.1275	.96035
0.12	.12029	.08022	1.00721	.00312	.11943	.07710	8.3733	.92290
0.13	.13037	.11517	1.00846	.00366	.12927	.11151	7.7356	.88849
0.14	.14046	.14755	1.00982	.00424	.13909	.14330	7.1895	.85670
0.15	0.15056	.17772	1.01127	.00487	0.14889	.17285	6.7166	.82715
0.16	.16068	.20597	1.01283	.00554	.15865	.20044	6.3032	.79956
0.17	.17082	.23254	1.01448	.00625	.16838	.22629	5.9389	.77371
0.18	.18097	.25762	1.01624	.00700	.17808	.25062	5.6154	.74938
0.19	.19115	.28136	1.01810	.00779	.18775	.27357	5.3263	.72643
0.20	0.20134	.30392	1.02007	.00863	0.19738	.29529	5.0665	.70471
0.21	.21155	.32541	1.02213	.00951	.20697	.31590	4.8317	.68410
0.22	.22178	.34592	1.02430	.01043	.21652	.33549	4.6186	.66451
0.23	.23203	.36555	1.02657	.01139	.22603	.35416	4.4242	.64584
0.24	.24231	.38437	1.02894	.01239	.23550	.37198	4.2464	.62802
0.25	0.25261	.40245	1.03141	.01343	0.24492	.38902	4.0830	.61098
0.26	.26294	.41986	1.03399	.01452	.25430	.40534	3.9324	.59466
0.27	.27329	.43663	1.03667	.01564	.26362	.42099	3.7933	.57901
0.28	.28367	.45282	1.03946	.01681	.27291	.43601	3.6643	.56399
0.29	.29408	.46847	1.04235	.01801	.28213	.45046	3.5444	.54954
0.30	0.30452	.48362	1.04534	.01926	0.29131	.46436	3.4327	.53564
0.31	.31499	.49830	1.04844	.02054	.30044	.47775	3.3285	.52225
0.32	.32549	.51254	1.05164	.02187	.30951	.49067	3.2309	.50933
0.33	.33602	.52637	1.05495	.02323	.31852	.50314	3.1395	.49686
0.34	.34659	.53981	1.05836	.02463	.32748	.51518	3.0536	.48482
0.35	0.35719	.55290	1.06188	.02607	0.33638	.52682	2.9729	.47318
0.36	.36783	.56564	1.06550	.02755	.34521	.53809	2.8968	.46191
0.37	.37850	.57807	1.06923	.02907	.35399	.54899	2.8249	.45101
0.38	.38921	.59019	1.07307	.03063	.36271	.55956	2.7570	.44044
0.39	.39996	.60202	1.07702	.03222	.37136	.56980	2.6928	.43020
0.40	0.41075	.61358	1.08107	.03385	0.37995	.57973	2.6319	.42027
0.41	.42158	.62488	1.08523	.03552	.38847	.58936	2.5742	.41064
0.42	.43246	.63594	1.08950	.03723	.39693	.59871	2.5193	.40129
0.43	.44337	.64677	1.09388	.03897	.40532	.60780	2.4672	.39220
0.44	.45434	.65738	1.09837	.04075	.41364	.61663	2.4175	.38337
0.45	0.46534	.66777	1.10297	.04256	0.42190	.62521	2.3702	.37479
0.46	.47640	.67797	1.10768	.04441	.43008	.63355	2.3251	.36645
0.47	.48750	.68797	1.11250	.04630	.43820	.64167	2.2821	.35833
0.48	.49865	.69779	1.11743	.04822	.44624	.64957	2.2409	.35043
0.49	.50984	.70744	1.12247	.05018	.45422	.65726	2.2016	.34274

HYPERBOLIC FUNCTIONS AND THEIR COMMON LOGARITHMS (Continued)

x	Sinh x		Cosh x		Tanh x		Coth x	
	Value	$\log_{10}$	Value	$\log_{10}$	Value	$\log_{10}$	Value	$\log_{10}$
0.50	0.52110	.71692	1.12763	.05217	0.46212	.66475	2.1640	.33525
0.51	.53240	.72624	1.13289	.05419	.46995	.67205	2.1279	.32795
0.52	.54375	.73540	1.13827	.05625	.47770	.67916	2.0934	.32084
0.53	.55516	.74442	1.14377	.05834	.48538	.68608	2.0602	.31392
0.54	.56663	.75330	1.14938	.06046	.49299	.69284	2.0284	.30716
0.55	0.57815	.76204	1.15510	.06262	0.50052	.69942	1.9979	.30058
0.56	.58973	.77065	1.16094	.06481	.50798	.70584	1.9686	.29416
0.57	.60137	.77914	1.16690	.06703	.51536	.71211	1.9404	.28789
0.58	.61307	.78751	1.17297	.06929	.52267	.71822	1.9133	.28178
0.59	.62483	.79576	1.17916	.07157	.52990	.72419	1.8872	.27581
0.60	0.63665	.80390	1.18547	.07389	0.53705	.73001	1.8620	.26999
0.61	.64854	.81194	1.19189	.07624	.54413	.73570	1.8378	.26430
0.62	.66049	.81987	1.19844	.07861	.55113	.74125	1.8145	.25875
0.63	.67251	.82770	1.20510	.08102	.55805	.74667	1.7919	.25333
0.64	.68459	.83543	1.21189	.08346	.56490	.75197	1.7702	.24803
0.65	0.69675	.84308	1.21879	.08593	0.57167	.75715	1.7493	.24285
0.66	.70897	.85063	1.22582	.08843	.57836	.76220	1.7290	.23780
0.67	.72126	.85809	1.23297	.09095	.58498	.76714	1.7095	.23286
0.68	.73363	.86548	1.24025	.09351	.59152	.77197	1.6906	.22803
0.69	.74607	.87278	1.24765	.09609	.59798	.77669	1.6723	.22331
0.70	0.75858	.88000	1.25517	.09870	0.60437	.78130	1.6546	.21870
0.71	.77117	.88715	1.26282	.10134	.61068	.78581	1.6375	.21419
0.72	.78384	.89423	1.27059	.10401	.61691	.79022	1.6210	.20978
0.73	.79659	.90123	1.27849	.10670	.62307	.79453	1.6050	.20547
0.74	.80941	.90817	1.28652	.10942	.62915	.79875	1.5895	.20125
0.75	0.82232	.91504	1.29468	.11216	0.63515	.80288	1.5744	.19712
0.76	.83530	.92185	1.30297	.11493	.64108	.80691	1.5599	.19309
0.77	.84838	.92859	1.31139	.11773	.64693	.81086	1.5458	.18914
0.78	.86153	.93527	1.31994	.12055	.65271	.81472	1.5321	.18528
0.79	.87478	.94190	1.32862	.12340	.65841	.81850	1.5188	.18150
0.80	0.88811	.94846	1.33743	.12627	0.66404	.82219	1.5059	.17781
0.81	.90152	.95498	1.34638	.12917	.66959	.82581	1.4935	.17419
0.82	.91503	.96144	1.35547	.13209	.67507	.82935	1.4813	.17065
0.83	.92863	.96784	1.36468	.13503	.68048	.83281	1.4696	.16719
0.84	.94233	.97420	1.37404	.13800	.68581	.83620	1.4581	.16380
0.85	0.95612	.98051	1.38353	.14099	0.69107	.83952	1.4470	.16048
0.86	.97000	.98677	1.39316	.14400	.69626	.84277	1.4362	.15723
0.87	.98398	.99299	1.40293	.14704	.70137	.84595	1.4258	.15405
0.88	.99806	.99916	1.41284	.15009	.70642	.84906	1.4156	.15094
0.89	1.01224	.00528	1.42289	.15317	.71139	.85211	1.4057	.14789
0.90	1.02652	.01137	1.43309	.15627	0.71630	.85509	1.3961	.14491
0.91	1.04090	.01741	1.44342	.15939	.72113	.85801	1.3867	.14199
0.92	1.05539	.02341	1.45390	.16254	.72590	.86088	1.3776	.13912
0.93	1.06998	.02937	1.46453	.16570	.73059	.86368	1.3687	.13632
0.94	1.08468	.03530	1.47530	.16888	.73522	.86642	1.3601	.13358
0.95	1.09948	.04119	1.48623	.17208	0.73978	.86910	1.3517	.13090
0.96	1.11440	.04704	1.49729	.17531	.74428	.87173	1.3436	.12827
0.97	1.12943	.05286	1.50851	.17855	.74870	.87431	1.3356	.12569
0.98	1.14457	.05864	1.51988	.18181	.75307	.87683	1.3279	.12317
0.99	1.15983	.06439	1.53141	.18509	.75736	.87930	1.3204	.12070

HYPERBOLIC FUNCTIONS AND THEIR COMMON LOGARITHMS (Continued)

x	Sinh x		Cosh x		Tanh x		Coth x	
	Value	$\log_{10}$	Value	$\log_{10}$	Value	$\log_{10}$	Value	$\log_{10}$
1.00	1.17520	.07011	1.54308	.18839	0.76159	.88172	1.3130	.11828
1.01	1.19069	.07580	1.55491	.19171	.76576	.88409	1.3059	.11591
1.02	1.20630	.08146	1.56689	.19504	.76987	.88642	1.2989	.11358
1.03	1.22203	.08708	1.57904	.19839	.77391	.88869	1.2921	.11131
1.04	1.23788	.09268	1.59134	.20176	.77789	.89092	1.2855	.10908
1.05	1.25386	.09825	1.60379	.20515	0.78181	.89310	1.2791	.10690
1.06	1.26996	.10379	1.61641	.20855	.78566	.89524	1.2728	.10476
1.07	1.28619	.10930	1.62919	.21197	.78946	.89733	1.2667	.10267
1.08	1.30254	.11479	1.64214	.21541	.79320	.89938	1.2607	.10062
1.09	1.31903	.12025	1.65525	.21886	.79688	.90139	1.2549	.09861
1.10	1.33565	.12569	1.66852	.22233	0.80050	.90336	1.2492	.09664
1.11	1.35240	.13111	1.68196	.22582	.80406	.90529	1.2437	.09471
1.12	1.36929	.13649	1.69557	.22931	.80757	.90718	1.2383	.09282
1.13	1.38631	.14186	1.70934	.23283	.81102	.90903	1.2330	.09097
1.14	1.40347	.14720	1.72329	.23636	.81441	.91085	1.2279	.08915
1.15	1.42078	.15253	1.73741	.23990	0.81775	.91262	1.2229	.08738
1.16	1.43822	.15783	1.75171	.24346	.82104	.91436	1.2180	.08564
1.17	1.45581	.16311	1.76618	.24703	.82427	.91607	1.2132	.08393
1.18	1.47355	.16836	1.78083	.25062	.82745	.91774	1.2085	.08226
1.19	1.49143	.17360	1.79565	.25422	.83058	.91938	1.2040	.08062
1.20	1.50946	.17882	1.81066	.25784	0.83365	.92099	1.1995	.07901
1.21	1.52764	.18402	1.82584	.26146	.83668	.92256	1.1952	.07744
1.22	1.54598	.18920	1.84121	.26510	.83965	.92410	1.1910	.07590
1.23	1.56447	.19437	1.85676	.26876	.84258	.92561	1.1868	.07439
1.24	1.58311	.19951	1.87250	.27242	.84546	.92709	1.1828	.07291
1.25	1.60192	.20464	1.88842	.27610	0.84828	.92854	1.1789	.07146
1.26	1.62088	.20975	1.90454	.27979	.85106	.92996	1.1750	.07004
1.27	1.64001	.21485	1.92084	.28349	.85380	.93135	1.1712	.06865
1.28	1.65930	.21993	1.93734	.28721	.85648	.93272	1.1676	.06728
1.29	1.67876	.22499	1.95403	.29093	.85913	.93406	1.1640	.06594
1.30	1.69838	.23004	1.97091	.29467	0.86172	.93537	1.1605	.06463
1.31	1.71818	.23507	1.98800	.29842	.86428	.93665	1.1570	.06335
1.32	1.73814	.24009	2.00528	.30217	.86678	.93791	1.1537	.06209
1.33	1.75828	.24509	2.02276	.30594	.86925	.93914	1.1504	.06086
1.34	1.77860	.25008	2.04044	.30972	.87167	.94035	1.1472	.05965
1.35	1.79909	.25505	2.05833	.31352	0.87405	.94154	1.1441	.05846
1.36	1.81977	.26002	2.07643	.31732	.87639	.94270	1.1410	.05730
1.37	1.84062	.26496	2.09473	.32113	.87869	.94384	1.1381	.05616
1.38	1.86166	.26990	2.11324	.32495	.88095	.94495	1.1351	.05505
1.39	1.88289	.27482	2.13196	.32878	.88317	.94604	1.1323	.05396
1.40	1.90430	.27974	2.15090	.33262	0.88535	.94712	1.1295	.05288
1.41	1.92591	.28464	2.17005	.33647	.88749	.94817	1.1268	.05183
1.42	1.94770	.28952	2.18942	.34033	.88960	.94919	1.1241	.05081
1.43	1.96970	.29440	2.20900	.34420	.89167	.95020	1.1215	.04980
1.44	1.99188	.29926	2.22881	.34807	.89370	.95119	1.1189	.04881
1.45	2.01427	.30412	2.24884	.35196	0.89569	.95216	1.1165	.04784
1.46	2.03686	.30896	2.26910	.35585	.89765	.95311	1.1140	.04689
1.47	2.05965	.31379	2.28958	.35976	.89958	.95404	1.1116	.04596
1.48	2.08265	.31862	2.31029	.36367	.90147	.95495	1.1093	.04505
1.49	2.10586	.32343	2.33123	.36759	.90332	.95584	1.1070	.04416

HYPERBOLIC FUNCTIONS AND THEIR COMMON LOGARITHMS (Continued)

x	Sinh x		Cosh x		Tanh x		Coth x	
	Value	$\log_{10}$	Value	$\log_{10}$	Value	$\log_{10}$	Value	$\log_{10}$
1.50	2.12928	.32823	2.35241	.37151	0.90515	.95672	1.1048	.04328
1.51	2.15291	.33303	2.37382	.37545	.90694	.95758	1.1026	.04242
1.52	2.17676	.33781	2.39547	.37939	.90870	.95842	1.1005	.04158
1.53	2.20082	.34258	2.41736	.38334	.91042	.95924	1.0984	.04076
1.54	2.22510	.34735	2.43949	.38730	.91212	.96005	1.0963	.03995
1.55	2.24961	.35211	2.46186	.39126	0.91379	.96084	1.0943	.03916
1.56	2.27434	.35686	2.48448	.39524	.91542	.96162	1.0924	.03838
1.57	2.29930	.36160	2.50735	.39921	.91703	.96238	1.0905	.03762
1.58	2.32449	.36633	2.53047	.40320	.91860	.96313	1.0886	.03687
1.59	2.34991	.37105	2.55384	.40719	.92015	.96386	1.0868	.03614
1.60	2.37557	.37577	2.57746	.41119	0.92167	.96457	1.0850	.03543
1.61	2.40146	.38048	2.60135	.41520	.92316	.96528	1.0832	.03472
1.62	2.42760	.38518	2.62549	.41921	.92462	.96597	1.0815	.03403
1.63	2.45397	.38987	2.64990	.42323	.92606	.96664	1.0798	.03336
1.64	2.48059	.39456	2.67457	.42725	.92747	.96730	1.0782	.03270
1.65	2.50746	.39923	2.69951	.43129	0.92886	.96795	1.0766	.03205
1.66	2.53459	.40391	2.72472	.43532	.93022	.96858	1.0750	.03142
1.67	2.56196	.40857	2.75021	.43937	.93155	.96921	1.0735	.03079
1.68	2.58959	.41323	2.77596	.44341	.93286	.96982	1.0720	.03018
1.69	2.61748	.41788	2.80200	.44747	.93415	.97042	1.0705	.02958
1.70	2.64563	.42253	2.82832	.45153	.93541	.97100	1.0691	.02900
1.71	2.67405	.42717	2.85491	.45559	.93665	.97158	1.0676	.02842
1.72	2.70273	.43180	2.88180	.45966	.93786	.97214	1.0663	.02786
1.73	2.73168	.43643	2.90897	.46374	.93906	.97269	1.0649	.02731
1.74	2.76091	.44105	2.93643	.46782	.94023	.97323	1.0636	.02677
1.75	2.79041	.44567	2.96419	.47191	0.94138	.97376	1.0623	.02624
1.76	2.82020	.45028	2.99224	.47600	.94250	.97428	1.0610	.02572
1.77	2.85026	.45488	3.02059	.48009	.94361	.97479	1.0598	.02521
1.78	2.88061	.45948	3.04925	.48419	.94470	.97529	1.0585	.02471
1.79	2.91125	.46408	3.07821	.48830	.94576	.97578	1.0574	.02422
1.80	2.94217	.46867	3.10747	.49241	0.94681	.97626	1.0562	.02374
1.81	2.97340	.47325	3.13705	.49652	.94783	.97673	1.0550	.02327
1.82	3.00492	.47783	3.16694	.50064	.94884	.97719	1.0539	.02281
1.83	3.03674	.48241	3.19715	.50476	.94983	.97764	1.0528	.02236
1.84	3.06886	.48698	3.22768	.50889	.95080	.97809	1.0518	.02191
1.85	3.10129	.49154	3.25853	.51302	0.95175	.97852	1.0507	.02148
1.86	3.13403	.49610	3.28970	.51716	.95268	.97895	1.0497	.02105
1.87	3.16709	.50066	3.32121	.52130	.95359	.97936	1.0487	.02064
1.88	3.20046	.50521	3.35305	.52544	.95449	.97977	1.0477	.02023
1.89	3.23415	.50976	3.38522	.52959	.95537	.98017	1.0467	.01983
1.90	3.26816	.51430	3.41773	.53374	0.95624	.98057	1.0458	.01943
1.91	3.30250	.51884	3.45058	.53789	.95709	.98095	1.0448	.01905
1.92	3.33718	.52338	3.48378	.54205	.95792	.98133	1.0439	.01867
1.93	3.37218	.52791	3.51733	.54621	.95873	.98170	1.0430	.01830
1.94	3.40752	.53244	3.55123	.55038	.95953	.98206	1.0422	.01794
1.95	3.44321	.53696	3.58548	.55455	0.96032	.98242	1.0413	.01758
1.96	3.47923	.54148	3.62009	.55872	.96109	.98276	1.0405	.01724
1.97	3.51561	.54600	3.65507	.56290	.96185	.98311	1.0397	.01689
1.98	3.55234	.55051	3.69041	.56707	.96259	.98344	1.0389	.01656
1.99	3.58942	.55502	3.72611	.57126	.96331	.98377	1.0381	.01623

HYPERBOLIC FUNCTIONS AND THEIR COMMON LOGARITHMS (Continued)

x	Sinh x Value	Sinh x $\log_{10}$	Cosh x Value	Cosh x $\log_{10}$	Tanh x Value	Tanh x $\log_{10}$	Coth x Value	Coth x $\log_{10}$
2.00	3.62686	.55953	3.76220	.57544	0.96403	.98409	1.0373	.01591
2.01	3.66466	.56403	3.79865	.57963	.96473	.98440	1.0366	.01560
2.02	3.70283	.56853	3.83549	.58382	.96541	.98471	1.0358	.01529
2.03	3.74138	.57303	3.87271	.58802	.96609	.98502	1.0351	.01498
2.04	3.78029	.57753	3.91032	.59221	.96675	.98531	1.0344	.01469
2.05	3.81958	.58202	3.94832	.59641	0.96740	.98560	1.0337	.01440
2.06	3.85926	.58650	3.98671	.60061	.96803	.98589	1.0330	.01411
2.07	3.89932	.59099	4.02550	.60482	.96865	.98617	1.0324	.01383
2.08	3.93977	.59547	4.06470	.60903	.96926	.98644	1.0317	.01356
2.09	3.98061	.59995	4.10430	.61324	.96986	.98671	1.0311	.01329
2.10	4.02186	.60443	4.14431	.61745	0.97045	.98697	1.0304	.01303
2.11	4.06350	.60890	4.18474	.62167	.97103	.98723	1.0298	.01277
2.12	4.10555	.61337	4.22558	.62589	.97159	.98748	1.0292	.01252
2.13	4.14801	.61784	4.26685	.63011	.97215	.98773	1.0286	.01227
2.14	4.19089	.62231	4.30855	.63433	.97269	.98798	1.0281	.01202
2.15	4.23419	.62677	4.35067	.63856	0.97323	.98821	1.0275	.01179
2.16	4.27791	.63123	4.39323	.64278	.97375	.98845	1.0270	.01155
2.17	4.32205	.63569	4.43623	.64701	.97426	.98868	1.0264	.01132
2.18	4.36663	.64015	4.47967	.65125	.97477	.98890	1.0259	.01110
2.19	4.41165	.64460	4.52356	.65548	.97526	.98912	1.0254	.01088
2.20	4.45711	.64905	4.56791	.65972	0.97574	.98934	1.0249	.01066
2.21	4.50301	.65350	4.61271	.66396	.97622	.98955	1.0244	.01045
2.22	4.54936	.65795	4.65797	.66820	.97668	.98975	1.0239	.01025
2.23	4.59617	.66240	4.70370	.67244	.97714	.98996	1.0234	.01004
2.24	4.64344	.66684	4.74989	.67668	.97759	.99016	1.0229	.00984
2.25	4.69117	.67128	4.79657	.68093	0.97803	.99035	1.0225	.00965
2.26	4.73937	.67572	4.84372	.68518	.97846	.99054	1.0220	.00946
2.27	4.78804	.68016	4.89136	.68943	.97888	.99073	1.0216	.00927
2.28	4.83720	.68459	4.93948	.69368	.97929	.99091	1.0211	.00909
2.29	4.88684	.68903	4.98810	.69794	.97970	.99109	1.0207	.00891
2.30	4.93696	.69346	5.03722	.70219	0.98010	.99127	1.0203	.00873
2.31	4.98758	.69789	5.08684	.70645	.98049	.99144	1.0199	.00856
2.32	5.03870	.70232	5.13697	.71071	.98087	.99161	1.0195	00839
2.33	5.09032	.70675	5.18762	.71497	.98124	.99178	1.0191	.00822
2.34	5.14245	.71117	5.23878	.71923	.98161	.99194	1.0187	.00806
2.35	5.19510	.71559	5.29047	.72349	0.98197	.99210	1.0184	.00790
2.36	5.24827	.72002	5.34269	.72776	.98233	.99226	1.0180	.00774
2.37	5.30196	.72444	5.39544	.73203	.98267	.99241	1.0176	.00759
2.38	5.35618	.72885	5.44873	.73630	.98301	.99256	1.0173	.00744
2.39	5.41093	.73327	5.50256	.74056	.98335	.99271	1.0169	.00729
2.40	5.46623	.73769	5.55695	.74484	0.98367	.99285	1.0166	.00715
2.41	5.52207	.74210	5.61189	.74911	.98400	.99299	1.0163	.00701
2.42	5.57847	.74652	5.66739	.75338	.98431	.99313	1.0159	.00687
2.43	5.63542	.75093	5.72346	.75766	.98462	.99327	1.0156	.00673
2.44	5.69294	.75534	5.78010	.76194	.98492	.99340	1.0153	.00660
2.45	5.75103	.75975	5.83732	.76621	0.98522	.99353	1.0150	.00647
2.46	5.80969	.75415	5.89512	.77049	.98551	.99366	1.0147	.00634
2.47	5.86893	.76856	5.95352	.77477	.98579	.99379	1.0144	.00621
2.48	5.92876	.77296	6.01250	.77906	.98607	.99391	1.0141	.00609
2.49	5.98918	.77737	6.07209	.78334	.98635	.99403	1.0138	.00597

HYPERBOLIC FUNCTIONS AND THEIR COMMON LOGARITHMS (Continued)

x	Sinh x		Cosh x		Tanh x		Coth x	
	Value	$\log_{10}$	Value	$\log_{10}$	Value	$\log_{10}$	Value	$\log_{10}$
2.50	6.05020	.78177	6.13229	.78762	0.98661	.99415	1.0136	.00585
2.51	6.11183	.78617	6.19310	.79191	.98688	.99426	1.0133	.00574
2.52	6.17407	.79057	6.25453	.79619	.98714	.99438	1.0130	.00562
2.53	6.23692	.79497	6.31658	.80048	.98739	.99449	1.0128	.00551
2.54	6.30040	.79937	6.37927	.80477	.98764	.99460	1.0125	.00540
2.55	6.36451	.80377	6.44259	.80906	0.98788	.99470	1.0123	.00530
2.56	6.42926	.80816	6.50656	.81335	.98812	.99481	1.0120	.00519
2.57	6.49464	.81256	6.57118	.81764	.98835	.99491	1.0118	.00509
2.58	6.56068	.81695	6.63646	.82194	.98858	.99501	1.0115	.00499
2.59	6.62738	.82134	6.70240	.82623	.98881	.99511	1.0113	.00489
2.60	6.69473	.82573	6.76901	.83052	0.98903	.99521	1.0111	.00479
2.61	6.76276	.83012	6.83629	.83482	.98924	.99530	1.0109	.00470
2.62	6.83146	.83451	6.90426	.83912	.98946	.99540	1.0107	.00460
2.63	6.90085	.83890	6.97292	.84341	.98966	.99549	1.0104	.00451
2.64	6.97092	.84329	7.04228	.84771	.98987	.99558	1.0102	.00442
2.65	7.04169	.84768	7.11234	.85201	0.99007	.99566	1.0100	.00434
2.66	7.11317	.85206	7.18312	.85631	.99026	.99575	1.0098	.00425
2.67	7.18536	.85645	7.25461	.86061	.99045	.99583	1.0096	.00417
2.68	7.25827	.86083	7.32683	.86492	.99064	.99592	1.0094	.00408
2.69	7.33190	.86522	7.39978	.86922	.99083	.99600	1.0093	.00400
2.70	7.40626	.86960	7.47347	.87352	0.99101	.99608	1.0091	.00392
2.71	7.48137	.87398	7.54791	.87783	.99118	.99615	1.0089	.00385
2.72	7.55722	.87836	7.62310	.88213	.99136	.99623	1.0087	.00377
2.73	7.63383	.88274	7.69905	.88644	.99153	.99631	1.0085	.00369
2.74	7.71121	.88712	7.77578	.89074	.99170	.99638	1.0084	.00362
2.75	7.78935	.89150	7.85328	.89505	0.99186	.99645	1.0082	.00355
2.76	7.86828	.89588	7.93157	.89936	.99202	.99652	1.0080	.00348
2.77	7.94799	.90026	8.01065	.90367	.99218	.99659	1.0079	.00341
2.78	8.02849	.90463	8.09053	.90798	.99233	.99666	1.0077	.00334
2.79	8.10980	.90901	8.17122	.91229	.99248	.99672	1.0076	.00328
2.80	8.19192	.91339	8.25273	.91660	0.99263	.99679	1.0074	.00321
2.81	8.27486	.91776	8.33506	.92091	.99278	.99685	1.0073	.00315
2.82	8.35862	.92213	8.41823	.92522	.99292	.99691	1.0071	.00309
2.83	8.44322	.92651	8.50224	.92953	.99306	.99698	1.0070	.00302
2.84	8.52867	.93088	8.58710	.93385	.99320	.99704	1.0069	.00296
2.85	8.61497	.93525	8.67281	.93816	0.99333	.99709	1.0067	.00291
2.86	8.70213	.93963	8.75940	.94247	.99346	.99715	1.0066	.00285
2.87	8.79016	.94400	8.84686	.94679	.99359	.99721	1.0065	.00279
2.88	8.87907	.94837	8.93520	.95110	.99372	.99726	1.0063	.00274
2.89	8.96887	.95274	9.02444	.95542	.99384	.99732	1.0062	.00268
2.90	9.05956	.95711	9.11458	.95974	0.99396	.99737	1.0061	.00263
2.91	9.15116	.96148	9.20564	.96405	.99408	.99742	1.0060	.00258
2.92	9.24368	.96584	9.29761	.96837	.99420	.99747	1.0058	.00253
2.93	9.33712	.97021	9.39051	.97269	.99431	.99752	1.0057	.00248
2.94	9.43149	.97458	9.48436	.97701	.99443	.99757	1.0056	.00243
2.95	9.52681	.97895	9.57915	.98133	0.99454	.99762	1.0055	.00238
2.96	9.62308	.98331	9.67490	.98565	.99464	.99767	1.0054	.00233
2.97	9.72031	.98768	9.77161	.98997	.99475	.99771	1.0053	.00229
2.98	9.81851	.99205	9.86930	.99429	.99485	.99776	1.0052	.00224
2.99	9.91770	.99641	9.96798	.99861	.99496	.99780	1.0051	.00220

HYPERBOLIC FUNCTIONS AND THEIR COMMON LOGARITHMS (Continued)

x	Sinh x		Cosh x		Tanh x		Coth x	
	Value	$\log_{10}$	Value	$\log_{10}$	Value	$\log_{10}$	Value	$\log_{10}$
3.0	10.0179	.00078	10.0677	.00293	0.99505	.99785	1.0050	.00215
3.1	11.0765	.04440	11.1215	.04616	.99595	.99824	1.0041	.00176
3.2	12.2459	.08799	12.2866	.08943	.99668	.99856	1.0033	.00144
3.3	13.5379	.13155	13.5748	.13273	.99728	.99882	1.0027	.00118
3.4	14.9654	.17509	14.9987	.17605	.99777	.99903	1.0022	.00097
3.5	16.5426	.21860	16.5728	.21940	0.99818	.99921	1.0018	.00079
3.6	18.2855	.26211	18.3128	.26275	.99851	.99935	1.0015	.00065
3.7	20.2113	.30559	20.2360	.30612	.99878	.99947	1.0012	.00053
3.8	22.3394	.34907	22.3618	.34951	.99900	.99957	1.0010	.00043
3.9	24.6911	.39254	24.7113	.39290	.99918	.99964	1.0008	.00036
4.0	27.2899	.43600	27.3082	.43629	0.99933	.99971	1.0007	.00029
4.1	30.1619	.47946	30.1784	.47970	.99945	.99976	1.0005	.00024
4.2	33.3357	.52291	33.3507	.52310	.99955	.99980	1.0004	.00020
4.3	36.8431	.56636	36.8567	.56652	.99963	.99984	1.0004	.00016
4.4	40.7193	.60980	40.7316	.60993	.99970	.99987	1.0003	.00013
4.5	45.0030	.65324	45.0141	.65335	0.99975	.99989	1.0002	.00011
4.6	49.7371	.69668	49.7472	.69677	.99980	.99991	1.0002	.00009
4.7	54.9690	.74012	54.9781	.74019	.99983	.99993	1.0002	.00007
4.8	60.7511	.78355	60.7593	.78361	.99986	.99994	1.0001	.00006
4.9	67.1412	.82699	67.1486	.82704	.99989	.99995	1.0001	.00005
5.0	74.2032	.87042	74.2099	.87046	0.99991	.99996	1.0001	.00004
5.1	82.008	.91386	82.014	.91389	.99993	.99997	1.0001	.00003
5.2	90.633	.95729	90.639	.95731	.99994	.99997	1.0001	.00003
5.3	100.17	.00072	100.17	.00074	.99995	.99998	1.0000	.00002
5.4	110.70	.04415	110.71	.04417	.99996	.99998	1.0000	.00002
5.5	122.34	.08758	122.35	.08760	0.99997	.99999	1.0000	.00001
5.6	135.21	.13101	135.22	.13103	.99997	.99999	1.0000	.00001
5.7	149.43	.17444	149.44	.17445	.99998	.99999	1.0000	.00001
5.8	165.15	.21787	165.15	.21788	.99998	.99999	1.0000	.00001
5.9	182.52	.26130	182.52	.26131	.99998	.99999	1.0000	.00001
6.0	201.71	.30473	201.72	.30474	0.99999	.00000	1.0000	.00000
6.1	222.93	.34817	222.93	.34817	.99999	.00000	1.0000	.00000
6.2	246.37	.39159	246.38	.39161	.99999	.00000	1.0000	.00000
6.3	272.29	.43503	272.29	.43503	.99999	.00000	1.0000	.00000
6.4	300.92	.47845	300.92	.47845	.99999	.00000	1.0000	.00000
6.5	332.57	.52188	332.57	.52188	1.0000	.00000	1.0000	.00000
6.6	367.55	.56532	367.55	.56532	1.0000	.00000	1.0000	.00000
6.7	406.20	.60874	406.20	.60874	1.0000	.00000	1.0000	.00000
6.8	448.92	.65217	448.92	.65217	1.0000	.00000	1.0000	.00000
6.9	496.14	.69560	496.14	.69560	1.0000	.00000	1.0000	.00000
7.0	548.32	.73903	548.32	.73903	1.0000	.00000	1.0000	.00000
7.1	605.98	.78246	605.98	.78246	1.0000	.00000	1.0000	.00000
7.2	669.72	.82589	669.72	.82589	1.0000	.00000	1.0000	.00000
7.3	740.15	.86932	740.15	.86932	1.0000	.00000	1.0000	.00000
7.4	817.99	.91275	817.99	.91275	1.0000	.00000	1.0000	.00000
7.5	904.02	.95618	904.02	.95618	1.0000	.00000	1.0000	.00000
7.6	999.10	.99961	999.10	.99961	1.0000	.00000	1.0000	.00000
7.7	1104.2	.04305	1104.2	.04305	1.0000	.00000	1.0000	.00000
7.8	1220.3	.08647	1220.3	.08647	1.0000	.00000	1.0000	.00000
7.9	1348.6	.12988	1348.6	.12988	1.0000	.00000	1.0000	.00000

HYPERBOLIC FUNCTIONS AND THEIR COMMON LOGARITHMS (Continued)

x	Sinh x		Cosh x		Tanh x		Coth x	
	Value	$\log_{10}$	Value	$\log_{10}$	Value	$\log_{10}$	Value	$\log_{10}$
8.0	1490.5	.17333	1490.5	.17333	1.0000	.00000	1.0000	.00000
8.1	1647.2	.21675	1647.2	.21675	1.0000	.00000	1.0000	.00000
8.2	1820.5	.26019	1820.5	.26019	1.0000	.00000	1.0000	.00000
8.3	2011.9	.30360	2011.9	.30360	1.0000	.00000	1.0000	.00000
8.4	2223.5	.34704	2223.5	.34704	1.0000	.00000	1.0000	.00000
8.5	2457.4	.39048	2457.4	.39048	1.0000	.00000	1.0000	.00000
8.6	2715.8	.43390	2715.8	.43390	1.0000	.00000	1.0000	.00000
8.7	3001.5	.47734	3001.5	.47734	1.0000	.00000	1.0000	.00000
8.8	3317.1	.52076	3317.1	.52076	1.0000	.00000	1.0000	.00000
8.9	3666.0	.56419	3666.0	.56419	1.0000	.00000	1.0000	.00000
9.0	4051.5	.60762	4051.5	.60762	1.0000	.00000	1.0000	.00000
9.1	4477.6	.65105	4477.6	.65105	1.0000	.00000	1.0000	.00000
9.2	4948.6	.69448	4948.6	.69448	1.0000	.00000	1.0000	.00000
9.3	5469.0	.73791	5469.0	.73791	1.0000	.00000	1.0000	.00000
9.4	6044.2	.78134	6044.2	.78134	1.0000	.00000	1.0000	.00000
9.5	6679.9	.82477	6679.9	.82477	1.0000	.00000	1.0000	.00000
9.6	7382.4	.86820	7382.4	.86820	1.0000	.00000	1.0000	.00000
9.7	8158.8	.91163	8158.8	.91163	1.0000	.00000	1.0000	.00000
9.8	9016.9	.95506	9016.9	.95506	1.0000	.00000	1.0000	.00000
9.9	9965.2	.99849	9965.2	.99849	1.0000	.00000	1.0000	.00000
10.0	11013.2	.04191	11013.2	.04191	1.0000	.00000	1.0000	.00000

EXPONENTIAL AND HYPERBOLIC FUNCTIONS FOR πx

x	$e^{\pi x}$	$e^{-\pi x}$	$\sinh \pi x$	$\cosh \pi x$	$\tanh \pi x$
0.00	1.00000	1.00000	0.00000	1.00000	0.00000
0.01	1.03191	0.96907	0.03142	1.00049	0.03141
0.02	1.06485	0.93910	0.06287	1.00197	0.06275
0.03	1.09883	0.91006	0.09439	1.00444	0.09397
0.04	1.13390	0.88191	0.12599	1.00791	0.12501
0.05	1.17009	0.85464	0.15773	1.01236	0.15580
0.06	1.20743	0.82820	0.18961	1.01782	0.18629
0.07	1.24597	0.80259	0.22169	1.02428	0.21643
0.08	1.28573	0.77777	0.25398	1.03175	0.24617
0.09	1.32676	0.75371	0.28653	1.04024	0.27544
0.10	1.36911	0.73040	0.31935	1.04976	0.30422
0.11	1.41280	0.70781	0.35249	1.06031	0.33245
0.12	1.45789	0.68592	0.38598	1.07191	0.36009
0.13	1.50442	0.66471	0.41986	1.08456	0.38712
0.14	1.55243	0.64415	0.45414	1.09829	0.41350
0.15	1.60198	0.62423	0.48887	1.11310	0.43920
0.16	1.65310	0.60492	0.52409	1.12901	0.46420
0.17	1.70586	0.58621	0.55982	1.14604	0.48849
0.18	1.76030	0.56808	0.59611	1.16419	0.51204
0.19	1.81648	0.55051	0.63298	1.18350	0.53484
0.20	1.87446	0.53349	0.67048	1.20397	0.55689
0.21	1.93428	0.51699	0.70865	1.22563	0.57819
0.22	1.99601	0.50100	0.74751	1.24850	0.59872
0.23	2.05971	0.48550	0.78710	1.27261	0.61850
0.24	2.12545	0.47049	0.82748	1.29797	0.63752
0.25	2.19328	0.45594	0.86867	1.32461	0.65579
0.26	2.26328	0.44184	0.91072	1.35256	0.67333
0.27	2.33551	0.42817	0.95367	1.38184	0.69014
0.28	2.41005	0.41493	0.99756	1.41249	0.70624
0.29	2.48696	0.40210	1.04243	1.44453	0.72164
0.30	2.56633	0.38966	1.08834	1.47800	0.73636
0.31	2.64824	0.37761	1.13531	1.51292	0.75041
0.32	2.73275	0.36593	1.18341	1.54934	0.76382
0.33	2.81997	0.35461	1.23268	1.58729	0.77659
0.34	2.90997	0.34365	1.28316	1.62681	0.78876
0.35	3.00284	0.33302	1.33491	1.66793	0.80034
0.36	3.09867	0.32272	1.38798	1.71070	0.81135
0.37	3.19756	0.31274	1.44241	1.75515	0.82182
0.38	3.29961	0.30307	1.49827	1.80134	0.83176
0.39	3.40492	0.29369	1.55561	1.84931	0.84119
0.40	3.51359	0.28461	1.61449	1.89910	0.85013
0.41	3.62572	0.27581	1.67496	1.95076	0.85862
0.42	3.74143	0.26728	1.73708	2.00436	0.86665
0.43	3.86084	0.25901	1.80091	2.05993	0.87426
0.44	3.98406	0.25100	1.86653	2.11753	0.88147
0.45	4.11121	0.24324	1.93398	2.17722	0.88828
0.46	4.24241	0.23571	2.00335	2.23906	0.89473
0.47	4.37781	0.22842	2.07469	2.30312	0.90082
0.48	4.51753	0.22136	2.14808	2.36944	0.90658
0.49	4.66170	0.21451	2.22359	2.43811	0.91202
0.50	4.81048	0.20788	2.30130	2.50918	0.91715
0.51	4.96400	0.20145	2.38128	2.58273	0.92200
0.52	5.12243	0.19522	2.46360	2.65882	0.92658
0.53	5.28591	0.18918	2.54836	2.73754	0.93089
0.54	5.45460	0.18333	2.63564	2.81897	0.93497

EXPONENTIAL, HYPERBOLIC FUNCTIONS FOR πx (Continued)

x	$e^{\pi x}$	$e^{-\pi x}$	sinh πx	cosh πx	tanh. πx
0.55	5.62869	0.17766	2.72551	2.90317	0.93880
0.56	5.80832	0.17217	2.81808	2.99024	0.94242
0.57	5.99369	0.16684	2.91343	3.08027	0.94584
0.58	6.18498	0.16168	3.01165	3.17333	0.94905
0.59	6.38237	0.15668	3.11284	3.26953	0.95208
0.60	6.58606	0.15184	3.21711	3.36895	0.95493
0.61	6.79625	0.14714	3.32456	3.47170	0.95762
0.62	7.01315	0.14259	3.43528	3.57787	0.96015
0.63	7.23698	0.13818	3.54940	3.68758	0.96253
0.64	7.46794	0.13391	3.66702	3.80092	0.96477
0.65	7.70628	0.12976	3.78826	3.91802	0.96688
0.66	7.95222	0.12575	3.91323	4.03899	0.96887
0.67	8.20601	0.12186	4.04208	4.16394	0.97073
0.68	8.46790	0.11809	4.17491	4.29300	0.97249
0.69	8.73815	0.11444	4.31186	4.42630	0.97415
0.70	9.01703	0.11090	4.45306	4.56396	0.97570
0.71	9.30480	0.10747	4.59867	4.70614	0.97716
0.72	9.60176	0.10415	4.74881	4.85296	0.97854
0.73	9.90820	0.10093	4.90364	5.00456	0.97983
0.74	10.22442	0.09781	5.06331	5.16111	0.98105
0.75	10.55072	0.09478	5.22797	5.32275	0.98219
0.76	10.88745	0.09185	5.39780	5.48965	0.98327
0.77	11.23492	0.08901	5.57295	5.66196	0.98428
0.78	11.59347	0.08626	5.75361	5.83986	0.98523
0.79	11.96347	0.08359	5.93994	6.02353	0.98612
0.80	12.34528	0.08100	6.13214	6.21314	0.98696
0.81	12.73928	0.07850	6.33039	6.40889	0.98775
0.82	13.14585	0.07607	6.53489	6.61096	0.98849
0.83	13.56539	0.07372	6.74584	6.81955	0.98919
0.84	13.99833	0.07144	6.96344	7.03488	0.98985
0.85	14.44508	0.06923	7.18793	7.25715	0.99046
0.86	14.90609	0.06709	7.41950	7.48659	0.99104
0.87	15.38181	0.06501	7.65840	7.72341	0.99158
0.88	15.87271	0.06300	7.90486	7.96786	0.99209
0.89	16.37929	0.06105	8.15912	8.22017	0.99257
0.90	16.90202	0.05916	8.41243	8.48059	0.99302
0.91	17.44145	0.05733	8.69206	8.74939	0.99345
0.92	17.99808	0.05556	8.97126	9.02682	0.99384
0.93	18.57248	0.05384	9.25932	9.31316	0.99422
0.94	19.16522	0.05218	9.55652	9.60870	0.99457
0.95	19.77687	0.05056	9.86315	9.91372	0.99490
0.96	20.40804	0.04900	10.17952	10.22852	0.99521
0.97	21.05935	0.04748	10.50594	10.55342	0.99550
0.98	21.73146	0.04602	10.84272	10.88874	0.99577
0.99	22.42501	0.04459	11.19021	11.23480	0.99603
1.00	23.14069	0.04321	11.54874	11.59195	0.99627

Tables for Use in Hyperbolic and Related Functions

INVERSE HYPERBOLIC FUNCTIONS

x	$\sinh^{-1} x$	$\tanh^{-1} x$	$\operatorname{cosech}^{-1} x$	$\operatorname{sech}^{-1} x$
0.0	0.00000	0.00000	∞	∞
0.01	0.01000	0.01000	5.29834	5.29829
0.02	0.02000	0.02000	4.60527	4.60507
0.03	0.03000	0.03001	4.19993	4.19948
0.04	0.03999	0.04002	3.91242	3.91162
0.05	0.04998	0.05004	3.68950	3.68825
0.06	0.05996	0.06007	3.50746	3.50566
0.07	0.06994	0.07011	3.35363	3.35118
0.08	0.07991	0.08017	3.22047	3.21727
0.09	0.08988	0.09024	3.10311	3.09906
0.10	0.09983	0.10034	2.99822	2.99322
0.11	0.10978	0.11045	2.90343	2.89738
0.12	0.11971	0.12058	2.81699	2.80979
0.13	0.12964	0.13074	2.73757	2.72912
0.14	0.13955	0.14093	2.66412	2.65432
0.15	0.14944	0.15114	2.59585	2.58459
0.16	0.15933	0.16139	2.53207	2.51927
0.17	0.16919	0.17167	2.47225	2.45780
0.18	0.17904	0.18198	2.41595	2.39975
0.19	0.18888	0.19234	2.36278	2.34473
0.20	0.19869	0.20273	2.31244	2.29243
0.21	0.20849	0.21317	2.26464	2.24258
0.22	0.21826	0.22366	2.21916	2.19495
0.23	0.22802	0.23419	2.17579	2.14933
0.24	0.23775	0.24477	2.13436	2.10554
0.25	0.24747	0.25541	2.09471	2.06344
0.26	0.25716	0.26611	2.05671	2.02288
0.27	0.26682	0.27686	2.02023	1.98374
0.28	0.27646	0.28768	1.98516	1.94591
0.29	0.28608	0.29857	1.95141	1.90930
0.30	0.29567	0.30952	1.91890	1.87382
0.31	0.30524	0.32055	1.88753	1.83939
0.32	0.31478	0.33165	1.85725	1.80594
0.33	0.32429	0.34283	1.82799	1.77340
0.34	0.33377	0.35409	1.79968	1.74172
0.35	0.34322	0.36544	1.77228	1.71083
0.36	0.35265	0.37689	1.74573	1.68070
0.37	0.36204	0.38842	1.71999	1.65127
0.38	0.37140	0.40006	1.69502	1.62250
0.39	0.38073	0.41180	1.67078	1.59436
0.40	0.39004	0.42365	1.64723	1.56680
0.41	0.39930	0.43561	1.62434	1.53979
0.42	0.40854	0.44769	1.60209	1.51331
0.43	0.41774	0.45990	1.58043	1.48731
0.44	0.42691	0.47223	1.55935	1.46178
0.45	0.43605	0.48470	1.53882	1.43669
0.46	0.44515	0.49731	1.51881	1.41200
0.47	0.45422	0.51007	1.49931	1.38771
0.48	0.46325	0.52298	1.48029	1.36379
0.49	0.47225	0.53606	1.46174	1.34021
0.50	0.48121	0.54931	1.44364	1.31696

INVERSE HYPERBOLIC FUNCTIONS (Continued)

x	$\sinh^{-1} x$	$\tanh^{-1} x$	$\operatorname{cosech}^{-1} x$	$\operatorname{sech}^{-1} x$
0.50	0.48121	0.54931	1.44364	1.31696
0.51	0.49014	0.56273	1.42596	1.29401
0.52	0.49903	0.57634	1.40870	1.27136
0.53	0.50788	0.59015	1.39183	1.24898
0.54	0.51670	0.60416	1.37535	1.22686
0.55	0.52548	0.61838	1.35924	1.20497
0.56	0.53422	0.63283	1.34348	1.18331
0.57	0.54293	0.64752	1.32807	1.16186
0.58	0.55160	0.66246	1.31299	1.14060
0.59	0.56023	0.67767	1.29824	1.11952
0.60	0.56882	0.69315	1.28380	1.09861
0.61	0.57738	0.70892	1.26965	1.07785
0.62	0.58590	0.72501	1.25580	1.05723
0.63	0.59438	0.74142	1.24223	1.03673
0.64	0.60282	0.75817	1.22894	1.01635
0.65	0.61122	0.77530	1.21591	0.99606
0.66	0.61959	0.79281	1.20314	0.97585
0.67	0.62792	0.81074	1.19062	0.95572
0.68	0.63620	0.82911	1.17834	0.93564
0.69	0.64446	0.84796	1.16629	0.91560
0.70	0.65267	0.86730	1.15448	0.89559
0.71	0.66084	0.88718	1.14288	0.87559
0.72	0.66897	0.90764	1.13151	0.85558
0.73	0.67707	0.92873	1.12034	0.83555
0.74	0.68513	0.95048	1.10938	0.81549
0.75	0.69315	0.97296	1.09861	0.79537
0.76	0.70113	0.99622	1.08804	0.77517
0.77	0.70907	1.02033	1.07766	0.75487
0.78	0.71697	1.04537	1.06746	0.73445
0.79	0.72484	1.07143	1.05744	0.71388
0.80	0.73267	1.09861	1.04759	0.69315
0.81	0.74046	1.12703	1.03792	0.67221
0.82	0.74821	1.15682	1.02840	0.65103
0.83	0.75592	1.18814	1.01905	0.62958
0.84	0.76360	1.22117	1.00986	0.60781
0.85	0.77124	1.25615	1.00082	0.58568
0.86	0.77884	1.29334	0.99193	0.56313
0.87	0.78640	1.33308	0.98319	0.54008
0.88	0.79393	1.37577	0.97459	0.51647
0.89	0.80142	1.42193	0.96613	0.49220
0.90	0.80887	1.47222	0.95780	0.46715
0.91	0.81628	1.52752	0.94961	0.44116
0.92	0.82366	1.58903	0.94154	0.41406
0.93	0.83100	1.65839	0.93361	0.38560
0.94	0.83830	1.73805	0.92580	0.35542
0.95	0.84557	1.83178	0.91810	0.32304
0.96	0.85280	1.94591	0.91053	0.28768
0.97	0.86000	2.09230	0.90307	0.24807
0.98	0.86716	2.29756	0.89573	0.20169
0.99	0.87428	2.64665	0.88850	0.14201
1.00	0.88137	∞	0.88137	0.00000

INVERSE HYPERBOLIC FUNCTIONS (Continued)

x	$\sinh^{-1} x$	$\cosh^{-1} x$	$\operatorname{cosech}^{-1} x$	$\coth^{-1} x$
1.00	0.88137	0.00000	0.88137	∞
1.01	0.88843	0.14130	0.87436	2.65165
1.02	0.89545	0.19967	0.86744	2.30756
1.03	0.90243	0.24434	0.86063	2.10730
1.04	0.90938	0.28191	0.85391	1.96591
1.05	0.91629	0.31492	0.84730	1.85679
1.06	0.92317	0.34470	0.84078	1.76806
1.07	0.93002	0.37202	0.83435	1.69340
1.08	0.93683	0.39738	0.82801	1.62905
1.09	0.94360	0.42114	0.82177	1.57255
1.10	0.95035	0.44357	0.81561	1.52226
1.11	0.95706	0.46485	0.80954	1.47698
1.12	0.96373	0.48513	0.80355	1.43584
1.13	0.97038	0.50453	0.79764	1.39817
1.14	0.97699	0.52316	0.79182	1.36346
1.15	0.98357	0.54110	0.78607	1.33129
1.16	0.99011	0.55840	0.78041	1.30134
1.17	0.99663	0.57514	0.77482	1.27334
1.18	1.00311	0.59135	0.76930	1.24706
1.19	1.00956	0.60708	0.76386	1.22232
1.20	1.01597	0.62236	0.75849	1.19895
1.21	1.02236	0.63724	0.75319	1.17682
1.22	1.02871	0.65173	0.74796	1.15582
1.23	1.03504	0.66586	0.74279	1.13584
1.24	1.04133	0.67966	0.73770	1.11680
1.25	1.04759	0.69315	0.73267	1.09861
1.26	1.05382	0.70634	0.72770	1.08122
1.27	1.06003	0.71924	0.72280	1.06456
1.28	1.06620	0.73189	0.71796	1.04857
1.29	1.07234	0.74428	0.71318	1.03321
1.30	1.07845	0.75643	0.70846	1.01844
1.31	1.08453	0.76836	0.70380	1.00422
1.32	1.09059	0.78007	0.69920	0.99050
1.33	1.09661	0.79157	0.69465	0.97727
1.34	1.10261	0.80288	0.69016	0.96448
1.35	1.10857	0.81400	0.68572	0.95212
1.36	1.11451	0.82494	0.68134	0.94016
1.37	1.12042	0.83570	0.67701	0.92857
1.38	1.12630	0.84630	0.67273	0.91734
1.39	1.13216	0.85673	0.66851	0.90645
1.40	1.13798	0.86701	0.66433	0.89588
1.41	1.14378	0.87715	0.66020	0.88561
1.42	1.14955	0.88714	0.65612	0.87563
1.43	1.15530	0.89699	0.65209	0.86593
1.44	1.16101	0.90670	0.64811	0.85649
1.45	1.16670	0.91629	0.64417	0.84730
1.46	1.17237	0.92575	0.64028	0.83835
1.47	1.17801	0.93509	0.63643	0.82962
1.48	1.18362	0.94432	0.63263	0.82111
1.49	1.18920	0.95343	0.62886	0.81282
1.50	1.19476	0.96242	0.62515	0.80472

INVERSE HYPERBOLIC FUNCTIONS (Continued)

x	$\sinh^{-1} x$	$\cosh^{-1} x$	$\operatorname{cosech}^{-1} x$	$\coth^{-1} x$
1.50	1.19476	0.96242	0.62515	0.80472
1.51	1.20030	0.97131	0.62147	0.79681
1.52	1.20581	0.98010	0.61783	0.78909
1.53	1.21129	0.98879	0.61424	0.78155
1.54	1.21675	0.99737	0.61068	0.77418
1.55	1.22218	1.00587	0.60716	0.76697
1.56	1.22759	1.01426	0.60368	0.75991
1.57	1.23298	1.02257	0.60024	0.75301
1.58	1.23834	1.03079	0.59684	0.74626
1.59	1.24367	1.03892	0.59347	0.73965
1.60	1.24898	1.04697	0.59014	0.73317
1.61	1.25427	1.05493	0.58685	0.72682
1.62	1.25954	1.06282	0.58359	0.72061
1.63	1.26478	1.07063	0.58036	0.71451
1.64	1.26999	1.07836	0.57717	0.70853
1.65	1.27519	1.08601	0.57401	0.70267
1.66	1.28036	1.09360	0.57089	0.69692
1.67	1.28551	1.10111	0.56780	0.69128
1.68	1.29064	1.10855	0.56474	0.68574
1.69	1.29574	1.11592	0.56171	0.68030
1.70	1.30082	1.12323	0.55871	0.67496
1.71	1.30588	1.13047	0.55574	0.66972
1.72	1.31092	1.13765	0.55281	0.66457
1.73	1.31593	1.14476	0.54990	0.65951
1.74	1.32093	1.15182	0.54702	0.65453
1.75	1.32590	1.15881	0.54417	0.64964
1.76	1.33085	1.16574	0.54135	0.64483
1.77	1.33578	1.17262	0.53856	0.64011
1.78	1.34069	1.17944	0.53579	0.63546
1.79	1.34557	1.18620	0.53305	0.63088
1.80	1.35044	1.19291	0.53034	0.62638
1.81	1.35529	1.19957	0.52766	0.62195
1.82	1.36011	1.20617	0.52500	0.61759
1.83	1.36492	1.21272	0.52237	0.61330
1.84	1.36970	1.21922	0.51976	0.60908
1.85	1.37447	1.22567	0.51718	0.60492
1.86	1.37921	1.23207	0.51462	0.60082
1.87	1.38394	1.23842	0.51208	0.59679
1.88	1.38864	1.24473	0.50957	0.59281
1.89	1.39333	1.25098	0.50709	0.58890
1.90	1.39800	1.25720	0.50462	0.58504
1.91	1.40265	1.26336	0.50218	0.58123
1.92	1.40728	1.26949	0.49977	0.57748
1.93	1.41188	1.27557	0.49737	0.57379
1.94	1.41648	1.28160	0.49500	0.57014
1.95	1.42105	1.28760	0.49265	0.56655
1.96	1.42560	1.29355	0.49032	0.56301
1.97	1.43014	1.29946	0.48801	0.55951
1.98	1.43466	1.30533	0.48572	0.55606
1.99	1.43915	1.31117	0.48346	0.55266
2.00	1.44364	1.31696	0.48121	0.54931

Tables for Use in Hyperbolic and Related Functions

INVERSE HYPERBOLIC FUNCTIONS (Continued)

x	$\sinh^{-1} x$	$\cosh^{-1} x$	$\operatorname{cosech}^{-1} x$	$\coth^{-1} x$
2.00	1.44364	1.31696	0.48121	0.54931
2.10	1.48748	1.37286	0.45982	0.51805
2.20	1.52966	1.42542	0.44019	0.49041
2.30	1.57028	1.47504	0.42213	0.46578
2.40	1.60944	1.52208	0.40547	0.44365
2.50	1.64723	1.56680	0.39004	0.42365
2.60	1.68374	1.60944	0.37571	0.40547
2.70	1.71905	1.65019	0.36239	0.38885
2.80	1.75323	1.68924	0.34996	0.37361
2.90	1.78634	1.72671	0.33834	0.35956
3.00	1.81845	1.76275	0.32745	0.34657
3.10	1.84960	1.79746	0.31723	0.33452
3.20	1.87986	1.83094	0.30763	0.32331
3.30	1.90927	1.86328	0.29857	0.31285
3.40	1.93788	1.89456	0.29003	0.30307
3.50	1.96572	1.92485	0.28196	0.29389
3.60	1.99284	1.95421	0.27432	0.28527
3.70	2.01926	1.98270	0.26708	0.27716
3.80	2.04503	2.01037	0.26021	0.26950
3.90	2.07017	2.03727	0.25368	0.26226
4.00	2.09471	2.06344	0.24747	0.25541
4.10	2.11869	2.08892	0.24155	0.24892
4.20	2.14211	2.11375	0.23590	0.24275
4.30	2.16502	2.13796	0.23051	0.23689
4.40	2.18742	2.16158	0.22536	0.23131
4.50	2.20935	2.18464	0.22043	0.22599
4.60	2.23081	2.20717	0.21571	0.22092
4.70	2.25184	2.22920	0.21119	0.21607
4.80	2.27244	2.25073	0.20685	0.21143
4.90	2.29264	2.27180	0.20269	0.20699
5.00	2.31244	2.29243	0.19869	0.20273
5.10	2.33186	2.31263	0.19484	0.19865
5.20	2.35093	2.33243	0.19114	0.19473
5.30	2.36964	2.35183	0.18758	0.19097
5.40	2.38801	2.37086	0.18414	0.18735
5.50	2.40606	2.38953	0.18083	0.18386
5.60	2.42379	2.40784	0.17764	0.18051
5.70	2.44122	2.42583	0.17455	0.17727
5.80	2.45836	2.44349	0.17157	0.17415
5.90	2.47521	2.46084	0.16869	0.17114
6.00	2.49178	2.47789	0.16590	0.16824
6.10	2.50809	2.49465	0.16321	0.16543
6.20	2.52414	2.51113	0.16060	0.16271
6.30	2.53994	2.52734	0.15807	0.16008
6.40	2.55549	2.54329	0.15562	0.15754
6.50	2.57081	2.55898	0.15325	0.15508
6.60	2.58591	2.57443	0.15094	0.15269
6.70	2.60078	2.58964	0.14871	0.15038
6.80	2.61543	2.60462	0.14653	0.14813
6.90	2.62988	2.61938	0.14442	0.14596
7.00	2.64412	2.63392	0.14238	0.14384

GUDERMANNIAN FUNCTION

x	0	1	2	3	4	5	6	7	8	9
0.0	0.00000	0.01000	0.02000	0.03000	0.03999	0.04998	0.05996	0.06994	0.07991	0.08988
0.1	0.09983	0.10978	0.11971	0.12964	0.13954	0.14944	0.15932	0.16919	0.17904	0.18887
0.2	0.19868	0.20847	0.21825	0.22800	0.23773	0.24744	0.25712	0.26678	0.27641	0.28602
0.3	0.29560	0.30515	0.31467	0.32417	0.33363	0.34307	0.35247	0.36184	0.37117	0.38047
0.4	0.38974	0.39897	0.40817	0.41733	0.42645	0.43554	0.44459	0.45359	0.46256	0.47149
0.5	0.48038	0.48923	0.49803	0.50680	0.51552	0.52420	0.53284	0.54143	0.54997	0.55848
0.6	0.56694	0.57535	0.58372	0.59204	0.60031	0.60854	0.61672	0.62486	0.63294	0.64098
0.7	0.64897	0.65692	0.66481	0.67266	0.68045	0.68820	0.69590	0.70355	0.71115	0.71870
0.8	0.72620	0.73366	0.74106	0.74841	0.75571	0.76297	0.77017	0.77732	0.78443	0.79148
0.9	0.79848	0.80544	0.81234	0.81919	0.82599	0.83275	0.83945	0.84611	0.85271	0.85926
1.0	0.86577	0.87223	0.87863	0.88499	0.89130	0.89756	0.90377	0.90993	0.91604	0.92211
1.1	0.92813	0.93410	0.94002	0.94589	0.95172	0.95750	0.96323	0.96892	0.97455	0.98015
1.2	0.98569	0.99119	0.99665	1.00205	1.00742	1.01274	1.01801	1.02324	1.02842	1.03356
1.3	1.03866	1.04371	1.04872	1.05368	1.05860	1.06348	1.06832	1.07312	1.07787	1.08258
1.4	1.08725	1.09188	1.09647	1.10101	1.10552	1.10999	1.11441	1.11880	1.12315	1.12746
1.5	1.13173	1.13596	1.14015	1.14431	1.14843	1.15251	1.15655	1.16056	1.16453	1.16846
1.6	1.17236	1.17622	1.18005	1.18384	1.18760	1.19132	1.19500	1.19866	1.20228	1.20586
1.7	1.20941	1.21293	1.21642	1.21987	1.22330	1.22668	1.23004	1.23337	1.23666	1.23993
1.8	1.24316	1.24636	1.24954	1.25268	1.25579	1.25888	1.26193	1.26496	1.26795	1.27092
1.9	1.27386	1.27677	1.27966	1.28251	1.28534	1.28815	1.29092	1.29367	1.29639	1.29909
2.0	1.30176	1.30441	1.30703	1.30962	1.31219	1.31473	1.31726	1.31975	1.32222	1.32467
2.1	1.32710	1.32950	1.33188	1.33423	1.33656	1.33887	1.34116	1.34343	1.34567	1.34789
2.2	1.35009	1.35227	1.35443	1.35656	1.35868	1.36077	1.36285	1.36490	1.36694	1.36895
2.3	1.37095	1.37292	1.37488	1.37682	1.37873	1.38063	1.38251	1.38438	1.38622	1.38805
2.4	1.38986	1.39165	1.39342	1.39518	1.39691	1.39864	1.40034	1.40203	1.40370	1.40535
2.5	1.40699	1.40862	1.41022	1.41181	1.41339	1.41495	1.41649	1.41802	1.41954	1.42104
2.6	1.42252	1.42399	1.42545	1.42689	1.42832	1.42973	1.43113	1.43251	1.43388	1.43524
2.7	1.43659	1.43792	1.43924	1.44054	1.44183	1.44311	1.44438	1.44564	1.44688	1.44811
2.8	1.44933	1.45053	1.45173	1.45291	1.45408	1.45524	1.45638	1.45752	1.45864	1.45976
2.9	1.46086	1.46195	1.46303	1.46410	1.46516	1.46621	1.46725	1.46828	1.46930	1.47031
3.0	1.47130	1.47229	1.47327	1.47424	1.47520	1.47615	1.47709	1.47802	1.47894	1.47986
3.1	1.48076	1.48165	1.48254	1.48342	1.48428	1.48514	1.48600	1.48684	1.48767	1.48850
3.2	1.48932	1.49013	1.49093	1.49172	1.49251	1.49329	1.49406	1.49482	1.49558	1.49632
3.3	1.49706	1.49780	1.49852	1.49924	1.49995	1.50066	1.50135	1.50204	1.50273	1.50340
3.4	1.50407	1.50474	1.50539	1.50605	1.50669	1.50733	1.50796	1.50858	1.50920	1.50981
3.5	1.51042	1.51102	1.51161	1.51220	1.51279	1.51336	1.51393	1.51450	1.51506	1.51561
3.6	1.51616	1.51671	1.51724	1.51778	1.51830	1.51883	1.51934	1.51985	1.52036	1.52086
3.7	1.52136.	1.52185	1.52234	1.52282	1.52330	1.52377	1.52424	1.52470	1.52516	1.52561
3.8	1.52606	1.52651	1.52695	1.52738	1.52782	1.52824	1.52867	1.52909	1.52950	1.52991
3.9	1.53032	1.53072	1.53112	1.53151	1.53190	1.53229	1.53267	1.53305	1.53343	1.53380
4.0	1.53417	1.53453	1.53489	1.53525	1.53561	1.53596	1.53630	1.53664	1.53698	1.53732
4.1	1.53765	1.53798	1.53831	1.53863	1.53895	1.53927	1.53958	1.53989	1.54020	1.54051
4.2	1.54081	1.54111	1.54140	1.54169	1.54198	1.54227	1.54255	1.54283	1.54311	1.54339
4.3	1.54366	1.54393	1.54420	1.54446	1.54472	1.54498	1.54524	1.54550	1.54575	1.54600
4.4	1.54624	1.54649	1.54673	1.54697	1.54721	1.54744	1.54767	1.54790	1.54813	1.54836
4.5	1.54858	1.54880	1.54902	1.54924	1.54945	1.54966	1.54987	1.55008	1.55029	1.55049
4.6	1.55069	1.55089	1.55109	1.55129	1.55148	1.55167	1.55186	1.55205	1.55224	1.55242
4.7	1.55261	1.55279	1.55297	1.55314	1.55332	1.55349	1.55367	1.55384	1.55400	1.55417
4.8	1.55434	1.55450	1.55466	1.55482	1.55498	1.55514	1.55530	1.55545	1.55560	1.55575
4.9	1.55590	1.55605	1.55620	1.55634	1.55649	1.55663	1.55677	1.55691	1.55705	1.55719

GUDERMANNIAN FUNCTION (Continued)

x	0	1	2	3	4	5	6	7	8	9
5.0	1.55732	1.55745	1.55759	1.55772	1.55785	1.55798	1.55811	1.55823	1.55836	1.55848
5.1	1.55860	1.55872	1.55884	1.55896	1.55908	1.55920	1.55931	1.55943	1.55954	1.55965
5.2	1.55976	1.55987	1.55998	1.56009	1.56020	1.56030	1.56041	1.56051	1.56061	1.56071
5.3	1.56081	1.56091	1.56101	1.56111	1.56120	1.56130	1.56139	1.56149	1.56158	1.56167
5.4	1.56176	1.56185	1.56194	1.56203	1.56212	1.56220	1.56229	1.56237	1.56246	1.56254
5.5	1.56262	1.56270	1.56278	1.56286	1.56294	1.56302	1.56310	1.56318	1.56325	1.56333
5.6	1.56340	1.56347	1.56355	1.56362	1.56369	1.56376	1.56383	1.56390	1.56397	1.56404
5.7	1.56410	1.56417	1.56424	1.56430	1.56437	1.56443	1.56449	1.56456	1.56462	1.56468
5.8	1.56474	1.56480	1.56486	1.56492	1.56498	1.56504	1.56509	1.56515	1.56521	1.56526
5.9	1.56532	1.56537	1.56543	1.56548	1.56553	1.56558	1.56564	1.56569	1.56574	1.56579
6.0	1.56584	1.56589	1.56594	1.56599	1.56603	1.56608	1.56613	1.56617	1.56622	1.56627
6.1	1.56631	1.56636	1.56640	1.56644	1.56649	1.56653	1.56657	1.56661	1.56666	1.56670
6.2	1.56674	1.56678	1.56682	1.56686	1.56690	1.56694	1.56697	1.56701	1.56705	1.56709
6.3	1.56712	1.56716	1.56720	1.56723	1.56727	1.56730	1.56734	1.56737	1.56741	1.56744
6.4	1.56747	1.56751	1.56754	1.56757	1.56760	1.56764	1.56767	1.56770	1.56773	1.56776
6.5	1.56779	1.56782	1.56785	1.56788	1.56791	1.56794	1.56796	1.56799	1.56802	1.56805
6.6	1.56808	1.56810	1.56813	1.56816	1.56818	1.56821	1.56823	1.56826	1.56828	1.56831
6.7	1.56833	1.56836	1.56838	1.56841	1.56843	1.56845	1.56848	1.56850	1.56852	1.56855
6.8	1.56857	1.56859	1.56861	1.56863	1.56866	1.56868	1.56870	1.56872	1.56874	1.56876
6.9	1.56878	1.56880	1.56882	1.56884	1.56886	1.56888	1.56890	1.56892	1.56894	1.56895
7.0	1.56897	1.56899	1.56901	1.56903	1.56904	1.56906	1.56908	1.56910	1.56911	1.56913
7.1	1.56915	1.56916	1.56918	1.56919	1.56921	1.56923	1.56924	1.56926	1.56927	1.56929
7.2	1.56930	1.56932	1.56933	1.56935	1.56936	1.56938	1.56939	1.56940	1.56942	1.56943
7.3	1.56945	1.56946	1.56947	1.56949	1.56950	1.56951	1.56952	1.56954	1.56955	1.56956
7.4	1.56957	1.56959	1.56960	1.56961	1.56962	1.56963	1.56965	1.56966	1.56967	1.56968
7.5	1.56969	1.56970	1.56971	1.56972	1.56973	1.56974	1.56975	1.56976	1.56978	1.56979
7.6	1.56980	1.56981	1.56982	1.56983	1.56983	1.56984	1.56985	1.56986	1.56987	1.56988
7.7	1.56989	1.56990	1.56991	1.56992	1.56993	1.56993	1.56994	1.56995	1.56996	1.56997
7.8	1.56998	1.56999	1.56999	1.57000	1.57001	1.57002	1.57002	1.57003	1.57004	1.57005
7.9	1.57005	1.57006	1.57007	1.57008	1.57008	1.57009	1.57010	1.57010	1.57011	1.57012
8.0	1.57013	1.57013	1.57014	1.57015	1.57015	1.57016	1.57016	1.57017	1.57018	1.57018
8.1	1.57019	1.57020	1.57020	1.57021	1.57021	1.57022	1.57022	1.57023	1.57024	1.57024
8.2	1.57025	1.57025	1.57026	1.57026	1.57027	1.57027	1.57028	1.57028	1.57029	1.57029
8.3	1.57030	1.57030	1.57031	1.57031	1.57032	1.57032	1.57033	1.57033	1.57034	1.57034
8.4	1.57035	1.57035	1.57036	1.57036	1.57036	1.57037	1.57037	1.57038	1.57038	1.57039
8.5	1.57039	1.57039	1.57040	1.57040	1.57041	1.57041	1.57041	1.57042	1.57042	1.57042
8.6	1.57043	1.57043	1.57044	1.57044	1.57044	1.57045	1.57045	1.57045	1.57046	1.57046
8.7	1.57046	1.57047	1.57047	1.57047	1.57048	1.57048	1.57048	1.57049	1.57049	1.57049
8.8	1.57049	1.57050	1.57050	1.57050	1.57051	1.57051	1.57051	1.57052	1.57052	1.57052
8.9	1.57052	1.57053	1.57053	1.57053	1.57053	1.57054	1.57054	1.57054	1.57054	1.57055
9.0	1.57055	1.57055	1.57055	1.57056	1.57056	1.57056	1.57056	1.57057	1.57057	1.57057
9.1	1.57057	1.57058	1.57058	1.57058	1.57058	1.57058	1.57059	1.57059	1.57059	1.57059
9.2	1.57059	1.57060	1.57060	1.57060	1.57060	1.57060	1.57061	1.57061	1.57061	1.57061
9.3	1.57061	1.57062	1.57062	1.57062	1.57062	1.57062	1.57062	1.57063	1.57063	1.57063
9.4	1.57063	1.57063	1.57063	1.57064	1.57064	1.57064	1.57064	1.57064	1.57064	1.57065
9.5	1.57065	1.57065	1.57065	1.57065	1.57065	1.57065	1.57066	1.57066	1.57066	1.57066
9.6	1.57066	1.57066	1.57066	1.57066	1.57067	1.57067	1.57067	1.57067	1.57067	1.57067
9.7	1.57067	1.57067	1.57068	1.57068	1.57068	1.57068	1.57068	1.57068	1.57068	1.57068
9.8	1.57069	1.57069	1.57069	1.57069	1.57069	1.57069	1.57069	1.57069	1.57069	1.57069
9.9	1.57070	1.57070	1.57070	1.57070	1.57070	1.57070	1.57070	1.57070	1.57070	1.57070

INVERSE GUDERMANNIAN FUNCTION

x	0	1	2	3	4	5	6	7	8	9
0.0	0.00000	0.01000	0.02000	0.03000	0.04001	0.05002	0.06004	0.07006	0.08009	0.09012
0.1	0.10017	0.11022	0.12029	0.13037	0.14046	0.15057	0.16069	0.17082	0.18098	0.19115
0.2	0.20135	0.21156	0.22180	0.23206	0.24234	0.25265	0.26298	0.27334	0.28373	0.29415
0.3	0.30460	0.31509	0.32561	0.33616	0.34675	0.35737	0.36804	0.37874	0.38949	0.40028
0.4	0.41111	0.42199	0.43292	0.44390	0.45493	0.46600	0.47714	0.48833	0.49957	0.51087
0.5	0.52224	0.53366	0.54515	0.55671	0.56834	0.58003	0.59180	0.60364	0.61555	0.62755
0.6	0.63962	0.65178	0.66402	0.67636	0.68878	0.70129	0.71390	0.72661	0.73942	0.75233
0.7	0.76535	0.77848	0.79172	0.80508	0.81856	0.83217	0.84590	0.85976	0.87376	0.88790
0.8	0.90218	0.91660	0.93118	0.94592	0.96082	0.97589	0.99113	1.00654	1.02215	1.03794
0.9	1.05392	1.07011	1.08651	1.10313	1.11997	1.13704	1.15435	1.17192	1.18974	1.20783
1.0	1.22619	1.24485	1.26380	1.28306	1.30265	1.32258	1.34285	1.36349	1.38451	1.40593
1.1	1.42776	1.45003	1.47275	1.49594	1.51963	1.54384	1.56860	1.59394	1.61987	1.64645
1.2	1.67370	1.70166	1.73037	1.75987	1.79022	1.82147	1.85367	1.88689	1.92120	1.95667
1.3	1.99340	2.03147	2.07100	2.11210	2.15491	2.19959	2.24630	2.29524	2.34666	2.40080
1.4	2.45800	2.51861	2.58307	2.65193	2.72583	2.80558	2.89219	2.98695	3.09160	3.20843
1.5	3.34068	3.49307	3.67286	3.89217	4.17343	4.56609	5.22169	7.82865		

ANALYTIC GEOMETRY

Dr. Howard Eves

RECTANGULAR COORDINATES IN A PLANE

Rectangular (Cartesian) Coordinates

Let $X'X$ (called the *x-axis*) and $Y'Y$ (called the *y-axis*) be two perpendicular lines (here taken horizontally and vertically, respectively) intersecting in point O (called the *origin*). Then any point P in the plane of the axes is located by the distance x (called the *abscissa*) and the distance y (called the *ordinate*) from $Y'Y$ and $X'X$, respectively, to P, where x is taken as positive to the right and negative to the left of $Y'Y$, and y is taken as positive above and negative below $X'X$. The ordered pair of numbers, (x,y), are called *rectangular coordinates* of the point P.

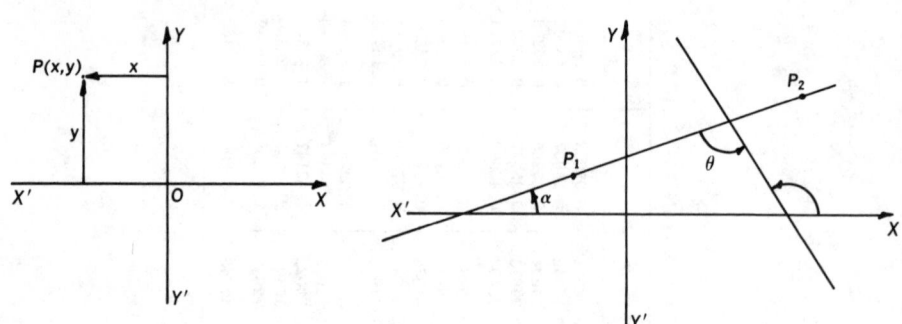

Points, Slopes, Angles

Let $P_1(x_1,y_1)$ and $P_2(x_2,y_2)$ be any two points and let α be the angle measured counterclockwise from $X'X$ to P_1P_2.

Distance between P_1 and P_2: $\quad\sqrt{(x_2 - x_1)^2 + (y_2 - y_1)^2}$

Point dividing P_1P_2 in ratio $\dfrac{r}{s}$: $\quad\left(\dfrac{rx_2 + sx_1}{r + s},\ \dfrac{ry_2 + sy_1}{r + s}\right)$

Midpoint of P_1P_2: $\quad\left(\dfrac{x_1 + x_2}{2},\ \dfrac{y_1 + y_2}{2}\right)$

Slope m of P_1P_2: $\quad m = \tan \alpha = \dfrac{y_2 - y_1}{x_2 - x_1}$

Angle θ between two lines of slopes m_1 and m_2: $\quad\tan \theta = \dfrac{m_2 - m_1}{1 + m_1m_2}$

For parallel lines: $\quad m_1 = m_2$

For perpendicular lines: $\quad m_1m_2 = -1$

Points P_1, P_2, P_3 are collinear if and only if $\quad\begin{vmatrix} x_1 & y_1 & 1 \\ x_2 & y_2 & 1 \\ x_3 & y_3 & 1 \end{vmatrix} = 0.$

368

Polygonal Areas

Area of triangle $P_1 P_2 P_3$:

$$\frac{1}{2}\begin{vmatrix} x_1 & y_1 & 1 \\ x_2 & y_2 & 1 \\ x_3 & y_3 & 1 \end{vmatrix} = \tfrac{1}{2}(x_1 y_2 + x_2 y_3 + x_3 y_1 - y_1 x_2 - y_2 x_3 - y_3 x_1)$$

Area of polygon $P_1 P_2 \cdots P_n$:

$$\tfrac{1}{2}(x_1 y_2 + x_2 y_3 + \cdots + x_{n-1} y_n + x_n y_1 - y_1 x_2 - y_2 x_3 - \cdots - y_{n-1} x_n - y_n x_1)$$

Note. The parenthesis in the last formula is remembered by the device

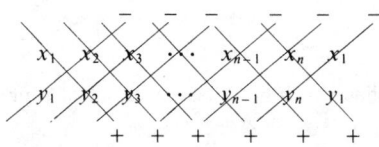

Here one adds the products of coordinates on the lines slanting downward to the right and subtracts the products of coordinates on the lines slanting upward to the right. The area is positive or negative according as $P_1 P_2 \cdots P_n$ is a counterclockwise or clockwise polygon.

Straight Lines

Line parallel to y-axis:	$x = a$
Line parallel to x-axis:	$y = b$
Slope y-intercept form:	$y = mx + b$
Intercept form:	$\dfrac{x}{a} + \dfrac{y}{b} = 1$
Point-slope form:	$y - y_1 = m(x - x_1)$
Two-point form:	$\dfrac{y - y_1}{x - x_1} = \dfrac{y_2 - y_1}{x_2 - x_1}$

or

$$\begin{vmatrix} x & y & 1 \\ x_1 & y_1 & 1 \\ x_2 & y_2 & 1 \end{vmatrix} = 0$$

Normal form:	$x \cos \omega + y \sin \omega = p$
General form:	$Ax + By + C = 0$
Slope:	$m = -\dfrac{A}{B}$
Intercepts:	$a = -\dfrac{C}{A}, \quad b = -\dfrac{C}{B}$

To reduce $Ax + By + C = 0$ to normal form, divide by $\pm \sqrt{A^2 + B^2}$, where the sign of the radical is chosen opposite to the sign of C when $C \neq 0$ and the same as the sign of B when $C = 0$.

Distance from $Ax + By + C = 0$ to P_1: $\dfrac{A x_1 + B y_1 + C}{\pm \sqrt{A^2 + B^2}}$

Angle θ between lines $A_1 x + B_1 y + C_1 = 0$
and $A_2 x + B_2 y + C_2 = 0$

$$\tan \theta = \frac{A_1 B_2 - A_2 B_1}{A_1 A_2 + B_1 B_2}$$

Lines parallel: $\qquad A_1 B_2 = A_2 B_1$

Lines perpendicular: $\qquad A_1 A_2 = -B_1 B_2$

Lines $A_1 x + B_1 y + C_1 = 0, A_2 x + B_2 y + C_2 = 0, A_3 x + B_3 y + C_3 = 0$ are concurrent if and only if

$$\begin{vmatrix} A_1 & B_1 & C_1 \\ A_2 & B_2 & C_2 \\ A_3 & B_3 & C_3 \end{vmatrix} = 0.$$

Line of Best Fit

In seeking the straight line which best fits a given set of n points $P_1(x_1, y_1)$, $P_2(x_2, y_2)$, $\cdots$, $P_n(x_n, y_n)$, calculate

$$\bar{x} = \frac{x_1 + x_2 + \cdots + x_n}{n}, \quad \bar{y} = \frac{y_1 + y_2 + \cdots + y_n}{n},$$

$$m = \frac{(x_1 y_1 + x_2 y_2 + \cdots + x_n y_n) - n \bar{x} \bar{y}}{(x_1^2 + x_2^2 + \cdots + x_n^2) - n \bar{x}^2}.$$

Then the sought line is given by

$$y - \bar{y} = m(x - \bar{x}).$$

Circles

Center at origin, radius r: $\qquad x^2 + y^2 = r^2$

Center at (h, k), radius r: $\qquad (x - h)^2 + (y - k)^2 = r^2$

General form: $\qquad \begin{cases} Ax^2 + Ay^2 + Dx + Ey + F = 0, A \neq 0 \\ x^2 + y^2 + 2dx + 2ey + f = 0 \end{cases}$

Center: $\qquad (-d, -e)$

Radius: $\qquad r = \sqrt{d^2 + e^2 - f}$

Circle on $P_1 P_2$ as diameter: $\qquad (x - x_1)(x - x_2) + (y - y_1)(y - y_2) = 0$

Three-point form: $\qquad \begin{vmatrix} x^2 + y^2 & x & y & 1 \\ x_1^2 + y_1^2 & x_1 & y_1 & 1 \\ x_2^2 + y_2^2 & x_2 & y_2 & 1 \\ x_3^2 + y_3^2 & x_3 & y_3 & 1 \end{vmatrix} = 0$

Conic Sections

A *conic section* is the locus of a point P that moves in the plane of a fixed point F (called a *focus*) and a fixed line d (called a *directrix*), F not on d, such that the ratio of the distance of P from F to its distance from d is a constant e (called the *eccentricity*).

If $e = 1$, the conic is a *parabola*; if $e < 1$, an *ellipse*; if $e > 1$, a *hyperbola*.

Focus, (0,0); directrix, $x = -a$: $\quad x^2 + y^2 = e^2 (x + a)^2$

Parabolas (e = 1)

Let p = distance from the vertex to the focus, e = eccentricity.

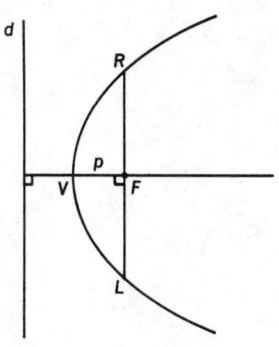

V: vertex
F: focus
d: directrix
LR: latus rectum
line VF: axis

Latus rectum:	$4p$
Distance from vertex to directrix:	p
Vertex at origin, focus at $(p,0)$:	$y^2 = 4px$
Vertex at origin, focus at $(-p,0)$:	$y^2 = -4px$
Vertex at origin, focus at $(0,p)$:	$x^2 = 4py$
Vertex at origin, focus at $(0,-p)$:	$x^2 = -4py$
Vertex, (h,k); focus, $(h + p,k)$:	$(y - k)^2 = 4p(x - h)$
Vertex, (h,k); focus, $(h - p,k)$:	$(y - k)^2 = -4p(x - h)$
Vertex, (h,k); focus, $(h,k + p)$:	$(x - h)^2 = 4p(y - k)$
Vertex, (h,k); focus, $(h,k - p)$:	$(x - h)^2 = -4p(y - k)$
General form, axis parallel to $X'X$:	$Cy^2 + Dx + Ey + F = 0$
General form, axis parallel to $Y'Y$:	$\begin{cases} Ax^2 + Dx + Ey + F = 0 \\ y = ax^2 + bx + c \end{cases}$
General form, axis oblique to coordinate axes:	$Ax^2 + Bxy + Cy^2 + Dx + Ey + F = 0,$ $B^2 - 4AC = 0$

Ellipses (e < 1)

Let $2a$ = major axis, $2b$ = minor axis, e = eccentricity.

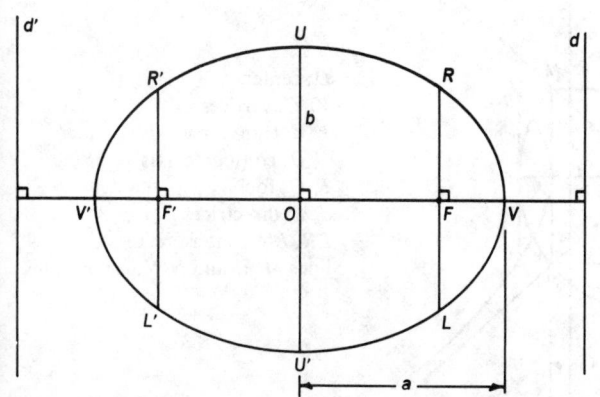

O: center
V, V': vertices
$V'V$: major axis = $2a$
$U'U$: minor axis = $2b$
F, F': foci
d, d': directrices
$LR, L'R'$: latera recta

Eccentricity:	$e = \dfrac{\sqrt{a^2 - b^2}}{a}$
Latus rectum:	$\dfrac{2b^2}{a}$
Distance from center to either focus:	$\sqrt{a^2 - b^2}$
Distance from center to either directrix:	$\dfrac{a}{e}$
Sum of distances from any point on ellipse to the foci:	$2a$
Center at origin, foci on $X'X$:	$\dfrac{x^2}{a^2} + \dfrac{y^2}{b^2} = 1$
Center at origin, foci on $Y'Y$:	$\dfrac{x^2}{b^2} + \dfrac{y^2}{a^2} = 1$
Center at (h,k), major axis parallel to $X'X$:	$\dfrac{(x - h)^2}{a^2} + \dfrac{(y - k)^2}{b^2} = 1$
Center at (h,k), major axis parallel to $Y'Y$:	$\dfrac{(x - h)^2}{b^2} + \dfrac{(y - k)^2}{a^2} = 1$
General form, axes parallel to coordinate axes:	$Ax^2 + Cy^2 + Dx + Ey + F = 0, AC > 0$
General form, axes oblique to coordinate axes:	$Ax^2 + Bxy + Cy^2 + Dx + Ey + F = 0,$ $B^2 - 4AC < 0$

For a *circle*: $a = b$, $e = 0$, foci coincide at the center of the circle, directrices are at infinity.

Hyperbolas ($e > 1$)

Let $2a$ = transverse axis, $2b$ = conjugate axis, e = eccentricity.

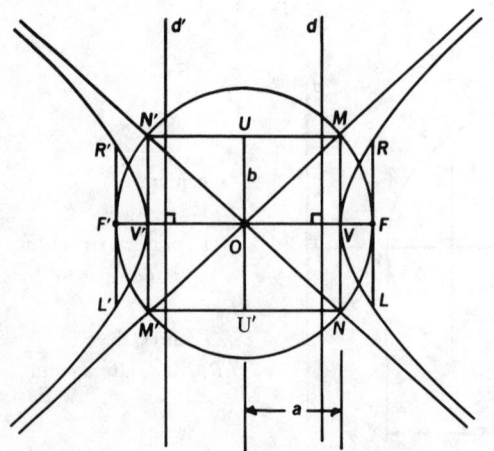

O: center
V, V': vertices
$V'V$: transverse axis = $2a$
$U'U$: conjugate axis = $2b$
F, F': foci
d, d': directrices
$LR, L'R'$: latera recta
lines $M'M$ and $N'N$: asymptotes

Eccentricity:	$e = \dfrac{\sqrt{a^2 + b^2}}{a}$
Latus rectum:	$\dfrac{2b^2}{a}$
Distance from center to either focus:	$\sqrt{a^2 + b^2}$
Distance from center to either directrix:	$\dfrac{a}{e}$
Difference of distances of any point on hyperbola from foci:	$2a$
Center at origin, foci on $X'X$:	$\dfrac{x^2}{a^2} - \dfrac{y^2}{b^2} = 1$
Slopes of asymptotes:	$\pm \dfrac{b}{a}$
Center at origin, foci on $Y'Y$:	$\dfrac{y^2}{a^2} - \dfrac{x^2}{b^2} = 1$
Slopes of asymptotes:	$\pm \dfrac{a}{b}$
Center at (h,k), transverse axis parallel to $X'X$:	$\dfrac{(x - h)^2}{a^2} - \dfrac{(y - k)^2}{b^2} = 1$
Slopes of asymptotes:	$\pm \dfrac{b}{a}$
Center at (h, k), transverse axis parallel to $Y'Y$:	$\dfrac{(y - k)^2}{a^2} - \dfrac{(x - h)^2}{b^2} = 1$
Slopes of asymptotes:	$\pm \dfrac{a}{b}$
Center at origin, $X'X$ and $Y'Y$ for asymptotes:	$xy = c$
Center at (h,k), asymptotes parallel to $X'X$ and $Y'Y$:	$(x - h)(y - k) = c$
General form, axes parallel to coordinate axes:	$Ax^2 + Cy^2 + Dx + Ey + F = 0, AC < 0$
General form, axes oblique to coordinate axes:	$Ax^2 + Bxy + Cy^2 + Dx + Ey + F = 0,$ $B^2 - 4AC > 0$

For a *rectangular hyperbola*: $a = b$, $e = \sqrt{2}$, asymptotes are perpendicular.

General Equation of Second Degree

The nature of the graph of the general quadratic equation in x and y,

$$ax^2 + 2hxy + by^2 + 2gx + 2fy + c = 0,$$

is described in the following table in terms of the values of

$$\Delta = \begin{vmatrix} a & h & g \\ h & b & f \\ g & f & c \end{vmatrix}, \quad J = \begin{vmatrix} a & h \\ h & b \end{vmatrix},$$

$$I = a + b, \quad K = \begin{vmatrix} a & g \\ g & c \end{vmatrix} + \begin{vmatrix} b & f \\ f & c \end{vmatrix}.$$

Case	$\triangle$	J	$\triangle/I$	K	Conic
1	$\neq 0$	> 0	< 0		real ellipse
2	$\neq 0$	> 0	> 0		imaginary ellipse
3	$\neq 0$	< 0			hyperbola
4	$\neq 0$	0			parabola
5	0	< 0			real intersecting lines
6	0	> 0			conjugate complex intersecting lines
7	0	0		< 0	real distinct parallel lines
8	0	0		> 0	conjugate complex parallel lines
9	0	0		0	coincident lines

In cases 1, 2, and 3, the center (x_0, y_0) of the conic is given by the simultaneous solution of the equations

$$ax + hy + g = 0, \quad hx + by + f = 0.$$

The equations of the axes of the conic are

$$y - y_0 = m(x - x_0), \quad y - y_0 = -\frac{1}{m}(x - x_0),$$

where m is the positive root of

$$hm^2 + (a - b)m - h = 0.$$

Transformation of Coordinates

To transform an equation of a curve from an old system of rectangular coordinates (x, y) to a new system of rectangular coordinates (x', y'), substitute for each old variable in the equation of the curve its expression in terms of the new variables.

Translation: $\begin{cases} x = x' + h \\ y = y' + k \end{cases}$ The new axes are parallel to the old axes and the coordinates of the new origin in terms of the old system are (h, k).

Rotation: $\begin{cases} x = x' \cos\theta - y' \sin\theta \\ y = x' \sin\theta + y' \cos\theta \end{cases}$ The new origin is coincident with the old origin and the new axes make an angle θ with the old axes.

To remove the xy-term from the equation

$$ax^2 + 2hxy + by^2 + 2gx + 2fy + c = 0,$$

rotate the coordinate axes about the origin through the acute angle $\theta = \arctan m$, where m is the positive root of

$$hm^2 + (a - b)m - h = 0.$$

OBLIQUE COORDINATES IN A PLANE

Oblique (Cartesian) Coordinates

Let $X'X$ (called the *x-axis*, here taken horizontally) and $Y'Y$ (called the *y-axis*) be two lines intersecting in point O (called the *origin*), and denote by ω the counterclockwise angle from $X'X$ to $Y'Y$. Then any point P in the plane of the axes is located by the distance x (called the *abscissa*) measured parallel to the x-axis and the distance y (called the *ordinate*) measured parallel to the *y*-axis from $Y'Y$ and $X'X$, respectively, to *P*, where *x* is taken as positive to the right and negative to the left of $Y'Y$, and *y* is taken as positive above and negative below $X'X$. The ordered pair of numbers, (x,y), are called *oblique coordinates* of the point *P*. If $\omega = 90°$, this coordinate system becomes a rectangular (Cartesian) coordinate system.

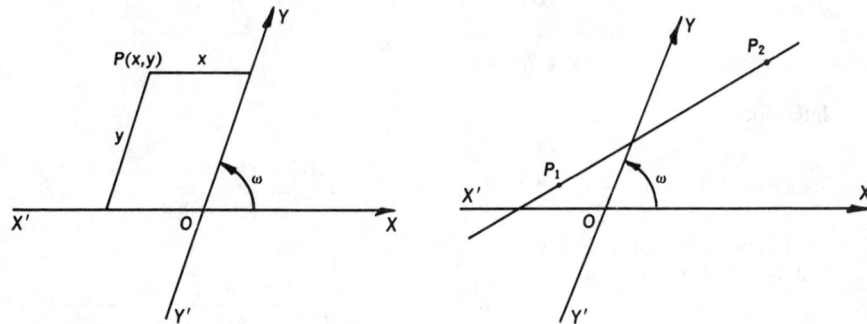

Points

Let $P_1(x_1,y_1)$ and $P_2(x_2,y_2)$ be any two points.
Distance between P_1 and P_2:

$$\sqrt{(x_2 - x_1)^2 + (y_2 - y_1)^2 + 2(x_2 - x_1)(y_2 - y_1)\cos \omega}$$

Point dividing $P_1 P_2$ in ratio $\dfrac{r}{s}$:
$$\left(\frac{rx_2 + sx_1}{r + s}, \frac{ry_2 + sy_1}{r + s}\right)$$

Midpoint of $P_1 P_2$:
$$\left(\frac{x_1 + x_2}{2}, \frac{y_1 + y_2}{2}\right)$$

Points P_1, P_2, P_3 are collinear if and only if $\begin{vmatrix} x_1 & y_1 & 1 \\ x_2 & y_2 & 1 \\ x_3 & y_3 & 1 \end{vmatrix} = 0.$

Polygonal Areas

Area of triangle $P_1 P_2 P_3$:

$$\sin \omega \begin{vmatrix} x_1 & y_1 & 1 \\ x_2 & y_2 & 1 \\ x_3 & y_3 & 1 \end{vmatrix} = \tfrac{1}{2}(\sin \omega)(x_1 y_2 + x_2 y_3 + x_3 y_1 - y_1 x_2 - y_2 x_3 - y_3 x_1)$$

Area of polygon $P_1 P_2 \cdots P_n$:

$$\tfrac{1}{2}(\sin \omega)(x_1 y_2 + x_2 y_3 + \cdots + x_{n-1} y_n + x_n y_1 - y_1 x_2 - y_2 x_3 - \cdots - y_{n-1} x_n - y_n x_1)$$

The area is positive or negative according as $P_1 P_2 \cdots P_n$ is a counterclockwise or clockwise polygon.

Straight Lines

Line parallel to *y*-axis: $x = a$

Line parallel to *x*-axis: $y = b$

Intercept form: $\dfrac{x}{a} + \dfrac{y}{b} = 1$

Two-point form: $\dfrac{y - y_1}{x - x_1} = \dfrac{y_2 - y_1}{x_2 - x_1}$,   or $\begin{vmatrix} x & y & 1 \\ x_1 & y_1 & 1 \\ x_2 & y_2 & 1 \end{vmatrix} = 0$

General form: $Ax + By + C = 0$

Intercepts: $a = -\dfrac{C}{A}$, $b = -\dfrac{C}{B}$

Distance from $Ax + By + C = 0$ to P_1: $\dfrac{(Ax_1 + By_1 + C) \sin \omega}{\pm \sqrt{A^2 + B^2 - 2AB \cos \omega}}$

Angle θ between lines $A_1 x + B_1 y + C_1 = 0$
  and $A_2 x + B_2 y + C_2 = 0$:

$$\tan \theta = \frac{(A_1 B_2 - A_2 B_1) \sin \omega}{A_1 A_2 + B_1 B_2 - (A_1 B_2 + A_2 B_1) \cos \omega}$$

Lines parallel: $A_1 B_2 = A_2 B_1$

Lines perpendicular: $A_1 A_2 + B_1 B_2 = (A_1 B_2 + A_2 B_1) \cos \omega$

Lines $A_1 x + B_1 y + C_1 = 0$, $A_2 x + B_2 y + C_2 = 0$, $A_3 x + B_3 y + C_3 = 0$ are concurrent if and only if

$$\begin{vmatrix} A_1 & B_1 & C_1 \\ A_2 & B_2 & C_2 \\ A_3 & B_3 & C_3 \end{vmatrix} = 0.$$

Circles

Center at (h, k), radius r: $(x - h)^2 + (y - k)^2 + 2(x - h)(y - k) \cos \omega = r^2$

Transformation of Coordinates

Translation: $\begin{cases} x = x' + h \\ y = y' + k \end{cases}$ The new axes are parallel to the old axes and the coordinates of the new origin in terms of the old system are (h, k).

From one oblique system to another, origin fixed:
$$\begin{cases} x = \dfrac{x' \sin (\omega - \theta) + y' \sin (\omega - \omega' - \theta)}{\sin \omega} \\[2ex] y = \dfrac{x' \sin \theta + y' \sin (\omega' + \theta)}{\sin \omega} \end{cases}$$

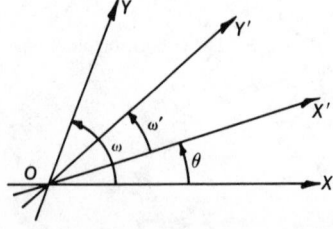

The old and new origins coincide; the old axes intersect at angle ω; the new axes intersect at angle ω'; the counterclockwise angle from x-axis to x'-axis is θ.

POLAR COORDINATES IN A PLANE

Polar Coordinates

In a plane, let OX (called the *initial line*) be a fixed ray radiating from point O (called the *pole* or *origin*). Then any point P, other than O, in the plane is located by angle θ (called the *vectorial angle*) measured from OX to the line determined by O and P and the distance r (called the *radius vector*) from O to P, where θ is taken as positive if measured counterclockwise and negative if measured clockwise, and r is taken as positive if measured along the terminal side of angle θ and negative if measured along the terminal side of θ produced through the pole. Such an ordered pair of numbers, (r, θ), are called *polar coordinates* of the point P. The polar coordinates of the pole O are taken as $(0, \theta)$, where θ is arbitrary. It follows that, for a given initial line and pole, each point of the plane has infinitely many polar coordinates, but each pair of coordinates corresponds to only one point.

Example

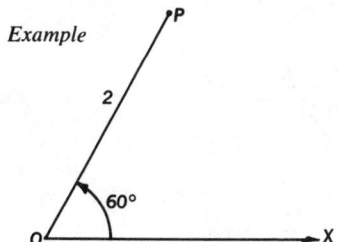

Some polar coordinates of P are: $(2, 60°)$, $(2, 420°)$, $(2, -300°)$, $(-2, 240°)$, $(-2, -120°)$.

Points

Distance between P_1 and P_2: $\sqrt{r_1^2 + r_2^2 - 2r_1 r_2 \cos(\theta_1 - \theta_2)}$
Points P_1, P_2, P_3 are collinear if and only if

$$r_2 r_3 \sin(\theta_3 - \theta_2) + r_3 r_1 \sin(\theta_1 - \theta_3) + r_1 r_2 \sin(\theta_2 - \theta_1) = 0.$$

Polygonal Areas

Area of triangle $P_1 P_2 P_3$:

$$\tfrac{1}{2}[r_1 r_2 \sin(\theta_2 - \theta_1) + r_2 r_3 \sin(\theta_3 - \theta_2) + r_3 r_1 \sin(\theta_1 - \theta_3)]$$

Area of polygon $P_1 P_2 \cdots P_n$:

$$\tfrac{1}{2}[r_1 r_2 \sin(\theta_2 - \theta_1) + r_2 r_3 \sin(\theta_3 - \theta_2) + \cdots + r_{n-1} r_n \sin(\theta_n - \theta_{n-1}) + r_n r_1 \sin(\theta_1 - \theta_n)]$$

The area is positive or negative according as $P_1 P_2 \cdots P_n$ is a counterclockwise or clockwise polygon.

Straight Lines

Let p = distance of line from O, ω = counterclockwise angle from OX to the perpendicular through O to the line.

Normal form: $r \cos(\theta - \omega) = p$
Two-point form: $r[r_1 \sin(\theta - \theta_1) - r_2 \sin(\theta - \theta_2)] = r_1 r_2 \sin(\theta_2 - \theta_1)$

Circles

Center at pole, radius a: $r = a$
Center at $(a, 0)$ and passing
    through the pole: $r = 2a \cos \theta$

Center at $\left(a, \dfrac{\pi}{2}\right)$ and passing

through the pole: $\qquad\qquad\qquad\qquad r = 2a \sin \theta$

Center (h, α), radius a: $\qquad\qquad r^2 - 2hr \cos (\theta - \alpha) + h^2 - a^2 = 0$

Conics

Let $2p$ = distance from directrix to focus, e = eccentricity.

Focus at pole, directrix to left of pole: $\qquad r = \dfrac{2ep}{1 - e \cos \theta}$

Focus at pole, directrix to right of pole: $\qquad r = \dfrac{2ep}{1 + e \cos \theta}$

Focus at pole, directrix below pole: $\qquad r = \dfrac{2ep}{1 - e \sin \theta}$

Focus at pole, directrix above pole: $\qquad r = \dfrac{2ep}{1 + e \sin \theta}$

Parabola with vertex at pole, directrix to left of pole: $\qquad r = \dfrac{4p \cos \theta}{\sin^2 \theta}$

Ellipse with center at pole, semiaxes a and b horizontal and vertical, respectively: $\qquad r^2 = \dfrac{a^2 b^2}{a^2 \sin^2 \theta + b^2 \cos^2 \theta}$

Hyperbola with center at pole, semiaxes a and b horizontal and vertical, respectively: $\qquad r^2 = \dfrac{a^2 b^2}{a^2 \sin^2 \theta - b^2 \cos^2 \theta}$

Relations Between Rectangular and Polar Coordinates

Let the positive x-axis coincide with the initial line and let r be nonnegative.

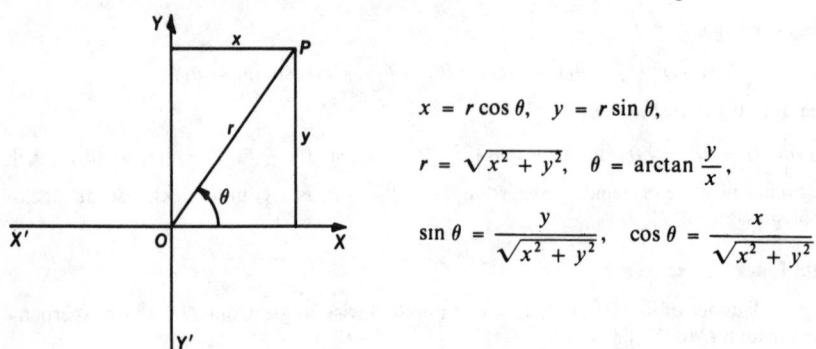

$$x = r \cos \theta, \quad y = r \sin \theta,$$

$$r = \sqrt{x^2 + y^2}, \quad \theta = \arctan \frac{y}{x},$$

$$\sin \theta = \frac{y}{\sqrt{x^2 + y^2}}, \quad \cos \theta = \frac{x}{\sqrt{x^2 + y^2}}$$

RECTANGULAR COORDINATES IN SPACE

Rectangular (Cartesian) Coordinates

Let $X'X$, $Y'Y$, $Z'Z$ (called the *x-axis*, the *y-axis*, and the *z-axis*, respectively) be three mutually perpendicular lines in space intersecting in a point O (called the *origin*), forming in this way three mutually perpendicular planes XOY, XOZ, YOZ (called the *xy-*

plane, the *xz-plane*, and the *yz-plane*, respectively). Then any point P of space is located by its signed distances x, y, z from the *yz*-plane, the *xz*-plane, and the *xy*-plane, respectively, where x and y are the rectangular coordinates with respect to the axes $X'X$ and $Y'Y$ of the orthogonal projection P' of P on the *xy*-plane (here taken horizontally) and z is taken as positive above and negative below the *xy*-plane. The ordered triple of numbers, (x, y, z), are called *rectangular coordinates* of the point P.

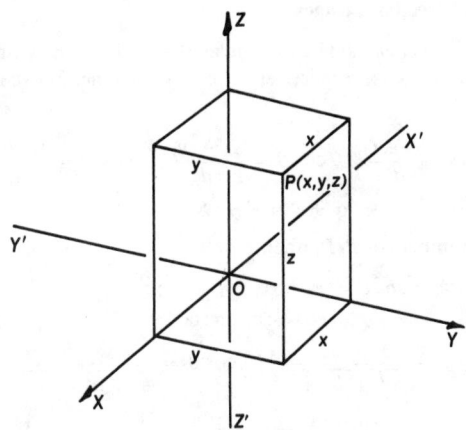

Points

Let $P_1(x_1, y_1, z_1)$ and $P_2(x_2, y_2, z_2)$ be any two points.

Distance between P_1 and P_2: $\sqrt{(x_2 - x_1)^2 + (y_2 - y_1)^2 + (z_2 - z_1)^2}$

Point dividing $P_1 P_2$ in ratio $\dfrac{r}{s}$: $\left(\dfrac{rx_2 + sx_1}{r + s}, \ \dfrac{ry_2 + sy_1}{r + s}, \ \dfrac{rz_2 + sz_1}{r + s} \right)$

Midpoint of $P_1 P_2$: $\left(\dfrac{x_1 + x_2}{2}, \ \dfrac{y_1 + y_2}{2} \quad \dfrac{z_1 + z_2}{2} \right)$

Points P_1, P_2, P_3 are collinear if and only if

$$x_2 - x_1 : y_2 - y_1 : z_2 - z_1 = x_3 - x_1 : y_3 - y_1 : z_3 - z_1.$$

Points P_1, P_2, P_3, P_4 are coplanar if and only if $\begin{vmatrix} x_1 & y_1 & z_1 & 1 \\ x_2 & y_2 & z_2 & 1 \\ x_3 & y_3 & z_3 & 1 \\ x_4 & y_4 & z_4 & 1 \end{vmatrix} = 0.$

Area of triangle $P_1 P_2 P_3$:

$$\frac{1}{2} \sqrt{ \begin{vmatrix} y_1 & z_1 & 1 \\ y_2 & z_2 & 1 \\ y_3 & z_3 & 1 \end{vmatrix}^2 + \begin{vmatrix} z_1 & x_1 & 1 \\ z_2 & x_2 & 1 \\ z_3 & x_3 & 1 \end{vmatrix}^2 + \begin{vmatrix} x_1 & y_1 & 1 \\ x_2 & y_2 & 1 \\ x_3 & y_3 & 1 \end{vmatrix}^2 }$$

$$\text{Volume of tetrahedron } P_1P_2P_3P_4: \quad \frac{1}{6}\begin{vmatrix} x_1 & y_1 & z_1 & 1 \\ x_2 & y_2 & z_2 & 1 \\ x_3 & y_3 & z_3 & 1 \\ x_4 & y_4 & z_4 & 1 \end{vmatrix}$$

Direction Numbers and Direction Cosines

Let α, β, γ (called *direction angles*) be the angles that P_1P_2, or any line parallel to P_1P_2, makes with the x-, y-, and z-axis, respectively. Let d = distance between P_1 and P_2.

Direction cosines of P_1P_2:

$$\cos\alpha = \frac{x_2 - x_1}{d}, \quad \cos\beta = \frac{y_2 - y_1}{d}, \quad \cos\gamma = \frac{z_2 - z_1}{d}$$

$$\cos^2\alpha + \cos^2\beta + \cos^2\gamma = 1$$

If a, b, c are direction numbers of P_1P_2, then:

$$a : b : c = x_2 - x_1 : y_2 - y_1 : z_2 - z_1$$
$$= \cos\alpha : \cos\beta : \cos\gamma$$

$$\cos\alpha = \frac{a}{\pm\sqrt{a^2 + b^2 + c^2}}, \quad \cos\beta = \frac{b}{\pm\sqrt{a^2 + b^2 + c^2}},$$

$$\cos\gamma = \frac{c}{\pm\sqrt{a^2 + b^2 + c^2}}$$

Angle between two lines with direction angles $\alpha_1, \beta_1, \gamma_1$ and $\alpha_2, \beta_2, \gamma_2$:

$$\cos\theta = \cos\alpha_1 \cos\alpha_2 + \cos\beta_1 \cos\beta_2 + \cos\gamma_1 \cos\gamma_2$$

For parallel lines: $\alpha_1 = \alpha_2, \ \beta_1 = \beta_2, \ \gamma_1 = \gamma_2$

For perpendicular lines:

$$\cos\alpha_1 \cos\alpha_2 + \cos\beta_1 \cos\beta_2 + \cos\gamma_1 \cos\gamma_2 = 0$$

Angle between two lines with directions (a_1, b_1, c_1) and (a_2, b_2, c_2):

$$\cos\theta = \frac{a_1 a_2 + b_1 b_2 + c_1 c_2}{\sqrt{a_1^2 + b_1^2 + c_1^2}\ \sqrt{a_2^2 + b_2^2 + c_2^2}}$$

$$\sin\theta = \frac{\sqrt{(b_1 c_2 - c_1 b_2)^2 + (c_1 a_2 - a_1 c_2)^2 + (a_1 b_2 - b_1 a_2)^2}}{\sqrt{a_1^2 + b_1^2 + c_1^2}\ \sqrt{a_2^2 + b_2^2 + c_2^2}}$$

For parallel lines: $a_1 : b_1 : c_1 = a_2 : b_2 : c_2$

For perpendicular lines: $a_1 a_2 + b_1 b_2 + c_1 c_2 = 0$

The direction

$$(b_1 c_2 - c_1 b_2, c_1 a_2 - a_1 c_2, a_1 b_2 - b_1 a_2)$$

is perpendicular to both directions (a_1, b_1, c_1) and (a_2, b_2, c_2).

The directions (a_1, b_1, c_1), (a_2, b_2, c_2), (a_3, b_3, c_3) are parallel to a common plane if and only if

$$\begin{vmatrix} a_1 & b_1 & c_1 \\ a_2 & b_2 & c_2 \\ a_3 & b_3 & c_3 \end{vmatrix} = 0.$$

Straight Lines

Point-direction form:
$$\frac{x - x_1}{a} = \frac{y - y_1}{b} = \frac{z - z_1}{c}$$

Two-point form:
$$\frac{x - x_1}{x_2 - x_1} = \frac{y - y_1}{y_2 - y_1} = \frac{z - z_1}{z_2 - z_1}$$

Parametric form: $x = x_1 + ta, \; y = y_1 + tb, \; z = z_1 + tc$

General form:
$$\begin{cases} A_1x + B_1y + C_1z + D_1 = 0 \\ A_2x + B_2y + C_2z + D_2 = 0 \end{cases}$$

Direction of line: $(B_1C_2 - C_1B_2, C_1A_2 - A_1C_2, A_1B_2 - B_1A_2)$

Projection of segment P_1P_2 on any line having the direction (a, b, c):

$$\frac{(x_2 - x_1)a + (y_2 - y_1)b + (z_2 - z_1)c}{\sqrt{a^2 + b^2 + c^2}}$$

Distance from point P_0 to line through P_1 in direction (a, b, c):

$$\sqrt{\frac{\begin{vmatrix} y_0 - y_1 & z_0 - z_1 \\ b & c \end{vmatrix}^2 + \begin{vmatrix} z_0 - z_1 & x_0 - x_1 \\ c & a \end{vmatrix}^2 + \begin{vmatrix} x_0 - x_1 & y_0 - y_1 \\ a & b \end{vmatrix}^2}{a^2 + b^2 + c^2}}$$

Distance between line through P_1 in direction (a_1, b_1, c_1) and line through P_2 in direction (a_2, b_2, c_2):

$$\pm \frac{\begin{vmatrix} x_2 - x_1 & y_2 - y_1 & z_2 - z_1 \\ a_1 & b_1 & c_1 \\ a_2 & b_2 & c_2 \end{vmatrix}}{\sqrt{\begin{vmatrix} b_1 & c_1 \\ b_2 & c_2 \end{vmatrix}^2 + \begin{vmatrix} c_1 & a_1 \\ c_2 & a_2 \end{vmatrix}^2 + \begin{vmatrix} a_1 & b_1 \\ a_2 & b_2 \end{vmatrix}^2}}$$

The line through P_1 in direction (a_1, b_1, c_1) and the line through P_2 in direction (a_2, b_2, c_2) intersect if and only if

$$\begin{vmatrix} x_2 - x_1 & y_2 - y_1 & z_2 - z_1 \\ a_1 & b_1 & c_1 \\ a_2 & b_2 & c_2 \end{vmatrix} = 0.$$

Planes

General form: $Ax + By + Cz + D = 0$
    Direction of normal: (A, B, C)
Perpendicular to yz-plane: $By + Cz + D = 0$
Perpendicular to xz-plane: $Ax + Cz + D = 0$
Perpendicular to xy-plane: $Ax + By + D = 0$
Perpendicular to x-axis: $Ax + D = 0$
Perpendicular to y-axis: $By + D = 0$
Perpendicular to z-axis: $Cz + D = 0$

Intercept form:
$$\frac{x}{a} + \frac{y}{b} + \frac{z}{c} = 1$$

Plane through point P_1 and perpendicular to direction (a, b, c):

$$a(x - x_1) + b(y - y_1) + c(z - z_1) = 0$$

Plane through point P_1 and parallel to directions (a_1,b_1,c_1) and (a_2,b_2,c_2):

$$\begin{vmatrix} x - x_1 & y - y_1 & z - z_1 \\ a_1 & b_1 & c_1 \\ a_2 & b_2 & c_2 \end{vmatrix} = 0$$

Plane through points P_1 and P_2 parallel to direction (a,b,c):

$$\begin{vmatrix} x - x_1 & y - y_1 & z - z_1 \\ x_2 - x_1 & y_2 - y_1 & z_2 - z_1 \\ a & b & c \end{vmatrix} = 0$$

Three-point form:

$$\begin{vmatrix} x & y & z & 1 \\ x_1 & y_1 & z_1 & 1 \\ x_2 & y_2 & z_2 & 1 \\ x_3 & y_3 & z_3 & 1 \end{vmatrix} = 0 \quad \text{or} \quad \begin{vmatrix} x - x_1 & y - y_1 & z - z_1 \\ x_2 - x_1 & y_2 - y_1 & z_2 - z_1 \\ x_3 - x_1 & y_3 - y_1 & z_3 - z_1 \end{vmatrix} = 0$$

Normal form (p = distance from origin to plane; α, β, γ are direction angles of perpendicular to plane from origin):

$$x \cos \alpha + y \cos \beta + z \cos \gamma = p$$

To reduce $Ax + By + Cz + D = 0$ to normal form, divide by $\pm \sqrt{A^2 + B^2 + C^2}$, where the sign of the radical is chosen opposite to the sign of D when $D \neq 0$, the same as the sign of C when $D = 0$ and $C \neq 0$, the same as the sign of B when $C = D = 0$.

Distance from point P_1 to plane $Ax + By + Cz + D = 0$:

$$\frac{Ax_1 + By_1 + Cz_1 + D}{\pm \sqrt{A^2 + B^2 + C^2}}$$

Angle θ between planes $A_1x + B_1y + C_1z + D_1 = 0$ and $A_2x + B_2y + C_2z + D_2 = 0$:

$$\cos \theta = \frac{A_1A_2 + B_1B_2 + C_1C_2}{\sqrt{A_1^2 + B_1^2 + C_1^2} \sqrt{A_2^2 + B_2^2 + C_2^2}}$$

Planes parallel: $\quad A_1:B_1:C_1 = A_2:B_2:C_2$

Planes perpendicular: $\quad A_1A_2 + B_1B_2 + C_1C_2 = 0$

Spheres

Center at origin, radius r: $\quad x^2 + y^2 + z^2 = r^2$

Center at (g,h,k), radius r: $\quad (x - g)^2 + (y - h)^2 + (z - k)^2 = r^2$

General form: $\quad \begin{cases} Ax^2 + Ay^2 + Az^2 + Dx + Ey + Fz + M = 0, \quad A \neq 0 \\ x^2 + y^2 + z^2 + 2dx + 2ey + 2fz + m = 0 \end{cases}$

Center: $\quad (-d, -e, -f)$

Radius: $\quad r = \sqrt{d^2 + e^2 + f^2 - m}$

Sphere on $P_1 P_2$ as diameter:

$$(x - x_1)(x - x_2) + (y - y_1)(y - y_2) + (z - z_1)(z - z_2) = 0$$

Four-point form:
$$\begin{vmatrix} x^2 + y^2 + z^2 & x & y & z & 1 \\ x_1^2 + y_1^2 + z_1^2 & x_1 & y_1 & z_1 & 1 \\ x_2^2 + y_2^2 + z_2^2 & x_2 & y_2 & z_2 & 1 \\ x_3^2 + y_3^2 + z_3^2 & x_3 & y_3 & z_3 & 1 \\ x_4^2 + y_4^2 + z_4^2 & x_4 & y_4 & z_4 & 1 \end{vmatrix} = 0$$

The Seventeen Quadric Surfaces in Standard Form

1. Real ellipsoid: $\qquad\qquad x^2/a^2 + y^2/b^2 + z^2/c^2 = 1$
2. Imaginary ellipsoid: $\qquad\; x^2/a^2 + y^2/b^2 + z^2/c^2 = -1$
3. Hyperboloid of one sheet: $\; x^2/a^2 + y^2/b^2 - z^2/c^2 = 1$
4. Hyperboloid of two sheets: $x^2/a^2 + y^2/b^2 - z^2/c^2 = -1$
5. Real quadric cone: $\qquad\; x^2/a^2 + y^2/b^2 - z^2/c^2 = 0$
6. Imaginary quadric cone: $\;\; x^2/a^2 + y^2/b^2 + z^2/c^2 = 0$
7. Elliptic paraboloid: $\qquad x^2/a^2 + y^2/b^2 + 2z = 0$
8. Hyperbolic paraboloid: $\;\; x^2/a^2 - y^2/b^2 + 2z = 0$
9. Real elliptic cylinder: $\qquad x^2/a^2 + y^2/b^2 = 1$
10. Imaginary elliptic cylinder: $\; x^2/a^2 + y^2/b^2 = -1$
11. Hyperbolic cylinder: $\qquad x^2/a^2 - y^2/b^2 = -1$
12. Real intersecting planes: $\; x^2/a^2 - y^2/b^2 = 0$
13. Imaginary intersecting planes: $x^2/a^2 + y^2/b^2 = 0$
14. Parabolic cylinder: $\qquad\; x^2 + 2rz = 0$
15. Real parallel planes: $\qquad x^2 = a^2$
16. Imaginary parallel planes: $\; x^2 = -a^2$
17. Coincident planes: $\qquad\; x^2 = 0$

General Equation of Second Degree

The nature of the graph of the general quadratic equation in x, y, z,

$$ax^2 + by^2 + cz^2 + 2fyz + 2gzx + 2hxy + 2px + 2qy + 2rz + d = 0,$$

is described in the following table in terms of $\rho_3, \rho_4, \Delta, k_1, k_2, k_3$, where

$$e = \begin{bmatrix} a & h & g \\ h & b & f \\ g & f & c \end{bmatrix}, \quad E = \begin{bmatrix} a & h & g & p \\ h & b & f & q \\ g & f & c & r \\ p & q & r & d \end{bmatrix},$$

$$\rho_3 = \text{rank } e, \quad \rho_4 = \text{rank } E,$$

$$\Delta = \text{determinant of } E,$$

k_1, k_2, k_3 are the roots of $\begin{vmatrix} a - x & h & g \\ h & b - x & f \\ g & f & c - x \end{vmatrix} = 0.$

Case	ρ_3	ρ_4	Sign of Δ	Nonzero k's same sign?	Quadric Surface
1	3	4	−	yes	Real ellipsoid
2	3	4	+	yes	Imaginary ellipsoid
3	3	4	+	no	Hyperboloid of one sheet
4	3	4	−	no	Hyperboloid of two sheets
5	3	3		no	Real quadric cone
6	3	3		yes	Imaginary quadric cone
7	2	4	−	yes	Elliptic paraboloid
8	2	4	+	no	Hyperbolic paraboloid
9	2	3		yes	Real elliptic cylinder
10	2	3		yes	Imaginary elliptic cylinder
11	2	3		no	Hyperbolic cylinder
12	2	2		no	Real intersecting planes
13	2	2		yes	Imaginary intersecting planes
14	1	3			Parabolic cylinder
15	1	2			Real parallel planes
16	1	2			Imaginary parallel planes
17	1	1			Coincident planes

Cylindrical and Conical Surfaces

Any equation in just two of the variables x, y, z represents a *cylindrical surface* whose elements are parallel to the axis of the missing variable.

Any equation homogeneous in the variables x, y, z represents a *conical surface* whose vertex is at the origin.

Transformation of Coordinates

To transform an equation of a surface from an old system of rectangular coordinates (x, y, z) to a new system of rectangular coordinates (x', y', z'), substitute for each old variable in the equation of the surface its expression in terms of the new variables.

Translation:

$x = x' + h$ The new axes are parallel to the old axes and the coordinates of
$y = y' + k$ the new origin in terms of the old system are (h, k, l).
$z = z' + l$

Rotation about the origin:

$x = \lambda_1 x' + \lambda_2 y' + \lambda_3 z'$ The new origin is coincident with the old origin and
$y = \mu_1 x' + \mu_2 y' + \mu_3 z'$ the x'-axis, y'-axis, z'-axis have direction cosines
$z = \nu_1 x' + \nu_2 y' + \nu_3 z'$ $(\lambda_1, \mu_1, \nu_1), (\lambda_2, \mu_2, \nu_2), (\lambda_3, \mu_3, \nu_3)$, respectively, with respect to the old system of axes.

$x' = \lambda_1 x + \mu_1 y + \nu_1 z$
$y' = \lambda_2 x + \mu_2 y + \nu_2 z$
$z' = \lambda_3 x + \mu_3 y + \nu_3 z$

Cylindrical Coordinates

If (r, θ, z) are the cylindrical coordinates and (x, y, z) the rectangular coordinates of a point P, then

$$x = r \cos \theta, \quad r = \sqrt{x^2 + y^2},$$

$$y = r \sin \theta, \quad \theta = \arctan \frac{y}{x},$$

$$z = z, \qquad z = z.$$

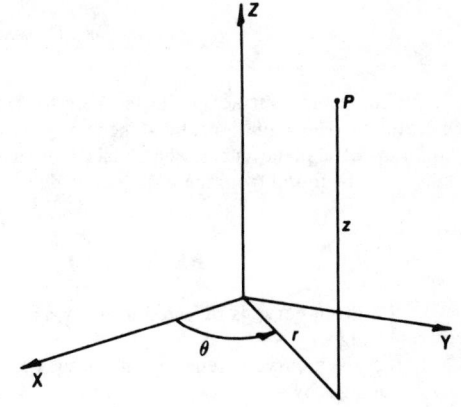

Spherical Coordinates

If (ρ, θ, ϕ) are the spherical coordinates and (x, y, z) the rectangular coordinates of a point P, then

$$x = \rho \cos \theta \sin \phi$$
$$y = \rho \sin \theta \sin \phi$$
$$z = \rho \cos \phi$$
$$\phi = \arccos \frac{z}{\sqrt{x^2 + y^2 + z^2}},$$

$$\theta = \arctan \frac{y}{x}.$$

$$p^2 = x^2 + y^2 + z^2$$

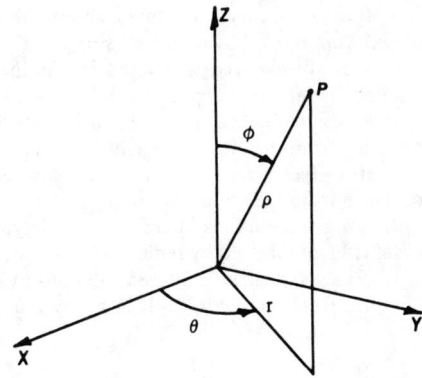

CURVES AND SURFACES

Dr. Howard Eves

The curves and surfaces collected here for reference appear frequently in mathematical literature. The equations most generally associated with each figure are given. The equation of a plane curve when placed otherwise on the coordinate frame of reference may often be found from the given equation by the following rules.

RECTANGULAR COORDINATES

1. If a given curve is reflected in the x-axis, the new equation is obtained from the old by replacing y by $-y$.

2. If a given curve is reflected in the y-axis, the new equation is obtained from the old by replacing x by $-x$.

3. If a given curve is reflected in the origin, the new equation is obtained from the old by replacing x by $-x$ and y by $-y$.

4. If a given curve is reflected in the line $y = x$, the new equation is obtained from the old by interchanging x and y.

5. If a given curve is rotated about the origin through 90°, the new equation is obtained from the old by replacing x by y and y by $-x$.

6. If a given curve is rotated about the origin through $-90°$, the new equation is obtained from the old by replacing x by $-y$ and y by x.

7. If a given curve is translated a distance h in the x-direction, the new equation is obtained from the old by replacing x by $x - h$.

8. If a given curve is translated a distance k in the y-direction, the new equation is obtained from the old by replacing y by $y - k$.

9. If a given curve is altered by multiplying all the abscissas by a, the new equation is obtained from the old by replacing x by x/a.

10. If a given curve is altered by multiplying all the ordinates by b, the new equation is obtained from the old by replacing y by y/b.

POLAR COORDINATES

1. If a given curve is reflected in the polar axis, the new equation is obtained from the old by replacing θ by $-\theta$, or by replacing r by $-r$ and θ by $\pi - \theta$.

2. If a given curve is reflected in the 90° axis, the new equation is obtained from the old by replacing θ by $\pi - \theta$, or by replacing r by $-r$ and θ by $-\theta$.

3. If a given curve is reflected in the pole, the new equation is obtained from the old by replacing θ by $\pi + \theta$, or by replacing r by $-r$.

4. If a given curve is rotated about the pole through an angle α, the new equation is obtained from the old by replacing θ by $\theta - \alpha$.

PLANE CURVES

Archimedean spiral
  See: Spiral of Archimedes

Astroid
  See: Hypocycloid of four cusps

Bifolium

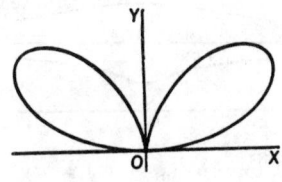

$$(x^2 + y^2)^2 = ax^2y$$
$$r = a \sin \theta \cos^2 \theta$$

Cardioid

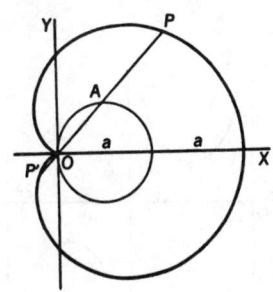

$$(x^2 + y^2 - ax)^2 = a^2(x^2 + y^2)$$
$$r = a(\cos \theta + 1)$$
or
$$r = a(\cos \theta - 1)$$
$$[P'A = AP = a]$$

Cassinian curves
  See: Ovals of Cassini

Catenary, Hyperbolic cosine

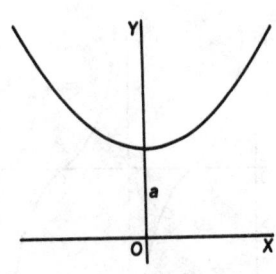

$$y = \frac{a}{2} (e^{x/a} + e^{-x/a}) = a \cosh \frac{x}{a}$$

Circle
(a)

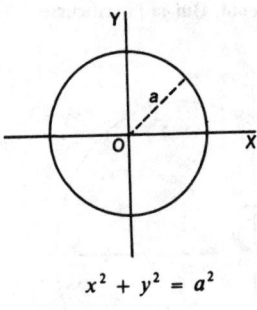

$$x^2 + y^2 = a^2$$
$$r = a$$

(b)

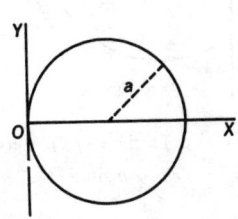

$$x^2 + y^2 = 2ax$$
$$r = 2a \cos \theta$$

(c)

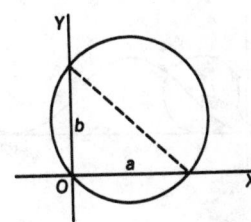

$$x^2 + y^2 = ax + by$$
$$r = a \cos \theta + b \sin \theta$$

Cissoid of Diocles

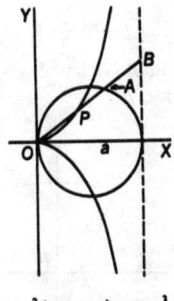

$$y^2(a - x) = x^3$$
$$r = a \sin \theta \tan \theta$$
$$[OP = AB]$$

Cochleoid, Oui-ja board curve

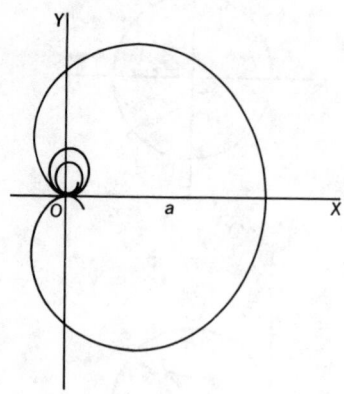

$$(x^2 + y^2)\tan^{-1}(y/x) = ay$$
$$r\theta = a\sin\theta$$

Companion to the cycloid

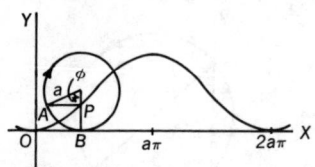

$$\begin{cases} x = a\phi \\ y = a(1 - \cos\phi) \end{cases}$$
$$[OB = \widehat{AB}]$$

(This is a sinusoid)

Conchoid of Nicomedes
(a) $a < b$

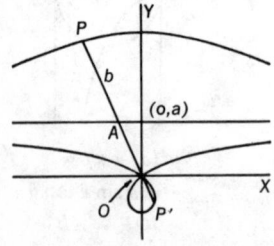

(b) $a > b$

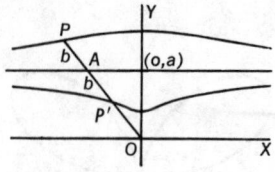

$$(y - a)^2(x^2 + y^2) = b^2y^2$$
$$r = a\csc\theta \pm b$$
$$[P'A = AP = b]$$

Conic sections
See: Circle; Ellipse; Hyperbola; Parabola

Cosecant curve

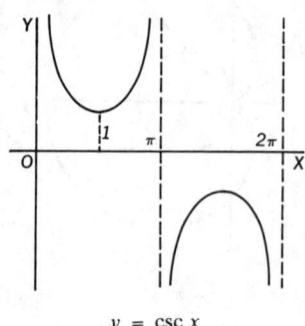

$$y = \csc x$$

Cosine curve

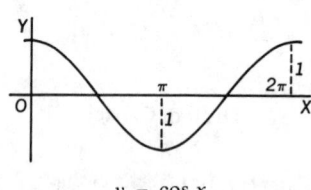

$$y = \cos x$$

Cotangent curve

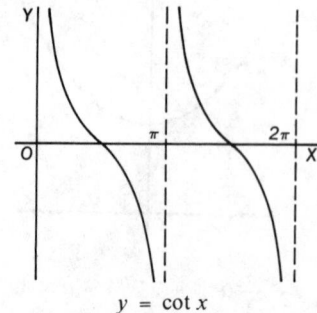

$$y = \cot x$$

Cubical parabola (special)

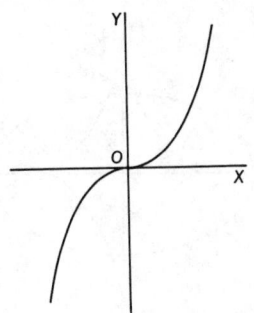

$$y = ax^3, \quad a > 0$$

$$r^2 = \frac{1}{a} \sec^2 \theta \tan \theta, \quad a > 0$$

Cubical parabola (general)

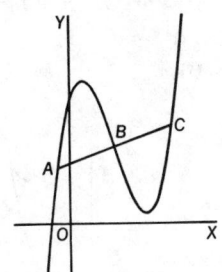

$$y = ax^3 + bx^2 + cx + d, \quad a > 0$$
$$[AB = BC]$$
(abscissa of $B = -b/3a$)

Curtate cycloid, Trochoids
See: Cycloid, curtate

Cycloid (cusp at origin)

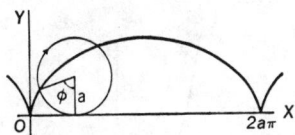

$$x = a \arccos \frac{a - y}{a} \mp \sqrt{2ay - y^2}$$

$$\begin{cases} x = a(\phi - \sin \phi) \\ y = a(1 - \cos \phi) \end{cases}$$

(For one arch: arc length $= 8a$;
area $= 3\pi a^2$)

Cycloid (vertex at origin)

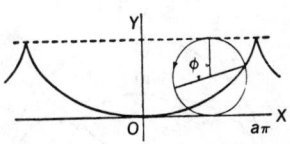

$$x = 2a \arcsin \sqrt{y/2a} + \sqrt{2ay - y^2}$$

$$\begin{cases} x = a(\phi + \sin \phi) \\ y = a(1 - \cos \phi) \end{cases}$$

Cycloid, curtate

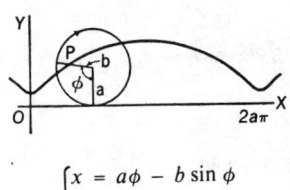

$$\begin{cases} x = a\phi - b \sin \phi \\ y = a - b \cos \phi \end{cases}$$
$$a > b$$

Cycloid, prolate

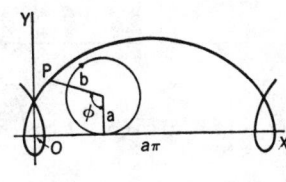

$$\begin{cases} x = a\phi - b \sin \phi \\ y = a - b \cos \phi \end{cases}$$
$$a < b$$

Deltoid
See: Hypocycloid of three cusps

Ellipse

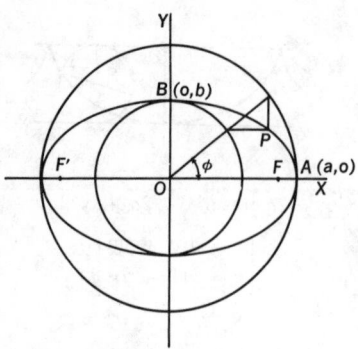

$$x^2/a^2 + y^2/b^2 = 1$$

$$\begin{cases} x = a \cos \phi \\ y = b \sin \phi \end{cases}$$

$$[BF' = BF = a, \quad PF' + PF = 2a]$$

Epicycloid

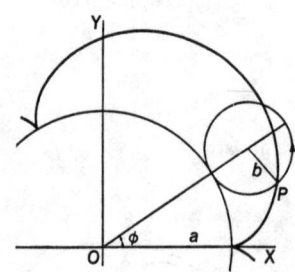

$$\begin{cases} x = (a + b) \cos \phi - b \cos\!\left(\dfrac{a + b}{b}\,\phi\right) \\ y = (a + b) \sin \phi - b \sin\!\left(\dfrac{a + b}{b}\,\phi\right) \end{cases}$$

Equiangular spiral
  See: Spiral, logarithmic or equiangular

Equilateral hyperbola
  See: Hyperbola, equilateral or rectangular

Evolute of ellipse

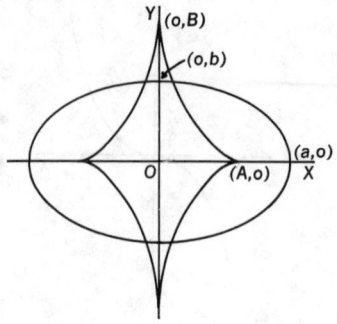

$$(ax)^{2/3} + (by)^{2/3} = (a^2 - b^2)^{2/3}$$

$$\begin{cases} x = A \cos^3 \phi \\ y = B \sin^3 \phi \end{cases}$$

$$[A = (a^2 - b^2)/a, \quad B = (a^2 - b^2)/b]$$

Exponential curve
  (1) $a > 0$

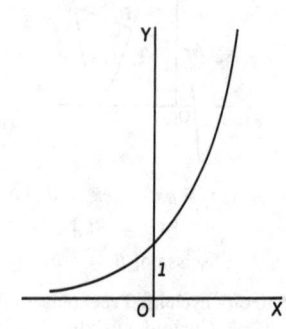

  (2) $a < 0$

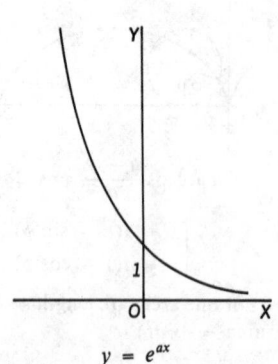

$$y = e^{ax}$$

Folium of Descartes

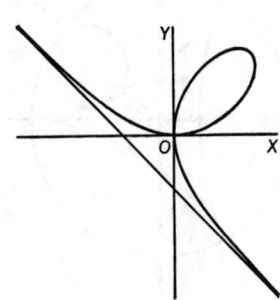

$$x^3 + y^3 - 3axy = 0$$
$$\begin{cases} x = 3a\phi/(1 + \phi^3) \\ y = 3a\phi^2/(1 + \phi^3) \end{cases}$$
$$r = \frac{3a \sin \theta \cos \theta}{\sin^3 \theta + \cos^3 \theta}$$

[asymptote: $x + y + a = 0$]

Gamma function

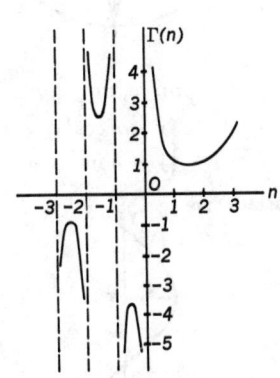

$$\Gamma(n) = \int_0^\infty x^{n-1} e^{-x} dx \quad (n > 0)$$

$$\Gamma(n) = \frac{\Gamma(n + 1)}{n} \quad (0 > n \ne -1, -2, -3, \ldots)$$

Hyperbola

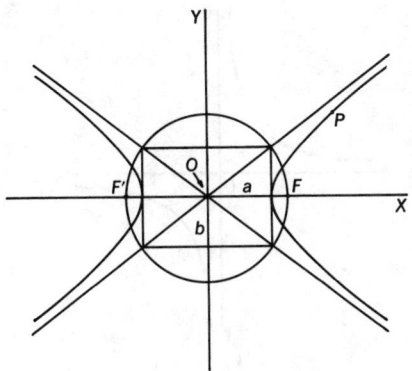

$$x^2/a^2 - y^2/b^2 = 1$$
$$[F'P - FP = 2a]$$

Hyperbola, equilateral or **rectangular**

(1)

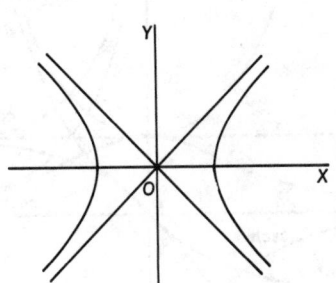

$$x^2 - y^2 = a^2$$

(2)

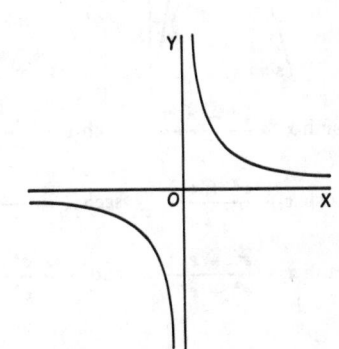

$$xy = k, \quad k > 0$$

(3)

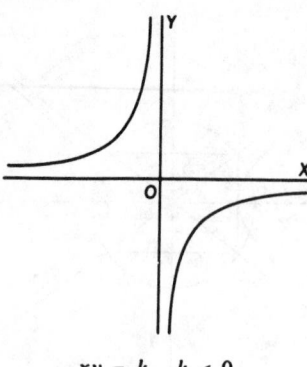

$$xy = k, \quad k < 0$$

Hyperbolic functions*

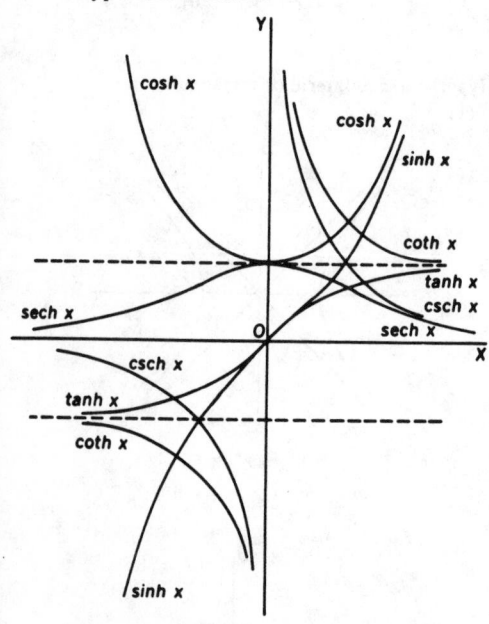

$$\sinh x = \frac{e^x - e^{-x}}{2} \qquad \operatorname{csch} x = \frac{2}{e^x - e^{-x}}$$

$$\cosh x = \frac{e^x + e^{-x}}{2} \qquad \operatorname{sech} x = \frac{2}{e^x + e^{-x}}$$

$$\tanh x = \frac{e^x - e^{-x}}{e^x + e^{-x}} \qquad \coth x = \frac{e^x + e^{-x}}{e^x - e^{-x}}$$

Hyperbolic spiral
   See: Spiral, hyperbolic or reciprocal

*See page 344 for inverse hyperbolic functions.

Hypocycloid of three cusps, Deltoid

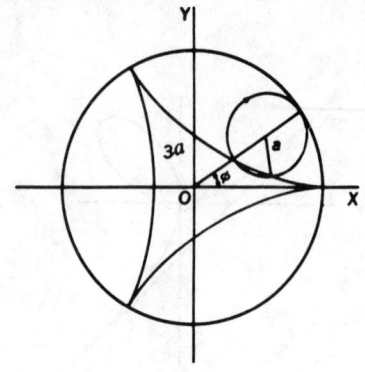

$$\begin{cases} x = 2a \cos \phi + a \cos 2\phi \\ y = 2a \sin \phi - a \sin 2\phi \end{cases}$$

Hypocycloid of four cusps, Astroid

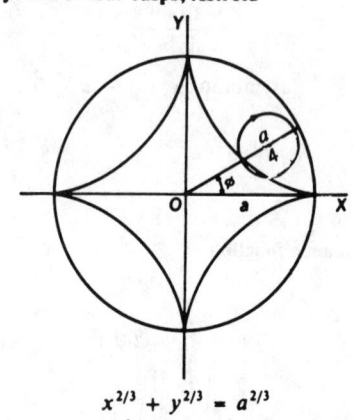

$$x^{2/3} + y^{2/3} = a^{2/3}$$
$$\begin{cases} x = a \cos^3 \phi \\ y = a \sin^3 \phi \end{cases}$$

Inverse cosine curve

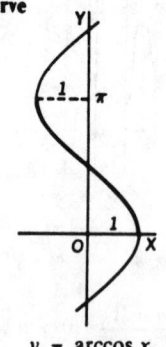

$$y = \arccos x$$

Inverse sine curve

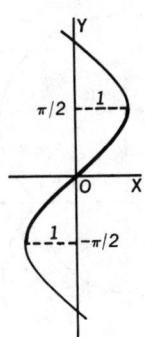

$y = \arcsin x$

Inverse tangent curve

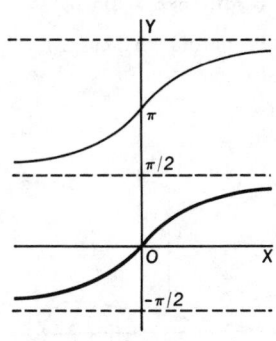

$y = \arctan x$

Involute of circle

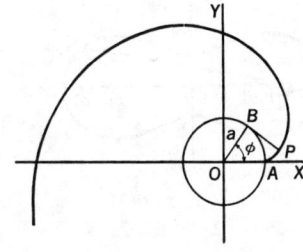

$$\begin{cases} x = a \cos \phi + a\phi \sin \phi \\ y = a \sin \phi - a\phi \cos \phi \end{cases}$$

$$[BP = \widehat{BA}]$$

Lemniscate of Bernoulli, Two-leaved rose

(a)

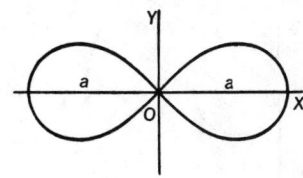

$$(x^2 + y^2)^2 = a^2(x^2 - y^2)$$
$$r^2 = a^2 \cos 2\theta$$

(b)

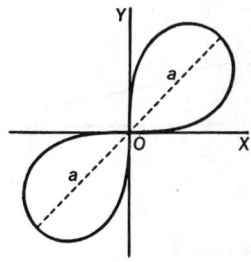

$$(x^2 + y^2)^2 = 2a^2xy$$
$$r^2 = a^2 \sin 2\theta$$

Limaçon of Pascal
(1) $a > b$

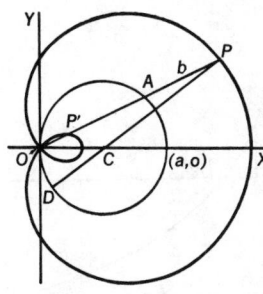

[If $a = 2b$, the curve is called the *trisectrix*, since then $\sphericalangle OPD = \frac{1}{3} \sphericalangle OCD$.]

(2) $a = b$
   See: Cardioid

(3) $a < b$

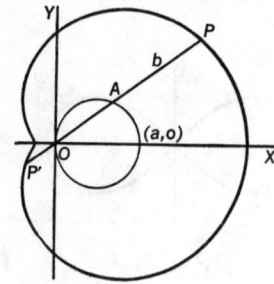

$$(x^2 + y^2 - ax)^2 = b^2(x^2 + y^2)$$
$$r = b + a \cos \theta$$
$$[P'A = AP = b]$$

Lituus

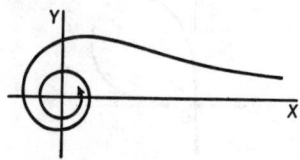

$$r^2\theta = a^2$$

Logarithmic curve
(1) $a > 1$

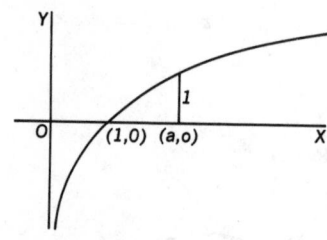

(2) $0 < a < 1$

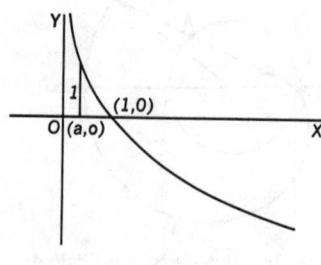

$$y = \log_a x$$

Logarithmic spiral
See: Spiral, logarithmic or equiangular

Nephroid

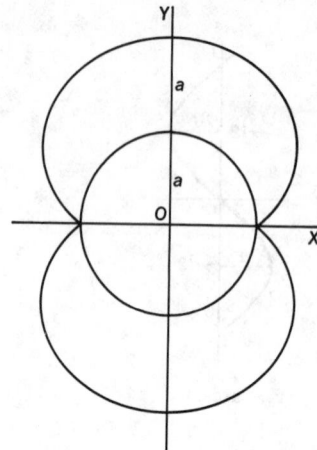

$$\begin{cases} x = \tfrac{1}{2}a(3\cos\phi - \cos 3\phi) \\ y = \tfrac{1}{2}a(3\sin\phi - \sin 3\phi) \end{cases}$$

[The nephroid is a 2-cusped epicycloid.]

Oui-ja board curve
See: Cochleoid

Ovals of Cassini
(1) $b > k$

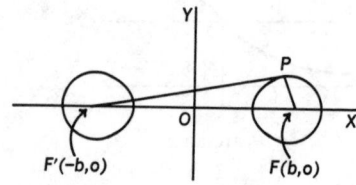

(2) $b = k$
See: Lemniscate of Bernoulli
(3) $b < k$

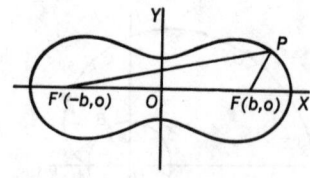

$$(x^2 + y^2 + b^2)^2 - 4b^2x^2 = k^4$$
$$r^4 + b^4 - 2r^2b^2\cos 2\theta = k^4$$
$$[F'P \cdot FP = k^2]$$

[These curves are sections of a torus on planes parallel to the axis of the torus.]

Parabola
(1)

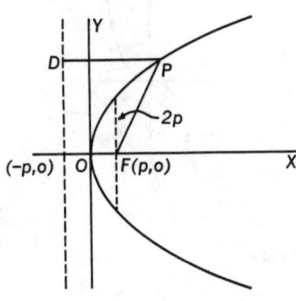

$$y^2 = 4px$$
$$[DP = FP]$$

(2)

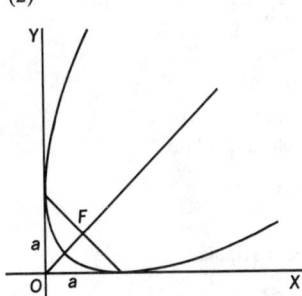

$$\pm x^{1/2} \pm y^{1/2} = a^{1/2}$$
$$(x - y)^2 - 2a(x + y) + a^2 = 0$$

(3)

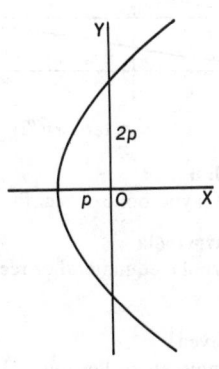

$$r = 2p/(1 - \cos\theta)$$

(4)

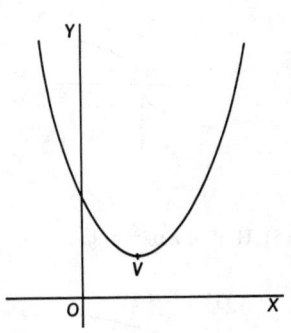

$$y = ax^2 + bx + c, \quad a > 0$$
$$[\text{abscissa of vertex} = -b/2a]$$

Parabolic spiral
  See: Spiral, parabolic

Power functions
(1)

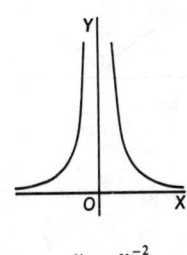

$$y = x^{-2}$$

(2) Equilateral hyperbola

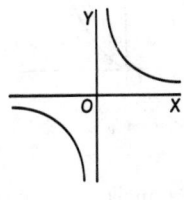

$$y = x^{-1}$$

(3)

$$y = x^{-1/2}$$

(4) Cubical parabola

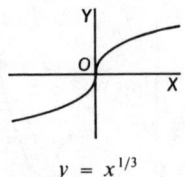

$$y = x^{1/3}$$

(5) Half of a parabola

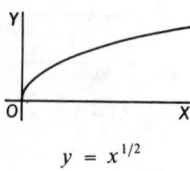

$$y = x^{1/2}$$

(6) Semicubical parabola

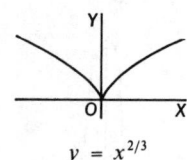

$$y = x^{2/3}$$

(7) Half of semicubical parabola

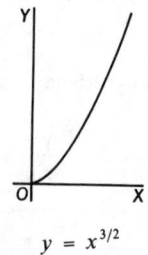

$$y = x^{3/2}$$

(8) Parabola

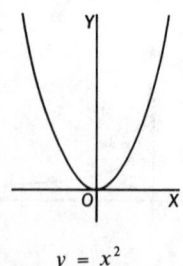

$$y = x^2$$

(9) Cubical parabola

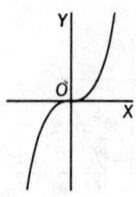

$$y = x^3$$

Probability curve

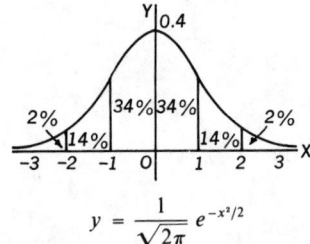

$$y = \frac{1}{\sqrt{2\pi}} e^{-x^2/2}$$

Prolate cycloid
See: Cycloid, prolate

Pursuit curve
See: Tractrix

Quadratrix of Hippias

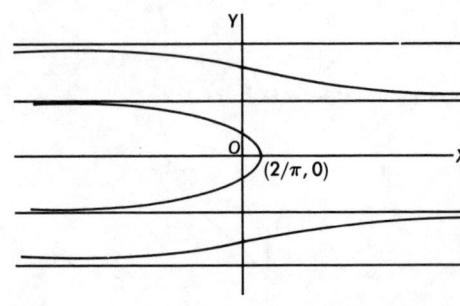

$$y = x \tan (\pi y/2)$$

Reciprocal spiral
See: Spiral, hyperbolic or reciprocal

Rectangular hyperbola
See: Hyperbola, equilateral or rectangular

Rose curves
(1) Two-leaved
See: Lemniscate of Bernoulli, Two-leaved rose

(2) Three-leaved

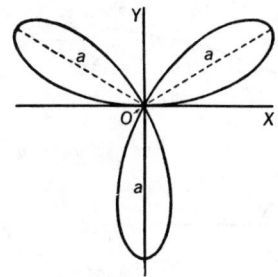

$$r = a \sin 3\theta$$

(3) Three-leaved

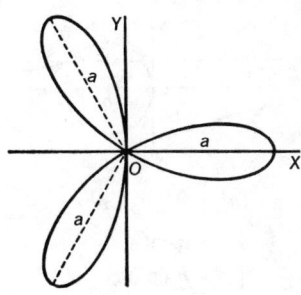

$$r = a \cos 3\theta$$

(4) Four-leaved

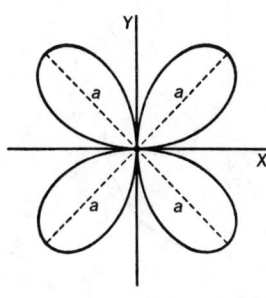

$$r = a \sin 2\theta$$

(5) Four-leaved

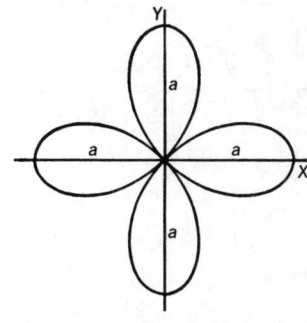

$$r = a \cos 2\theta$$

(6) *n*-leaved

The roses $r = a \sin n\theta$ and $r = a \cos n\theta$, have, for n an even integer, $2n$ leaves; for n an odd integer, n leaves. The roses $r^2 = a \sin n\theta$ and $r^2 = a \cos n\theta$, have, for n an even integer, n leaves; for n an odd integer, $2n$ leaves.

Secant curve

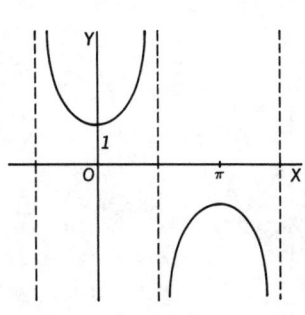

$$y = \sec x$$

Semicubical parabola

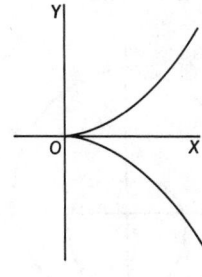

$$y^2 = ax^3$$

$$r = \frac{1}{a} \tan^2 \theta \sec \theta$$

Serpentine curve

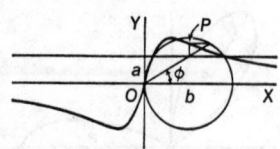

$$(a^2 + x^2)y = abx$$

$$\begin{cases} x = a \cot \phi \\ y = b \sin \phi \cos \phi \end{cases}$$

Sine curve

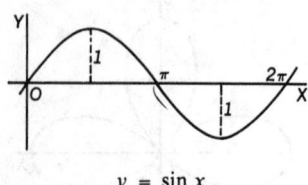

$$y = \sin x$$

Sinusoid

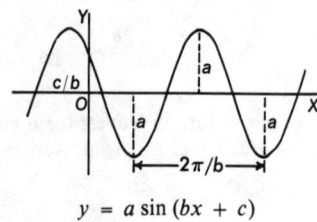

$$y = a \sin(bx + c)$$

Spiral of Archimedes

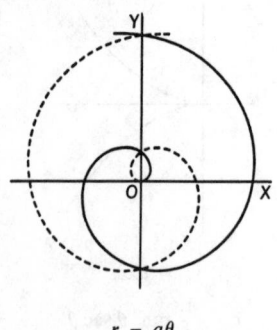

$$r = a\theta$$

Spiral, hyperbolic or reciprocal

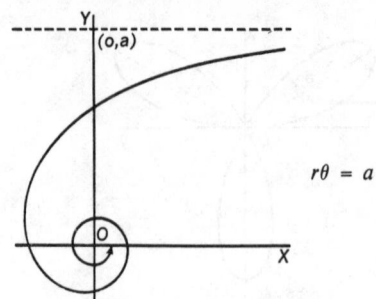

$$r\theta = a$$

Spiral, logarithmic or equiangular

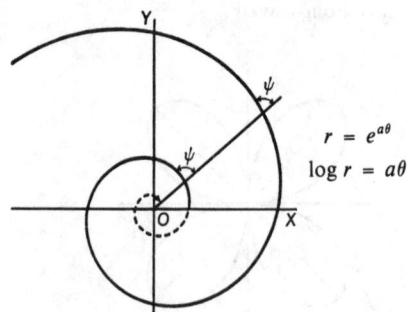

$$r = e^{a\theta}$$

$$\log r = a\theta$$

Spiral, parabolic

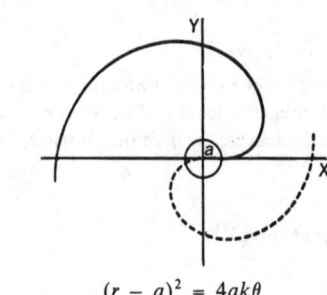

$$(r - a)^2 = 4ak\theta$$

Strophoid

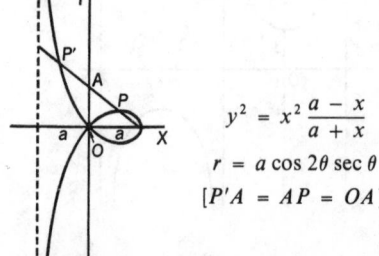

$$y^2 = x^2 \frac{a - x}{a + x}$$

$$r = a \cos 2\theta \sec \theta$$

$$[P'A = AP = OA]$$

Tangent curve

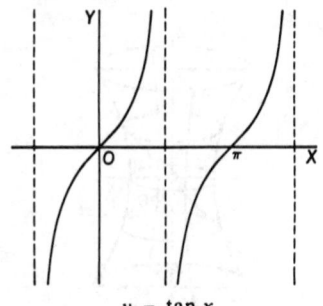

$y = \tan x$

Trajectory (a parabola)

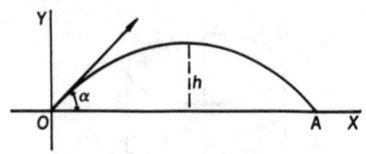

$$y = x \tan \alpha - gx^2/(2v_0^2 \cos^2 \alpha)$$
$$x = (v_0 \cos \alpha) t$$
$$y = (v_0 \sin \alpha) t - gt^2/2$$

Trigonometric functions

See: Cosecant curve; Cosine curve; Cotangent curve; Secant curve Sine curve; Tangent curve

Trisectrix

See: Limaçon of Pascal (1)

Tractrix, Pursuit curve

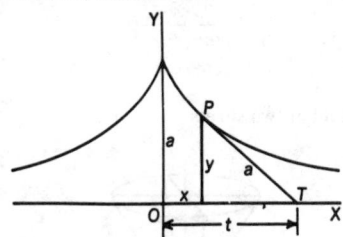

$$x = a \operatorname{sech}^{-1}(y/a) - \sqrt{a^2 - y^2}$$
$$\begin{cases} x = t - a \tanh(t/a) \\ y = a \operatorname{sech}(t/a) \end{cases}$$
$$[PT = a]$$

Witch of Agnesi

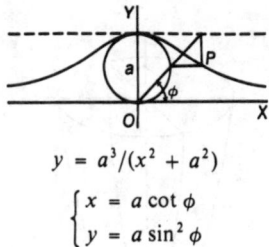

$$y = a^3/(x^2 + a^2)$$
$$\begin{cases} x = a \cot \phi \\ y = a \sin^2 \phi \end{cases}$$

*QUADRIC SURFACES

Ellipsoid

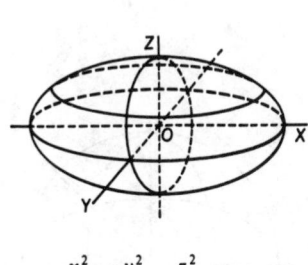

$$\frac{x^2}{a^2} + \frac{y^2}{b^2} + \frac{z^2}{c^2} = 1$$

Elliptic cone

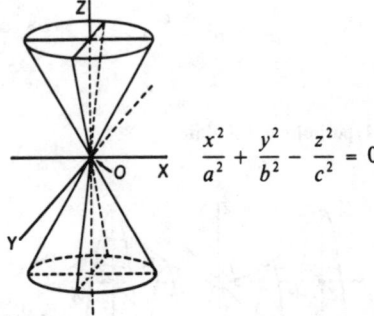

$$\frac{x^2}{a^2} + \frac{y^2}{b^2} - \frac{z^2}{c^2} = 0$$

*Each of the equations is given for the case where the origin is located at $(0,0,0)$, the center of the quadric surface. If, however, the center of the surface is at (h, k, l), replace x by $x - h$, y by $y - k$, and z by $z - l$, and the particular standardized form will be that of the surface with center at (h, k, l). For example, the elliptic paraboloid would be

$$\frac{(x - h)^2}{a^2} + \frac{(y - k)^2}{b^2} = c(z - l).$$

Elliptic cylinder

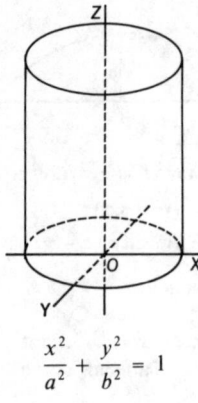

$$\frac{x^2}{a^2} + \frac{y^2}{b^2} = 1$$

Elliptic paraboloid

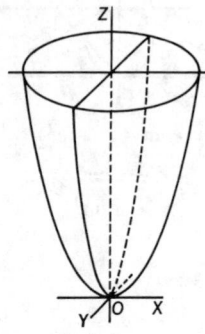

$$\frac{x^2}{a^2} + \frac{y^2}{b^2} = cz$$

Hyperbolic paraboloid

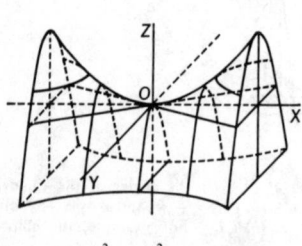

$$\frac{x^2}{a^2} - \frac{y^2}{b^2} = cz$$

Hyperboloid of one sheet

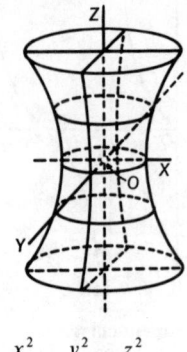

$$\frac{x^2}{a^2} + \frac{y^2}{b^2} - \frac{z^2}{c^2} = 1$$

Hyperboloid of two sheets

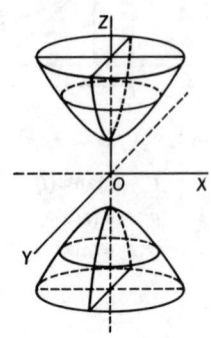

$$\frac{z^2}{c^2} - \frac{x^2}{a^2} - \frac{y^2}{b^2} = 1$$

Sphere

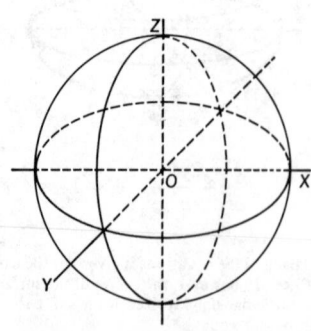

$$x^2 + y^2 + z^2 = a^2$$

PATTERNS OF REGULAR POLYHEDRA

Tetrahedron

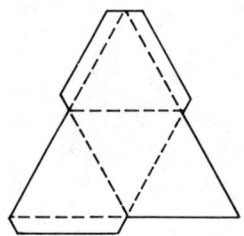

Octahedron

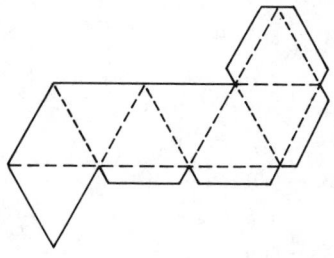

Hexahedron, or Cube

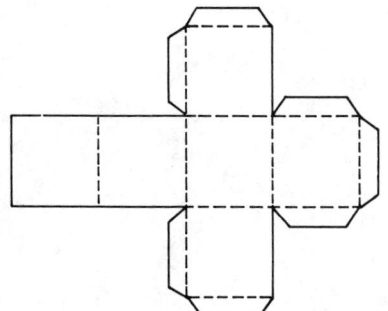

Icosahedron

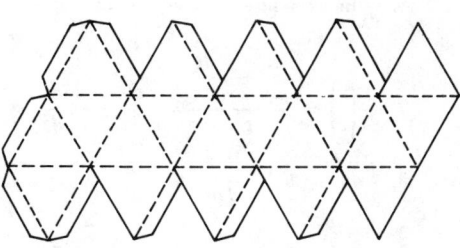

Dodecahedron

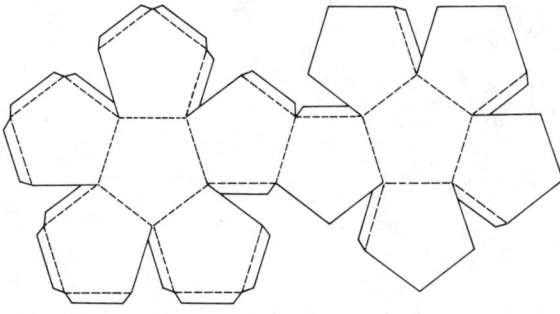

*Derivatives

In the following formulas u, v, w represent functions of x, while a, c, n represent fixed real numbers. All arguments in the trigonometric functions are measured in radians, and all inverse trigonometric and hyperbolic functions represent principal values.

1. $\dfrac{d}{dx}(a) = 0$

2. $\dfrac{d}{dx}(x) = 1$

3. $\dfrac{d}{dx}(au) = a\dfrac{du}{dx}$

4. $\dfrac{d}{dx}(u + v - w) = \dfrac{du}{dx} + \dfrac{dv}{dx} - \dfrac{dw}{dx}$

5. $\dfrac{d}{dx}(uv) = u\dfrac{dv}{dx} + v\dfrac{du}{dx}$

6. $\dfrac{d}{dx}(uvw) = uv\dfrac{dw}{dx} + vw\dfrac{du}{dx} + uw\dfrac{dv}{dx}$ and so on to n factors

7. $\dfrac{d}{dx}\left(\dfrac{u}{v}\right) = \dfrac{v\dfrac{du}{dx} - u\dfrac{dv}{dx}}{v^2} = \dfrac{1}{v}\dfrac{du}{dx} - \dfrac{u}{v^2}\dfrac{dv}{dx}$

8. $\dfrac{d}{dx}(u^n) = nu^{n-1}\dfrac{du}{dx}$

9. $\dfrac{d}{dx}(\sqrt{u}) = \dfrac{1}{2\sqrt{u}}\dfrac{du}{dx}$

10. $\dfrac{d}{dx}\left(\dfrac{1}{u}\right) = -\dfrac{1}{u^2}\dfrac{du}{dx}$

11. $\dfrac{d}{dx}\left(\dfrac{1}{u^n}\right) = -\dfrac{n}{u^{n+1}}\dfrac{du}{dx}$

12. $\dfrac{d}{dx}\left(\dfrac{u^n}{v^m}\right) = \dfrac{u^{n-1}}{v^{m+1}}\left(nv\dfrac{du}{dx} - mu\dfrac{dv}{dx}\right)$

13. $\dfrac{d}{dx}(u^n v^m) = u^{n-1}v^{m-1}\left(nv\dfrac{du}{dx} + mu\dfrac{dv}{dx}\right)$

14. $\dfrac{d}{dx}[f(u)] = \dfrac{d}{du}[f(u)] \cdot \dfrac{du}{dx}$

* Let $y = f(x)$ and $\dfrac{dy}{dx} = \dfrac{d[f(x)]}{dx} = f'(x)$ define respectively a function and its derivative for any value x in their common domain. The differential for the function at such a value x is accordingly defined as

$$dy = d[f(x)] = \frac{dy}{dx}dx = \frac{d[f(x)]}{dx}dx = f'(x)\,dx$$

Each derivative formula has an associated differential formula. For example, formula 6 above has the differential formula

$$d(uvw) = uv\,dw + vw\,du + uw\,dv$$

402

DERIVATIVES (Continued)

15. $\dfrac{d^2}{dx^2}[f(u)] = \dfrac{df(u)}{du} \cdot \dfrac{d^2u}{dx^2} + \dfrac{d^2f(u)}{du^2} \cdot \left(\dfrac{du}{dx}\right)^2$

16. $\dfrac{d^n}{dx^n}[uv] = \binom{n}{0} v \dfrac{d^n u}{dx^n} + \binom{n}{1} \dfrac{dv}{dx} \dfrac{d^{n-1}u}{dx^{n-1}} + \binom{n}{2} \dfrac{d^2v}{dx^2} \dfrac{d^{n-2}u}{dx^{n-2}}$

$$+ \cdots + \binom{n}{k} \dfrac{d^k v}{dx^k} \dfrac{d^{n-k}u}{dx^{n-k}} + \cdots + \binom{n}{n} u \dfrac{d^n v}{dx^n}$$

where $\binom{n}{r} = \dfrac{n!}{r!(n-r)!}$ the binomial coefficient, n non-negative integer and $\binom{n}{0} = 1$.

17. $\dfrac{du}{dx} = \dfrac{1}{\dfrac{dx}{du}}$ if $\dfrac{dx}{du} \neq 0$

18. $\dfrac{d}{dx}(\log_a u) = (\log_a e)\dfrac{1}{u}\dfrac{du}{dx}$

19. $\dfrac{d}{dx}(\log_e u) = \dfrac{1}{u}\dfrac{du}{dx}$

20. $\dfrac{d}{dx}(a^u) = a^u(\log_e a)\dfrac{du}{dx}$

21. $\dfrac{d}{dx}(e^u) = e^u \dfrac{du}{dx}$

22. $\dfrac{d}{dx}(u^v) = vu^{v-1}\dfrac{du}{dx} + (\log_e u)u^v\dfrac{dv}{dx}$

23. $\dfrac{d}{dx}(\sin u) = \dfrac{du}{dx}(\cos u)$

24. $\dfrac{d}{dx}(\cos u) = -\dfrac{du}{dx}(\sin u)$

25. $\dfrac{d}{dx}(\tan u) = \dfrac{du}{dx}(\sec^2 u)$

26. $\dfrac{d}{dx}(\cot u) = -\dfrac{du}{dx}(\csc^2 u)$

27. $\dfrac{d}{dx}(\sec u) = \dfrac{du}{dx}\sec u \cdot \tan u$

28. $\dfrac{d}{dx}(\csc u) = -\dfrac{du}{dx}\csc u \cdot \cot u$

29. $\dfrac{d}{dx}(\text{vers } u) = \dfrac{du}{dx}\sin u$

30. $\dfrac{d}{dx}(\arcsin u) = \dfrac{1}{\sqrt{1-u^2}}\dfrac{du}{dx}$, $\left(-\dfrac{\pi}{2} \leq \arcsin u \leq \dfrac{\pi}{2}\right)$

DERIVATIVES (Continued)

31. $\dfrac{d}{dx}(\text{arc cos } u) = -\dfrac{1}{\sqrt{1 - u^2}}\dfrac{du}{dx}$, $(0 \le \text{arc cos } u \le \pi)$

32. $\dfrac{d}{dx}(\text{arc tan } u) = \dfrac{1}{1 + u^2}\dfrac{du}{dx}$, $\left(-\dfrac{\pi}{2} < \text{arc tan } u < \dfrac{\pi}{2}\right)$

33. $\dfrac{d}{dx}(\text{arc cot } u) = -\dfrac{1}{1 + u^2}\dfrac{du}{dx}$, $(0 \le \text{arc cot } u \le \pi)$

34. $\dfrac{d}{dx}(\text{arc sec } u) = \dfrac{1}{u\sqrt{u^2 - 1}}\dfrac{du}{dx}$, $\left(0 \le \text{arc sec } u < \dfrac{\pi}{2}, -\pi \le \text{arc sec } u < -\dfrac{\pi}{2}\right)$

35. $\dfrac{d}{dx}(\text{arc csc } u) = -\dfrac{1}{u\sqrt{u^2 - 1}}\dfrac{du}{dx}$, $\left(0 < \text{arc csc } u \le \dfrac{\pi}{2}, -\pi < \text{arc csc } u \le -\dfrac{\pi}{2}\right)$

36. $\dfrac{d}{dx}(\text{arc vers } u) = \dfrac{1}{\sqrt{2u - u^2}}\dfrac{du}{dx}$, $(0 \le \text{arc vers } u \le \pi)$

37. $\dfrac{d}{dx}(\sinh u) = \dfrac{du}{dx}(\cosh u)$

38. $\dfrac{d}{dx}(\cosh u) = \dfrac{du}{dx}(\sinh u)$

39. $\dfrac{d}{dx}(\tanh u) = \dfrac{du}{dx}(\text{sech}^2 u)$

40. $\dfrac{d}{dx}(\coth u) = -\dfrac{du}{dx}(\text{csch}^2 u)$

41. $\dfrac{d}{dx}(\text{sech } u) = -\dfrac{du}{dx}(\text{sech } u \cdot \tanh u)$

42. $\dfrac{d}{dx}(\text{csch } u) = -\dfrac{du}{dx}(\text{csch } u \cdot \coth u)$

43. $\dfrac{d}{dx}(\sinh^{-1} u) = \dfrac{d}{dx}[\log(u + \sqrt{u^2 + 1})] = \dfrac{1}{\sqrt{u^2 + 1}}\dfrac{du}{dx}$

44. $\dfrac{d}{dx}(\cosh^{-1} u) = \dfrac{d}{dx}[\log(u + \sqrt{u^2 - 1})] = \dfrac{1}{\sqrt{u^2 - 1}}\dfrac{du}{dx}$, $(u > 1, \cosh^{-1} u > 0)$

45. $\dfrac{d}{dx}(\tanh^{-1} u) = \dfrac{d}{dx}\left[\dfrac{1}{2}\log\dfrac{1 + u}{1 - u}\right] = \dfrac{1}{1 - u^2}\dfrac{du}{dx}$, $(u^2 < 1)$

46. $\dfrac{d}{dx}(\coth^{-1} u) = \dfrac{d}{dx}\left[\dfrac{1}{2}\log\dfrac{u + 1}{u - 1}\right] = \dfrac{1}{1 - u^2}\dfrac{du}{dx}$, $(u^2 > 1)$

47. $\dfrac{d}{dx}(\text{sech}^{-1} u) = \dfrac{d}{dx}\left[\log\dfrac{1 + \sqrt{1 - u^2}}{u}\right] = -\dfrac{1}{u\sqrt{1 - u^2}}\dfrac{du}{dx}$, $(0 < u < 1, \text{sech}^{-1} u > 0)$

48. $\dfrac{d}{dx}(\text{csch}^{-1} u) = \dfrac{d}{dx}\left[\log\dfrac{1 + \sqrt{1 + u^2}}{u}\right] = -\dfrac{1}{|u|\sqrt{1 + u^2}}\dfrac{du}{dx}$

49. $\dfrac{d}{dq} \displaystyle\int_p^q f(x)\, dx = f(q), \qquad [p \text{ constant}]$

50. $\dfrac{d}{dp} \displaystyle\int_p^q f(x)\, dx = -f(p), \qquad [q \text{ constant}]$

51. $\dfrac{d}{da} \displaystyle\int_p^q f(x, a)\, dx = \int_p^q \dfrac{\partial}{\partial a}[f(x, a)]\, dx + f(q, a)\dfrac{dq}{da} - f(p, a)\dfrac{dp}{da}$

INTEGRATION

The following is a brief discussion of some integration techniques. A more complete discussion can be found in a number of good text books. However, the purpose of this introduction is simply to discuss a few of the important techniques which may be used, in conjunction with the integral table which follows, to integrate particular functions.

No matter how extensive the integral table, it is a fairly uncommon occurrence to find in the table the exact integral desired. Usually some form of transformation will have to be made. The simplest type of transformation, and yet the most general, is substitution. Simple forms of substitution, such as $y = ax$, are employed almost unconsciously by experienced users of integral tables. Other substitutions may require more thought. In some sections of the tables, appropriate substitutions are suggested for integrals which are similar to, but not exactly like, integrals in the table. Finding the right substitution is largely a matter of intuition and experience.

Several precautions must be observed when using substitutions:

1. Be sure to make the substitution in the dx term, as well as everywhere else in the integral.
2. Be sure that the function substituted is one-to-one and continuous. If this is not the case, the integral must be restricted in such a way as to make it true. See the example following.
3. With definite integrals, the limits should also be expressed in terms of the new dependent variable. With indefinite integrals, it is necessary to perform the reverse substitution to obtain the answer in terms of the original independent variable. This may also be done for definite integrals, but it is usually easier to change the limits.

Example:

$$\int \frac{x^4}{\sqrt{a^2 - x^2}} dx$$

Here we make the substitution $x = |a| \sin \theta$. Then $dx = |a| \cos \theta \, d\theta$, and

$$\sqrt{a^2 - x^2} = \sqrt{a^2 - a^2 \sin^2 \theta} = |a|\sqrt{1 - \sin^2 \theta} = |a \cos \theta|$$

Notice the absolute value signs. It is very important to keep in mind that a square root radical always denotes the positive square root, and to assure the sign is always kept positive. Thus $\sqrt{x^2} = |x|$. Failure to observe this is a common cause of errors in integration.

Notice also that the indicated substitution is not a one-to-one function, that is, it does not have a unique inverse. Thus we must restrict the range of θ in such a way as to make the function one-to-one. Fortunately, this is easily done by solving for θ

$$\theta = \sin^{-1} \frac{x}{|a|}$$

and restricting the inverse sine to the principal values, $-\frac{\pi}{2} \le \theta \le \frac{\pi}{2}$.

Thus the integral becomes

$$\int \frac{a^4 \sin^4 \theta |a| \cos \theta \, d\theta}{|a| |\cos \theta|}$$

Now, however, in the range of values chosen for θ, $\cos \theta$ is always positive. Thus we may remove the absolute value signs from $\cos \theta$ in the denominator. (This is one of the reasons that the principal values of the inverse trigonometric functions are defined as they are.)

Then the cos θ terms cancel, and the integral becomes

$$a^4 \int \sin^4 \theta \, d\theta$$

By application of integral formulas 299 and 296, we integrate this to

$$-a^4 \frac{\sin^3 \theta \cos \theta}{4} - \frac{3a^4}{8} \cos \theta \sin \theta + \frac{3a^4}{8} \theta + C$$

We now must perform the inverse substitution to get the result in terms of x. We have

$$\theta = \sin^{-1} \frac{x}{|a|}$$

$$\sin \theta = \frac{x}{|a|}$$

Then

$$\cos \theta = \pm \sqrt{1 - \sin^2 \theta} = \pm \sqrt{1 - \frac{x^2}{a^2}} = \pm \frac{\sqrt{a^2 - x^2}}{|a|}.$$

Because of the previously mentioned fact that cos θ is positive, we may omit the $\pm$ sign. The reverse substitution then produces the final answer

$$\int \frac{x^4}{\sqrt{a^2 - x^2}} \, dx = -\tfrac{1}{4}x^3 \sqrt{a^2 - x^2} - \tfrac{3}{8}a^2 x \sqrt{a^2 - x^2} + \frac{3a^4}{8} \sin^{-1} \frac{x}{|a|} + C.$$

Any rational function of x may be integrated, if the denominator is factored into linear and irreducible quadratic factors. The function may then be broken into partial fractions, and the individual partial fractions integrated by use of the appropriate formula from the integral table. See the section on partial fractions for further information.

Many integrals may be reduced to rational functions by proper substitutions. For example,

$$z = \tan \frac{x}{2}$$

will reduce any rational function of the six trigonometric functions of x to a rational function of z. (Frequently there are other substitutions which are simpler to use, but this one will always work. See integral formula number 484.)

Any rational function of x and $\sqrt{ax + b}$ may be reduced to a rational function of z by making the substitution

$$z = \sqrt{ax + b}.$$

Other likely substitutions will be suggested by looking at the form of the integrand.

The other main method of transforming integrals is integration by parts. This involves applying formula number 5 or 6 in the accompanying integral table. The critical factor in this method is the choice of the functions u and v. In order for the method to be successful, $v = \int dv$ and $\int v \, du$ must be easier to integrate than the original integral. Again, this choice is largely a matter of intuition and experience.

Example:

$$\int x \sin x \, dx$$

Two obvious choices are $u = x$, $dv = \sin x \, dx$, or $u = \sin x$, $dv = x \, dx$. Since a preliminary mental calculation indicates that $\int v \, du$ in the second choice would be more, rather than less, complicated than the original integral (it would contain x^2), we use the first choice.

$$u = x \qquad\qquad du = dx$$
$$dv = \sin x\, dx \qquad\qquad v = -\cos x$$
$$\int x \sin x\, dx = \int u\, dv = uv - \int v\, du = -x \cos x + \int \cos x\, dx$$
$$= \sin x - x \cos x$$

Of course, this result could have been obtained directly from the integral table, but it provides a simple example of the method. In more complicated examples the choice of u and v may not be so obvious, and several different choices may have to be tried. Of course, there is no guarantee that any of them will work.

Integration by parts may be applied more than once, or combined with substitution. A fairly common case is illustrated by the following example.

Example:

$$\int e^x \sin x\, dx$$

Let

$$u = e^x \qquad \text{Then} \quad du = e^x\, dx$$
$$dv = \sin x\, dx \qquad\qquad v = -\cos x$$
$$\int e^x \sin x\, dx = \int u\, dv = uv - \int v\, du = -e^x \cos x + \int e^x \cos x\, dx$$

In this latter integral,

$$\text{let} \quad u = e^x \qquad \text{Then} \quad du = e^x\, dx$$
$$dv = \cos x\, dx \qquad\qquad v = \sin x$$
$$\int e^x \sin x\, dx = -e^x \cos x + \int e^x \cos x\, dx = -e^x \cos x + \int u\, dv$$
$$= -e^x \cos x + uv - \int v\, du$$
$$= -e^x \cos x + e^x \sin x - \int e^x \sin x\, dx$$

This looks as if a circular transformation has taken place, since we are back at the same integral we started from. However, the above equation can be solved algebraically for the required integral:

$$\int e^x \sin x\, dx = \tfrac{1}{2}(e^x \sin x - e^x \cos x)$$

In the second integration by parts, if the parts had been chosen as $u = \cos x$, $dv = e^x\, dx$, we would indeed have made a circular transformation, and returned to the starting place. In general, when doing repeated integration by parts, one should never choose the function u at any stage to be the same as the function v at the previous stage, or a constant times the previous v.

The following rule is called the extended rule for integration by parts. It is the result of $n + 1$ successive applications of integration by parts.

If

$$g_1(x) = \int g(x)\,dx, \qquad g_2(x) = \int g_1(x)\,dx,$$

$$g_3(x) = \int g_2(x)\,dx, \ldots, g_m(x) = \int g_{m-1}(x)\,dx, \ldots,$$

then

$$\int f(x) \cdot g(x)\,dx = f(x) \cdot g_1(x) - f'(x) \cdot g_2(x) + f''(x) \cdot g_3(x) - + \cdots$$

$$+ (-1)^n f^{(n)}(x) g_{n+1}(x) + (-1)^{n+1} \int f^{(n+1)}(x) g_{n+1}(x)\,dx.$$

A useful special case of the above rule is when $f(x)$ is a polynomial of degree n. Then $f^{(n+1)}(x) = 0$, and

$$\int f(x) \cdot g(x)\,dx = f(x) \cdot g_1(x) - f'(x) \cdot g_2(x) + f''(x) \cdot g_3(x) - + \cdots + (-1)^n f^{(n)}(x) g_{n+1}(x) + C$$

Example:
If $f(x) = x^2, g(x) = \sin x$

$$\int x^2 \sin x\,dx = -x^2 \cos x + 2x \sin x + 2 \cos x + C$$

Another application of this formula occurs if

$$f''(x) = af(x) \quad \text{and} \quad g''(x) = bg(x),$$

where a and b are unequal constants. In this case, by a process similar to that used in the above example for $\int e^x \sin x\,dx$, we get the formula

$$\int f(x)g(x)\,dx = \frac{f(x) \cdot g'(x) - f'(x) \cdot g(x)}{b - a} + C$$

This formula could have been used in the example mentioned. Here is another example.

Example:
If $f(x) = e^{2x}, g(x) = \sin 3x$, then $a = 4, b = -9$, and

$$\int e^{2x} \sin 3x\,dx = \frac{3 e^{2x} \cos 3x - 2 e^{2x} \sin 3x}{-9 - 4} + C = \frac{e^{2x}}{13}(2 \sin 3x - 3 \cos 3x) + C$$

The following additional points should be observed when using this table.

1. A constant of integration is to be supplied with the answers for indefinite integrals.
2. Logarithmic expressions are to base $e = 2.71828\ldots$, unless otherwise specified, and are to be evaluated for the absolute value of the arguments involved therein.
3. All angles are measured in radians, and inverse trigonometric and hyperbolic functions represent principal values, unless otherwise indicated.
4. If the application of a formula produces either a zero denominator or the square root of a negative number in the result, there is usually available another form of the answer which avoids this difficulty. In many of the results, the excluded values are specified, but when such are omitted it is presumed that one can tell what these should be, especially when difficulties of the type herein mentioned are obtained.
5. When inverse trigonometric functions occur in the integrals, be sure that any replacements made for them are strictly in accordance with the rules for such functions. This causes

little difficulty when the argument of the inverse trigonometric function is positive, since then all angles involved are in the first quadrant. However, if the argument is negative, special care must be used. Thus if $u > 0$,

$$\sin^{-1} u = \cos^{-1}\sqrt{1 - u^2} = \csc^{-1}\frac{1}{u}, \text{ etc.}$$

However, if $u < 0$,

$$\sin^{-1} u = -\cos^{-1}\sqrt{1 - u^2} = -\pi - \csc^{-1}\frac{1}{u}, \text{ etc.}$$

See the section on inverse trigonometric functions for a full treatment of the allowable substitutions.

6. In integrals 340–345 and some others, the right side includes expressions of the form

$$A \tan^{-1}[B + C \tan f(x)].$$

In these formulas, the $\tan^{-1}$ does not necessarily represent the principal value. Instead of always employing the principal branch of the inverse tangent function, one must instead use that branch of the inverse tangent function upon which $f(x)$ lies for any particular choice of x.

Example:

$$\int_0^{4\pi} \frac{dx}{2 + \sin x} = \frac{2}{\sqrt{3}}\tan^{-1}\frac{2\tan\frac{x}{2} + 1}{\sqrt{3}}\Bigg]_0^{4\pi}$$

$$= \frac{2}{\sqrt{3}}\left[\tan^{-1}\frac{2\tan 2\pi + 1}{\sqrt{3}} - \tan^{-1}\frac{2\tan 0 + 1}{\sqrt{3}}\right]$$

$$= \frac{2}{\sqrt{3}}\left[\frac{13\pi}{6} - \frac{\pi}{6}\right] = \frac{4\pi}{\sqrt{3}} = \frac{4\sqrt{3}\pi}{3}$$

Here

$$\tan^{-1}\frac{2\tan 2\pi + 1}{\sqrt{3}} = \tan^{-1}\frac{1}{\sqrt{3}} = \frac{13\pi}{6},$$

since $f(x) = 2\pi$; and

$$\tan^{-1}\frac{2\tan 0 + 1}{\sqrt{3}} = \tan^{-1}\frac{1}{\sqrt{3}} = \frac{\pi}{6},$$

since $f(x) = 0$.

7. B_n and E_n where used in Integrals represents the Bernoulli and Euler numbers as defined in the tables contained from pages 482 to 488.

INTEGRALS

ELEMENTARY FORMS

1. $\int a\,dx = ax$

2. $\int a \cdot f(x)\,dx = a\int f(x)\,dx$

3. $\int \phi(y)\,dx = \int \frac{\phi(y)}{y'}\,dy,$ where $y' = \dfrac{dy}{dx}$

4. $\int (u + v)\,dx = \int u\,dx + \int v\,dx,$ where u and v are any functions of x

5. $\int u\,dv = u\int dv - \int v\,du = uv - \int v\,du$

6. $\int u\dfrac{dv}{dx}\,dx = uv - \int v\dfrac{du}{dx}\,dx$

7. $\int x^n\,dx = \dfrac{x^{n+1}}{n+1},$ except $n = -1$

8. $\int \dfrac{f'(x)\,dx}{f(x)} = \log f(x),$ $(df(x) = f'(x)\,dx)$

9. $\int \dfrac{dx}{x} = \log x$

10. $\int \dfrac{f'(x)\,dx}{2\sqrt{f(x)}} = \sqrt{f(x)},$ $(df(x) = f'(x)\,dx)$

11. $\int e^x\,dx = e^x$

12. $\int e^{ax}\,dx = e^{ax}/a$

13. $\int b^{ax}\,dx = \dfrac{b^{ax}}{a\log b},$ $(b > 0)$

14. $\int \log x\,dx = x\log x - x$

15. $\int a^x \log a\,dx = a^x,$ $(a > 0)$

16. $\int \dfrac{dx}{a^2 + x^2} = \dfrac{1}{a}\tan^{-1}\dfrac{x}{a}$

INTEGRALS (Continued)

17. $\displaystyle\int \frac{dx}{a^2 - x^2} = \begin{cases} \dfrac{1}{a}\tanh^{-1}\dfrac{x}{a} \\ \qquad \text{or} \\ \dfrac{1}{2a}\log\dfrac{a+x}{a-x}, \quad (a^2 > x^2) \end{cases}$

18. $\displaystyle\int \frac{dx}{x^2 - a^2} = \begin{cases} -\dfrac{1}{a}\coth^{-1}\dfrac{x}{a} \\ \qquad \text{or} \\ \dfrac{1}{2a}\log\dfrac{x-a}{x+a}, \quad (x^2 > a^2) \end{cases}$

19. $\displaystyle\int \frac{dx}{\sqrt{a^2 - x^2}} = \begin{cases} \sin^{-1}\dfrac{x}{|a|} \\ \qquad \text{or} \\ -\cos^{-1}\dfrac{x}{|a|}, \quad (a^2 > x^2) \end{cases}$

20. $\displaystyle\int \frac{dx}{\sqrt{x^2 \pm a^2}} = \log\left(x + \sqrt{x^2 \pm a^2}\right)$

21. $\displaystyle\int \frac{dx}{x\sqrt{x^2 - a^2}} = \frac{1}{|a|}\sec^{-1}\frac{x}{a}$

22. $\displaystyle\int \frac{dx}{x\sqrt{a^2 \pm x^2}} = -\frac{1}{a}\log\left(\frac{a + \sqrt{a^2 \pm x^2}}{x}\right)$

FORMS CONTAINING $(a + bx)$

For forms containing $a + bx$, but not listed in the table, the substitution $u = \dfrac{a + bx}{x}$ may prove helpful.

23. $\displaystyle\int (a + bx)^n\, dx = \frac{(a + bx)^{n+1}}{(n+1)b}, \quad (n \neq -1)$

24. $\displaystyle\int x(a + bx)^n\, dx$

$$= \frac{1}{b^2(n+2)}(a + bx)^{n+2} - \frac{a}{b^2(n+1)}(a + bx)^{n+1}, \quad (n \neq -1, -2)$$

25. $\displaystyle\int x^2(a + bx)^n\, dx = \frac{1}{b^3}\left[\frac{(a + bx)^{n+3}}{n+3} - 2a\frac{(a + bx)^{n+2}}{n+2} + a^2\frac{(a + bx)^{n+1}}{n+1}\right]$

INTEGRALS (Continued)

26. $\int x^m (a + bx)^n \, dx =$
$$\begin{cases} \dfrac{x^{m+1}(a+bx)^n}{m+n+1} + \dfrac{an}{m+n+1} \int x^m (a+bx)^{n-1} \, dx \\[4pt] \qquad\qquad\qquad \text{or} \\[4pt] \dfrac{1}{a(n+1)} \left[-x^{m+1}(a+bx)^{n+1} \right. \\[10pt] \qquad\qquad\qquad\qquad \left. + (m+n+2) \int x^m (a+bx)^{n+1} \, dx \right] \\[4pt] \qquad\qquad\qquad \text{or} \\[4pt] \dfrac{1}{b(m+n+1)} \left[x^m (a+bx)^{n+1} - ma \int x^{m-1}(a+bx)^n \, dx \right] \end{cases}$$

27. $\displaystyle \int \frac{dx}{a+bx} = \frac{1}{b} \log (a + bx)$

28. $\displaystyle \int \frac{dx}{(a+bx)^2} = - \frac{1}{b(a+bx)}$

29. $\displaystyle \int \frac{dx}{(a+bx)^3} = - \frac{1}{2b(a+bx)^2}$

30. $\displaystyle \int \frac{x \, dx}{a+bx} = \begin{cases} \dfrac{1}{b^2} [a + bx - a \log (a + bx)] \\[4pt] \qquad\qquad \text{or} \\[4pt] \dfrac{x}{b} - \dfrac{a}{b^2} \log (a + bx) \end{cases}$

31. $\displaystyle \int \frac{x \, dx}{(a+bx)^2} = \frac{1}{b^2} \left[\log (a + bx) + \frac{a}{a+bx} \right]$

32. $\displaystyle \int \frac{x \, dx}{(a+bx)^n} = \frac{1}{b^2} \left[\frac{-1}{(n-2)(a+bx)^{n-2}} + \frac{a}{(n-1)(a+bx)^{n-1}} \right], \qquad n \neq 1, 2$

33. $\displaystyle \int \frac{x^2 \, dx}{a+bx} = \frac{1}{b^3} \left[\frac{1}{2}(a+bx)^2 - 2a(a+bx) + a^2 \log (a + bx) \right]$

34. $\displaystyle \int \frac{x^2 \, dx}{(a+bx)^2} = \frac{1}{b^3} \left[a + bx - 2a \log (a + bx) - \frac{a^2}{a+bx} \right]$

35. $\displaystyle \int \frac{x^2 \, dx}{(a+bx)^3} = \frac{1}{b^3} \left[\log (a + bx) + \frac{2a}{a+bx} - \frac{a^2}{2(a+bx)^2} \right]$

36. $\displaystyle \int \frac{x^2 \, dx}{(a+bx)^n} = \frac{1}{b^3} \left[\frac{-1}{(n-3)(a+bx)^{n-3}} \right.$
$$\left. + \frac{2a}{(n-2)(a+bx)^{n-2}} - \frac{a^2}{(n-1)(a+bx)^{n-1}} \right], \qquad n \neq 1, 2, 3$$

INTEGRALS (Continued)

37. $\displaystyle\int \frac{dx}{x(a + bx)} = -\frac{1}{a}\log\frac{a + bx}{x}$

38. $\displaystyle\int \frac{dx}{x(a + bx)^2} = \frac{1}{a(a + bx)} - \frac{1}{a^2}\log\frac{a + bx}{x}$

39. $\displaystyle\int \frac{dx}{x(a + bx)^3} = \frac{1}{a^3}\left[\frac{1}{2}\left(\frac{2a + bx}{a + bx}\right)^2 + \log\frac{x}{a + bx}\right]$

40. $\displaystyle\int \frac{dx}{x^2(a + bx)} = -\frac{1}{ax} + \frac{b}{a^2}\log\frac{a + bx}{x}$

41. $\displaystyle\int \frac{dx}{x^3(a + bx)} = \frac{2bx - a}{2a^2x^2} + \frac{b^2}{a^3}\log\frac{x}{a + bx}$

42. $\displaystyle\int \frac{dx}{x^2(a + bx)^2} = -\frac{a + 2bx}{a^2x(a + bx)} + \frac{2b}{a^3}\log\frac{a + bx}{x}$

FORMS CONTAINING $c^2 \pm x^2$, $x^2 - c^2$

43. $\displaystyle\int \frac{dx}{c^2 + x^2} = \frac{1}{c}\tan^{-1}\frac{x}{c}$

44. $\displaystyle\int \frac{dx}{c^2 - x^2} = \frac{1}{2c}\log\frac{c + x}{c - x}, \qquad (c^2 > x^2)$

45. $\displaystyle\int \frac{dx}{x^2 - c^2} = \frac{1}{2c}\log\frac{x - c}{x + c}, \qquad (x^2 > c^2)$

46. $\displaystyle\int \frac{x\,dx}{c^2 \pm x^2} = \pm\frac{1}{2}\log(c^2 \pm x^2)$

47. $\displaystyle\int \frac{x\,dx}{(c^2 \pm x^2)^{n+1}} = \mp\frac{1}{2n(c^2 \pm x^2)^n}$

48. $\displaystyle\int \frac{dx}{(c^2 \pm x^2)^n} = \frac{1}{2c^2(n - 1)}\left[\frac{x}{(c^2 \pm x^2)^{n-1}} + (2n - 3)\int \frac{dx}{(c^2 \pm x^2)^{n-1}}\right]$

49. $\displaystyle\int \frac{dx}{(x^2 - c^2)^n} = \frac{1}{2c^2(n - 1)}\left[-\frac{x}{(x^2 - c^2)^{n-1}} - (2n - 3)\int \frac{dx}{(x^2 - c^2)^{n-1}}\right]$

50. $\displaystyle\int \frac{x\,dx}{x^2 - c^2} = \frac{1}{2}\log(x^2 - c^2)$

51. $\displaystyle\int \frac{x\,dx}{(x^2 - c^2)^{n+1}} = -\frac{1}{2n(x^2 - c^2)^n}$

INTEGRALS (Continued)

FORMS CONTAINING $a + bx$ and $c + dx$

$$u = a + bx, \qquad v = c + dx, \qquad k = ad - bc$$

If $k = 0$, then $v = \dfrac{c}{a} u$

52. $\displaystyle \int \frac{dx}{u \cdot v} = \frac{1}{k} \cdot \log\left(\frac{v}{u}\right)$

53. $\displaystyle \int \frac{x\,dx}{u \cdot v} = \frac{1}{k}\left[\frac{a}{b}\log(u) - \frac{c}{d}\log(v)\right]$

54. $\displaystyle \int \frac{dx}{u^2 \cdot v} = \frac{1}{k}\left(\frac{1}{u} + \frac{d}{k}\log\frac{v}{u}\right)$

55. $\displaystyle \int \frac{x\,dx}{u^2 \cdot v} = \frac{-a}{bku} - \frac{c}{k^2}\log\frac{v}{u}$

56. $\displaystyle \int \frac{x^2\,dx}{u^2 \cdot v} = \frac{a^2}{b^2 ku} + \frac{1}{k^2}\left[\frac{c^2}{d}\log(v) + \frac{a(k - bc)}{b^2}\log(u)\right]$

57. $\displaystyle \int \frac{dx}{u^n \cdot v^m} = \frac{1}{k(m - 1)}\left[\frac{-1}{u^{n-1} \cdot v^{m-1}} - (m + n - 2)b\int \frac{dx}{u^n \cdot v^{m-1}}\right]$

58. $\displaystyle \int \frac{u}{v}\,dx = \frac{bx}{d} + \frac{k}{d^2}\log(v)$

59. $\displaystyle \int \frac{u^m\,dx}{v^n} = \begin{cases} \dfrac{-1}{k(n-1)}\left[\dfrac{u^{m+1}}{v^{n-1}} + b(n - m - 2)\displaystyle\int \frac{u^m}{v^{n-1}}\,dx\right] \\[2mm] \text{or} \\[2mm] \dfrac{-1}{d(n - m - 1)}\left[\dfrac{u^m}{v^{n-1}} + mk\displaystyle\int \frac{u^{m-1}}{v^n}\,dx\right] \\[2mm] \text{or} \\[2mm] \dfrac{-1}{d(n - 1)}\left[\dfrac{u^m}{v^{n-1}} - mb\displaystyle\int \frac{u^{m-1}}{v^{n-1}}\,dx\right] \end{cases}$

FORMS CONTAINING $(a + bx^n)$

60. $\displaystyle \int \frac{dx}{a + bx^2} = \frac{1}{\sqrt{ab}}\tan^{-1}\frac{x\sqrt{ab}}{a}, \qquad (ab > 0)$

61. $\displaystyle \int \frac{dx}{a + bx^2} = \begin{cases} \dfrac{1}{2\sqrt{-ab}}\log\dfrac{a + x\sqrt{-ab}}{a - x\sqrt{-ab}}, \qquad (ab < 0) \\[2mm] \text{or} \\[2mm] \dfrac{1}{\sqrt{-ab}}\tanh^{-1}\dfrac{x\sqrt{-ab}}{a}, \qquad (ab < 0) \end{cases}$

INTEGRALS (Continued)

62. $\displaystyle \int \frac{dx}{a^2 + b^2 x^2} = \frac{1}{ab} \tan^{-1} \frac{bx}{a}$

63. $\displaystyle \int \frac{x\,dx}{a + bx^2} = \frac{1}{2b} \log(a + bx^2)$

64. $\displaystyle \int \frac{x^2\,dx}{a + bx^2} = \frac{x}{b} - \frac{a}{b} \int \frac{dx}{a + bx^2}$

65. $\displaystyle \int \frac{dx}{(a + bx^2)^2} = \frac{x}{2a(a + bx^2)} + \frac{1}{2a} \int \frac{dx}{a + bx^2}$

66. $\displaystyle \int \frac{dx}{a^2 - b^2 x^2} = \frac{1}{2ab} \log \frac{a + bx}{a - bx}$

67. $\displaystyle \int \frac{dx}{(a + bx^2)^{m+1}} = \begin{cases} \dfrac{1}{2ma} \dfrac{x}{(a + bx^2)^m} + \dfrac{2m - 1}{2ma} \displaystyle\int \dfrac{dx}{(a + bx^2)^m} \\[2mm] \qquad\qquad\text{or} \\[2mm] \dfrac{(2m)!}{(m!)^2}\left[\dfrac{x}{2a} \displaystyle\sum_{r=1}^{m} \dfrac{r!(r - 1)!}{(4a)^{m-r}(2r)!(a + bx^2)^r} + \dfrac{1}{(4a)^m} \int \dfrac{dx}{a + bx^2}\right] \end{cases}$

68. $\displaystyle \int \frac{x\,dx}{(a + bx^2)^{m+1}} = -\frac{1}{2bm(a + bx^2)^m}$

69. $\displaystyle \int \frac{x^2\,dx}{(a + bx^2)^{m+1}} = \frac{-x}{2mb(a + bx^2)^m} + \frac{1}{2mb} \int \frac{dx}{(a + bx^2)^m}$

70. $\displaystyle \int \frac{dx}{x(a + bx^2)} = \frac{1}{2a} \log \frac{x^2}{a + bx^2}$

71. $\displaystyle \int \frac{dx}{x^2(a + bx^2)} = -\frac{1}{ax} - \frac{b}{a} \int \frac{dx}{a + bx^2}$

72. $\displaystyle \int \frac{dx}{x(a + bx^2)^{m+1}} = \begin{cases} \dfrac{1}{2am(a + bx^2)^m} + \dfrac{1}{a} \displaystyle\int \dfrac{dx}{x(a + bx^2)^m} \\[2mm] \qquad\qquad\text{or} \\[2mm] \dfrac{1}{2a^{m+1}}\left[\displaystyle\sum_{r=1}^{m} \dfrac{a^r}{r(a + bx^2)^r} + \log \dfrac{x^2}{a + bx^2}\right] \end{cases}$

73. $\displaystyle \int \frac{dx}{x^2(a + bx^2)^{m+1}} = \frac{1}{a} \int \frac{dx}{x^2(a + bx^2)^m} - \frac{b}{a} \int \frac{dx}{(a + bx^2)^{m+1}}$

74. $\displaystyle \int \frac{dx}{a + bx^3} = \frac{k}{3a}\left[\frac{1}{2} \log \frac{(k + x)^3}{a + bx^3} + \sqrt{3} \tan^{-1} \frac{2x - k}{k\sqrt{3}}\right], \qquad \left(k = \sqrt[3]{\frac{a}{b}}\right)$

75. $\displaystyle \int \frac{x\,dx}{a + bx^3} = \frac{1}{3bk}\left[\frac{1}{2} \log \frac{a + bx^3}{(k + x)^3} + \sqrt{3} \tan^{-1} \frac{2x - k}{k\sqrt{3}}\right], \qquad \left(k = \sqrt[3]{\frac{a}{b}}\right)$

INTEGRALS (Continued)

76. $\int \dfrac{x^2 \, dx}{a + bx^3} = \dfrac{1}{3b} \log(a + bx^3)$

77. $\int \dfrac{dx}{a + bx^4} = \dfrac{k}{2a} \left[\dfrac{1}{2} \log \dfrac{x^2 + 2kx + 2k^2}{x^2 - 2kx + 2k^2} + \tan^{-1} \dfrac{2kx}{2k^2 - x^2} \right],$

$$\left(ab > 0, k = \sqrt[4]{\dfrac{a}{4b}} \right)$$

78. $\int \dfrac{dx}{a + bx^4} = \dfrac{k}{2a} \left[\dfrac{1}{2} \log \dfrac{x + k}{x - k} + \tan^{-1} \dfrac{x}{k} \right], \qquad \left(ab < 0, k = \sqrt[4]{-\dfrac{a}{b}} \right)$

79. $\int \dfrac{x \, dx}{a + bx^4} = \dfrac{1}{2bk} \tan^{-1} \dfrac{x^2}{k}, \qquad \left(ab > 0, k = \sqrt{\dfrac{a}{b}} \right)$

80. $\int \dfrac{x \, dx}{a + bx^4} = \dfrac{1}{4bk} \log \dfrac{x^2 - k}{x^2 + k}, \qquad \left(ab < 0, k = \sqrt{-\dfrac{a}{b}} \right)$

81. $\int \dfrac{x^2 \, dx}{a + bx^4} = \dfrac{1}{4bk} \left[\dfrac{1}{2} \log \dfrac{x^2 - 2kx + 2k^2}{x^2 + 2kx + 2k^2} + \tan^{-1} \dfrac{2kx}{2k^2 - x^2} \right],$

$$\left(ab > 0, k = \sqrt[4]{\dfrac{a}{4b}} \right)$$

82. $\int \dfrac{x^2 \, dx}{a + bx^4} = \dfrac{1}{4bk} \left[\log \dfrac{x - k}{x + k} + 2 \tan^{-1} \dfrac{x}{k} \right], \qquad \left(ab < 0, k = \sqrt[4]{-\dfrac{a}{b}} \right)$

83. $\int \dfrac{x^3 \, dx}{a + bx^4} = \dfrac{1}{4b} \log(a + bx^4)$

84. $\int \dfrac{dx}{x(a + bx^n)} = \dfrac{1}{an} \log \dfrac{x^n}{a + bx^n}$

85. $\int \dfrac{dx}{(a + bx^n)^{m+1}} = \dfrac{1}{a} \int \dfrac{dx}{(a + bx^n)^m} - \dfrac{b}{a} \int \dfrac{x^n \, dx}{(a + bx^n)^{m+1}}$

86. $\int \dfrac{x^m \, dx}{(a + bx^n)^{p+1}} = \dfrac{1}{b} \int \dfrac{x^{m-n} \, dx}{(a + bx^n)^p} - \dfrac{a}{b} \int \dfrac{x^{m-n} \, dx}{(a + bx^n)^{p+1}}$

87. $\int \dfrac{dx}{x^m(a + bx^n)^{p+1}} = \dfrac{1}{a} \int \dfrac{dx}{x^m(a + bx^n)^p} - \dfrac{b}{a} \int \dfrac{dx}{x^{m-n}(a + bx^n)^{p+1}}$

INTEGRALS (Continued)

$$88. \int x^m(a + bx^n)^p \, dx = \begin{cases} \dfrac{1}{b(np + m + 1)}\left[x^{m-n+1}(a + bx^n)^{p+1} \right. \\ \qquad\qquad \left. - a(m - n + 1)\displaystyle\int x^{m-n}(a + bx^n)^p \, dx \right] \\ \text{or} \\ \dfrac{1}{np + m + 1}\left[x^{m+1}(a + bx^n)^p \right. \\ \qquad\qquad \left. + anp\displaystyle\int x^m(a + bx^n)^{p-1} \, dx \right] \\ \text{or} \\ \dfrac{1}{a(m + 1)}\left[x^{m+1}(a + bx^n)^{p+1} \right. \\ \qquad\qquad \left. - (m + 1 + np + n)b\displaystyle\int x^{m+n}(a + bx^n)^p \, dx \right] \\ \text{or} \\ \dfrac{1}{an(p + 1)}\left[-x^{m+1}(a + bx^n)^{p+1} \right. \\ \qquad\qquad \left. + (m + 1 + np + n)\displaystyle\int x^m(a + bx^n)^{p+1} \, dx \right] \end{cases}$$

FORMS CONTAINING $c^3 \pm x^3$

$$89. \int \frac{dx}{c^3 \pm x^3} = \pm\frac{1}{6c^2}\log\frac{(c \pm x)^3}{c^3 \pm x^3} + \frac{1}{c^2\sqrt{3}}\tan^{-1}\frac{2x \mp c}{c\sqrt{3}}$$

$$90. \int \frac{dx}{(c^3 \pm x^3)^2} = \frac{x}{3c^3(c^3 \pm x^3)} + \frac{2}{3c^3}\int \frac{dx}{c^3 \pm x^3}$$

$$91. \int \frac{dx}{(c^3 \pm x^3)^{n+1}} = \frac{1}{3nc^3}\left[\frac{x}{(c^3 \pm x^3)^n} + (3n - 1)\int \frac{dx}{(c^3 \pm x^3)^n} \right]$$

$$92. \int \frac{x \, dx}{c^3 \pm x^3} = \frac{1}{6c}\log\frac{c^3 \pm x^3}{(c \pm x)^3} \pm \frac{1}{c\sqrt{3}}\tan^{-1}\frac{2x \mp c}{c\sqrt{3}}$$

$$93. \int \frac{x \, dx}{(c^3 \pm x^3)^2} = \frac{x^2}{3c^3(c^3 \pm x^3)} + \frac{1}{3c^3}\int \frac{x \, dx}{c^3 \pm x^3}$$

$$94. \int \frac{x \, dx}{(c^3 \pm x^3)^{p+1}} = \frac{1}{3nc^3}\left[\frac{x^2}{(c^3 \pm x^3)^n} + (3n - 2)\int \frac{x \, dx}{(c^3 \pm x^3)^n} \right]$$

$$95. \int \frac{x^2 \, dx}{c^3 \pm x^3} = \pm\frac{1}{3}\log(c^3 \pm x^3)$$

INTEGRALS (Continued)

96. $\displaystyle\int \frac{x^2\,dx}{(c^3 \pm x^3)^{n+1}} = \mp\frac{1}{3n(c^3 \pm x^3)^n}$

97. $\displaystyle\int \frac{dx}{x(c^3 \pm x^3)} = \frac{1}{3c^3}\log\frac{x^3}{c^3 \pm x^3}$

98. $\displaystyle\int \frac{dx}{x(c^3 \pm x^3)^2} = \frac{1}{3c^3(c^3 \pm x^3)} + \frac{1}{3c^6}\log\frac{x^3}{c^3 \pm x^3}$

99. $\displaystyle\int \frac{dx}{x(c^3 \pm x^3)^{n+1}} = \frac{1}{3nc^3(c^3 \pm x^3)^n} + \frac{1}{c^3}\int\frac{dx}{x(c^3 \pm x^3)^n}$

100. $\displaystyle\int \frac{dx}{x^2(c^3 \pm x^3)} = -\frac{1}{c^3 x} \mp \frac{1}{c^3}\int\frac{x\,dx}{c^3 \pm x^3}$

101. $\displaystyle\int \frac{dx}{x^2(c^3 \pm x^3)^{n+1}} = \frac{1}{c^3}\int\frac{dx}{x^2(c^3 \pm x^3)^n} \mp \frac{1}{c^3}\int\frac{x\,dx}{(c^3 \pm x^3)^{n+1}}$

FORMS CONTAINING $c^4 \pm x^4$

102. $\displaystyle\int \frac{dx}{c^4 + x^4} = \frac{1}{2c^3\sqrt{2}}\left[\frac{1}{2}\log\frac{x^2 + cx\sqrt{2} + c^2}{x^2 - cx\sqrt{2} + c^2} + \tan^{-1}\frac{cx\sqrt{2}}{c^2 - x^2}\right]$

103. $\displaystyle\int \frac{dx}{c^4 - x^4} = \frac{1}{2c^3}\left[\frac{1}{2}\log\frac{c + x}{c - x} + \tan^{-1}\frac{x}{c}\right]$

104. $\displaystyle\int \frac{x\,dx}{c^4 + x^4} = \frac{1}{2c^2}\tan^{-1}\frac{x^2}{c^2}$

105. $\displaystyle\int \frac{x\,dx}{c^4 - x^4} = \frac{1}{4c^2}\log\frac{c^2 + x^2}{c^2 - x^2}$

106. $\displaystyle\int \frac{x^2\,dx}{c^4 + x^4} = \frac{1}{2c\sqrt{2}}\left[\frac{1}{2}\log\frac{x^2 - cx\sqrt{2} + c^2}{x^2 + cx\sqrt{2} + c^2} + \tan^{-1}\frac{cx\sqrt{2}}{c^2 - x^2}\right]$

107. $\displaystyle\int \frac{x^2\,dx}{c^4 - x^4} = \frac{1}{2c}\left[\frac{1}{2}\log\frac{c + x}{c - x} - \tan^{-1}\frac{x}{c}\right]$

108. $\displaystyle\int \frac{x^3\,dx}{c^4 \pm x^4} = \pm\frac{1}{4}\log(c^4 \pm x^4)$

FORMS CONTAINING $(a + bx + cx^2)$

$$X = a + bx + cx^2 \text{ and } q = 4ac - b^2$$

If $q = 0$, then $X = c\left(x + \dfrac{b}{2c}\right)^2$, and formulas starting with 23 should be used in place of these.

109. $\displaystyle\int \frac{dx}{X} = \frac{2}{\sqrt{q}}\tan^{-1}\frac{2cx + b}{\sqrt{q}}, \qquad (q > 0)$

INTEGRALS (Continued)

110. $\displaystyle \int \frac{dx}{X} = \begin{cases} \dfrac{-2}{\sqrt{-q}} \tanh^{-1} \dfrac{2cx + b}{\sqrt{-q}} \\[2ex] \qquad\qquad \text{or} \\[2ex] \dfrac{1}{\sqrt{-q}} \log \dfrac{2cx + b - \sqrt{-q}}{2cx + b + \sqrt{-q}}, \end{cases} \quad (q < 0)$

111. $\displaystyle \int \frac{dx}{X^2} = \frac{2cx + b}{qX} + \frac{2c}{q} \int \frac{dx}{X}$

112. $\displaystyle \int \frac{dx}{X^3} = \frac{2cx + b}{q} \left(\frac{1}{2X^2} + \frac{3c}{qX} \right) + \frac{6c^2}{q^2} \int \frac{dx}{X}$

113. $\displaystyle \int \frac{dx}{X^{n+1}} = \begin{cases} \dfrac{2cx + b}{nqX^n} + \dfrac{2(2n - 1)c}{qn} \displaystyle\int \dfrac{dx}{X^n} \\[2ex] \qquad\qquad \text{or} \\[2ex] \dfrac{(2n)!}{(n!)^2} \left(\dfrac{c}{q} \right)^n \left[\dfrac{2cx + b}{q} \displaystyle\sum_{r=1}^{n} \left(\dfrac{q}{cX} \right)^r \left(\dfrac{(r - 1)!r!}{(2r)!} \right) + \displaystyle\int \dfrac{dx}{X} \right] \end{cases}$

114. $\displaystyle \int \frac{x\, dx}{X} = \frac{1}{2c} \log X - \frac{b}{2c} \int \frac{dx}{X}$

115. $\displaystyle \int \frac{x\, dx}{X^2} = -\frac{bx + 2a}{qX} - \frac{b}{q} \int \frac{dx}{X}$

116. $\displaystyle \int \frac{x\, dx}{X^{n+1}} = -\frac{2a + bx}{nqX^n} - \frac{b(2n - 1)}{nq} \int \frac{dx}{X^n}$

117. $\displaystyle \int \frac{x^2}{X} dx = \frac{x}{c} - \frac{b}{2c^2} \log X + \frac{b^2 - 2ac}{2c^2} \int \frac{dx}{X}$

118. $\displaystyle \int \frac{x^2}{X^2} dx = \frac{(b^2 - 2ac)x + ab}{cqX} + \frac{2a}{q} \int \frac{dx}{X}$

119. $\displaystyle \int \frac{x^m\, dx}{X^{n+1}} = -\frac{x^{m-1}}{(2n - m + 1)cX^n} - \frac{n - m + 1}{2n - m + 1} \cdot \frac{b}{c} \int \frac{x^{m-1}\, dx}{X^{n+1}}$

$$+ \frac{m - 1}{2n - m + 1} \cdot \frac{a}{c} \int \frac{x^{m-2}\, dx}{X^{n+1}}$$

120. $\displaystyle \int \frac{dx}{xX} = \frac{1}{2a} \log \frac{x^2}{X} - \frac{b}{2a} \int \frac{dx}{X}$

121. $\displaystyle \int \frac{dx}{x^2 X} = \frac{b}{2a^2} \log \frac{X}{x^2} - \frac{1}{ax} + \left(\frac{b^2}{2a^2} - \frac{c}{a} \right) \int \frac{dx}{X}$

122. $\displaystyle \int \frac{dx}{xX^n} = \frac{1}{2a(n - 1)X^{n-1}} - \frac{b}{2a} \int \frac{dx}{X^n} + \frac{1}{a} \int \frac{dx}{xX^{n-1}}$

INTEGRALS (Continued)

123. $\int \dfrac{dx}{x^m X^{n+1}} = -\dfrac{1}{(m-1)ax^{m-1}X^n} - \dfrac{n+m-1}{m-1}\cdot\dfrac{b}{a}\int \dfrac{dx}{x^{m-1}X^{n+1}}$

$$- \dfrac{2n+m-1}{m-1}\cdot\dfrac{c}{a}\int \dfrac{dx}{x^{m-2}X^{n+1}}$$

FORMS CONTAINING $\sqrt{a+bx}$

124. $\int \sqrt{a+bx}\,dx = \dfrac{2}{3b}\sqrt{(a+bx)^3}$

125. $\int x\sqrt{a+bx}\,dx = -\dfrac{2(2a-3bx)\sqrt{(a+bx)^3}}{15b^2}$

126. $\int x^2\sqrt{a+bx}\,dx = \dfrac{2(8a^2-12abx+15b^2x^2)\sqrt{(a+bx)^3}}{105b^3}$

127. $\int x^m\sqrt{a+bx}\,dx = \begin{cases} \dfrac{2}{b(2m+3)}\left[x^m\sqrt{(a+bx)^3} - ma\int x^{m-1}\sqrt{a+bx}\,dx\right] \\[2ex] \text{or} \\[2ex] \dfrac{2}{b^{m+1}}\sqrt{a+bx}\,\displaystyle\sum_{r=0}^{m}\dfrac{m!(-a)^{m-r}}{r!(m-r)!(2r+3)}(a+bx)^{r+1} \end{cases}$

128. $\int \dfrac{\sqrt{a+bx}}{x}\,dx = 2\sqrt{a+bx} + a\int \dfrac{dx}{x\sqrt{a+bx}}$

129. $\int \dfrac{\sqrt{a+bx}}{x^2}\,dx = -\dfrac{\sqrt{a+bx}}{x} + \dfrac{b}{2}\int \dfrac{dx}{x\sqrt{a+bx}}$

130. $\int \dfrac{\sqrt{a+bx}}{x^m}\,dx = -\dfrac{1}{(m-1)a}\left[\dfrac{\sqrt{(a+bx)^3}}{x^{m-1}} + \dfrac{(2m-5)b}{2}\int \dfrac{\sqrt{a+bx}}{x^{m-1}}\,dx\right]$

131. $\int \dfrac{dx}{\sqrt{a+bx}} = \dfrac{2\sqrt{a+bx}}{b}$

132. $\int \dfrac{x\,dx}{\sqrt{a+bx}} = -\dfrac{2(2a-bx)}{3b^2}\sqrt{a+bx}$

133. $\int \dfrac{x^2\,dx}{\sqrt{a+bx}} = \dfrac{2(8a^2-4abx+3b^2x^2)}{15b^3}\sqrt{a+bx}$

INTEGRALS (Continued)

134. $\displaystyle\int \frac{x^m\,dx}{\sqrt{a+bx}} = \begin{cases} \dfrac{2}{(2m+1)b}\left[x^m\sqrt{a+bx} - ma\displaystyle\int\frac{x^{m-1}\,dx}{\sqrt{a+bx}}\right] \\[4mm] \text{or} \\[2mm] \dfrac{2(-a)^m\sqrt{a+bx}}{b^{m+1}}\displaystyle\sum_{r=0}^{m}\frac{(-1)^r m!(a+bx)^r}{(2r+1)r!(m-r)!a^r} \end{cases}$

135. $\displaystyle\int \frac{dx}{x\sqrt{a+bx}} = \frac{1}{\sqrt{a}}\log\left(\frac{\sqrt{a+bx}-\sqrt{a}}{\sqrt{a+bx}+\sqrt{a}}\right), \qquad (a>0)$

136. $\displaystyle\int \frac{dx}{x\sqrt{a+bx}} = \frac{2}{\sqrt{-a}}\tan^{-1}\sqrt{\frac{a+bx}{-a}}, \qquad (a<0)$

137. $\displaystyle\int \frac{dx}{x^2\sqrt{a+bx}} = -\frac{\sqrt{a+bx}}{ax} - \frac{b}{2a}\int\frac{dx}{x\sqrt{a+bx}}$

138. $\displaystyle\int \frac{dx}{x^n\sqrt{a+bx}} = \begin{cases} -\dfrac{\sqrt{a+bx}}{(n-1)ax^{n-1}} - \dfrac{(2n-3)b}{(2n-2)a}\displaystyle\int\frac{dx}{x^{n-1}\sqrt{a+bx}} \\[4mm] \text{or} \\[2mm] \dfrac{(2n-2)!}{[(n-1)!]^2}\left[-\dfrac{\sqrt{a+bx}}{a}\displaystyle\sum_{r=1}^{n-1}\frac{r!(r-1)!}{x^r(2r)!}\left(-\frac{b}{4a}\right)^{n-r-1}\right. \\[4mm] \qquad\qquad\qquad\left. + \left(-\dfrac{b}{4a}\right)^{n-1}\displaystyle\int\frac{dx}{x\sqrt{a+bx}}\right] \end{cases}$

139. $\displaystyle\int (a+bx)^{\pm\frac{n}{2}}\,dx = \frac{2(a+bx)^{\frac{2\pm n}{2}}}{b(2\pm n)}$

140. $\displaystyle\int x(a+bx)^{\pm\frac{n}{2}}\,dx = \frac{2}{b^2}\left[\frac{(a+bx)^{\frac{4\pm n}{2}}}{4\pm n} - \frac{a(a+bx)^{\frac{2\pm n}{2}}}{2\pm n}\right]$

141. $\displaystyle\int \frac{dx}{x(a+bx)^{\frac{m}{2}}} = \frac{1}{a}\int\frac{dx}{x(a+bx)^{\frac{m-2}{2}}} - \frac{b}{a}\int\frac{dx}{(a+bx)^{\frac{m}{2}}}$

142. $\displaystyle\int \frac{(a+bx)^{\frac{n}{2}}\,dx}{x} = b\int(a+bx)^{\frac{n-2}{2}}\,dx + a\int\frac{(a+bx)^{\frac{n-2}{2}}}{x}\,dx$

143. $\displaystyle\int f(x,\sqrt{a+bx})\,dx = \frac{2}{b}\int f\left(\frac{z^2-a}{b}, z\right)z\,dz, \qquad (z=\sqrt{a+bx})$

FORMS CONTAINING $\sqrt{a + bx}$ and $\sqrt{c + dx}$

$$u = a + bx \qquad v = c + dx \qquad k = ad - bc$$

If $k = 0$, then $v = \dfrac{c}{a}u$, and formulas starting with 124 should be used in place of these.

144. $\displaystyle\int \frac{dx}{\sqrt{uv}} = \begin{cases} \dfrac{2}{\sqrt{bd}} \tanh^{-1} \dfrac{\sqrt{bduv}}{bv}, \quad bd > o, \, k < o \\[2ex] \text{or} \\[2ex] \dfrac{2}{\sqrt{bd}} \tanh^{-1} \dfrac{\sqrt{bduv}}{du}, \quad bd > o, \, k > o. \\[2ex] \text{or} \\[2ex] \dfrac{1}{\sqrt{bd}} \log \dfrac{(bv + \sqrt{bduv})^2}{v}, \qquad (bd > 0) \end{cases}$

145. $\displaystyle\int \frac{dx}{\sqrt{uv}} = \begin{cases} \dfrac{2}{\sqrt{-bd}} \tan^{-1} \dfrac{\sqrt{-bduv}}{bv} \\[2ex] \text{or} \\[2ex] -\dfrac{1}{\sqrt{-bd}} \sin^{-1} \left(\dfrac{2bdx + ad + bc}{|k|} \right), \qquad (bd < 0) \end{cases}$

146. $\displaystyle\int \sqrt{uv}\, dx = \frac{k + 2bv}{4bd} \sqrt{uv} - \frac{k^2}{8bd} \int \frac{dx}{\sqrt{uv}}$

147. $\displaystyle\int \frac{dx}{v\sqrt{u}} = \begin{cases} \dfrac{1}{\sqrt{kd}} \log \dfrac{d\sqrt{u} - \sqrt{kd}}{d\sqrt{u} + \sqrt{kd}} \\[2ex] \text{or} \\[2ex] \dfrac{1}{\sqrt{kd}} \log \dfrac{(d\sqrt{u} - \sqrt{kd})^2}{v}, \qquad (kd > 0) \end{cases}$

148. $\displaystyle\int \frac{dx}{v\sqrt{u}} = \frac{2}{\sqrt{-kd}} \tan^{-1} \frac{d\sqrt{u}}{\sqrt{-kd}}, \qquad (kd < 0)$

149. $\displaystyle\int \frac{x\, dx}{\sqrt{uv}} = \frac{\sqrt{uv}}{bd} - \frac{ad + bc}{2bd} \int \frac{dx}{\sqrt{uv}}$

150. $\displaystyle\int \frac{dx}{v\sqrt{uv}} = \frac{-2\sqrt{uv}}{kv}$

INTEGRALS (Continued)

151. $\displaystyle \int \frac{v\,dx}{\sqrt{uv}} = \frac{\sqrt{uv}}{b} - \frac{k}{2b}\int \frac{dx}{\sqrt{uv}}$

152. $\displaystyle \int \sqrt{\frac{v}{u}}\,dx = \frac{v}{|v|}\int \frac{v\,dx}{\sqrt{uv}}$

153. $\displaystyle \int v^m\sqrt{u}\,dx = \frac{1}{(2m+3)d}\left(2v^{m+1}\sqrt{u} + k\int \frac{v^m\,dx}{\sqrt{u}}\right)$

154. $\displaystyle \int \frac{dx}{v^m\sqrt{u}} = -\frac{1}{(m-1)k}\left(\frac{\sqrt{u}}{v^{m-1}} + \left(m-\frac{3}{2}\right)b\int \frac{dx}{v^{m-1}\sqrt{u}}\right)$

155. $\displaystyle \int \frac{v^m\,dx}{\sqrt{u}} = \begin{cases} \dfrac{2}{b(2m+1)}\left[v^m\sqrt{u} - mk\displaystyle\int \frac{v^{m-1}}{\sqrt{u}}\,dx\right] \\ \quad\text{or} \\ \dfrac{2(m!)^2\sqrt{u}}{b(2m+1)!}\displaystyle\sum_{r=0}^{m}\left(-\frac{4k}{b}\right)^{m-r}\frac{(2r)!}{(r!)^2}v^r \end{cases}$

FORMS CONTAINING $\sqrt{x^2 \pm a^2}$

156. $\displaystyle \int \sqrt{x^2 \pm a^2}\,dx = \tfrac{1}{2}[x\sqrt{x^2 \pm a^2} \pm a^2 \log(x + \sqrt{x^2 \pm a^2})]$

157. $\displaystyle \int \frac{dx}{\sqrt{x^2 \pm a^2}} = \log(x + \sqrt{x^2 \pm a^2})$

158. $\displaystyle \int \frac{dx}{x\sqrt{x^2 - a^2}} = \frac{1}{|a|}\sec^{-1}\frac{x}{a}$

159. $\displaystyle \int \frac{dx}{x\sqrt{x^2 + a^2}} = -\frac{1}{a}\log\left(\frac{a + \sqrt{x^2 + a^2}}{x}\right)$

160. $\displaystyle \int \frac{\sqrt{x^2 + a^2}}{x}\,dx = \sqrt{x^2 + a^2} - a\log\left(\frac{a + \sqrt{x^2 + a^2}}{x}\right)$

161. $\displaystyle \int \frac{\sqrt{x^2 - a^2}}{x}\,dx = \sqrt{x^2 - a^2} - |a|\sec^{-1}\frac{x}{a}$

162. $\displaystyle \int \frac{x\,dx}{\sqrt{x^2 \pm a^2}} = \sqrt{x^2 \pm a^2}$

163. $\displaystyle \int x\sqrt{x^2 \pm a^2}\,dx = \tfrac{1}{3}\sqrt{(x^2 \pm a^2)^3}$

INTEGRALS (Continued)

164. $\displaystyle\int \sqrt{(x^2 \pm a^2)^3}\, dx = \frac{1}{4}\Bigg[x\sqrt{(x^2 \pm a^2)^3} \pm \frac{3a^2 x}{2}\sqrt{x^2 \pm a^2}$
$$+ \frac{3a^4}{2}\log(x + \sqrt{x^2 \pm a^2})\Bigg]$$

165. $\displaystyle\int \frac{dx}{\sqrt{(x^2 \pm a^2)^3}} = \frac{\pm x}{a^2\sqrt{x^2 \pm a^2}}$

166. $\displaystyle\int \frac{x\, dx}{\sqrt{(x^2 \pm a^2)^3}} = \frac{-1}{\sqrt{x^2 \pm a^2}}$

167. $\displaystyle\int x\sqrt{(x^2 \pm a^2)^3}\, dx = \tfrac{1}{5}\sqrt{(x^2 \pm a^2)^5}$

168. $\displaystyle\int x^2\sqrt{x^2 \pm a^2}\, dx = \frac{x}{4}\sqrt{(x^2 \pm a^2)^3} \mp \frac{a^2}{8}x\sqrt{x^2 \pm a^2} - \frac{a^4}{8}\log(x + \sqrt{x^2 \pm a^2})$

169. $\displaystyle\int x^3\sqrt{x^2 + a^2}\, dx = (\tfrac{1}{5}x^2 - \tfrac{2}{15}a^2)\sqrt{(a^2 + x^2)^3}$

170. $\displaystyle\int x^3\sqrt{x^2 - a^2}\, dx = \frac{1}{5}\sqrt{(x^2 - a^2)^5} + \frac{a^2}{3}\sqrt{(x^2 - a^2)^3}$

171. $\displaystyle\int \frac{x^2\, dx}{\sqrt{x^2 \pm a^2}} = \frac{x}{2}\sqrt{x^2 \pm a^2} \mp \frac{a^2}{2}\log(x + \sqrt{x^2 \pm a^2})$

172. $\displaystyle\int \frac{x^3\, dx}{\sqrt{x^2 \pm a^2}} = \frac{1}{3}\sqrt{(x^2 \pm a^2)^3} \mp a^2\sqrt{x^2 \pm a^2}$

173. $\displaystyle\int \frac{dx}{x^2\sqrt{x^2 \pm a^2}} = \mp\frac{\sqrt{x^2 \pm a^2}}{a^2 x}$

174. $\displaystyle\int \frac{dx}{x^3\sqrt{x^2 + a^2}} = -\frac{\sqrt{x^2 + a^2}}{2a^2 x^2} + \frac{1}{2a^3}\log\frac{a + \sqrt{x^2 + a^2}}{x}$

175. $\displaystyle\int \frac{dx}{x^3\sqrt{x^2 - a^2}} = \frac{\sqrt{x^2 - a^2}}{2a^2 x^2} + \frac{1}{2|a^3|}\sec^{-1}\frac{x}{a}$

176. $\displaystyle\int x^2\sqrt{(x^2 \pm a^2)^3}\, dx = \frac{x}{6}\sqrt{(x^2 \pm a^2)^5} \mp \frac{a^2 x}{24}\sqrt{(x^2 \pm a^2)^3} - \frac{a^4 x}{16}\sqrt{x^2 \pm a^2}$
$$\mp \frac{a^6}{16}\log(x + \sqrt{x^2 \pm a^2})$$

177. $\displaystyle\int x^3\sqrt{(x^2 \pm a^2)^3}\, dx = \frac{1}{7}\sqrt{(x^2 \pm a^2)^7} \mp \frac{a^2}{5}\sqrt{(x^2 \pm a^2)^5}$

INTEGRALS (Continued)

178. $\displaystyle\int \frac{\sqrt{x^2 \pm a^2}\,dx}{x^2} = -\frac{\sqrt{x^2 \pm a^2}}{x} + \log\left(x + \sqrt{x^2 \pm a^2}\right)$

179. $\displaystyle\int \frac{\sqrt{x^2 + a^2}}{x^3}\,dx = -\frac{\sqrt{x^2 + a^2}}{2x^2} - \frac{1}{2a}\log\frac{a + \sqrt{x^2 + a^2}}{x}$

180. $\displaystyle\int \frac{\sqrt{x^2 - a^2}}{x^3}\,dx = -\frac{\sqrt{x^2 - a^2}}{2x^2} + \frac{1}{2|a|}\sec^{-1}\frac{x}{a}$

181. $\displaystyle\int \frac{\sqrt{x^2 \pm a^2}}{x^4}\,dx = \mp\frac{\sqrt{(x^2 \pm a^2)^3}}{3a^2x^3}$

182. $\displaystyle\int \frac{x^2\,dx}{\sqrt{(x^2 \pm a^2)^3}} = \frac{-x}{\sqrt{x^2 \pm a^2}} + \log\left(x + \sqrt{x^2 \pm a^2}\right)$

183. $\displaystyle\int \frac{x^3\,dx}{\sqrt{(x^2 \pm a^2)^3}} = \sqrt{x^2 \pm a^2} \pm \frac{a^2}{\sqrt{x^2 \pm a^2}}$

184. $\displaystyle\int \frac{dx}{x\sqrt{(x^2 + a^2)^3}} = \frac{1}{a^2\sqrt{x^2 + a^2}} - \frac{1}{a^3}\log\frac{a + \sqrt{x^2 + a^2}}{x}$

185. $\displaystyle\int \frac{dx}{x\sqrt{(x^2 - a^2)^3}} = -\frac{1}{a^2\sqrt{x^2 - a^2}} - \frac{1}{|a^3|}\sec^{-1}\frac{x}{a}$

186. $\displaystyle\int \frac{dx}{x^2\sqrt{(x^2 \pm a^2)^3}} = -\frac{1}{a^4}\left[\frac{\sqrt{x^2 \pm a^2}}{x} + \frac{x}{\sqrt{x^2 \pm a^2}}\right]$

187. $\displaystyle\int \frac{dx}{x^3\sqrt{(x^2 + a^2)^3}} = -\frac{1}{2a^2x^2\sqrt{x^2 + a^2}} - \frac{3}{2a^4\sqrt{x^2 + a^2}}$

$$+ \frac{3}{2a^5}\log\frac{a + \sqrt{x^2 + a^2}}{x}$$

188. $\displaystyle\int \frac{dx}{x^3\sqrt{(x^2 - a^2)^3}} = \frac{1}{2a^2x^2\sqrt{x^2 - a^2}} - \frac{3}{2a^4\sqrt{x^2 - a^2}} - \frac{3}{2|a^5|}\sec^{-1}\frac{x}{a}$

189. $\displaystyle\int \frac{x^m}{\sqrt{x^2 \pm a^2}}\,dx = \frac{1}{m}x^{m-1}\sqrt{x^2 \pm a^2} \mp \frac{m-1}{m}a^2 \int \frac{x^{m-2}}{\sqrt{x^2 \pm a^2}}\,dx$

190. $\displaystyle\int \frac{x^{2m}}{\sqrt{x^2 \pm a^2}}\,dx = \frac{(2m)!}{2^{2m}(m!)^2}\left[\sqrt{x^2 \pm a^2}\sum_{r=1}^{m}\frac{r!(r-1)!}{(2r)!}(\mp a^2)^{m-r}(2x)^{2r-1}\right.$

$$\left. + (\mp a^2)^m \log\left(x + \sqrt{x^2 \pm a^2}\right)\right]$$

191. $\displaystyle\int \frac{x^{2m+1}}{\sqrt{x^2 \pm a^2}}\,dx = \sqrt{x^2 \pm a^2}\sum_{r=0}^{m}\frac{(2r)!(m!)^2}{(2m+1)!(r!)^2}(\mp 4a^2)^{m-r}x^{2r}$

INTEGRALS (Continued)

192. $\displaystyle\int \frac{dx}{x^m\sqrt{x^2 \pm a^2}} = \mp \frac{\sqrt{x^2 \pm a^2}}{(m-1)a^2x^{m-1}} \mp \frac{(m-2)}{(m-1)a^2}\int \frac{dx}{x^{m-2}\sqrt{x^2 \pm a^2}}$

193. $\displaystyle\int \frac{dx}{x^{2m}\sqrt{x^2 \pm a^2}} = \sqrt{x^2 \pm a^2}\sum_{r=0}^{m-1} \frac{(m-1)!\,m!\,(2r)!\,2^{2m-2r-1}}{(r!)^2(2m)!(\mp a^2)^{m-r}x^{2r+1}}$

194. $\displaystyle\int \frac{dx}{x^{2m+1}\sqrt{x^2 + a^2}} = \frac{(2m)!}{(m!)^2}\left[\frac{\sqrt{x^2 + a^2}}{a^2}\sum_{r=1}^{m}(-1)^{m-r+1}\frac{r!(r-1)!}{2(2r)!(4a^2)^{m-r}x^{2r}}\right.$

$$\left. + \frac{(-1)^{m+1}}{2^{2m}a^{2m+1}}\log\frac{\sqrt{x^2 + a^2} + a}{x}\right]$$

195. $\displaystyle\int \frac{dx}{x^{2m+1}\sqrt{x^2 - a^2}} = \frac{(2m)!}{(m!)^2}\left[\frac{\sqrt{x^2 - a^2}}{a^2}\sum_{r=1}^{m}\frac{r!(r-1)!}{2(2r)!(4a^2)^{m-r}x^{2r}}\right.$

$$\left. + \frac{1}{2^{2m}|a|^{2m+1}}\sec^{-1}\frac{x}{a}\right]$$

196. $\displaystyle\int \frac{dx}{(x-a)\sqrt{x^2 - a^2}} = -\frac{\sqrt{x^2 - a^2}}{a(x-a)}$

197. $\displaystyle\int \frac{dx}{(x+a)\sqrt{x^2 - a^2}} = \frac{\sqrt{x^2 - a^2}}{a(x+a)}$

198. $\displaystyle\int f(x,\sqrt{x^2 + a^2})\,dx = a\int f(a\tan u, a\sec u)\sec^2 u\,du, \qquad \left(u = \tan^{-1}\frac{x}{a}, a > 0\right)$

199. $\displaystyle\int f(x,\sqrt{x^2 - a^2})\,dx = a\int f(a\sec u, a\tan u)\sec u\tan u\,du, \qquad \left(u = \sec^{-1}\frac{x}{a},\right.$

$$\left. a > 0\right)$$

FORMS CONTAINING $\sqrt{a^2 - x^2}$

200. $\displaystyle\int \sqrt{a^2 - x^2}\,dx = \frac{1}{2}\left[x\sqrt{a^2 - x^2} + a^2\sin^{-1}\frac{x}{|a|}\right]$

201. $\displaystyle\int \frac{dx}{\sqrt{a^2 - x^2}} = \begin{cases} \sin^{-1}\dfrac{x}{|a|} \\ \text{or} \\ -\cos^{-1}\dfrac{x}{|a|} \end{cases}$

202. $\displaystyle\int \frac{dx}{x\sqrt{a^2 - x^2}} = -\frac{1}{a}\log\left(\frac{a + \sqrt{a^2 - x^2}}{x}\right)$

INTEGRALS (Continued)

203. $\displaystyle\int \frac{\sqrt{a^2-x^2}}{x}\,dx = \sqrt{a^2-x^2} - a\log\left(\frac{a+\sqrt{a^2-x^2}}{x}\right)$

204. $\displaystyle\int \frac{x\,dx}{\sqrt{a^2-x^2}} = -\sqrt{a^2-x^2}$

205. $\displaystyle\int x\sqrt{a^2-x^2}\,dx = -\tfrac{1}{3}\sqrt{(a^2-x^2)^3}$

206. $\displaystyle\int \sqrt{(a^2-x^2)^3}\,dx = \frac{1}{4}\left[x\sqrt{(a^2-x^2)^3} + \frac{3a^2x}{2}\sqrt{a^2-x^2} + \frac{3a^4}{2}\sin^{-1}\frac{x}{|a|}\right]$

207. $\displaystyle\int \frac{dx}{\sqrt{(a^2-x^2)^3}} = \frac{x}{a^2\sqrt{a^2-x^2}}$

208. $\displaystyle\int \frac{x\,dx}{\sqrt{(a^2-x^2)^3}} = \frac{1}{\sqrt{a^2-x^2}}$

209. $\displaystyle\int x\sqrt{(a^2-x^2)^3}\,dx = -\tfrac{1}{5}\sqrt{(a^2-x^2)^5}$

210. $\displaystyle\int x^2\sqrt{a^2-x^2}\,dx = -\frac{x}{4}\sqrt{(a^2-x^2)^3} + \frac{a^2}{8}\left(x\sqrt{a^2-x^2} + a^2\sin^{-1}\frac{x}{|a|}\right)$

211. $\displaystyle\int x^3\sqrt{a^2-x^2}\,dx = (-\tfrac{1}{5}x^2 - \tfrac{2}{15}a^2)\sqrt{(a^2-x^2)^3}$

212. $\displaystyle\int x^2\sqrt{(a^2-x^2)^3}\,dx = -\frac{1}{6}x\sqrt{(a^2-x^2)^5} + \frac{a^2x}{24}\sqrt{(a^2-x^2)^3}$

$$+\frac{a^4x}{16}\sqrt{a^2-x^2} + \frac{a^6}{16}\sin^{-1}\frac{x}{|a|}$$

213. $\displaystyle\int x^3\sqrt{(a^2-x^2)^3}\,dx = \frac{1}{7}\sqrt{(a^2-x^2)^7} - \frac{a^2}{5}\sqrt{(a^2-x^2)^5}$

214. $\displaystyle\int \frac{x^2\,dx}{\sqrt{a^2-x^2}} = -\frac{x}{2}\sqrt{a^2-x^2} + \frac{a^2}{2}\sin^{-1}\frac{x}{|a|}$

215. $\displaystyle\int \frac{dx}{x^2\sqrt{a^2-x^2}} = -\frac{\sqrt{a^2-x^2}}{a^2x}$

216. $\displaystyle\int \frac{\sqrt{a^2-x^2}}{x^2}\,dx = -\frac{\sqrt{a^2-x^2}}{x} - \sin^{-1}\frac{x}{|a|}$

217. $\displaystyle\int \frac{\sqrt{a^2-x^2}}{x^3}\,dx = -\frac{\sqrt{a^2-x^2}}{2x^2} + \frac{1}{2a}\log\frac{a+\sqrt{a^2-x^2}}{x}$

218. $\displaystyle\int \frac{\sqrt{a^2-x^2}}{x^4}\,dx = -\frac{\sqrt{(a^2-x^2)^3}}{3a^2x^3}$

INTEGRALS (Continued)

219. $\displaystyle\int \frac{x^2\,dx}{\sqrt{(a^2-x^2)^3}} = \frac{x}{\sqrt{a^2-x^2}} - \sin^{-1}\frac{x}{|a|}$

220. $\displaystyle\int \frac{x^3\,dx}{\sqrt{a^2-x^2}} = -\frac{2}{3}(a^2-x^2)^{\frac{1}{2}} - x^2(a^2-x^2)^{\frac{1}{2}} = -\frac{1}{3}\sqrt{a^2-x^2}(x^2+2a^2)$

221. $\displaystyle\int \frac{x^3\,dx}{\sqrt{(a^2-x^2)^3}} = 2(a^2-x^2)^{\frac{1}{2}} + \frac{x^2}{(a^2-x^2)^{\frac{1}{2}}} = -\frac{a^2}{\sqrt{a^2-x^2}} + \sqrt{a^2-x^2}$

222. $\displaystyle\int \frac{dx}{x^3\sqrt{a^2-x^2}} = -\frac{\sqrt{a^2-x^2}}{2a^2x^2} - \frac{1}{2a^3}\log\frac{a+\sqrt{a^2-x^2}}{x}$

223. $\displaystyle\int \frac{dx}{x\sqrt{(a^2-x^2)^3}} = \frac{1}{a^2\sqrt{a^2-x^2}} - \frac{1}{a^3}\log\frac{a+\sqrt{a^2-x^2}}{x}$

224. $\displaystyle\int \frac{dx}{x^2\sqrt{(a^2-x^2)^3}} = \frac{1}{a^4}\left[-\frac{\sqrt{a^2-x^2}}{x} + \frac{x}{\sqrt{a^2-x^2}} \right]$

225. $\displaystyle\int \frac{dx}{x^3\sqrt{(a^2-x^2)^3}} = -\frac{1}{2a^2x^2\sqrt{a^2-x^2}} + \frac{3}{2a^4\sqrt{a^2-x^2}}$

$$-\frac{3}{2a^5}\log\frac{a+\sqrt{a^2-x^2}}{x}$$

226. $\displaystyle\int \frac{x^m}{\sqrt{a^2-x^2}}\,dx = -\frac{x^{m-1}\sqrt{a^2-x^2}}{m} + \frac{(m-1)a^2}{m}\int \frac{x^{m-2}}{\sqrt{a^2-x^2}}\,dx$

227. $\displaystyle\int \frac{x^{2m}}{\sqrt{a^2-x^2}}\,dx = \frac{(2m)!}{(m!)^2}\left[-\sqrt{a^2-x^2}\sum_{r=1}^{m}\frac{r!(r-1)!}{2^{2m-2r+1}(2r)!}a^{2m-2r}x^{2r-1}\right.$

$$\left. +\frac{a^{2m}}{2^{2m}}\sin^{-1}\frac{x}{|a|} \right]$$

228. $\displaystyle\int \frac{x^{2m+1}}{\sqrt{a^2-x^2}}\,dx = -\sqrt{a^2-x^2}\sum_{r=0}^{m}\frac{(2r)!(m!)^2}{(2m+1)!(r!)^2}(4a^2)^{m-r}x^{2r}$

229. $\displaystyle\int \frac{dx}{x^m\sqrt{a^2-x^2}} = -\frac{\sqrt{a^2-x^2}}{(m-1)a^2x^{m-1}} + \frac{m-2}{(m-1)a^2}\int \frac{dx}{x^{m-2}\sqrt{a^2-x^2}}$

230. $\displaystyle\int \frac{dx}{x^{2m}\sqrt{a^2-x^2}} = -\sqrt{a^2-x^2}\sum_{r=0}^{m-1}\frac{(m-1)!m!(2r)!2^{2m-2r-1}}{(r!)^2(2m)!a^{2m-2r}x^{2r+1}}$

231. $\displaystyle\int \frac{dx}{x^{2m+1}\sqrt{a^2-x^2}} = \frac{(2m)!}{(m!)^2}\left[-\frac{\sqrt{a^2-x^2}}{a^2}\sum_{r=1}^{m}\frac{r!(r-1)!}{2(2r)!(4a^2)^{m-r}x^{2r}}\right.$

$$\left. +\frac{1}{2^{2m}a^{2m+1}}\log\frac{a-\sqrt{a^2-x^2}}{x} \right]$$

INTEGRALS (Continued)

232. $\displaystyle \int \frac{dx}{(b^2 - x^2)\sqrt{a^2 - x^2}} = \frac{1}{2b\sqrt{a^2 - b^2}} \log \frac{(b\sqrt{a^2 - x^2} + x\sqrt{a^2 - b^2})^2}{b^2 - x^2},$

$$(a^2 > b^2)$$

233. $\displaystyle \int \frac{dx}{(b^2 - x^2)\sqrt{a^2 - x^2}} = \frac{1}{b\sqrt{b^2 - a^2}} \tan^{-1} \frac{x\sqrt{b^2 - a^2}}{b\sqrt{a^2 - x^2}}, \qquad (b^2 > a^2)$

234. $\displaystyle \int \frac{dx}{(b^2 + x^2)\sqrt{a^2 - x^2}} = \frac{1}{b\sqrt{a^2 + b^2}} \tan^{-1} \frac{x\sqrt{a^2 + b^2}}{b\sqrt{a^2 - x^2}}$

235. $\displaystyle \int \frac{\sqrt{a^2 - x^2}}{b^2 + x^2} dx = \frac{\sqrt{a^2 + b^2}}{|b|} \sin^{-1} \frac{x\sqrt{a^2 + b^2}}{|a|\sqrt{x^2 + b^2}} - \sin^{-1} \frac{x}{|a|}$

236. $\displaystyle \int f(x, \sqrt{a^2 - x^2}) \, dx = a \int f(a \sin u, a \cos u) \cos u \, du, \qquad \left(u = \sin^{-1} \frac{x}{a}, \, a > 0 \right)$

FORMS CONTAINING $\sqrt{a + bx + cx^2}$

$$X = a + bx + cx^2, \, q = 4ac - b^2, \text{ and } k = \frac{4c}{q}$$

If $q = 0$, then $\sqrt{X} = \sqrt{c} \left| x + \dfrac{b}{2c} \right|$

237. $\displaystyle \int \frac{dx}{\sqrt{X}} = \begin{cases} \dfrac{1}{\sqrt{c}} \log (2\sqrt{cX} + 2cx + b) \\[2mm] \qquad\text{or} \\[2mm] \dfrac{1}{\sqrt{c}} \sinh^{-1} \dfrac{2cx + b}{\sqrt{q}}, \qquad (c > 0) \end{cases}$

238. $\displaystyle \int \frac{dx}{\sqrt{X}} = -\frac{1}{\sqrt{-c}} \sin^{-1} \frac{2cx + b}{\sqrt{-q}}, \qquad (c < 0)$

239. $\displaystyle \int \frac{dx}{X\sqrt{X}} = \frac{2(2cx + b)}{q\sqrt{X}}$

240. $\displaystyle \int \frac{dx}{X^2\sqrt{X}} = \frac{2(2cx + b)}{3q\sqrt{X}} \left(\frac{1}{X} + 2k \right)$

241. $\displaystyle \int \frac{dx}{X^n\sqrt{X}} = \begin{cases} \dfrac{2(2cx + b)\sqrt{X}}{(2n - 1)qX^n} + \dfrac{2k(n - 1)}{2n - 1} \displaystyle\int \frac{dx}{X^{n-1}\sqrt{X}} \\[3mm] \qquad\qquad\text{or} \\[3mm] \dfrac{(2cx + b)(n!)(n - 1)!4^n k^{n-1}}{q[(2n)!]\sqrt{X}} \displaystyle\sum_{r=0}^{n-1} \frac{(2r)!}{(4kX)^r(r!)^2} \end{cases}$

INTEGRALS (Continued)

242. $\displaystyle \int \sqrt{X}\, dx = \frac{(2cx + b)\sqrt{X}}{4c} + \frac{1}{2k}\int \frac{dx}{\sqrt{X}}$

243. $\displaystyle \int X\sqrt{X}\, dx = \frac{(2cx + b)\sqrt{X}}{8c}\left(X + \frac{3}{2k}\right) + \frac{3}{8k^2}\int \frac{dx}{\sqrt{X}}$

244. $\displaystyle \int X^2\sqrt{X}\, dx = \frac{(2cx + b)\sqrt{X}}{12c}\left(X^2 + \frac{5X}{4k} + \frac{15}{8k^2}\right) + \frac{5}{16k^3}\int \frac{dx}{\sqrt{X}}$

245. $\displaystyle \int X^n\sqrt{X}\, dx = \begin{cases} \dfrac{(2cx + b)X^n\sqrt{X}}{4(n + 1)c} + \dfrac{2n + 1}{2(n + 1)k}\displaystyle\int X^{n-1}\sqrt{X}\, dx \\[2ex] \text{or} \\[2ex] \dfrac{(2n + 2)!}{[(n + 1)!]^2(4k)^{n+1}}\left[\dfrac{k(2cx + b)\sqrt{X}}{c}\displaystyle\sum_{r=0}^{n}\dfrac{r!(r + 1)!(4kX)^r}{(2r + 2)!} \right. \\[3ex] \hspace{6cm}\left. + \displaystyle\int \dfrac{dx}{\sqrt{X}}\right] \end{cases}$

246. $\displaystyle \int \frac{x\, dx}{\sqrt{X}} = \frac{\sqrt{X}}{c} - \frac{b}{2c}\int \frac{dx}{\sqrt{X}}$

247. $\displaystyle \int \frac{x\, dx}{X\sqrt{X}} = -\frac{2(bx + 2a)}{q\sqrt{X}}$

248. $\displaystyle \int \frac{x\, dx}{X^n\sqrt{X}} = -\frac{\sqrt{X}}{(2n - 1)cX^n} - \frac{b}{2c}\int \frac{dx}{X^n\sqrt{X}}$

249. $\displaystyle \int \frac{x^2\, dx}{\sqrt{X}} = \left(\frac{x}{2c} - \frac{3b}{4c^2}\right)\sqrt{X} + \frac{3b^2 - 4ac}{8c^2}\int \frac{dx}{\sqrt{X}}$

250. $\displaystyle \int \frac{x^2\, dx}{X\sqrt{X}} = \frac{(2b^2 - 4ac)x + 2ab}{cq\sqrt{X}} + \frac{1}{c}\int \frac{dx}{\sqrt{X}}$

251. $\displaystyle \int \frac{x^2\, dx}{X^n\sqrt{X}} = \frac{(2b^2 - 4ac)x + 2ab}{(2n - 1)cqX^{n-1}\sqrt{X}} + \frac{4ac + (2n - 3)b^2}{(2n - 1)cq}\int \frac{dx}{X^{n-1}\sqrt{X}}$

252. $\displaystyle \int \frac{x^3\, dx}{\sqrt{X}} = \left(\frac{x^2}{3c} - \frac{5bx}{12c^2} + \frac{5b^2}{8c^3} - \frac{2a}{3c^2}\right)\sqrt{X} + \left(\frac{3ab}{4c^2} - \frac{5b^3}{16c^3}\right)\int \frac{dx}{\sqrt{X}}$

253. $\displaystyle \int \frac{x^n\, dx}{\sqrt{X}} = \frac{1}{nc}x^{n-1}\sqrt{X} - \frac{(2n - 1)b}{2nc}\int \frac{x^{n-1}\, dx}{\sqrt{X}} - \frac{(n - 1)a}{nc}\int \frac{x^{n-2}\, dx}{\sqrt{X}}$

INTEGRALS (Continued)

254. $\displaystyle \int x\sqrt{X}\,dx = \frac{X\sqrt{X}}{3c} - \frac{b(2cx + b)}{8c^2}\sqrt{X} - \frac{b}{4ck}\int \frac{dx}{\sqrt{X}}$

255. $\displaystyle \int xX\sqrt{X}\,dx = \frac{X^2\sqrt{X}}{5c} - \frac{b}{2c}\int X\sqrt{X}\,dx$

256. $\displaystyle \int xX^n\sqrt{X}\,dx = \frac{X^{n+1}\sqrt{X}}{(2n + 3)c} - \frac{b}{2c}\int X^n\sqrt{X}\,dx$

257. $\displaystyle \int x^2\sqrt{X}\,dx = \left(x - \frac{5b}{6c}\right)\frac{X\sqrt{X}}{4c} + \frac{5b^2 - 4ac}{16c^2}\int \sqrt{X}\,dx$

258. $\displaystyle \int \frac{dx}{x\sqrt{X}} = -\frac{1}{\sqrt{a}}\log\frac{2\sqrt{aX} + bx + 2a}{x}, \qquad (a > 0)$

259. $\displaystyle \int \frac{dx}{x\sqrt{X}} = \frac{1}{\sqrt{-a}}\sin^{-1}\left(\frac{bx + 2a}{|x|\sqrt{-q}}\right), \qquad (a < 0)$

260. $\displaystyle \int \frac{dx}{x\sqrt{X}} = -\frac{2\sqrt{X}}{bx}, \qquad (a = 0)$

261. $\displaystyle \int \frac{dx}{x^2\sqrt{X}} = -\frac{\sqrt{X}}{ax} - \frac{b}{2a}\int \frac{dx}{x\sqrt{X}}$

262. $\displaystyle \int \frac{\sqrt{X}\,dx}{x} = \sqrt{X} + \frac{b}{2}\int \frac{dx}{\sqrt{X}} + a\int \frac{dx}{x\sqrt{X}}$

263. $\displaystyle \int \frac{\sqrt{X}\,dx}{x^2} = -\frac{\sqrt{X}}{x} + \frac{b}{2}\int \frac{dx}{x\sqrt{X}} + c\int \frac{dx}{\sqrt{X}}$

FORMS INVOLVING $\sqrt{2ax - x^2}$

264. $\displaystyle \int \sqrt{2ax - x^2}\,dx = \frac{1}{2}\left[(x - a)\sqrt{2ax - x^2} + a^2\sin^{-1}\frac{x - a}{|a|}\right]$

265. $\displaystyle \int \frac{dx}{\sqrt{2ax - x^2}} = \begin{cases} \cos^{-1}\dfrac{a - x}{|a|} \\[2mm] \text{or} \\[2mm] \sin^{-1}\dfrac{x - a}{|a|} \end{cases}$

INTEGRALS (Continued)

266. $\displaystyle \int x^n \sqrt{2ax - x^2}\, dx = \begin{cases} -\dfrac{x^{n-1}(2ax - x^2)^{\frac{3}{2}}}{n + 2} + \dfrac{(2n + 1)a}{n + 2} \displaystyle\int x^{n-1}\sqrt{2ax - x^2}\, dx \\[2mm] \text{or} \\[2mm] \sqrt{2ax - x^2}\left[\dfrac{x^{n+1}}{n + 2} - \displaystyle\sum_{r=0}^{n} \dfrac{(2n + 1)!(r!)^2 a^{n-r+1}}{2^{n-r}(2r + 1)!(n + 2)!n!} x^r \right] \\[3mm] \qquad + \dfrac{(2n + 1)!a^{n+2}}{2^n n!(n + 2)!}\sin^{-1}\dfrac{x - a}{|a|} \end{cases}$

267. $\displaystyle \int \frac{\sqrt{2ax - x^2}}{x^n}\, dx = \frac{(2ax - x^2)^{\frac{3}{2}}}{(3 - 2n)ax^n} + \frac{n - 3}{(2n - 3)a}\int \frac{\sqrt{2ax - x^2}}{x^{n-1}}\, dx$

268. $\displaystyle \int \frac{x^n\, dx}{\sqrt{2ax - x^2}} = \begin{cases} \dfrac{-x^{n-1}\sqrt{2ax - x^2}}{n} + \dfrac{a(2n - 1)}{n}\displaystyle\int \dfrac{x^{n-1}}{\sqrt{2ax - x^2}}\, dx \\[2mm] \text{or} \\[2mm] -\sqrt{2ax - x^2}\displaystyle\sum_{r=1}^{n} \dfrac{(2n)!r!(r - 1)!a^{n-r}}{2^{n-r}(2r)!(n!)^2} x^{r-1} \\[3mm] \qquad + \dfrac{(2n)!a^n}{2^n(n!)^2}\sin^{-1}\dfrac{x - a}{|a|} \end{cases}$

269. $\displaystyle \int \frac{dx}{x^n\sqrt{2ax - x^2}} = \begin{cases} \dfrac{\sqrt{2ax - x^2}}{a(1 - 2n)x^n} + \dfrac{n - 1}{(2n - 1)a}\displaystyle\int \dfrac{dx}{x^{n-1}\sqrt{2ax - x^2}} \\[2mm] \text{or} \\[2mm] -\sqrt{2ax - x^2}\displaystyle\sum_{r=0}^{n-1} \dfrac{2^{n-r}(n - 1)!n!(2r)!}{(2n)!(r!)^2 a^{n-r}x^{r+1}} \end{cases}$

270. $\displaystyle \int \frac{dx}{(2ax - x^2)^{\frac{3}{2}}} = \frac{x - a}{a^2\sqrt{2ax - x^2}}$

271. $\displaystyle \int \frac{x\, dx}{(2ax - x^2)^{\frac{3}{2}}} = \frac{x}{a\sqrt{2ax - x^2}}$

MISCELLANEOUS ALGEBRAIC FORMS

272. $\displaystyle \int \frac{dx}{\sqrt{2ax + x^2}} = \log\left(x + a + \sqrt{2ax + x^2}\right)$

273. $\displaystyle \int \sqrt{ax^2 + c}\, dx = \frac{x}{2}\sqrt{ax^2 + c} + \frac{c}{2\sqrt{a}}\log\left(x\sqrt{a} + \sqrt{ax^2 + c}\right), \qquad (a > 0)$

274. $\displaystyle \int \sqrt{ax^2 + c}\, dx = \frac{x}{2}\sqrt{ax^2 + c} + \frac{c}{2\sqrt{-a}}\sin^{-1}\left(x\sqrt{-\frac{a}{c}}\right), \qquad (a < 0)$

INTEGRALS (Continued)

275. $\displaystyle\int\sqrt{\frac{1+x}{1-x}}\,dx = \sin^{-1}x - \sqrt{1-x^2}$

276. $\displaystyle\int\frac{dx}{x\sqrt{ax^n+c}} = \begin{cases} \dfrac{1}{n\sqrt{c}}\log\dfrac{\sqrt{ax^n+c}-\sqrt{c}}{\sqrt{ax^n+c}+\sqrt{c}} \\[2mm] \text{or} \\[2mm] \dfrac{2}{n\sqrt{c}}\log\dfrac{\sqrt{ax^n+c}-\sqrt{c}}{\sqrt{x^n}}, \quad (c>0) \end{cases}$

277. $\displaystyle\int\frac{dx}{x\sqrt{ax^n+c}} = \frac{2}{n\sqrt{-c}}\sec^{-1}\sqrt{-\frac{ax^n}{c}}, \quad (c<0)$

278. $\displaystyle\int\frac{dx}{\sqrt{ax^2+c}} = \frac{1}{\sqrt{a}}\log(x\sqrt{a}+\sqrt{ax^2+c}), \quad (a>0)$

279. $\displaystyle\int\frac{dx}{\sqrt{ax^2+c}} = \frac{1}{\sqrt{-a}}\sin^{-1}\left(x\sqrt{-\frac{a}{c}}\right), \quad (a<0)$

280. $\displaystyle\int(ax^2+c)^{m+\frac{1}{2}}\,dx = \begin{cases} \dfrac{x(ax^2+c)^{m+\frac{1}{2}}}{2(m+1)} + \dfrac{(2m+1)c}{2(m+1)}\displaystyle\int(ax^2+c)^{m-\frac{1}{2}}\,dx \\[2mm] \text{or} \\[2mm] x\sqrt{ax^2+c}\,\displaystyle\sum_{r=0}^{m}\dfrac{(2m+1)!(r!)^2 c^{m-r}}{2^{2m-2r+1}m!(m+1)!(2r+1)!}(ax^2+c)^r \\[2mm] + \dfrac{(2m+1)!c^{m+1}}{2^{2m+1}m!(m+1)!}\displaystyle\int\dfrac{dx}{\sqrt{ax^2+c}} \end{cases}$

281. $\displaystyle\int x(ax^2+c)^{m+\frac{1}{2}}\,dx = \frac{(ax^2+c)^{m+\frac{3}{2}}}{(2m+3)a}$

282. $\displaystyle\int\frac{(ax^2+c)^{m+\frac{1}{2}}}{x}\,dx = \begin{cases} \dfrac{(ax^2+c)^{m+\frac{1}{2}}}{2m+1} + c\displaystyle\int\dfrac{(ax^2+c)^{m-\frac{1}{2}}}{x}\,dx \\[2mm] \text{or} \\[2mm] \sqrt{ax^2+c}\,\displaystyle\sum_{r=0}^{m}\dfrac{c^{m-r}(ax^2+c)^r}{2r+1} + c^{m+1}\displaystyle\int\dfrac{dx}{x\sqrt{ax^2+c}} \end{cases}$

283. $\displaystyle\int\frac{dx}{(ax^2+c)^{m+\frac{1}{2}}} = \begin{cases} \dfrac{x}{(2m-1)c(ax^2+c)^{m-\frac{1}{2}}} + \dfrac{2m-2}{(2m-1)c}\displaystyle\int\dfrac{dx}{(ax^2+c)^{m-\frac{1}{2}}} \\[2mm] \text{or} \\[2mm] \dfrac{x}{\sqrt{ax^2+c}}\,\displaystyle\sum_{r=0}^{m-1}\dfrac{2^{2m-2r-1}(m-1)!m!(2r)!}{(2m)!(r!)^2 c^{m-r}(ax^2+c)^r} \end{cases}$

INTEGRALS (Continued)

284. $\displaystyle\int \frac{dx}{x^m\sqrt{ax^2 + c}} = -\frac{\sqrt{ax^2 + c}}{(m - 1)cx^{m-1}} - \frac{(m - 2)a}{(m - 1)c}\int \frac{dx}{x^{m-2}\sqrt{ax^2 + c}}$

285. $\displaystyle\int \frac{1 + x^2}{(1 - x^2)\sqrt{1 + x^4}}\, dx = \frac{1}{\sqrt{2}}\log \frac{x\sqrt{2} + \sqrt{1 + x^4}}{1 - x^2}$

286. $\displaystyle\int \frac{1 - x^2}{(1 + x^2)\sqrt{1 + x^4}}\, dx = \frac{1}{\sqrt{2}}\tan^{-1}\frac{x\sqrt{2}}{\sqrt{1 + x^4}}$

287. $\displaystyle\int \frac{dx}{x\sqrt{x^n + a^2}} = -\frac{2}{na}\log \frac{a + \sqrt{x^n + a^2}}{\sqrt{x^n}}$

288. $\displaystyle\int \frac{dx}{x\sqrt{x^n - a^2}} = -\frac{2}{na}\sin^{-1}\frac{a}{\sqrt{x^n}}$

289. $\displaystyle\int \sqrt{\frac{x}{a^3 - x^3}}\, dx = \frac{2}{3}\sin^{-1}\left(\frac{x}{a}\right)^{\frac{3}{2}}$

FORMS INVOLVING TRIGONOMETRIC FUNCTIONS

290. $\displaystyle\int (\sin ax)\, dx = -\frac{1}{a}\cos ax$

291. $\displaystyle\int (\cos ax)\, dx = \frac{1}{a}\sin ax$

292. $\displaystyle\int (\tan ax)\, dx = -\frac{1}{a}\log \cos ax = \frac{1}{a}\log \sec ax$

293. $\displaystyle\int (\cot ax)\, dx = \frac{1}{a}\log \sin ax = -\frac{1}{a}\log \csc ax$

294. $\displaystyle\int (\sec ax)\, dx = \frac{1}{a}\log (\sec ax + \tan ax) = \frac{1}{a}\log \tan \left(\frac{\pi}{4} + \frac{ax}{2}\right)$

295. $\displaystyle\int (\csc ax)\, dx = \frac{1}{a}\log (\csc ax - \cot ax) = \frac{1}{a}\log \tan \frac{ax}{2}$

296. $\displaystyle\int (\sin^2 ax)\, dx = -\frac{1}{2a}\cos ax \sin ax + \frac{1}{2}x = \frac{1}{2}x - \frac{1}{4a}\sin 2ax$

297. $\displaystyle\int (\sin^3 ax)\, dx = -\frac{1}{3a}(\cos ax)(\sin^2 ax + 2)$

298. $\displaystyle\int (\sin^4 ax)\, dx = \frac{3x}{8} - \frac{\sin 2ax}{4a} + \frac{\sin 4ax}{32a}$

299. $\displaystyle\int (\sin^n ax)\, dx = -\frac{\sin^{n-1} ax \cos ax}{na} + \frac{n - 1}{n}\int (\sin^{n-2} ax)\, dx$

INTEGRALS (Continued)

300. $\displaystyle\int (\sin^{2m} ax)\,dx = -\frac{\cos ax}{a}\sum_{r=0}^{m-1}\frac{(2m)!(r!)^2}{2^{2m-2r}(2r+1)!(m!)^2}\sin^{2r+1} ax + \frac{(2m)!}{2^{2m}(m!)^2}x$

301. $\displaystyle\int (\sin^{2m+1} ax)\,dx = -\frac{\cos ax}{a}\sum_{r=0}^{m}\frac{2^{2m-2r}(m!)^2(2r)!}{(2m+1)!(r!)^2}\sin^{2r} ax$

302. $\displaystyle\int (\cos^2 ax)\,dx = \frac{1}{2a}\sin ax\cos ax + \frac{1}{2}x = \frac{1}{2}x + \frac{1}{4a}\sin 2ax$

303. $\displaystyle\int (\cos^3 ax)\,dx = \frac{1}{3a}(\sin ax)(\cos^2 ax + 2)$

304. $\displaystyle\int (\cos^4 ax)\,dx = \frac{3x}{8} + \frac{\sin 2ax}{4a} + \frac{\sin 4ax}{32a}$

305. $\displaystyle\int (\cos^n ax)\,dx = \frac{1}{na}\cos^{n-1} ax \sin ax + \frac{n-1}{n}\int (\cos^{n-2} ax)\,dx$

306. $\displaystyle\int (\cos^{2m} ax)\,dx = \frac{\sin ax}{a}\sum_{r=0}^{m-1}\frac{(2m)!(r!)^2}{2^{2m-2r}(2r+1)!(m!)^2}\cos^{2r+1} ax + \frac{(2m)!}{2^{2m}(m!)^2}x$

307. $\displaystyle\int (\cos^{2m+1} ax)\,dx = \frac{\sin ax}{a}\sum_{r=0}^{m}\frac{2^{2m-2r}(m!)^2(2r)!}{(2m+1)!(r!)^2}\cos^{2r} ax$

308. $\displaystyle\int \frac{dx}{\sin^2 ax} = \int (\csc^2 ax)\,dx = -\frac{1}{a}\cot ax$

309. $\displaystyle\int \frac{dx}{\sin^m ax} = \int (\csc^m ax)\,dx = -\frac{1}{(m-1)a}\cdot\frac{\cos ax}{\sin^{m-1} ax} + \frac{m-2}{m-1}\int \frac{dx}{\sin^{m-2} ax}$

310. $\displaystyle\int \frac{dx}{\sin^{2m} ax} = \int (\csc^{2m} ax)\,dx = -\frac{1}{a}\cos ax \sum_{r=0}^{m-1}\frac{2^{2m-2r-1}(m-1)!\,m!(2r)!}{(2m)!(r!)^2\sin^{2r+1} ax}$

311. $\displaystyle\int \frac{dx}{\sin^{2m+1} ax} = \int (\csc^{2m+1} ax)\,dx =$

$\displaystyle -\frac{1}{a}\cos ax \sum_{r=0}^{m-1}\frac{(2m)!(r!)^2}{2^{2m-2r}(m!)^2(2r+1)!\sin^{2r+2} ax} + \frac{1}{a}\cdot\frac{(2m)!}{2^{2m}(m!)^2}\log\tan\frac{ax}{2}$

312. $\displaystyle\int \frac{dx}{\cos^2 ax} = \int (\sec^2 ax)\,dx = \frac{1}{a}\tan ax$

313. $\displaystyle\int \frac{dx}{\cos^n ax} = \int (\sec^n ax)\,dx = \frac{1}{(n-1)a}\cdot\frac{\sin ax}{\cos^{n-1} ax} + \frac{n-2}{n-1}\int \frac{dx}{\cos^{n-2} ax}$

314. $\displaystyle\int \frac{dx}{\cos^{2m} ax} = \int (\sec^{2m} ax)\,dx = \frac{1}{a}\sin ax \sum_{r=0}^{m-1}\frac{2^{2m-2r-1}(m-1)!\,m!(2r)!}{(2m)!(r!)^2\cos^{2r+1} ax}$

INTEGRALS (Continued)

315. $\displaystyle\int \frac{dx}{\cos^{2m+1} ax} = \int (\sec^{2m+1} ax)\, dx =$

$$\frac{1}{a}\sin ax \sum_{r=0}^{m-1} \frac{(2m)!(r!)^2}{2^{2m-2r}(m!)^2(2r+1)!\cos^{2r+2} ax}$$

$$+ \frac{1}{a}\cdot\frac{(2m)!}{2^{2m}(m!)^2}\log(\sec ax + \tan ax)$$

316. $\displaystyle\int (\sin mx)(\sin nx)\, dx = \frac{\sin(m-n)x}{2(m-n)} - \frac{\sin(m+n)x}{2(m+n)}, \qquad (m^2 \neq n^2)$

317. $\displaystyle\int (\cos mx)(\cos nx)\, dx = \frac{\sin(m-n)x}{2(m-n)} + \frac{\sin(m+n)x}{2(m+n)}, \qquad (m^2 \neq n^2)$

318. $\displaystyle\int (\sin ax)(\cos ax)\, dx = \frac{1}{2a}\sin^2 ax$

319. $\displaystyle\int (\sin mx)(\cos nx)\, dx = -\frac{\cos(m-n)x}{2(m-n)} - \frac{\cos(m+n)x}{2(m+n)}, \qquad (m^2 \neq n^2)$

320. $\displaystyle\int (\sin^2 ax)(\cos^2 ax)\, dx = -\frac{1}{32a}\sin 4ax + \frac{x}{8}$

321. $\displaystyle\int (\sin ax)(\cos^m ax)\, dx = -\frac{\cos^{m+1} ax}{(m+1)a}$

322. $\displaystyle\int (\sin^m ax)(\cos ax)\, dx = \frac{\sin^{m+1} ax}{(m+1)a}$

323. $\displaystyle\int (\cos^m ax)(\sin^n ax)\, dx = \begin{cases} \dfrac{\cos^{m-1} ax \sin^{n+1} ax}{(m+n)a} \\[2ex] \qquad + \dfrac{m-1}{m+n}\displaystyle\int (\cos^{m-2} ax)(\sin^n ax)\, dx \\[2ex] \text{or} \\[2ex] -\dfrac{\sin^{n-1} ax \cos^{m+1} ax}{(m+n)a} \\[2ex] \qquad + \dfrac{n-1}{m+n}\displaystyle\int (\cos^m ax)(\sin^{n-2} ax)\, dx \end{cases}$

324. $\displaystyle\int \frac{\cos^m ax}{\sin^n ax}\, dx = \begin{cases} -\dfrac{\cos^{m+1} ax}{(n-1)a\sin^{n-1} ax} - \dfrac{m-n+2}{n-1}\displaystyle\int \dfrac{\cos^m ax}{\sin^{n-2} ax}\, dx \\[2ex] \text{or} \\[2ex] \dfrac{\cos^{m-1} ax}{a(m-n)\sin^{n-1} ax} + \dfrac{m-1}{m-n}\displaystyle\int \dfrac{\cos^{m-2} ax}{\sin^n ax}\, dx \end{cases}$

INTEGRALS (Continued)

325. $\displaystyle\int \frac{\sin^m ax}{\cos^n ax}\,dx = \begin{cases} \dfrac{\sin^{m+1} ax}{a(n-1)\cos^{n-1} ax} - \dfrac{m-n+2}{n-1}\displaystyle\int \dfrac{\sin^m ax}{\cos^{n-2} ax}\,dx \\[2mm] \quad\text{or} \\[2mm] -\dfrac{\sin^{m-1} ax}{a(m-n)\cos^{n-1} ax} + \dfrac{m-1}{m-n}\displaystyle\int \dfrac{\sin^{m-2} ax}{\cos^n ax}\,dx \end{cases}$

326. $\displaystyle\int \frac{\sin ax}{\cos^2 ax}\,dx = \frac{1}{a\cos ax} = \frac{\sec ax}{a}$

327. $\displaystyle\int \frac{\sin^2 ax}{\cos ax}\,dx = -\frac{1}{a}\sin ax + \frac{1}{a}\log\tan\left(\frac{\pi}{4} + \frac{ax}{2}\right)$

328. $\displaystyle\int \frac{\cos ax}{\sin^2 ax}\,dx = -\frac{1}{a\sin ax} = -\frac{\csc ax}{a}$

329. $\displaystyle\int \frac{dx}{(\sin ax)(\cos ax)} = \frac{1}{a}\log\tan ax$

330. $\displaystyle\int \frac{dx}{(\sin ax)(\cos^2 ax)} = \frac{1}{a}\left(\sec ax + \log\tan\frac{ax}{2}\right)$

331. $\displaystyle\int \frac{dx}{(\sin ax)(\cos^n ax)} = \frac{1}{a(n-1)\cos^{n-1} ax} + \int \frac{dx}{(\sin ax)(\cos^{n-2} ax)}$

332. $\displaystyle\int \frac{dx}{(\sin^2 ax)(\cos ax)} = -\frac{1}{a}\csc ax + \frac{1}{a}\log\tan\left(\frac{\pi}{4} + \frac{ax}{2}\right)$

333. $\displaystyle\int \frac{dx}{(\sin^2 ax)(\cos^2 ax)} = -\frac{2}{a}\cot 2ax$

334. $\displaystyle\int \frac{dx}{\sin^m ax \cos^n ax} = \begin{cases} -\dfrac{1}{a(m-1)(\sin^{m-1} ax)(\cos^{n-1} ax)} \\[2mm] \qquad\qquad + \dfrac{m+n-2}{m-1}\displaystyle\int \dfrac{dx}{(\sin^{m-2} ax)(\cos^n ax)} \\[2mm] \quad\text{or} \\[2mm] \dfrac{1}{a(n-1)\sin^{m-1} ax \cos^{n-1} ax} \\[2mm] \qquad\qquad - \dfrac{m+n-2}{n-1}\displaystyle\int \dfrac{dx}{\sin^m ax \cos^{n-2} ax} \end{cases}$

335. $\displaystyle\int \sin(a+bx)\,dx = -\frac{1}{b}\cos(a+bx)$

336. $\displaystyle\int \cos(a+bx)\,dx = \frac{1}{b}\sin(a+bx)$

337. $\displaystyle\int \frac{dx}{1 \pm \sin ax} = \mp\frac{1}{a}\tan\left(\frac{\pi}{4} \mp \frac{ax}{2}\right)$

INTEGRALS (Continued)

338. $\displaystyle\int \frac{dx}{1 + \cos ax} = \frac{1}{a} \tan \frac{ax}{2}$

339. $\displaystyle\int \frac{dx}{1 - \cos ax} = -\frac{1}{a} \cot \frac{ax}{2}$

*340. $\displaystyle\int \frac{dx}{a + b \sin x} = \begin{cases} \dfrac{2}{\sqrt{a^2 - b^2}} \tan^{-1} \dfrac{a \tan \frac{x}{2} + b}{\sqrt{a^2 - b^2}} \\[6pt] \quad\text{or} \\[6pt] \dfrac{1}{\sqrt{b^2 - a^2}} \log \dfrac{a \tan \frac{x}{2} + b - \sqrt{b^2 - a^2}}{a \tan \frac{x}{2} + b + \sqrt{b^2 - a^2}} \end{cases}$

*341. $\displaystyle\int \frac{dx}{a + b \cos x} = \begin{cases} \dfrac{2}{\sqrt{a^2 - b^2}} \tan^{-1} \dfrac{\sqrt{a^2 - b^2} \tan \frac{x}{2}}{a + b} \\[6pt] \quad\text{or} \\[6pt] \dfrac{1}{\sqrt{b^2 - a^2}} \log \left(-\dfrac{\sqrt{b^2 - a^2} \tan \frac{x}{2} + a + b}{\sqrt{b^2 - a^2} \tan \frac{x}{2} - a - b} \right) \end{cases}$

*342. $\displaystyle\int \frac{dx}{a + b \sin x + c \cos x}$

$$= \begin{cases} \dfrac{1}{\sqrt{b^2 + c^2 - a^2}} \log \dfrac{b - \sqrt{b^2 + c^2 - a^2} + (a - c) \tan \frac{x}{2}}{b + \sqrt{b^2 + c^2 - a^2} + (a - c) \tan \frac{x}{2}}, & \text{if } a^2 < b^2 + c^2, a \neq c \\[6pt] \quad\text{or} \\[6pt] \dfrac{2}{\sqrt{a^2 - b^2 - c^2}} \tan^{-1} \dfrac{b + (a - c) \tan \frac{x}{2}}{\sqrt{a^2 - b^2 - c^2}}, & \text{if } a^2 > b^2 + c^2 \\[6pt] \quad\text{or} \\[6pt] \dfrac{1}{a} \left[\dfrac{a - (b + c) \cos x - (b - c) \sin x}{a - (b - c) \cos x + (b + c) \sin x} \right], & \text{if } a^2 = b^2 + c^2, a \neq c. \end{cases}$$

*343. $\displaystyle\int \frac{\sin^2 x \, dx}{a + b \cos^2 x} = \frac{1}{b} \sqrt{\frac{a + b}{a}} \tan^{-1}\left(\sqrt{\frac{a}{a + b}} \tan x \right) - \frac{x}{b}, \qquad (ab > 0, \text{ or } |a| > |b|)$

*See note 6 – page 410.

INTEGRALS (Continued)

*344. $\displaystyle\int \frac{dx}{a^2 \cos^2 x + b^2 \sin^2 x} = \frac{1}{ab} \tan^{-1}\left(\frac{b \tan x}{a}\right)$

*345. $\displaystyle\int \frac{\cos^2 cx}{a^2 + b^2 \sin^2 cx}\, dx = \frac{\sqrt{a^2 + b^2}}{ab^2 c} \tan^{-1} \frac{\sqrt{a^2 + b^2}\, \tan cx}{a} - \frac{x}{b^2}$

346. $\displaystyle\int \frac{\sin cx \cos cx}{a \cos^2 cx + b \sin^2 cx}\, dx = \frac{1}{2c(b - a)} \log\left(a \cos^2 cx + b \sin^2 cx\right)$

347. $\displaystyle\int \frac{\cos cx}{a \cos cx + b \sin cx}\, dx = \int \frac{dx}{a + b \tan cx} =$

$$\frac{1}{c(a^2 + b^2)}\left[acx + b \log\left(a \cos cx + b \sin cx\right)\right]$$

348. $\displaystyle\int \frac{\sin cx}{a \sin cx + b \cos cx}\, dx = \int \frac{dx}{a + b \cot cx} =$

$$\frac{1}{c(a^2 + b^2)}\left[acx - b \log\left(a \sin cx + b \cos cx\right)\right]$$

*349. $\displaystyle\int \frac{dx}{a \cos^2 x + 2b \cos x \sin x + c \sin^2 x} =$

$$\begin{cases} \dfrac{1}{2\sqrt{b^2 - ac}} \log \dfrac{c \tan x + b - \sqrt{b^2 - ac}}{c \tan x + b + \sqrt{b^2 - ac}}, \\ \qquad\qquad\qquad\qquad\qquad\qquad (b^2 > ac) \\ \text{or} \\ \dfrac{1}{\sqrt{ac - b^2}} \tan^{-1} \dfrac{c \tan x + b}{\sqrt{ac - b^2}}, \quad (b^2 < ac) \\ \text{or} \\ -\dfrac{1}{c \tan x + b}, \qquad (b^2 = ac) \end{cases}$$

350. $\displaystyle\int \frac{\sin ax}{1 \pm \sin ax}\, dx = \pm x + \frac{1}{a} \tan\left(\frac{\pi}{4} \mp \frac{ax}{2}\right)$

351. $\displaystyle\int \frac{dx}{(\sin ax)(1 \pm \sin ax)} = \frac{1}{a} \tan\left(\frac{\pi}{4} \mp \frac{ax}{2}\right) + \frac{1}{a} \log \tan \frac{ax}{2}$

352. $\displaystyle\int \frac{dx}{(1 + \sin ax)^2} = -\frac{1}{2a} \tan\left(\frac{\pi}{4} - \frac{ax}{2}\right) - \frac{1}{6a} \tan^3\left(\frac{\pi}{4} - \frac{ax}{2}\right)$

353. $\displaystyle\int \frac{dx}{(1 - \sin ax)^2} = \frac{1}{2a} \cot\left(\frac{\pi}{4} - \frac{ax}{2}\right) + \frac{1}{6a} \cot^3\left(\frac{\pi}{4} - \frac{ax}{2}\right)$

354. $\displaystyle\int \frac{\sin ax}{(1 + \sin ax)^2}\, dx = -\frac{1}{2a} \tan\left(\frac{\pi}{4} - \frac{ax}{2}\right) + \frac{1}{6a} \tan^3\left(\frac{\pi}{4} - \frac{ax}{2}\right)$

*See note 6–page 410.

INTEGRALS (Continued)

355. $\displaystyle\int \frac{\sin ax}{(1 - \sin ax)^2}\,dx = -\frac{1}{2a}\cot\left(\frac{\pi}{4} - \frac{ax}{2}\right) + \frac{1}{6a}\cot^3\left(\frac{\pi}{4} - \frac{ax}{2}\right)$

356. $\displaystyle\int \frac{\sin x\,dx}{a + b\sin x} = \frac{x}{b} - \frac{a}{b}\int \frac{dx}{a + b\sin x}$

357. $\displaystyle\int \frac{dx}{(\sin x)(a + b\sin x)} = \frac{1}{a}\log\tan\frac{x}{2} - \frac{b}{a}\int \frac{dx}{a + b\sin x}$

358. $\displaystyle\int \frac{dx}{(a + b\sin x)^2} = \frac{b\cos x}{(a^2 - b^2)(a + b\sin x)} + \frac{a}{a^2 - b^2}\int \frac{dx}{a + b\sin x}$

359. $\displaystyle\int \frac{\sin x\,dx}{(a + b\sin x)^2} = \frac{a\cos x}{(b^2 - a^2)(a + b\sin x)} + \frac{b}{b^2 - a^2}\int \frac{dx}{a + b\sin x}$

*360. $\displaystyle\int \frac{dx}{a^2 + b^2\sin^2 cx} = \frac{1}{ac\sqrt{a^2 + b^2}}\tan^{-1}\frac{\sqrt{a^2 + b^2}\,\tan cx}{a}$

*361. $\displaystyle\int \frac{dx}{a^2 - b^2\sin^2 cx} = \begin{cases} \dfrac{1}{ac\sqrt{a^2 - b^2}}\tan^{-1}\dfrac{\sqrt{a^2 - b^2}\,\tan cx}{a}, & (a^2 > b^2) \\[2ex] \text{or} \\[1ex] \dfrac{1}{2ac\sqrt{b^2 - a^2}}\log\dfrac{\sqrt{b^2 - a^2}\,\tan cx + a}{\sqrt{b^2 - a^2}\,\tan cx - a}, & (a^2 < b^2) \end{cases}$

362. $\displaystyle\int \frac{\cos ax}{1 + \cos ax}\,dx = x - \frac{1}{a}\tan\frac{ax}{2}$

363. $\displaystyle\int \frac{\cos ax}{1 - \cos ax}\,dx = -x - \frac{1}{a}\cot\frac{ax}{2}$

364. $\displaystyle\int \frac{dx}{(\cos ax)(1 + \cos ax)} = \frac{1}{a}\log\tan\left(\frac{\pi}{4} + \frac{ax}{2}\right) - \frac{1}{a}\tan\frac{ax}{2}$

365. $\displaystyle\int \frac{dx}{(\cos ax)(1 - \cos ax)} = \frac{1}{a}\log\tan\left(\frac{\pi}{4} + \frac{ax}{2}\right) - \frac{1}{a}\cot\frac{ax}{2}$

366. $\displaystyle\int \frac{dx}{(1 + \cos ax)^2} = \frac{1}{2a}\tan\frac{ax}{2} + \frac{1}{6a}\tan^3\frac{ax}{2}$

367. $\displaystyle\int \frac{dx}{(1 - \cos ax)^2} = -\frac{1}{2a}\cot\frac{ax}{2} - \frac{1}{6a}\cot^3\frac{ax}{2}$

368. $\displaystyle\int \frac{\cos ax}{(1 + \cos ax)^2}\,dx = \frac{1}{2a}\tan\frac{ax}{2} - \frac{1}{6a}\tan^3\frac{ax}{2}$

369. $\displaystyle\int \frac{\cos ax}{(1 - \cos ax)^2}\,dx = \frac{1}{2a}\cot\frac{ax}{2} - \frac{1}{6a}\cot^3\frac{ax}{2}$

*See note 6–page 410.

INTEGRALS (Continued)

370. $\displaystyle\int \frac{\cos x\, dx}{a + b\cos x} = \frac{x}{b} - \frac{a}{b}\int \frac{dx}{a + b\cos x}$

371. $\displaystyle\int \frac{dx}{(\cos x)(a + b\cos x)} = \frac{1}{a}\log\tan\left(\frac{x}{2} + \frac{\pi}{4}\right) - \frac{b}{a}\int \frac{dx}{a + b\cos x}$

372. $\displaystyle\int \frac{dx}{(a + b\cos x)^2} = \frac{b\sin x}{(b^2 - a^2)(a + b\cos x)} - \frac{a}{b^2 - a^2}\int \frac{dx}{a + b\cos x}$

373. $\displaystyle\int \frac{\cos x}{(a + b\cos x)^2}\, dx = \frac{a\sin x}{(a^2 - b^2)(a + b\cos x)} - \frac{b}{a^2 - b^2}\int \frac{dx}{a + b\cos x}$

*374. $\displaystyle\int \frac{dx}{a^2 + b^2 - 2ab\cos cx} = \frac{2}{c(a^2 - b^2)}\tan^{-1}\left(\frac{a + b}{a - b}\tan\frac{cx}{2}\right)$

*375. $\displaystyle\int \frac{dx}{a^2 + b^2\cos^2 cx} = \frac{1}{ac\sqrt{a^2 + b^2}}\tan^{-1}\frac{a\tan cx}{\sqrt{a^2 + b^2}}$

*376. $\displaystyle\int \frac{dx}{a^2 - b^2\cos^2 cx} = \begin{cases} \dfrac{1}{ac\sqrt{a^2 - b^2}}\tan^{-1}\dfrac{a\tan cx}{\sqrt{a^2 - b^2}}, & (a^2 > b^2) \\[2ex] \text{or} \\[1ex] \dfrac{1}{2ac\sqrt{b^2 - a^2}}\log\dfrac{a\tan cx - \sqrt{b^2 - a^2}}{a\tan cx + \sqrt{b^2 - a^2}}, & (b^2 > a^2) \end{cases}$

377. $\displaystyle\int \frac{\sin ax}{1 \pm \cos ax}\, dx = \mp\frac{1}{a}\log(1 \pm \cos ax)$

378. $\displaystyle\int \frac{\cos ax}{1 \pm \sin ax}\, dx = \pm\frac{1}{a}\log(1 \pm \sin ax)$

379. $\displaystyle\int \frac{dx}{(\sin ax)(1 \pm \cos ax)} = \pm\frac{1}{2a(1 \pm \cos ax)} + \frac{1}{2a}\log\tan\frac{ax}{2}$

380. $\displaystyle\int \frac{dx}{(\cos ax)(1 \pm \sin ax)} = \mp\frac{1}{2a(1 \pm \sin ax)} + \frac{1}{2a}\log\tan\left(\frac{\pi}{4} + \frac{ax}{2}\right)$

381. $\displaystyle\int \frac{\sin ax}{(\cos ax)(1 \pm \cos ax)}\, dx = \frac{1}{a}\log(\sec ax \pm 1)$

382. $\displaystyle\int \frac{\cos ax}{(\sin ax)(1 \pm \sin ax)}\, dx = -\frac{1}{a}\log(\csc ax \pm 1)$

383. $\displaystyle\int \frac{\sin ax}{(\cos ax)(1 \pm \sin ax)}\, dx = \frac{1}{2a(1 \pm \sin ax)} \pm \frac{1}{2a}\log\tan\left(\frac{\pi}{4} + \frac{ax}{2}\right)$

384. $\displaystyle\int \frac{\cos ax}{(\sin ax)(1 \pm \cos ax)}\, dx = -\frac{1}{2a(1 \pm \cos ax)} \pm \frac{1}{2a}\log\tan\frac{ax}{2}$

*See note 6–page 410.

INTEGRALS (Continued)

385. $\displaystyle\int \frac{dx}{\sin ax \pm \cos ax} = \frac{1}{a\sqrt{2}} \log \tan\left(\frac{ax}{2} \pm \frac{\pi}{8}\right)$

386. $\displaystyle\int \frac{dx}{(\sin ax \pm \cos ax)^2} = \frac{1}{2a} \tan\left(ax \mp \frac{\pi}{4}\right)$

387. $\displaystyle\int \frac{dx}{1 + \cos ax \pm \sin ax} = \pm\frac{1}{a} \log\left(1 \pm \tan\frac{ax}{2}\right)$

388. $\displaystyle\int \frac{dx}{a^2 \cos^2 cx - b^2 \sin^2 cx} = \frac{1}{2abc} \log\frac{b \tan cx + a}{b \tan cx - a}$

389. $\displaystyle\int x(\sin ax)\,dx = \frac{1}{a^2} \sin ax - \frac{x}{a} \cos ax$

390. $\displaystyle\int x^2(\sin ax)\,dx = \frac{2x}{a^2} \sin ax - \frac{a^2x^2 - 2}{a^3} \cos ax$

391. $\displaystyle\int x^3(\sin ax)\,dx = \frac{3a^2x^2 - 6}{a^4} \sin ax - \frac{a^2x^3 - 6x}{a^3} \cos ax$

392. $\displaystyle\int x^m \sin ax\,dx = \begin{cases} -\dfrac{1}{a}x^m \cos ax + \dfrac{m}{a}\displaystyle\int x^{m-1} \cos ax\,dx \\[2mm] \qquad\text{or} \\[2mm] \cos ax \displaystyle\sum_{r=0}^{\left[\frac{m}{2}\right]} (-1)^{r+1} \frac{m!}{(m-2r)!}\cdot\frac{x^{m-2r}}{a^{2r+1}} \\[4mm] + \sin ax \displaystyle\sum_{r=0}^{\left[\frac{m-1}{2}\right]} (-1)^{r} \frac{m!}{(m-2r-1)!}\cdot\frac{x^{m-2r-1}}{a^{2r+2}} \end{cases}$

Note: $[s]$ means greatest integer $\le s$; $[3\tfrac{1}{2}] = 3$, $[\tfrac{1}{2}] = 0$, etc.

393. $\displaystyle\int x(\cos ax)\,dx = \frac{1}{a^2} \cos ax + \frac{x}{a} \sin ax$

394. $\displaystyle\int x^2(\cos ax)\,dx = \frac{2x \cos ax}{a^2} + \frac{a^2x^2 - 2}{a^3} \sin ax$

395. $\displaystyle\int x^3(\cos ax)\,dx = \frac{3a^2x^2 - 6}{a^4} \cos ax + \frac{a^2x^3 - 6x}{a^3} \sin ax$

396. $\displaystyle\int x^m(\cos ax)\,dx = \begin{cases} \dfrac{x^m \sin ax}{a} - \dfrac{m}{a}\displaystyle\int x^{m-1} \sin ax\,dx \\[2mm] \qquad\text{or} \\[2mm] \sin ax \displaystyle\sum_{r=0}^{\left[\frac{m}{2}\right]} (-1)^{r} \frac{m!}{(m-2r)!}\cdot\frac{x^{m-2r}}{a^{2r+1}} \\[4mm] + \cos ax \displaystyle\sum_{r=0}^{\left[\frac{m-1}{2}\right]} (-1)^{r} \frac{m!}{(m-2r-1)!}\cdot\frac{x^{m-2r-1}}{a^{2r+2}} \end{cases}$

See note integral 392.

INTEGRALS (Continued)

397. $\int \dfrac{\sin ax}{x}\,dx = \displaystyle\sum_{n=0}^{\infty} (-1)^n \dfrac{(ax)^{2n+1}}{(2n+1)(2n+1)!}$

398. $\int \dfrac{\cos ax}{x}\,dx = \log x + \displaystyle\sum_{n=1}^{\infty} (-1)^n \dfrac{(ax)^{2n}}{2n(2n)!}$

399. $\int x(\sin^2 ax)\,dx = \dfrac{x^2}{4} - \dfrac{x\sin 2ax}{4a} - \dfrac{\cos 2ax}{8a^2}$

400. $\int x^2(\sin^2 ax)\,dx = \dfrac{x^3}{6} - \left(\dfrac{x^2}{4a} - \dfrac{1}{8a^3}\right)\sin 2ax - \dfrac{x\cos 2ax}{4a^2}$

401. $\int x(\sin^3 ax)\,dx = \dfrac{x\cos 3ax}{12a} - \dfrac{\sin 3ax}{36a^2} - \dfrac{3x\cos ax}{4a} + \dfrac{3\sin ax}{4a^2}$

402. $\int x(\cos^2 ax)\,dx = \dfrac{x^2}{4} + \dfrac{x\sin 2ax}{4a} + \dfrac{\cos 2ax}{8a^2}$

403. $\int x^2(\cos^2 ax)\,dx = \dfrac{x^3}{6} + \left(\dfrac{x^2}{4a} - \dfrac{1}{8a^3}\right)\sin 2ax + \dfrac{x\cos 2ax}{4a^2}$

404. $\int x(\cos^3 ax)\,dx = \dfrac{x\sin 3ax}{12a} + \dfrac{\cos 3ax}{36a^2} + \dfrac{3x\sin ax}{4a} + \dfrac{3\cos ax}{4a^2}$

405. $\int \dfrac{\sin ax}{x^m}\,dx = -\dfrac{\sin ax}{(m-1)x^{m-1}} + \dfrac{a}{m-1}\int \dfrac{\cos ax}{x^{m-1}}\,dx$

406. $\int \dfrac{\cos ax}{x^m}\,dx = -\dfrac{\cos ax}{(m-1)x^{m-1}} - \dfrac{a}{m-1}\int \dfrac{\sin ax}{x^{m-1}}\,dx$

407. $\int \dfrac{x}{1 \pm \sin ax}\,dx = \mp \dfrac{x\cos ax}{a(1 \pm \sin ax)} + \dfrac{1}{a^2}\log(1 \pm \sin ax)$

408. $\int \dfrac{x}{1 + \cos ax}\,dx = \dfrac{x}{a}\tan\dfrac{ax}{2} + \dfrac{2}{a^2}\log\cos\dfrac{ax}{2}$

409. $\int \dfrac{x}{1 - \cos ax}\,dx = -\dfrac{x}{a}\cot\dfrac{ax}{2} + \dfrac{2}{a^2}\log\sin\dfrac{ax}{2}$

410. $\int \dfrac{x + \sin x}{1 + \cos x}\,dx = x\tan\dfrac{x}{2}$

411. $\int \dfrac{x - \sin x}{1 - \cos x}\,dx = -x\cot\dfrac{x}{2}$

412. $\int \sqrt{1 - \cos ax}\,dx = -\dfrac{2\sin ax}{a\sqrt{1 - \cos ax}} = -\dfrac{2\sqrt{2}}{a}\cos\left(\dfrac{ax}{2}\right)$

413. $\int \sqrt{1 + \cos ax}\,dx = \dfrac{2\sin ax}{a\sqrt{1 + \cos ax}} = \dfrac{2\sqrt{2}}{a}\sin\left(\dfrac{ax}{2}\right)$

INTEGRALS (Continued)

414. $\int \sqrt{1 + \sin x} \, dx = \pm 2 \left(\sin \dfrac{x}{2} - \cos \dfrac{x}{2} \right),$

[use $+$ if $(8k - 1)\dfrac{\pi}{2} < x \le (8k + 3)\dfrac{\pi}{2}$, otherwise $-$; k an integer]

415. $\int \sqrt{1 - \sin x} \, dx = \pm 2 \left(\sin \dfrac{x}{2} + \cos \dfrac{x}{2} \right),$

[use $+$ if $(8k - 3)\dfrac{\pi}{2} < x \le (8k + 1)\dfrac{\pi}{2}$, otherwise $-$; k an integer]

416. $\int \dfrac{dx}{\sqrt{1 - \cos x}} = \pm \sqrt{2} \log \tan \dfrac{x}{4},$

[use $+$ if $4k\pi < x < (4k + 2)\pi$, otherwise $-$; k an integer]

417. $\int \dfrac{dx}{\sqrt{1 + \cos x}} = \pm \sqrt{2} \log \tan \left(\dfrac{x + \pi}{4} \right),$

[use $+$ if $(4k - 1)\pi < x < (4k + 1)\pi$, otherwise $-$; k an integer]

418. $\int \dfrac{dx}{\sqrt{1 - \sin x}} = \pm \sqrt{2} \log \tan \left(\dfrac{x}{4} - \dfrac{\pi}{8} \right),$

[use $+$ if $(8k + 1)\dfrac{\pi}{2} < x < (8k + 5)\dfrac{\pi}{2}$, otherwise $-$; k an integer]

419. $\int \dfrac{dx}{\sqrt{1 + \sin x}} = \pm \sqrt{2} \log \tan \left(\dfrac{x}{4} + \dfrac{\pi}{8} \right),$

[use $+$ if $(8k - 1)\dfrac{\pi}{2} < x < (8k + 3)\dfrac{\pi}{2}$, otherwise $-$; k an integer]

420. $\int (\tan^2 ax) \, dx = \dfrac{1}{a} \tan ax - x$

421. $\int (\tan^3 ax) \, dx = \dfrac{1}{2a} \tan^2 ax + \dfrac{1}{a} \log \cos ax$

422. $\int (\tan^4 ax) \, dx = \dfrac{\tan^3 ax}{3a} - \dfrac{1}{a} \tan x + x$

423. $\int (\tan^n ax) \, dx = \dfrac{\tan^{n-1} ax}{a(n - 1)} - \int (\tan^{n-2} ax) \, dx$

424. $\int (\cot^2 ax) \, dx = -\dfrac{1}{a} \cot ax - x$

425. $\int (\cot^3 ax) \, dx = -\dfrac{1}{2a} \cot^2 ax - \dfrac{1}{a} \log \sin ax$

426. $\int (\cot^4 ax) \, dx = -\dfrac{1}{3a} \cot^3 ax + \dfrac{1}{a} \cot ax + x$

427. $\displaystyle \int (\cot^n ax)\, dx = -\frac{\cot^{n-1} ax}{a(n-1)} - \int (\cot^{n-2} ax)\, dx$

428. $\displaystyle \int \frac{x}{\sin^2 ax}\, dx = \int x(\csc^2 ax)\, dx = -\frac{x \cot ax}{a} + \frac{1}{a^2}\log \sin ax$

429. $\displaystyle \int \frac{x}{\sin^n ax}\, dx = \int x(\csc^n ax)\, dx = -\frac{x \cos ax}{a(n-1)\sin^{n-1} ax}$

$$-\frac{1}{a^2(n-1)(n-2)\sin^{n-2} ax} + \frac{(n-2)}{(n-1)}\int \frac{x}{\sin^{n-2} ax}\, dx$$

430. $\displaystyle \int \frac{x}{\cos^2 ax}\, dx = \int x(\sec^2 ax)\, dx = \frac{1}{a}x \tan ax + \frac{1}{a^2}\log \cos ax$

431. $\displaystyle \int \frac{x}{\cos^n ax}\, dx = \int x(\sec^n ax)\, dx = \frac{x \sin ax}{a(n-1)\cos^{n-1} ax}$

$$-\frac{1}{a^2(n-1)(n-2)\cos^{n-2} ax} + \frac{n-2}{n-1}\int \frac{x}{\cos^{n-2} ax}\, dx$$

432. $\displaystyle \int \frac{\sin ax}{\sqrt{1 + b^2 \sin^2 ax}}\, dx = -\frac{1}{ab}\sin^{-1}\frac{b \cos ax}{\sqrt{1 + b^2}}$

433. $\displaystyle \int \frac{\sin ax}{\sqrt{1 - b^2 \sin^2 ax}}\, dx = -\frac{1}{ab}\log (b \cos ax + \sqrt{1 - b^2 \sin^2 ax})$

434. $\displaystyle \int (\sin ax)\sqrt{1 + b^2 \sin^2 ax}\, dx = -\frac{\cos ax}{2a}\sqrt{1 + b^2 \sin^2 ax}$

$$-\frac{1 + b^2}{2ab}\sin^{-1}\frac{b \cos ax}{\sqrt{1 + b^2}}$$

435. $\displaystyle \int (\sin ax)\sqrt{1 - b^2 \sin^2 ax}\, dx = -\frac{\cos ax}{2a}\sqrt{1 - b^2 \sin^2 ax}$

$$-\frac{1 - b^2}{2ab}\log (b \cos ax + \sqrt{1 - b^2 \sin^2 ax})$$

436. $\displaystyle \int \frac{\cos ax}{\sqrt{1 + b^2 \sin^2 ax}}\, dx = \frac{1}{ab}\log (b \sin ax + \sqrt{1 + b^2 \sin^2 ax})$

437. $\displaystyle \int \frac{\cos ax}{\sqrt{1 - b^2 \sin^2 ax}}\, dx = \frac{1}{ab}\sin^{-1}(b \sin ax)$

438. $\displaystyle \int (\cos ax)\sqrt{1 + b^2 \sin^2 ax}\, dx = \frac{\sin ax}{2a}\sqrt{1 + b^2 \sin^2 ax}$

$$+\frac{1}{2ab}\log (b \sin ax + \sqrt{1 + b^2 \sin^2 ax})$$

INTEGRALS (Continued)

439. $\int (\cos ax)\sqrt{1 - b^2 \sin^2 ax}\, dx = \dfrac{\sin ax}{2a}\sqrt{1 - b^2 \sin^2 ax} + \dfrac{1}{2ab}\sin^{-1}(b\sin ax)$

440. $\int \dfrac{dx}{\sqrt{a + b\tan^2 cx}} = \dfrac{\pm 1}{c\sqrt{a - b}}\sin^{-1}\left(\sqrt{\dfrac{a - b}{a}}\sin cx\right), \qquad (a > |b|)$

[use + if $(2k - 1)\dfrac{\pi}{2} < x \le (2k + 1)\dfrac{\pi}{2}$, otherwise $-$; k an integer]

FORMS INVOLVING INVERSE TRIGONOMETRIC FUNCTIONS

441. $\int (\sin^{-1} ax)\, dx = x\sin^{-1} ax + \dfrac{\sqrt{1 - a^2 x^2}}{a}$

442. $\int (\cos^{-1} ax)\, dx = x\cos^{-1} ax - \dfrac{\sqrt{1 - a^2 x^2}}{a}$

443. $\int (\tan^{-1} ax)\, dx = x\tan^{-1} ax - \dfrac{1}{2a}\log(1 + a^2 x^2)$

444. $\int (\cot^{-1} ax)\, dx = x\cot^{-1} ax + \dfrac{1}{2a}\log(1 + a^2 x^2)$

445. $\int (\sec^{-1} ax)\, dx = x\sec^{-1} ax - \dfrac{1}{a}\log(ax + \sqrt{a^2 x^2 - 1})$

446. $\int (\csc^{-1} ax)\, dx = x\csc^{-1} ax + \dfrac{1}{a}\log(ax + \sqrt{a^2 x^2 - 1})$

447. $\int \left(\sin^{-1}\dfrac{x}{a}\right) dx = x\sin^{-1}\dfrac{x}{a} + \sqrt{a^2 - x^2}, \qquad (a > 0)$

448. $\int \left(\cos^{-1}\dfrac{x}{a}\right) dx = x\cos^{-1}\dfrac{x}{a} - \sqrt{a^2 - x^2}, \qquad (a > 0)$

449. $\int \left(\tan^{-1}\dfrac{x}{a}\right) dx = x\tan^{-1}\dfrac{x}{a} - \dfrac{a}{2}\log(a^2 + x^2)$

450. $\int \left(\cot^{-1}\dfrac{x}{a}\right) dx = x\cot^{-1}\dfrac{x}{a} + \dfrac{a}{2}\log(a^2 + x^2)$

451. $\int x[\sin^{-1}(ax)]\, dx = \dfrac{1}{4a^2}[(2a^2 x^2 - 1)\sin^{-1}(ax) + ax\sqrt{1 - a^2 x^2}]$

452. $\int x[\cos^{-1}(ax)]\, dx = \dfrac{1}{4a^2}[(2a^2 x^2 - 1)\cos^{-1}(ax) - ax\sqrt{1 - a^2 x^2}]$

INTEGRALS (Continued)

453. $\displaystyle\int x^n[\sin^{-1}(ax)]\,dx = \frac{x^{n+1}}{n+1}\sin^{-1}(ax) - \frac{a}{n+1}\int\frac{x^{n+1}\,dx}{\sqrt{1-a^2x^2}}, \qquad (n \neq -1)$

454. $\displaystyle\int x^n[\cos^{-1}(ax)]\,dx = \frac{x^{n+1}}{n+1}\cos^{-1}(ax) + \frac{a}{n+1}\int\frac{x^{n+1}\,dx}{\sqrt{1-a^2x^2}}, \qquad (n \neq -1)$

455. $\displaystyle\int x(\tan^{-1}ax)\,dx = \frac{1+a^2x^2}{2a^2}\tan^{-1}ax - \frac{x}{2a}$

456. $\displaystyle\int x^n(\tan^{-1}ax)\,dx = \frac{x^{n+1}}{n+1}\tan^{-1}ax - \frac{a}{n+1}\int\frac{x^{n+1}}{1+a^2x^2}\,dx$

457. $\displaystyle\int x(\cot^{-1}ax)\,dx = \frac{1+a^2x^2}{2a^2}\cot^{-1}ax + \frac{x}{2a}$

458. $\displaystyle\int x^n(\cot^{-1}ax)\,dx = \frac{x^{n+1}}{n+1}\cot^{-1}ax + \frac{a}{n+1}\int\frac{x^{n+1}}{1+a^2x^2}\,dx$

459. $\displaystyle\int\frac{\sin^{-1}(ax)}{x^2}\,dx = a\log\left(\frac{1-\sqrt{1-a^2x^2}}{x}\right) - \frac{\sin^{-1}(ax)}{x}$

460. $\displaystyle\int\frac{\cos^{-1}(ax)\,dx}{x^2} = -\frac{1}{x}\cos^{-1}(ax) + a\log\frac{1+\sqrt{1-a^2x^2}}{x}$

461. $\displaystyle\int\frac{\tan^{-1}(ax)\,dx}{x^2} = -\frac{1}{x}\tan^{-1}(ax) - \frac{a}{2}\log\frac{1+a^2x^2}{x^2}$

462. $\displaystyle\int\frac{\cot^{-1}ax}{x^2}\,dx = -\frac{1}{x}\cot^{-1}ax - \frac{a}{2}\log\frac{x^2}{a^2x^2+1}$

463. $\displaystyle\int(\sin^{-1}ax)^2\,dx = x(\sin^{-1}ax)^2 - 2x + \frac{2\sqrt{1-a^2x^2}}{a}\sin^{-1}ax$

464. $\displaystyle\int(\cos^{-1}ax)^2\,dx = x(\cos^{-1}ax)^2 - 2x - \frac{2\sqrt{1-a^2x^2}}{a}\cos^{-1}ax$

465. $\displaystyle\int(\sin^{-1}ax)^n\,dx = \begin{cases} x(\sin^{-1}ax)^n + \dfrac{n\sqrt{1-a^2x^2}}{a}(\sin^{-1}ax)^{n-1} \\ \qquad\qquad -n(n-1)\displaystyle\int(\sin^{-1}ax)^{n-2}\,dx \\ \text{or} \\ \displaystyle\sum_{r=0}^{\left[\frac{n}{2}\right]}(-1)^r\frac{n!}{(n-2r)!}x(\sin^{-1}ax)^{n-2r} \\ \qquad + \displaystyle\sum_{r=0}^{\left[\frac{n-1}{2}\right]}(-1)^r\frac{n!\sqrt{1-a^2x^2}}{(n-2r-1)!a}(\sin^{-1}ax)^{n-2r-1} \end{cases}$

Note: $[s]$ means greatest integer $\leq s$. Thus $[3.5]$ means 3; $[5] = 5$, $[\frac{1}{2}] = 0$.

INTEGRALS (Continued)

466. $\displaystyle\int (\cos^{-1} ax)^n \, dx = \begin{cases} x(\cos^{-1} ax)^n - \dfrac{n\sqrt{1 - a^2 x^2}}{a}(\cos^{-1} ax)^{n-1} \\ \qquad\qquad\qquad - n(n-1)\displaystyle\int (\cos^{-1} ax)^{n-2} \, dx \\ \qquad\qquad\text{or} \\ \displaystyle\sum_{r=0}^{\left[\frac{n}{2}\right]} (-1)^r \dfrac{n!}{(n-2r)!} x(\cos^{-1} ax)^{n-2r} \\ \qquad - \displaystyle\sum_{r=0}^{\left[\frac{n-1}{2}\right]} (-1)^r \dfrac{n!\sqrt{1 - a^2 x^2}}{(n-2r-1)!a}(\cos^{-1} ax)^{n-2r-1} \end{cases}$

467. $\displaystyle\int \frac{1}{\sqrt{1 - a^2 x^2}}(\sin^{-1} ax) \, dx = \frac{1}{2a}(\sin^{-1} ax)^2$

468. $\displaystyle\int \frac{x^n}{\sqrt{1 - a^2 x^2}}(\sin^{-1} ax) \, dx = -\frac{x^{n-1}}{na^2}\sqrt{1 - a^2 x^2}\,\sin^{-1} ax + \frac{x^n}{n^2 a}$
$$+ \frac{n-1}{na^2}\int \frac{x^{n-2}}{\sqrt{1 - a^2 x^2}}\sin^{-1} ax \, dx$$

469. $\displaystyle\int \frac{1}{\sqrt{1 - a^2 x^2}}(\cos^{-1} ax) \, dx = -\frac{1}{2a}(\cos^{-1} ax)^2$

470. $\displaystyle\int \frac{x^n}{\sqrt{1 - a^2 x^2}}(\cos^{-1} ax) \, dx = -\frac{x^{n-1}}{na^2}\sqrt{1 - a^2 x^2}\,\cos^{-1} ax - \frac{x^n}{n^2 a}$
$$+ \frac{n-1}{na^2}\int \frac{x^{n-2}}{\sqrt{1 - a^2 x^2}}\cos^{-1} ax \, dx$$

471. $\displaystyle\int \frac{\tan^{-1} ax}{a^2 x^2 + 1} \, dx = \frac{1}{2a}(\tan^{-1} ax)^2$

472. $\displaystyle\int \frac{\cot^{-1} ax}{a^2 x^2 + 1} \, dx = -\frac{1}{2a}(\cot^{-1} ax)^2$

473. $\displaystyle\int x \sec^{-1} ax \, dx = \frac{x^2}{2}\sec^{-1} ax - \frac{1}{2a^2}\sqrt{a^2 x^2 - 1}$

474. $\displaystyle\int x^n \sec^{-1} ax \, dx = \frac{x^{n+1}}{n+1}\sec^{-1} ax - \frac{1}{n+1}\int \frac{x^n \, dx}{\sqrt{a^2 x^2 - 1}}$

475. $\displaystyle\int \frac{\sec^{-1} ax}{x^2} \, dx = -\frac{\sec^{-1} ax}{x} + \frac{\sqrt{a^2 x^2 - 1}}{x}$

476. $\displaystyle\int x \csc^{-1} ax \, dx = \frac{x^2}{2}\csc^{-1} ax + \frac{1}{2a^2}\sqrt{a^2 x^2 - 1}$

477. $\displaystyle\int x^n \csc^{-1} ax \, dx = \frac{x^{n+1}}{n+1}\csc^{-1} ax + \frac{1}{n+1}\int \frac{x^n \, dx}{\sqrt{a^2 x^2 - 1}}$

INTEGRALS (Continued)

478. $\displaystyle\int \frac{\csc^{-1} ax}{x^2} dx = -\frac{\csc^{-1} ax}{x} - \frac{\sqrt{a^2x^2 - 1}}{x}$

FORMS INVOLVING TRIGONOMETRIC SUBSTITUTIONS

479. $\displaystyle\int f(\sin x)\, dx = 2 \int f\left(\frac{2z}{1 + z^2}\right) \frac{dz}{1 + z^2}, \qquad \left(z = \tan\frac{x}{2}\right)$

480. $\displaystyle\int f(\cos x)\, dx = 2 \int f\left(\frac{1 - z^2}{1 + z^2}\right) \frac{dz}{1 + z^2}, \qquad \left(z = \tan\frac{x}{2}\right)$

*481. $\displaystyle\int f(\sin x)\, dx = \int f(u)\frac{du}{\sqrt{1 - u^2}}, \qquad (u = \sin x)$

*482. $\displaystyle\int f(\cos x)\, dx = -\int f(u)\frac{du}{\sqrt{1 - u^2}}, \qquad (u = \cos x)$

*483. $\displaystyle\int f(\sin x, \cos x)\, dx = \int f(u, \sqrt{1 - u^2})\frac{du}{\sqrt{1 - u^2}}, \qquad (u = \sin x)$

484. $\displaystyle\int f(\sin x, \cos x)\, dx = 2 \int f\left(\frac{2z}{1 + z^2}, \frac{1 - z^2}{1 + z^2}\right) \frac{dz}{1 + z^2}, \qquad \left(z = \tan\frac{x}{2}\right)$

LOGARITHMIC FORMS

485. $\displaystyle\int (\log x)\, dx = x \log x - x$

486. $\displaystyle\int x(\log x)\, dx = \frac{x^2}{2} \log x - \frac{x^2}{4}$

487. $\displaystyle\int x^2(\log x)\, dx = \frac{x^3}{3} \log x - \frac{x^3}{9}$

488. $\displaystyle\int x^n(\log ax)\, dx = \frac{x^{n+1}}{n + 1} \log ax - \frac{x^{n+1}}{(n + 1)^2}$

489. $\displaystyle\int (\log x)^2\, dx = x(\log x)^2 - 2x \log x + 2x$

490. $\displaystyle\int (\log x)^n\, dx = \begin{cases} x(\log x)^n - n \int (\log x)^{n-1}\, dx, \qquad (n \neq -1) \\ \text{or} \\ (-1)^n n! \, x \displaystyle\sum_{r=0}^{n} \frac{(-\log x)^r}{r!} \end{cases}$

---

* The square roots appearing in these formulas may be plus or minus, depending on the quadrant of *x*. Care must be used to give them the proper sign.

INTEGRALS (Continued)

491. $\displaystyle\int \frac{(\log x)^n}{x}\,dx = \frac{1}{n+1}(\log x)^{n+1}$

492. $\displaystyle\int \frac{dx}{\log x} = \log(\log x) + \log x + \frac{(\log x)^2}{2\cdot 2!} + \frac{(\log x)^3}{3\cdot 3!} + \cdots$

493. $\displaystyle\int \frac{dx}{x\log x} = \log(\log x)$

494. $\displaystyle\int \frac{dx}{x(\log x)^n} = -\frac{1}{(n-1)(\log x)^{n-1}}$

495. $\displaystyle\int \frac{x^m\,dx}{(\log x)^n} = -\frac{x^{m+1}}{(n-1)(\log x)^{n-1}} + \frac{m+1}{n-1}\int \frac{x^m\,dx}{(\log x)^{n-1}}$

496. $\displaystyle\int x^m(\log x)^n\,dx = \begin{cases} \dfrac{x^{m+1}(\log x)^n}{m+1} - \dfrac{n}{m+1}\displaystyle\int x^m(\log x)^{n-1}\,dx \\[2ex] \text{or} \\[1ex] (-1)^n \dfrac{n!}{m+1}x^{m+1}\displaystyle\sum_{r=0}^{n} \dfrac{(-\log x)^r}{r!(m+1)^{n-r}} \end{cases}$

497. $\displaystyle\int x^p \cos(b\,\ln x)\,dx = \frac{x^{p+1}}{(p+1)^2+b^2}\cdot [b\sin(b\,\ln x) + (p+1)\cos(b\,\ln x)] + c$

498. $\displaystyle\int x^p \sin(b\,\ln x)\,dx = \frac{x^{p+1}}{(p+1)^2+b^2}\cdot [(p+1)\sin(b\,\ln x) - b\cos(b\,\ln x)] + c$

499. $\displaystyle\int [\log(ax+b)]\,dx = \frac{ax+b}{a}\log(ax+b) - x$

500. $\displaystyle\int \frac{\log(ax+b)}{x^2}\,dx = \frac{a}{b}\log x - \frac{ax+b}{bx}\log(ax+b)$

501. $\displaystyle\int x^m[\log(ax+b)]\,dx = \frac{1}{m+1}\left[x^{m+1} - \left(-\frac{b}{a}\right)^{m+1}\right]\log(ax+b)$
$$-\frac{1}{m+1}\left(-\frac{b}{a}\right)^{m+1}\sum_{r=1}^{m+1}\frac{1}{r}\left(-\frac{ax}{b}\right)^r$$

502. $\displaystyle\int \frac{\log(ax+b)}{x^m}\,dx = -\frac{1}{m-1}\frac{\log(ax+b)}{x^{m-1}} + \frac{1}{m-1}\left(-\frac{a}{b}\right)^{m-1}\log\frac{ax+b}{x}$
$$+\frac{1}{m-1}\left(-\frac{a}{b}\right)^{m-1}\sum_{r=1}^{m-2}\frac{1}{r}\left(-\frac{b}{ax}\right)^r, \quad (m>2)$$

503. $\displaystyle\int \left[\log \frac{x+a}{x-a}\right]\,dx = (x+a)\log(x+a) - (x-a)\log(x-a)$

504. $\displaystyle\int x^m\left[\log \frac{x+a}{x-a}\right]\,dx = \frac{x^{m+1}-(-a)^{m+1}}{m+1}\log(x+a) - \frac{x^{m+1}-a^{m+1}}{m+1}\log(x-a)$
$$+\frac{2a^{m+1}}{m+1}\sum_{r=1}^{\left[\frac{m+1}{2}\right]}\frac{1}{m-2r+2}\left(\frac{x}{a}\right)^{m-2r+2}$$

See note integral 392.

INTEGRALS (Continued)

505. $\displaystyle\int \frac{1}{x^2}\left[\log\frac{x+a}{x-a}\right] dx = \frac{1}{x}\log\frac{x-a}{x+a} - \frac{1}{a}\log\frac{x^2-a^2}{x^2}$

506. $\displaystyle\int (\log X)\, dx =$

$$\begin{cases} \left(x + \dfrac{b}{2c}\right)\log X - 2x + \dfrac{\sqrt{4ac-b^2}}{c}\tan^{-1}\dfrac{2cx+b}{\sqrt{4ac-b^2}}, \\ \hspace{6cm} (b^2 - 4ac < 0) \\[2mm] \text{or} \\[2mm] \left(x + \dfrac{b}{2c}\right)\log X - 2x + \dfrac{\sqrt{b^2-4ac}}{c}\tanh^{-1}\dfrac{2cx+b}{\sqrt{b^2-4ac}}, \\ \hspace{6cm} (b^2 - 4ac > 0) \\[2mm] \text{where} \\[2mm] X = a + bx + cx^2 \end{cases}$$

507. $\displaystyle\int x^n(\log X)\, dx = \frac{x^{n+1}}{n+1}\log X - \frac{2c}{n+1}\int\frac{x^{n+2}}{X}\, dx - \frac{b}{n+1}\int\frac{x^{n+1}}{X}\, dx$

$$\text{where } X = a + bx + cx^2$$

508. $\displaystyle\int [\log(x^2 + a^2)]\, dx = x\log(x^2 + a^2) - 2x + 2a\tan^{-1}\frac{x}{a}$

509. $\displaystyle\int [\log(x^2 - a^2)]\, dx = x\log(x^2 - a^2) - 2x + a\log\frac{x+a}{x-a}$

510. $\displaystyle\int x[\log(x^2 \pm a^2)]\, dx = \tfrac{1}{2}(x^2 \pm a^2)\log(x^2 \pm a^2) - \tfrac{1}{2}x^2$

511. $\displaystyle\int [\log(x + \sqrt{x^2 \pm a^2})]\, dx = x\log(x + \sqrt{x^2 \pm a^2}) - \sqrt{x^2 \pm a^2}$

512. $\displaystyle\int x[\log(x + \sqrt{x^2 \pm a^2})]\, dx = \left(\frac{x^2}{2} \pm \frac{a^2}{4}\right)\log(x + \sqrt{x^2 \pm a^2}) - \frac{x\sqrt{x^2 \pm a^2}}{4}$

513. $\displaystyle\int x^m[\log(x + \sqrt{x^2 \pm a^2})]\, dx = \frac{x^{m+1}}{m+1}\log(x + \sqrt{x^2 \pm a^2})$

$$-\frac{1}{m+1}\int\frac{x^{m+1}}{\sqrt{x^2 \pm a^2}}\, dx$$

514. $\displaystyle\int \frac{\log(x + \sqrt{x^2 + a^2})}{x^2}\, dx = -\frac{\log(x + \sqrt{x^2 + a^2})}{x} - \frac{1}{a}\log\frac{a + \sqrt{x^2 + a^2}}{x}$

515. $\displaystyle\int \frac{\log(x + \sqrt{x^2 - a^2})}{x^2}\, dx = -\frac{\log(x + \sqrt{x^2 - a^2})}{x} + \frac{1}{|a|}\sec^{-1}\frac{x}{a}$

INTEGRALS (Continued)

516. $\displaystyle\int x^n \log(x^2 - a^2)\, dx = \frac{1}{n+1}\Bigg[x^{n+1} \log(x^2 - a^2) - a^{n+1} \log(x - a)$

See note integral 392. $\hspace{2cm} -(-a)^{n+1} \log(x+a) - 2 \displaystyle\sum_{r=0}^{\left[\frac{n}{2}\right]} \frac{a^{2r} x^{n-2r+1}}{n - 2r + 1} \Bigg]$

EXPONENTIAL FORMS

517. $\displaystyle\int e^x\, dx = e^x$

518. $\displaystyle\int e^{-x}\, dx = -e^{-x}$

519. $\displaystyle\int e^{ax}\, dx = \frac{e^{ax}}{a}$

520. $\displaystyle\int x\, e^{ax}\, dx = \frac{e^{ax}}{a^2}(ax - 1)$

521. $\displaystyle\int x^m e^{ax}\, dx = \begin{cases} \dfrac{x^m e^{ax}}{a} - \dfrac{m}{a} \displaystyle\int x^{m-1} e^{ax}\, dx \\[2mm] \text{or} \\[2mm] e^{ax} \displaystyle\sum_{r=0}^{m} (-1)^r \dfrac{m!\, x^{m-r}}{(m-r)!\, a^{r+1}} \end{cases}$

522. $\displaystyle\int \frac{e^{ax}\, dx}{x} = \log x + \frac{ax}{1!} + \frac{a^2 x^2}{2 \cdot 2!} + \frac{a^3 x^3}{3 \cdot 3!} + \cdots$

523. $\displaystyle\int \frac{e^{ax}}{x^m}\, dx = -\frac{1}{m-1}\frac{e^{ax}}{x^{m-1}} + \frac{a}{m-1}\int \frac{e^{ax}}{x^{m-1}}\, dx$

524. $\displaystyle\int e^{ax} \log x\, dx = \frac{e^{ax} \log x}{a} - \frac{1}{a}\int \frac{e^{ax}}{x}\, dx$

525. $\displaystyle\int \frac{dx}{1 + e^x} = x - \log(1 + e^x) = \log\frac{e^x}{1 + e^x}$

526. $\displaystyle\int \frac{dx}{a + be^{px}} = \frac{x}{a} - \frac{1}{ap} \log(a + be^{px})$

527. $\displaystyle\int \frac{dx}{ae^{mx} + be^{-mx}} = \frac{1}{m\sqrt{ab}} \tan^{-1}\left(e^{mx}\sqrt{\frac{a}{b}}\right), \qquad (a > 0, b > 0)$

528. $\displaystyle\int \frac{dx}{ae^{mx} - be^{-mx}} = \begin{cases} \dfrac{1}{2m\sqrt{ab}} \log \dfrac{\sqrt{a}\, e^{mx} - \sqrt{b}}{\sqrt{a}\, e^{mx} + \sqrt{b}} \\[3mm] \text{or} \\[3mm] \dfrac{-1}{m\sqrt{ab}} \tanh^{-1}\left(\sqrt{\dfrac{a}{b}}\, e^{mx}\right), \qquad (a > 0, b > 0) \end{cases}$

INTEGRALS (Continued)

529. $\displaystyle\int (a^x - a^{-x})\,dx = \frac{a^x + a^{-x}}{\log a}$

530. $\displaystyle\int \frac{e^{ax}}{b + ce^{ax}}\,dx = \frac{1}{ac}\log\,(b + ce^{ax})$

531. $\displaystyle\int \frac{x\,e^{ax}}{(1 + ax)^2}\,dx = \frac{e^{ax}}{a^2(1 + ax)}$

532. $\displaystyle\int x\,e^{-x^2}\,dx = -\tfrac{1}{2}e^{-x^2}$

533. $\displaystyle\int e^{ax}\,[\sin\,(bx)]\,dx = \frac{e^{ax}[a\sin\,(bx) - b\cos\,(bx)]}{a^2 + b^2}$

534. $\displaystyle\int e^{ax}\,[\sin\,(bx)][\sin\,(cx)]\,dx = \frac{e^{ax}[(b - c)\sin\,(b - c)x + a\cos\,(b - c)x]}{2[a^2 + (b - c)^2]}$

$$-\frac{e^{ax}[(b + c)\sin\,(b + c)x + a\cos\,(b + c)x]}{2[a^2 + (b + c)^2]}$$

535. $\displaystyle\int e^{ax}[\sin\,(bx)][\cos\,(cx)]\,dx = \begin{cases} \dfrac{e^{ax}[a\sin\,(b - c)x - (b - c)\cos\,(b - c)x]}{2[a^2 + (b - c)^2]} \\[2mm] \quad + \dfrac{e^{ax}[a\sin\,(b + c)x - (b + c)\cos\,(b + c)x]}{2[a^2 + (b + c)^2]} \\[2mm] \qquad\qquad \text{or} \\[2mm] \dfrac{e^{ax}}{\rho}[(a\sin bx - b\cos bx)[\cos\,(cx - \alpha)] \\[2mm] \qquad\qquad\qquad -c(\sin bx)\sin\,(cx - \alpha)] \\[2mm] \text{where} \\[2mm] \rho = \sqrt{(a^2 + b^2 - c^2)^2 + 4a^2c^2}, \\[2mm] \rho\cos\alpha = a^2 + b^2 - c^2, \qquad \rho\sin\alpha = 2ac \end{cases}$

536. $\displaystyle\int e^{ax}[\sin\,(bx)][\sin\,(bx + c)]\,dx$

$$= \frac{e^{ax}\cos c}{2a} - \frac{e^{ax}[a\cos\,(2bx + c) + 2b\sin\,(2bx + c)]}{2(a^2 + 4b^2)}$$

537. $\displaystyle\int e^{ax}[\sin\,(bx)][\cos\,(bx + c)]\,dx$

$$= \frac{-e^{ax}\sin c}{2a} + \frac{e^{ax}[a\sin\,(2bx + c) - 2b\cos\,(2bx + c)]}{2(a^2 + 4b^2)}$$

538. $\displaystyle\int e^{ax}[\cos\,(bx)]\,dx = \frac{e^{ax}}{a^2 + b^2}[a\cos\,(bx) + b\sin\,(bx)]$

INTEGRALS (Continued)

539. $\int e^{ax}[\cos(bx)][\cos(cx)]\,dx = \dfrac{e^{ax}[(b-c)\sin(b-c)x + a\cos(b-c)x]}{2[a^2 + (b-c)^2]}$

$$+ \dfrac{e^{ax}[(b+c)\sin(b+c)x + a\cos(b+c)x]}{2[a^2 + (b+c)^2]}$$

540. $\int e^{ax}[\cos(bx)][\cos(bx + c)]\,dx$

$$= \dfrac{e^{ax}\cos c}{2a} + \dfrac{e^{ax}[a\cos(2bx + c) + 2b\sin(2bx + c)]}{2(a^2 + 4b^2)}$$

541. $\int e^{ax}[\cos(bx)][\sin(bx + c)]\,dx$

$$= \dfrac{e^{ax}\sin c}{2a} + \dfrac{e^{ax}[a\sin(2bx + c) - 2b\cos(2bx + c)]}{2(a^2 + 4b^2)}$$

542. $\int e^{ax}[\sin^n bx]\,dx = \dfrac{1}{a^2 + n^2b^2}\Bigg[(a\sin bx - nb\cos bx)\, e^{ax}\sin^{n-1}bx$

$$+ n(n-1)b^2 \int e^{ax}[\sin^{n-2}bx]\,dx \Bigg]$$

543. $\int e^{ax}[\cos^n bx]\,dx = \dfrac{1}{a^2 + n^2b^2}\Bigg[(a\cos bx + nb\sin bx)\, e^{ax}\cos^{n-1}bx$

$$+ n(n-1)b^2 \int e^{ax}[\cos^{n-2}bx]\,dx \Bigg]$$

544. $\int x^m e^x \sin x\,dx = \dfrac{1}{2}x^m e^x(\sin x - \cos x) - \dfrac{m}{2}\int x^{m-1} e^x \sin x\,dx$

$$+ \dfrac{m}{2}\int x^{m-1} e^x \cos x\,dx$$

545. $\int x^m e^{ax}[\sin bx]\,dx = \begin{cases} x^m e^{ax}\dfrac{a\sin bx - b\cos bx}{a^2 + b^2} \\[2mm] \qquad - \dfrac{m}{a^2 + b^2}\int x^{m-1} e^{ax}(a\sin bx - b\cos bx)\,dx \\[2mm] \qquad\qquad \text{or} \\[2mm] e^{ax}\displaystyle\sum_{r=0}^{m} \dfrac{(-1)^r m!\, x^{m-r}}{\rho^{r+1}(m-r)!}\sin[bx - (r+1)\alpha] \\[2mm] \qquad\qquad \text{where} \\[2mm] \rho = \sqrt{a^2 + b^2}, \qquad \rho\cos\alpha = a, \qquad \rho\sin\alpha = b \end{cases}$

546. $\int x^m e^x \cos x\,dx = \dfrac{1}{2}x^m e^x(\sin x + \cos x)$

$$- \dfrac{m}{2}\int x^{m-1} e^x \sin x\,dx - \dfrac{m}{2}\int x^{m-1} e^x \cos x\,dx$$

456

Calculus

INTEGRALS (Continued)

547. $\displaystyle\int x^m e^{ax}\cos bx\,dx =$
$$\begin{cases} x^m e^{ax}\dfrac{a\cos bx + b\sin bx}{a^2+b^2} \\[2mm] \quad -\dfrac{m}{a^2+b^2}\displaystyle\int x^{m-1}e^{ax}(a\cos bx + b\sin bx)\,dx \\[2mm] \text{or} \\[2mm] e^{ax}\displaystyle\sum_{r=0}^{m}\dfrac{(-1)^r m!\,x^{m-r}}{\rho^{r+1}(m-r)!}\cos[bx-(r+1)\alpha] \\[2mm] \text{where} \\[2mm] \rho=\sqrt{a^2+b^2}, \qquad \rho\cos\alpha=a, \qquad \rho\sin\alpha=b \end{cases}$$

548. $\displaystyle\int e^{ax}(\cos^m x)(\sin^n x)\,dx =$
$$\begin{cases} \dfrac{e^{ax}\cos^{m-1}x\,\sin^n x[a\cos x+(m+n)\sin x]}{(m+n)^2+a^2} \\[2mm] \quad -\dfrac{na}{(m+n)^2+a^2}\displaystyle\int e^{ax}(\cos^{m-1}x)(\sin^{n-1}x)\,dx \\[2mm] \quad +\dfrac{(m-1)(m+n)}{(m+n)^2+a^2}\displaystyle\int e^{ax}(\cos^{m-2}x)(\sin^n x)\,dx \\[2mm] \text{or} \\[2mm] \dfrac{e^{ax}\cos^m x\,\sin^{n-1}x[a\sin x-(m+n)\cos x]}{(m+n)^2+a^2} \\[2mm] \quad +\dfrac{ma}{(m+n)^2+a^2}\displaystyle\int e^{ax}(\cos^{m-1}x)(\sin^{n-1}x)\,dx \\[2mm] \quad +\dfrac{(n-1)(m+n)}{(m+n)^2+a^2}\displaystyle\int e^{ax}(\cos^m x)(\sin^{n-2}x)\,dx \\[2mm] \text{or} \\[2mm] \dfrac{e^{ax}(\cos^{m-1}x)(\sin^{n-1}x)(a\sin x\cos x+m\sin^2 x-n\cos}{(m+n)^2+a^2} \\[2mm] \quad +\dfrac{m(m-1)}{(m+n)^2+a^2}\displaystyle\int e^{ax}(\cos^{m-2}x)(\sin^n x)\,dx \\[2mm] \quad +\dfrac{n(n-1)}{(m+n)^2+a^2}\displaystyle\int e^{ax}(\cos^m x)(\sin^{n-2}x)\,dx \\[2mm] \text{or} \\[2mm] \dfrac{e^{ax}(\cos^{m-1}x)(\sin^{n-1}x)(a\cos x\sin x+m\sin^2 x-n\cos^2}{(m+n)^2+a^2} \\[2mm] \quad +\dfrac{m(m-1)}{(m+n)^2+a^2}\displaystyle\int e^{ax}(\cos^{m-2}x)(\sin^{n-2}x)\,dx \\[2mm] \quad +\dfrac{(n-m)(n+m-1)}{(m+n)^2+a^2}\displaystyle\int e^{ax}(\cos^m x)(\sin^{n-2}x)\,dx \end{cases}$$

INTEGRALS (Continued)

549. $\int x\, e^{ax}(\sin bx)\, dx = \dfrac{x\, e^{ax}}{a^2 + b^2}(a \sin bx - b \cos bx)$

$$-\frac{e^{ax}}{(a^2 + b^2)^2}[(a^2 - b^2)\sin bx - 2ab \cos bx]$$

550. $\int x\, e^{ax}(\cos bx)\, dx = \dfrac{x\, e^{ax}}{a^2 + b^2}(a \cos bx + b \sin bx)$

$$-\frac{e^{ax}}{(a^2 + b^2)^2}[(a^2 - b^2)\cos bx + 2ab \sin bx]$$

551. $\int \dfrac{e^{ax}}{\sin^n x}\, dx = -\dfrac{e^{ax}[a \sin x + (n - 2)\cos x]}{(n - 1)(n - 2)\sin^{n-1} x} + \dfrac{a^2 + (n - 2)^2}{(n - 1)(n - 2)}\int \dfrac{e^{ax}}{\sin^{n-2} x}\, dx$

552. $\int \dfrac{e^{ax}}{\cos^n x}\, dx = -\dfrac{e^{ax}[a \cos x - (n - 2)\sin x]}{(n - 1)(n - 2)\cos^{n-1} x} + \dfrac{a^2 + (n - 2)^2}{(n - 1)(n - 2)}\int \dfrac{e^{ax}}{\cos^{n-2} x}\, dx$

553. $\int e^{ax} \tan^n x\, dx = e^{ax}\dfrac{\tan^{n-1} x}{n - 1} - \dfrac{a}{n - 1}\int e^{ax} \tan^{n-1} x\, dx - \int e^{ax} \tan^{n-2} x\, dx$

HYPERBOLIC FORMS

554. $\int (\sinh x)\, dx = \cosh x$

555. $\int (\cosh x)\, dx = \sinh x$

556. $\int (\tanh x)\, dx = \log \cosh x$

557. $\int (\coth x)\, dx = \log \sinh x$

558. $\int (\operatorname{sech} x)\, dx = \tan^{-1}(\sinh x)$

559. $\int \operatorname{csch} x\, dx = \log \tanh \left(\dfrac{x}{2}\right)$

560. $\int x(\sinh x)\, dx = x \cosh x - \sinh x$

561. $\int x^n(\sinh x)\, dx = x^n \cosh x - n \int x^{n-1}(\cosh x)\, dx$

562. $\int x(\cosh x)\, dx = x \sinh x - \cosh x$

563. $\int x^n(\cosh x)\, dx = x^n \sinh x - n \int x^{n-1}(\sinh x)\, dx$

INTEGRALS (Continued)

564. $\displaystyle\int (\text{sech } x)(\tanh x)\, dx = -\,\text{sech } x$

565. $\displaystyle\int (\text{csch } x)(\coth x)\, dx = -\,\text{csch } x$

566. $\displaystyle\int (\sinh^2 x)\, dx = \frac{\sinh 2x}{4} - \frac{x}{2}$

567. $\displaystyle\int (\sinh^m x)(\cosh^n x)\, dx =$
$$\begin{cases} \dfrac{1}{m+n}(\sinh^{m+1} x)(\cosh^{n-1} x) \\[2mm] \qquad\qquad +\dfrac{n-1}{m+n}\displaystyle\int (\sinh^m x)(\cosh^{n-2} x)\, dx \\[4mm] \text{or} \\[2mm] \dfrac{1}{m+n}\sinh^{m-1} x \cosh^{n+1} x \\[2mm] \qquad -\dfrac{m-1}{m+n}\displaystyle\int (\sinh^{m-2} x)(\cosh^n x)\, dx, \quad (m+n \neq 0) \end{cases}$$

568. $\displaystyle\int \frac{dx}{(\sinh^m x)(\cosh^n x)} =$
$$\begin{cases} -\dfrac{1}{(m-1)(\sinh^{m-1} x)(\cosh^{n-1} x)} \\[2mm] \qquad -\dfrac{m+n-2}{m-1}\displaystyle\int \dfrac{dx}{(\sinh^{m-2} x)(\cosh^n x)}, \quad (m \neq 1) \\[4mm] \text{or} \\[2mm] \dfrac{1}{(n-1)\sinh^{m-1} x \cosh^{n-1} x} \\[2mm] \qquad +\dfrac{m+n-2}{n-1}\displaystyle\int \dfrac{dx}{(\sinh^m x)(\cosh^{n-2} x)}, \quad (n \neq 1) \end{cases}$$

569. $\displaystyle\int (\tanh^2 x)\, dx = x - \tanh x$

570. $\displaystyle\int (\tanh^n x)\, dx = -\frac{\tanh^{n-1} x}{n-1} + \int (\tanh^{n-2} x)\, dx, \quad (n \neq 1)$

571. $\displaystyle\int (\text{sech}^2 x)\, dx = \tanh x$

572. $\displaystyle\int (\cosh^2 x)\, dx = \frac{\sinh 2x}{4} + \frac{x}{2}$

573. $\displaystyle\int (\coth^2 x)\, dx = x - \coth x$

574. $\displaystyle\int (\coth^n x)\, dx = -\frac{\coth^{n-1} x}{n-1} + \int \coth^{n-2} x\, dx, \quad (n \neq 1)$

INTEGRALS (Continued)

575. $\int (\text{csch}^2\, x)\, dx = -\text{ctnh}\, x$

576. $\int (\sinh mx)(\sinh nx)\, dx = \dfrac{\sinh (m+n)x}{2(m+n)} - \dfrac{\sinh (m-n)x}{2(m-n)}, \qquad (m^2 \neq n^2)$

577. $\int (\cosh mx)(\cosh nx)\, dx = \dfrac{\sinh (m+n)x}{2(m+n)} + \dfrac{\sinh (m-n)x}{2(m-n)}, \qquad (m^2 \neq n^2)$

578. $\int (\sinh mx)(\cosh nx)\, dx = \dfrac{\cosh (m+n)x}{2(m+n)} + \dfrac{\cosh (m-n)x}{2(m-n)}, \qquad (m^2 \neq n^2)$

579. $\int \left(\sinh^{-1}\dfrac{x}{a}\right) dx = x \sinh^{-1}\dfrac{x}{a} - \sqrt{x^2 + a^2}, \qquad (a > 0)$

580. $\int x\left(\sinh^{-1}\dfrac{x}{a}\right) dx = \left(\dfrac{x^2}{2} + \dfrac{a^2}{4}\right)\sinh^{-1}\dfrac{x}{a} - \dfrac{x}{4}\sqrt{x^2 + a^2}, \qquad (a > 0)$

581. $\int x^n(\sinh^{-1} x)\, dx = \dfrac{x^{n+1}}{n+1}\sinh^{-1} x - \dfrac{1}{n+1}\int \dfrac{x^{n+1}}{(1+x^2)^{\frac{1}{2}}}\, dx, \qquad (n \neq -1)$

582. $\int \left(\cosh^{-1}\dfrac{x}{a}\right) dx = \begin{cases} x \cosh^{-1}\dfrac{x}{a} - \sqrt{x^2 - a^2}, & \left(\cosh^{-1}\dfrac{x}{a} > 0\right) \\[1em] \text{or} \\[1em] x \cosh^{-1}\dfrac{x}{a} + \sqrt{x^2 - a^2}, & \left(\cosh^{-1}\dfrac{x}{a} < 0\right), \end{cases} \qquad (a > 0)$

583. $\int x\left(\cosh^{-1}\dfrac{x}{a}\right) dx = \dfrac{2x^2 - a^2}{4}\cosh^{-1}\dfrac{x}{a} - \dfrac{x}{4}(x^2 - a^2)^{\frac{1}{2}}$

584. $\int x^n(\cosh^{-1} x)\, dx = \dfrac{x^{n+1}}{n+1}\cosh^{-1} x - \dfrac{1}{n+1}\int \dfrac{x^{n+1}}{(x^2 - 1)^{\frac{1}{2}}}\, dx, \qquad (n \neq -1)$

585. $\int \left(\tanh^{-1}\dfrac{x}{a}\right) dx = x \tanh^{-1}\dfrac{x}{a} + \dfrac{a}{2}\log (a^2 - x^2), \qquad \left(\left|\dfrac{x}{a}\right| < 1\right)$

586. $\int \left(\coth^{-1}\dfrac{x}{a}\right) dx = x \coth^{-1}\dfrac{x}{a} + \dfrac{a}{2}\log (x^2 - a^2), \qquad \left(\left|\dfrac{x}{a}\right| > 1\right)$

587. $\int x\left(\tanh^{-1}\dfrac{x}{a}\right) dx = \dfrac{x^2 - a^2}{2}\tanh^{-1}\dfrac{x}{a} + \dfrac{ax}{2}, \qquad \left(\left|\dfrac{x}{a}\right| < 1\right)$

588. $\int x^n\left(\tanh^{-1} x\right) dx = \dfrac{x^{n+1}}{n+1}\tanh^{-1} x - \dfrac{1}{n+1}\int \dfrac{x^{n+1}}{1 - x^2}\, dx, \qquad (n \neq -1)$

589. $\int x\left(\coth^{-1}\dfrac{x}{a}\right) dx = \dfrac{x^2 - a^2}{2}\coth^{-1}\dfrac{x}{a} + \dfrac{ax}{2}, \qquad \left(\left|\dfrac{x}{a}\right| > 1\right)$

590. $\int x^n(\coth^{-1} x)\, dx = \dfrac{x^{n+1}}{n+1}\coth^{-1} x + \dfrac{1}{n+1}\int \dfrac{x^{n+1}}{x^2 - 1}\, dx, \qquad (n \neq -1)$

INTEGRALS (Continued)

591. $\int (\operatorname{sech}^{-1} x)\, dx = x \operatorname{sech}^{-1} x + \sin^{-1} x$

592. $\int x \operatorname{sech}^{-1} x\, dx = \dfrac{x^2}{2} \operatorname{sech}^{-1} x - \dfrac{1}{2}\sqrt{1 - x^2}$

593. $\int x^n \operatorname{sech}^{-1} x\, dx = \dfrac{x^{n+1}}{n+1} \operatorname{sech}^{-1} x + \dfrac{1}{n+1}\int \dfrac{x^n}{(1 - x^2)^{\frac{1}{2}}}\, dx, \qquad (n \ne -1)$

594. $\int \operatorname{csch}^{-1} x\, dx = x \operatorname{csch}^{-1} x + \dfrac{x}{|x|}\sinh^{-1} x$

595. $\int x \operatorname{csch}^{-1} x\, dx = \dfrac{x^2}{2} \operatorname{csch}^{-1} x + \dfrac{1}{2}\dfrac{x}{|x|}\sqrt{1 + x^2}$

596. $\int x^n \operatorname{csch}^{-1} x\, dx = \dfrac{x^{n+1}}{n+1} \operatorname{csch}^{-1} x + \dfrac{1}{n+1}\dfrac{x}{|x|}\int \dfrac{x^n}{(x^2 + 1)^{\frac{1}{2}}}\, dx, \qquad (n \ne -1)$

DEFINITE INTEGRALS

597. $\displaystyle\int_0^\infty x^{n-1} e^{-x}\, dx = \int_0^1 \left(\log\dfrac{1}{x}\right)^{n-1} dx = \dfrac{1}{n}\prod_{m=1}^\infty \dfrac{\left(1 + \dfrac{1}{m}\right)^n}{1 + \dfrac{n}{m}}$

$$= \Gamma(n),\ n \ne 0, -1, -2, -3, \ldots \qquad \text{(Gamma Function)}$$

598. $\displaystyle\int_0^\infty t^n p^{-t}\, dt = \dfrac{n!}{(\log p)^{n+1}}, \qquad (n = 0, 1, 2, 3, \ldots \text{ and } p > 0)$

599. $\displaystyle\int_0^\infty t^{n-1} e^{-(a+1)t}\, dt = \dfrac{\Gamma(n)}{(a+1)^n}, \qquad (n > 0, a > -1)$

600. $\displaystyle\int_0^1 x^m \left(\log\dfrac{1}{x}\right)^n dx = \dfrac{\Gamma(n+1)}{(m+1)^{n+1}}, \qquad (m > -1, n > -1)$

601. $\Gamma(n)$ is finite if $n > 0$, $\Gamma(n + 1) = n\Gamma(n)$

602. $\Gamma(n) \cdot \Gamma(1 - n) = \dfrac{\pi}{\sin n\pi}$

603. $\Gamma(n) = (n - 1)!$ if $n = $ integer > 0

604. $\Gamma(\frac{1}{2}) = 2\displaystyle\int_0^\infty e^{-t^2}\, dt = \sqrt{\pi} = 1.7724538509\cdots = (-\frac{1}{2})!$

605. $\Gamma(n + \frac{1}{2}) = \dfrac{1 \cdot 3 \cdot 5 \ldots (2n - 1)}{2^n}\sqrt{\pi} \qquad n = 1, 2, 3, \ldots$

606. $\Gamma(-n + \frac{1}{2}) = \dfrac{(-1)^n 2^n \sqrt{\pi}}{1 \cdot 3 \cdot 5 \ldots (2n - 1)} \qquad n = 1, 2, 3, \ldots$

DEFINITE INTEGRALS (Continued)

607. $\displaystyle\int_0^1 x^{m-1}(1-x)^{n-1}\,dx = \int_0^\infty \frac{x^{m-1}}{(1+x)^{m+n}}\,dx = \frac{\Gamma(m)\Gamma(n)}{\Gamma(m+n)} = B(m,n)$

(Beta function)

608. $\displaystyle B(m,n) = B(n,m) = \frac{\Gamma(m)\Gamma(n)}{\Gamma(m+n)}$, where m and n are any positive real numbers.

609. $\displaystyle\int_a^b (x-a)^m(b-x)^n\,dx = (b-a)^{m+n+1}\frac{\Gamma(m+1)\cdot\Gamma(n+1)}{\Gamma(m+n+2)}$,

$(m > -1, n > -1, b > a)$

610. $\displaystyle\int_1^\infty \frac{dx}{x^m} = \frac{1}{m-1}$, $\quad [m > 1]$

611. $\displaystyle\int_0^\infty \frac{dx}{(1+x)x^p} = \pi\csc p\pi$, $\quad [p < 1]$

612. $\displaystyle\int_0^\infty \frac{dx}{(1-x)x^p} = -\pi\cot p\pi$, $\quad [p < 1]$

613. $\displaystyle\int_0^\infty \frac{x^{p-1}\,dx}{1+x} = \frac{\pi}{\sin p\pi}$

$= B(p, 1-p) = \Gamma(p)\Gamma(1-p)$, $\quad [0 < p < 1]$

614. $\displaystyle\int_0^\infty \frac{x^{m-1}\,dx}{1+x^n} = \frac{\pi}{n\sin\dfrac{m\pi}{n}}$, $\quad [0 < m < n]$

615. $\displaystyle\int_0^\infty \frac{x^a\,dx}{(m+x^b)^c} = m^{\frac{a+1-bc}{b}}\frac{\left[\Gamma\left(\dfrac{a+1}{b}\right)\Gamma\left(c-\dfrac{a+1}{b}\right)\right]}{b\,\Gamma(c)}$

$\left(a > -1, b > 0, m > 0, c > \dfrac{a+1}{b}\right)$

616. $\displaystyle\int_0^\infty \frac{dx}{(1+x)\sqrt{x}} = \pi$

617. $\displaystyle\int_0^\infty \frac{a\,dx}{a^2+x^2} = \frac{\pi}{2}$, if $a > 0$; 0, if $a = 0$; $-\frac{\pi}{2}$, if $a < 0$

618. $\displaystyle\int_0^a (a^2-x^2)^{\frac{n}{2}}\,dx = \frac{1}{2}\int_{-a}^a (a^2-x^2)^{\frac{n}{2}}\,dx = \frac{1\cdot3\cdot5\ldots n}{2\cdot4\cdot6\ldots(n+1)}\cdot\frac{\pi}{2}\cdot a^{n+1}$ $\quad$ (n odd)

619. $\displaystyle\int_0^a x^m(a^2-x^2)^{\frac{n}{2}}\,dx = \begin{cases}\dfrac{1}{2}a^{m+n+1}B\left(\dfrac{m+1}{2}, \dfrac{n+2}{2}\right)\\[2mm]\text{or}\\[2mm]\dfrac{1}{2}a^{m+n+1}\dfrac{\Gamma\left(\dfrac{m+1}{2}\right)\Gamma\left(\dfrac{n+2}{2}\right)}{\Gamma\left(\dfrac{m+n+3}{2}\right)}\end{cases}$

DEFINITE INTEGRALS (Continued)

620. $\displaystyle\int_0^{\pi/2} (\sin^n x)\, dx = \begin{cases} \displaystyle\int_0^{\pi/2} (\cos^n x)\, dx \\[2mm] \text{or} \\[2mm] \dfrac{1\cdot 3\cdot 5\cdot 7\ldots(n-1)}{2\cdot 4\cdot 6\cdot 8\ldots(n)}\,\dfrac{\pi}{2}, \qquad (n \text{ an even integer, } n \neq 0) \\[3mm] \text{or} \\[2mm] \dfrac{2\cdot 4\cdot 6\cdot 8\ldots(n-1)}{1\cdot 3\cdot 5\cdot 7\ldots(n)}, \qquad (n \text{ an odd integer, } n \neq 1) \\[3mm] \text{or} \\[2mm] \dfrac{\sqrt{\pi}}{2}\,\dfrac{\Gamma\!\left(\dfrac{n+1}{2}\right)}{\Gamma\!\left(\dfrac{n}{2}+1\right)}, \qquad (n > -1) \end{cases}$

621. $\displaystyle\int_0^{\infty} \frac{\sin mx\, dx}{x} = \frac{\pi}{2},\ \text{if } m > 0;\ 0,\ \text{if } m = 0;\ -\frac{\pi}{2},\ \text{if } m < 0$

622. $\displaystyle\int_0^{\infty} \frac{\cos x\, dx}{x} = \infty$

623. $\displaystyle\int_0^{\infty} \frac{\tan x\, dx}{x} = \frac{\pi}{2}$

624. $\displaystyle\int_0^{\pi} \sin ax\cdot \sin bx\, dx = \int_0^{\pi} \cos ax\cdot \cos bx\, dx = 0, \qquad (a \neq b;\, a, b \text{ integers})$

625. $\displaystyle\int_0^{\pi/a} [\sin(ax)][\cos(ax)]\, dx = \int_0^{\pi} [\sin(ax)][\cos(ax)]\, dx = 0$

626. $\displaystyle\int_0^{\pi} [\sin(ax)][\cos(bx)]\, dx = \frac{2a}{a^2 - b^2},\ \text{if } a - b \text{ is odd, or } 0 \text{ if } a - b \text{ is even}$

627. $\displaystyle\int_0^{\infty} \frac{\sin x \cos mx\, dx}{x}$

$$= 0,\ \text{if } m < -1 \text{ or } m > 1;\ \frac{\pi}{4},\ \text{if } m = \pm 1;\ \frac{\pi}{2},\ \text{if } m^2 < 1$$

628. $\displaystyle\int_0^{\infty} \frac{\sin ax \sin bx}{x^2}\, dx = \frac{\pi a}{2}, \qquad (a \leq b)$

629. $\displaystyle\int_0^{\pi} \sin^2 mx\, dx = \int_0^{\pi} \cos^2 mx\, dx = \frac{\pi}{2}$

630. $\displaystyle\int_0^{\infty} \frac{\sin^2(px)}{x^2}\, dx = \frac{\pi p}{2}$

DEFINITE INTEGRALS (Continued)

631. $\displaystyle\int_0^\infty \frac{\sin x}{x^p}\,dx = \frac{\pi}{2\Gamma(p)\sin(p\pi/2)}, \qquad 0 < p < 1$

632. $\displaystyle\int_0^\infty \frac{\cos x}{x^p}\,dx = \frac{\pi}{2\Gamma(p)\cos(p\pi/2)}, \qquad 0 < p < 1$

633. $\displaystyle\int_0^\infty \frac{1 - \cos px}{x^2}\,dx = \frac{\pi p}{2}$

634. $\displaystyle\int_0^\infty \frac{\sin px \cos qx}{x}\,dx = \left\{ 0, \quad q > p > 0; \quad \frac{\pi}{2}, \quad p > q > 0; \quad \frac{\pi}{4}, \quad p = q > 0 \right\}$

635. $\displaystyle\int_0^\infty \frac{\cos(mx)}{x^2 + a^2}\,dx = \frac{\pi}{2|a|}\,e^{-|ma|}$

636. $\displaystyle\int_0^\infty \cos(x^2)\,dx = \int_0^\infty \sin(x^2)\,dx = \frac{1}{2}\sqrt{\frac{\pi}{2}}$

637. $\displaystyle\int_0^\infty \sin ax^n\,dx = \frac{1}{na^{1/n}}\,\Gamma(1/n)\sin\frac{\pi}{2n}, \qquad n > 1$

638. $\displaystyle\int_0^\infty \cos ax^n\,dx = \frac{1}{na^{1/n}}\,\Gamma(1/n)\cos\frac{\pi}{2n}, \qquad n > 1$

639. $\displaystyle\int_0^\infty \frac{\sin x}{\sqrt{x}}\,dx = \int_0^\infty \frac{\cos x}{\sqrt{x}}\,dx = \sqrt{\frac{\pi}{2}}$

640. (a) $\displaystyle\int_0^\infty \frac{\sin^3 x}{x}\,dx = \frac{\pi}{4}$ (b) $\displaystyle\int_0^\infty \frac{\sin^3 x}{x^2}\,dx\ \frac{3}{4}\log 3$

641. $\displaystyle\int_0^\infty \frac{\sin^3 x}{x^3}\,dx = \frac{3\pi}{8}$

642. $\displaystyle\int_0^\infty \frac{\sin^4 x}{x^4}\,dx = \frac{\pi}{3}$

643. $\displaystyle\int_0^{\pi/2} \frac{dx}{1 + a\cos x} = \frac{\cos^{-1} a}{\sqrt{1 - a^2}}, \qquad (a < 1)$

644. $\displaystyle\int_0^\pi \frac{dx}{a + b\cos x} = \frac{\pi}{\sqrt{a^2 - b^2}}, \qquad (a > b \geq 0)$

645. $\displaystyle\int_0^{2\pi} \frac{dx}{1 + a\cos x} = \frac{2\pi}{\sqrt{1 - a^2}}, \qquad (a^2 < 1)$

646. $\displaystyle\int_0^\infty \frac{\cos ax - \cos bx}{x}\,dx = \log\frac{b}{a}$

647. $\displaystyle\int_0^{\pi/2} \frac{dx}{a^2\sin^2 x + b^2\cos^2 x} = \frac{\pi}{2ab}$

DEFINITE INTEGRALS (Continued)

648. $\displaystyle\int_0^{\pi/2} \frac{dx}{(a^2 \sin^2 x + b^2 \cos^2 x)^2} = \frac{\pi(a^2 + b^2)}{4a^3b^3}$, $(a, b > 0)$

649. $\displaystyle\int_0^{\pi/2} \sin^{n-1} x \cos^{m-1} x \, dx = \frac{1}{2}B\left(\frac{n}{2}, \frac{m}{2}\right)$, m and n positive integers

650. $\displaystyle\int_0^{\pi/2} (\sin^{2n+1} \theta) \, d\theta = \frac{2 \cdot 4 \cdot 6 \ldots (2n)}{1 \cdot 3 \cdot 5 \ldots (2n + 1)}$, $(n = 1, 2, 3 \ldots)$

651. $\displaystyle\int_0^{\pi/2} (\sin^{2n} \theta) \, d\theta = \frac{1 \cdot 3 \cdot 5 \ldots (2n - 1)}{2 \cdot 4 \ldots (2n)}\left(\frac{\pi}{2}\right)$, $(n = 1, 2, 3 \ldots)$

652. $\displaystyle\int_0^{\pi/2} \frac{x}{\sin x} \, dx = 2\left\{\frac{1}{1^2} - \frac{1}{3^2} + \frac{1}{5^2} - \frac{1}{7^2} + \cdots\right\}$

653. $\displaystyle\int_0^{\pi/2} \frac{dx}{1 + \tan^m x} = \frac{\pi}{4}$

654. $\displaystyle\int_0^{\pi/2} \sqrt{\cos \theta} \, d\theta = \frac{(2\pi)^{\frac{3}{2}}}{[\Gamma(\frac{1}{4})]^2}$

655. $\displaystyle\int_0^{\pi/2} (\tan^h \theta) \, d\theta = \frac{\pi}{2 \cos\left(\dfrac{h\pi}{2}\right)}$, $(0 < h < 1)$

656. $\displaystyle\int_0^{\infty} \frac{\tan^{-1}(ax) - \tan^{-1}(bx)}{x} \, dx = \frac{\pi}{2} \log \frac{a}{b}$, $(a, b > 0)$

657. The area enclosed by a curve defined through the equation $x^{\frac{b}{c}} + y^{\frac{b}{c}} = a^{\frac{b}{c}}$ where $a > 0$, c a positive odd integer and b a positive even integer is given by

$$\frac{\left[\Gamma\left(\dfrac{c}{b}\right)\right]^2}{\Gamma\left(\dfrac{2c}{b}\right)}\left(\dfrac{2ca^2}{b}\right)$$

658. $\displaystyle I = \iiint\limits_R x^{h-1} y^{m-1} z^{n-1} \, dv$, where R denotes the region of space bounded by

the co-ordinate planes and that portion of the surface $\left(\dfrac{x}{a}\right)^p + \left(\dfrac{y}{b}\right)^q + \left(\dfrac{z}{c}\right)^k = 1$,

which lies in the first octant and where $h, m, n, p, q, k, a, b, c$, denote positive real numbers is given by

$$\int_0^a x^{h-1} \, dx \int_0^{b\left[1-\left(\frac{x}{a}\right)^p\right]^{\frac{1}{q}}} y^m \, dy \int_0^{c\left[1-\left(\frac{x}{a}\right)^p-\left(\frac{y}{b}\right)^q\right]^{\frac{1}{k}}} z^{n-1} \, dz$$

$$= \frac{a^h b^m c^n}{pqk} \frac{\Gamma\left(\dfrac{h}{p}\right)\Gamma\left(\dfrac{m}{q}\right)\Gamma\left(\dfrac{n}{k}\right)}{\Gamma\left(\dfrac{h}{p} + \dfrac{m}{q} + \dfrac{n}{k} + 1\right)}$$

DEFINITE INTEGRALS (Continued)

659. $\int_0^\infty e^{-ax}\,dx = \frac{1}{a}, \quad (a > 0)$

660. $\int_0^\infty \frac{e^{-ax} - e^{-bx}}{x}\,dx = \log\frac{b}{a}, \quad (a, b > 0)$

661. $\int_0^\infty x^n e^{-ax}\,dx = \begin{cases} \dfrac{\Gamma(n+1)}{a^{n+1}}, & (n > -1, a > 0) \\ \quad\text{or} \\ \dfrac{n!}{a^{n+1}}, & (a > 0, n \text{ positive integer}) \end{cases}$

662. $\int_0^\infty x^n \exp(-ax^p)\,dx = \frac{\Gamma(k)}{pa^k}, \quad \left(n > -1, p > 0, a > 0, k = \frac{n+1}{p}\right)$

663. $\int_0^\infty e^{-a^2 x^2}\,dx = \frac{1}{2a}\sqrt{\pi} = \frac{1}{2a}\Gamma\left(\frac{1}{2}\right), \quad (a > 0)$

664. $\int_0^\infty x e^{-x^2}\,dx = \frac{1}{2}$

665. $\int_0^\infty x^2 e^{-x^2}\,dx = \frac{\sqrt{\pi}}{4}$

666. $\int_0^\infty x^{2n} e^{-ax^2}\,dx = \frac{1 \cdot 3 \cdot 5 \ldots (2n-1)}{2^{n+1}a^n}\sqrt{\frac{\pi}{a}}$

667. $\int_0^\infty x^{2n+1} e^{-ax^2}\,dx = \frac{n!}{2a^{n+1}}, \quad (a > 0)$

668. $\int_0^1 x^m e^{-ax}\,dx = \frac{m!}{a^{m+1}}\left[1 - e^{-a}\sum_{r=0}^m \frac{a^r}{r!}\right]$

669. $\int_0^\infty e^{\left(-x^2 - \frac{a^2}{x^2}\right)}\,dx = \frac{e^{-2a}\sqrt{\pi}}{2}, \quad (a \geq 0)$

670. $\int_0^\infty e^{-nx}\sqrt{x}\,dx = \frac{1}{2n}\sqrt{\frac{\pi}{n}}$

671. $\int_0^\infty \frac{e^{-nx}}{\sqrt{x}}\,dx = \sqrt{\frac{\pi}{n}}$

672. $\int_0^\infty e^{-ax}(\cos mx)\,dx = \frac{a}{a^2 + m^2}, \quad (a > 0)$

673. $\int_0^\infty e^{-ax}(\sin mx)\,dx = \frac{m}{a^2 + m^2}, \quad (a > 0)$

Calculus

DEFINITE INTEGRALS (Continued)

674. $\displaystyle\int_0^\infty x\,e^{-ax}[\sin{(bx)}]\,dx = \frac{2ab}{(a^2+b^2)^2}, \qquad (a>0)$

675. $\displaystyle\int_0^\infty x\,e^{-ax}[\cos{(bx)}]\,dx = \frac{a^2-b^2}{(a^2+b^2)^2}, \qquad (a>0)$

676. $\displaystyle\int_0^\infty x^n\,e^{-ax}[\sin{(bx)}]\,dx = \frac{n![(a+ib)^{n+1}-(a-ib)^{n+1}]}{2i(a^2+b^2)^{n+1}}, \qquad (i^2=-1, a>0)$

677. $\displaystyle\int_0^\infty x^n\,e^{-ax}[\cos{(bx)}]\,dx = \frac{n![(a-ib)^{n+1}+(a+ib)^{n+1}]}{2(a^2+b^2)^{n+1}}, \qquad (i^2=-1, a>0)$

678. $\displaystyle\int_0^\infty \frac{e^{-ax}\sin x}{x}\,dx = \cot^{-1}a, \qquad (a>0)$

679. $\displaystyle\int_0^\infty e^{-a^2x^2}\cos bx\,dx = \frac{\sqrt{\pi}}{2a}\exp\left(-\frac{b^2}{4a^2}\right), \qquad (ab\neq 0)$

680. $\displaystyle\int_0^\infty e^{-t\cos\phi}\,t^{b-1}\sin{(t\sin\phi)}\,dt = [\Gamma(b)]\sin{(b\phi)}, \qquad \left(b>0, -\frac{\pi}{2}<\phi<\frac{\pi}{2}\right)$

681. $\displaystyle\int_0^\infty e^{-t\cos\phi}\,t^{b-1}[\cos{(t\sin\phi)}]\,dt = [\Gamma(b)]\cos{(b\phi)}, \qquad \left(b>0, -\frac{\pi}{2}<\phi<\frac{\pi}{2}\right)$

682. $\displaystyle\int_0^\infty t^{b-1}\cos t\,dt = [\Gamma(b)]\cos\left(\frac{b\pi}{2}\right), \qquad (0<b<1)$

683. $\displaystyle\int_0^\infty t^{b-1}(\sin t)\,dt = [\Gamma(b)]\sin\left(\frac{b\pi}{2}\right), \qquad (0<b<1)$

684. $\displaystyle\int_0^1 (\log x)^n\,dx = (-1)^n \cdot n!$

685. $\displaystyle\int_0^1 \left(\log\frac{1}{x}\right)^{\frac{1}{2}}\,dx = \frac{\sqrt{\pi}}{2}$

686. $\displaystyle\int_0^1 \left(\log\frac{1}{x}\right)^{-\frac{1}{2}}\,dx = \sqrt{\pi}$

687. $\displaystyle\int_0^1 \left(\log\frac{1}{x}\right)^n\,dx = n!$

688. $\displaystyle\int_0^1 x\log{(1-x)}\,dx = -\tfrac{3}{4}$

689. $\displaystyle\int_0^1 x\log{(1+x)}\,dx = \tfrac{1}{4}$

690. $\displaystyle\int_0^1 x^m(\log x)^n\,dx = \frac{(-1)^n n!}{(m+1)^{n+1}}, \qquad m>-1, n=0,1,2,\ldots$

If $n\neq 0,1,2,\ldots$ replace $n!$ by $\Gamma(n+1)$.

DEFINITE INTEGRALS (Continued)

691. $\int_0^1 \dfrac{\log x}{1 + x}\,dx = -\dfrac{\pi^2}{12}$

692. $\int_0^1 \dfrac{\log x}{1 - x}\,dx = -\dfrac{\pi^2}{6}$

693. $\int_0^1 \dfrac{\log (1 + x)}{x}\,dx = \dfrac{\pi^2}{12}$

694. $\int_0^1 \dfrac{\log (1 - x)}{x}\,dx = -\dfrac{\pi^2}{6}$

695. $\int_0^1 (\log x)[\log (1 + x)]\,dx = 2 - 2\log 2 - \dfrac{\pi^2}{12}$

696. $\int_0^1 (\log x)[\log (1 - x)]\,dx = 2 - \dfrac{\pi^2}{6}$

697. $\int_0^1 \dfrac{\log x}{1 - x^2}\,dx = -\dfrac{\pi^2}{8}$

698. $\int_0^1 \log\left(\dfrac{1 + x}{1 - x}\right) \cdot \dfrac{dx}{x} = \dfrac{\pi^2}{4}$

699. $\int_0^1 \dfrac{\log x\,dx}{\sqrt{1 - x^2}} = -\dfrac{\pi}{2}\log 2$

700. $\int_0^1 x^m\left[\log\left(\dfrac{1}{x}\right)\right]^n dx = \dfrac{\Gamma(n + 1)}{(m + 1)^{n+1}}, \quad$ if $m + 1 > 0, n + 1 > 0$

701. $\int_0^1 \dfrac{(x^p - x^q)\,dx}{\log x} = \log\left(\dfrac{p + 1}{q + 1}\right), \quad (p + 1 > 0, q + 1 > 0)$

702. $\int_0^1 \dfrac{dx}{\sqrt{\log\left(\dfrac{1}{x}\right)}} = \sqrt{\pi}$, (same as integral 686)

703. $\int_0^\infty \log\left(\dfrac{e^x + 1}{e^x - 1}\right) dx = \dfrac{\pi^2}{4}$

704. $\int_0^{\pi/2} (\log \sin x)\,dx = \int_0^{\pi/2} \log \cos x\,dx = -\dfrac{\pi}{2}\log 2$

705. $\int_0^{\pi/2} (\log \sec x)\,dx = \int_0^{\pi/2} \log \csc x\,dx = \dfrac{\pi}{2}\log 2$

706. $\int_0^\pi x(\log \sin x)\,dx = -\dfrac{\pi^2}{2}\log 2$

707. $\int_0^{\pi/2} (\sin x)(\log \sin x)\,dx = \log 2 - 1$

DEFINITE INTEGRALS (Continued)

708. $\int_0^{\pi/2} (\log \tan x)\, dx = 0$

709. $\int_0^{\pi} \log\left(a \pm b \cos x\right) dx = \pi \log\left(\dfrac{a + \sqrt{a^2 - b^2}}{2}\right), \qquad (a \geq b)$

710. $\int_0^{\pi} \log\left(a^2 - 2ab \cos x + b^2\right) dx = \begin{cases} 2\pi \log a, & a \geq b > 0 \\ 2\pi \log b, & b \geq a > 0 \end{cases}$

711. $\int_0^{\infty} \dfrac{\sin ax}{\sinh bx}\, dx = \dfrac{\pi}{2b} \tanh \dfrac{a\pi}{2b}$

712. $\int_0^{\infty} \dfrac{\cos ax}{\cosh bx}\, dx = \dfrac{\pi}{2b} \operatorname{sech} \dfrac{a\pi}{2b}$

713. $\int_0^{\infty} \dfrac{dx}{\cosh ax} = \dfrac{\pi}{2a}$

714. $\int_0^{\infty} \dfrac{x\, dx}{\sinh ax} = \dfrac{\pi^2}{4a^2}$

715. $\int_0^{\infty} e^{-ax}(\cosh bx)\, dx = \dfrac{a}{a^2 - b^2}, \qquad (0 \leq |b| < a)$

716. $\int_0^{\infty} e^{-ax}(\sinh bx)\, dx = \dfrac{b}{a^2 - b^2}, \qquad (0 \leq |b| < a)$

717. $\int_0^{\infty} \dfrac{\sinh ax}{e^{bx} + 1}\, dx = \dfrac{\pi}{2b} \csc \dfrac{a\pi}{b} - \dfrac{1}{2a}$

718. $\int_0^{\infty} \dfrac{\sinh ax}{e^{bx} - 1}\, dx = \dfrac{1}{2a} - \dfrac{\pi}{2b} \cot \dfrac{a\pi}{b}$

719. $\int_0^{\pi/2} \dfrac{dx}{\sqrt{1 - k^2 \sin^2 x}} = \dfrac{\pi}{2}\left[1 + \left(\dfrac{1}{2}\right)^2 k^2 + \left(\dfrac{1 \cdot 3}{2 \cdot 4}\right)^2 k^4 \right.$
$$\left. + \left(\dfrac{1 \cdot 3 \cdot 5}{2 \cdot 4 \cdot 6}\right)^2 k^6 + \cdots \right], \text{ if } k^2 < 1$$

720. $\int_0^{\pi/2} \sqrt{1 - k^2 \sin^2 x}\, dx = \dfrac{\pi}{2}\left[1 - \left(\dfrac{1}{2}\right)^2 k^2 - \left(\dfrac{1 \cdot 3}{2 \cdot 4}\right)^2 \dfrac{k^4}{3} \right.$
$$\left. - \left(\dfrac{1 \cdot 3 \cdot 5}{2 \cdot 4 \cdot 6}\right)^2 \dfrac{k^6}{5} - \cdots \right], \text{ if } k^2 < 1$$

721. $\int_0^{\infty} e^{-x} \log x\, dx = -\gamma = -0.5772157\ldots$

722. $\int_0^{\infty} e^{-x^2} \log x\, dx = -\dfrac{\sqrt{\pi}}{4}(\gamma + 2 \log 2)$

DEFINITE INTEGRALS (Continued)

723. $\int_0^\infty \left(\dfrac{1}{1 - e^{-x}} - \dfrac{1}{x} \right) e^{-x} dx = \gamma = 0.5772157 \ldots$ [Euler's Constant]

724. $\int_0^\infty \dfrac{1}{x} \left(\dfrac{1}{1 + x} - e^{-x} \right) dx = \gamma = 0.5772157 \ldots$

For n even:

725. $\cos^n x \quad = \quad \dfrac{1}{2^{n-1}} \displaystyle\sum_{k=0}^{\frac{n}{2}-1} \binom{n}{k} \cos (n - 2k) x + \dfrac{1}{2^n} \binom{n}{\frac{n}{2}}$

726. $\sin^n x \quad = \quad \dfrac{1}{2^{n-1}} \displaystyle\sum_{k=0}^{\frac{n}{2}-1} \binom{n}{k} \cos \left[(n - 2k)(\tfrac{\pi}{2} - x) \right] + \dfrac{1}{2^n} \binom{n}{\frac{n}{2}}$

For n odd:

727. $\cos^n x \quad = \quad \dfrac{1}{2^{n-1}} \displaystyle\sum_{k=0}^{\frac{n-1}{2}} \binom{n}{k} \cos (n - 2k) x \, .$

728. $\sin^n x \quad = \quad \dfrac{1}{2^{n-1}} \displaystyle\sum_{k=0}^{\frac{n-1}{2}} \binom{n}{k} \cos \left[(n - 2k) (\tfrac{\pi}{2} - x) \right]$

For n even:

729. $\int \cos^n x \, dx \quad = \quad \dfrac{1}{2^{n-1}} \displaystyle\sum_{k=0}^{\frac{n}{2}-1} \binom{n}{k} \dfrac{\sin (n - 2k) x}{(n - 2k)} + \dfrac{1}{2^n} \binom{n}{\frac{n}{2}} x$

730. $\int \sin^n x \, dx \quad = \quad \dfrac{1}{2^{n-1}} \displaystyle\sum_{k=0}^{\frac{n}{2}-1} \binom{n}{k} \dfrac{\sin \left[(n - 2k) (\tfrac{\pi}{2} - x) \right]}{2k - n} + \dfrac{1}{2^n} \binom{n}{\frac{n}{2}} x$

For n odd:

731. $\int \cos^n x \, dx \quad = \quad \dfrac{1}{2^{n-1}} \displaystyle\sum_{k=0}^{\frac{n-1}{2}} \binom{n}{k} \dfrac{\sin (n - 2k) x}{(n - 2k)}$

732. $\int \sin^n x \, dx \quad = \quad \dfrac{1}{2^{n-1}} \displaystyle\sum_{k=0}^{\frac{n-1}{2}} \binom{n}{k} \dfrac{\sin \left[n - 2k) (\tfrac{\pi}{2} - x) \right]}{2k - n}$

SERIES

The expression in parentheses following certain of the series indicates the region of convergence. If not otherwise indicated it is to be understood that the series converges for all finite values of x.

BINOMIAL

$$(x + y)^n = x^n + nx^{n-1}y + \frac{n(n-1)}{2!} x^{n-2}y^2$$

$$+ \frac{n(n-1)(n-2)}{3!} x^{n-3}y^3 + \cdots \quad (y^2 < x^2)$$

$$(1 \pm x)^n = 1 \pm nx + \frac{n(n-1)x^2}{2!} \pm \frac{n(n-1)(n-2)x^3}{3!} + \cdots \text{ etc.} \quad (x^2 < 1)$$

$$(1 \pm x)^{-n} = 1 \mp nx + \frac{n(n+1)x^2}{2!} \mp \frac{n(n+1)(n+2)x^3}{3!} + \cdots \text{ etc.} \quad (x^2 < 1)$$

$$(1 \pm x)^{-1} = 1 \mp x + x^2 \mp x^3 + x^4 \mp x^5 + \cdots \qquad\qquad (x^2 < 1)$$
$$(1 \pm x)^{-2} = 1 \mp 2x + 3x^2 \mp 4x^3 + 5x^4 \mp 6x^5 + \cdots \qquad (x^2 < 1)$$

REVERSION OF SERIES

Let a series be represented by

$$y = a_1 x + a_2 x^2 + a_3 x^3 + a_4 x^4 + a_5 x^5 + a_6 x^6 + \cdots \quad (a_1 \neq 0)$$

to find the coefficients of the series

$$x = A_1 y + A_2 y^2 + A_3 y^3 + A_4 y^4 + \cdots$$

$$A_1 = \frac{1}{a_1} \qquad A_2 = -\frac{a_2}{a_1^3} \qquad A_3 = \frac{1}{a_1^5} (2a_2^2 - a_1 a_3)$$

$$A_4 = \frac{1}{a_1^7} (5a_1 a_2 a_3 - a_1^2 a_4 - 5a_2^3)$$

$$A_5 = \frac{1}{a_1^9} (6a_1^2 a_2 a_4 + 3a_1^2 a_3^2 + 14a_2^4 - a_1^3 a_5 - 21a_1 a_2^2 a_3)$$

$$A_6 = \frac{1}{a_1^{11}} (7a_1^3 a_2 a_5 + 7a_1^3 a_3 a_4 + 84a_1 a_2^3 a_3 - a_1^4 a_6 - 28a_1^2 a_2^2 a_4 - 28a_1^2 a_2 a_3^2 - 42a_2^5)$$

$$A_7 = \frac{1}{a_1^{13}} (8a_1^4 a_2 a_6 + 8a_1^4 a_3 a_5 + 4a_1^4 a_4^2 + 120a_1^2 a_2^3 a_4$$

$$+ 180a_1^2 a_2^2 a_3^2 + 132a_2^6 - a_1^5 a_7$$

$$- 36a_1^3 a_2^2 a_5 - 72a_1^3 a_2 a_3 a_4 - 12a_1^3 a_3^3 - 330a_1 a_2^4 a_3)$$

TAYLOR

1. $f(x) = f(a) + (x - a)f'(a) + \dfrac{(x - a)^2}{2!} f''(a) + \dfrac{(x - a)^3}{3!} f'''(a)$

$$+ \cdots + \frac{(x - a)^n}{n!} f^{(n)}(a) + \cdots \text{ (Taylor's Series)}$$

(Increment form)

2. $f(x + h) = f(x) + hf'(x) + \dfrac{h^2}{2!} f''(x) + \dfrac{h^3}{3!} f'''(x) + \cdots$

$$= f(h) + xf'(h) + \dfrac{x^3}{2!} f''(h) + \dfrac{x^3}{3!} f'''(h) + \cdots$$

3. If $f(x)$ is a function possessing derivatives of all orders throughout the interval $a \leqq x \leqq b$, then there is a value X, with $a < X < b$, such that

$$f(b) = f(a) + (b - a)f'(a) + \dfrac{(b - a)^2}{2!} f''(a) + \cdots$$

$$+ \dfrac{(b - a)^{n-1}}{(n - 1)!} f^{(n-1)}(a) + \dfrac{(b - a)^n}{n!} f^{(n)}(X)$$

$$f(a + h) = f(a) + hf'(a) + \dfrac{h^2}{2!} f''(a) + \cdots + \dfrac{h^{n-1}}{(n - 1)!} f^{(n-1)}(a)$$

$$+ \dfrac{h^n}{n!} f^{(n)}(a + \theta h), \quad b = a + h, 0 < \theta < 1.$$

or

$$f(x) = f(a) + (x - a)f'(a) + \dfrac{(x - a)^2}{2!} f''(a) + \cdots + (x - a)^{n-1} \dfrac{f^{(n-1)}(a)}{(n - 1)!} + R_n,$$

where

$$R_n = \dfrac{f^{(n)}[a + \theta \cdot (x - a)]}{n!} (x - a)^n, \quad 0 < \theta < 1.$$

The above forms are known as Taylor's series with the remainder term.

4. *Taylor's series for a function of two variables*

If $\left(h \dfrac{\partial}{\partial x} + k \dfrac{\partial}{\partial y} \right) f(x, y) = h \dfrac{\partial f(x, y)}{\partial x} + k \dfrac{\partial f(x, y)}{\partial y}$;

$$\left(h \dfrac{\partial}{\partial x} + k \dfrac{\partial}{\partial y} \right)^2 f(x, y) = h^2 \dfrac{\partial^2 f(x, y)}{\partial x^2} + 2hk \dfrac{\partial^2 f(x, y)}{\partial x \partial y} + k^2 \dfrac{\partial^2 f(x, y)}{\partial y^2}$$

etc., and if $\left(h \dfrac{\partial}{\partial x} + k \dfrac{\partial}{\partial y} \right)^n f(x, y) \Big|_{\substack{x=a \\ y=b}}$ with the bar and subscripts means that after differentiation we are to replace x by a and y by b,

$$f(a + h, b + k) = f(a, b) + \left(h \dfrac{\partial}{\partial x} + k \dfrac{\partial}{\partial y} \right) f(x, y) \Big|_{\substack{x=a \\ y=b}} + \cdots$$

$$+ \dfrac{1}{n!} \left(h \dfrac{\partial}{\partial x} + k \dfrac{\partial}{\partial y} \right)^n f(x, y) \Big|_{\substack{x=a \\ y=b}} + \cdots$$

MACLAURIN

$$f(x) = f(0) + xf'(0) + \dfrac{x^2}{2!} f''(0) + \dfrac{x^3}{3!} f'''(0) + \cdots + x^{n-1} \dfrac{f^{(n-1)}(0)}{(n - 1)!} + R_n,$$

where

$$R_n = \dfrac{x^n f^{(n)}(\theta x)}{n!}, \quad 0 < \theta < 1.$$

EXPONENTIAL

$$e = 1 + \frac{1}{1!} + \frac{1}{2!} + \frac{1}{3!} + \frac{1}{4!} + \cdots$$

$$e^x = 1 + x + \frac{x^2}{2!} + \frac{x^3}{3!} + \frac{x^4}{4!} + \cdots \qquad \text{(all real values of } x\text{)}$$

$$a^x = 1 + x \log_e a + \frac{(x \log_e a)^2}{2!} + \frac{(x \log_e a)^3}{3!} + \cdots$$

$$e^x = e^a \left[1 + (x - a) + \frac{(x - a)^2}{2!} + \frac{(x - \cdot a)^3}{3!} + \cdots \right]$$

LOGARITHMIC

$$\log_e x = \frac{x - 1}{x} + \frac{1}{2}\left(\frac{x - 1}{x}\right)^2 + \frac{1}{3}\left(\frac{x - 1}{x}\right)^3 + \cdots \qquad (x > \tfrac{1}{2})$$

$$\log_e x = (x - 1) - \tfrac{1}{2}(x - 1)^2 + \tfrac{1}{3}(x - 1)^3 - \cdots \qquad (2 \geq x > 0)$$

$$\log_e x = 2\left[\frac{x - 1}{x + 1} + \frac{1}{3}\left(\frac{x - 1}{x + 1}\right)^3 + \frac{1}{5}\left(\frac{x - 1}{x + 1}\right)^5 + \cdots\right] \qquad (x > 0)$$

$$\log_e(1 + x) = x - \tfrac{1}{2}x^2 + \tfrac{1}{3}x^3 - \tfrac{1}{4}x^4 + \cdots \qquad (-1 < x \leq 1)$$

$$\log_e(n + 1) - \log_e(n - 1) = 2\left[\frac{1}{n} + \frac{1}{3n^3} + \frac{1}{5n^5} + \cdots\right]$$

$$\log_e(a + x) = \log_e a + 2\left[\frac{x}{2a + x} + \frac{1}{3}\left(\frac{x}{2a + x}\right)^3 + \frac{1}{5}\left(\frac{x}{2a + x}\right)^5 + \cdots\right]$$

$$(a > 0, -a < x < +\infty)$$

$$\log_e \frac{1 + x}{1 - x} = 2\left[x + \frac{x^3}{3} + \frac{x^5}{5} + \cdots + \frac{x^{2n-1}}{2n - 1} + \cdots\right], \qquad -1 < x < 1$$

$$\log_e x = \log_e a + \frac{(x - a)}{a} - \frac{(x - a)^2}{2a^2} + \frac{(x - a)^3}{3a^3} - + \cdots, \qquad 0 < x \leq 2a$$

TRIGONOMETRIC

$$\sin x = x - \frac{x^3}{3!} + \frac{x^5}{5!} - \frac{x^7}{7!} + \cdots \qquad \text{(all real values of } x\text{)}$$

$$\cos x = 1 - \frac{x^2}{2!} + \frac{x^4}{4!} - \frac{x^6}{6!} + \cdots \qquad \text{(all real values of } x\text{)}$$

$$\tan x = x + \frac{x^3}{3} + \frac{2x^5}{15} + \frac{17x^7}{315} + \frac{62x^9}{2835} + \cdots + \frac{(-1)^{n+1} \, 2^{2n} \, (2^{2n} - 1) \, B_{2n}}{(2n)!} x^{2n-1} + \cdots,$$

$$\left[x^2 < \frac{\pi^2}{4}, \text{ and } B_n \text{ represents the } n\text{'th Bernoulli number.}\right]$$

$$\cot x = \frac{1}{x} - \frac{x}{3} - \frac{x^3}{45} - \frac{2x^5}{945} - \frac{x^7}{4725} - \cdots - \frac{(-1)^{n+1}2^{2n}}{(2n)!} B_{2n}x^{2n-1} - \cdots,$$

$$[x^2 < \pi^2, \text{ and } B_n \text{ represents the } n\text{'th Bernoulli number.}]$$

$$\sec x = 1 + \frac{x^2}{2} + \frac{5}{24}x^4 + \frac{61}{720}x^6 + \frac{277}{8064}x^8 + \cdots + \frac{(-1)^n}{(2n)!}E_{2n}x^{2n} + \cdots,$$

$$\left[x^2 < \frac{\pi^2}{4}, \text{ and } E_n \text{ represents the } n\text{'th Euler number.}\right]$$

$$\csc x = \frac{1}{x} + \frac{x}{6} + \frac{7}{360}x^3 + \frac{31}{15,120}x^5 + \frac{127}{604,800}x^7 + \cdots$$

$$+ \frac{(-1)^{n+1}2(2^{2n-1}-1)}{(2n)!}B_{2n}x^{2n-1} + \cdots,$$

$$[x^2 < \pi^2, \text{ and } B_n \text{ represents } n\text{'th Bernoulli number.}]$$

$$\sin x = x\left(1 - \frac{x^2}{\pi^2}\right)\left(1 - \frac{x^2}{2^2\pi^2}\right)\left(1 - \frac{x^2}{3^2\pi^2}\right)\cdots \qquad (x^2 < \infty)$$

$$\cos x = \left(1 - \frac{4x^2}{\pi^2}\right)\left(1 - \frac{4x^2}{3^2\pi^2}\right)\left(1 - \frac{4x^2}{5^2\pi^2}\right)\cdots \qquad (x^2 < \infty)$$

$$\sin^{-1}x = x + \frac{x^3}{2\cdot 3} + \frac{1\cdot 3}{2\cdot 4\cdot 5}x^5 + \frac{1\cdot 3\cdot 5}{2\cdot 4\cdot 6\cdot 7}x^7 + \cdots \qquad \left(x^2 < 1, -\frac{\pi}{2} < \sin^{-1}x < \frac{\pi}{2}\right)$$

$$\cos^{-1}x = \frac{\pi}{2} - \left(x + \frac{x^3}{2\cdot 3} + \frac{1\cdot 3}{2\cdot 4\cdot 5}x^5 + \frac{1\cdot 3\cdot 5x^7}{2\cdot 4\cdot 6\cdot 7} + \cdots\right) \quad (x^2 < 1, 0 < \cos^{-1}x < \pi)$$

$$\tan^{-1}x = x - \frac{x^3}{3} + \frac{x^5}{5} - \frac{x^7}{7} + \cdots \qquad (x^2 < 1)$$

$$\tan^{-1}x = \frac{\pi}{2} - \frac{1}{x} + \frac{1}{3x^3} - \frac{1}{5x^5} + \frac{1}{7x^7} - \cdots \qquad (x > 1)$$

$$\tan^{-1}x = -\frac{\pi}{2} - \frac{1}{x} + \frac{1}{3x^3} - \frac{1}{5x^5} + \frac{1}{7x^7} - \cdots \qquad (x < -1)$$

$$\cot^{-1}x = \frac{\pi}{2} - x + \frac{x^3}{3} - \frac{x^5}{5} + \frac{x^7}{7} - \cdots \qquad (x^2 < 1)$$

$$\log_e \sin x = \log_e x - \frac{x^2}{6} - \frac{x^4}{180} - \frac{x^6}{2835} - \cdots \qquad (x^2 < \pi^2)$$

$$\log_e \cos x = -\frac{x^2}{2} - \frac{x^4}{12} - \frac{x^6}{45} - \frac{17x^8}{2520} - \cdots \qquad \left(x^2 < \frac{\pi^2}{4}\right)$$

$$\log_e \tan x = \log_e x + \frac{x^2}{3} + \frac{7x^4}{90} + \frac{62x^6}{2835} + \cdots \qquad \left(x^2 < \frac{\pi^2}{4}\right)$$

$$e^{\sin x} = 1 + x + \frac{x^2}{2!} - \frac{3x^4}{4!} - \frac{8x^5}{5!} - \frac{3x^6}{6!} + \frac{56x^7}{7!} + \cdots$$

$$e^{\cos x} = e\left(1 - \frac{x^2}{2!} + \frac{4x^4}{4!} - \frac{31x^6}{6!} + \cdots\right)$$

$$e^{\tan x} = 1 + x + \frac{x^2}{2!} + \frac{3x^3}{3!} + \frac{9x^4}{4!} + \frac{37x^5}{5!} + \cdots \qquad \left(x^2 < \frac{\pi^2}{4}\right)$$

$$\sin x = \sin a + (x - a)\cos a - \frac{(x - a)^2}{2!}\sin a$$

$$- \frac{(x - a)^3}{3!}\cos a + \frac{(x - a)^4}{4!}\sin a + \cdots$$

HYPERBOLIC AND INVERSE HYPERBOLIC
See page 337 for section on Hyperbolic Functions
See page 342 for section on Hyperbolic Series

FOURIER

(Also see Index for Cosine and Sine Transforms)

1. If $f(x)$ is a bounded periodic function of period $2L$ (i.e. $f(x + 2L) = f(x)$), and satisfies the *Dirichlet conditions*:

   a) In any period $f(x)$ is continuous, except possibly for a finite number of jump discontinuities

   b) In any period $f(x)$ has only a finite number of maxima and minima.

Then $f(x)$ may be represented by the *Fourier series*

$$\frac{a_0}{2} + \sum_{n=1}^{\infty} \left(a_n \cos \frac{n\pi x}{L} + b_n \sin \frac{n\pi x}{L} \right),$$

where a_n and b_n are as determined below. This series will converge to $f(x)$ at every point where $f(x)$ is continuous, and to

$$\frac{f(x^+) + f(x^-)}{2}$$

(i.e. the average of the left-hand and right-hand limits) at every point where $f(x)$ has a jump discontinuity.

$$a_n = \frac{1}{L} \int_{-L}^{L} f(x) \cos \frac{n\pi x}{L} \, dx, \quad n = 0, 1, 2, 3, \ldots;$$

$$b_n = \frac{1}{L} \int_{-L}^{L} f(x) \sin \frac{n\pi x}{L} \, dx, \quad n = 1, 2, 3, \ldots$$

We may also write

$$a_n = \frac{1}{L} \int_{\alpha}^{\alpha+2L} f(x) \cos \frac{n\pi x}{L} \, dx \text{ and } b_n = \frac{1}{L} \int_{\alpha}^{\alpha+2L} f(x) \sin \frac{n\pi x}{L} \, dx,$$

where α is any real number. Thus if $\alpha = 0$,

$$a_n = \frac{1}{L} \int_{0}^{2L} f(x) \cos \frac{n\pi x}{L} \, dx, \quad n = 0, 1, 2, 3, \ldots;$$

$$b_n = \frac{1}{L} \int_{0}^{2L} f(x) \sin \frac{n\pi x}{L} \, dx, \quad n = 1, 2, 3, \ldots$$

2. If in addition to the above restrictions, $f(x)$ is even (i.e. $f(-x) = f(x)$), the Fourier series reduces to

$$\frac{a_0}{2} + \sum_{n=1}^{\infty} a_n \cos \frac{n\pi x}{L}.$$

That is, $b_n = 0$. In this case, a simpler formula for a_n is

$$a_n = \frac{2}{L} \int_0^L f(x) \cos \frac{n\pi x}{L} \, dx, \quad n = 0, 1, 2, 3, \ldots$$

3. If in addition to the restrictions in (1), $f(x)$ is an odd function (i.e. $f(-x) = -f(x)$), then the Fourier series reduces to

$$\sum_{n=1}^{\infty} b_n \sin \frac{n\pi x}{L}.$$

That is, $a_n = 0$. In this case, a simpler formula for the b_n is

$$b_n = \frac{2}{L} \int_0^L f(x) \sin \frac{n\pi x}{L} \, dx, \quad n = 1, 2, 3, \ldots$$

4. If in addition to the restrictions in (2) above, $f(x) = -f(L - x)$, then a_n will be 0 for all even values of n, including $n = 0$. Thus in this case, the expansion reduces to

$$\sum_{m=1}^{\infty} a_{2m-1} \cos \frac{(2m - 1)\pi x}{L}.$$

5. If in addition to the restrictions in (3) above, $f(x) = f(L - x)$, then b_n will be 0 for all even values of n. Thus in this case, the expansion reduces to

$$\sum_{m=1}^{\infty} b_{2m-1} \sin \frac{(2m - 1)\pi x}{L}.$$

(The series in (4) and (5) are known as *odd-harmonic series*, since only the odd harmonics appear. Similar rules may be stated for even-harmonic series, but when a series appears in the even-harmonic form, it means that $2L$ has not been taken as the smallest period of $f(x)$. Since any integral multiple of a period is also a period, series obtained in this way will also work, but in general computation is simplified if $2L$ is taken to be the smallest period.)

6. If we write the Euler definitions for $\cos \theta$ and $\sin \theta$, we obtain the complex form of the Fourier Series known either as the "Complex Fourier Series" or the "Exponential Fourier Series" of $f(x)$. It is represented as

$$f(x) = \frac{1}{2} \sum_{n=-\infty}^{n=+\infty} c_n e^{i\omega_n x},$$

where

$$c_n = \frac{1}{L} \int_{-L}^{L} f(x) e^{-i\omega_n x} dx, \quad n = 0, \pm 1, \pm 2, \pm 3, \ldots$$

with $\omega_n = \frac{n\pi}{L}, \quad n = 0, \pm 1, \pm 2, \ldots$

The set of coefficients $\{c_n\}$ is often referred to as the Fourier spectrum.

7. If both sine and cosine terms are present and if $f(x)$ is of period $2L$ and expandable by a Fourier series, it can be represented as

$$f(x) = \frac{a_0}{2} + \sum_{n=1}^{\infty} c_n \cos\left(\frac{n\pi x}{L} + \phi_n\right),$$

where $a_n = c_n \cos \phi_n$, $\qquad b_n = c_n \cos \phi_n$, $\quad c_n = \sqrt{a_n^2 + b_n^2}$, $\quad \phi_n = \arctan\left(\frac{a_n}{b_n}\right)$

It can also be represented as

$$f(x) = \frac{a_0}{2} + \sum_{n=1}^{\infty} c_n \sin\left(\frac{n\pi x}{L} + \phi_n\right),$$

where $a_n = c_n \sin \phi_n$, $\qquad b_n = -c_n \sin \phi_n$, $\quad c_n = \sqrt{a_n^2 + b_n^2}$, $\quad \phi_n = \arctan\left(-\frac{b_n}{a_n}\right)$

where the quadrant of ϕ_n is chosen so as to make the formulas for a_n, b_n, and c_n hold.

8. The following table of trigonometric identities should be helpful for developing Fourier Series.

	n**	n even	n odd	$n/2$ odd	$n/2$ even
$\sin n\pi$	0	0	0	0	0
$\cos n\pi$	$(-1)^n$	$+1$	-1	$+1$	$+1$
*$\sin \dfrac{n\pi}{2}$		0	$(-1)^{(n-1)/2}$	0	0
*$\cos \dfrac{n\pi}{2}$		$(-1)^{n/2}$	0	-1	$+1$
$\sin \dfrac{n\pi}{4}$			$\dfrac{\sqrt{2}}{2}(-1)^{(n^2+4n+11)/8}$	$(-1)^{(n-2)/4}$	0

*A useful formula for $\sin \dfrac{n\pi}{2}$ and $\cos \dfrac{n\pi}{2}$ is given by

$$\sin \frac{n\pi}{2} = \frac{(i)^{n+1}}{2}[(-1)^n - 1] \text{ and } \cos \frac{n\pi}{2} = \frac{(i)^n}{2}[(-1)^n + 1], \text{ where } i^2 = -1.$$

** n any integer.

AUXILIARY FORMULAS FOR FOURIER SERIES

$$1 = \frac{4}{\pi}\left[\sin\frac{\pi x}{k} + \frac{1}{3}\sin\frac{3\pi x}{k} + \frac{1}{5}\sin\frac{5\pi x}{k} + \cdots\right] \qquad [0 < x < k]$$

$$x = \frac{2k}{\pi}\left[\sin\frac{\pi x}{k} - \frac{1}{2}\sin\frac{2\pi x}{k} + \frac{1}{3}\sin\frac{3\pi x}{k} - \cdots\right] \qquad [-k < x < k]$$

$$x = \frac{k}{2} - \frac{4k}{\pi^2}\left[\cos\frac{\pi x}{k} + \frac{1}{3^2}\cos\frac{3\pi x}{k} + \frac{1}{5^2}\cos\frac{5\pi x}{k} + \cdots\right] \qquad [0 < x < k]$$

$$x^2 = \frac{2k^2}{\pi^3}\left[\left(\frac{\pi^2}{1} - \frac{4}{1}\right)\sin\frac{\pi x}{k} - \frac{\pi^2}{2}\sin\frac{2\pi x}{k} + \left(\frac{\pi^2}{3} - \frac{4}{3^3}\right)\sin\frac{3\pi x}{k}\right.$$
$$\left. - \frac{\pi^2}{4}\sin\frac{4\pi x}{k} + \left(\frac{\pi^2}{5} - \frac{4}{5^3}\right)\sin\frac{5\pi x}{k} + \cdots\right] [0 < x < k]$$

$$x^2 = \frac{k^2}{3} - \frac{4k^2}{\pi^2}\left[\cos\frac{\pi x}{k} - \frac{1}{2^2}\cos\frac{2\pi x}{k} + \frac{1}{3^2}\cos\frac{3\pi x}{k} - \frac{1}{4^2}\cos\frac{4\pi x}{k} + \cdots\right]$$
$$[-k < x < k]$$

$$1 - \frac{1}{3} + \frac{1}{5} - \frac{1}{7} + \cdots = \frac{\pi}{4}$$

$$1 + \frac{1}{2^2} + \frac{1}{3^2} + \frac{1}{4^2} + \cdots = \frac{\pi^2}{6}$$

$$1 - \frac{1}{2^2} + \frac{1}{3^2} - \frac{1}{4^2} + \cdots = \frac{\pi^2}{12}$$

$$1 + \frac{1}{3^2} + \frac{1}{5^2} + \frac{1}{7^2} + \cdots = \frac{\pi^2}{8}$$

$$\frac{1}{2^2} + \frac{1}{4^2} + \frac{1}{6^2} + \frac{1}{8^2} + \cdots = \frac{\pi^2}{24}$$

*SUMS OF RECIPROCAL POWERS

n	$\zeta(n) = \sum\limits_{k=1}^{\infty} k^{-n}$				$\sum\limits_{k=1}^{\infty} (-1)^{k-1} k^{-n}$			
1	∞				0.69314	71805	59945	30942
2	1.64493	40668	48226	43637	0.82246	70334	24113	21824
3	1.20205	69031	59594	28540	0.90154	26773	69695	71405
4	1.08232	32337	11138	19152	0.94703	28294	97245	91758
5	1.03692	77551	43369	92633	0.97211	97704	46909	30594
6	1,01734	30619	84449	13971	0.98555	10912	97435	10410
7	1.00834	92773	81922	82684	0.99259	38199	22830	28267
8	1.00407	73561	97944	33938	0.99623	30018	52647	89923
9	1.00200	83928	26082	21442	0.99809	42975	41605	33077
10	1.00099	45751	27818	08534	0.99903	95075	98271	56564
11	1.00049	41886	04119	46456	0.99951	71434	98060	75414
12	1.00024	60865	53308	04830	0.99975	76851	43858	19085
13	1.00012	27133	47578	48915	0.99987	85427	63265	11549
14	1.00006	12481	35058	70483	0.99993	91703	45979	71817
15	1.00003	05882	36307	02049	0.99996	95512	13099	23808
16	1.00001	52822	59408	65187	0.99998	47642	14906	10644
17	1.00000	76371	97637	89976	0.99999	23782	92041	01198
18	1.00000	38172	93264	99984	0.99999	61878	69610	11348
19	1.00000	19082	12716	55394	0.99999	80935	08171	67511
20	1.00000	09539	62033	87280	0.99999	90466	11581	52212
21	1.00000	04769	32986	78781	0.99999	95232	58215	54282
22	1.00000	02384	50502	72773	0.99999	97616	13230	82255
23	1.00000	01192	19925	96531	0.99999	98808	01318	43950
24	1.00000	00596	08189	05126	0.99999	99403	98892	39463
25	1.00000	00298	03503	51465	0.99999	99701	98856	96283
26	1.00000	00149	01554	82837	0.99999	99850	99231	99657
27	1.00000	00074	50711	78984	0.99999	99925	49550	48496
28	1.00000	00037	25334	02479	0.99999	99962	74753	40011
29	1.00000	00018	62659	72351	0.99999	99981	37369	41811
30	1.00000	00009	31327	43242	0.99999	99990	68682	28145
31	1.00000	00004	65662	90650	0.99999	99995	34340	33145
32	1.00000	00002	32831	18337	0.99999	99997	67169	89595
33	1.00000	00001	16415	50173	0.99999	99998	83584	85805
34	1.00000	00000	58207	72088	0.99999	99999	41792	39905
35	1.00000	00000	29103	85044	0.99999	99999	70896	18953
36	1.00000	00000	14551	92189	0.99999	99999	85448	09143
37	1.00000	00000	07275	95984	0.99999	99999	92724	04461
38	1.00000	00000	03637	97955	0.99999	99999	96362	02193
39	1.00000	00000	01818	98965	0.99999	99999	98181	01084
40	1.00000	00000	00909	49478	0.99999	99999	99090	50538
41	1.00000	00000	00454	74738	0.99999	99999	99545	25268
42	1.00000	00000	00227	37368	0.99999	99999	99772	62633

For $n > 42$, $\sum\limits_{k=1}^{\infty} k^{-(n+1)} = \dfrac{1}{2}\left[1 + \sum\limits_{k=1}^{\infty} k^{-n}\right]$, $\sum\limits_{k=1}^{\infty} (-1)^{k-1} k^{-(n+1)} = \dfrac{1}{2}\left[1 + \sum\limits_{k=1}^{\infty} (-1)^{k-1} k^{-n}\right]$

* Note: By definition Riemann's Zeta Function is

$$\zeta(p) = \text{Zeta } (p) = 1 + \frac{1}{2^p} + \frac{1}{3^p} + \frac{1}{4^p} + \cdots$$

478

SUMS OF RECIPROCAL POWERS

n	$\sum_{k=0}^{\infty} (2k+1)^{-n}$				$\sum_{k=0}^{\infty} (-1)^k (2k+1)^{-n}$			
1	∞				0.78539	81633	97448	310
2	1.23370	05501	36169	82735	0.91596	55941	77219	015
3	1.05179	97902	64644	99972	0.96894	61462	59369	380
4	1.01467	80316	04192	05455	0.98894	45517	41105	336
5	1.00452	37627	95139	61613	0.99615	78280	77088	064
6	1.00144	70766	40942	12191	0.99868	52222	18438	135
7	1.00047	15486	52376	55476	0.99955	45078	90539	909
8	1.00015	51790	25296	11930	0.99984	99902	46829	656
9	1.00005	13451	83843	77259	0.99994	96841	87220	090
10	1.00001	70413	63044	82549	0.99998	31640	26196	877
11	1.00000	56660	51090	10935	0.99999	43749	73823	699
12	1.00000	18858	48583	11958	0.99999	81223	50587	882
13	1.00000	06280	55421	80232	0.99999	93735	83771	841
14	1.00000	02092	40519	21150	0.99999	97910	87248	734
15	1.00000	00697	24703	12929	0.99999	99303	40842	624
16	1.00000	00232	37157	37916	0.99999	99767	75950	903
17	1.00000	00077	44839	45587	0.99999	99922	57782	104
18	1.00000	00025	81437	55666	0.99999	99974	19086	745
19	1.00000	00008	60444	11452	0.99999	99991	39660	745
20	1.00000	00002	86807	69746	0.99999	99997	13213	274
21	1.00000	00000	95601	16531	0.99999	99999	04403	029
22	1.00000	00000	31866	77514	0.99999	99999	68134	064
23	1.00000	00000	10622	20241	0.99999	99999	89377	965
24	1.00000	00000	03540	72294	0.99999	99999	96459	311
25	1.00000	00000	01180	23874	0.99999	99999	98819	768
26	1.00000	00000	00393	41247	0.99999	99999	99606	589
27	1.00000	00000	00131	13740	0.99999	99999	99868	863
28	1.00000	00000	00043	71245	0.99999	99999	99956	288
29	1.00000	00000	00014	57081	0.99999	99999	99985	429
30	1.00000	00000	00004	85694	0.99999	99999	99995	143
31	1.00000	00000	00001	61898	0.99999	99999	99998	381
32	1.00000	00000	00000	53966	0.99999	99999	99999	460
33	1.00000	00000	00000	17989	0.99999	99999	99999	820
34	1.00000	00000	00000	05996	0.99999	99999	99999	940
35	1.00000	00000	00000	01999	0.99999	99999	99999	980
36	1.00000	00000	00000	00666	0.99999	99999	99999	993
37	1.00000	00000	00000	00222	0.99999	99999	99999	998
38	1.00000	00000	00000	00074	0.99999	99999	99999	999
39	1.00000	00000	00000	00025				
40	1.00000	00000	00000	00008				
41	1.00000	00000	00000	00003				
42	1.00000	00000	00000	00001				

*FOURIER EXPANSIONS FOR BASIC PERIODIC FUNCTIONS

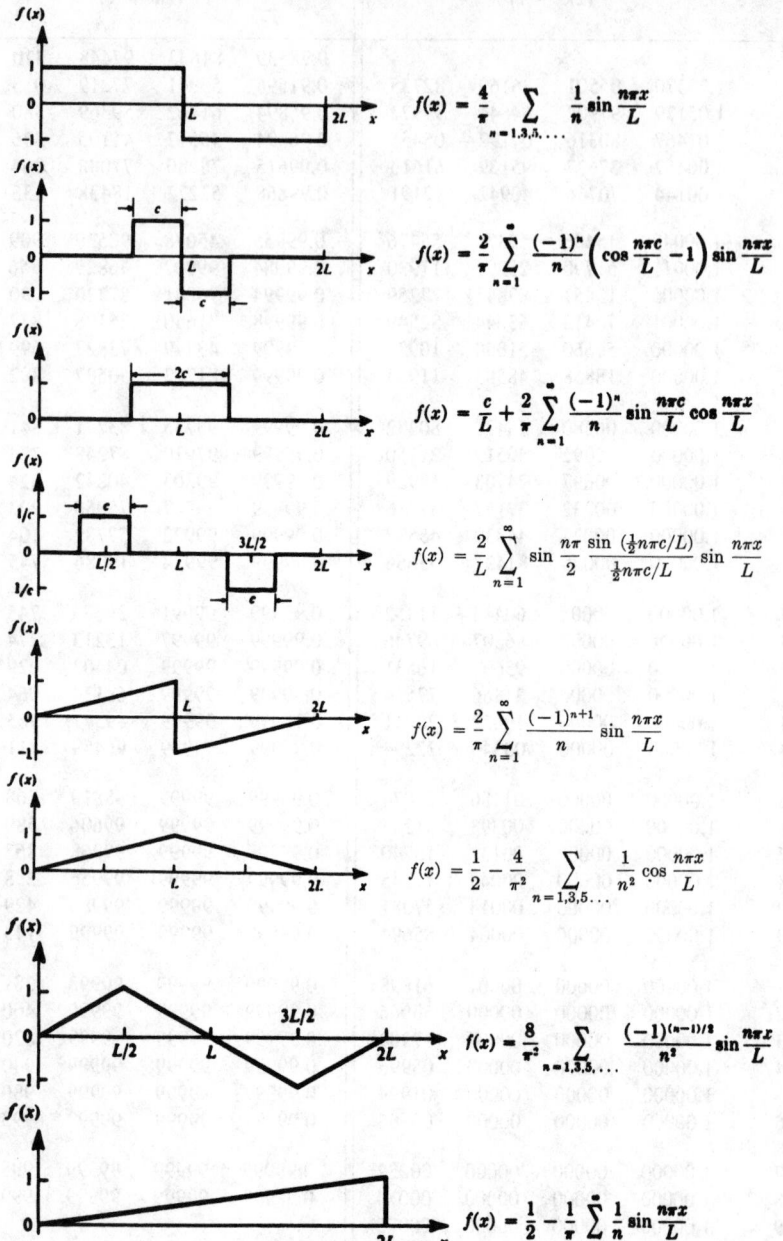

$$f(x) = \frac{4}{\pi} \sum_{n=1,3,5,\ldots} \frac{1}{n} \sin \frac{n\pi x}{L}$$

$$f(x) = \frac{2}{\pi} \sum_{n=1}^{\infty} \frac{(-1)^n}{n} \left(\cos \frac{n\pi c}{L} - 1 \right) \sin \frac{n\pi x}{L}$$

$$f(x) = \frac{c}{L} + \frac{2}{\pi} \sum_{n=1}^{\infty} \frac{(-1)^n}{n} \sin \frac{n\pi c}{L} \cos \frac{n\pi x}{L}$$

$$f(x) = \frac{2}{L} \sum_{n=1}^{\infty} \sin \frac{n\pi}{2} \frac{\sin \left(\frac{1}{2} n\pi c/L\right)}{\frac{1}{2} n\pi c/L} \sin \frac{n\pi x}{L}$$

$$f(x) = \frac{2}{\pi} \sum_{n=1}^{\infty} \frac{(-1)^{n+1}}{n} \sin \frac{n\pi x}{L}$$

$$f(x) = \frac{1}{2} - \frac{4}{\pi^2} \sum_{n=1,3,5\ldots} \frac{1}{n^2} \cos \frac{n\pi x}{L}$$

$$f(x) = \frac{8}{\pi^2} \sum_{n=1,3,5,\ldots} \frac{(-1)^{(n-1)/2}}{n^2} \sin \frac{n\pi x}{L}$$

$$f(x) = \frac{1}{2} - \frac{1}{\pi} \sum_{n=1}^{\infty} \frac{1}{n} \sin \frac{n\pi x}{L}$$

* Extracted from graphs and formulas, pages 372, 373, Differential Equations in Engineering Problems, Salvadori and Schwarz, published by Prentice-Hall, Inc., 1954.

*FOURIER EXPANSIONS FOR BASIC PERIODIC FUNCTIONS (Continued)

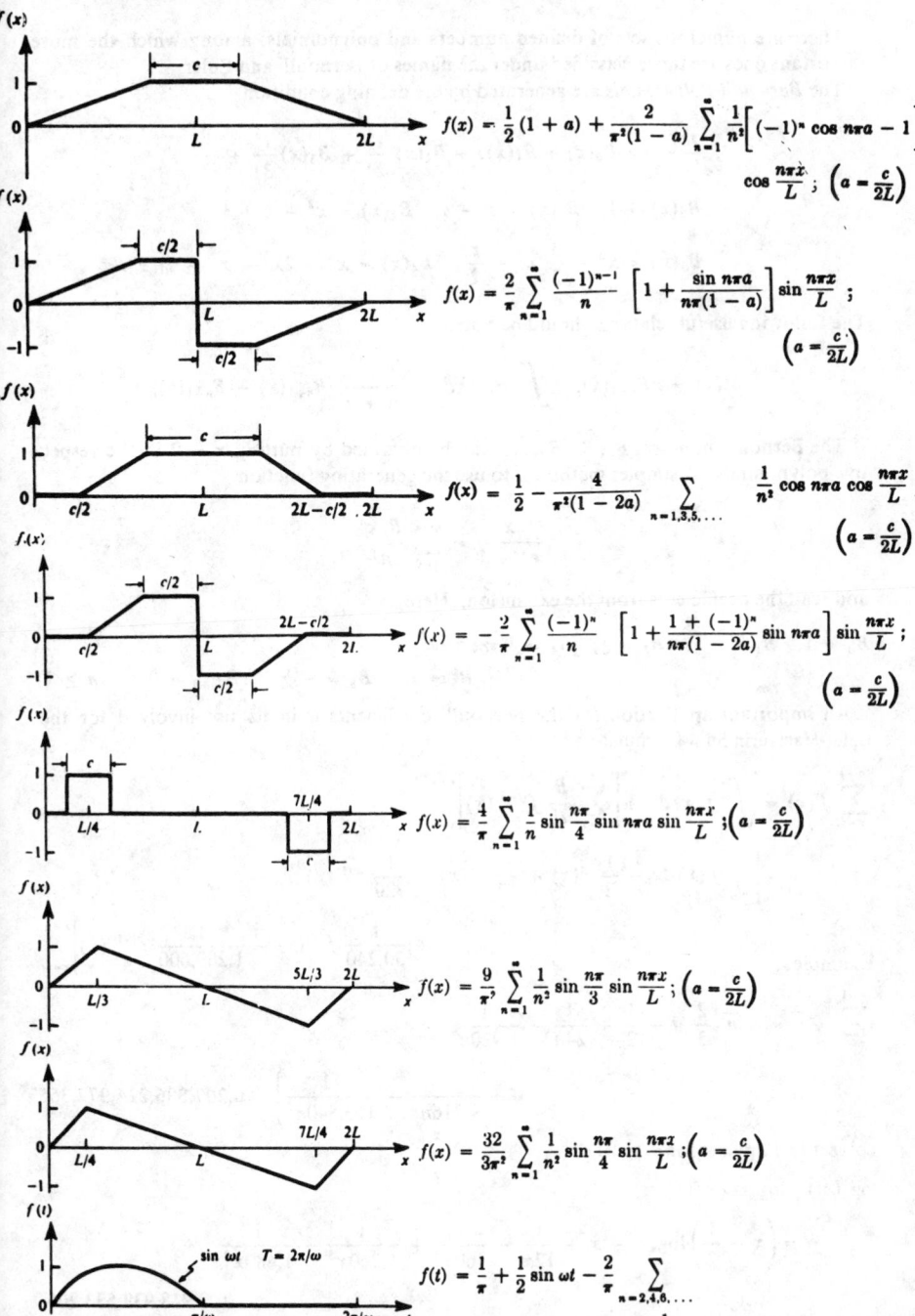

$$f(x) = \frac{1}{2}(1 + a) + \frac{2}{\pi^2(1-a)} \sum_{n=1}^{\infty} \frac{1}{n^2}\left[(-1)^n \cos n\pi a - 1\right] \cos \frac{n\pi x}{L} \; ; \; \left(a = \frac{c}{2L}\right)$$

$$f(x) = \frac{2}{\pi} \sum_{n=1}^{\infty} \frac{(-1)^{n-1}}{n}\left[1 + \frac{\sin n\pi a}{n\pi(1-a)}\right]\sin\frac{n\pi x}{L} \; ; \; \left(a = \frac{c}{2L}\right)$$

$$f(x) = \frac{1}{2} - \frac{4}{\pi^2(1-2a)} \sum_{n=1,3,5,\dots} \frac{1}{n^2}\cos n\pi a \cos\frac{n\pi x}{L} \; ; \; \left(a = \frac{c}{2L}\right)$$

$$f(x) = -\frac{2}{\pi} \sum_{n=1}^{\infty} \frac{(-1)^n}{n}\left[1 + \frac{1+(-1)^n}{n\pi(1-2a)}\sin n\pi a\right]\sin\frac{n\pi x}{L} \; ; \; \left(a = \frac{c}{2L}\right)$$

$$f(x) = \frac{4}{\pi} \sum_{n=1}^{\infty} \frac{1}{n}\sin\frac{n\pi}{4}\sin n\pi a \sin\frac{n\pi x}{L} \; ; \left(a = \frac{c}{2L}\right)$$

$$f(x) = \frac{9}{\pi^2} \sum_{n=1}^{\infty} \frac{1}{n^2}\sin\frac{n\pi}{3}\sin\frac{n\pi x}{L} \; ; \left(a = \frac{c}{2L}\right)$$

$$f(x) = \frac{32}{3\pi^2} \sum_{n=1}^{\infty} \frac{1}{n^2}\sin\frac{n\pi}{4}\sin\frac{n\pi x}{L} \; ; \left(a = \frac{c}{2L}\right)$$

$$f(t) = \frac{1}{\pi} + \frac{1}{2}\sin\omega t - \frac{2}{\pi} \sum_{n=2,4,6,\dots} \frac{1}{n^2-1}\cos n\omega t$$

* Extracted from graphs and·formulas, pages 372, 373, Differential Equations in Engineering Problems, Salvadori and Schwarz, published by Prentice-Hall, Inc., 1954.

BERNOULLI AND EULER NUMBERS—POLYNOMIALS

There are numerous sets of defined numbers and polynomials, among which the more important ones are those classified under the names of Bernoulli and Euler.

The *Bernoulli Polynomials* are generated by the defining condition

$$\frac{te^{tx}}{e^t - 1} = B_0(x) + B_1(x)t + B_2(x)\frac{t^2}{2!} + B_3(x)\frac{t^3}{3!} + \cdots$$

$$B_0(x) = 1, \quad B_1(x) = x - \tfrac{1}{2}, \quad B_2(x) = x^2 - x + \tfrac{1}{6}$$

$$B_3(x) = x^3 - \frac{3}{2}x^2 + \frac{x}{2}, \quad B_4(x) = x^4 - 2x^3 + x^2 - \tfrac{1}{30}, \ldots$$

The following useful relations should be noted

$$B_n'(x) = nB_{n-1}(x), \quad \int_a^x B_n(x)\,dx = \frac{1}{n+1}[B_{n+1}(x) - B_{n+1}(a)]$$

The Bernoulli numbers $B_0, B_1, B_2, \ldots$, can be obtained by putting $x = 0$ in the respective polynomials. A simpler method is to use the generating function

$$\frac{x}{e^x - 1} = \sum_{n=0}^{\infty} \frac{B_n x^n}{n!}$$

and read the coefficients from the expansion. Here,

$$B_0 = 1, \quad B_1 = -\tfrac{1}{2}, \quad B_2 = \tfrac{1}{6}, \quad B_4 = -\tfrac{1}{30},$$

$$B_6 = \tfrac{1}{42}, \quad B_8 = -\tfrac{1}{30}, \ldots B_{2n+1} = 0 \qquad (n \geq 1)$$

An important application for the Bernoulli coefficients is in its use involved for the Euler-Maclaurin Sum Formula:

$$\sum_{x=1}^{n-1} f(x) = \int_1^n f(x)\,dx + \left[\sum_{i=1}^{\infty} \frac{B_i}{i!} f^{(i-1)}(x)\right]_{x=1}^{x=n}$$

$$= \left[\int f(x)\,dx - \frac{1}{2}f(x) + \frac{1}{12}f'(x) - \frac{1}{720}f'''(x)\right.$$

$$\left. + \frac{1}{30,240}f^{(V)}(x) - \frac{1}{1,209,600}f^{(VII)}(x)\right]_{x=1}^{x=n}$$

Examples:

$$\sum_{x=1}^{n-1} \sqrt{x} = \sqrt{n}\left\{\frac{2}{3}n - \frac{1}{2} + \frac{1}{24n} - \frac{1}{1,920n^3}\right.$$

$$\left. + \frac{1}{9,216n^5} - \frac{11}{163,840n^7}\right\} - 0.207,886,224,977,355$$

correct to 12 places for $n \geq 10$.

$$\log_e(x!) = \log_e \Gamma(x + 1)$$

$$= \left(x + \frac{1}{2}\right)\log_e x - x + \frac{1}{12x} - \frac{1}{360x^3} + \frac{1}{1,260x^5} - \frac{1}{1,680x^7}$$

$$+ 0.918,938,533,205$$

accurate to 12 places for $x \geq 10$.

$f(x)$ (digamma function) $= \dfrac{d \log \Gamma(x)}{dx}$

$$= 1 + \frac{1}{2} + \frac{1}{3} + \cdots + \frac{1}{x-1} - \gamma$$

(Euler Constant) for x integer.

By Euler-Maclaurin

$$f(x) = \log_e x - \frac{1}{2x} - \frac{1}{12x^2} + \frac{1}{120x^4} - \frac{1}{252x^6} + \frac{1}{240x^8} - \frac{5}{660x^{10}} + \frac{691}{32{,}760x^{12}}$$

correct to 12 places for $x \geq 10$.

The Euler numbers together with their respective polynomials can be generated from

$$\frac{2e^{tx}}{e^t + 1} = \sum_{i=0}^{\infty} E_i(x) \frac{t^i}{i!}$$

and the relation

$$x^n = \frac{1}{2}\left[E_n(x+1) + E_n(x)\right]$$

The Euler polynomials are

$$E_0(x) = 1, \quad E_1(x) = x - \frac{1}{2}, \quad E_2(x) = x^2 - x$$

$$E_3(x) = x^3 - \frac{3}{2}x^2 + \frac{1}{4}, \quad E_4(x) = x^4 - 2x^3 + x$$

$$E_5(x) = x^5 - \frac{5}{2}x^4 + \frac{5}{2}x^2 - \frac{1}{2}$$

Tables which follow record the first fifteen polynomials of $B_k(x)$ and $E_k(x)$. The first sixty Bernoulli and Euler numbers are given in a separate table. The value of $x^n/n!$ is also important and this is given in a succeeding table for values of x from 1 to 9 and n from 1 to 50.

COEFFICIENTS b_k OF THE BERNOULLI POLYNOMIALS $B_n(x) = \sum_{k=0}^{n} b_k x^k$

$n \backslash k$	0	1	2	3	4	5	6	7	8	9	10	11	12	13	14	15
0	1															
1	$-\frac{1}{2}$	1														
2	$\frac{1}{6}$	-1	1													
3	0	$\frac{1}{2}$	$-\frac{3}{2}$	1												
4	$-\frac{1}{30}$	0	1	-2	1											
5	0	$-\frac{1}{6}$	0	$\frac{5}{3}$	$-\frac{5}{2}$	1										
6	$\frac{1}{42}$	0	$-\frac{1}{2}$	0	$\frac{5}{2}$	-3	1									
7	0	$\frac{1}{6}$	0	$-\frac{7}{6}$	0	$\frac{7}{2}$	$-\frac{7}{2}$	1								
8	$-\frac{1}{30}$	0	$\frac{2}{3}$	0	$-\frac{7}{3}$	0	$\frac{14}{3}$	-4	1							
9	0	$-\frac{3}{10}$	0	2	0	$-\frac{21}{5}$	0	6	$-\frac{9}{2}$	1						
10	$\frac{5}{66}$	0	$-\frac{3}{2}$	0	5	0	-7	0	$\frac{15}{2}$	-5	1					
11	0	$\frac{5}{6}$	0	$-\frac{11}{2}$	0	11	0	-11	0	$\frac{55}{6}$	$-\frac{11}{2}$	1				
12	$-\frac{691}{2730}$	0	5	0	$-\frac{33}{2}$	0	22	0	$-\frac{33}{2}$	0	11	-6	1			
13	0	$-\frac{691}{210}$	0	$\frac{65}{3}$	0	$-\frac{429}{10}$	0	$\frac{286}{7}$	0	$-\frac{143}{6}$	0	13	$-\frac{13}{2}$	1		
14	$\frac{7}{6}$	0	$-\frac{691}{30}$	0	$\frac{455}{6}$	0	$-\frac{1001}{10}$	0	$\frac{143}{3}$	0	$-\frac{1001}{30}$	0	$\frac{91}{6}$	-7	1	
15	0	$\frac{35}{2}$	0	$-\frac{691}{6}$	0	$\frac{455}{2}$	0	$-\frac{429}{2}$	0	$\frac{715}{6}$	0	$-\frac{91}{2}$	0	$\frac{35}{2}$	$-\frac{15}{2}$	1

COEFFICIENTS e_k OF THE EULER POLYNOMIALS $E_n(x) = \sum_{k=0}^{n} e_k x^k$

$n \backslash k$	0	1	2	3	4	5	6	7	8	9	10	11	12	13	14	15
0	1															
1	$-\frac{1}{2}$	1														
2	0	-1	1													
3	$\frac{1}{4}$	0	$-\frac{3}{2}$	1												
4	0	1	0	-2	1											
5	$-\frac{1}{2}$	0	$\frac{5}{2}$	0	$-\frac{5}{2}$	1										
6	0	-3	0	5	0	-3	1									
7	$\frac{17}{8}$	0	$-\frac{21}{2}$	0	$\frac{35}{4}$	0	$-\frac{7}{2}$	1								
8	0	17	0	-28	0	14	0	-4	1							
9	$-\frac{31}{2}$	0	$\frac{153}{2}$	0	-63	0	21	0	$-\frac{9}{2}$	1						
10	0	-155	0	255	0	-126	0	30	0	-5	1					
11	$\frac{691}{4}$	0	$-\frac{1705}{2}$	0	$\frac{2805}{4}$	0	-231	0	$\frac{165}{4}$	0	$-\frac{11}{2}$	1				
12	0	2073	0	-3410	0	1683	0	-396	0	55	0	-6	1			
13	$-\frac{5461}{2}$	0	$\frac{26949}{2}$	0	$-\frac{22165}{2}$	0	$\frac{7293}{2}$	0	$-\frac{1287}{2}$	0	$\frac{143}{2}$	0	$-\frac{13}{2}$	1		
14	0	-38227	0	62881	0	-31031	0	7293	0	-1001	0	91	0	-7	1	
15	$\frac{929569}{16}$	0	$-\frac{573405}{2}$	0	$\frac{943215}{4}$	0	$-\frac{155155}{2}$	0	$\frac{109395}{8}$	0	$-\frac{3003}{2}$	0	$\frac{455}{4}$	0	$-\frac{15}{2}$	1

BERNOULLI NUMBERS
$$B_n = N/D$$

n	N	D	B_n
0	1	1	(0) 1.0000 00000
1	−1	2	(−1) −5.0000 00000*
2	1	6	(−1) 1.6666 66667
4	−1	30	(−2) −3.3333 33333
6	1	42	(−2) 2.3809 52381
8	−1	30	(−2) −3.3333 33333
10	5	66	(−2) 7.5757 57576
12	−691	2730	(−1) −2.5311 35531
14	7	6	(0) 1.1666 66667
16	−3617	510	(0) −7.0921 56863
18	43867	798	(1) 5.4971 17794
20	−1 74611	330	(2) −5.2912 42424
22	8 54513	138	(3) 6.1921 23188
24	−2363 64091	2730	(4) −8.6580 25311
26	85 53103	6	(6) 1.4255 17167
28	−2 37494 61029	870	(7) −2.7298 23107
30	861 58412 76005	14322	(8) 6.0158 08739
32	−770 93210 41217	510	(10) −1.5116 31577
34	257 76878 58367	6	(11) 4.2961 46431
36	−26315 27155 30534 77373	19 19190	(13) −1.3711 65521
38	2 92999 39138 41559	6	(14) 4.8833 23190
40	−2 61082 71849 64491 22051	13530	(16) −1.9296 57934
42	15 20097 64391 80708 02691	1806	(17) 8.4169 30476
44	−278 33269 57930 10242 35023	690	(19) −4.0338 07185
46	5964 51111 59391 21632 77961	282	(21) 2.1150 74864
48	−560 94033 68997 81768 62491 27547	46410	(23) −1.2086 62652
50	49 50572 05241 07964 82124 77525	66	(24) 7.5008 66746
52	−80116 57181 35489 95734 79249 91853	1590	(26) −5.0387 78101
54	29 14996 36348 84862 42141 81238 12691	798	(28) 3.6528 77648
56	−2479 39292 93132 26753 68541 57396 63229	870	(30) −2.8498 76930
58	84483 61334 88800 41862 04677 59940 36021	354	(32) 2.3865 42750
60	−121 52331 40483 75557 20403 04994 07982 02460 41491	567 86730	(34) −2.1399 94926

*The floating decimal point notation is used here. For example for $n = 1$, $B_1 = -\frac{1}{2} = -.500000 = (-5.00000)(10^{-1}) = (-1) - 5.0000,0000$.

EULER NUMBERS

n	E_n
0	1
2	-1
4	5
6	-61
8	1385
10	-50521
12	27 02765
14	-1993 60981
16	1 93915 12145
18	-240 48796 75441
20	37037 11882 37525
22	-69 34887 43931 37901
24	15514 53416 35570 86905
26	-40 87072 50929 31238 92361
28	12522 59641 40362 98654 68285
30	-44 15438 93249 02310 45536 82821
32	17751 93915 79539 28943 66647 89665
34	-80 72329 92358 87898 06216 82474 53281
36	41222 06033 95177 02122 34707 96712 59045
38	-234 89580 52704 31082 52017 82857 61989 47741
40	1 48511 50718 11498 00178 77156 78140 58266 84425
42	-1036 46227 33519 61211 93979 57304 74518 59763 10201
44	7 94757 94225 97592 70360 80405 10088 07061 95192 73805
46	-6667 53751 66855 44977 43502 84747 73748 19752 41076 84661
48	60 96278 64556 85421 58691 68574 28768 43153 97653 90444 35185
50	-60532 85248 18862 18963 14383 78511 16490 88103 49822 51468 15121
52	650 61624 86684 60884 77158 70634 08082 29834 83644 23676 53855 76565
54	-7 54665 99390 08739 09806 14325 65889 73674 42122 40024 71169 98586 45581
56	9420 32189 64202 41204 20228 62376 90583 22720 93888 52599 64600 93949 05945
58	-126 22019 25180 62187 19903 40923 72874 89255 48234 10611 91825 59406 99649 20041
60	181089 11496 57923 04965 45807 74165 21586 88733 48734 92363 14106 00809 54542 31325

BERNOULLI AND EULER POLYNOMIALS

$$x^n/n!$$

$n \backslash x$	2		3		4		5	
1	(0) 2.0000	00000	(0) 3.0000	00000	(0) 4.0000	00000	(0) 5.0000	00000
2	(0) 2.0000	00000	(0) 4.5000	00000	(0) 8.0000	00000	(1) 1.2500	00000
3	(0) 1.3333	33333	(0) 4.5000	00000	(1) 1.0666	66667	(1) 2.0833	33333
4	(− 1) 6.6666	66667	(0) 3.3750	00000	(1) 1.0666	66667	(1) 2.6041	66667
5	(− 1) 2.6666	66667	(0) 2.0250	00000	(0) 8.5333	33333	(1) 2.6041	66667
6	(− 2) 8.8888	88889	(0) 1.0125	00000	(0) 5.6888	88889	(1) 2.1701	38889
7	(− 2) 2.5396	82540	(− 1) 4.3392	85714	(0) 3.2507	93651	(1) 1.5500	99206
8	(− 3) 6.3492	06349	(− 1) 1.6272	32143	(0) 1.6253	96825	(0) 9.6881	20040
9	(− 3) 1.4109	34744	(− 2) 5.4241	07143	(− 1) 7.2239	85891	(0) 5.3822	88911
10	(− 4) 2.8218	69489	(− 2) 1.6272	32144	(− 1) 2.8895	94356	(0) 2.6911	44455
11	(− 5) 5.1306	71797	(− 3) 4.4379	05844	(− 1) 1.0507	61584	(0) 1.2232	47480
12	(− 6) 8.5511	19662	(− 3) 1.1094	76461	(− 2) 3.5025	38614	(− 1) 5.0968	64499
13	(− 6) 1.3155	56871	(− 4) 2.5603	30295	(− 2) 1.0777	04189	(− 1) 1.9603	32500
14	(− 7) 1.8793	66959	(− 5) 5.4864	22060	(− 3) 3.0791	54825	(− 2) 7.0011	87499
15	(− 8) 2.5058	22612	(− 5) 1.0972	84412	(− 4) 8.2110	79534	(− 2) 2.3337	29166
16	(− 9) 3.1322	78264	(− 6) 2.0574	08272	(− 4) 2.0527	69883	(− 3) 7.2929	03644
17	(−10) 3.6850	33252	(− 7) 3.6307	20481	(− 5) 4.8300	46785	(− 3) 2.1449	71660
18	(−11) 4.0944	81391	(− 8) 6.0512	00801	(− 5) 1.0733	43730	(− 4) 5.9582	54611
19	(−12) 4.3099	80412	(− 9) 9.5545	27582	(− 6) 2.2596	71011	(− 4) 1.5679	61740
20	(−13) 4.3099	80413	(− 9) 1.4331	79137	(− 7) 4.5193	42021	(− 5) 3.9199	04350
21	(−14) 4.1047	43250	(−10) 2.0473	98768	(− 8) 8.6082	70516	(− 6) 9.3331	05595
22	(−15) 3.7315	84772	(−11) 2.7919	07410	(− 8) 1.5651	40093	(− 6) 2.1211	60362
23	(−16) 3.2448	56324	(−12) 3.6416	18361	(− 9) 2.7219	82772	(− 7) 4.6112	18179
24	(−17) 2.7040	46937	(−13) 4.5520	22952	(−10) 4.5366	37953	(− 8) 9.6067	04540
25	(−18) 2.1632	37550	(−14) 5.4624	27543	(−11) 7.2586	20726	(− 8) 1.9213	40908
26	(−19) 1.6640	28884	(−15) 6.3028	01010	(−11) 1.1167	10881	(− 9) 3.6948	86362
27	(−20) 1.2326	13988	(−16) 7.0031	12233	(−12) 1.6543	86490	(−10) 6.8423	82151
28	(−22) 8.8043	85630	(−17) 7.5033	34535	(−13) 2.3634	09271	(−10) 1.2218	53956
29	(−23) 6.0719	90089	(−18) 7.7620	70209	(−14) 3.2598	74857	(−11) 2.1066	44751
30	(−24) 4.0479	93393	(−19) 7.7620	70209	(−15) 4.3464	99810	(−12) 3.5110	74585
31	(−25) 2.6116	08641	(−20) 7.5116	80847	(−16) 5.6083	86851	(−13) 5.6630	23524
32	(−26) 1.6322	55401	(−21) 7.0422	00795	(−17) 7.0104	83564	(−14) 8.8484	74257
33	(−28) 9.8924	56972	(−22) 6.4020	00722	(−18) 8.4975	55834	(−14) 1.3406	77918
34	(−29) 5.8190	92337	(−23) 5.6488	24167	(−19) 9.9971	24511	(−15) 1.9715	85173
35	(−30) 3.3251	95620	(−24) 4.8418	49286	(−19) 1.1425	28515	(−16) 2.8165	50246
36	(−31) 1.8473	30900	(−25) 4.0348	74405	(−20) 1.2694	76128	(−17) 3.9118	75343
37	(−33) 9.9855	72436	(−26) 3.2715	19788	(−21) 1.3724	06625	(−18) 5.2863	18032
38	(−34) 5.2555	64439	(−27) 2.5827	78779	(−22) 1.4446	38552	(−19) 6.9556	81619
39	(−35) 2.6951	61251	(−28) 1.9867	52908	(−23) 1.4816	80567	(−20) 8.9175	40539
40	(−36) 1.3475	80626	(−29) 1.4900	64681	(−24) 1.4816	80567	(−20) 1.1146	92567
41	(−38) 6.5735	64028	(−30) 1.0902	91230	(−25) 1.4455	42017	(−21) 1.3593	81180
42	(−39) 3.1302	68584	(−32) 7.7877	94498	(−26) 1.3767	06682	(−22) 1.6183	10928
43	(−40) 1.4559	38876	(−33) 5.4333	44999	(−27) 1.2806	57379	(−23) 1.8817	56893
44	(−42) 6.6179	03983	(−34) 3.7045	53408	(−28) 1.1642	33981	(−24) 2.1383	60106
45	(−43) 2.9412	90659	(−35) 2.4697	02271	(−29) 1.0348	74650	(−25) 2.3759	55673
46	(−44) 1.2788	22026	(−36) 1.6106	75399	(−31) 8.9989	09998	(−26) 2.5825	60514
47	(−46) 5.4417	95855	(−37) 1.0280	90677	(−32) 7.6586	46807	(−27) 2.7474	04803
48	(−47) 2.2674	14940	(−39) 6.4255	66736	(−33) 6.3822	05674	(−28) 2.8618	80003
49	(−49) 9.2547	54855	(−40) 3.9340	20450	(−34) 5.2099	63815	(−29) 2.9202	85717
50	(−50) 3.7019	10942	(−41) 2.3604	12270	(−35) 4.1679	71052	(−30) 2.9202	85717

Series

BERNOULLI AND EULER POLYNOMIALS

$$x^n/n!$$

$n\backslash x$	6		7		8		9	
1	(0) 6.0000	00000	(0) 7.0000	00000	(0) 8.0000	00000	(0) 9.0000	00000
*2	(1) 1.8000	00000	(1) 2.4500	00000	(1) 3.2000	00000	(1) 4.0500	00000
3	(1) 3.6000	00000	(1) 5.7166	66667	(1) 8.5333	33333	(2) 1.2150	00000
4	(1) 5.4000	00000	(2) 1.0004	16667	(2) 1.7066	66667	(2) 2.7337	50000
5	(1) 6.4800	00000	(2) 1.4005	83333	(2) 2.7306	66667	(2) 4.9207	50000
6	(1) 6.4800	00000	(2) 1.6340	13889	(2) 3.6408	88889	(2) 7.3811	25000
7	(1) 5.5542	85714	(2) 1.6340	13889	(2) 4.1610	15873	(2) 9.4900	17857
8	(1) 4.1657	14286	(2) 1.4297	62153	(2) 4.1610	15873	(3) 1.0676	27009
9	(1) 2.7771	42857	(2) 1.1120	37230	(2) 3.6986	80776	(3) 1.0676	27009
10	(1) 1.6662	85714	(1) 7.7842	60610	(2) 2.9589	44621	(2) 9.6086	43080
11	(0) 9.0888	31169	(1) 4.9536	20388	(2) 2.1519	59724	(2) 7.8616	17066
12	(0) 4.5444	15584	(1) 2.8896	11893	(2) 1.4346	39816	(2) 5.8962	12799
13	(0) 2.0974	22577	(1) 1.5559	44865	(1) 8.8285	52715	(2) 4.0819	93476
14	(− 1) 8.9889	53903	(0) 7.7797	24327	(1) 5.0448	87266	(2) 2.6241	38663
15	(− 1) 3.5955	81561	(0) 3.6305	38019	(1) 2.6906	06542	(2) 1.5744	83198
16	(− 1) 1.3483	43085	(0) 1.5883	60383	(1) 1.3453	03271	(1) 8.8564	67988
17	(− 2) 4.7588	57949	(− 1) 6.5403	07461	(0) 6.3308	38921	(1) 4.6887	18347
18	(− 2) 1.5862	85983	(− 1) 2.5434	52902	(0) 2.8137	06187	(1) 2.3443	59173
19	(− 3) 5.0093	24157	(− 2) 9.3706	15954	(0) 1.1847	18395	(1) 1.1104	85924
20	(− 3) 1.5027	97247	(− 2) 3.2797	15584	(− 1) 4.7388	73579	(0) 4.9971	86660
21	(− 4) 4.2937	06421	(− 2) 1.0932	38528	(− 1) 1.8052	85173	(0) 2.1416	51426
22	(− 4) 1.1710	10841	(− 3) 3.4784	86224	(− 2) 6.5646	73356	(− 1) 8.7613	01286
23	(− 5) 3.0548	10892	(− 3) 1.0586	69721	(− 2) 2.2833	64645	(− 1) 3.4283	35286
24	(− 6) 7.6370	27230	(− 4) 3.0877	86685	(− 3) 7.6112	15485	(− 1) 1.2856	25732
25	(− 6) 1.8328	86535	(− 5) 8.6458	02719	(− 3) 2.4355	88956	(− 2) 4.6282	52637
26	(− 7) 4.2297	38158	(− 5) 2.3277	16117	(− 4) 7.4941	19863	(− 2) 1.6020	87451
27	(− 8) 9.3994	18129	(− 6) 6.0348	19562	(− 4) 2.2204	79959	(− 3) 5.3402	91503
28	(− 8) 2.0141	61028	(− 6) 1.5087	04890	(− 5) 6.3442	28454	(− 3) 1.7165	22269
29	(− 9) 4.1672	29712	(− 7) 3.6417	01460	(− 5) 1.7501	31987	(− 4) 5.3271	38075
30	(−10) 8.3344	59424	(− 8) 8.4973	03406	(− 6) 4.6670	18634	(− 4) 1.5981	41423
31	(−10) 1.6131	21179	(− 8) 1.9187	45930	(− 6) 1.2043	91905	(− 5) 4.6397	65421
32	(−11) 3.0246	02211	(− 9) 4.1972	56723	(− 7) 3.0109	79764	(− 5) 1.3049	34025
33	(−12) 5.4992	76746	(−10) 8.9032	71836	(− 8) 7.2993	44881	(− 6) 3.5589	10976
34	(−13) 9.7046	06022	(−10) 1.8330	26555	(− 8) 1.7174	92913	(− 7) 9.4206	46701
35	(−13) 1.6636	46746	(−11) 3.6660	53108	(− 9) 3.9256	98086	(− 7) 2.4224	52008
36	(−14) 2.7727	44578	(−12) 7.1284	36600	(−10) 8.7237	73527	(− 8) 6.0561	30022
37	(−15) 4.4963	42559	(−12) 1.3486	23141	(−10) 1.8862	21303	(− 8) 1.4731	12708
38	(−16) 7.0994	88250	(−13) 2.4843	05785	(−11) 3.9709	92217	(− 9) 3.4889	51151
39	(−16) 1.0922	28962	(−14) 4.4590	10384	(−12) 8.1456	25061	(−10) 8.0514	25733
40	(−17) 1.6383	43443	(−15) 7.8032	68172	(−12) 1.6291	25012	(−10) 1.8115	70790
41	(−18) 2.3975	75770	(−15) 1.3322	65298	(−13) 3.1787	80512	(−11) 3.9766	18807
42	(−19) 3.4251	08241	(−16) 2.2204	42162	(−14) 6.0548	20021	(−12) 8.5213	26014
43	(−20) 4.7792	20803	(−17) 3.6146	73288	(−14) 1.1264	78144	(−12) 1.7835	33352
44	(−21) 6.5171	19276	(−18) 5.7506	16594	(−15) 2.0481	42079	(−13) 3.6481	36401
45	(−22) 8.6894	92369	(−19) 8.9454	03592	(−16) 3.6411	41473	(−14) 7.2962	72804
46	(−22) 1.1334	12048	(−19) 1.3612	ˉ7068	(−17) 6.3324	19955	(−14) 1.4275	31635
47	(−23) 1.4469	08998	(−20) 2.0274	04144	(−17) 1.0778	58716	(−15) 2.7335	71217
48	(−24) 1.8086	36247	(−21) 2.9566	31045	(−18) 1.7964	31193	(−16) 5.1254	46033
49	(−25) 2.2146	56629	(−22) 4.2237	58634	(−19) 2.9329	48887	(−17) 9.4140	84548
50	(−26) 2.6575	87955	(−23) 5.9132	62088	(−20) 4.6927	18219	(−17) 1 6945	35219

*The floating decimal point notation is used here. For example (1) 1.8000,000 = (1.8000,000) 10.

STIRLING NUMBERS

Stirling numbers

The Stirling numbers are used for reducing factorials such as $x^{(n)}$ to polynomials in x and vice versa.

Stirling numbers of the first kind

The factorial polynomial $x^{(n)}$ is defined and represented by

$$x^{(n)} = x(x - 1)(x - 2) \cdots (x - n + 1)$$

where $x^{(0)}$ is 1 by definition.

If n is a non-negative integer, then

$$x^{(n)} = s_{n1}x + s_{n2}x^2 + \cdots + s_{nn}x^n.$$

Here the numbers $s_{n1}, s_{n2}, s_{n3}, \ldots$, are Stirling numbers of the first kind. A table listing these numbers with an example using same follows.

STIRLING NUMBERS OF THE FIRST KIND

n	s_{n1}	s_{n2}	s_{n3}	s_{n4}	s_{n5}	s_{n6}	s_{n7}	s_{n8}
1	1	0	0	0	0	0	0	0
2	-1	1	0	0	0	0	0	0
3	2	-3	1	0	0	0	0	0
4	-6	11	-6	1	0	0	0	0
5	24	-50	35	-10	1	0	0	0
6	-120	274	-225	85	-15	1	0	0
7	720	$-1\ 764$	1 624	-735	175	-21	1	0
8	$-5\ 040$	13 068	$-13\ 132$	6 769	$-1\ 960$	322	-28	1

The table may be continued by using the recurrence formula

$$s_{ni} = s_{n-1,i-1} - (n - 1)s_{n-1,i}, \quad i = 1, 2, \ldots, n$$

where $s_{n0} = 0$ for all n.

Example

Express $3x^{(3)} + 2x^{(1)}$ using Stirling's numbers of the first kind

$$3x^{(3)} = 3(2x - 3x^2 + x^3)$$
$$= 6x - 9x^2 + 3x^3$$
$$2x^{(1)} = 2x$$
$$\therefore 3x^{(3)} + 2x^{(1)} = 8x - 9x^2 + 3x^3$$

This may be verified by carrying out the indicated operations as follows

$$3x^{(3)} + 2x^{(1)} = 3(x)(x - 1)(x - 2) + 2x$$
$$= 3x^3 - 9x^2 + 6x + 2x$$
$$= 8x - 9x^2 + 3x^3$$

Stirling numbers of the second kind

For every non-negative integer n the function defined by x^n can be expressed as a linear combination of factorial powers of x not higher than the n'th. In other words

$$x^n = t_{n1}x^{(1)} + t_{n2}x^{(2)} + \cdots + t_{nn}x^{(n)}.$$

The numbers $t_{n1}, t_{n2}, \ldots, t_{nn}$ are called Stirling's numbers of the second kind.

A table listing these numbers with an example using same follows.

STIRLING NUMBERS OF THE SECOND KIND

n	t_{n1}	t_{n2}	t_{n3}	t_{n4}	t_{n5}	t_{n6}	t_{n7}	t_{n8}
1	1	0	0	0	0	0	0	0
2	1	1	0	0	0	0	0	0
3	1	3	1	0	0	0	0	0
4	1	7	6	1	0	0	0	0
5	1	15	25	10	1	0	0	0
6	1	31	90	65	15	1	0	0
7	1	63	301	350	140	21	1	0
8	1	127	966	1 701	1 050	266	28	1

This table may be continued by using the recurrence formula

$$t_{ni} = it_{n-1,i} + t_{n-1,i-1}, \quad i = 1, 2, \ldots, n$$

where $t_{n0} = 0$ for all n.

Example

Express $2x^3 - 3x^2 + x + 2$ by use of factorial powers

$$2x^3 = 2[x^{(1)} + 3x^{(2)} + x^{(3)}] = 2x^{(1)} + 6x^{(2)} + 2x^{(3)}$$
$$-3x^2 = -3[x^{(1)} + x^{(2)}] \qquad = -3x^{(1)} - 3x^{(2)}$$
$$x = x^{(1)} \qquad\qquad\qquad = x^{(1)}$$
$$+2 = +2x^{(0)} \qquad\qquad\quad = 2x^{(0)}$$

$$\therefore 2x^3 - 3x^2 + x + 2 = 2 + 3x^{(2)} + 2x^{(3)}$$

DIFFERENTIAL EQUATIONS

SPECIAL FORMULAS

Certain types of differential equations occur sufficiently often to justify the use of formulas for the corresponding particular solutions. The following set of tables I to XIV covers all first, second and nth order ordinary linear differential equations with constant coefficients for which the right members are of the form $P(x)e^{rx} \sin sx$ or $P(x)e^{rx} \cos sx$, where r and s are constants and $P(x)$ is a polynomial of degree n.

When the right member of a reducible linear partial differential equation with constant coefficients is not zero, particular solutions for certain types of right members are contained in tables XV to XXI. In these tables both F and P are used to denote polynomials, and it is assumed that no denominator is zero. In any formula the roles of x and y may be reversed throughout, changing a formula in which x dominates to one in which y dominates. Tables XIX, XX, XXI are applicable whether the equations are reducible or not. The symbol $\binom{m}{n}$ stands for $\dfrac{m!}{(m-n)!n!}$ and is the $n+1$ st coefficient in the expansion of $(a+b)^m$. Also $0! = 1$ by definition.

The tables as herewith given are those contained in the text *Differential Equations* by Ginn and Company (1955) and are published with their kind permission and that of the author, Professor Frederick H. Steen.

Solution of Linear Differential Equations with Constant Coefficients

Any linear differential equation with constant coefficients may be written in the form

$$p(D)y = R(x),$$

where D is the differential operator

$$Dy = \frac{dy}{dx},$$

$p(D)$ is a polynomial in D,
y is the dependent variable,
x is the independent variable,
$R(x)$ is an arbitrary function of x.

A power of D represents repeated differentiation, that is

$$D^n y = \frac{d^n y}{dx^n}.$$

For such an equation, the general solution may be written in the form

$$y = y_c + y_p,$$

where y_p is any particular solution, and y_c is called the *complementary function*. This complementary function is defined as the general solution of the *homogeneous equation*, which is the original differential equation with the right side replaced by zero, i.e.

$$p(D)y = 0$$

The complementary function y_c may be determined as follows:

1. Factor the polynomial $p(D)$ into real and complex linear factors, just as if D were a variable instead of an operator.

2. For each non-repeated linear factor of the form $(D - a)$, where a is real, write down a term of the form

$$ce^{ax},$$

where c is an arbitrary constant.

3. For each repeated real linear factor of the form $(D - a)^n$, write down n terms of the form

$$c_1 e^{ax} + c_2 x e^{ax} + c_3 x^2 e^{ax} + \cdots + c_n x^{n-1} e^{ax},$$

where the c_i's are arbitrary constants.

4. For each non-repeated conjugate complex pair of factors of the form $(D - a + ib)(D - a - ib)$, write down 2 terms of the form

$$c_1 e^{ax} \cos bx + c_2 e^{ax} \sin bx$$

5. For each repeated conjugate complex pair of factors of the form $(D - a + ib)^n (D - a - ib)^n$, write down $2n$ terms of the form

$$c_1 e^{ax} \cos bx + c_2 e^{ax} \sin bx + c_3 x e^{ax} \cos bx + c_4 x e^{ax} \sin bx + \cdots$$
$$+ c_{2n-1} x^{n-1} e^{ax} \cos bx + c_{2n} x^{n-1} e^{ax} \sin bx$$

6. The sum of all the terms thus written down is the complementary function y_c.

To find the particular solution y_p, use the following tables, as shown in the examples. For cases not shown in the tables, there are various methods of finding y_p. The most general method is called *variation of parameters*. The following example illustrates the method:

Find y_p for $(D^2 - 4)y = e^x$.

This example can be solved most easily by use of equation 63 in the tables following. However it is given here as an example of the method of variation of parameters.

The complementary function is

$$y_c = c_1 e^{2x} + c_2 e^{-2x}$$

To find y_p, replace the constants in the complementary function with unknown functions,

$$y_p = u e^{2x} + v e^{-2x}.$$

We now prepare to substitute this assumed solution into the original equation. We begin by taking all the necessary derivatives:

$$y_p = u e^{2x} + v e^{-2x}$$
$$y_p' = 2u e^{2x} - 2v e^{-2x} + u' e^{2x} + v' e^{-2x}$$

For each derivative of y_p except the highest, we set the sum of all the terms containing u' and v' to 0. Thus the above equation becomes

$$u' e^{2x} + v' e^{-2x} = 0 \quad \text{and} \quad y_p' = 2u e^{2x} - 2v e^{-2x}$$

Continuing to differentiate, we have

$$y_p'' = 4u e^{2x} + 4v e^{-2x} + 2u' e^{2x} - 2v' e^{-2x}$$

When we substitute into the original equation, all the terms not containing u' or v' cancel out. This is a consequence of the method by which y_p was set up.

Thus all that is necessary is to write down the terms containing u' or v' in the highest order derivative of y_p, multiply by the constant coefficient of the highest power of D in $p(D)$, and set it equal to $R(x)$. Together with the previous terms in u' and v' which were set equal to 0, this gives us as many linear equations in the first derivatives of the unknown functions as there are unknown functions. The first derivatives may then be solved for by algebra, and the unknown functions found by integration. In the present example, this becomes

$$u'e^{2x} + v'e^{-2x} = 0$$
$$2u'e^{2x} - 2v'e^{-2x} = e^x.$$

We eliminate v' and u' separately, getting

$$4u'e^{2x} = e^x$$
$$4v'e^{-2x} = -e^x.$$

Thus

$$u' = \tfrac{1}{4}e^{-x}$$
$$v' = -\tfrac{1}{4}e^{3x}.$$

Therefore, by integrating

$$u = -\tfrac{1}{4}e^{-x}$$
$$v = -\tfrac{1}{12}e^{3x}.$$

A constant of integration is not needed, since we need only one particular solution. Thus

$$y_p = ue^{2x} + ve^{-2x} = -\tfrac{1}{4}e^{-x}e^{2x} - \tfrac{1}{12}e^{3x}e^{-2x}$$
$$= -\tfrac{1}{4}e^x - \tfrac{1}{12}e^x = -\tfrac{1}{3}e^x,$$

and the general solution is

$$y = y_c + y_p = c_1e^{2x} + c_2e^{-2x} - \tfrac{1}{3}e^x.$$

The following examples illustrate the use of the tables.

Example 1. Solve $(D^2 - 4)y = \sin 3x$.
Substitution of $q = -4, s = 3$ in formula 24 gives

$$y_p = \frac{\sin 3x}{-9 - 4},$$

wherefore the general solution is

$$y = c_1e^{2x} + c_2e^{-2x} - \frac{\sin 3x}{13}.$$

Example 2. Obtain a particular solution of $(D^2 - 4D + 5)y = x^2e^{3x}\sin x$.
Applying formula 40 with $a = 2, b = 1, r = 3, s = 1, P(x) = x^2, s + b = 2, s - b = 0$, $a - r = -1, (a - r)^2 + (s + b)^2 = 5, (a - r)^2 + (s - b)^2 = 1$, we have

$$y_p = \frac{e^{3x}\sin x}{2}\left[\left(\frac{2}{5} - \frac{0}{1}\right)x^2 + \left(\frac{2(-1)2}{25} - \frac{2(-1)0}{1}\right)2x\right.$$
$$\left. + \left(\frac{3 \cdot 1 \cdot 2 - 2^3}{125} - \frac{3 \cdot 1 \cdot 0 - 0}{1}\right)2\right]$$
$$- \frac{e^{3x}\cos x}{2}\left[\left(\frac{-1}{5} - \frac{-1}{1}\right)x^2 + \left(\frac{1 - 4}{25} - \frac{1 - 0}{1}\right)2x\right.$$
$$\left. + \left(\frac{-1 - 3(-1)4}{125} - \frac{-1 - 3(-1)0}{1}\right)2\right]$$

$$= \left(\tfrac{1}{5}x^2 - \tfrac{4}{25}x - \tfrac{2}{125}\right)e^{3x}\sin x + \left(-\tfrac{2}{5}x^2 + \tfrac{28}{25}x - \tfrac{136}{125}\right)e^{3x}\cos x.$$

The special formulas effect a very considerable saving of time in problems of this type.

Example 3.   Obtain a particular solution of $(D^2 - 4D + 5)y = x^2 e^{2x} \cos x$. (Compare with Example 2.)

Formula 40 is not applicable here since for this equation $r = a$, $s = b$, wherefore the denominator $(a - r)^2 + (s - b)^2 = 0$. We turn instead to formula 44. Substituting $a = 2, b = 1, P(x) = x^2$ and replacing sin by cos, cos by $-\sin$, we obtain

$$y_p = \frac{e^{2x} \cos x}{4} (x^2 - \tfrac{2}{4}) + \frac{e^{2x} \sin x}{2} \int (x^2 - \tfrac{1}{2}) dx$$

$$= \left(\frac{x^2}{4} - \frac{1}{8}\right) e^{2x} \cos x + \left(\frac{x^3}{6} - \frac{x}{4}\right) e^{2x} \sin x,$$

which is the required solution.

Example 4.   Find z_p for $(D_x - 3D_y)z = \ln(y + 3x)$.

Referring to Table XV we note that formula 69 (not 68) is applicable. This gives

$$z_p = x \ln(y + 3x).$$

It is easily seen that $-\dfrac{y}{3} \ln(y + 3x)$ would serve equally well.

Example 5.   Solve $(D_x + 2D_y - 4)z = y \cos(y - 2x)$.

Since R in formula 76 contains a polynomial in x, not y, we rewrite the given equation in the form

$$(D_y + \tfrac{1}{2}D_x - 2)z = \tfrac{1}{2}y \cos(y - 2x).$$

Then

$$z_c = e^{2y} F(x - \tfrac{1}{2}y) = e^{2y} f(2x - y),$$

and by the formula

$$z_p = -\tfrac{1}{2} \cos(y - 2x) \cdot \left(\frac{y}{2} + \frac{\tfrac{1}{2}}{2}\right)$$

$$= -\tfrac{1}{8}(2y + 1) \cos(y - 2x).$$

Example 6.   Find z_p for $(D_x + 4D_y)^3 z = (2x - y)^2$.

Using formula 79, we obtain

$$z_p = \frac{\int\int\int u^2 du^3}{[2 + 4(-1)]^3} = \frac{u^5}{5 \cdot 4 \cdot 3 \cdot (-8)} = -\frac{(2x - y)^5}{480}.$$

Example 7.   Find z_p for $(D_x^3 + 5D_x^2 D_y - 7D_x + 4)z = e^{2x+3y}$.

By formula 87

$$z_p = \frac{e^{2x+3y}}{2^3 + 5 \cdot 2^2 \cdot 3 - 7 \cdot 2 + 4} = \frac{e^{2x+3y}}{58}.$$

Example 8.   Find z_p for

$$(D_x^4 + 6D_x^3 D_y + D_x D_y + D_y^2 + 9)z = \sin(3x + 4y).$$

Since every term in the left member is of *even* degree in the two operators D_x and D_y, formula 90 is applicable.

It gives

$$z_p = \frac{\sin(3x + 4y)}{(-9)^2 + 6(-9)(-12) + (-12) + (-16) + 9}$$

$$= \frac{\sin(3x + 4y)}{710}$$

DIFFERENTIAL EQUATIONS

TABLE I: $(D-a)y = R$

R	y_p
1. e^{rx}	$\dfrac{e^{rx}}{r-a}$
2. $\sin sx$*	$-\dfrac{a\sin sx + s\cos sx}{a^2+s^2} = -\dfrac{1}{\sqrt{a^2+s^2}}\sin\left(sx+\tan^{-1}\dfrac{s}{a}\right)$
3. $P(x)$	$-\dfrac{1}{a}\left[P(x) + \dfrac{P'(x)}{a} + \dfrac{P''(x)}{a^2} + \cdots + \dfrac{P^{(n)}(x)}{a^n}\right]$
4. $e^{rx}\sin sx$*	Replace a by $a-r$ in formula 2 and multiply by e^{rx}.
5. $P(x)e^{rx}$	Replace a by $a-r$ in formula 3 and multiply by e^{rx}.
6. $P(x)\sin sx$*	$-\sin sx\left[\dfrac{a}{a^2+s^2}P(x) + \dfrac{a^2-s^2}{(a^2+s^2)^2}P'(x) + \dfrac{a^3-3as^2}{(a^2+s^2)^3}P''(x) + \cdots\right.$
	$\left. + \dfrac{a^k - \binom{k}{2}a^{k-2}s^2 + \binom{k}{4}a^{k-4}s^4 - \cdots}{(a^2+s^2)^k}P^{(k-1)}(x) + \cdots\right]$
	$-\cos sx\left[\dfrac{s}{a^2+s^2}P(x) + \dfrac{2as}{(a^2+s^2)^2}P'(x) + \dfrac{3a^2s-s^3}{(a^2+s^2)^3}P''(x) + \cdots\right.$
	$\left. + \dfrac{\binom{k}{1}a^{k-1}s - \binom{k}{3}a^{k-3}s^3 + \cdots}{(a^2+s^2)^k}P^{(k-1)}(x) + \cdots\right]$
7. $P(x)e^{rx}\sin sx$*	Replace a by $a-r$ in formula 6 and multiply by e^{rx}.
8. e^{ax}	xe^{ax}
9. $e^{ax}\sin sx$*	$-\dfrac{e^{ax}\cos sx}{s}$
10. $P(x)e^{ax}$	$e^{ax}\displaystyle\int P(x)\,dx$
11. $P(x)e^{ax}\sin sx$*	$\dfrac{e^{ax}\sin sx}{s}\left[\dfrac{P'(x)}{s^3} - \dfrac{P'''(x)}{s^3} + \dfrac{P^v(x)}{s^5} - \cdots\right] - \dfrac{e^{ax}\cos sx}{s}\left[P(x) - \dfrac{P''(x)}{s^2} + \dfrac{P^{iv}(x)}{s^4} - \cdots\right]$

* For cos sx in R replace "sin" by "cos" and "cos" by "$-\sin$" in y_p.

$$D^n = \dfrac{d^n}{dx^n} \qquad \binom{m}{n} = \dfrac{m!}{(m-n)!\,n!} \qquad 0! = 1$$

DIFFERENTIAL EQUATIONS (Continued)

TABLE II: $(D-a)^2 y = R$

R	y_p
12. e^{rx}	$\dfrac{e^{rx}}{(r-a)^2}$
13. $\sin sx$*	$\dfrac{1}{(a^2+s^2)^2}\left[(a^2-s^2)\sin sx + 2as\cos sx\right] = \dfrac{1}{a^2+s^2}\sin\left(sx+\tan^{-1}\dfrac{2as}{a^2-s^2}\right)$
14. $P(x)$	$\dfrac{1}{a^2}\left[P(x)+\dfrac{2P'(x)}{a}+\dfrac{3P''(x)}{a^2}+\cdots+\dfrac{(n+1)P^{(n)}(x)}{a^n}\right]$
15. $e^{rx}\sin sx$*	Replace a by $a-r$ in formula 13 and multiply by e^{rx}.
16. $P(x)e^{rx}$	Replace a by $a-r$ in formula 14 and multiply by e^{rx}.
17. $P(x)\sin sx$*	$\sin sx\left[\dfrac{a^2-s^2}{(a^2+s^2)^2}P(x)+2\dfrac{a^3-3as^2}{(a^2+s^2)^3}P'(x)+3\dfrac{a^4-6a^2s^2+s^4}{(a^2+s^2)^4}P''(x)+\cdots\right.$ $\left.+(k-1)\dfrac{a^k-\binom{k}{2}a^{k-2}s^2+\binom{k}{4}a^{k-4}s^4-\cdots}{(a^2+s^2)^k}P^{(k-2)}(x)+\cdots\right]$ $+\cos sx\left[\dfrac{2as}{(a^2+s^2)^2}P(x)+2\dfrac{3a^2s-s^3}{(a^2+s^2)^3}P'(x)+3\dfrac{4a^3s-4as^3}{(a^2+s^2)^4}P''(x)+\cdots\right.$ $\left.+(k-1)\dfrac{\binom{k}{1}a^{k-1}s-\binom{k}{3}a^{k-3}s^3+\cdots}{(a^2+s^2)^k}P^{(k-2)}(x)+\cdots\right]$
18. $P(x)e^{rx}\sin sx$*	Replace a by $a-r$ in formula 17 and multiply by e^{rx}.
19. e^{ax}	$\frac{1}{2}x^2 e^{ax}$
20. $e^{ax}\sin sx$*	$-\dfrac{e^{ax}\sin sx}{s^2}$
21. $P(x)e^{ax}$	$e^{ax}\displaystyle\iint P(x)dx\,dx$
22. $P(x)e^{ax}\sin sx$*	$-\dfrac{e^{ax}\sin sx}{s^2}\left[P(x)-\dfrac{3P''(x)}{s^2}+\dfrac{5P^{iv}(x)}{s^4}-\dfrac{7P^{vi}(x)}{s^6}+\cdots\right]$ $-\dfrac{e^{ax}\cos sx}{s^2}\left[\dfrac{2P'(x)}{s}-\dfrac{4P'''(x)}{s^3}+\dfrac{6P^{v}(x)}{s^5}-\cdots\right]$

* For cos sx in R replace "sin" by "cos" and "cos" by "− sin" in y_p.

DIFFERENTIAL EQUATIONS (Continued)

TABLE III: $(D^2 + q)y = R$

R	y_p
23. e^{rx}	$\dfrac{e^{rx}}{r^2+q}$
24. $\sin sx$*	$\dfrac{\sin sx}{-s^2+q}$
25. $P(x)$	$\dfrac{1}{q}\left[P(x) - \dfrac{P''(x)}{q} + \dfrac{P^{iv}(x)}{q^2} - \cdots + (-1)^k \dfrac{P^{(2k)}(x)}{q^k} \cdots\right]$
26. $e^x \sin sx$*	$\dfrac{(r^2 - s^2 + q)e^x \sin sx - 2\cdot rse^x \cos sx}{(r^2 - s^2 + q)^2 + (2rs)^2} = \dfrac{e^{rx}}{\sqrt{(r^2 - s^2 + q)^2 + (2rs)^2}}\sin\left[sx - \tan^{-1}\dfrac{2rs}{r^2 - s^2 + q}\right]$
27. $P(x)e^{rx}$	$\dfrac{e^{rx}}{r^2+q}\left[P(x) - \dfrac{2r}{r^2+q}P'(x) + \dfrac{3r^2-q}{(r^2+q)^2}P''(x) - \dfrac{4r^3-4qr}{(r^2+q)^3}P'''(x) - \cdots + (-1)^{k-1}\dfrac{\binom{k}{1}r^{k-1} - \binom{k}{3}r^{k-3}q + \binom{k}{5}r^{k-5}q^2 - \cdots}{(r^2+q)^{k-1}}P^{(k-1)}(x) + \cdots\right]$
28. $P(x)\sin sx$*	$\dfrac{\sin sx}{(-s^2+q)}\left[P(x) - \dfrac{3s^2+q}{(-s^2+q)^2}P''(x) + \dfrac{5s^4+10s^2q+q^2}{(-s^2+q)^4}P^{iv}(x) + \cdots + (-1)^k\dfrac{\binom{2k+1}{1}s^{2k} + \binom{2k+1}{3}s^{2k-2}q + \binom{2k+1}{5}s^{2k-4}q^2 + \cdots}{(-s^2+q)^{2k}}P^{(2k)}(x) + \cdots\right]$ $- s\cos sx\left[\dfrac{2P'(x)}{(-s^2+q)} - \dfrac{4s^2+4q}{(-s^2+q)^3}P'''(x) + \cdots + (-1)^{k+1}\dfrac{\binom{2k}{1}s^{2k-2} - \binom{2k}{3}s^{2k-4}q + \cdots}{(-s^2+q)^{2k-1}}P^{(2k-1)}(x) + \cdots\right]$

TABLE IV: $(D^2 + b^2)y = R$

R	y_p
29. $\sin bx$*	$-\dfrac{x\cos bx}{2b}$
30. $P(x)\sin bx$*	$\dfrac{\sin bx}{(2b)^2}\left[P(x) - \dfrac{P''(x)}{(2b)^2} + \dfrac{P^{iv}(x)}{(2b)^4} - \cdots\right] - \dfrac{\cos bx}{2b}\int\left[P(x) - \dfrac{P''(x)}{(2b)^2} + \cdots\right]dx$

*For cos sx in R replace "sin" by "cos" and "cos" by "− sin" in y_p.

DIFFERENTIAL EQUATIONS (Continued)

TABLE V: $(D^2 + pD + q)y = R$

R	y_p
31. e^{rx}	$\dfrac{e^{rx}}{r^2 + pr + q}$
32. $\sin sx$*	$\dfrac{(q - s^2)\sin sx - ps\cos sx}{(q-s^2)^2 + (ps)^2} = \dfrac{1}{\sqrt{(q-s^2)^2 + (ps)^2}}\sin\left(sx - \tan^{-1}\dfrac{ps}{q-s^2}\right)$

33. $P(x)$

$$\dfrac{1}{q}\left[P(x) - \dfrac{p}{q}P'(x) + \dfrac{p^2 - q}{q^2}P''(x) - \dfrac{p^3 - 2pq}{q^3}P'''(x) + \cdots\right.$$
$$\left. + (-1)^n\dfrac{p^n - \binom{n-1}{1}p^{n-2}q + \binom{n-2}{2}p^{n-4}q^2 - \cdots}{q^n}P^{(n)}(x)\right]$$

34. $e^{rx}\sin sx$*   Replace p by $p + 2r$, q by $q + pr + r^2$ in formula 32 and multiply by e^{rx}.

35. $P(x)e^{rx}$ Replace p by $p + 2r$, q by $q + pr + r^2$ in formula 33 and multiply by e^{rx}.

TABLE VI: $(D - b)(D - a)y = R$

36. $P(x)\sin sx$*

$$\dfrac{\sin sx}{b-a}\left[\left(\dfrac{a}{a^2+s^2} - \dfrac{b}{b^2+s^2}\right)P(x) + \left(\dfrac{a^2 - s^2}{(a^2+s^2)^2} - \dfrac{b^2 - s^2}{(b^2+s^2)^2}\right)P'(x)\right.$$
$$+ \left.\left(\dfrac{a^3 - 3as^2}{(a^2+s^2)^3} - \dfrac{b^3 - 3bs^2}{(b^2+s^2)^3}\right)P''(x) + \cdots\right]$$

$$+ \dfrac{\cos sx}{b-a}\left[\left(\dfrac{s}{a^2+s^2} - \dfrac{s}{b^2+s^2}\right)P(x) + \left(\dfrac{2as}{(a^2+s^2)^2} - \dfrac{2bs}{(b^2+s^2)^2}\right)P'(x)\right.$$
$$+ \left.\left(\dfrac{3a^2s - s^3}{(a^2+s^2)^3} - \dfrac{3b^2s - s^3}{(b^2+s^2)^3}\right)P''(x) + \cdots\right]^\dagger$$

37. $P(x)e^{rx}\sin sx$*   Replace a by $a - r$, b by $b - r$ in formula 36 and multiply by e^{rx}.

38. $P(x)e^{ax}$

$$\dfrac{e^{ax}}{a-b}\left[\int\int P(x)dx + \dfrac{P(x)}{(b-a)} + \dfrac{P'(x)}{(b-a)^2} + \dfrac{P''(x)}{(b-a)^3} + \cdots + \dfrac{P^{(n)}(x)}{(b-a)^{n+1}}\right]$$

* For cos sx in R replace "sin" by "cos" and "cos" by "− sin" in y_p.

† For additional terms, compare with formula 6.

DIFFERENTIAL EQUATIONS (Continued)

TABLE VII: $(D^2 - 2aD + a^2 + b^2)y = R$

R	y_p
39. $P(x)\sin sx*$	$\dfrac{\sin sx}{2b}\left[\left(\dfrac{s+b}{a^2+(s+b)^2}-\dfrac{s-b}{a^2+(s-b)^2}\right)P(x)+\left(\dfrac{2a(s+b)}{[a^2+(s+b)^2]^2}-\dfrac{2a(s-b)}{[a^2+(s-b)^2]^2}\right)P'(x)\right.$
	$\left.+\left(\dfrac{3a^2(s+b)-(s+b)^3}{[a^2+(s+b)^2]^3}-\dfrac{3a^2(s-b)-(s-b)^3}{[a^2+(s-b)^2]^3}\right)P''(x)+\cdots\right]$
	$-\dfrac{\cos sx}{2b}\left[\left(\dfrac{a}{a^2+(s+b)^2}-\dfrac{a}{a^2+(s-b)^2}\right)P(x)+\left(\dfrac{a^2-(s+b)^2}{[a^2+(s+b)^2]^2}-\dfrac{a^2-(s-b)^2}{[a^2+(s-b)^2]^2}\right)P'(x)\right.$
	$\left.+\left(\dfrac{a^3-3a(s+b)^2}{[a^2+(s+b)^2]^3}-\dfrac{a^3-3a(s-b)^2}{[a^2+(s-b)^2]^3}\right)P''(x)+\cdots\right]^{\dagger}$
40. $P(x)e^{rx}\sin sx*$	Replace a by $a-r$ in formula 39 and multiply by e^{rx}.
41. $P(x)e^{ax}$	$\dfrac{e^{ax}}{b^2}\left[P(x)-\dfrac{P''(x)}{b^2}+\dfrac{P^{\mathrm{iv}}(x)}{b^4}-\cdots\right]$
42. $e^{ax}\sin sx*$	$\dfrac{e^{ax}\sin sx}{-s^2+b^2}$
43. $e^{ax}\sin bx*$	$-\dfrac{xe^{ax}\cos bx}{2b}$
44. $P(x)e^{ax}\sin bx*$	$\dfrac{e^{ax}\sin bx}{(2b)^2}\left[P(x)-\dfrac{P''(x)}{(2b)^2}+\dfrac{P^{\mathrm{iv}}(x)}{(2b)^4}-\cdots\right]-\dfrac{e^{ax}\cos bx}{2b}\int\left[P(x)-\dfrac{P''(x)}{(2b)^2}+\dfrac{P^{\mathrm{iv}}(x)}{(2b)^4}-\cdots\right]dx$

* For $\cos sx$ in R replace "sin" by "cos" and "cos" by " $-$ sin" in y_p.
† For additional terms, compare with formula 6.

DIFFERENTIAL EQUATIONS (Continued)

TABLE VIII: $f(D)y = [D^n + a_{n-1}D^{n-1} + \cdots + a_1D + a_0]y = R$

R	y_p
45. e^{rx}	$\dfrac{e^{rx}}{f(r)}$
46. $\sin sx$*	$\dfrac{[a_0 - a_2s^2 + a_4s^4 - \cdots]\sin sx - [a_1s - a_3s^3 + a_5s^5 + \cdots]\cos sx}{[a_0 - a_2s^2 + a_4s^4 - \cdots]^2 + [a_1s - a_3s^3 + a_5s^5 - \cdots]^2}$

TABLE IX: $f(D^2)y = R$

47. $\sin sx$*	$\dfrac{\sin sx}{f(-s^2)} = \dfrac{\sin sx}{a_0 - a_2s^2 + \cdots \pm s^{2n}}$

TABLE X: $(D - a)^n y = R$

48. e^{rx}	$\dfrac{e^{rx}}{(r-a)^n}$
49. $\sin sx$*	$\dfrac{(-1)^n}{(a^2 + s^2)^n}\left\{\left[a^n - \binom{n}{2}a^{n-2}s^2 + \binom{n}{4}a^{n-4}s^4 - \cdots\right]\sin sx + \left[\binom{n}{1}a^{n-1}s - \binom{n}{3}a^{n-3}s^3 + \cdots\right]\cos sx\right\}$
50. $P(x)$	$\dfrac{(-1)^n}{a^n}\left[P(x) + \binom{n}{1}\dfrac{P'(x)}{a} + \binom{n+1}{2}\dfrac{P''(x)}{a^2} + \binom{n+2}{3}\dfrac{P'''(x)}{a^3} + \cdots\right]$
51. $e^{rx}\sin sx$*	Replace a by $a - r$ in formula 49 and multiply by e^{rx}.
52. $e^{rx}P(x)$	Replace a by $a - r$ in formula 50 and multiply by e^{rx}.

* For $\cos sx$ in R replace "sin" by "cos" and "cos" by "$-$ sin" in y_p.

DIFFERENTIAL EQUATIONS (Continued)

TABLE XI: $(D - a)^n f(D)y = R$

53. $P(x)\sin sx^*$

$(-1)^n \sin sx[A_nP(x) + \binom{n}{1}A_{n+1}P'(x) + \binom{n+1}{2}A_{n+2}P''(x) + \binom{n+2}{3}A_{n+3}P'''(x) + \cdots]$
$+ (-1)^n \cos sx[B_nP(x) + \binom{n}{1}B_{n+1}P'(x) + \binom{n+1}{2}B_{n+2}P''(x) + \binom{n+2}{3}B_{n+3}P'''(x) + \cdots]$

$$A_1 = \frac{a}{a^2 + s^2}, \quad A_2 = \frac{a^2 - s^2}{(a^2 + s^2)^2}, \quad \cdots, \quad A_k = \frac{a^k - \binom{k}{2}a^{k-2}s^2 + \binom{k}{4}a^{k-4}s^4 - \cdots}{(a^2 + s^2)^k}$$

$$B_1 = \frac{s}{a^2 + s^2}, \quad B_2 = \frac{2as}{(a^2 + s^2)^2}, \quad \cdots, \quad B_k = \frac{\binom{k}{1}a^{k-1}s - \binom{k}{3}a^{k-3}s^3 + \cdots}{(a^2 + s^2)^k}$$

54. $P(x)e^{rx}\sin sx^*$ Replace a by $a - r$ in formula 53 and multiply by e^{rx}.

55. $e^{ax}P(x)$ $e^{ax}\displaystyle\iint \cdots \int P(x)\,dx^n$

56. $P(x)e^{ax}\sin sx^*$

$$\frac{(-1)^{\frac{n-1}{2}}e^{ax}\sin sx}{s^n}\left[\binom{n}{n-1}\frac{P'(x)}{s} - \binom{n+2}{n-1}\frac{P'''(x)}{s^3} + \binom{n+4}{n-1}\frac{P^{v}(x)}{s^5} - \cdots\right]$$
$$+ \frac{(-1)^{\frac{n+1}{2}}e^{ax}\cos sx}{s^n}\left[\binom{n-1}{n-1}P(x) - \binom{n+1}{n-1}\frac{P''(x)}{s^2} + \binom{n+3}{n-1}\frac{P^{iv}(x)}{s^4} - \cdots\right] \quad (n \text{ odd})$$

$$\frac{(-1)^{\frac{n}{2}}e^{ax}\sin sx}{s^n}\left[\binom{n-1}{n-1}P(x) - \binom{n+1}{n-1}\frac{P''(x)}{s^2} + \binom{n+3}{n-1}\frac{P^{iv}(x)}{s^4} - \cdots\right]$$
$$+ \frac{(-1)^{\frac{n}{2}}e^{ax}\cos sx}{s^n}\left[\binom{n}{n-1}\frac{P'(x)}{s} - \binom{n+2}{n-1}\frac{P'''(x)}{s^3} + \binom{n+4}{n-1}\frac{P^{v}(x)}{s^5} - \cdots\right] \quad (n \text{ even})$$

57. e^{ax} $\dfrac{x^n}{n!} \cdot \dfrac{e^{ax}}{f(a)}$

* For cos sx in R replace "sin" by "cos" and "cos" by "− sin" in y_p.

DIFFERENTIAL EQUATIONS (Continued)

TABLE XII: $(D^2 + q)^n y = R$

R	y_p
58. e^{rx}	$e^{rx}/(r^2 + q)^n$
59. $\sin sx$*	$\sin sx/(q - s^2)^n$
60. $P(x)$	$\dfrac{1}{q^n}\left[P(x) - \binom{n}{1}\dfrac{P''(x)}{q} + \binom{n+1}{2}\dfrac{P^{iv}(x)}{q^2} - \binom{n+2}{3}\dfrac{P^{vi}(x)}{q^3} + \cdots\right]$
61. $e^{rx}\sin sx$*	$\dfrac{e^{rx}}{(A^2 + B^2)^n}\{[A^n - \binom{r}{2}A^{n-2}B^2 + \binom{n}{4}A^{n-4}B^4 - \cdots]\sin sx - [\binom{n}{1}A^{n-1}B - \binom{n}{3}A^{n-3}B^3 + \cdots]\cos sx\}$

$$A = r^2 - s^2 + q, \qquad B = 2rs$$

TABLE XIII: $(D^2 + b^2)^n y = R$

62. $\sin bx$*	$(-1)^{\frac{n+1}{2}}\dfrac{x^n\cos bx}{n!(2b)^n}$ (n odd), $(-1)^{\frac{n}{2}}\dfrac{x^n\sin bx}{n!(2b)^n}$ (n even)

TABLE XIV: $(D^n - q)y = R$

63. e^{rx}	$e^{rx}/(r^n - q)$
64. $P(x)$	$-\dfrac{1}{q}\left[P(x)\dfrac{P^{(n)}(x)}{q} + \dfrac{P^{(2n)}(x)}{q^2} + \cdots\right]$
65. $\sin sx$*	$-\dfrac{q\sin sx + (-1)^{\frac{n-1}{2}}s^n\cos sx}{q^2 + s^{2n}}$ (n odd), $\dfrac{\sin sx}{(-s^2)^{n/2} - q}$ (n even)
66. $e^{rx}\sin sx$*	$\dfrac{Ae^{rx}\sin sr - Be^{rx}\cos sx}{A^2 + B^2} = \dfrac{e^{rx}}{\sqrt{A^2 + B^2}}\sin\left(sx - \tan^{-1}\dfrac{B}{A}\right)$

$$A = [r^n - \binom{n}{2}r^{n-2}s^2 + \binom{n}{4}r^{n-4}s^4 - \cdots] - q, \qquad B = [\binom{n}{1}r^{n-1}s - \binom{n}{3}r^{n-3}s^3 + \cdots]$$

* For cos sx in R replace "sin" by "cos" and "cos" by "− sin" in y_p.

DIFFERENTIAL EQUATIONS (Continued)

TABLE XV: $(D_x + mD_y)z = R$

R	z_p
67. e^{ax+by}	$\dfrac{e^{ax+by}}{a+mb}$
68. $f(ax+by)$	$\dfrac{\int f(u)du}{a+mb}$, $u = ax + by$
69. $f(y-mx)$	$xf(y-mx)$
70. $\phi(x,y)f(y-mx)$	$f(y-mx)\int \phi(x, a+mx)dx$ $\quad (a = y - mx \text{ after integration})$

TABLE XVI: $(D_x + mD_y - k)z = R$

R	
71. e^{ax+by}	$\dfrac{e^{ax+by}}{a+mb-k}$
72. $\sin(ax+by)^*$	$-\dfrac{(a+bm)\cos(ax+by)+k\sin(ax+by)}{(a+bm)^2+k^2}$
73. $e^{\alpha x+\beta y}\sin(ax+by)$	Replace k in 72 by $k - \alpha - m\beta$ and multiply by $e^{\alpha x+\beta y}$
74. $e^{zk}f(ax+by)$	$\dfrac{e^{zk}\int f(u)du}{a+mb}$, $u = ax + by$
75. $f(y-mx)$	$-\dfrac{f(y-mx)}{k}$
76. $P(x)f(y-mx)$	$-\dfrac{1}{k}f(y-mx)\left[P(x) + \dfrac{P'(x)}{k} + \dfrac{P''(x)}{k^2} + \cdots + \dfrac{P^{(n)}(x)}{k^n}\right]$
77. $e^{kx}f(y-mx)$	$xe^{kx}f(y-mx)$

* For cos $(ax + by)$ replace "sin" by "cos," and "cos" by "— sin" in z_p.

$$D_x = \frac{\partial}{\partial x}; \quad D_y = \frac{\partial}{\partial y}; \quad D_x^k D_y^r = \frac{\partial^{k+r}}{\partial_x^k \partial_y^r}$$

DIFFERENTIAL EQUATIONS (Continued)

TABLE XVII: $(D_x + mD_y)^n z = R$

R	z_p
78. e^{ax+by}	$\dfrac{e^{ax+by}}{(a+mb)^n}$
79. $f(ax+by)$	$\dfrac{\int\int\cdots\int f(u)du^n}{(a+mb)^n}$, $u = ax+by$
80. $f(y-mx)$	$\dfrac{x^n}{n!}f(y-mx)$
81. $\phi(x,y)f(y+mx)$	$f(y-mx)\int\int\cdots\int\phi(x, a+mx)dx^n$ $(a = y - mx$ after integration$)$

TABLE XVIII: $(D_x + mD_y - k)^n z = R$

R	
82. e^{ax+by}	$\dfrac{e^{ax+by}}{(a+mb-k)^n}$
83. $f(y-mx)$	$\dfrac{(-1)^n f(y-mx)}{k^n}$
84. $P(x)f(y-mx)$	$\dfrac{(-1)^n}{k^n}f(y-mx)\left[P(x) + \binom{n}{1}\dfrac{P'(x)}{k} + \binom{n+1}{2}\dfrac{P''(x)}{k^2} + \binom{n+2}{3}\dfrac{P'''(x)}{k^3} + \cdots\right]$
85. $e^{kx}f(ax+by)$	$\dfrac{e^{kx}\int\int\cdots\int f(u)du^n}{(a+mb)^n}$, $u = ax+by$
86. $e^{kx}f(y-mx)$	$\dfrac{x^n}{n!}e^{kx}f(y-mx)$

DIFFERENTIAL EQUATIONS (Continued)

TABLE XIX: $[D_x^n + a_1 D_x^{n-1}D_y + a_2 D_x^{n-2}D_y^2 + \cdots + a^n D_y^n]z = R$

87. e^{ax+by} $\qquad \dfrac{e^{ax+by}}{a + a_1 a^{n-1}b + a_2 a^{n-2}b^2 + \cdots + a_n b^n}$

88. $f(ax + by)$ $\qquad \dfrac{\int\int\cdots\int f(u)du^n}{a^n + a_1 a^{n-1}b + a_2 a^{n-2}b^2 + \cdots + a^n b^n}$, $\quad (u = ax + by)$

TABLE XX: $F(D_x, D_y)z = R$

89. e^{ax+by} $\qquad \dfrac{e^{ax+by}}{F(a, b)}$

TABLE XXI: $F(D_x^2, D_xD_y, D_y^2)z = R$

90. $\sin(ax + by)$* $\qquad \dfrac{\sin(ax + by)}{F(-a^2, -ab, -b^2)}$

* For cos $(ax + by)$ replace "sin" by "cos", and "cos" by "−sin" in z.

THE LAPLACE TRANSFORM

DR. R. E. GASKELL

If $F(t)$ is a piecewise continuous real-valued function of the real variable $t (0 \leqq t < \infty)$, and if $F(t)$ is of exponential order, that is if $|F(t)| < Me^{at} (t > T; M, a, T$ positive constants) then the *Laplace transform* of $F(t)$,

$$L\{F(t)\} = f(s) = \int_0^\infty e^{-st} F(t) \, dt, \tag{1}$$

exists in the half-plane of the complex variable s for which the real part of s is greater than some fixed value s_0, i.e., $R(s) \geq s_0$. Furthermore

$$F(t) = \frac{1}{2\pi i} \int_{a-i\infty}^{a+i\infty} e^{st} f(s) \, ds, \tag{2}$$

where $a > s_0$. The important property

$$
\begin{aligned}
L\{F^{(r)}(t)\} &= \int_0^\infty e^{-st} \left(\frac{d^r F}{dt^r} \right) dt \\
&= s^r f(s) - \sum_{n=0}^{r-1} s^{r-1-n} F^{(n)}(+0)
\end{aligned}
\tag{3}
$$

makes the Laplace transform very useful for solving linear differential equations with constant coefficients, and many boundary value problems.

	$F(t)$	$f(s)$
1	$F(t)$	$\displaystyle\int_0^\infty e^{-st}F(t)\,dt$
2	$AF(t) + BG(t)$	$Af(s) + Bg(s)$
3	$F'(t)$	$sf(s) - F(+0)$
4	$F^{(n)}(t)$	$s^n f(s) - s^{n-1}F(+0) - s^{n-2}F'(+0) - \cdots$ $- F^{(n-1)}(+0)$
5	$\displaystyle\int_0^t F(\tau)\,d\tau$	$\dfrac{1}{s} f(s)$
6	$\displaystyle\int_0^t \int_0^r F(\lambda)\,d\lambda\,d\tau$	$\dfrac{1}{s^2} f(s)$
7	$\displaystyle\int_0^t F_1(t - \tau)F_2(\tau)\,d\tau = F_1{*}F_2$	$f_1(s)\,f_2(s)$
8	$tF(t)$	$-f'(s)$
9	$t^n F(t)$	$(-1)^n f^{(n)}(s)$
10	$\dfrac{1}{t} F(t)$	$\displaystyle\int_s^\infty f(x)\,dx$
11	$e^{at} F(t)$	$f(s - a)$
12	$F(t - b)$, where $F(t) = 0$ when $t < 0$	$e^{-bs} f(s)$
13	$\dfrac{1}{c} F\left(\dfrac{t}{c}\right)$	$f(cs)$
14	$\dfrac{1}{c} e^{(bt)/c}\, F\left(\dfrac{t}{c}\right)$	$f(cs - b)$
15	$F(t + a) = F(t)$	$\dfrac{\displaystyle\int_0^a e^{-st}F(t)\,dt}{1 - e^{-as}}$
16	$F(t + a) = -F(t)$	$\dfrac{\displaystyle\int_0^a e^{-st}F(t)\,dt}{1 + e^{-as}}$
17	$F_1(t)$, the half-wave rectification of $F(t)$ in No. 16	$\dfrac{f(s)}{1 - e^{-as}}$
18	$F_2(t)$, the full-wave rectification of $F(t)$ in No. 16	$f(s) \coth \dfrac{as}{2}$
19	$\displaystyle\sum_1^m \dfrac{p(a_n)}{q'(a_n)} e^{a_n t}$	$\dfrac{p(s)}{q(s)}$, $q(s) = (s - a_1)(s - a_2)\cdots(s - a_m)$
20	$e^{at} \displaystyle\sum_{n=1}^r \dfrac{\phi^{(r-n)}(a)}{(r - n)!} \dfrac{t^{n-1}}{(n - 1)!} + \cdots$	$\dfrac{p(s)}{q(s)} = \dfrac{\phi(s)}{(s - a)^r}$

[1]These tables of Laplace Operations, Laplace Transforms, and Finite Fourier sine and cosine transforms were taken from "Modern Operational Mathematics in Engineering", by permission of the author, R. V. Churchill, and the publisher, McGraw-Hill Book Company, Inc.

LAPLACE TRANSFORMS

	$f(s)$	$F(t)$
1	$\dfrac{1}{s}$	$\mu(t)$, unit step function
2	$\dfrac{1}{s^2}$	t
3	$\dfrac{1}{s^n}$ $(n = 1, 2, \ldots)$	$\dfrac{t^{n-1}}{(n-1)!}$
4	$\dfrac{1}{\sqrt{s}}$	$\dfrac{1}{\sqrt{\pi t}}$
5	$s^{-3/2}$	$2\sqrt{\dfrac{t}{\pi}}$
6	$s^{-[n+(1/2)]}$ $(n = 1, 2, \ldots)$	$\dfrac{2^n t^{n-(1/2)}}{1 \cdot 3 \cdot 5 \cdots (2n-1)\sqrt{\pi}}$
7	$\dfrac{\Gamma(k)}{s^k}$ $(k > 0)$	t^{k-1}
8	$\dfrac{1}{s-a}$	e^{at}
9	$\dfrac{1}{(s-a)^2}$	te^{at}
10	$\dfrac{1}{(s-a)^n}$ $(n = 1, 2, \ldots)$	$\dfrac{1}{(n-1)!}\, t^{n-1} e^{at}$
11	$\dfrac{\Gamma(k)}{(s-a)^k}$ $(k > 0)$	$t^{k-1} e^{at}$
12*	$\dfrac{1}{(s-a)(s-b)}$	$\dfrac{1}{a-b}(e^{at} - e^{bt})$
13*	$\dfrac{s}{(s-a)(s-b)}$	$\dfrac{1}{a-b}(ae^{at} - be^{bt})$
14*	$\dfrac{1}{(s-a)(s-b)(s-c)}$	$-\dfrac{(b-c)e^{at} + (c-a)e^{bt} + (a-b)e^{ct}}{(a-b)(b-c)(c-a)}$
15	$\dfrac{1}{s^2 + a^2}$	$\dfrac{1}{a}\sin at$
16	$\dfrac{s}{s^2 + a^2}$	$\cos at$
17	$\dfrac{1}{s^2 - a^2}$	$\dfrac{1}{a}\sinh at$
18	$\dfrac{s}{s^2 - a^2}$	$\cosh at$

*Here a, b, and (in 14) c represent distinct constants.

LAPLACE TRANSFORMS (Continued)

	$f(s)$	$F(t)$
19	$\dfrac{1}{s(s^2 + a^2)}$	$\dfrac{1}{a^2}(1 - \cos at)$
20	$\dfrac{1}{s^2(s^2 + a^2)}$	$\dfrac{1}{a^3}(at - \sin at)$
21	$\dfrac{1}{(s^2 + a^2)^2}$	$\dfrac{1}{2a^3}(\sin at - at \cos at)$
22	$\dfrac{s}{(s^2 + a^2)^2}$	$\dfrac{t}{2a} \sin at$
23	$\dfrac{s^2}{(s^2 + a^2)^2}$	$\dfrac{1}{2a}(\sin at + at \cos at)$
24	$\dfrac{s^2 - a^2}{(s^2 + a^2)^2}$	$t \cos at$
25	$\dfrac{s}{(s^2 + a^2)(s^2 + b^2)} \ (a^2 \neq b^2)$	$\dfrac{\cos at - \cos bt}{b^2 - a^2}$
26	$\dfrac{1}{(s - a)^2 + b^2}$	$\dfrac{1}{b} e^{at} \sin bt$
27	$\dfrac{s - a}{(s - a)^2 + b^2}$	$e^{at} \cos bt$
27.1	$\dfrac{1}{[(s + a)^2 + b^2]^n}$	$\dfrac{-e^{-at}}{4^{n-1} b^{2n}} \displaystyle\sum_{r=1}^{n} \binom{2n - r - 1}{n - 1} (-2t)^{r-1} \dfrac{d^r}{dt^r}[\cos(bt)]$
27.2	$\dfrac{s}{[(s + a)^2 + b^2]^n}$	$\dfrac{e^{-at}}{4^{n-1} b^{2n}} \Bigg\{ \displaystyle\sum_{r=1}^{n} \binom{2n - r - 1}{n - 1}$ $(-2t)^{r-1} \dfrac{d^r}{dt^r}[a \cos(bt) + b \sin(bt)]$ $-2b \displaystyle\sum_{r=1}^{n-1} r\binom{2n - r - 2}{n - 1}$ $(-2t)^{r-1} \dfrac{d^r}{dt^r}[\sin bt] \Bigg\}$
28	$\dfrac{3a^2}{s^3 + a^3}$	$e^{-at} - e^{(at)/2}\left(\cos \dfrac{at\sqrt{3}}{2} - \sqrt{3} \sin \dfrac{at\sqrt{3}}{2}\right)$
29	$\dfrac{4a^3}{s^4 + 4a^4}$	$\sin at \cosh at - \cos at \sinh at$
30	$\dfrac{s}{s^4 + 4a^4}$	$\dfrac{1}{2a^2} \sin at \sinh at$

LAPLACE TRANSFORMS (Continued)

	$f(s)$	$F(t)$
31	$\dfrac{1}{s^4 - a^4}$	$\dfrac{1}{2a^3}(\sinh at - \sin at)$
32	$\dfrac{s}{s^4 - a^4}$	$\dfrac{1}{2a^2}(\cosh at - \cos at)$
33	$\dfrac{8a^3 s^2}{(s^2 + a^2)^3}$	$(1 + a^2 t^2)\sin at - \cos at$
34*	$\dfrac{1}{s}\left(\dfrac{s-1}{s}\right)^n$	$L_n(t) = \dfrac{e^t}{n!}\dfrac{d^n}{dt^n}(t^n e^{-t})$
35	$\dfrac{s}{(s-a)^{3/2}}$	$\dfrac{1}{\sqrt{\pi t}}e^{at}(1 + 2at)$
36	$\sqrt{s-a} - \sqrt{s-b}$	$\dfrac{1}{2\sqrt{\pi t^3}}(e^{bt} - e^{at})$
37	$\dfrac{1}{\sqrt{s} + a}$	$\dfrac{1}{\sqrt{\pi t}} - ae^{a^2 t}\operatorname{erfc}(a\sqrt{t})$
38	$\dfrac{\sqrt{s}}{s - a^2}$	$\dfrac{1}{\sqrt{\pi t}} + ae^{a^2 t}\operatorname{erf}(a\sqrt{t})$
39	$\dfrac{\sqrt{s}}{s + a^2}$	$\dfrac{1}{\sqrt{\pi t}} - \dfrac{2a}{\sqrt{\pi}}e^{-a^2 t}\displaystyle\int_0^{a\sqrt{t}} e^{\lambda^2}\,d\lambda$
40	$\dfrac{1}{\sqrt{s}(s - a^2)}$	$\dfrac{1}{a}e^{a^2 t}\operatorname{erf}(a\sqrt{t})$
41	$\dfrac{1}{\sqrt{s}(s + a^2)}$	$\dfrac{2}{a\sqrt{\pi}}e^{-a^2 t}\displaystyle\int_0^{a\sqrt{t}} e^{\lambda^2}\,d\lambda$
42	$\dfrac{b^2 - a^2}{(s - a^2)(b + \sqrt{s})}$	$e^{a^2 t}[b - a\operatorname{erf}(a\sqrt{t})] - be^{b^2 t}\operatorname{erfc}(b\sqrt{t})$
43	$\dfrac{1}{\sqrt{s}(\sqrt{s} + a)}$	$e^{a^2 t}\operatorname{erfc}(a\sqrt{t})$
44	$\dfrac{1}{(s + a)\sqrt{s + b}}$	$\dfrac{1}{\sqrt{b - a}}e^{-at}\operatorname{erf}(\sqrt{b - a}\sqrt{t})$
45	$\dfrac{b^2 - a^2}{\sqrt{s}(s - a^2)(\sqrt{s} + b)}$	$e^{a^2 t}\left[\dfrac{b}{a}\operatorname{erf}(a\sqrt{t}) - 1\right] + e^{b^2 t}\operatorname{erfc}(b\sqrt{t})$
46†	$\dfrac{(1 - s)^n}{s^{n+(1/2)}}$	$\dfrac{n!}{(2n)!\sqrt{\pi t}}H_{2n}(\sqrt{t})$
47	$\dfrac{(1 - s)^n}{s^{n+(3/2)}}$	$-\dfrac{n!}{\sqrt{\pi}(2n + 1)!}H_{2n+1}(\sqrt{t})$

*$L_n(t)$ is the Laguerre polynomial of degree n.

†$H_n(x)$ is the Hermite polynomial, $H_n(x) = e^{x^2}\dfrac{d^n}{dx^n}(e^{-x^2})$.

LAPLACE TRANSFORMS (Continued)

	$f(s)$	$F(t)$
48†	$\dfrac{\sqrt{s + 2a}}{\sqrt{s}} - 1$	$ae^{-at}[I_1(at) + I_0(at)]$
49	$\dfrac{1}{\sqrt{s + a}\,\sqrt{s + b}}$	$e^{-(1/2)(a+b)t} I_0\left(\dfrac{a - b}{2}\, t\right)$
50	$\dfrac{\Gamma(k)}{(s + a)^k (s + b)^k}\ (k \geq 0)$	$\sqrt{\pi}\left(\dfrac{t}{a - b}\right)^{k - (1/2)} e^{-(1/2)(a+b)t} I_{k - (1/2)}\left(\dfrac{a - b}{2}\, t\right)$
51	$\dfrac{1}{(s + a)^{1/2}(s + b)^{3/2}}$	$te^{-(1/2)(a+b)t}\left[I_0\left(\dfrac{a - b}{2}\, t\right) + I_1\left(\dfrac{a - b}{2}\, t\right)\right]$
52	$\dfrac{\sqrt{s + 2a} - \sqrt{s}}{\sqrt{s + 2a} + \sqrt{s}}$	$\dfrac{1}{t}\, e^{-at} I_1(at)$
53	$\dfrac{(a - b)^k}{(\sqrt{s + a} + \sqrt{s + b})^{2k}}\ (k > 0)$	$\dfrac{k}{t}\, e^{-(1/2)(a+b)t} I_k\left(\dfrac{a - b}{2}\, t\right)$
54	$\dfrac{(\sqrt{s + a} + \sqrt{s})^{-2\nu}}{\sqrt{s}\,\sqrt{s + a}}\ (\nu > -1)$	$\dfrac{1}{a^\nu}\, e^{-(1/2)(at)} I_\nu\left(\dfrac{1}{2}\, at\right)$
55	$\dfrac{1}{\sqrt{s^2 + a^2}}$	$J_0(at)$
56	$\dfrac{(\sqrt{s^2 + a^2} - s)^\nu}{\sqrt{s^2 + a^2}}\ (\nu > -1)$	$a^\nu J_\nu(at)$
57	$\dfrac{1}{(s^2 + a^2)^k}\ (k > 0)$	$\dfrac{\sqrt{\pi}}{\Gamma(k)}\left(\dfrac{t}{2a}\right)^{k - (1/2)} J_{k - (1/2)}(at)$
58	$(\sqrt{s^2 + a^2} - s)^k\,(k > 0)$	$\dfrac{ka^k}{t}\, J_k(at)$
59	$\dfrac{(s - \sqrt{s^2 - a^2})^\nu}{\sqrt{s^2 - a^2}}\ (\nu > -1)$	$a^\nu I_\nu(at)$
60	$\dfrac{1}{(s^2 - a^2)^k}\ (k > 0)$	$\dfrac{\sqrt{\pi}}{\Gamma(k)}\left(\dfrac{t}{2a}\right)^{k - (1/2)} I_{k - (1/2)}(at)$
61	$\dfrac{e^{-ks}}{s}$	$S_k(t) = \begin{cases} 0 \text{ when } 0 < t < k \\ 1 \text{ when } t > k \end{cases}$
62	$\dfrac{e^{-ks}}{s^2}$	$\begin{cases} 0 \text{ when } 0 < t < k \\ t - k \text{ when } t > k \end{cases}$
63	$\dfrac{e^{-ks}}{s^\mu}\ (\mu > 0)$	$\begin{cases} 0 & \text{when } 0 < t < k \\ \dfrac{(t - k)^{\mu - 1}}{\Gamma(\mu)} & \text{when } t > k \end{cases}$
64	$\dfrac{1 - e^{-ks}}{s}$	$\begin{cases} 1 \text{ when } 0 < t < k \\ 0 \text{ when } t > k \end{cases}$

†$I_n(x) = i^{-n} J_n(ix)$, where J_n is Bessel's function of the first kind.

LAPLACE TRANSFORMS (Continued)

	$f(s)$	$F(t)$
65	$\dfrac{1}{s(1 - e^{-ks})} = \dfrac{1 + \coth \frac{1}{2}ks}{2s}$	$S(k,t) = n$ when $\quad (n-1)k < t < nk(n = 1,2,\ldots)$
66	$\dfrac{1}{s(e^{ks} - a)}$	$\begin{cases} 0 \text{ when } 0 < t < k \\ 1 + a + a^2 + \cdots + a^{n-1} \\ \quad \text{when } nk < t < (n+1)k(n = 1,2,\ldots) \end{cases}$
67	$\dfrac{1}{s} \tanh ks$	$M(2k,t) = (-1)^{n-1}$ $\quad$ when $2k(n-1) < t < 2kn$ $\qquad\qquad (n = 1,2,\ldots)$
68	$\dfrac{1}{s(1 + e^{-ks})}$	$\dfrac{1}{2} M(k,t) + \dfrac{1}{2} = \dfrac{1 - (-1)^n}{2}$ $\quad$ when $(n-1)k < t < nk$
69*	$\dfrac{1}{s^2} \tanh ks$	$H(2k,t)$
70	$\dfrac{1}{s \sinh ks}$	$2S(2k, t + k) - 2 = 2(n - 1)$ $\quad$ when $(2n - 3)k < t < (2n - 1)k \quad (t > 0)$
71	$\dfrac{1}{s \cosh ks}$	$M(2k, t + 3k) + 1 = 1 + (-1)^n$ $\quad$ when $(2n - 3)k < t < (2n - 1)k \quad (t > 0)$
72	$\dfrac{1}{s} \coth ks$	$2S(2k, t) - 1 = 2n - 1$ $\qquad\qquad$ when $2k(n - 1) < t < 2kn$
73	$\dfrac{k}{s^2 + k^2} \coth \dfrac{\pi s}{2k}$	$\lvert \sin kt \rvert$
74	$\dfrac{1}{(s^2 + 1)(1 - e^{-\pi s})}$	$\begin{cases} \sin t \text{ when } (2n - 2)\pi < t < (2n - 1)\pi \\ 0 \quad \text{when } (2n - 1)\pi < t < 2n\pi \end{cases}$
75	$\dfrac{1}{s} e^{-k/s}$	$J_0(2 \sqrt{kt})$
76	$\dfrac{1}{\sqrt{s}} e^{-k/s}$	$\dfrac{1}{\sqrt{\pi t}} \cos 2 \sqrt{kt}$
77	$\dfrac{1}{\sqrt{s}} e^{k/s}$	$\dfrac{1}{\sqrt{\pi t}} \cosh 2 \sqrt{kt}$
78	$\dfrac{1}{s^{3/2}} e^{-k/s}$	$\dfrac{1}{\sqrt{\pi k}} \sin 2 \sqrt{kt}$
79	$\dfrac{1}{s^{3/2}} e^{k/s}$	$\dfrac{1}{\sqrt{\pi k}} \sinh 2 \sqrt{kt}$
80	$\dfrac{1}{s^{\mu}} e^{-k/s}(\mu > 0)$	$\left(\dfrac{t}{k}\right)^{(\mu-1)/2} J_{\mu-1}(2 \sqrt{kt})$

*$H(2k,t) = k + (r - k)(-1)^n$ where $t = 2kn + r; 0 \le r < 2k; n = 0,1,2,\ldots$.

LAPLACE TRANSFORMS (Continued)

	$f(s)$	$F(t)$
81	$\dfrac{1}{s^{\mu}} e^{k/s} (\mu > 0)$	$\left(\dfrac{t}{k}\right)^{(\mu-1)/2} I_{\mu-1}(2\sqrt{kt})$
82	$e^{-k\sqrt{s}}(k > 0)$	$\dfrac{k}{2\sqrt{\pi t^3}} \exp\left(-\dfrac{k^2}{4t}\right)$
83	$\dfrac{1}{s} e^{-k\sqrt{s}}(k \geq 0)$	$\operatorname{erfc}\left(\dfrac{k}{2\sqrt{t}}\right)$
84	$\dfrac{1}{\sqrt{s}} e^{-k\sqrt{s}}(k \geq 0)$	$\dfrac{1}{\sqrt{\pi t}} \exp\left(-\dfrac{k^2}{4t}\right)$
85	$s^{-3/2} e^{-k\sqrt{s}}(k \geq 0)$	$2\sqrt{\dfrac{t}{\pi}} \exp\left(-\dfrac{k^2}{4t}\right) - k\operatorname{erfc}\left(\dfrac{k}{2\sqrt{t}}\right)$
86	$\dfrac{ae^{-k\sqrt{s}}}{s(a + \sqrt{s})} (k \geq 0)$	$-e^{ak}e^{a^2 t}\operatorname{erfc}\left(a\sqrt{t} + \dfrac{k}{2\sqrt{t}}\right) + \operatorname{erfc}\left(\dfrac{k}{2\sqrt{t}}\right)$
87	$\dfrac{e^{-k\sqrt{s}}}{\sqrt{s}(a + \sqrt{s})} (k \geq 0)$	$e^{ak}e^{a^2 t}\operatorname{erfc}\left(a\sqrt{t} + \dfrac{k}{2\sqrt{t}}\right)$
88	$\dfrac{e^{-k\sqrt{s(s+a)}}}{\sqrt{s(s+a)}}$	$\begin{cases} 0 & \text{when } 0 < t < k \\ e^{-(1/2)(at)} I_0(\tfrac{1}{2}a\sqrt{t^2 - k^2}) & \text{when } t > k \end{cases}$
89	$\dfrac{e^{-k\sqrt{s^2+a^2}}}{\sqrt{s^2+a^2}}$	$\begin{cases} 0 & \text{when } 0 < t < k \\ J_0(a\sqrt{t^2 - k^2}) & \text{when } t > k \end{cases}$
90	$\dfrac{e^{-k\sqrt{s^2-a^2}}}{\sqrt{s^2-a^2}}$	$\begin{cases} 0 & \text{when } 0 < t < k \\ I_0(a\sqrt{t^2 - k^2}) & \text{when } t > k \end{cases}$
91	$\dfrac{e^{-k(\sqrt{s^2+a^2}-s)}}{\sqrt{s^2+a^2}} (k \geq 0)$	$J_0(a\sqrt{t^2 + 2kt})$
92	$e^{-ks} - e^{-k\sqrt{s^2+a^2}}$	$\begin{cases} 0 & \text{when } 0 < t < k \\ \dfrac{ak}{\sqrt{t^2 - k^2}} J_1(a\sqrt{t^2 - k^2}) & \text{when } t > k \end{cases}$
93	$e^{-k\sqrt{s^2+a^2}} - \cdot e^{-ks}$	$\begin{cases} 0 & \text{when } 0 < t < k \\ \dfrac{ak}{\sqrt{t^2 - k^2}} I_1(a\sqrt{t^2 - k^2}) & \text{when } t > k \end{cases}$
94	$\dfrac{a^{\nu} e^{-k\sqrt{s^2-a^2}}}{\sqrt{s^2+a^2}(\sqrt{s^2+a^2}+s)^{\nu}}$ $(\nu > -1)$	$\begin{cases} 0 & \text{when } 0 < t < k \\ \left(\dfrac{t - k}{t + k}\right)^{(1/2)\nu} J_{\nu}(a\sqrt{t^2 - k^2}) & \text{when } t > k \end{cases}$
95	$\dfrac{1}{s} \log s$	$\Gamma'(1) - \log t \; [\Gamma'(1) = -0.5772]$
96	$\dfrac{1}{s^k} \log s \; (k > 0)$	$t^{k-1}\left\{\dfrac{\Gamma'(k)}{[\Gamma(k)]^2} - \dfrac{\log t}{\Gamma(k)}\right\}$
97	$\dfrac{\log s}{s - a} \; (a > 0)$	$e^{at}[\log a - \operatorname{Ei}(-at)]$

LAPLACE TRANSFORMS (Continued)

	$f(s)$	$F(t)$
98	$\dfrac{\log s}{s^2 + 1}$	$\cos t\, \mathrm{Si}(t) - \sin t\, \mathrm{Ci}(t)$
99	$\dfrac{s \log s}{s^2 + 1}$	$-\sin t\, \mathrm{Si}(t) - \cos t\, \mathrm{Ci}(t)$
100	$\dfrac{1}{s} \log (1 + ks)\, (k > 0)$	$-\mathrm{Ei}\left(-\dfrac{t}{k}\right)$
101	$\log \dfrac{s - a}{s - b}$	$\dfrac{1}{t}\, (e^{bt} - e^{at})$
102	$\dfrac{1}{s} \log (1 + k^2 s^2)$	$-2\mathrm{Ci}\left(\dfrac{t}{k}\right)$
103	$\dfrac{1}{s} \log (s^2 + a^2)\ \ (a > 0)$	$2 \log a - 2\mathrm{Ci}(at)$
104	$\dfrac{1}{s^2} \log (s^2 + a^2)\ \ (a > 0)$	$\dfrac{2}{a}\, [at \log a + \sin at - at\, \mathrm{Ci}(at)]$
105	$\log \dfrac{s^2 + a^2}{s^2}$	$\dfrac{2}{t}\, (1 - \cos at)$
106	$\log \dfrac{s^2 - a^2}{s^2}$	$\dfrac{2}{t}\, (1 - \cosh at)$
107	$\arctan \dfrac{k}{s}$	$\dfrac{1}{t} \sin kt$
108	$\dfrac{1}{s} \arctan \dfrac{k}{s}$	$\mathrm{Si}(kt)$
109	$e^{k^2 s^2} \mathrm{erfc}\, (ks)\ \ (k > 0)$	$\dfrac{1}{k \sqrt{\pi}} \exp\left(-\dfrac{t^2}{4k^2}\right)$
110	$\dfrac{1}{s}\, e^{k^2 s^2} \mathrm{erfc}\, (ks)\ \ (k > 0)$	$\mathrm{erf}\left(\dfrac{t}{2k}\right)$
111	$e^{ks} \mathrm{erfc}\, (\sqrt{ks})\ \ (k > 0)$	$\dfrac{\sqrt{k}}{\pi \sqrt{t(t + k)}}$
112	$\dfrac{1}{\sqrt{s}}\, \mathrm{erfc}\, (\sqrt{ks})$	$\begin{cases} 0 & \text{when } 0 < t < k \\ (\pi t)^{-1/2} & \text{when } t > k \end{cases}$
113	$\dfrac{1}{\sqrt{s}}\, e^{ks} \mathrm{erfc}\, (\sqrt{ks})\,(k > 0)$	$\dfrac{1}{\sqrt{\pi(t + k)}}$
114	$\mathrm{erf}\left(\dfrac{k}{\sqrt{s}}\right)$	$\dfrac{1}{\pi t} \sin (2k \sqrt{t})$
115	$\dfrac{1}{\sqrt{s}}\, e^{k^2/s} \mathrm{erfc}\left(\dfrac{k}{\sqrt{s}}\right)$	$\dfrac{1}{\sqrt{\pi t}}\, e^{-2k \sqrt{t}}$

LAPLACE TRANSFORMS (Continued)

	$f(s)$	$F(t)$
115.1	$-e^{as}\,\mathrm{Ei}(-as)$	$\dfrac{1}{t+a}$; $(a > 0)$
115.2	$\dfrac{1}{a} + se^{as}\,\mathrm{Ei}(-as)$	$\dfrac{1}{(t+a)^2}$; $(a > 0)$
115.3	$\left[\dfrac{\pi}{2} - \mathrm{Si}(s)\right]\cos s + \mathrm{Ci}(s)\sin s$	$\dfrac{1}{t^2+1}$
116*	$K_0(ks)$	$\begin{cases} 0 & \text{when } 0 < t < k \\ (t^2 - k^2)^{-1/2} & \text{when } t > k \end{cases}$
117	$K_0(k\sqrt{s})$	$\dfrac{1}{2t}\exp\left(-\dfrac{k^2}{4t}\right)$
118	$\dfrac{1}{s}\,e^{ks}K_1(ks)$	$\dfrac{1}{k}\sqrt{t(t+2k)}$
119	$\dfrac{1}{\sqrt{s}}\,K_1(k\sqrt{s})$	$\dfrac{1}{k}\exp\left(-\dfrac{k^2}{4t}\right)$
120	$\dfrac{1}{\sqrt{s}}\,e^{k/s}K_0\left(\dfrac{k}{s}\right)$	$\dfrac{2}{\sqrt{\pi t}}\,K_0(2\sqrt{2kt})$
121	$\pi e^{-ks}I_0(ks)$	$\begin{cases} [t(2k - t)]^{-1/2} & \text{when } 0 < t < 2k \\ 0 & \text{when } t > 2k \end{cases}$
122†	$e^{-ks}I_1(ks)$	$\begin{cases} \dfrac{k - t}{\pi k\sqrt{t(2k - t)}} & \text{when } 0 < t < 2k \\ 0 & \text{when } t > 2k \end{cases}$

*$K_n(x)$ is Bessel's function of the second kind for the imaginary argument.

†Several additional transforms, especially those involving other Bessel functions, can be found in the tables by G. A. Campbell and R. M. Foster, "Fourier Integrals for Practical Applications", or "Vol. 1, Bateman Manuscript Project, Transform Tables, McGraw-Hill, 1955", or N. W. McLachlan and P. Humbert, "Formulaire pour le calcul symbolique". In the tables by Campbell and Foster, only those entries containing the condition $0 < g$ or $k < g$, where g is our t, are Laplace transforms.

THE Z TRANSFORM

B. Girling

When $F(t)$, a continuous function of time, is sampled at regular intervals of period T the usual Laplace transform techniques are modified. The diagramatic form of a simple sampler together with its associated input-output waveforms is shown below

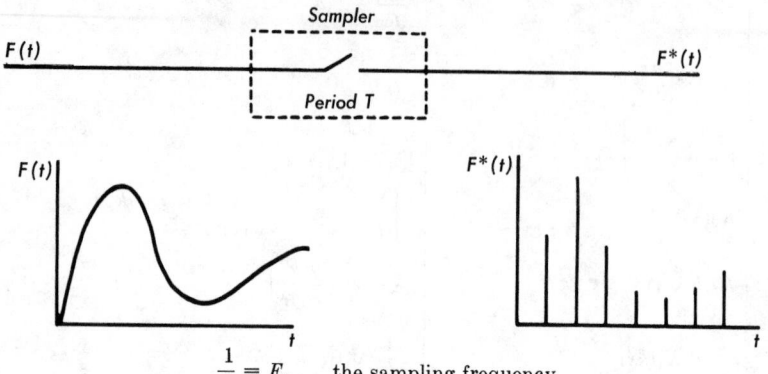

$$\frac{1}{T} \equiv F_s \qquad \text{the sampling frequency}$$

Defining the set of impulse functions $\delta_T(t)$ by

$$\delta_T(t) \equiv \sum_{n=0}^{\infty} \delta(t - nT)$$

the input-output relationship of the sampler becomes

$$F^*(t) = F(t) \cdot \delta_T(t)$$

$$= \sum_{n=0}^{\infty} F(nT) \cdot \delta(t - nT).$$

While for a given $F(t)$ and T the $F^*(t)$ is unique, the converse is not true.

The Laplace transform can be used to define $F^*(s)$ as follows

$$L\{F^*(t)\} \equiv f^*(s)$$

$$= \sum_{n=0}^{\infty} F(nT) \cdot e^{-nTs}.$$

The variable 'z' is introduced by means of the transformation

$$z = e^{Ts}$$

and since any function of s can now be replaced by a corresponding function of z we have

$$f(z) = \sum_{n=0}^{\infty} F(nT) \cdot z^{-n}$$

where $$f^*(s) \equiv f(z)$$

and $$s = \frac{1}{T} \ln Z$$

The Z operator can now be defined in terms of the Laplace operator by the relationship

$$Z\{F(t)\} \equiv L\{F^*(t)\}$$

THE Z TRANSFORM (Continued)

An alternative definition (quoted without proof) is

$$Z\{F(t)\} = \sum \text{ residues of } \left[\left(\frac{1}{1 - e^{Tz}z^{-1}}\right) \cdot f(z)\right]$$

The inverse z transform

$$Z^{-1}\{f(z)\} \equiv F^*(t)$$

$$= \frac{1}{2\pi j} \oint f(z) \cdot z^{n-1}\, dz$$

where the contour of integration encloses all the singularities of the integrand.
In the following table Greek letters denote constants.

$F(t)$	$f(z) = Z\{F(t)\}$
$\alpha F(t)$	$\alpha f(z)$
$F(t) + G(t)$	$f(z) + g(z)$
$F(t + T)$	$zf(z) - zF(0)$
$F(t + 2T)$	$z^2 f(z) - z^2 F(0) - zF(T)$
$F(t + mT)$	$z^m f(z) - \displaystyle\sum_{r=0}^{m-1} z^{m-r}F(rT)$
	$= z^m f(z)$ when $F(rT) = 0,\, 0 \leq r \leq m - 1$
$F(t - mT)$	$z^{-m}f(z)$
$e^{\alpha t}F(t)$	$f(e^{-\alpha T}z)$
$e^{-\alpha t}F(t)$	$f(e^{\alpha T}z)$
$t \cdot F(t)$	$-Tz\dfrac{d}{dz}f(z)$
$t^{-1}F(t)$	$-\dfrac{1}{T}\displaystyle\int_0^z \dfrac{f(z)}{z}\, dz$
$\displaystyle\sum_{m=0}^{T/t} F(mT)$	$\left(\dfrac{z}{z-1}\right)f(z)$

The following limits are also valid

$$\lim_{t \to 0} F(t) = \lim_{z \to \infty} f(z)$$

$$\lim_{t \to \infty} F^*(t) = \lim_{z \to 1} \left[\left(\frac{z-1}{z}\right)f(z)\right]$$

In the table which follows, the Heavyside unit step function is defined by

$$H(t - nT) \equiv \begin{cases} 1; t \geq nT \\ 0; t < nT. \end{cases}$$

THE Z TRANSFORM (Continued)

$F(t)$	$f(z)$
$\delta(t)$	1
$\delta(t - mT)$	$\dfrac{1}{z^m}$
$H(t)$	$\dfrac{z}{z - 1}$
$H(t - T)$	$\dfrac{1}{z - 1}$
$H(t - mT)$	$\dfrac{z}{z^m \cdot (z - 1)}$
$H(t) - H(t - T)$	1
$H(t) - H(t - 2T)$	$1 + \dfrac{1}{z}$
$H(t - mT) - H(t - \overline{m + 1}T)$	$\dfrac{1}{z}m$
$\dfrac{T}{t} H(t - T)$	$\ln\left(\dfrac{z}{z - 1}\right)$
t	$\dfrac{Tz}{(z - 1)^2}$
t^2	$\dfrac{T^2 z(z + 1)}{(z - 1)^3}$
t^3	$\dfrac{T^3 z(z^2 + 4z + 1)}{(z - 1)^4}$
t^n	$(-1)^n \lim\limits_{\chi \to 0} \dfrac{\partial^n}{\partial \chi^n}\left(\dfrac{z}{z - e^{-\chi T}}\right)$
$1 - a^{\omega t}$	$\dfrac{z(1 - a^{\omega T})}{(z - 1)(z - a^{\omega T})}$
$a^{\omega t}$	$\dfrac{z}{(z - a^{\omega T})}$
$ta^{\omega t}$	$\dfrac{Tz a^{\omega T}}{(z - a^{\omega T})^2}$
$t^2 a^{\omega t}$	$\dfrac{T^2 a^{\omega T} z(z + a^{\omega T})}{(z - a^{\omega T})^3}$
$\sin \omega t$	$\dfrac{z \sin \omega T}{z^2 - 2z \cos \omega T + 1}$
$\cos \omega t$	$\dfrac{z(z - \cos \omega T)}{z^2 - 2z \cos \omega T + 1}$
$\sinh \omega t$	$\dfrac{z \sinh \omega T}{z^2 - 2z \cosh \omega T + 1}$
$\cosh \omega t$	$\dfrac{z(z - \cosh \omega T)}{z^2 - 2z \cosh \omega T + 1}$
$e^{-\alpha t} \sin \omega t$	$\dfrac{z e^{-\alpha T} \sin \omega T}{z^2 - 2z e^{-T} \cos \omega T + e^{-2\alpha T}}$
$e^{-\alpha t} \cos \omega t$	$\dfrac{z(z - e^{-\alpha T} \cos \omega T)}{z^2 - 2z e^{-T} \cos \omega T + e^{-2\alpha T}}$
$e^{-\alpha t} \sinh \omega t$	$\dfrac{z e^{-\alpha T} \sinh \omega T}{z^2 - 2z e^{-\alpha T} \cosh \omega T + e^{-2\alpha T}}$
$e^{-\alpha t} \cosh \omega t$	$\dfrac{z(z - e^{-\alpha T} \cosh \omega T)}{z^2 - 2z e^{-\alpha T} \cosh \omega T + e^{-2\alpha T}}$

THE Z TRANSFORM (Continued)

$F(t)$	$f(z)$
$-\dfrac{1}{a}\left[\delta(t) - a^{t/T}\right]$	$\dfrac{1}{z - a}$
$\dfrac{1}{(a - b)}\left[a^{\left(\frac{t}{T}-1\right)} - b^{\left(\frac{T}{t}-1\right)}\right]$	$\dfrac{1}{(z - a)(z - b)}$
$\dfrac{1}{(a - b)}\left[a^{\frac{t}{T}} - b^{\frac{t}{T}}\right]$	$\dfrac{z}{(z - a)(z - b)}$
$\dfrac{1}{(a - b)}\left[(a - c)a^{\left(\frac{t}{T}-1\right)} - (b - c)b^{\left(\frac{t}{T}-1\right)}\right]$	$\dfrac{z - c}{(z - a)(z - b)}$
$\dfrac{1}{(a - b)}\left[a^{\left(\frac{T}{t}+1\right)} - b^{\left(\frac{T}{t}+1\right)}\right]$	$\dfrac{z^2}{(z - a)(z - b)}$
$\left(\dfrac{T}{t}\right)!$	$e^{1/z}$
$\left(\dfrac{T}{2T}\right)!$	$\cosh(z^{-\frac{1}{2}})$

Methods of evaluating inverse z transforms.

(1) Cauchy's residue theorem.

For $t = nT$,

$$G(nT) = \sum_{\text{all } z_k} [\text{residues of } g(z)z^{n-1} \text{ at } z_k]$$

where the z_k define all the poles of $g(z)z^{n-1}$.

(2) Partial fractions.

Expand $g(z)/z$ into partial fractions. The product of z with each of the partial fractions will then be recognizable from the standard forms in the table of z transforms. Note however that the continuous functions obtained are only valid at the sampling instants.

(3) Power series expansion by long division using detached coefficients.

$g(z)$ is expanded into a power series in z^{-1} and the coefficient of the term in z^{-n} is the value of $g(nT)$ i.e. the value of $G(t)$ at the nth sampling instant.

The z transform as a means of determining approximately the inverse Laplace transform.

Since

$$z \equiv e^{Ts}$$

$$s^{-1} = \frac{T}{2}\left[\frac{1}{v} - \frac{v}{3} - \frac{4v^3}{45} - \frac{44v^5}{945} - \cdots\right]$$

where

$$v \equiv \frac{1 - z^{-1}}{1 + z^{-1}},$$

the series being very rapid in its convergence. Given $g(s)$, to find its inverse Laplace transform the following operations are carried out:-

(i) Divide the numerator and denominator of $g(s)$ by the highest power of s yielding as an alternative form for $g(s)$ the quotient of two polynomials in s^{-1}.

(ii) Chose as a numerical value of T, that which makes $2\pi/T$ much larger than the imaginary part of the poles of $G(s)$.

(iii) Substitute into the alternative form for $g(s)$ obtained in (i) above the expansion for s^{-n} determined from the following short table of approximations.

THE Z TRANSFORM (Continued)

Do not at this stage insert the numerical value for T as tabulations with different intervals may be required.

(iv) Divide by T.

(v) Insert the chosen value for T and divide the numerator by the denominator.

(vi) The coefficient of z^{-n} is the required value of the function at $t = nT$.

s^{-n}	z transform (approximate)
s^{-1}	$\dfrac{T}{2}\left[\dfrac{1 + z^{-1}}{1 - z^{-1}}\right]$
s^{-2}	$\dfrac{T^2}{12}\left[\dfrac{1 + 10z^{-1} + z^{-2}}{(1 - z^{-1})^2}\right]$
s^{-3}	$\dfrac{T^3}{3}\left[\dfrac{z^{-1} + z^{-2}}{(1 - z^{-1})^3}\right]$
s^{-4}	$\dfrac{T^4}{144}\left[\dfrac{1 + 20z^{-1} + 102z^{-2} + 20z^{-3} + z^{-4}}{(1 - z^{-1})^4}\right]$
s^{-5}	$\dfrac{T^5}{24}\left[\dfrac{z^{-1} + 11z^{-2} + 11z^{-3} + z^{-4}}{(1 - z^{-1})^5}\right]$
s^{-6}	$\dfrac{T^6}{4}\left[\dfrac{z^{-2} + 2z^{-3} + z^{-4}}{(1 - z^{-1})^6}\right]$
s^{-7}	$\dfrac{T^7}{8}\left[\dfrac{z^{-2} + 3z^{-3} + 3z^{-4} + z^{-5}}{(1 - z^{-1})^7}\right]$

THE FINITE FOURIER TRANSFORM

DR. R. E. GASKELL

For a piecewise continuous function $F(x)$ over a finite interval $0 \leq x \leq \pi$, the *finite Fourier cosine transform* of $F(x)$ is

$$f_c(n) = \int_0^\pi F(x) \cos nx \, dx \quad (n = 0, 1, 2, \ldots). \tag{4}$$

If x ranges over the interval $0 \leq x \leq L$, the substitution $x' = \pi x / L$ allows the use of this definition, also. The inverse transform is written

$$\bar{F}(x) = \frac{1}{\pi} f_c(0) - \frac{2}{\pi} \sum_{n=1}^{\infty} f_c(n) \cos nx \quad (0 < x < \pi) \tag{5}$$

where $\bar{F}(x) = \dfrac{[F(x + 0) + F(x - 0)]}{2}$. We observe that $\bar{F}(x) = F(x)$ at points of continuity. The formula

$$f_c^{(2)}(n) = \int_0^\pi F''(x) \cos nx \, dx$$
$$= -n^2 f_c(n) - F'(0) + (-1)^n F'(\pi) \tag{6}$$

makes the finite Fourier cosine transform useful in certain boundary value problems.

Analogously, the *finite Fourier sine transform* of $F(x)$ is

$$f_s(n) = \int_0^\pi F(x) \sin nx \, dx \quad (n = 1, 2, 3, \ldots) \tag{7}$$

and

$$\bar{F}(x) = \frac{2}{\pi} \sum_{n=1}^{\infty} f_s(n) \sin nx \quad (0 < x < \pi) \tag{8}$$

Corresponding to (6) we have

$$f_s^{(2)}(n) = \int_0^\pi F''(x) \sin nx \, dx$$
$$= -n^2 f_s(n) - nF(0) - n(-1)^n F(\pi). \tag{9}$$

FOURIER TRANSFORMS

If $F(x)$ is defined for $x \geq 0$ and is piecewise continuous over any finite interval, and if

$$\int_0^\infty F(x) \, dx.$$

is absolutely convergent, then

$$f_c(\alpha) = \sqrt{\frac{2}{\pi}} \int_0^\infty F(x) \cos(\alpha x) \, dx \tag{10}$$

is the *Fourier cosine transform* of $F(x)$. Furthermore,

$$\bar{F}(x) = \sqrt{\frac{2}{\pi}} \int_0^\infty f_c(\alpha) \cos(\alpha x) \, d\alpha. \tag{11}$$

If $\lim\limits_{x \to \infty} \dfrac{d^n F}{dx^n} = 0$, an important property of the Fourier cosine transform

$$f_c^{(2r)}(\alpha) = \sqrt{\frac{2}{\pi}} \int_0^\infty \left(\frac{d^{2r} F}{dx^{2r}}\right) \cos(\alpha x)\, dx$$

$$= -\sqrt{\frac{2}{\pi}} \sum_{n=0}^{r-1} (-1)^n a_{2r-2n-1} \alpha^{2n} + (-1)^r \alpha^{2r} f_c(\alpha) \tag{12}$$

where $\lim\limits_{x \to 0} \dfrac{d^r F}{dx^r} = a_r$, makes it useful in the solution of many problems.

Under the same conditions,

$$f_s(\alpha) = \sqrt{\frac{2}{\pi}} \int_0^\infty F(x) \sin(\alpha x)\, dx \tag{13}$$

defines the *Fourier sine transform* of $F(x)$, and

$$\bar{F}(x) = \sqrt{\frac{2}{\pi}} \int_0^\infty f_s(\alpha) \sin(\alpha x)\, d\alpha. \tag{14}$$

Corresponding to (12) we have

$$f_s^{(2r)}(\alpha) = \sqrt{\frac{2}{\pi}} \int_0^\infty \frac{d^{2r} F}{dx^{2r}} \sin(\alpha x)\, dx$$

$$= -\sqrt{\frac{2}{\pi}} \sum_{n=1}^r (-1)^n \alpha^{2n-1} a_{2r-2n} + (-1)^{r-1} \alpha^{2r} f_s(\alpha). \tag{15}$$

Similarly, if $F(x)$ is defined for $-\infty < x < \infty$, and if $\displaystyle\int_{-\infty}^\infty F(x)\, dx$ is absolutely convergent, then

$$f(\alpha) = \frac{1}{\sqrt{2\pi}} \int_{-\infty}^\infty F(x) e^{i\alpha x}\, dx \tag{16}$$

is the *Fourier transform* of $F(x)$, and

$$\bar{F}(x) = \frac{1}{\sqrt{2\pi}} \int_{-\infty}^\infty f(\alpha) e^{-i\alpha x}\, d\alpha. \tag{17}$$

Also, if

$$\lim_{|x| \to \infty} \left|\frac{d^n F}{dx^n}\right| = 0 \quad (n = 1, 2, \ldots, r-1),$$

then

$$f^{(r)}(\alpha) = \frac{1}{\sqrt{2\pi}} \int_{-\infty}^\infty F^{(r)}(x) e^{i\alpha x}\, dx = (-i\alpha)^r f(\alpha). \tag{18}$$

FOURIER TRANSFORMS
FINITE SINE TRANSFORMS

	$f_s(n)$	$F(x)$
1	$f_s(n) = \displaystyle\int_0^\pi F(x) \sin nx \, dx \ (n = 1, 2, \cdots)$	$F(x)$
2	$(-1)^{n+1} f_s(n)$	$F(\pi - x)$
3	$\dfrac{1}{n}$	$\dfrac{\pi - x}{\pi}$
4	$\dfrac{(-1)^{n+1}}{n}$	$\dfrac{x}{\pi}$
5	$\dfrac{1 - (-1)^n}{n}$	1
6	$\dfrac{2}{n^2} \sin \dfrac{n\pi}{2}$	$\begin{cases} x & \text{when } 0 < x < \pi/2 \\ \pi - x & \text{when } \pi/2 < x < \pi \end{cases}$
7	$\dfrac{(-1)^{n+1}}{n^3}$	$\dfrac{x(\pi^2 - x^2)}{6\pi}$
8	$\dfrac{1 - (-1)^n}{n^3}$	$\dfrac{x(\pi - x)}{2}$
9	$\dfrac{\pi^2(-1)^{n-1}}{n} - \dfrac{2[1 - (-1)^n]}{n^3}$	x^2
10	$\pi(-1)^n \left(\dfrac{6}{n^3} - \dfrac{\pi^2}{n} \right)$	x^3
11	$\dfrac{n}{n^2 + c^2} [1 - (-1)^n e^{c\pi}]$	e^{cx}
12	$\dfrac{n}{n^2 + c^2}$	$\dfrac{\sinh c(\pi - x)}{\sinh c\pi}$
13	$\dfrac{n}{n^2 - k^2} \ (k \neq 0, 1, 2, \cdots)$	$\dfrac{\sin k(\pi - x)}{\sin k\pi}$
14	$\begin{cases} \dfrac{\pi}{2} & \text{when } n = m \\ 0 & \text{when } n \neq m \end{cases} \quad (m = 1, 2, \cdots)$	$\sin mx$
15	$\dfrac{n}{n^2 - k^2} [1 - (-1)^n \cos k\pi]$ $(k \neq 1, 2, \cdots)$	$\cos kx$
16	$\begin{cases} \dfrac{n}{n^2 - m^2} [1 - (-1)^{n+m}] \\ \qquad \text{when } n \neq m = 1, 2, \cdots \\ 0 \qquad \text{when } n = m \end{cases}$	$\cos mx$
17	$\dfrac{n}{(n^2 - k^2)^2} \ (k \neq 0, 1, 2, \cdots)$	$\dfrac{\pi \sin kx}{2k \sin^2 k\pi} - \dfrac{x \cos k(\pi - x)}{2k \sin k\pi}$
18	$\dfrac{b^n}{n} \ (|b| \leq 1)$	$\dfrac{2}{\pi} \arctan \dfrac{b \sin x}{1 - b \cos x}$
19	$\dfrac{1 - (-1)^n}{n} b^n \ (|b| \leq 1)$	$\dfrac{2}{\pi} \arctan \dfrac{2b \sin x}{1 - b^2}$

FINITE COSINE TRANSFORMS

	$f_c(n)$	$F(x)$
1	$f_c(n) = \displaystyle\int_0^\pi F(x) \cos nx\, dx \quad (n = 0, 1, 2, \cdots)$	$F(x)$
2	$(-1)^n f_c(n)$	$F(\pi - x)$
3	0 when $n = 1, 2, \cdots;\ f_c(0) = \pi$	1
4	$\dfrac{2}{n} \sin \dfrac{n\pi}{2};\ f_c(0) = 0$	$\begin{cases} 1 \text{ when } 0 < x < \pi/2 \\ -1 \text{ when } \pi/2 < x < \pi \end{cases}$
5	$-\dfrac{1 - (-1)^n}{n^2};\ f_c(0) = \dfrac{\pi^2}{2}$	x
6	$\dfrac{(-1)^n}{n^2};\ f_c(0) = \dfrac{\pi^2}{6}$	$\dfrac{x^2}{2\pi}$
7	$\dfrac{1}{n^2};\ f_c(0) = 0$	$\dfrac{(\pi - x)^2}{2\pi} - \dfrac{\pi}{6}$
8	$3\pi^2 \dfrac{(-1)^n}{n^2} - 6 \dfrac{1 - (-1)^n}{n^4};\ f_c(0) = \dfrac{\pi^4}{4}$	x^3
9	$\dfrac{(-1)^n e^c \pi - 1}{n^2 + c^2}$	$\dfrac{1}{c} e^{cx}$
10	$\dfrac{1}{n^2 + c^2}$	$\dfrac{\cosh c(\pi - x)}{c \sinh c\pi}$
11	$\dfrac{k}{n^2 - k^2} [(-1)^n \cos \pi k - 1]$ $(k \neq 0, 1, 2, \cdots)$	$\sin kx$
12	$\dfrac{(-1)^{n+m} - 1}{n^2 - m^2};\ f_c(m) = 0 \quad (m = 1, 2, \cdots)$	$\dfrac{1}{m} \sin mx$
13	$\dfrac{1}{n^2 - k^2} \quad (k \neq 0, 1, 2, \cdots)$	$-\dfrac{\cos k(\pi - x)}{k \sin k\pi}$
14	0 when $n = 1, 2, \cdots;$ $f_c(m) = \dfrac{\pi}{2} \quad (m = 1, 2, \cdots)$	$\cos mx$

FOURIER SINE TRANSFORMS[1]

$F(x)$	$f_s(\alpha)$
1 $\begin{cases} 1 & (0 < x < a) \\ 0 & (x > a) \end{cases}$	$\sqrt{\dfrac{2}{\pi}} \left[\dfrac{1 - \cos \alpha}{\alpha} \right]$
2 $x^{p-1} \, (0 < p < 1)$	$\sqrt{\dfrac{2}{\pi}} \, \dfrac{\Gamma(p)}{\alpha^p} \sin \dfrac{p\pi}{2}$
3 $\begin{cases} \sin x & (0 < x < a) \\ 0 & (x > a) \end{cases}$	$\dfrac{1}{\sqrt{2\pi}} \left[\dfrac{\sin[a(1 - \alpha)]}{1 - \alpha} - \dfrac{\sin[a(1 + \alpha)]}{1 + \alpha} \right]$
4 e^{-x}	$\sqrt{\dfrac{2}{\pi}} \left[\dfrac{\alpha}{1 + \alpha^2} \right]$
5 $xe^{-x^2/2}$	$\alpha e^{-\alpha^2/2}$
6 $\cos \dfrac{x^2}{2}$	$\sqrt{2} \left[\sin \dfrac{\alpha^2}{2} C\!\left(\dfrac{\alpha^2}{2}\right) - \cos \dfrac{\alpha^2}{2} S\!\left(\dfrac{\alpha^2}{2}\right) \right]$ *
7 $\sin \dfrac{x^2}{2}$	$\sqrt{2} \left[\cos \dfrac{\alpha^2}{2} C\!\left(\dfrac{\alpha^2}{2}\right) + \sin \dfrac{\alpha^2}{2} S\!\left(\dfrac{\alpha^2}{2}\right) \right]$ *

*$C(y)$ and $S(y)$ are the Fresnel integrals

$$C(y) = \frac{1}{\sqrt{2\pi}} \int_0^y \frac{1}{\sqrt{t}} \cos t \, dt,$$

$$S(y) = \frac{1}{\sqrt{2\pi}} \int_0^y \frac{1}{\sqrt{t}} \sin t \, dt.$$

[1] More extensive tables of the Fourier sine and cosine transforms can be found in Fritz Oberhettinger, "Tabellen zur-Fourier Transformation," Springer (1957).

FOURIER COSINE TRANSFORMS

$F(x)$	$f_c(\alpha)$
1 $\begin{cases} 1 & (0 < x < a) \\ 0 & (x > a) \end{cases}$	$\sqrt{\dfrac{2}{\pi}} \, \dfrac{\sin a\alpha}{\alpha}$
2 $x^{p-1} \quad (0 < p < 1)$	$\sqrt{\dfrac{2}{\pi}} \, \dfrac{\Gamma(p)}{\alpha^p} \cos \dfrac{p\pi}{2}$
3 $\begin{cases} \cos x & (0 < x < a) \\ 0 & (x > a) \end{cases}$	$\dfrac{1}{\sqrt{2\pi}} \left[\dfrac{\sin[a(1 - \alpha)]}{1 - \alpha} + \dfrac{\sin[a(1 + \alpha)]}{1 + \alpha} \right]$
4 e^{-x}	$\sqrt{\dfrac{2}{\pi}} \left(\dfrac{1}{1 + \alpha^2} \right)$
5 $e^{-x^2/2}$	$e^{-\alpha^2/2}$
6 $\cos \dfrac{x^2}{2}$	$\cos\!\left(\dfrac{\alpha^2}{2} - \dfrac{\pi}{4} \right)$
7 $\sin \dfrac{x^2}{2}$	$\cos\!\left(\dfrac{\alpha^2}{2} + \dfrac{\pi}{4} \right)$

FOURIER TRANSFORMS[1]

	$F(x)$	$f(\alpha)$
1	$\dfrac{\sin ax}{x}$	$\begin{cases} \sqrt{\dfrac{\pi}{2}} & \lvert \alpha \rvert < a \\ 0 & \lvert \alpha \rvert > a \end{cases}$
2	$\begin{cases} e^{iwx} & (p < x < q) \\ 0 & (x < p,\ x > q) \end{cases}$	$\dfrac{i}{\sqrt{2\pi}}\ \dfrac{e^{ip(w+\alpha)} - e^{iq(w+\alpha)}}{(w+\alpha)}$
3	$\begin{cases} e^{-cx+iwx} & (x > 0) \\ 0 & (x < 0) \end{cases} \quad (c > 0)$	$\dfrac{i}{\sqrt{2\pi}(w + \alpha + ic)}$
4	$e^{-px^2} \quad R(p) > 0$	$\dfrac{1}{\sqrt{2p}}\, e^{-\alpha^2/4p}$
5	$\cos px^2$	$\dfrac{1}{\sqrt{2p}}\cos\left[\dfrac{\alpha^2}{4p} - \dfrac{\pi}{4}\right]$
6	$\sin px^2$	$\dfrac{1}{\sqrt{2p}}\cos\left[\dfrac{\alpha^2}{4p} + \dfrac{\pi}{4}\right]$
7	$\lvert x \rvert^{-p} \quad (0 < p < 1)$	$\sqrt{\dfrac{2}{\pi}}\ \dfrac{\Gamma(1-p)\sin\dfrac{p\pi}{2}}{\lvert \alpha \rvert^{(1-p)}}$
8	$\dfrac{e^{-a\lvert x \rvert}}{\sqrt{\lvert x \rvert}}$	$\dfrac{\sqrt{\sqrt{(a^2+\alpha^2)} + a}}{\sqrt{a^2+\alpha^2}}$
9	$\dfrac{\cosh ax}{\cosh \pi x} \quad (-\pi < a < \pi)$	$\sqrt{\dfrac{2}{\pi}}\ \dfrac{\cos\dfrac{a}{2}\cosh\dfrac{\alpha}{2}}{\cosh\alpha + \cos a}$
10	$\dfrac{\sinh ax}{\sinh \pi x} \quad (-\pi < a < \pi)$	$\dfrac{1}{\sqrt{2\pi}}\ \dfrac{\sin a}{\cosh\alpha + \cos a}$
11	$\begin{cases} \dfrac{1}{\sqrt{a^2 - x^2}} & (\lvert x \rvert < a) \\ 0 & (\lvert x \rvert > a) \end{cases}$	$\sqrt{\dfrac{\pi}{2}}\, J_0(a\alpha)$
12	$\dfrac{\sin[b\sqrt{a^2+x^2}]}{\sqrt{a^2+x^2}}$	$\begin{cases} 0 & (\lvert \alpha \rvert > b) \\ \sqrt{\dfrac{\pi}{2}}\, J_0(a\sqrt{b^2-\alpha^2}) & (\lvert \alpha \rvert < b) \end{cases}$
13	$\begin{cases} P_n(x) & (\lvert x \rvert < 1) \\ 0 & (\lvert x \rvert > 1) \end{cases}$	$\dfrac{i^n}{\sqrt{\alpha}}\, J_{n+\frac{1}{2}}(\alpha)$
14	$\begin{cases} \dfrac{\cos[b\sqrt{a^2-x^2}]}{\sqrt{a^2-x^2}} & (\lvert x \rvert < a) \\ 0 & (\lvert x \rvert > a) \end{cases}$	$\sqrt{\dfrac{\pi}{2}}\, J_0(a\sqrt{\alpha^2+b^2})$
15	$\begin{cases} \dfrac{\cosh[b\sqrt{a^2-x^2}]}{\sqrt{a^2-x^2}} & (\lvert x \rvert < a) \\ 0 & (\lvert x \rvert > a) \end{cases}$	$\sqrt{\dfrac{\pi}{2}}\, J_0(a\sqrt{\alpha^2-b^2})$

[1]More extensive tables of Fourier transforms can be found in W. Magnus and F. Oberhettinger, "Formulas and Theorems of the Special Functions of Mathematical Physics," pp. 116–120. Chelsea (1949).

The following functions appear among the entries of the tables on transforms.

Function	Definition	Name
$Ei(x)$	$\displaystyle\int_{-\infty}^{x} \frac{e^{v}}{v}\, dv$; or sometimes defined as $$-Ei(-x) = \int_{x}^{\infty} \frac{e^{-v}}{v}\, dv$$	Sine, Cosine, and Exponential Integral tables pages 515–517
$Si(x)$	$\displaystyle\int_{0}^{x} \frac{\sin v}{v}\, dv$	Sine, Cosine, and Exponential Integral tables pages 515–517
$Ci(x)$	$\displaystyle\int_{\infty}^{x} \frac{\cos v}{v}\, dv$; or sometimes defined as negative of this integral	Sine, Cosine, and Exponential Integral tables pages 515–517
$erf(x)$	$\displaystyle\frac{2}{\sqrt{\pi}} \int_{0}^{x} e^{-v^{2}}\, dv$	Error function page 576
$erfc(x)$	$\displaystyle 1 - erf(x) = \frac{2}{\sqrt{\pi}} \int_{x}^{\infty} e^{-v^{2}}\, dv$	Complementary function to error function
$L_{n}(x)$	$\displaystyle\frac{e^{x}}{n!} \frac{d^{n}}{dx^{n}} (x^{n} e^{-x}), \quad n = 0, 1, \cdots$	Laguerre polynomial of degree n

ORTHOGONAL POLYNOMIALS

I

Name: Legendre   *Symbol*: $P_n(x)$ *Interval*: $[-1, 1]$

Differential Equation: $(1 - x^2)y'' - 2xy' + n(n + 1)y = 0$
$$y = P_n(x)$$

Explicit Expression: $P_n(x) = \dfrac{1}{2^n} \displaystyle\sum_{m=0}^{[n/2]} (-1)^m \binom{n}{m} \binom{2n - 2m}{n} x^{n-2m}$

Recurrence Relation: $(n + 1)P_{n+1}(x) = (2n + 1)xP_n(x) - nP_{n-1}(x)$

Weight: 1   *Standardization*: $P_n(1) = 1$

Norm: $\displaystyle\int_{-1}^{+1} [P_n(x)]^2 dx = \dfrac{2}{2n + 1}$

Rodrigues' Formula: $P_n(x) = \dfrac{(-1)^n}{2^n n!} \dfrac{d^n}{dx^n} \{(1 - x^2)^n\}$

Generating Function: $R^{-1} = \displaystyle\sum_{n=0}^{\infty} P_n(x)z^n; \quad -1 < x < 1, \quad |z| < 1,$
$$R = \sqrt{1 - 2xz + z^2}.$$

Inequality: $|P_n(x)| \le 1, \, -1 \le x \le 1$.

II

Name: Tschebysheff, First Kind   *Symbol*: $T_n(x)$ *Interval*: $[-1, 1]$

Differential Equation: $(1 - x^2)y'' - xy' + n^2 y = 0$
$$y = T_n(x)$$

Explicit Expression: $\dfrac{n}{2} \displaystyle\sum_{m=0}^{[n/2]} (-1)^m \dfrac{(n - m - 1)!}{m!(n - 2m)!} (2x)^{n-2m} = \cos(n \arccos x) = T_n(x)$

Recurrence Relation: $T_{n+1}(x) = 2xT_n(x) - T_{n-1}(x)$

Weight: $(1 - x^2)^{-1/2}$ *Standardization*: $T_n(1) = 1$

Norm: $\displaystyle\int_{-1}^{+1} (1 - x^2)^{-1/2}[T_n(x)]^2 dx = \begin{cases} \pi/2, & n \ne 0 \\ \pi, & n = 0 \end{cases}$

Rodrigues' Formula: $\dfrac{(-1)^n(1 - x^2)^{1/2}\sqrt{\pi}}{2^{n+1}\Gamma(n + \frac{1}{2})} \dfrac{d^n}{dx^n} \{(1 - x^2)^{n-(1/2)}\} = T_n(x)$

Generating Function: $\dfrac{1 - xz}{1 - 2xz + z^2} = \displaystyle\sum_{n=0}^{\infty} T_n(x)z^n, \, -1 < x < 1, \, |z| < 1$.

Inequality: $|T_n(x)| \le 1, \, -1 \le x \le 1$.

III

Name: Tschebysheff, Second Kind   *Symbol*: $U_n(x)$ *Interval*: $[-1, 1]$

Differential Equation: $(1 - x^2)y'' - 3xy' + n(n + 2)y = 0$

$$y = U_n(x)$$

Explicit Expression:
$$U_n(x) = \sum_{m=0}^{[n/2]} (-1)^m \frac{(m - n)!}{m!(n - 2m)!} (2x)^{n-2m}$$

$$U_n(\cos\theta) = \frac{\sin[(n + 1)\theta]}{\sin\theta}$$

Recurrence Relation: $U_{n+1}(x) = 2xU_n(x) - U_{n-1}(x)$

Weight: $(1 - x^2)^{1/2}$ *Standardization*: $U_n(1) = n + 1$

Norm:
$$\int_{-1}^{+1} (1 - x^2)^{1/2}[U_n(x)]^2 dx = \frac{\pi}{2}$$

Rodrigues' Formula:
$$U_n(x) = \frac{(-1)^n(n + 1)\sqrt{\pi}}{(1 - x^2)^{1/2}2^{n+1}\Gamma(n + \tfrac{3}{2})} \frac{d^n}{dx^n}\{(1 - x^2)^{n+(1/2)}\}$$

Generating Function:
$$\frac{1}{1 - 2xz + z^2} = \sum_{n=0}^{\infty} U_n(x)z^n, \quad -1 < x < 1, \; |z| < 1.$$

Inequality: $|U_n(x)| \le n + 1, \; -1 \le x \le 1.$

IV

Name: Jacobi   *Symbol*: $P_n^{(\alpha,\beta)}(x)$ *Interval*: $[-1, 1]$

Differential Equation:

$$(1 - x^2)y'' + [\beta - \alpha - (\alpha + \beta + 2)x]y' + n(n + \alpha + \beta + 1)y = 0$$

$$y = P_n^{(\alpha,\beta)}(x)$$

Explicit Expression:
$$P_n^{(\alpha,\beta)}(x) = \frac{1}{2^n} \sum_{m=0}^{n} \binom{n + \alpha}{m}\binom{n + \beta}{n - m} (x - 1)^{n-m}(x + 1)^m$$

Recurrence Relation: $2(n + 1)(n + \alpha + \beta + 1)(2n + \alpha + \beta)P_{n+1}^{(\alpha,\beta)}(x)$

$$= (2n + \alpha + \beta + 1)[(\alpha^2 - \beta^2) + (2n + \alpha + \beta + 2)$$
$$\times (2n + \alpha + \beta)x] P_n^{(\alpha,\beta)}(x)$$
$$- 2(n + \alpha)(n + \beta)(2n + \alpha + \beta + 2) P_{n-1}^{(\alpha,\beta)}(x)$$

Weight: $(1 - x)^\alpha(1 + x)^\beta; \; \alpha, \beta > 1$ *Standardization*: $P_n^{(\alpha,\beta)}(x) = \binom{n + \alpha}{n}$

Norm:
$$\int_{-1}^{+1} (1 - x)^\alpha(1 + x)^\beta[P_n^{(\alpha,\beta)}(x)]^2 dx = \frac{2^{\alpha+\beta+1}\Gamma(n + \alpha + 1)\Gamma(n + \beta + 1)}{(2n + \alpha + \beta + 1)n!\Gamma(n + \alpha + \beta + 1)}$$

Rodrigues' Formula:
$$P_n^{(\alpha,\beta)}(x) = \frac{(-1)^n}{2^n n!(1 - x)^\alpha(1 + x)^\beta} \frac{d^n}{dx^n}\{(1 - x)^{n+\alpha}(1 + x)^{n+\beta}\}$$

IV (Continued)

Generating Function: $R^{-1}(1 - z + R)^{-\alpha}(1 + z + R)^{-\beta} = \sum_{n=0}^{\infty} 2^{-\alpha-\beta} P_n^{(\alpha,\beta)}(x) z^n,$

$$R = \sqrt{1 - 2xz + z^2}, \ |z| < 1$$

Inequality: $\max_{-1 \leq x \leq 1} | P_n^{(\alpha,\beta)}(x) | = \begin{cases} \dbinom{n + q}{n} \sim n^q \text{ if } q = \max(\alpha, \beta) \geq -\frac{1}{2} \\ | P_n^{(\alpha,\beta)}(x') | \sim n^{-1/2} \text{ if } q < -\frac{1}{2} \\ x' \text{ is one of the two maximum points nearest} \\ \dfrac{\beta - \alpha}{\alpha + \beta + 1} \end{cases}$

V

Name: Generalized Laguerre   *Symbol*: $L_n^{(\alpha)}(x)$ *Interval*: $[0, \infty]$

Differential Equation: $xy'' + (\alpha + 1 - x)y' + ny = 0$

$$y = L_n^{(\alpha)}(x)$$

Explicit Expression: $L_n^{(\alpha)}(x) = \sum_{m=0}^{n} (-1)^m \binom{n + \alpha}{n - m} \frac{1}{m!} x^m$

Recurrence Relation: $(n + 1) L_{n+1}^{(\alpha)}(x) = [(2n + \alpha + 1) - x] L_n^{(\alpha)}(x) - (n + \alpha) L_{n-1}^{(\alpha)}(x)$

Weight: $x^\alpha e^{-x}, \alpha > -1$ *Standardization*: $L_n^{(\alpha)}(x) = \dfrac{(-1)^n}{n!} x^n + \cdots$

Norm: $\displaystyle\int_0^{\infty} x^\alpha e^{-x} [L_n^{(\alpha)}(x)]^2 \, dx = \frac{\Gamma(n + \alpha + 1)}{n!}$

Rodrigues' Formula: $L_n^{(\alpha)}(x) = \dfrac{1}{n! \, x^\alpha e^{-x}} \dfrac{d^n}{dx^n} \{x^{n+\alpha} e^{-x}\}$

Generating Function: $(1 - z)^{-\alpha-1} \exp\left(\dfrac{xz}{z - 1}\right) = \sum_{n=0}^{\infty} L_n^{(\alpha)}(x) z^n$

Inequality: $| L_n^{(\alpha)}(x) | \leq \dfrac{\Gamma(n + \alpha + 1)}{n! \, \Gamma(\alpha + 1)} e^{x/2}; \quad \begin{matrix} x \geq 0 \\ \alpha > 0 \end{matrix}$

$$| L_n^{(\alpha)}(x) | \leq \left[2 - \frac{\Gamma(\alpha + n + 1)}{n! \, \Gamma(\alpha + 1)}\right] e^{x/2}; \quad \begin{matrix} x \geq 0 \\ -1 < \alpha < 0 \end{matrix}$$

SINE, COSINE, AND EXPONENTIAL INTEGRALS

$$Si(x) = \int_0^x \frac{\sin v}{v} \, dv; \qquad Ci(x) = \int_\infty^x \frac{\cos v}{v} \, dv;$$

$$Ei(x) = \int_{-\infty}^x \frac{e^v}{v} \, dv; \qquad -Ei(-x) = \int_x^\infty \frac{e^{-v}}{v} \, dv$$

x	$Si(x)$	$Ci(x)$	$Ei(x)$	$-Ei(-x)$
0.0	0.00000	$-\infty$	$-\infty$	$+\infty$
0.1	0.09994	-1.72787	-1.62281	1.82292
0.2	.19956	-1.04221	$-$ .82176	1.22265
0.3	.29850	$-$ .64917	$-$ .30267	.90568
0.4	.39646	$-$ .37881	.10477	.70238
0.5	.49311	$-$ .17778	.45422	.55977
0.6	.58813	$-$ .02227	.76988	.45438
0.7	.68122	.10051	1.06491	.37377
0.8	.77210	.19828	1.34740	.31060
0.9	.86047	.27607	1.62281	.26018
1.0	.94608	.33740	1.89512	.21938
1.1	1.02869	.38487	2.16738	.18599
1.2	1.10805	.42046	2.44209	.15841
1.3	1.18396	.44574	2.72140	.13545
1.4	1.25623	.46201	3.00721	.11622
1.5	1.32468	.47036	3.30129	.10002
1.6	1.38918	.47173	3.60532	.08631
1.7	1.44959	.46697	3.92096	.07465
1.8	1.50582	.45681	4.24987	.06471
1.9	1.55778	.44194	4.59371	.05620
2.0	1.60541	.42298	4.95423	.04890
2.1	1.64870	.40051	5.33324	.04261
2.2	1.68762	.37507	5.73261	.03719
2.3	1.72221	.34718	6.15438	.03250
2.4	1.75249	.31729	6.60067	.02844
2.5	1.77852	.28587	7.07377	.02491
2.6	1.80039	.25334	7.57611	.02185
2.7	1.81821	.22008	8.11035	.01918
2.8	1.83210	.18649	8.67930	.01686
2.9	1.84219	.15290	9.28602	.01482
3.0	1.84865	.11963	9.93383	.01305
3.1	1.85166	.08699	10.6263	.01149
3.2	1.85140	.05526	11.3673	.01013
3.3	1.84808	.02468	12.1610	.00894
3.4	1.84191	$-$ .00452	13.0121	.00789
3.5	1.83313	$-$ .03213	13.9254	.00697
3.6	1.82195	$-$ .05797	14.9063	.00616
3.7	1.80862	$-$ .08190	15.9606	.00545
3.8	1.79339	$-$ .10378	17.0948	.00482
3.9	1.77650	$-$ .12350	18.3157	.00427
4.0	1.75820	$-$ .14098	19.6309	.00378
4.1	1.73874	$-$ .15617	21.0485	.00335
4.2	1.71837	$-$ .16901	22.5774	.00297
4.3	1.69732	$-$ .17951	24.2274	.00263
4.4	1.67583	$-$ .18766	26.0090	.00234

SINE, COSINE, AND EXPONENTIAL INTEGRALS (Continued)

x	$Si(x)$	$Ci(x)$	$Ei(x)$	$-Ei(-x)$
4.5	1.65414	− .19349	27.9337	.00207
4.6	1.63246	− .19705	30.0141	.00184
4.7	1.61100	− .19839	32.2639	.00164
4.8	1.58998	− .19760	34.6979	.00145
4.9	1.56956	− .19478	37.3325	.00129
5.0	1.54993	− .19003	40.1853	.00115
5.1	1.53125	− .18348	43.2757	.00102
5.2	1.51367	− .17525	46.6249	.00091
5.3	1.49732	− .16551	50.2557	.00081
5.4	1.48230	− .15439	54.1935	.00072
5.5	1.46872	− .14205	58.4655	.00064
5.6	1.45667	− .12867	63.1018	.00057
5.7	1.44620	− .11441	68.1350	.00051
5.8	1.43736	− .09944	73.6008	.00045
5.9	1.43018	− .08393	79.5382	.00040
6.0	1.42469	− .06806	85.9898	.00036
6.1	1.42087	− .05198	93.0020	.00032
6.2	1.41871	− .03587	100.626	.00029
6.3	1.41817	− .01989	108.916	.00026
6.4	1.41922	− .00418	117.935	.00023
6.5	1.42179	+ .01110	127.747	.00020
6.6	1.42582	+ .02582	138.426	.00018
6.7	1.43121	.03986	150.050	.00016
6.8	1.43787	.05308	162.707	.00014
6.9	1.44570	.06539	176.491	.00013
7.0	1.45460	.07670	191.505	.00012
7.1	1.46443	.08691	207.863	.00010
7.2	1.47509	.09596	225.688	.00009
7.3	1.48644	.10379	245.116	.00008
7.4	1.49834	.11036	266.296	.00007
7.5	1.51068	.11563	289.388	.00007
7.6	1.52331	.11960	314.572	.00006
7.7	1.53611	.12225	342.040	.00005
7.8	1.54894	.12359	372.006	.00005
7.9	1.56167	.12364	404.701	.00004
8.0	1.57419	.12243	440.380	.00004
8.1	1.58637	.12002	479.322	.00003
8.2	1.59810	.11644	521.831	.00003
8.3	1.60928	.11177	568.242	.00003
8.4	1.61981	.10607	681.919	.00002
8.5	1.62960	.09943	674.264	.00002
8.6	1.63857	.09194	734.714	.00002
8.7	1.64665	.08368	800.749	.00002
8.8	1.65379	.07476	872.895	.00002
8.9	1.65993	.06528	951.728	.00001
9.0	1.66504	.05535	1037.88	.00001
9.1	1.66908	.04507	1132.04	.00001
9.2	1.67205	.03455	1234.96	.00001
9.3	1.67393	.02391	1347.48	.00001
9.4	1.67473	.01325	1470.51	.00001

SINE, COSINE, AND EXPONENTIAL INTEGRALS (Continued)

x	Si(x)	Ci(x)	Ei(x)	−Ei(−x)
9.5	1.67446	.00268	1605.03	.00001
9.6	1.67316	− .00771	1752.14	.00001
9.7	1.67084	− .01780	1913.05	.00001
9.8	1.66757	− .02752	2089.05	.00001
9.9	1.66338	− .03676	2281.58	.00000
10.0	1.65835	− .04546	2492.23	.00000
10.5	1.62294	− .07828	3883.74	.00000
11.0	1.57831	− .08956	6071.41	.00000
11.5	1.53572	− .07857	9518.20	.00000
12.0	1.50497	− .04978	14959.5	.00000
12.5	1.49234	− .01141	23565.1	.00000
13.0	1.49936	+ .02676	37197.7	.00000
13.5	1.52291	+ .05576	58827.0	.00000
14.0	1.55621	.06940	93193.0	.00000
14.5	1.59072	.06554	147866.	.00000
15.0	1.61819	.04628	234955.	.00000

*GAMMA FUNCTION

Values of $\Gamma(n) = \int_0^\infty e^{-z}z^{n-1}dz$; $\Gamma(n+1) = n\Gamma(n)$

n	Γ (n)	n	Γ (n)	n	Γ (n)	n	Γ (n)
1.00	1.00000	1.25	.90640	1.50	.88623	1.75	.91906
1.01	.99433	1.26	.90440	1.51	.88659	1.76	.92137
1.02	.98884	1.27	.90250	1.52	.88704	1.77	.92376
1.03	.98355	1.28	.90072	1.53	.88757	1.78	.92623
1.04	.97844	1.29	.89904	1.54	.88818	1.79	.92877
1.05	.97350	1.30	.89747	1.55	.88887	1.80	.93138
1.06	.96874	1.31	.89600	1.56	.88964	1.81	.93408
1.07	.96415	1.32	.89464	1.57	.89049	1.82	.93685
1.08	.95973	1.33	.89338	1.58	.89142	1.83	.93969
1.09	.95546	1.34	.89222	1.59	.89243	1.84	.94261
1.10	.95135	1.35	.89115	1.60	.89352	1.85	.94561
1.11	.94740	1.36	.89018	1.61	.89468	1.86	.94869
1.12	.94359	1.37	.88931	1.62	.89592	1.87	.95184
1.13	.93993	1.38	.88854	1.63	.89724	1.88	.95507
1.14	.93642	1.39	.88785	1.64	.89864	1.89	.95838
1.15	.93304	1.40	.88726	1.65	.90012	1.90	.96177
1.16	.92980	1.41	.88676	1.66	.90167	1.91	.96523
1.17	.92670	1.42	.88636	1.67	.90330	1.92	.96877
1.18	.92373	1.43	.88604	1.68	.90500	1.93	.97240
1.19	.92089	1.44	.88581	1.69	.90678	1.94	.97610
1.20	.91817	1.45	.88566	1.70	.90864	1.95	.97988
1.21	.91558	1.46	.88560	1.71	.91057	1.96	.98374
1.22	.91311	1.47	.88563	1.72	.91258	1.97	.98768
1.23	.91075	1.48	.88575	1.73	.91466	1.98	.99171
1.24	.90852	1.49	.88595	1.74	.91683	1.99	.99581
						2.00	1.00000

* For large positive values of x, $\Gamma(x)$ approximates Stirling's asymptotic series

$$x^x e^{-x} \sqrt{\frac{2\pi}{x}} \left[1 + \frac{1}{12x} + \frac{1}{288x^2} - \frac{139}{51840x^3} - \frac{571}{2488320x^4} + \cdots \right].$$

BESSEL FUNCTIONS

1. Bessel's differential equation for a real variable x is

$$x^2 \frac{d^2 y}{dx^2} + x \frac{dy}{dx} + (x^2 - n^2) y = 0$$

2. When n is not an integer, two independent solutions of the equation are $J_n(x)$ and $J_{-n}(x)$, where

$$J_n(x) = \sum_{k=0}^{\infty} \frac{(-1)^k}{k!\,\Gamma(n + k + 1)} \left(\frac{x}{2}\right)^{n+2k}$$

3. If n is an integer $J_{-n}(x) = (-1)^n J_n(x)$, where

$$J_n(x) = \frac{x^n}{2^n n!} \left\{ 1 - \frac{x^2}{2^2 \cdot 1!(n + 1)} + \frac{x^4}{2^4 \cdot 2!(n + 1)(n + 2)} \right.$$
$$\left. - \frac{x^6}{2^6 \cdot 3!(n + 1)(n + 2)(n + 3)} + \cdots \right\}$$

4. For $n = 0$ and $n = 1$, this formula becomes

$$J_0(x) = 1 - \frac{x^2}{2^2 (1!)^2} + \frac{x^4}{2^4 (2!)^2} - \frac{x^6}{2^6 (3!)^2} + \frac{x^8}{2^8 (4!)^2} - \cdots$$

$$J_1(x) = \frac{x}{2} - \frac{x^3}{2^3 \cdot 1!2!} + \frac{x^5}{2^5 \cdot 2!3!} - \frac{x^7}{2^7 \cdot 3!4!} + \frac{x^9}{2^9 \cdot 4!5!} - \cdots$$

5. When x is large and positive, the following asymptotic series may be used

$$J_0(x) = \left(\frac{2}{\pi x}\right)^{\frac{1}{2}} \left\{ P_0(x) \cos\left(x - \frac{\pi}{4}\right) - Q_0(x) \sin\left(x - \frac{\pi}{4}\right) \right\}$$

$$J_1(x) = \left(\frac{2}{\pi x}\right)^{\frac{1}{2}} \left\{ P_1(x) \cos\left(x - \frac{3\pi}{4}\right) - Q_1(x) \sin\left(x - \frac{3\pi}{4}\right) \right\},$$

where

$$P_0(x) \sim 1 - \frac{1^2 \cdot 3^2}{2!(8x)^2} + \frac{1^2 \cdot 3^2 \cdot 5^2 \cdot 7^2}{4!(8x)^4} - \frac{1^2 \cdot 3^2 \cdot 5^2 \cdot 7^2 \cdot 9^2 \cdot 11^2}{6!(8x)^6} + \cdots$$

$$Q_0(x) \sim - \frac{1^2}{1!8x} + \frac{1^2 \cdot 3^2 \cdot 5^2}{3!(8x)^3} - \frac{1^2 \cdot 3^2 \cdot 5^2 \cdot 7^2 \cdot 9^2}{5!(8x)^5} + - \cdots$$

$$P_1(x) \sim 1 + \frac{1^2 \cdot 3 \cdot 5}{2!(8x)^2} - \frac{1^2 \cdot 3^2 \cdot 5^2 \cdot 7 \cdot 9}{4!(8x)^4} + \frac{1^2 \cdot 3^2 \cdot 5^2 \cdot 7^2 \cdot 9^2 \cdot 11 \cdot 13}{6!(8x)^6} - + \cdots$$

$$Q_1(x) \sim \frac{1 \cdot 3}{1!8x} - \frac{1^2 \cdot 3^2 \cdot 5 \cdot 7}{3!(8x)^3} + \frac{1^2 \cdot 3^2 \cdot 5^2 \cdot 7^2 \cdot 9 \cdot 11}{5!(8x)^5} - \cdots$$

[In $P_1(x)$ the signs alternate from $+$ to $-$ after the first term]

6. If $x > 25$, it is convenient to use the formulas

$$J_0(x) = A_0(x) \sin x + B_0(x) \cos x$$
$$J_1(x) = B_1(x) \sin x - A_1(x) \cos x,$$

where

$$A_0(x) = \frac{P_0(x) - Q_0(x)}{(\pi x)^{\frac{1}{2}}} \quad \text{and} \quad A_1(x) = \frac{P_1(x) - Q_1(x)}{(\pi x)^{\frac{1}{2}}}$$

$$B_0(x) = \frac{P_0(x) + Q_0(x)}{(\pi x)^{\frac{1}{2}}} \quad \text{and} \quad B_1(x) = \frac{P_1(x) + Q_1(x)}{(\pi x)^{\frac{1}{2}}}$$

7. The zeros of $J_0(x)$ and $J_1(x)$

If $j_{0,s}$ and $j_{1,s}$ are the s'th zeros of $J_0(x)$ and $J_1(x)$ respectively, and if $a = 4s - 1$, $b = 4s + 1$

$$j_{0,s} \sim \frac{1}{4} \pi a \left\{ 1 + \frac{2}{\pi^2 a^2} - \frac{62}{3\pi^4 a^4} + \frac{15{,}116}{15\pi^6 a^6} - \frac{12{,}554{,}474}{105\pi^8 a^8} + \frac{8{,}368{,}654{,}292}{315\pi^{10} a^{10}} - + \cdots \right\}$$

$$j_{1,s} \sim \frac{1}{4} \pi b \left\{ 1 - \frac{6}{\pi^2 b^2} + \frac{6}{\pi^4 b^4} - \frac{4716}{5\pi^6 b^6} + \frac{3{,}902{,}418}{35\pi^8 b^8} - \frac{895{,}167{,}324}{35\pi^{10} b^{10}} + \cdots \right\}$$

$$J_1(j_{0,s}) \sim \frac{(-1)^{s+1} 2^{\frac{3}{2}}}{\pi a^{\frac{1}{2}}} \left\{ 1 - \frac{56}{3\pi^4 a^4} + \frac{9664}{5\pi^6 a^6} - \frac{7{,}381{,}280}{21\pi^8 a^8} + \cdots \right\}$$

$$J_0(j_{1,s}) \sim \frac{(-1)^s 2^{\frac{3}{2}}}{\pi b^{\frac{1}{2}}} \left\{ 1 + \frac{24}{\pi^4 b^4} - \frac{19{,}584}{10\pi^6 b^6} + \frac{2{,}466{,}720}{7\pi^8 b^8} - \cdots \right\}$$

8. Table of zeros for $J_0(x)$ and $J_1(x)$

$$J_1(\alpha_n) = 0 \qquad J_0(\beta_n) = 0$$

Roots α_n	$J_1(\alpha_n)$	Roots β_n	$J_0(\beta_n)$
2.4048	0.5191	0.0000	1.0000
5.5201	-0.3403	3.8317	-0.4028
8.6537	0.2715	7.0156	0.3001
11.7915	-0.2325	10.1735	-0.2497
14.9309	0.2065	13.3237	0.2184
18.0711	-0.1877	16.4706	-0.1965
21.2116	0.1733	19.6159	0.1801

9. Recurrence formulas

$$J_{n-1}(x) + J_{n+1}(x) = \frac{2n}{x} J_n(x) \qquad\qquad nJ_n(x) + xJ_n'(x) = xJ_{n-1}(x)$$

$$J_{n-1}(x) - J_{n+1}(x) = 2J_n'(x) \qquad\qquad nJ_n(x) - xJ_n'(x) = xJ_{n+1}(x)$$

10. If J_n is written for $J_n(x)$ and $J_n^{(k)}$ is written for $\frac{d^k}{dx^k} \{J_n(x)\}$, then the following derivative relationships are important

$$J_0^{(r)} = -J_1^{(r-1)}$$

$$J_0^{(2)} = -J_0 + \frac{1}{x} J_1 = \frac{1}{2} (J_2 - J_0)$$

$$J_0^{(3)} = \frac{1}{x} J_0 + \left(1 - \frac{2}{x^2}\right) J_1 = \frac{1}{4} (-J_3 + 3J_1)$$

$$J_0^{(4)} = \left(1 - \frac{3}{x^2}\right) J_0 - \left(\frac{2}{x} - \frac{6}{x^3}\right) J_1 = \frac{1}{8} (J_4 - 4J_2 + 3J_0), \text{ etc.}$$

11. Half order Bessel functions

$$J_{\frac{1}{2}}(x) = \sqrt{\frac{2}{\pi x}} \sin x$$

$$J_{-\frac{1}{2}}(x) = \sqrt{\frac{2}{\pi x}} \cos x$$

$$J_{n+\frac{1}{2}}(x) = -x^{n+\frac{1}{2}} \frac{d}{dx} \{x^{-(n+\frac{1}{2})} J_{n+\frac{1}{2}}(x)\}$$

$$J_{n-\frac{1}{2}}(x) = x^{-(n+\frac{1}{2})} \frac{d}{dx} \{x^{n+\frac{1}{2}} J_{n+\frac{1}{2}}(x)\}$$

n	$\left(\dfrac{\pi x}{2}\right)^{\frac{1}{2}} J_{n+\frac{1}{2}}(x)$	$\left(\dfrac{\pi x}{2}\right)^{\frac{1}{2}} J_{-(n+\frac{1}{2})}(x)$
0	$\sin x$	$\cos x$
1	$\dfrac{\sin x}{x} - \cos x$	$-\dfrac{\cos x}{x} - \sin x$
2	$\left(\dfrac{3}{x^2} - 1\right) \sin x - \dfrac{3}{x} \cos x$	$\left(\dfrac{3}{x^2} - 1\right) \cos x + \dfrac{3}{x} \sin x$
3	$\left(\dfrac{15}{x^3} - \dfrac{6}{x}\right) \sin x - \left(\dfrac{15}{x^2} - 1\right) \cos x$	$-\left(\dfrac{15}{x^3} - \dfrac{6}{x}\right) \cos x - \left(\dfrac{15}{x^2} - 1\right) \sin x$
	etc.	

12. Additional solutions to Bessel's equation are

$Y_n(x)$ (also called Weber's function, and sometimes denoted by $N_n(x)$)
$H_n^{(1)}(x)$ and $H_n^{(2)}(x)$ (also called Hankel functions)

These solutions are defined as follows

$$Y_n(x) = \begin{cases} \dfrac{J_n(x) \cos(n\pi) - J_{-n}(x)}{\sin(n\pi)} & n \text{ not an integer} \\ \lim\limits_{v \to n} \dfrac{J_v(x) \cos(v\pi) - J_{-v}(x)}{\sin(v\pi)} & n \text{ an integer} \end{cases}$$

$$H_n^{(1)}(x) = J_n(x) + iY_n(x)$$
$$H_n^{(2)}(x) = J_n(x) - iY_n(x)$$

The additional properties of these functions may all be derived from the above relations and the known properties of $J_n(x)$.

13. Complete solutions to Bessel's equation may be written as

$$c_1 J_n(x) + c_2 J_{-n}(x) \qquad \text{if } n \text{ is not an integer,}$$

or

$$c_1 J_n(x) + c_2 Y_n(x)$$
$$c_1 H_n^{(1)}(x) + c_2 H_n^{(2)}(x)$$

or $\left.\begin{array}{c} \\ \\ \end{array}\right\}$ for any value of n

14. The modified (or hyperbolic) Bessel's differential equation is

$$x^2 \frac{d^2y}{dx^2} + x \frac{dy}{dx} - (x^2 + n^2)y = 0$$

15. When n is not an integer, two independent solutions of the equation are $I_n(x)$ and $I_{-n}(x)$, where

$$I_n(x) = \sum_{k=0}^{\infty} \frac{1}{k!\,\Gamma(n + k + 1)} \left(\frac{x}{2}\right)^{n+2k}$$

16. If n is an integer,

$$I_n(x) = I_{-n}(x) = \frac{x^n}{2^n n!} \left\{ 1 + \frac{x^2}{2^2 \cdot 1!(n + 1)} + \frac{x^4}{2^4 \cdot 2!(n + 1)(n + 2)} \right.$$
$$\left. + \frac{x^6}{2^6 \cdot 3!(n + 1)(n + 2)(n + 3)} + \cdots \right\}$$

17. For $n = 0$ and $n = 1$, this formula becomes

$$I_0(x) = 1 + \frac{x^2}{2^2(1!)^2} + \frac{x^4}{2^4(2!)^2} + \frac{x^6}{2^6(3!)^2} + \frac{x^8}{2^8(4!)^2} + \cdots$$

$$I_1(x) = \frac{x}{2} + \frac{x^3}{2^3 \cdot 1!2!} + \frac{x^5}{2^5 \cdot 2!3!} + \frac{x^7}{2^7 \cdot 3!4!} + \frac{x^9}{2^9 \cdot 4!5!} + \cdots$$

18. Another solution to the modified Bessel's equation is

$$K_n(x) = \begin{cases} \dfrac{1}{2}\,\pi\,\dfrac{I_{-n}(x) - I_n(x)}{\sin(n\pi)} & n \text{ not an integer} \\[3mm] \lim_{v \to n} \dfrac{1}{2}\,\pi\,\dfrac{I_{-v}(x) - I_v(x)}{\sin(v\pi)} & n \text{ an integer} \end{cases}$$

This function is linearly independent of $I_n(x)$ for all values of n. Thus the complete solution to the modified Bessel's equation may be written as

$$c_1 I_n(x) + c_2 I_{-n}(x) \qquad n \text{ not an integer}$$

or

$$c_1 I_n(x) + c_2 K_n(x) \qquad \text{any } n$$

19. The following relations hold among the various Bessel functions:

$$I_n(z) = i^{-m} J_m(iz)$$
$$Y_n(iz) = (i)^{n+1} I_n(z) - \frac{2}{\pi}\, i^{-n} K_n(z)$$

Most of the properties of the modified Bessel function may be deduced from the known properties of $J_n(x)$ by use of these relations and those previously given.

20. Recurrence formulas

$$I_{n-1}(x) - I_{n+1}(x) = \frac{2n}{x}\, I_n(x) \qquad\qquad I_{n-1}(x) + I_{n+1}(x) = 2I_n'(x)$$

$$I_{n-1}(x) - \frac{n}{x}\, I_n(x) = I_n'(x) \qquad\qquad\qquad I_n'(x) = I_{n+1}(x) + \frac{n}{x}\, I_n(z)$$

Special Function Tables

BESSEL FUNCTIONS $J_0(x)$ AND $J_1(x)$

x	$J_0(x)$	$J_1(x)$	x	$J_0(x)$	$J_1(x)$	x	$J_0(x)$	$J_1(x)$
0.0	1.0000	.0000	**5.0**	−.1776	−.3276	**10.0**	−.2459	.0435
0.1	.9975	.0499	5.1	−.1443	−.3371	10.1	−.2490	.0184
0.2	.9900	.0995	5.2	−.1103	−.3432	10.2	−.2496	−.0066
0.3	.9776	.1483	5.3	−.0758	−.3460	10.3	−.2477	−.0313
0.4	.9604	.1960	5.4	−.0412	−.3453	10.4	−.2434	−.0555
0.5	.9385	.2423	**5.5**	−.0068	−.3414	**10.5**	−.2366	−.0789
0.6	.9120	.2867	5.6	.0270	−.3343	10.6	−.2276	−.1012
0.7	.8812	.3290	5.7	.0599	−.3241	10.7	−.2164	−.1224
0.8	.8463	.3688	5.8	.0917	−.3110	10.8	−.2032	−.1422
0.9	.8075	.4059	5.9	.1220	−.2951	10.9	−.1881	−.1603
1.0	.7652	.4401	**6.0**	.1506	−.2767	**11.0**	−.1712	−.1768
1.1	.7196	.4709	6.1	.1773	−.2559	11.1	−.1528	−.1913
1.2	.6711	.4983	6.2	.2017	−.2329	11.2	−.1330	−.2039
1.3	.6201	.5220	6.3	.2238	−.2081	11.3	−.1121	−.2143
1.4	.5669	.5419	6.4	.2433	−.1816	11.4	−.0902	−.2225
1.5	.5118	.5579	**6.5**	.2601	−.1538	**11.5**	−.0677	−.2284
1.6	.4554	.5699	6.6	.2740	−.1250	11.6	−.0446	−.2320
1.7	.3980	.5778	6.7	.2851	−.0953	11.7	−.0213	−.2333
1.8	.3400	.5815	6.8	.2931	−.0652	11.8	.0020	−.2323
1.9	.2818	.5812	6.9	.2981	−.0349	11.9	.0250	−.2290
2.0	.2239	.5767	**7.0**	.3001	−.0047	**12.0**	.0477	−.2234
2.1	.1666	.5683	7.1	.2991	.0252	12.1	.0697	−.2157
2.2	.1104	.5560	7.2	.2951	.0543	12.2	.0908	−.2060
2.3	.0555	.5399	7.3	.2882	.0826	12.3	.1108	−.1943
2.4	.0025	.5202	7.4	.2786	.1096	12.4	.1296	−.1807
2.5	−.0484	.4971	**7.5**	.2663	.1352	**12.5**	.1469	−.1655
2.6	−.0968	.4708	7.6	.2516	.1592	12.6	.1626	−.1487
2.7	−.1424	.4416	7.7	.2346	.1813	12.7	.1766	−.1307
2.8	−.1850	.4097	7.8	.2154	.2014	12.8	.1887	−.1114
2.9	−.2243	.3754	7.9	.1944	.2192	12.9	.1988	−.0912
3.0	−.2601	.3391	**8.0**	.1717	.2346	**13.0**	.2069	−.0703
3.1	−.2921	.3009	8.1	.1475	.2476	13.1	.2129	−.0489
3.2	−.3202	.2613	8.2	.1222	.2580	13.2	.2167	−.0271
3.3	−.3443	.2207	8.3	.0960	.2657	13.3	.2183	−.0052
3.4	−.3643	.1792	8.4	.0692	.2708	13.4	.2177	.0166
3.5	−.3801	.1374	**8.5**	.0419	.2731	**13.5**	.2150	.0380
3.6	−.3918	.0955	8.6	.0146	.2728	13.6	.2101	.0590
3.7	−.3992	.0538	8.7	−.0125	.2697	13.7	.2032	.0791
3.8	−.4026	.0128	8.8	−.0392	.2641	13.8	.1943	.0984
3.9	−.4018	−.0272	8.9	−.0653	.2559	13.9	.1836	.1165
4.0	−.3971	−.0660	**9.0**	−.0903	.2453	**14.0**	.1711	.1334
4.1	−.3887	−.1033	9.1	−.1142	.2324	14.1	.1570	.1488
4.2	−.3766	−.1386	9.2	−.1367	.2174	14.2	.1414	.1626
4.3	−.3610	−.1719	9.3	−.1577	.2004	14.3	.1245	.1747
4.4	−.3423	−.2028	9.4	−.1768	.1816	14.4	.1065	.1850
4.5	−.3205	−.2311	**9.5**	−.1939	.1613	**14.5**	.0875	.1934
4.6	−.2961	−.2566	9.6	−.2090	.1395	14.6	.0679	.1999
4.7	−.2693	−.2791	9.7	−.2218	.1166	14.7	.0476	.2043
4.8	−.2404	−.2985	9.8	−.2323	.0928	14.8	.0271	.2066
4.9	−.2097	−.3147	9.9	−.2403	.0684	14.9	.0064	.2069

BESSEL FUNCTIONS FOR SPHERICAL COORDINATES

$$j_n(x) = \sqrt{\frac{\pi}{2x}}\, J_{(n+\frac{1}{2})}(x), \ \ y_n(x) = \sqrt{\frac{\pi}{2x}}\, Y_{(n+\frac{1}{2})}(x) = (-1)^{n+1} \sqrt{\frac{\pi}{2x}}\, J_{-(n+\frac{1}{2})}(x)$$

x	$j_0(x)$	$y_0(x)$	$j_1(x)$	$y_1(x)$	$j_2(x)$	$y_2(x)$
0.0	1.0000	$-\infty$	0.0000	$-\infty$	0.0000	$-\infty$
0.1	0.9983	-9.9500	0.0333	-100.50	0.0007	-3005.0
0.2	0.9933	-4.9003	0.0664	-25.495	0.0027	-377.52
0.4	0.9735	-2.3027	0.1312	-6.7302	0.0105	-48.174
0.6	0.9411	-1.3756	0.1929	-3.2337	0.0234	-14.793
0.8	0.8967	-0.8709	0.2500	-1.9853	0.0408	-6.5740
1.0	0.8415	-0.5403	0.3012	-1.3818	0.0620	-3.6050
1.2	0.7767	-0.3020	0.3453	-1.0283	0.0865	-2.2689
1.4	0.7039	-0.1214	0.3814	-0.7906	0.1133	-1.5728
1.6	0.6247	$+0.0182$	0.4087	-0.6133	0.1416	-1.1682
1.8	0.5410	0.1262	0.4268	-0.4709	0.1703	-0.9111
2.0	0.4546	0.2081	0.4354	-0.3506	0.1984	-0.7340
2.2	0.3675	0.2675	0.4345	-0.2459	0.2251	-0.6028
2.4	0.2814	0.3072	0.4245	-0.1534	0.2492	-0.4990
2.6	0.1983	0.3296	0.4058	-0.0715	0.2700	-0.4121
2.8	0.1196	0.3365	0.3792	$+0.0005$	0.2867	-0.3359
3.0	$+0.0470$	0.3300	0.3457	0.0630	0.2986	-0.2670
3.2	-0.0182	0.3120	0.3063	0.1157	0.3054	-0.2035
3.4	-0.0752	0.2844	0.2622	0.1588	0.3066	-0.1442
3.6	-0.1229	0.2491	0.2150	0.1921	0.3021	-0.0890
3.8	-0.1610	0.2081	0.1658	0.2158	0.2919	-0.0378
4.0	-0.1892	0.1634	0.1161	0.2301	0.2763	$+0.0091$
4.2	-0.2075	0.1167	0.0673	0.2353	0.2556	0.0514
4.4	-0.2163	0.0698	$+0.0207$	0.2321	0.2304	0.0884
4.6	-0.2160	$+0.0244$	-0.0226	0.2213	0.2013	0.1200
4.8	-0.2075	-0.0182	-0.0615	0.2037	0.1691	0.1456
5.0	-0.1918	-0.0567	-0.0951	0.1804	0.1347	0.1650
5.2	-0.1699	-0.0901	-0.1228	0.1526	0.0991	0.1781
5.4	-0.1431	-0.1175	-0.1440	0.1213	0.0631	0.1850
5.6	-0.1127	-0.1385	-0.1586	0.0880	$+0.0277$	0.1856
5.8	-0.0801	-0.1527	-0.1665	0.0538	-0.0060	0.1805
6.0	-0.0466	-0.1600	-0.1678	$+0.0199$	-0.0373	0.1700
6.2	-0.0134	-0.1607	-0.1629	-0.0125	-0.0654	0.1547
6.4	$+0.0182$	-0.1552	-0.1523	-0.0425	-0.0896	0.1353
6.6	0.0472	-0.1440	-0.1368	-0.0690	-0.1094	0.1126
6.8	0.0727	-0.1278	-0.1172	-0.0915	-0.1243	0.0875
7.0	0.0939	-0.1077	-0.0943	-0.1092	-0.1343	0.0609
7.2	0.1102	-0.0845	-0.0692	-0.1220	-0.1391	0.0337
7.4	0.1215	-0.0593	-0.0429	-0.1295	-0.1388	$+0.0068$
7.6	0.1274	-0.0331	-0.0163	-0.1317	-0.1338	-0.0189
7.8	0.1280	-0.0069	$+0.0095$	-0.1289	-0.1244	-0.0427
8.0	0.1237	$+0.0182$	0.0336	-0.1214	-0.1111	-0.0637

Taken from Vibration and Sound with the permission of Philip Morse, author, and McGraw-Hill Book Company, Inc., publisher.

Special Function Tables

HYPERBOLIC BESSEL FUNCTIONS

$$I_m(x) = i^{-m} J_m(ix)$$

x	$I_0(x)$	$I_1(x)$	$I_2(x)$
0.0	1.0000	0.0000	0.0000
0.1	1.0025	0.0501	0.0012
0.2	1.0100	0.1005	0.0050
0.4	1.0404	0.2040	0.0203
0.6	1.0920	0.3137	0.0464
0.8	1.1665	0.4329	0.0844
1.0	1.2661	0.5652	0.1357
1.2	1.3937	0.7147	0.2026
1.4	1.5534	0.8861	0.2875
1.6	1.7500	1.0848	0.3940
1.8	1.9896	1.3172	0.5260
2.0	2.2796	1.5906	0.6889
2.2	2.6291	1.9141	0.8891
2.4	3.0493	2.2981	1.1342
2.6	3.5533	2.7554	1.4337
2.8	4.1573	3.3011	1.7994
3.0	4.8808	3.9534	2.2452
3.2	5.7472	4.7343	2.7883
3.4	6.7848	5.6701	3.4495
3.6	8.0277	6.7927	4.2540
3.8	9.5169	8.1404	5.2325
4.0	11.302	9.7595	6.4222
4.2	13.442	11.706	7.8684
4.4	16.010	14.046	9.6258
4.6	19.093	16.863	11.761
4.8	22.794	20.253	14.355
5.0	27.240	24.336	17.506
5.2	32.584	29.254	21.332
5.4	39.009	35.182	25.978
5.6	46.738	42.328	31.620
5.8	56.038	50.946	38.470
6.0	67.234	61.342	46.787
6.2	80.718	73.886	56.884
6.4	96.962	89.026	69.141
6.6	116.54	107.30	84.021
6.8	140.14	129.38	102.08
7.0	168.59	156.04	124.01
7.2	202.92	188.25	150.63
7.4	244.34	227.17	182.94
7.6	294.33	274.22	222.17
7.8	354.68	331.10	269.79
8.0	427.56	399.87	327.60

Taken from *Vibration and Sound* with the permission of Philip Morse, author, and McGraw-Hill Book Company, Inc., publisher.

ELLIPTIC INTEGRALS OF THE FIRST, SECOND AND THIRD KIND

An elliptic integral has the form $\int R(x, \sqrt{f(x)}\, dx$, where R represents a rational function and $f(x) = a + bx + cx^2 + dx^3 + ex^4$, an algebraic function of the third or fourth degree.

1. Elliptic integrals of the *first kind* are represented by

$$F(k, \phi) = \int_0^\phi \frac{d\Phi}{\sqrt{1 - k^2 \sin^2 \Phi}}$$

$$= \int_0^x \frac{d\xi}{\sqrt{(1 - \xi^2)(1 - k^2\xi^2)}}, \quad x = \sin \phi,\ k^2 < 1.$$

2. Elliptic integrals of the second kind are represented by

$$E(k, \phi) = \int_0^\phi \sqrt{1 - k^2 \sin^2 \Phi}\; d\Phi$$

$$= \int_0^x \frac{\sqrt{1 - k^2\xi^2}}{\sqrt{1 - \xi^2}}\; d\xi, \quad x = \sin \phi,\ k^2 < 1.$$

3. Elliptic integrals of the third kind are represented as

$$\pi(k, n, \phi) = \int_0^\phi \frac{d\Phi}{(1 + n \sin^2 \Phi)\sqrt{1 - k^2 \sin^2 \Phi}},$$

$$k^2 < 1,\ n \text{ an integer.}$$

Elliptic integrals of the third kind are also presented as

$$\pi_1(k, n, x) = \int_0^x \frac{d\xi}{(1 + n\xi^2)\sqrt{(1 - \xi^2)(1 - k^2\xi^2)}},$$

$$x = \sin \phi,\ k^2 < 1,\ n \text{ an integer.}$$

4. The complete integrals are

$$K = F\left(k, \frac{\pi}{2}\right) = \frac{\pi}{2}\left[1 + \left(\frac{1}{2}\right)^2 k^2 + \left(\frac{3}{2\cdot 4}\right)^2 k^4 \right.$$

$$\left. + \left(\frac{3\cdot 5}{2\cdot 4\cdot 6}\right)^2 k^6 + \cdots \right]$$

$$E = E\left(k, \frac{\pi}{2}\right) = \frac{\pi}{2}\left[1 - \left(\frac{1}{2^2}\right) k^2 - \left(\frac{3^2}{2^2\cdot 4^2}\right)\frac{k^4}{3} \right.$$

$$\left. - \left(\frac{3^2\cdot 5^2}{2^2\cdot 4^2\cdot 6^2}\right)\frac{k^6}{5} - \left(\frac{3^2\cdot 5^2\cdot 7^2}{2^2\cdot 4^2\cdot 6^2\cdot 8^2}\right)\frac{k^8}{7} - \cdots \right].$$

$$K' = F\left(\sqrt{1 - k^2}, \frac{\pi}{2}\right), \quad E' = E\left(\sqrt{1 - k^2}, \frac{\pi}{2}\right)$$

5. The following relation holds between K, K', E, E', namely

$$KE' + EK' - KK' = \frac{\pi}{2} \qquad \text{Legendre's relation}$$

E: see 2 above. $\quad E' = \int_0^{\pi/2} (1 - k'^2 \sin^2 \phi)^{\frac{1}{2}} d\phi. \quad k' = \sqrt{(1 - k^2)}$

$$K = \int_0^{\pi/2} (1 - k^2 \sin^2 \phi)^{-\frac{1}{2}} d\phi \qquad K' = \int_0^{\pi/2} (1 - k'^2 \sin^2 \phi)^{-\frac{1}{2}} d\phi$$

ELLIPTIC INTEGRALS OF THE FIRST, SECOND AND THIRD KIND (Continued)

6. To evaluate elliptic integrals for values outside the range contained in the following tables, these relations are useful

$$F(k, \pi) = 2K; E(k, \pi) = 2E$$

$$F(k, \phi + m\pi) = mF(k, \pi) + F(k, \phi) = 2mK + F(k, \phi)$$
$$m = 0, 1, 2, 3, \ldots$$

$$E(k, \phi + m\pi) = mE(k, \pi) + E(k, \phi) = 2mE + E(k, \phi)$$
$$m = 0, 1, 2, 3, \ldots$$

7. If $u = F(k, \phi) = \int_0^\phi \dfrac{d\Phi}{\sqrt{1 - k^2 \sin^2 \Phi}}$ $\qquad (k^2 < 1)$,

= elliptic integral of the first kind.

$$u = \int_0^x \frac{dx}{\sqrt{(1 - \xi^2)(1 - k^2\xi^2)}}, \text{ where } x = \sin \phi.$$

ϕ is called the amplitude of u or am u.

k is called the modulus.

$$k' = \sqrt{1 - k^2} = \text{the complementary modulus.}$$

$\sin \phi = \text{sn } u = x \qquad \tan \phi = \text{tn } u = \dfrac{x}{\sqrt{1 - x^2}}.$

$\cos \phi = \text{cn } u = \sqrt{1 - x^2}.$ $\qquad\qquad \Delta\phi = \text{dn } u = \sqrt{1 - k^2x^2}.$

am $0 = 0$. $\qquad\qquad\qquad\qquad\qquad$ sn $0 = 0$.

cn $0 = 1$. $\qquad\qquad\qquad\qquad\qquad$ dn $0 = 1$.

am $(-u) = -$am u. $\qquad\qquad\qquad$ sn $(-u) = -$sn u.

cn $(-u) = $ cn u. $\qquad\qquad\qquad\quad$ dn $(-u) = $ dn u.

tn $(-u) = -$tn u.

$\text{sn}^2 u + \text{cn}^2 u = 1$.

$\text{dn}^2 u + k^2 \text{ sn}^2 u = 1$.

$\text{dn}^2 u - k^2 \text{ cn}^2 u = 1 - k^2 = k'^2$.

$$\text{sn } u = u - (1 + k^2) \frac{u^3}{3!} + (1 + 14k^2 + k^4) \frac{u^5}{5!}$$
$$- (1 + 135k^2 + 135k^4 + k^6) \frac{u^7}{7!} + \cdots$$

Periods: $4k$ and $2ik'$

$$\text{cn } u = 1 - \frac{u^2}{2!} + (1 + 4k^2) \frac{u^4}{4!} - (1 + 44k^2 + 16k^4) \frac{u^6}{6!} + \cdots$$

Periods: $4k$ and $2k + 2ik'$

$$\text{dn } u = 1 - k^2 \frac{u^2}{2!} + k^2(4 + k^2) \frac{u^4}{4!} - k^2(16 + 44k^2 + k^4) \frac{u^6}{6!} + \cdots$$

Periods: $2k$ and $4ik'$

*ELLIPTIC INTEGRALS OF THE FIRST KIND: $F(k, \phi)$

$$F(k, \phi) = \int_0^\phi \frac{d\Phi}{\sqrt{1 - k^2 \sin^2 \Phi}}, \qquad \theta = \sin^{-1} k$$

ϕ \ θ	5°	10°	15°	20°	25°	30°	35°	40°	45°
1°	0.0175	0.0175	0.0175	0.0175	0.0175	0.0175	0.0175	0.0175	0.0175
2°	0.0349	0.0349	0.0349	0.0349	0.0349	0.0349	0.0349	0.0349	0.0349
3°	0.0524	0.0524	0.0524	0.0524	0.0524	0.0524	0.0524	0.0524	0.0524
4°	0.0698	0.0698	0.0698	0.0698	0.0698	0.0698	0.0698	0.0698	0.0698
5°	0.0873	0.0873	0.0873	0.0873	0.0873	0.0873	0.0873	0.0873	0.0873
6°	0.1047	0.1047	0.1047	0.1047	0.1048	0.1048	0.1048	0.1048	0.1048
7°	0.1222	0.1222	0.1222	0.1222	0.1222	0.1222	0.1223	0.1223	0.1223
8°	0.1396	0.1396	0.1397	0.1397	0.1397	0.1397	0.1398	0.1398	0.1399
9°	0.1571	0.1571	0.1571	0.1572	0.1572	0.1572	0.1573	0.1573	0.1574
10°	0.1745	0.1746	0.1746	0.1746	0.1747	0.1748	0.1748	0.1749	0.1750
11°	0.1920	0.1920	0.1921	0.1921	0.1922	0.1923	0.1924	0.1925	0.1926
12°	0.2095	0.2095	0.2095	0.2096	0.2097	0.2098	0.2099	0.2101	0.2102
13°	0.2269	0.2270	0.2270	0.2271	0.2272	0.2274	0.2275	0.2277	0.2279
14°	0.2444	0.2444	0.2445	0.2446	0.2448	0.2450	0.2451	0.2453	0.2456
15°	0.2618	0.2619	0.2620	0.2621	0.2623	0.2625	0.2628	0.2630	0.2633
16°	0.2793	0.2794	0.2795	0.2797	0.2799	0.2802	0.2804	0.2808	0.2811
17°	0.2967	0.2968	0.2970	0.2972	0.2975	0.2978	0.2981	0.2985	0.2989
18°	0.3142	0.3143	0.3145	0.3148	0.3151	0.3154	0.3159	0.3163	0.3167
19°	0.3317	0.3318	0.3320	0.3323	0.3327	0.3331	0.3336	0.3341	0.3347
20°	0.3491	0.3493	0.3495	0.3499	0.3503	0.3508	0.3514	0.3520	0.3526
21°	0.3666	0.3668	0.3671	0.3675	0.3680	0.3685	0.3692	0.3699	0.3706
22°	0.3840	0.3842	0.3846	0.3851	0.3856	0.3863	0.3871	0.3879	0.3887
23°	0.4015	0.4017	0.4021	0.4027	0.4033	0.4041	0.4049	0.4059	0.4068
24°	0.4190	0.4192	0.4197	0.4203	0.4210	0.4219	0.4229	0.4239	0.4250
25°	0.4364	0.4367	0.4372	0.4379	0.4387	0.4397	0.4408	0.4420	0.4433
26°	0.4539	0.4542	0.4548	0.4556	0.4565	0.4576	0.4588	0.4602	0.4616
27°	0.4714	0.4717	0.4724	0.4732	0.4743	0.4755	0.4769	0.4784	0.4800
28°	0.4888	0.4893	0.4899	0.4909	0.4921	0.4934	0.4950	0.4967	0.4985
29°	0.5063	0.5068	0.5075	0.5086	0.5099	0.5114	0.5132	0.5150	0.5170
30°	0.5238	0.5243	0.5251	0.5263	0.5277	0.5294	0.5313	0.5334	0.5356
31°	0.5412	0.5418	0.5427	0.5440	0.5456	0.5475	0.5496	0.5519	0.5543
32°	0.5587	0.5593	0.5603	0.5617	0.5635	0.5656	0.5679	0.5704	0.5731
33°	0.5762	0.5769	0.5780	0.5795	0.5814	0.5837	0.5862	0.5890	0.5920
34°	0.5937	0.5944	0.5956	0.5973	0.5994	0.6018	0.6046	0.6077	0.6109
35°	0.6111	0.6119	0.6133	0.6151	0.6173	0.6200	0.6231	0.6264	0.6300
36°	0.6286	0.6295	0.6309	0.6329	0.6353	0.6383	0.6416	0.6452	0.6491
37°	0.6461	0.6470	0.6486	0.6507	0.6534	0.6565	0.6602	0.6641	0.6684
38°	0.6636	0.6646	0.6662	0.6685	0.6714	0.6749	0.6788	0.6831	0.6877
39°	0.6810	0.6821	0.6839	0.6864	0.6895	0.6932	0.6975	0.7021	0.7071
40°	0.6985	0.6997	0.7016	0.7043	0.7076	0.7116	0.7162	0.7213	0.7267
41°	0.7160	0.7173	0.7193	0.7222	0.7258	0.7301	0.7350	0.7405	0.7463
42°	0.7335	0.7348	0.7370	0.7401	0.7440	0.7486	0.7539	0.7598	0.7661
43°	0.7510	0.7524	0.7548	0.7580	0.7622	0.7671	0.7728	0.7791	0.7859
44°	0.7685	0.7700	0.7725	0.7760	0.7804	0.7857	0.7918	0.7986	0.8059
45°	0.7859	0.7876	0.7903	0.7940	0.7987	0.8044	0.8109	0.8181	0.8260

* For useful information about these tables see preceding page.

*ELLIPTIC INTEGRALS OF THE FIRST KIND: $F(k, \phi)$ (Continued)

$$F(k, \phi) = \int_0^\phi \frac{d\Phi}{\sqrt{1 - k^2 \sin^2 \Phi}}, \qquad \theta = \sin^{-1} k$$

θ \ ϕ	50°	55°	60°	65°	70°	75°	80°	85°	90°
1°	0.0175	0.0175	0.0175	0.0175	0.0175	0.0175	0.0175	0.0175	0.0175
2°	0.0349	0.0349	0.0349	0.0349	0.0349	0.0349	0.0349	0.0349	0.0349
3°	0.0524	0.0524	0.0524	0.0524	0.0524	0.0524	0.0524	0.0524	0.0524
4°	0.0698	0.0699	0.0699	0.0699	0.0699	0.0699	0.0699	0.0699	0.0699
5°	0.0873	0.0873	0.0873	0.0874	0.0874	0.0874	0.0874	0.0874	0.0874
6°	0.1048	0.1048	0.1049	0.1049	0.1049	0.1049	0.1049	0.1049	0.1049
7°	0.1224	0.1224	0.1224	0.1224	0.1224	0.1225	0.1225	0.1225	0.1225
8°	0.1399	0.1399	0.1400	0.1400	0.1400	0.1401	0.1401	0.1401	0.1401
9°	0.1575	0.1575	0.1576	0.1576	0.1577	0.1577	0.1577	0.1577	0.1577
10°	0.1751	0.1751	0.1752	0.1753	0.1753	0.1754	0.1754	0.1754	0.1754
11°	0.1927	0.1928	0.1929	0.1930	0.1930	0.1931	0.1931	0.1932	0.1932
12°	0.2103	0.2105	0.2106	0.2107	0.2108	0.2109	0.2109	0.2110	0.2110
13°	0.2280	0.2282	0.2284	0.2285	0.2286	0.2287	0.2288	0.2288	0.2289
14°	0.2458	0.2460	0.2462	0.2464	0.2465	0.2466	0.2467	0.2468	0.2468
15°	0.2636	0.2638	0.2641	0.2643	0.2645	0.2646	0.2647	0.2648	0.2648
16°	0.2814	0.2817	0.2820	0.2823	0.2825	0.2827	0.2828	0.2829	0.2830
17°	0.2993	0.2997	0.3000	0.3003	0.3006	0.3008	0.3010	0.3011	0.3012
18°	0.3172	0.3177	0.3181	0.3185	0.3188	0.3191	0.3193	0.3194	0.3195
19°	0.3352	0.3357	0.3362	0.3367	0.3371	0.3374	0.3377	0.3378	0.3379
20°	0.3533	0.3539	0.3545	0.3550	0.3555	0.3559	0.3561	0.3563	0.3564
21°	0.3714	0.3721	0.3728	0.3734	0.3740	0.3744	0.3747	0.3749	0.3750
22°	0.3896	0.3904	0.3912	0.3919	0.3926	0.3931	0.3935	0.3937	0.3938
23°	0.4078	0.4088	0.4097	0.4105	0.4113	0.4119	0.4123	0.4126	0.4127
24°	0.4261	0.4272	0.4283	0.4292	0.4301	0.4308	0.4313	0.4316	0.4317
25°	0.4446	0.4458	0.4470	0.4481	0.4490	0.4498	0.4504	0.4508	0.4509
26°	0.4630	0.4645	0.4658	0.4670	0.4681	0.4690	0.4697	0.4701	0.4702
27°	0.4816	0.4832	0.4847	0.4861	0.4873	0.4884	0.4891	0.4896	0.4897
28°	0.5003	0.5021	0.5038	0.5053	0.5067	0.5079	0.5087	0.5092	0.5094
29°	0.5190	0.5210	0.5229	0.5247	0.5262	0.5275	0.5285	0.5291	0.5293
30°	0.5379	0.5401	0.5422	0.5442	0.5459	0.5474	0.5484	0.5491	0.5493
31°	0.5568	0.5593	0.5617	0.5639	0.5658	0.5674	0.5686	0.5693	0.5696
32°	0.5759	0.5786	0.5812	0.5837	0.5858	0.5876	0.5889	0.5898	0.5900
33°	0.5950	0.5980	0.6010	0.6037	0.6060	0.6080	0.6095	0.6104	0.6107
34°	0.6143	0.6176	0.6208	0.6238	0.6265	0.6287	0.6303	0.6313	0.6317
35°	0.6336	0.6373	0.6408	0.6441	0.6471	0.6495	0.6513	0.6525	0.6528
36°	0.6531	0.6571	0.6610	0.6647	0.6679	0.6706	0.6726	0.6739	0.6743
37°	0.6727	0.6771	0.6814	0.6854	0.6890	0.6919	0.6941	0.6955	0.6960
38°	0.6925	0.6973	0.7019	0.7063	0.7102	0.7135	0.7159	0.7175	0.7180
39°	0.7123	0.7176	0.7227	0.7275	0.7318	0.7353	0.7380	0.7397	0.7403
40°	0.7323	0.7380	0.7436	0.7488	0.7535	0.7575	0.7604	0.7623	0.7629
41°	0.7524	0.7586	0.7647	0.7704	0.7756	0.7799	0.7831	0.7852	0.7859
42°	0.7727	0.7794	0.7860	0.7922	0.7979	0.8026	0.8062	0.8084	0.8092
43°	0.7931	0.8004	0.8075	0.8143	0.8204	0.8256	0.8295	0.8320	0.8328
44°	0.8136	0.8215	0.8293	0.8367	0.8433	0.8490	0.8533	0.8560	0.8569
45°	0.8343	0.8428	0.8512	0.8592	0.8665	0.8727	0.8774	0.8804	0.8814

*ELLIPTIC INTEGRALS OF THE FIRST KIND: $F(k, \phi)$ (Continued)

$$F(k, \phi) = \int_0^\phi \frac{d\Phi}{\sqrt{1 - k^2 \sin^2 \Phi}}, \qquad \theta = \sin^{-1} k$$

θ / ϕ	5°	10°	15°	20°	25°	30°	35°	40°	45°
46°	0.8034	0.8052	0.8080	0.8120	0.8170	0.8230	0.8300	0.8378	0.8462
47°	0.8209	0.8227	0.8258	0.8300	0.8353	0.8418	0.8492	0.8575	0.8666
48°	0.8384	0.8403	0.8436	0.8480	0.8537	0.8606	0.8685	0.8773	0.8870
49°	0.8559	0.8579	0.8614	0.8661	0.8721	0.8794	0.8878	0.8972	0.9076
50°	0.8734	0.8756	0.8792	0.8842	0.8905	0.8982	0.9072	0.9173	0.9283
51°	0.8909	0.8932	0.8970	0.9023	0.9090	0.9172	0.9267	0.9374	0.9491
52°	0.9084	0.9108	0.9148	0.9204	0.9275	0.9361	0.9462	0.9575	0.9701
53°	0.9259	0.9284	0.9326	0.9385	0.9460	0.9551	0.9658	0.9778	0.9912
54°	0.9434	0.9460	0.9505	0.9567	0.9646	0.9742	0.9855	0.9982	1.0124
55°	0.9609	0.9637	0.9683	0.9748	0.9832	0.9933	1.0052	1.0187	1.0337
56°	0.9784	0.9813	0.9862	0.9930	1.0018	1.0125	1.0250	1.0393	1.0552
57°	0.9959	0.9989	1.0041	1.0112	1.0204	1.0317	1.0449	1.0600	1.0768
58°	1.0134	1.0166	1.0219	1.0295	1.0391	1.0509	1.0648	1.0807	1.0985
59°	1.0309	1.0342	1.0398	1.0477	1.0578	1.0702	1.0848	1.1016	1.1204
60°	1.0484	1.0519	1.0577	1.0660	1.0766	1.0896	1.1049	1.1226	1.1424
61°	1.0659	1.0695	1.0757	1.0843	1.0953	1.1089	1.1250	1.1436	1.1646
62°	1.0834	1.0872	1.0936	1.1026	1.1141	1.1284	1.1452	1.1648	1.1868
63°	1.1009	1.1049	1.1115	1.1209	1.1330	1.1478	1.1655	1.1860	1.2093
64°	1.1184	1.1225	1.1295	1.1392	1.1518	1.1674	1.1859	1.2073	1.2318
65°	1.1359	1.1402	1.1474	1.1575	1.1707	1.1869	1.2063	1.2288	1.2545
66°	1.1534	1.1579	1.1654	1.1759	1.1896	1.2065	1.2267	1.2503	1.2773
67°	1.1709	1.1756	1.1833	1.1943	1.2085	1.2262	1.2472	1.2719	1.3002
68°	1.1884	1.1932	1.2013	1.2127	1.2275	1.2458	1.2678	1.2936	1.3232
69°	1.2059	1.2109	1.2193	1.2311	1.2465	1.2655	1.2885	1.3154	1.3464
70°	1.2234	1.2286	1.2373	1.2495	1.2655	1.2853	1.3092	1.3372	1.3697
71°	1.2410	1.2463	1.2553	1.2680	1.2845	1.3051	1.3299	1.3592	1.3931
72°	1.2585	1.2640	1.2733	1.2864	1.3036	1.3249	1.3507	1.3812	1.4167
73°	1.2760	1.2817	1.2913	1.3049	1.3226	1.3448	1.3715	1.4033	1.4403
74°	1.2935	1.2994	1.3093	1.3234	1.3417	1.3647	1.3924	1.4254	1.4640
75°	1.3110	1.3171	1.3273	1.3418	1.3608	1.3846	1.4134	1.4477	1.4879
76°	1.3285	1.3348	1.3454	1.3603	1.3800	1.4045	1.4344	1.4700	1.5118
77°	1.3460	1.3525	1.3634	1.3788	1.3991	1.4245	1.4554	1.4923	1.5359
78°	1.3636	1.3702	1.3814	1.3974	1.4183	1.4445	1.4765	1.5147	1.5600
79°	1.3811	1.3879	1.3995	1.4159	1.4374	1.4645	1.4976	1.5372	1.5842
80°	1.3986	1.4056	1.4175	1.4344	1.4566	1.4846	1.5187	1.5597	1.6085
81°	1.4161	1.4234	1.4356	1.4530	1.4758	1.5046	1.5399	1.5823	1.6328
82°	1.4336	1.4411	1.4536	1.4715	1.4950	1.5247	1.5611	1.6049	1.6572
83°	1.4512	1.4588	1.4717	1.4901	1.5143	1.5448	1.5823	1.6276	1.6817
84°	1.4687	1.4765	1.4897	1.5086	1.5335	1.5649	1.6035	1.6502	1.7062
85°	1.4862	1.4942	1.5078	1.5272	1.5527	1.5850	1.6248	1.6730	1.7308
86°	1.5037	1.5120	1.5259	1.5457	1.5720	1.6052	1.6461	1.6957	1.7554
87°	1.5212	1.5297	1.5439	1.5643	1.5912	1.6253	1.6673	1.7184	1.7801
88°	1.5388	1.5474	1.5620	1.5829	1.6105	1.6454	1.6886	1.7412	1.8047
89°	1.5563	1.5651	1.5801	1.6015	1.6297	1.6656	1.7099	1.7640	1.8294
90°	1.5738	1.5828	1.5981	1.6200	1.6490	1.6858	1.7312	1.7863	1.8541

*ELLIPTIC INTEGRALS OF THE FIRST KIND: $F(k, \phi)$ (Continued)

$$F(k, \phi) = \int_0^\phi \frac{d\Phi}{\sqrt{1 - k^2 \sin^2 \Phi}}, \qquad \theta = \sin^{-1} k$$

ϕ \ θ	50°	55°	60°	65°	70°	75°	80°	85°	90°
46°	0.8552	0.8643	0.8734	0.8821	0.8900	0.8968	0.9019	0.9052	0.9063
47°	0.8761	0.8860	0.8958	0.9053	0.9139	0.9212	0.9269	0.9304	0.9316
48°	0.8973	0.9079	0.9185	0.9287	0.9381	0.9461	0.9523	0.9561	0.9575
49°	0.9186	0.9300	0.9415	0.9525	0.9627	0.9714	0.9781	0.9824	0.9838
50°	0.9401	0.9523	0.9647	0.9766	0.9876	0.9971	1.0044	1.0091	1.0107
51°	0.9617	0.9748	0.9881	1.0010	1.0130	1.0233	1.0313	1.0364	1.0381
52°	0.9835	0.9976	1.0118	1.0258	1.0387	1.0499	1.0587	1.0642	1.0662
53°	1.0055	1.0205	1.0359	1.0509	1.0649	1.0771	1.0866	1.0927	1.0948
54°	1.0277	1.0437	1.0602	1.0764	1.0915	1.1048	1.1152	1.1219	1.1242
55°	1.0500	1.0672	1.0848	1.1022	1.1186	1.1331	1.1444	1.1517	1.1542
56°	1.0725	1.0908	1.1097	1.1285	1.1462	1.1619	1.1743	1.1823	1.1851
57°	1.0952	1.1147	1.1349	1.1551	1.1743	1.1914	1.2049	1.2136	1.2167
58°	1.1180	1.1389	1.1605	1.1822	1.2030	1.2215	1.2362	1.2458	1.2492
59°	1.1411	1.1632	1.1864	1.2097	1.2321	1.2522	1.2684	1.2789	1.2826
60°	1.1643	1.1879	1.2125	1.2376	1.2619	1.2837	1.3014	1.3129	1.3170
61°	1.1877	1.2128	1.2392	1.2660	1.2922	1.3159	1.3352	1.3480	1.3524
62°	1.2113	1.2379	1.2661	1.2949	1.3231	1.3490	1.3701	1.3841	1.3890
63°	1.2351	1.2633	1.2933	1.3242	1.3547	1.3828	1.4059	1.4214	1.4268
64°	1.2591	1.2890	1.3209	1.3541	1.3870	1.4175	1.4429	1.4599	1.4659
65°	1.2833	1.3149	1.3489	1.3844	1.4199	1.4532	1.4810	1.4998	1.5065
66°	1.3076	1.3411	1.3773	1.4153	1.4536	1.4898	1.5203	1.5411	1.5485
67°	1.3321	1.3675	1.4060	1.4467	1.4880	1.5274	1.5610	1.5840	1.5923
68°	1.3568	1.3942	1.4351	1.4786	1.5232	1.5661	1.6030	1.6287	1.6379
69°	1.3817	1.4212	1.4646	1.5111	1.5591	1.6059	1.6466	1.6752	1.6856
70°	1.4068	1.4484	1.4944	1.5441	1.5959	1.6468	1.6918	1.7237	1.7354
71°	1.4320	1.4759	1.5246	1.5777	1.6335	1.6891	1.7388	1.7745	1.7877
72°	1.4574	1.5036	1.5552	1.6118	1.6720	1.7326	1.7876	1.8277	1.8427
73°	1.4830	1.5315	1.5862	1.6465	1.7113	1.7774	1.8384	1.8837	1.9008
74°	1.5087	1.5597	1.6175	1.6818	1.7516	1.8237	1.8915	1.9427	1.9623
75°	1.5345	1.5882	1.6492	1.7176	1.7927	1.8715	1.9468	2.0050	2.0276
76°	1.5606	1.6168	1.6812	1.7540	1.8347	1.9207	2.0047	2.0711	2.0973
77°	1.5867	1.6457	1.7136	1.7909	1.8777	1.9716	2.0653	2.1414	2.1721
78°	1.6130	1.6748	1.7462	1.8284	1.9215	2.0240	2.1288	2.2164	2.2528
79°	1.6394	1.7040	1.7792	1.8664	1.9663	2.0781	2.1954	2.2969	2.3404
80°	1.6660	1.7335	1.8125	1.9048	2.0119	2.1339	2.2653	2.3836	2.4362
81°	1.6926	1.7631	1.8461	1.9438	2.0584	2.1913	2.3387	2.4775	2.5421
82°	1.7193	1.7929	1.8799	1.9831	2.1057	2.2504	2.4157	2.5795	2.6603
83°	1.7462	1.8228	1.9140	2.0229	2.1537	2.3110	2.4965	2.6911	2.7942
84°	1.7731	1.8528	1.9482	2.0630	2.2024	2.3731	2.5811	2.8136	2.9487
85°	1.8001	1.8830	1.9826	2.1035	2.2518	2.4366	2.6694	2.9487	3.1313
86°	1.8271	1.9132	2.0172	2.1442	2.3017	2.5013	2.7612	3.0978	3.3547
87°	1.8542	1.9435	2,0519	2.1852	2.3520	2.5670	2.8561	3.2620	3.6425
88°	1.8813	1.9739	2.0867	2.2263	2.4026	2.6336	2.9537	3.4412	4.0481
89°	1.9084	2.0043	2.1216	2.2675	2.4535	2.7007	3.0530	3.6328	4.7413
90°	1.9356	2.0347	2.1565	2.3088	2.5046	2.7681	3.1534	3.8317	———

ELLIPTIC INTEGRALS OF THE SECOND KIND: $E(k, \phi)$

$$E(k, \phi) = \int_0^\phi \sqrt{(1 - k^2 \sin^2 \Phi)}d\Phi, \quad \theta = \sin^{-1} k$$

θ / ϕ	5°	10°	15°	20°	25°	30°	35°	40°	45°
1°	0.0175	0.0175	0.0175	0.0175	0.0175	0.0175	0.0175	0.0175	0.0175
2°	0.0349	0.0349	0.0349	0.0349	0.0349	0.0349	0.0349	0.0349	0.0349
3°	0.0524	0.0524	0.0524	0.0524	0.0524	0.0524	0.0524	0.0523	0.0523
4°	0.0698	0.0698	0.0698	0.0698	0.0698	0.0698	0.0698	0.0698	0.0698
5°	0.0873	0.0873	0.0873	0.0873	0.0872	0.0872	0.0872	0.0872	0.0872
6°	0.1047	0.1047	0.1047	0.1047	0.1047	0.1047	0.1047	0.1046	0.1046
7°	0.1222	0.1222	0.1222	0.1221	0.1221	0.1221	0.1221	0.1220	0.1220
8°	0.1396	0.1396	0.1396	0.1396	0.1395	0.1395	0.1395	0.1394	0.1394
9°	0.1571	0.1571	0.1570	0.1570	0.1570	0.1569	0.1569	0.1568	0.1568
10°	0.1745	0.1745	0.1745	0.1744	0.1744	0.1743	0.1742	0.1742	0.1741
11°	0.1920	0.1920	0.1919	0.1918	0.1918	0.1917	0.1916	0.1915	0.1914
12°	0.2094	0.2094	0.2093	0.2093	0.2092	0.2091	0.2089	0.2088	0.2087
13°	0.2269	0.2268	0.2268	0.2267	0.2265	0.2264	0.2263	0.2261	0.2259
14°	0.2443	0.2443	0.2442	0.2441	0.2439	0.2437	0.2436	0.2433	0.2431
15°	0.2618	0.2617	0.2616	0.2615	0.2613	0.2611	0.2608	0.2606	0.2603
16°	0.2792	0.2791	0.2790	0.2788	0.2786	0.2784	0.2781	0.2778	0.2775
17°	0.2967	0.2966	0.2964	0.2962	0.2959	0.2956	0.2953	0.2949	0.2946
18°	0.3141	0.3140	0.3138	0.3136	0.3133	0.3129	0.3125	0.3121	0.3116
19°	0.3316	0.3314	0.3312	0.3309	0.3305	0.3301	0.3296	0.3291	0.3286
20°	0.3490	0.3489	0.3486	0.3483	0.3478	0.3473	0.3468	0.3462	0.3456
21°	0.3665	0.3663	0.3660	0.3656	0.3651	0.3645	0.3639	0.3632	0.3625
22°	0.3839	0.3837	0.3834	0.3829	0.3823	0.3817	0.3809	0.3802	0.3793
23°	0.4013	0.4011	0.4007	0.4002	0.3996	0.3988	0.3980	0.3971	0.3961
24°	0.4188	0.4185	0.4181	0.4175	0.4168	0.4159	0.4150	0.4139	0.4129
25°	0.4362	0.4359	0.4354	0.4348	0.4339	0.4330	0.4319	0.4308	0.4296
26°	0.4537	0.4533	0.4528	0.4520	0.4511	0.4500	0.4488	0.4475	0.4462
27°	0.4711	0.4707	0.4701	0.4693	0.4682	0.4670	0.4657	0.4643	0.4628
28°	0.4886	0.4881	0.4874	0.4865	0.4854	0.4840	0.4825	0.4809	0.4793
29°	0.5060	0.5055	0.5048	0.5037	0.5025	0.5010	0.4993	0.4975	0.4957
30°	0.5234	0.5229	0.5221	0.5209	0.5195	0.5179	0.5161	0.5141	0.5120
31°	0.5409	0.5403	0.5394	0.5381	0.5366	0.5348	0.5327	0.5306	0.5283
32°	0.5583	0.5577	0.5567	0.5553	0.5536	0.5516	0.5494	0.5470	0.5446
33°	0.5757	0.5751	0.5740	0.5725	0.5706	0.5684	0.5660	0.5634	0.5607
34°	0.5932	0.5924	0.5912	0.5896	0.5876	0.5852	0.5826	0.5797	0.5768
35°	0.6106	0.6098	0.6085	0.6067	0.6045	0.6019	0.5991	0.5960	0.5928
36°	0.6280	0.6272	0.6258	0.6238	0.6214	0.6186	0.6155	0.6122	0.6087
37°	0.6455	0.6445	0.6430	0.6409	0.6383	0.6353	0.6319	0.6283	0.6245
38°	0.6629	0.6619	0.6602	0.6580	0.6552	0.6519	0.6483	0.6444	0.6403
39°	0.6803	0.6792	0.6775	0.6750	0.6720	0.6685	0.6646	0.6604	0.6559
40°	0.6977	0.6966	0.6947	0.6921	0.6888	0.6851	0.6808	0.6763	0.6715
41°	0.7152	0.7139	0.7119	0.7091	0.7056	0.7016	0.6970	0.6921	0.6870
42°	0.7326	0.7313	0.7291	0.7261	0.7224	0.7180	0.7132	0.7079	0.7024
43°	0.7500	0.7486	0.7463	0.7431	0.7391	0.7345	0.7293	0.7237	0.7178
44°	0.7674	0.7659	0.7634	0.7600	0.7558	0.7508	0.7453	0.7393	0.7330
45°	0.7849	0.7832	0.7806	0.7770	0.7725	0.7672	0.7613	0.7549	0.7482

ELLIPTIC INTEGRALS OF THE SECOND KIND: $E(k, \phi)$ (Continued)

$$E(k, \phi) = \int_0^\phi \sqrt{(1 - k^2 \sin^2 \Phi)}d\Phi, \quad \theta = \sin^{-1} k$$

ϕ \ θ	50°	55°	60°	65°	70°	75°	80°	85°	90°
1°	0.0175	0.0175	0.0175	0.0175	0.0175	0.0175	0.0175	0.0175	0.0175
2°	0.0349	0.0349	0.0349	0.0349	0.0349	0.0349	0.0349	0.0349	0.0349
3°	0.0523	0.0523	0.0523	0.0523	0.0523	0.0523	0.0523	0.0523	0.0523
4°	0.0698	0.0698	0.0698	0.0698	0.0698	0.0698	0.0698	0.0698	0.0698
5°	0.0872	0.0872	0.0872	0.0872	0.0872	0.0872	0.0872	0.0872	0.0872
6°	0.1046	0.1046	0.1046	0.1046	0.1046	0.1045	0.1045	0.1045	0.1045
7°	0.1220	0.1220	0.1219	0.1219	0.1219	0.1219	0.1219	0.1219	0.1219
8°	0.1394	0.1393	0.1393	0.1393	0.1392	0.1392	0.1392	0.1392	0.1392
9°	0.1567	0.1566	0.1566	0.1566	0.1565	0.1565	0.1565	0.1564	0.1564
10°	0.1740	0.1739	0.1739	0.1738	0.1738	0.1737	0.1737	0.1737	0.1736
11°	0.1913	0.1912	0.1911	0.1910	0.1909	0.1909	0.1908	0.1908	0.1908
12°	0.2085	0.2084	0.2083	0.2082	0.2081	0.2080	0.2080	0.2079	0.2079
13°	0.2258	0.2256	0.2254	0.2253	0.2252	0.2251	0.2250	0.2250	0.2250
14°	0.2429	0.2427	0.2425	0.2424	0.2422	0.2421	0.2420	0.2419	0.2419
15°	0.2601	0.2598	0.2596	0.2594	0.2592	0.2590	0.2589	0.2588	0.2588
16°	0.2771	0.2768	0.2765	0.2763	0.2761	0.2759	0.2757	0.2757	0.2756
17°	0.2942	0.2938	0.2935	0.2932	0.2929	0.2927	0.2925	0.2924	0.2924
18°	0.3112	0.3107	0.3103	0.3099	0.3096	0.3094	0.3092	0.3091	0.3090
19°	0.3281	0.3276	0.3271	0.3267	0.3263	0.3260	0.3258	0.3256	0.3256
20°	0.3450	0.3444	0.3438	0.3433	0.3429	0.3425	0.3422	0.3421	0.3420
21°	0.3618	0.3611	0.3604	0.3598	0.3593	0.3589	0.3586	0.3584	0.3584
22°	0.3785	0.3777	0.3770	0.3763	0.3757	0.3752	0.3749	0.3747	0.3746
23°	0.3952	0.3943	0.3935	0.3927	0.3920	0.3915	0.3911	0.3908	0.3907
24°	0.4118	0.4108	0.4098	0.4090	0.4082	0.4076	0.4071	0.4068	0.4067
25°	0.4284	0.4272	0.4261	0.4251	0.4243	0.4236	0.4230	0.4227	0.4226
26°	0.4449	0.4436	0.4423	0.4412	0.4402	0.4394	0.4389	0.4385	0.4384
27°	0.4613	0.4598	0.4584	0.4572	0.4561	0.4552	0.4545	0.4541	0.4540
28°	0.4776	0.4760	0.4744	0.4730	0.4718	0.4708	0.4701	0.4696	0.4695
29°	0.4938	0.4920	0.4903	0.4887	0.4874	0.4863	0.4855	0.4850	0.4848
30°	0.5100	0.5080	0.5061	0.5044	0.5029	0.5016	0.5007	0.5002	0.5000
31°	0.5261	0.5239	0.5218	0.5199	0.5182	0.5169	0.5159	0.5152	0.5150
32°	0.5421	0.5396	0.5373	0.5352	0.5334	0.5319	0.5308	0.5301	0.5299
33°	0.5580	0.5553	0.5528	0.5505	0.5485	0.5468	0.5456	0.5449	0.5446
34°	0.5738	0.5709	0.5681	0.5656	0.5634	0.5616	0.5603	0.5595	0.5592
35°	0.5895	0.5863	0.5833	0.5806	0.5782	0.5762	0.5748	0.5739	0.5736
36°	0.6051	0.6017	0.5984	0.5954	0.5928	0.5907	0.5891	0.5881	0.5878
37°	0.6207	0.6169	0.6134	0.6101	0.6073	0.6050	0.6032	0.6022	0.6018
38°	0.6361	0.6321	0.6282	0.6247	0.6216	0.6191	0.6172	0.6160	0.6157
39°	0.6515	0.6471	0.6429	0.6391	0.6357	0.6330	0.6310	0.6297	0.6293
40°	0.6667	0.6620	0.6575	0.6533	0.6497	0.6468	0.6446	0.6432	0.6428
41°	0.6818	0.6767	0.6719	0.6674	0.6636	0.6604	0.6580	0.6566	0.6561
42°	0.6969	0.6914	0.6862	0.6814	0.6772	0.6738	0.6712	0.6697	0.6691
43°	0.7118	0.7059	0.7003	0.6952	0.6907	0.6870	0.6843	0.6826	0.6820
44°	0.7266	0.7204	0.7144	0.7088	0.7040	0.7000	0.6971	0.6953	0.6947
45°	0.7414	0.7346	0.7282	0.7223	0.7171	0.7129	0.7097	0.7078	0.7071

ELLIPTIC INTEGRALS OF THE SECOND KIND: $E(k, \phi)$ (Continued)

$$E(k, \phi) = \int_0^\phi \sqrt{(1 - k^2 \sin^2 \Phi)}d\Phi, \quad \theta = \sin^{-1} k$$

θ / ϕ	5°	10°	15°	20°	25°	30°	35°	40°	45°
46°	0.8023	0.8006	0.7977	0.7939	0.7891	0.7835	0.7772	0.7704	0.7633
47°	0.8197	0.8179	0.8149	0.8108	0.8057	0.7998	0.7931	0.7858	0.7782
48°	0.8371	0.8352	0.8320	0.8277	0.8223	0.8160	0.8089	0.8012	0.7931
49°	0.8545	0.8525	0.8491	0.8446	0.8389	0.8322	0.8247	0.8165	0.8079
50°	0.8719	0.8698	0.8663	0.8614	0.8554	0.8483	0.8404	0.8317	0.8227
51°	0.8894	0.8871	0.8834	0.8783	0.8719	0.8644	0.8560	0.8469	0.8373
52°	0.9068	0.9044	0.9004	0.8951	0.8884	0.8805	0.8716	0.8620	0.8518
53°	0.9242	0.9217	0.9175	0.9119	0.9048	0.8965	0.8872	0.8770	0.8663
54°	0.9416	0.9389	0.9345	0.9287	0.9212	0.9125	0.9026	0.8919	0.8806
55°	0.9590	0.9562	0.9517	0.9454	0.9376	0.9284	0.9181	0.9068	0.8949
56°	0.9764	0.9735	0.9687	0.9622	0.9540	0.9443	0.9335	0.9216	0.9091
57°	0.9938	0.9908	0.9858	0.9789	0.9703	0.9602	0.9488	0.9363	0.9232
58°	1.0112	1.0080	1.0028	0.9956	0.9866	0.9760	0.9641	0.9510	0.9372
59°	1.0286	1.0253	1.0198	1.0123	1.0029	1.9918	0.9793	0.9656	0.9511
60°	1.0460	1.0426	1.0368	1.0290	1.0191	1.0076	0.9945	0.9801	0.9650
61°	1.0634	1.0598	1.0538	1.0456	1.0354	1.0233	1.0096	0.9946	0.9787
62°	1.0808	1.0771	1.0708	1.0623	1.0516	1.0389	1.0246	1 0090	0.9924
63°	1.0982	1.0943	1.0878	1.0789	1.0678	1.0546	1.0397	1.0233	1.0060
64°	1.1156	1.1115	1.1048	1.0955	1.0839	1.0702	1.0547	1.0376	1.0195
65°	1.1330	1.1288	1.1218	1.1121	1.1001	1.0858	1.0696	1.0518	1.0329
66°	1.1504	1.1460	1.1387	1.1287	1.1162	1.1013	1.0845	1.0660	1.0463
67°	1.1678	1.1632	1.1557	1.1453	1.1323	1.1168	1.0993	1.0801	1.0596
68°	1.1852	1.1805	1.1726	1.1618	1.1483	1.1323	1.1141	1.0941	1.0728
69°	1.2026	1.1977	1.1896	1.1784	1.1644	1.1478	1.1289	1.1081	1.0859
70°	1.2200	1.2149	1.2065	1.1949	1.1804	1.1632	1.1436	1.1221	1.0990
71°	1.2374	1.2321	1.2234	1.2114	1.1964	1.1786	1.1583	1.1359	1.1120
72°	1.2548	1.2493	1.2403	1.2280	1.2124	1.1939	1.1729	1.1498	1.1250
73°	1.2722	1.2666	1.2573	1.2445	1.2284	1.2093	1.1875	1.1636	1.1379
74°	1.2896	1.2838	1.2742	1.2609	1.2443	1.2246	1.2021	1.1773	1.1507
75°	1.3070	1.3010	1.2911	1.2774	1.2603	1.2399	1.2167	1.1910	1.1635
76°	1.3244	1.3182	1.3080	1.2939	1.2762	1.2552	1.2312	1.2047	1.1762
77°	1.3418	1.3354	1.3249	1.3104	1.2921	1.2704	1.2457	1.2183	1.1889
78°	1.3592	1.3526	1.3417	1.3268	1.3080	1.2856	1.2601	1.2319	1.2015
79°	1.3765	1.3698	1.3586	1.3432	1.3239	1.3009	1.2746	1.2454	1.2141
80°	1.3939	1.3870	1.3755	1.3597	1.3398	1.3161	1.2890	1.2590	1.2266
81°	1.4113	1.4042	1.3924	1.3761	1.3556	1.3312	1.3034	1.2725	1.2391
82°	1.4287	1.4214	1.4093	1.3925	1.3715	1.3464	1.3177	1.2859	1.2516
83°	1.4461	1.4386	1.4261	1.4090	1.3873	1.3616	1.3321	1.2994	1.2640
84°	1.4635	1.4558	1.4430	1.4254	1.4032	1.3767	1.3464	1.3128	1.2765
85°	1.4809	1.4729	1.4598	1.4418	1.4190	1.3919	1.3608	1.3262	1.2889
86°	1.4983	1.4901	1.4767	1.4582	1.4348	1.4070	1.3751	1.3396	1.3012
87°	1.5156	1.5073	1.4936	1.4746	1.4507	1.4221	1.3894	1.3530	1.3136
88°	1.5330	1.5245	1.5104	1.4910	1.4665	1.4372	1.4037	1.3664	1.3260
89°	1.5504	1.5417	1.5273	1.5074	1.4823	1.4523	1.4180	1.3798	1.3383
90°	1.5678	1.5589	1.5442	1.5238	1.4981	1.4675	1.4323	1.3931	1.3506

ELLIPTIC INTEGRALS OF THE SECOND KIND: $E(k, \phi)$ (Continued)

$$E(k, \phi) = \int_0^\phi \sqrt{(1 - k^2 \sin^2 \Phi)}d\Phi, \quad \theta = \sin^{-1} k$$

θ \ ϕ	50°	55°	60°	65°	70°	75°	80°	85°	90°
46°	0.7560	0.7488	0.7419	0.7356	0.7301	0.7255	0.7221	0.7200	0.7193
47°	0.7705	0.7628	0.7555	0.7488	0.7429	0.7380	0.7344	0.7321	0.7314
48°	0.7849	0.7768	0.7690	0.7618	0.7555	0.7502	0.7464	0.7440	0.7431
49°	0.7992	0.7905	0.7822	0.7746	0.7679	0.7623	0.7581	0.7556	0.7547
50°	0.8134	0.8042	0.7954	0.7872	0.7801	0.7741	0.7697	0.7670	0.7660
51°	0.8275	0.8177	0.8084	0.7997	0.7921	0.7858	0.7811	0.7781	0.7771
52°	0.8414	0.8311	0.8212	0.8120	0.8039	0.7972	0.7922	0.7891	0.7880
53°	0.8553	0.8444	0.8339	0.8241	0.8155	0.8084	0.8031	0.7998	0.7986
54°	0.8690	0.8575	0.8464	0.8361	0.8270	0.8194	0.8137	0.8102	0.8090
55°	0.8827	0.8705	0.8588	0.8479	0.8382	0.8302	0.8242	0.8204	0.8192
56°	0.8962	0.8834	0.8710	0.8595	0.8493	0.8408	0.8344	0.8304	0.8290
57°	0.9096	0.8961	0.8831	0.8709	0.8601	0.8511	0.8443	0.8401	0.8387
58°	0.9230	0.9088	0.8950	0.8822	0.8707	0.8612	0.8540	0.8496	0.8480
59°	0.9362	0.9213	0.9068	0.8932	0.8812	0.8711	0.8635	0.8588	0.8572
60°	0.9493	0.9336	0.9184	0.9042	0.8914	0.8808	0.8728	0.8677	0.8660
61°	0.9623	0.9459	0.9299	0.9149	0.9015	0.8903	0.8817	0.8764	0.8746
62°	0.9752	0.9580	0.9412	0.9254	0.9113	0.8995	0.8905	0.8849	0.8829
63°	0.9880	0.9700	0.9524	0.9358	0.9210	0.9085	0.8990	0.8930	0.8910
64°	1.0007	0.9818	0.9634	0.9460	0.9304	0.9173	0.9072	0.9009	0.8988
65°	1.0133	0.9936	0.9743	0.9561	0.9397	0.9258	0.9152	0.9086	0.9063
66°	1.0258	1.0052	0.9850	0.9659	0.9487	0.9341	0.9230	0.9159	0.9135
67°	1.0383	1.0167	0.9956	0.9756	0.9576	0.9422	0.9305	0.9230	0.9205
68°	1.0506	1.0281	1.0061	0.9852	0.9662	0.9501	0.9377	0.9299	0.9272
69°	1.0628	1.0394	1.0164	0.9946	0.9747	0.9578	0.9447	0.9364	0.9336
70°	1.0750	1.0506	1.0266	1.0038	0.9830	0.9652	0.9514	0.9427	0.9397
71°	1.0871	1.0617	1.0367	1.0129	0.9911	0.9724	0.9579	0.9487	0.9455
72°	1.0991	1.0727	1.0467	1.0218	0.9990	0.9794	0.9642	0.9544	0.9511
73°	1.1110	1.0836	1.0565	1.0306	1.0067	0.9862	0.9702	0.9599	0.9563
74°	1.1228	1.0944	1.0662	1.0392	1.0143	0.9928	0.9759	0.9650	0.9613
75°	1.1346	1.1051	1.0759	1.0477	1.0217	0.9992	0.9814	0.9699	0.9659
76°	1.1463	1.1158	1.0854	1.0561	1.0290	1.0053	0.9867	0.9745	0.9703
77°	1.1580	1.1263	1.0948	1.0643	1.0361	1.0113	0.9917	0.9789	0.9744
78°	1.1695	1.1368	1.1041	1.0724	1.0430	1.0171	0.9965	0.9829	0.9781
79°	1.1811	1.1472	1.1133	1.0805	1.0498	1.0228	1.0011	0.9867	0.9816
80°	1.1926	1.1576	1.1225	1.0884	1.0565	1.0282	1.0054	0.9902	0.9848
81°	1.2040	1.1678	1.1316	1.0962	1.0630	1.0335	1.0096	0.9935	0.9877
82°	1.2154	1.1781	1.1406	1.1040	1.0695	1.0387	1.0135	0.9965	0.9903
83°	1.2267	1.1883	1.1495	1.1116	1.0758	1.0437	1.0173	0.9992	0.9925
84°	1.2381	1.1984	1.1584	1.1192	1.0821	1.0486	1.0209	1.0017	0.9945
85°	1.2493	1.2085	1.1673	1.1267	1.0882	1.0534	1.0244	1.0039	0.9962
86°	1.2606	1.2186	1.1761	1.1342	1.0944	1.0581	1.0277	1.0060	0.9976
87°	1.2719	1.2286	1.1848	1.1417	1.1004	1.0628	1.0309	1.0078	0.9986
88°	1.2831	1.2386	1.1936	1.1491	1.1064	1.0673	1.0340	1.0095	0.9994
89°	1.2943	1.2487	1.2023	1.1565	1.1124	1.0719	1.0371	1.0111	0.9998
90°	1.3055	1.2587	1.2111	1.1638	1.1184	1.0764	1.0401	1.0127	1.0000

COMPLETE ELLIPTIC INTEGRALS

$$K = \int_0^{\pi/2} \frac{d\Phi}{\sqrt{1 - k^2 \sin^2 \Phi}} = F\left(k, \frac{\pi}{2}\right)$$

$\sin^{-1} k$	K	$\log K$	$\sin^{-1} k$	K	$\log K$
0°	1.5708	0.196120	**40°**	1.7868	0.252068
1	1.5709	0.196153	41	1.7992	0.255085
2	1.5713	0.196252	42	1.8122	0.258197
3	1.5719	0.196418	43	1.8256	0.261406
4	1.5727	0.196649	44	1.8396	0.264716
5	1.5738	0.196947	**45**	1.8541	0.268127
6	1.5751	0.197312	46	1.8691	0.271644
7	1.5767	0.197743	47	1.8848	0.275267
8	1.5785	0.198241	48	1.9011	0.279001
9	1.5805	0.198806	49	1.9180	0.282848
10	1.5828	0.199438	**50**	1.9356	0.286811
11	1.5854	0.200137	51	1.9539	0.290895
12	1.5882	0.200904	52	1.9729	0.295101
13	1.5913	0.201740	53	1.9927	0.299435
14	1.5946	0.202643	54	2.0133	0.303901
15	1.5981	0.203615	**55**	2.0347	0.308504
16	1.6020	0.204657	56	2.0571	0.313247
17	1.6061	0.205768	57	2.0804	0.318138
18	1.6105	0.206948	58	2.1047	0.323182
19	1.6151	0.208200	59	2.1300	0.328384
20	1.6200	0.209522	**60**	2.1565	0.333753
21	1.6252	0.210916	61	2.1842	0.339295
22	1.6307	0.212382	62	2.2132	0.345020
23	1.6365	0.213921	63	2.2435	0.350936
24	1.6426	0.215533	64	2.2754	0.357053
25	1.6490	0.217219	**65**	2.3088	0.363384
26	1.6557	0.218981	66	2.3439	0.369940
27	1.6627	0.220818	67	2.3809	0.376736
28	1.6701	0.222732	68	2.4198	0.383787
29	1.6777	0.224723	69	2.4610	0.391112
30	1.6858	0.226793	**70**	2.5046	0.398730
31	1.6941	0.228943	71	2.5507	0.406665
32	1.7028	0.231173	72	2.5998	0.414943
33	1.7119	0.233485	73	2.6521	0.423596
34	1.7214	0.235880	74	2.7081	0.432660
35	1.7312	0.238359	**75**	2.7681	0.442176
36	1.7415	0.240923	76	2.8327	0.452196
37	1.7522	0.243575	77	2.9026	0.462782
38	1.7633	0.246315	78	2.9786	0.474008
39	1.7748	0.249146	79	3.0617	0.485967
40	1.7868	0.252068	**80**	3.1534	0.498777

COMPLETE ELLIPTIC INTEGRALS (Continued)

$$K = \int_0^{\pi/2} \frac{d\Phi}{\sqrt{1 - k^2 \sin^2 \Phi}} = F\left(k, \frac{\pi}{2}\right)$$

$\sin^{-1} k$	K	$\log K$	$\sin^{-1} k$	K	$\log K$
80°	3.1534	0.498777	**85°**	3.8317	0.583396
81	3.2553	0.512591	86	4.0528	0.607751
82	3.3699	0.527613	87	4.3387	0.637355
83	3.5004	0.544120	88	4.7427	0.676027
84	3.6519	0.562514	89	5.4349	0.735192
85	3.8317	0.583396	**90**	∞	∞

Values of K for $\sin^{-1} k$ = 85° to 89° by 0.1° and 89° to 90° by minutes

$\sin^{-1} k$	K	$\log K$	$\sin^{-1} k$		K	$\log K$
85.0°	3.832	0.58343	**89°**	**0′**	5.435	0.73520
85.1	3.852	0.58569	89	2	5.469	0.73791
85.2	3.872	0.58794	89	4	5.504	0.74068
85.3	3.893	0.59028	89	6	5.540	0.74351
85.4	3.914	0.59262	89	8	5.578	0.74648
85.5	3.936	0.59506	**89**	**10**	5.617	0.74950
85.6	3.958	0.59748	89	12	5.658	0.75266
85.7	3.981	0.59999	89	14	5.700	0.75587
85.8	4.004	0.60249	89	16	5.745	0.75929
85.9	4.028	0.60509	89	18	5.791	0.76275
86.0	4.053	0.60778	**89**	**20**	5.840	0.76641
86.1	4.078	0.61045	89	22	5.891	0.77019
86.2	4.104	0.61321	89	24	5.946	0.77422
86.3	4.130	0.61595	89	26	6.003	0.77837
86.4	4.157	0.61878	89	28	6.063	0.78269
86.5	4.185	0.62170	**89**	**30**	6.128	0.78732
86.6	4.214	0.62469	89	32	6.197	0.79218
86.7	4.244	0.62778	89	34	6.271	0.79734
86.8	4.274	0.63083	89	36	6.351	0.80284
86.9	4.306	0.63407	89	38	6.438	0.80875
87.0	4.339	0.63739	**89**	**40**	6.533	0.81511
87.1	4.372	0.64068	89	41	6.584	0.81849
87.2	4.407	0.64414	89	42	6.639	0.82210
87.3	4.444	0.64777	89	43	6.696	0.82582
87.4	4.481	0.65137	89	44	6.756	0.82969
87.5	4.520	0.65514	**89**	**45**	6.821	0.83385
87.6	4.561	0.65916	89	46	6.890	0.83822
87.7	4.603	0.66304	89	47	6.964	0.84286
87.8	4.648	0.66727	89	48	7.044	0.84782
87.9	4.694	0.67154	89	49	7.131	0.85315
88.0	4.743	0.67605	**89**	**50**	7.226	0.85890
88.1	4.794	0.68070	89	51	7.332	0.86522
88.2	4.848	0.68556	89	52	7.449	0.87210
88.3	4.905	0.69064	89	53	7.583	0.87984
88.4	4.965	0.69592	89	54	7.737	0.88857
88.5	5.030	0.70157	**89**	**55**	7.919	0.89867
88.6	5.099	0.70749	89	56	8.143	0.91078
88.7	5.173	0.71374	89	57	8.430	0.92583
88.8	5.253	0.72041	89	58	8.836	0.94626
88.9	5.340	0.72754	89	59	9.529	0.97905
89.0	5.435	0.73520	**90**	**0**	∞	∞

COMPLETE ELLIPTIC INTEGRALS (Continued)

$$E = \int_0^{\pi/2} \sqrt{1 - k^2 \sin^2 \Phi} \cdot d\Phi = E\left(k, \frac{\pi}{2}\right)$$

$\sin^{-1} k$	E	$\log E$	$\sin^{-1} k$	E	$\log E$
0°	1.5708	0.196120	45°	1.3506	0.130541
1	1.5707	0.196087	46	1.3418	0.127690
2	1.5703	0.195988	47	1.3329	0.124788
3	1.5697	0.195822	48	1.3238	0.121836
4	1.5689	0.195591	49	1.3147	0.118836
5	1.5678	0.195293	50	1.3055	0.115790
6	1.5665	0.194930	51	1.2963	0.112698
7	1.5649	0.194500	52	1.2870	0.109563
8	1.5632	0.194004	53	1.2776	0.106386
9	1.5611	0.193442	54	1.2681	0.103169
10	1.5589	0.192815	55	1.2587	0.099915
11	1.5564	0.192121	56	1.2492	0.096626
12	1.5537	0.191362	57	1.2397	0.093303
13	1.5507	0.190537	58	1.2301	0.089950
14	1.5476	0.189646	59	1.2206	0.086569
15	1.5442	0.188690	60	1.2111	0.083164
16	1.5405	0.187668	61	1.2015	0.079738
17	1.5367	0.186581	62	1.1920	0.076293
18	1.5326	0.185428	63	1.1826	0.072834
19	1.5283	0.184210	64	1.1732	0.069364
20	1.5238	0.182928	65	1.1638	0.065889
21	1.5191	0.181580	66	1.1545	0.062412
22	1.5141	0.180168	67	1.1453	0.058937
23	1.5090	0.178691	68	1.1362	0.055472
24	1.5037	0.177150	69	1.1272	0.052020
25	1.4981	0.175545	70	1.1184	0.048589
26	1.4924	0.173876	71	1.1096	0.045183
27	1.4864	0.172144	72	1.1011	0.041812
28	1.4803	0.170348	73	1.0927	0.038481
29	1.4740	0.168489	74	1.0844	0.035200
30	1.4675	0.166567	75	1.0764	0.031976
31	1.4608	0.164583	76	1.0686	0.028819
32	1.4539	0.162537	77	1.0611	0.025740
33	1.4469	0.160429	78	1.0538	0.022749
34	1.4397	0.158261	79	1.0468	0.019858
35	1.4323	0.156031	80	1.0401	0.017081
36	1.4248	0.153742	81	1.0338	0.014432
37	1.4171	0.151393	82	1.0278	0.011927
38	1.4092	0.148985	83	1.0223	0.009584
39	1.4013	0.146519	84	1.0172	0.007422
40	1.3931	0.143995	85	1.0127	0.005465
41	1.3849	0.141414	86	1.0086	0.003740
42	1.3765	0.138778	87	1.0053	0.002278
43	1.3680	0.136086	88	1.0026	0.001121
44	1.3594	0.133340	89	1.0008	0.000326
45	1.3506	0.130541	90°	1.0000	0.000000

VECTOR ANALYSIS

Definitions

Any quantity which is completely determined by its magnitude is called a *scalar*. Examples of such are mass, density, temperature, etc. Any quantity which is completely determined by its magnitude and direction is called a *vector*. Examples of such are velocity, acceleration, force, etc. A vector quantity is represented by a directed line segment, the length of which represents the magnitude of the vector. A vector quantity is usually represented by a boldfaced letter such as V. Two vectors V_1 and V_2 are equal to one another if they have equal magnitudes and are acting in the same directions. A negative vector, written as $-V$, is one which acts in the opposite direction to V, but is of equal magnitude to it. If we represent the magnitude of V by v, we write $|V| = v$. A vector parallel to V, but equal to the reciprocal of its magnitude is written as V^{-1} or as $\dfrac{1}{V}$.

The *unit vector* $\dfrac{V}{v}$ $(v \neq 0)$ is that vector which has the same direction as V, but has a magnitude of unity (sometimes represented as V_0 or $\hat{v}$).

Vector Algebra

The vector sum of V_1 and V_2 is represented by $V_1 + V_2$. The vector sum of V_1 and $-V_2$, or the difference of the vector V_2 from V_1 is represented by $V_1 - V_2$.

If r is a scalar, then $rV = Vr$, and represents a vector r times the magnitude of V, in the same direction as V if r is positive, and in the opposite direction if r is negative. If r and s are scalars, V_1, V_2, V_3, vectors, then the following rules of scalars and vectors hold:

$$V_1 + V_2 = V_2 + V_1$$
$$(r + s)V_1 = rV_1 + sV_1; \qquad r(V_1 + V_2) = rV_1 + rV_2$$
$$V_1 + (V_2 + V_3) = (V_1 + V_2) + V_3 = V_1 + V_2 + V_3$$

Vectors in Space

A plane is described by two distinct vectors V_1 and V_2. Should these vectors not intersect each other, then one is displaced parallel to itself until they do (fig. 1.) Any other vector V lying in this plane is given by

$$V = rV_1 + sV_2$$

VECTOR ANALYSIS (Continued)

A *position vector* specifies the position in space of a point relative to a fixed origin. If therefore V_1 and V_2 are the position vectors of the points A and B, relative to the origin O, then any point P on the line AB has a position vector V given by

$$V = rV_1 + (1 - r)V_2$$

The scalar "r" can be taken as the parametric representation of P since $r = 0$ implies $P = B$ and $r = 1$ implies $P = A$. (fig. 2). If P divides the line AB in the ratio $r:s$ then

$$V = \left(\frac{r}{r + s}\right)V_1 + \left(\frac{s}{r + s}\right)V_2$$

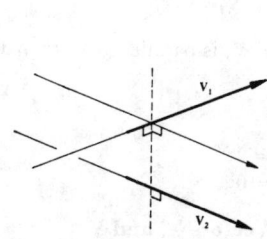

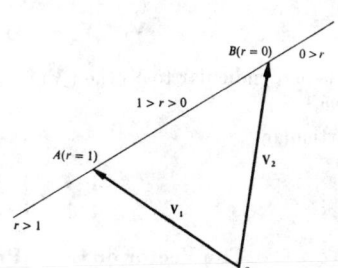

Fig. 1.　　　　　　　　　　　　　　Fig. 2.

The vectors V_1, V_2, V_3, . . . , V_n are said to be *linearly dependent* if there exist scalars $r_1, r_2, r_3, \ldots, r_n$, not all zero, such that

$$r_1V_1 + r_2V_2 + \cdots + r_nV_n = 0$$

A vector V is linearly dependent upon the set of vectors V_1, V_2, V_3, . . . , V_n if

$$V = r_1V_1 + r_2V_2 + r_3V_3 + \cdots + r_nV_n$$

Three vectors are linearly dependent if and only if they are co-planar.

All points in space can be uniquely determined by linear dependence upon three *base vectors* i.e. three vectors any one of which is linearly independent of the other two. The simplest set of base vectors are the unit vectors along the coordinate Ox, Oy and Oz axes. These are usually designated by $\mathbf{i}$, $\mathbf{j}$ and $\mathbf{k}$ respectively.

If V is a vector in space, and a, b and c are the respective magnitudes of the projections of the vector along the axes then

$$V = a\mathbf{i} + b\mathbf{j} + c\mathbf{k}$$

and
$$v = \sqrt{a^2 + b^2 + c^2}$$

and the direction cosines of V are

$$\cos \alpha = a/v, \quad \cos \beta = b/v, \quad \cos \gamma = c/v.$$

The law of addition yields

$$V_1 + V_2 = (a_1 + a_2)\mathbf{i} + (b_1 + b_2)\mathbf{j} + (c_1 + c_2)\mathbf{k}$$

The Scalar, Dot, or Inner Product of Two Vectors V_1 and V_2

This product is represented as $V_1 \cdot V_2$ and is defined to be equal to $v_1 v_2 \cos \theta$, where θ is the angle from V_1 to V_2, i.e.,

$$V_1 \cdot V_2 = v_1 v_2 \cos \theta$$

The following rules apply for this product:

$$V_1 \cdot V_2 = a_1 a_2 + b_1 b_2 + c_1 c_2 = V_2 \cdot V_1$$

It should be noted that this verifies that scalar multiplication is commutative.

$$(V_1 + V_2) \cdot V_3 = V_1 \cdot V_3 + V_2 \cdot V_3$$
$$V_1 \cdot (V_2 + V_3) = V_1 \cdot V_2 + V_1 \cdot V_3$$

If V_1 is perpendicular to V_2 then $V_1 \cdot V_2 = 0$, and if V_1 is parallel to V_2 then $V_1 \cdot V_2 = v_1 v_2 = rw_1^2$

In particular

$$i \cdot i = j \cdot j = k \cdot k = 1,$$
and
$$i \cdot j = j \cdot k = k \cdot i = 0$$

The Vector or Cross Product of Vectors V_1 and V_2

This product is represented as $V_1 \times V_2$ and is defined to be equal to $v_1 v_2 (\sin \theta) 1$, where θ is the angle from V_1 to V_2 and 1 is a unit vector perpendicular to the plane of V_1 and V_2 and so directed that a right-handed screw driven in the direction of 1 would carry V_1 into V_2, i.e.,

$$V_1 \times V_2 = v_1 v_2 (\sin \theta) 1$$
and
$$\tan \theta = \frac{|V_1 \times V_2|}{V_1 \cdot V_2}$$

The following rules apply for vector products:

$$V_1 \times V_2 = -V_2 \times V_1$$
$$V_1 \times (V_2 + V_3) = V_1 \times V_2 + V_1 \times V_3$$
$$(V_1 + V_2) \times V_3 = V_1 \times V_3 + V_2 \times V_3$$
$$V_1 \times (V_2 \times V_3) = V_2(V_3 \cdot V_1 - V_3(V_1 \cdot V_2)$$
$$i \times i = j \times j = k \times k = 0 \cdot 1 \text{ (zero vector)}$$
$$= 0$$

$$i \times j = k, \qquad j \times k = i, \qquad k \times i = j$$

If $V_1 = a_1 i + b_1 j + c_1 k,$ $\qquad V_2 = a_2 i + b_2 j + c_2 k,$ $\qquad V_3 = a_3 i + b_3 j + c_3 k,$

then

$$V_1 \times V_2 = \begin{vmatrix} i & j & k \\ a_1 & b_1 & c_1 \\ a_2 & b_2 & c_2 \end{vmatrix} = (b_1 c_2 - b_2 c_1)i + (c_1 a_2 - c_2 a_1)j + (a_1 b_2 - a_2 b_1)k$$

It should be noted that, since $V_1 \times V_2 = -V_2 \times V_1$, the vector product is not commutative.

Scalar Triple Product

There is only one possible interpretation of the expression $\mathbf{V}_1 \cdot \mathbf{V}_2 \times \mathbf{V}_3$ and that is $\mathbf{V}_1 \cdot (\mathbf{V}_2 \times \mathbf{V}_3)$ which is obviously a scalar.

Further $\mathbf{V}_1 \cdot (\mathbf{V}_2 \times \mathbf{V}_3) = (\mathbf{V}_1 \times \mathbf{V}_2) \cdot \mathbf{V}_3 = \mathbf{V}_2 \cdot (\mathbf{V}_3 \times \mathbf{V}_1)$

$$= \begin{vmatrix} a_1 & b_1 & c_1 \\ a_2 & b_2 & c_2 \\ a_3 & b_3 & c_3 \end{vmatrix}$$

$$= v_1 v_2 v_3 \cos \phi \sin \theta,$$

Where θ is the angle between $\mathbf{V}_2$ and $\mathbf{V}_3$ and ϕ is the angle between $\mathbf{V}_1$ and the normal to the plane of $\mathbf{V}_2$ and $\mathbf{V}_3$.

This product is called the *scalar triple product* and is written as $[\mathbf{V}_1\mathbf{V}_2\mathbf{V}_3]$.

The determinant indicates that it can be considered as the volume of the parallelepiped whose three determining edges are $\mathbf{V}_1$, $\mathbf{V}_2$ and $\mathbf{V}_3$.

It also follows that cyclic permutation of the subscripts does not change the value of the scalar triple product so that

$$[\mathbf{V}_1\mathbf{V}_2\mathbf{V}_3] = [\mathbf{V}_2\mathbf{V}_3\mathbf{V}_1] = [\mathbf{V}_3\mathbf{V}_1\mathbf{V}_2]$$

but $[\mathbf{V}_1\mathbf{V}_2\mathbf{V}_3] = -[\mathbf{V}_2\mathbf{V}_1\mathbf{V}_3]$ etc. and $[\mathbf{V}_1\mathbf{V}_1\mathbf{V}_2] \equiv 0$ etc.

Given three non-coplanar reference vectors $\mathbf{V}_1$, $\mathbf{V}_2$ and $\mathbf{V}_3$, the *reciprocal system is* given by $\mathbf{V}_1^*$, $\mathbf{V}_2^*$ and $\mathbf{V}_3^*$, where

$$1 = v_1 v_1^* = v_2 v_2^* = v_3 v_3^*$$

$$0 = v_1 v_2^* = v_1 v_3^* = v_2 v_1^* \quad \text{etc.}$$

$$\mathbf{V}_1^* = \frac{\mathbf{V}_2 \times \mathbf{V}_3}{[\mathbf{V}_1\mathbf{V}_2\mathbf{V}_3]}, \qquad \mathbf{V}_2^* = \frac{\mathbf{V}_3 \times \mathbf{V}_1}{[\mathbf{V}_1\mathbf{V}_2\mathbf{V}_3]}, \qquad \mathbf{V}_3^* = \frac{\mathbf{V}_1 \times \mathbf{V}_2}{[\mathbf{V}_1\mathbf{V}_2\mathbf{V}_3]}$$

The system $\mathbf{i}, \mathbf{j}, \mathbf{k}$ is its own reciprocal.

Vector Triple Product

The product $\mathbf{V}_1 \times (\mathbf{V}_2 \times \mathbf{V}_3)$ defines the *vector triple product*. Obviously, in this case, the brackets are vital to the definition.

$$\mathbf{V}_1 \times (\mathbf{V}_2 \times \mathbf{V}_3) = (\mathbf{V}_1 \cdot \mathbf{V}_3)\mathbf{V}_2 - (\mathbf{V}_1 \cdot \mathbf{V}_2)\mathbf{V}_3$$

$$= \begin{vmatrix} \mathbf{i} & \mathbf{j} & \mathbf{k} \\ a_1 & b_1 & c_1 \\ \begin{vmatrix} b_2 & c_2 \\ b_3 & c_3 \end{vmatrix} & \begin{vmatrix} c_2 & a_2 \\ c_3 & a_3 \end{vmatrix} & \begin{vmatrix} a_2 & b_2 \\ a_3 & b_3 \end{vmatrix} \end{vmatrix}$$

i.e. it is a vector, perpendicular to $\mathbf{V}_1$, lying in the plane of $\mathbf{V}_2$, $\mathbf{V}_3$.

Similarly
$$(\mathbf{V}_1 \times \mathbf{V}_2) \times \mathbf{V}_3 = \begin{vmatrix} \mathbf{i} & \mathbf{j} & \mathbf{k} \\ \begin{vmatrix} b_1 & c_1 \\ b_2 & c_2 \end{vmatrix} & \begin{vmatrix} c_1 & a_1 \\ c_2 & a_2 \end{vmatrix} & \begin{vmatrix} a_1 & b_1 \\ a_2 & b_2 \end{vmatrix} \\ a_3 & b_3 & c_3 \end{vmatrix}$$

$$\mathbf{V}_1 \times (\mathbf{V}_2 \times \mathbf{V}_3) + \mathbf{V}_2 \times (\mathbf{V}_3 \times \mathbf{V}_1) + \mathbf{V}_3 \times (\mathbf{V}_1 + \mathbf{V}_2) \equiv 0$$

If $\mathbf{V}_1 \times (\mathbf{V}_2 \times \mathbf{V}_3) = (\mathbf{V}_1 \times \mathbf{V}_2) \times \mathbf{V}_3$ then $\mathbf{V}_1, \mathbf{V}_2, \mathbf{V}_3$ form an *orthogonal set*. Thus $\mathbf{i}, \mathbf{j}, \mathbf{k}$ form an orthogonal set.

Geometry of the Plane, Straight Line and Sphere

The position vectors of the fixed points A, B, C, D relative to O are $\mathbf{V}_1, \mathbf{V}_2, \mathbf{V}_3, \mathbf{V}_4$ and the position vector of the variable point P is $\mathbf{V}$.

The vector form of the equation of the straight line through A parallel to $\mathbf{V}_2$ is

$$\mathbf{V} = \mathbf{V}_1 + r\mathbf{V}_2$$

$$\text{or} \quad (\mathbf{V} - \mathbf{V}_1) = r\mathbf{V}_2$$

$$\text{or} \quad (\mathbf{V} - \mathbf{V}_1) \times \mathbf{V}_2 = 0$$

while that of the plane through A perpendicular to $\mathbf{V}_2$ is

$$(\mathbf{V} - \mathbf{V}_1) \cdot \mathbf{V}_2 = 0$$

The equation of the line AB is

$$\mathbf{V} = r\mathbf{V}_1 + (1 - r)\mathbf{V}_2$$

and those of the bisectors of the angles between $\mathbf{V}_1$ and $\mathbf{V}_2$ are

$$\mathbf{V} = r\left(\frac{\mathbf{V}_1}{v} \pm \frac{\mathbf{V}_2}{v_2}\right)$$

$$\text{or} \quad \mathbf{V} = r(\hat{\mathbf{v}}_1 \pm \hat{\mathbf{v}}_2)$$

The perpendicular from C to the line through A parallel to $\mathbf{V}_2$ has as its equation

$$\mathbf{V} = \mathbf{V}_1 - \mathbf{V}_3 - \hat{\mathbf{v}}_2 \cdot (\mathbf{V}_1 - \mathbf{V}_3)\hat{\mathbf{v}}_2.$$

The condition for the intersection of the two lines,

$$\mathbf{V} = \mathbf{V}_1 + r\mathbf{V}_3$$

$$\text{and} \quad \mathbf{V} = \mathbf{V}_2 + s\mathbf{V}_4$$

$$\text{is} \quad [(\mathbf{V}_1 - \mathbf{V}_2)\mathbf{V}_3\mathbf{V}_4] = 0.$$

The common perpendicular to the above two lines is the line of intersection of the two planes

$$[(\mathbf{V} - \mathbf{V}_1)\mathbf{V}_3(\mathbf{V}_3 \times \mathbf{V}_4)] = 0$$

$$\text{and} \quad [(\mathbf{V} - \mathbf{V}_2)\mathbf{V}_4(\mathbf{V}_3 \times \mathbf{V}_4)] = 0$$

and the length of this perpendicular is

$$\frac{[(\mathbf{V}_1 - \mathbf{V}_2)\mathbf{V}_3\mathbf{V}_4]}{|\mathbf{V}_3 \times \mathbf{V}_4|}.$$

The equation of the line perpendicular to the plane ABC is

$$\mathbf{V} = \mathbf{V}_1 \times \mathbf{V}_2 + \mathbf{V}_2 \times \mathbf{V}_3 + \mathbf{V}_3 \times \mathbf{V}_1$$

and the distance of the plane from the origin is

$$\frac{[\mathbf{V}_1\mathbf{V}_2\mathbf{V}_3]}{|(\mathbf{V}_2 - \mathbf{V}_1) \times (\mathbf{V}_3 - \mathbf{V}_1)|}.$$

In general the vector equation

$$\mathbf{V} \cdot \mathbf{V}_2 = r$$

defines the plane which is perpendicular to $\mathbf{V}_2$, and the perpendicular distance from A to this plane is

$$\frac{r - \mathbf{V}_1 \cdot \mathbf{V}_2}{v_2}.$$

The distance from A, measured along a line parallel to $\mathbf{V}_3$, is

$$\frac{r - \mathbf{V}_1 \cdot \mathbf{V}_2}{\mathbf{V}_2 \cdot \hat{\mathbf{v}}_3} \quad \text{or} \quad \frac{r - \mathbf{V}_1 \cdot \mathbf{V}_2}{v_2 \cos \theta}$$

where θ is the angle beween $\mathbf{V}_2$ and $\mathbf{V}_3$.
(If this plane contains the point C then $r = \mathbf{V}_3 \cdot \mathbf{V}_2$ and if it passes through the origin then $r = 0$.)

Given two planes

$$\mathbf{V} \cdot \mathbf{V}_1 = r$$
$$\mathbf{V} \cdot \mathbf{V}_2 = s$$

then any plane through the line of intersection of these two planes is given by

$$\mathbf{V} \cdot (\mathbf{V}_1 + \lambda \mathbf{V}_2) = r + \lambda s$$

where λ is a scalar parameter. In particular $\lambda = \pm v_1/v_2$ yields the equation of the two planes bisecting the angle between the given planes.

The plane through A parallel to the plane of $\mathbf{V}_2$, $\mathbf{V}_3$ is

$$\mathbf{V} = \mathbf{V}_1 + r\mathbf{V}_2 + s\mathbf{V}_3$$

$$\text{or} \quad (\mathbf{V} - \mathbf{V}_1) \cdot \mathbf{V}_2 \times \mathbf{V}_3 = 0$$

$$\text{or} \quad [\mathbf{V}\mathbf{V}_2\mathbf{V}_3] - [\mathbf{V}_1\mathbf{V}_2\mathbf{V}_3] = 0$$

so that the expansion in rectangular Cartesian coordinates yields

$$\begin{vmatrix} (x - a_1) & (y - b_1) & (z - c_1) \\ a_2 & b_2 & c_2 \\ a_3 & b_3 & c_3 \end{vmatrix} = 0 \qquad (\mathbf{V} \equiv x\mathbf{i} + y\mathbf{j} + z\mathbf{k})$$

which is obviously the usual linear equation in x, y and z.

The plane through AB parallel to $\mathbf{V}_3$ is given by

$$[(\mathbf{V} - \mathbf{V}_1)(\mathbf{V}_1 - \mathbf{V}_2)\mathbf{V}_3] = 0$$

$$\text{or} \quad [\mathbf{V}\mathbf{V}_2\mathbf{V}_3] - [\mathbf{V}\mathbf{V}_1\mathbf{V}_3] - [\mathbf{V}_1\mathbf{V}_2\mathbf{V}_3] = 0$$

The plane through the three points A, B and C is

$$\mathbf{V} = \mathbf{V}_1 + s(\mathbf{V}_2 - \mathbf{V}_1) + t(\mathbf{V}_3 - \mathbf{V}_1)$$

$$\text{or} \qquad \mathbf{V} = r\mathbf{V}_1 + s\mathbf{V}_2 + t\mathbf{V}_3 \qquad (r + s + t \equiv 1)$$

$$\text{or} \qquad [(\mathbf{V} - \mathbf{V}_1)(\mathbf{V}_1 - \mathbf{V}_2)(\mathbf{V}_2 - \mathbf{V}_3)] = 0$$

$$\text{or} \qquad [\mathbf{V}\mathbf{V}_1\mathbf{V}_2] + [\mathbf{V}\mathbf{V}_2\mathbf{V}_3] + [\mathbf{V}\mathbf{V}_3\mathbf{V}_1] - [\mathbf{V}_1\mathbf{V}_2\mathbf{V}_3] = 0$$

For four points A, B, C, D to be coplanar, then

$$r\mathbf{V}_1 + s\mathbf{V}_2 + t\mathbf{V}_3 + u\mathbf{V}_4 \equiv 0 \equiv r + s + t + u$$

The following formulas relate to a sphere when the vectors are taken to lie in three dimensional space and to a circle when the space is two dimensional. For a circle in three dimensions take the intersection of the sphere with a plane.

The equation of a sphere with center O and radius OA is

$$\mathbf{V} \cdot \mathbf{V} = v_1^2 \qquad \text{(not } \mathbf{V} = \mathbf{V}_1\text{)}$$

or $\qquad (\mathbf{V} - \mathbf{V}_1) \cdot (\mathbf{V} + \mathbf{V}_1) = 0$

while that of a sphere with center B radius v_1 is

$$(\mathbf{V} - \mathbf{V}_2) \cdot (\mathbf{V} - \mathbf{V}_2) = v_1^2$$

or $\qquad \mathbf{V} \cdot (\mathbf{V} - 2\mathbf{V}_2) = v_1^2 - v_2^2$

If the above sphere passes through the origin then

$$\mathbf{V} \cdot (\mathbf{V} - 2\mathbf{V}_2) = 0$$

(note that in two dimensional polar coordinates this is simply)

$$r = 2a \cdot \cos \theta$$

while in three dimensional Cartesian coordinates it is

$$x^2 + y^2 + z^2 - 2(a_2 x + b_2 y + c_2 x) = 0.$$

The equation of a sphere having the points A and B as the extremities of a diameter is

$$(\mathbf{V} - \mathbf{V}_1) \cdot (\mathbf{V} - \mathbf{V}_2) = 0.$$

The square of the length of the tangent from C to the sphere with center B and radius v_1 is given by

$$(\mathbf{V}_3 - \mathbf{V}_2) \cdot (\mathbf{V}_3 - \mathbf{V}_2) = v_1^2$$

The condition that the plane $\mathbf{V} \cdot \mathbf{V}_3 = s$ is tangential to the sphere $(\mathbf{V} - \mathbf{V}_2) \cdot (\mathbf{V} - \mathbf{V}_2) = v_1^2$ is

$$(s - \mathbf{V}_3 \cdot \mathbf{V}_2) \cdot (s - \mathbf{V}_3 \cdot \mathbf{V}_2) = v_1^2 v_3^2.$$

The equation of the tangent plane at D, on the surface of sphere $(\mathbf{V} - \mathbf{V}_2) \cdot (\mathbf{V} - \mathbf{V}_2) = v_1^2$, is

$$(\mathbf{V} - \mathbf{V}_4) \cdot (\mathbf{V}_4 - \mathbf{V}_2) = 0$$

or $\qquad \mathbf{V} \cdot \mathbf{V}_4 - \mathbf{V}_2 \cdot (\mathbf{V} + \mathbf{V}_4) = v_1^2 - v_2^2$

The condition that the two circles $(\mathbf{V} - \mathbf{V}_2) \cdot (\mathbf{V} - \mathbf{V}_2) = v_1^2$ and $(\mathbf{V} - \mathbf{V}_4) \cdot (\mathbf{V} - \mathbf{V}_4) = v_3^2$ intersect orthogonally is clearly

$$(\mathbf{V}_2 - \mathbf{V}_4) \cdot (\mathbf{V}_2 - \mathbf{V}_4) = v_1^2 + v_3^2$$

The polar plane of D with respect to the circle

$$(\mathbf{V} - \mathbf{V}_2) \cdot (\mathbf{V} - \mathbf{V}_2) = v_1^2 \quad \text{is}$$

$$\mathbf{V} \cdot \mathbf{V}_4 - \mathbf{V}_2 \cdot (\mathbf{V} + \mathbf{V}_4) = v_1^2 - v_2^2$$

Any sphere through the intersection of the two spheres $(\mathbf{V} - \mathbf{V}_2) \cdot (\mathbf{V} - \mathbf{V}_2) = v_1^2$ and $(\mathbf{V} - \mathbf{V}_4) \cdot (\mathbf{V} - \mathbf{V}_4) = v_3^2$ is given by

$$(\mathbf{V} - \mathbf{V}_2) \cdot (\mathbf{V} - \mathbf{V}_2) + \lambda(\mathbf{V} - \mathbf{V}_4) \cdot (\mathbf{V} - \mathbf{V}_4) = v_1^2 + \lambda v_3^2$$

while the radical plane of two such spheres is

$$\mathbf{V} \cdot (\mathbf{V}_2 - \mathbf{V}_4) = -\tfrac{1}{2}(v_1^2 - v_2^2 - v_3^2 + v_4^2)$$

Differentiation of Vectors

If $\mathbf{V}_1 = a_1\mathbf{i} + b_1\mathbf{j} + c_1\mathbf{k}$, and $\mathbf{V}_2 = a_2\mathbf{i} + b_2\mathbf{j} + c_2\mathbf{k}$, and if $\mathbf{V}_1$ and $\mathbf{V}_2$ are functions of the scalar t, then

$$\frac{d}{dt}(\mathbf{V}_1 + \mathbf{V}_2 + \cdots) = \frac{d\mathbf{V}_1}{dt} + \frac{d\mathbf{V}_2}{dt} + \cdots ,$$

$$\text{where} \quad \frac{d\mathbf{V}_1}{dt} = \frac{da_1}{dt}\mathbf{i} + \frac{db_1}{dt}\mathbf{j} + \frac{dc_1}{dt}\mathbf{k}, \text{ etc.}$$

$$\frac{d}{dt}(\mathbf{V}_1 \cdot \mathbf{V}_2) = \frac{d\mathbf{V}_1}{dt} \cdot \mathbf{V}_2 + \mathbf{V}_1 \cdot \frac{d\mathbf{V}_2}{dt}$$

$$\frac{d}{dt}(\mathbf{V}_1 \times \mathbf{V}_2) = \frac{d\mathbf{V}_1}{dt} \times \mathbf{V}_2 + \mathbf{V}_1 \times \frac{d\mathbf{V}_2}{dt}$$

$$\mathbf{V} \cdot \frac{d\mathbf{V}}{dt} = v \cdot \frac{dv}{dt}$$

In particular, if $\mathbf{V}$ is a vector of constant length then the right hand side of the last equation is identically zero showing that $\mathbf{V}$ is perpendicular to its derivative.

The derivatives of the triple products are

$$\frac{d}{dt}[\mathbf{V}_1\mathbf{V}_2\mathbf{V}_3] = \left[\left(\frac{d\mathbf{V}_1}{dt}\right)\mathbf{V}_2\mathbf{V}_3\right] + \left[\mathbf{V}_1\left(\frac{d\mathbf{V}_2}{dt}\right)\mathbf{V}_3\right] + \left[\mathbf{V}_1\mathbf{V}_2\left(\frac{d\mathbf{V}_3}{dt}\right)\right]$$

$$\text{and} \quad \frac{d}{dt}\left\{\mathbf{V}_1 \times (\mathbf{V}_2 \times \mathbf{V}_3)\right\} = \left(\frac{d\mathbf{V}_1}{dt}\right) \times (\mathbf{V}_2 \times \mathbf{V}_3) + \mathbf{V}_1$$

$$\times \left(\left(\frac{d\mathbf{V}_2}{dt}\right) \times \mathbf{V}_3\right) + \mathbf{V}_1 \times \left(\mathbf{V}_2 \times \left(\frac{d\mathbf{V}_3}{dt}\right)\right).$$

Geometry of Curves in Space

s = the *length of arc*, measured from some fixed point on the curve (fig. 3).

$\mathbf{V}_1$ = the position vector of the point A on the curve

$\mathbf{V}_1 + \delta\mathbf{V}_1$ = the position vector of the point P in the neighborhood of A

$\hat{\mathbf{t}}$ = the *unit tangent* to the curve at the point A, measured in the direction of s increasing.

The *normal plane* is that plane which is perpendicular to the unit tangent. The principal normal is defined as the intersection of the normal plane with the plane defined by $\mathbf{V}_1$ and $\mathbf{V}_1 + \delta\mathbf{V}_1$ in the limit as $\delta\mathbf{V}_1 - 0$.

$\hat{\mathbf{n}}$ = the *unit normal* (principal) at the point A. The plane defined by $\hat{\mathbf{t}}$ and $\hat{\mathbf{n}}$ is called the *osculating plane* (alternatively plane of curvature or local plane).

ρ = the radius of curvature at A

$\delta\theta$ = the angle subtended at the origin by $\delta\mathbf{V}_1$.

$$\kappa = \frac{d\theta}{ds} = \frac{1}{\rho}$$

$\hat{\mathbf{b}}$ = the *unit binormal* i.e. the unit vector which is parallel to $\hat{\mathbf{t}} \times \hat{\mathbf{n}}$ at the point A:
λ = the *torsion* of the curve at A

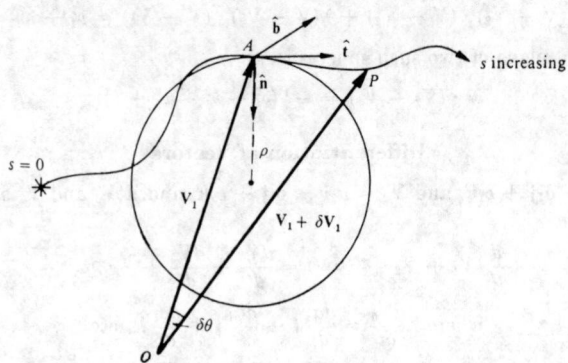

Figure 3.

Frenet's Formulas:

$$\frac{d\hat{\mathbf{t}}}{ds} = \kappa\hat{\mathbf{n}}$$

$$\frac{d\hat{\mathbf{n}}}{ds} = -\kappa\hat{\mathbf{t}} + \lambda\hat{\mathbf{b}}$$

$$\frac{d\hat{\mathbf{b}}}{ds} = -\lambda\hat{\mathbf{n}}$$

The following formulas are also applicable:

Unit tangent $\qquad\qquad\qquad \hat{\mathbf{t}} = \dfrac{d\mathbf{V}_1}{ds}$

Equation of the tangent $\qquad (\mathbf{V} - \mathbf{V}_1) \times \hat{\mathbf{t}} = 0$
$\qquad\qquad\qquad$ or $\qquad \mathbf{V} = \mathbf{V}_1 + q\hat{\mathbf{t}}$

Unit normal $\qquad\qquad\qquad \hat{\mathbf{n}} = \dfrac{1}{\kappa}\dfrac{d^2\mathbf{V}_1}{ds^2}$

Equation of the normal plane $\qquad (\mathbf{V} - \mathbf{V}_1) \cdot \hat{\mathbf{t}} = 0$

Equation of the normal $\qquad\quad (\mathbf{V} - \mathbf{V}_1) \times \hat{\mathbf{n}} = 0$
$\qquad\qquad\qquad$ or $\qquad \mathbf{V} = \mathbf{V}_1 + r\hat{\mathbf{n}}$

Unit binormal $\qquad\qquad \hat{\mathbf{b}} = \hat{\mathbf{t}} \times \hat{\mathbf{n}}$

Equation of the binormal $\qquad (\mathbf{V} - \mathbf{V}_1) \times \hat{\mathbf{b}} = 0$
$\qquad\qquad$ or $\qquad\qquad \mathbf{V} = \mathbf{V}_1 + u\hat{\mathbf{b}}$

$\qquad\qquad$ or $\qquad\qquad \mathbf{V} = \mathbf{V}_1 + w\dfrac{d\mathbf{V}_1}{ds} \times \dfrac{d^2\mathbf{V}_1}{ds^2}$

Equation of the osculating plane:

$$[(\mathbf{V} - \mathbf{V}_1)\hat{\mathbf{t}}\hat{\mathbf{n}}] = 0$$

$\qquad\qquad$ or $\qquad \left[(\mathbf{V} - \mathbf{V}_1)\left(\dfrac{d\mathbf{V}_1}{ds}\right)\left(\dfrac{d^2\mathbf{V}_1}{ds^2}\right)\right] = 0$

A *geodetic line* on a surface is a curve, the osculating plane of which is everywhere normal to the surface.

The differential equation of the geodetic is

$$[\hat{n}\,d\mathbf{V}_1\,d^2\mathbf{V}_1] = 0$$

Differential Operators—Rectangular Coordinates

$$dS = \frac{\partial S}{\partial x} \cdot dx + \frac{\partial S}{\partial y} \cdot dy + \frac{\partial S}{\partial z} \cdot dz$$

By definition

$$\nabla \equiv \text{del} \equiv \mathbf{i}\frac{\partial}{\partial x} + \mathbf{j}\frac{\partial}{\partial y} + \mathbf{k}\frac{\partial}{\partial z}$$

$$\nabla^2 \equiv \text{Laplacian} \equiv \frac{\partial^2}{\partial x^2} + \frac{\partial^2}{\partial y^2} + \frac{\partial^2}{\partial z^2}$$

If S is a scalar function, then

$$\nabla S \equiv \text{grad } S \equiv \frac{\partial S}{dx}\mathbf{i} + \frac{\partial S}{dy}\mathbf{j} + \frac{\partial S}{dz}\mathbf{k}$$

Grad S defines both the direction and magnitude of the maximum rate of increase of S at any point. Hence the name *gradient* and also its vectorial nature. ∇S is independent of the choice of rectangular coordinates.

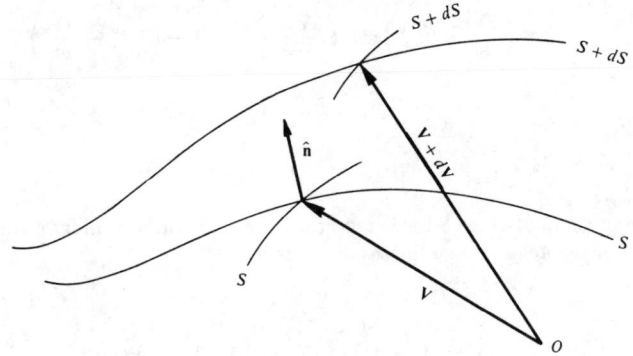

Figure 4

$$\nabla S = \frac{\partial S}{\partial n}\hat{n}$$

where $\hat{n}$ is the unit normal to the surface $S = $ constant, in the direction of S increasing. The total derivative of S at a point having the position vector $\mathbf{V}$ is given by (fig. 4)

$$dS = \frac{\partial S}{\partial n}\hat{n} \cdot d\mathbf{V}$$

$$= d\mathbf{V} \cdot \nabla S$$

and the directional derivative of S in the direction of $\mathbf{U}$ is

$$\mathbf{U} \cdot \nabla S = \mathbf{U} \cdot (\nabla S) = (\mathbf{U} \cdot \nabla)S$$

Similarly the directional derivative of the vector $\mathbf{V}$ in the direction of $\mathbf{U}$ is

$$(\mathbf{U} \cdot \nabla)\mathbf{V}$$

The *distributive* law holds for finding a gradient. Thus if S and T are scalar functions

$$\nabla(S + T) = \nabla S + \nabla T$$

The *associative* law becomes the rule for differentiating a product:

$$\nabla(ST) = S\nabla T + T\nabla S$$

If $\mathbf{V}$ is a vector function with the magnitudes of the components parallel to the three coordinate axes V_x, V_y, V_z, then

$$\nabla \cdot \mathbf{V} \equiv \operatorname{div} \mathbf{V} = \frac{\partial V_x}{\partial x} + \frac{\partial V_y}{\partial y} + \frac{\partial V_z}{\partial z}$$

The divergence obeys the distributive law. Thus, if $\mathbf{V}$ and $\mathbf{U}$ are vectors functions, then

$$\nabla \cdot (\mathbf{V} + \mathbf{U}) = \nabla \cdot \mathbf{V} + \nabla \cdot \mathbf{U}$$
$$\nabla \cdot (S\mathbf{V}) = (\nabla S) \cdot \mathbf{V} + S(\nabla \cdot \mathbf{V})$$
$$\nabla \cdot (\mathbf{U} \times \mathbf{V}) = \mathbf{V} \cdot (\nabla \times \mathbf{U}) - \mathbf{U} \cdot (\nabla \times \mathbf{V})$$

As with the gradient of a scalar, the divergence of a vector is invariant under a transformation from one set of rectangular coordinates to another.

$$\nabla \times \mathbf{V} \equiv \operatorname{curl} \mathbf{V} \quad (\text{sometimes } \nabla \wedge \mathbf{V} \text{ or rot } \mathbf{V})$$

$$\equiv \left(\frac{\partial V_z}{\partial y} - \frac{\partial V_y}{\partial z}\right)\mathbf{i} + \left(\frac{\partial V_x}{\partial z} - \frac{\partial V_z}{\partial x}\right)\mathbf{j} + \left(\frac{\partial V_y}{\partial x} - \frac{\partial V_x}{\partial y}\right)\mathbf{k}$$

$$= \begin{vmatrix} \mathbf{i} & \mathbf{j} & \mathbf{k} \\ \dfrac{\partial}{\partial x} & \dfrac{\partial}{\partial y} & \dfrac{\partial}{\partial z} \\ V_x & V_y & V_z \end{vmatrix}$$

The *curl* (or *rotation*) of a vector is a vector which is invariant under a transformation from one set of rectangular coordinates to another.

$$\nabla \times (\mathbf{U} + \mathbf{V}) = \nabla \times \mathbf{U} + \nabla \times \mathbf{V}$$
$$\nabla \times (S\mathbf{V}) = (\nabla S) \times \mathbf{V} + S(\nabla \times \mathbf{V})$$
$$\nabla \times (\mathbf{U} \times \mathbf{V}) = (\mathbf{V} \cdot \nabla)\mathbf{U} - (\mathbf{U} \cdot \nabla)\mathbf{V} + \mathbf{U}(\nabla \cdot \mathbf{V}) - \mathbf{V}(\nabla \cdot \mathbf{U})$$

$$\operatorname{grad}(\mathbf{U} \cdot \mathbf{V}) = \nabla(\mathbf{U} \cdot \mathbf{V})$$
$$= (\mathbf{V} \cdot \nabla)\mathbf{U} + (\mathbf{U} \cdot \nabla)\mathbf{V} + \mathbf{V} \times (\nabla \times \mathbf{U}) + \mathbf{U} \times (\nabla \times \mathbf{V})$$

If
$$\mathbf{V} = V_x\mathbf{i} + V_y\mathbf{j} + V_z\mathbf{k}$$
$$\nabla \cdot \mathbf{V} = \nabla V_x \cdot \mathbf{i} + \nabla V_y \cdot \mathbf{j} + \nabla V_z \cdot \mathbf{k}$$
and
$$\nabla \times \mathbf{V} = \nabla V_x \times \mathbf{i} + \nabla V_y \times \mathbf{j} + \nabla V_z \times \mathbf{k}$$

The operator ∇ can be used more than once. The number of possibilities where ∇ is used twice are

$$\nabla \cdot (\nabla \theta) \equiv \operatorname{div} \operatorname{grad} \theta$$
$$\nabla \times (\nabla \theta) \equiv \operatorname{curl} \operatorname{grad} \theta$$
$$\nabla(\nabla \cdot \mathbf{V}) \equiv \operatorname{grad} \operatorname{div} \mathbf{V}$$
$$\nabla \cdot (\nabla \times \mathbf{V}) \equiv \operatorname{div} \operatorname{curl} \mathbf{V}$$
$$\nabla \times (\nabla \times \mathbf{V}) \equiv \operatorname{curl} \operatorname{curl} \mathbf{V}$$

Thus: div grad $S \equiv \nabla \cdot (\nabla S) \equiv$ Laplacian $S \equiv \nabla^2 S$

$$\equiv \frac{\partial^2 S}{\partial x^2} + \frac{\partial^2 S}{\partial y^2} + \frac{\partial^2 S}{\partial z^2}$$

curl grad $S \equiv 0$;   curl curl $\mathbf{V} \equiv$ grad div $\mathbf{V} - \nabla^2 \mathbf{V}$;

div curl $\mathbf{V} \equiv \qquad 0$

Taylor's expansion in three dimensions can be written

$$f(\mathbf{V} + \boldsymbol{\varepsilon}) = e^{\boldsymbol{\varepsilon} \cdot \nabla} f(\mathbf{V})$$

where $\mathbf{V} = x\mathbf{i} + y\mathbf{j} + z\mathbf{k}$

and $\boldsymbol{\varepsilon} = h\mathbf{i} + l\mathbf{j} + m\mathbf{k}$

(note the analogy with $f_p = e^{phD} f_0$ in finite difference methods).

Orthogonal Curvilinear Coordinates

If at a point P there exist three uniform point functions u, v and w so that the surfaces $u = $ const., $v = $ const., and $w = $ const., intersect in three distinct curves through P then the surfaces are called the *coordinate surfaces* through P. The three lines of intersection are referred to as the *coordinate lines* and their tangents a, b, and c as the *coordinate axes*. When the coordinate axes form an orthogonal set the system is said to define *orthogonal curvilinear coordinates* at P.

Consider an infinitesimal volume enclosed by the surfaces u, v, w, $u + du$, $v + dv$, and $w + dw$ (fig. 5).

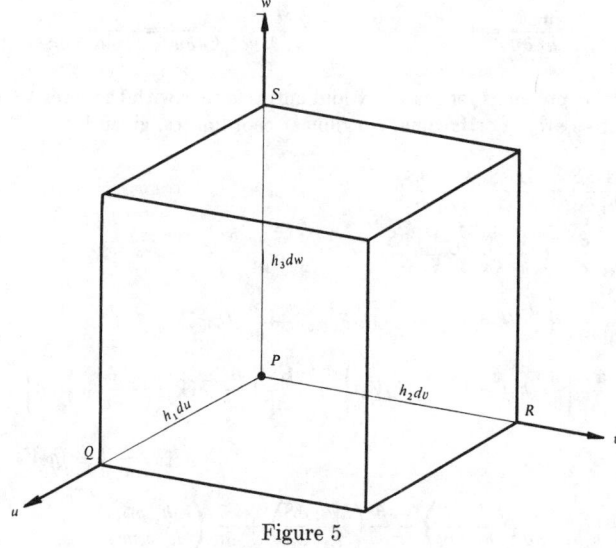

Figure 5

The surface $PRS \equiv u =$ const., and the face of the curvilinear figure immediately opposite this is $u + du =$ const. etc.

In terms of these surface constants

$$
\begin{aligned}
P &= P(u,v,w) \\
Q &= Q(u + du,v,w) \quad \text{and} \quad PQ = h_1 du \\
R &= R(u,v + dv,w) \quad\quad\quad\quad\; PR = h_2 dv \\
S &= S(u,v,w + dw) \quad\quad\quad\; PS = h_3 dw
\end{aligned}
$$

where h_1, h_2, and h_3 are functions of u, v, and w.

In rectangular Cartesians $\mathbf{i}$, $\mathbf{j}$, $\mathbf{k}$

$$
h_1 = 1, \qquad h_2 = 1, \qquad h_3 = 1.
$$

$$
\frac{\hat{\mathbf{a}}}{h_1}\frac{\partial}{\partial u} = \mathbf{i}\,\frac{\partial}{\partial x}, \qquad
\frac{\hat{\mathbf{b}}}{h_2}\frac{\partial}{\partial v} = \mathbf{j}\,\frac{\partial}{\partial y}, \qquad
\frac{\hat{\mathbf{c}}}{h_3}\frac{\partial}{\partial w} = \mathbf{k}\,\frac{\partial}{\partial z}.
$$

In cylindrical coordinates $\hat{\mathbf{r}}$, $\hat{\boldsymbol{\phi}}$, $\hat{\mathbf{k}}$

$$
h_1 = 1, \qquad h_2 = r \qquad h_3 = 1.
$$

$$
\frac{\hat{\mathbf{a}}}{h_1}\frac{\partial}{\partial u} = \hat{\mathbf{r}}\,\frac{\partial}{\partial r}, \qquad
\frac{\hat{\mathbf{b}}}{h_2}\frac{\partial}{\partial v} = \frac{\hat{\boldsymbol{\phi}}}{r}\frac{\partial}{\partial \phi} \qquad
\frac{\hat{\mathbf{c}}}{h_3}\frac{\partial}{\partial w} = \hat{\mathbf{k}}\,\frac{\partial}{\partial z}
$$

In spherical coordinates $\hat{\mathbf{r}}$, $\hat{\boldsymbol{\theta}}$, $\hat{\boldsymbol{\phi}}$

$$
h_1 = 1, \qquad h_2 = r, \qquad h_3 = r\sin\theta
$$

$$
\frac{\hat{\mathbf{a}}}{h_1}\frac{\partial}{\partial u} = \hat{\mathbf{r}}\,\frac{\partial}{\partial r}, \qquad
\frac{\mathbf{b}}{h_2}\frac{\partial}{\partial v} = \frac{\hat{\boldsymbol{\phi}}}{r}\frac{\partial}{\partial \theta}, \qquad
\frac{\hat{\mathbf{c}}}{h_3}\frac{\partial}{\partial w} = \frac{\hat{\boldsymbol{\phi}}}{r\sin\theta}\frac{\partial}{\partial \phi}
$$

The general expressions for grad, div and curl together with those for ∇^2 and the directional derivative are, in orthogonal curvilinear coordinates, given by

$$
\nabla S = \frac{\hat{\mathbf{a}}}{h_1}\frac{\partial S}{\partial u} + \frac{\hat{\mathbf{b}}}{h_2}\frac{\partial S}{\partial v} + \frac{\hat{\mathbf{c}}}{h_3}\frac{\partial S}{\partial w}
$$

$$
(\mathbf{V}\cdot\nabla)S = \frac{V_1}{h_1}\frac{\partial S}{\partial u} + \frac{V_2}{h_2}\frac{\partial S}{\partial v} + \frac{V_3}{h_3}\frac{\partial S}{\partial w}
$$

$$
\nabla\cdot\mathbf{V} = \frac{1}{h_1 h_2 h_3}\left\{\frac{\partial}{\partial u}(h_2 h_3 V_1) + \frac{\partial}{\partial v}(h_3 h_1 V_2) + \frac{\partial}{\partial w}(h_1 h_2 V_3)\right\}
$$

$$
\nabla\times\mathbf{V} = \frac{\hat{\mathbf{a}}}{h_2 h_3}\left\{\frac{\partial}{\partial v}(h_3 V_3) - \frac{\partial}{\partial w}(h_2 V_2)\right\} + \frac{\hat{\mathbf{b}}}{h_3 h_1}\left\{\frac{\partial}{\partial w}(h_1 V_1) - \frac{\partial}{\partial u}(h_3 V_3)\right\}
$$

$$
+ \frac{\hat{\mathbf{c}}}{h_1 h_2}\left\{\frac{\partial}{\partial u}(h_2 V_2) - \frac{\partial}{\partial v}(h_1 V_1)\right\}
$$

$$
\nabla^2 S = \frac{1}{h_1 h_2 h_3}\left\{\frac{\partial}{\partial u}\left(\frac{h_2 h_3}{h_1}\frac{\partial S}{\partial u}\right) + \frac{\partial}{\partial v}\left(\frac{h_3 h_1}{h_2}\frac{\partial S}{\partial v}\right) + \frac{\partial}{\partial w}\left(\frac{h_1 h_2}{h_3}\frac{\partial S}{\partial w}\right)\right\}
$$

FORMULAS OF VECTOR ANALYSIS

	Rectangular coordinates	Cylindrical coordinates	Spherical coordinates
Conversion to rectangular coordinates		$x = r\cos\varphi \quad y = r\sin\varphi \quad z = z$	$x = r\cos\varphi\sin\theta \quad y = r\sin\varphi\sin\theta$ $z = r\cos\theta$
Gradient	$\nabla\phi = \dfrac{\partial\phi}{\partial x}\mathbf{i} + \dfrac{\partial\phi}{\partial y}\mathbf{j} + \dfrac{\partial\phi}{\partial z}\mathbf{k}$	$\nabla\phi = \dfrac{\partial\phi}{\partial r}\mathbf{r} + \dfrac{1}{r}\dfrac{\partial\phi}{\partial\varphi}\boldsymbol{\phi} + \dfrac{\partial\phi}{\partial z}\mathbf{k}$	$\nabla\phi = \dfrac{\partial\phi}{\partial r}\mathbf{r} + \dfrac{1}{r}\dfrac{\partial\phi}{\partial\theta}\boldsymbol{\theta} + \dfrac{1}{r\sin\theta}\dfrac{\partial\phi}{\partial\varphi}\boldsymbol{\phi}$
Divergence	$\nabla\cdot\mathbf{A} = \dfrac{\partial A_x}{\partial x} + \dfrac{\partial A_y}{\partial y} + \dfrac{\partial A_z}{\partial z}$	$\nabla\cdot\mathbf{A} = \dfrac{1}{r}\dfrac{\partial(rA_r)}{\partial r} + \dfrac{1}{r}\dfrac{\partial A_\varphi}{\partial\varphi} + \dfrac{\partial A_z}{\partial z}$	$\nabla\cdot\mathbf{A} = \dfrac{1}{r^2}\dfrac{\partial(r^2 A_r)}{\partial r} + \dfrac{1}{r\sin\theta}\dfrac{\partial(A_\theta\sin\theta)}{\partial\theta} + \dfrac{1}{r\sin\theta}\dfrac{\partial A_\varphi}{\partial\varphi}$
Curl	$\nabla\times\mathbf{A} = \begin{vmatrix} \mathbf{i} & \mathbf{j} & \mathbf{k} \\ \dfrac{\partial}{\partial x} & \dfrac{\partial}{\partial y} & \dfrac{\partial}{\partial z} \\ A_x & A_y & A_z \end{vmatrix}$	$\nabla\times\mathbf{A} = \begin{vmatrix} \dfrac{1}{r}\mathbf{r} & \boldsymbol{\phi} & \dfrac{1}{r}\mathbf{k} \\ \dfrac{\partial}{\partial r} & \dfrac{\partial}{\partial\varphi} & \dfrac{\partial}{\partial z} \\ A_r & rA_\varphi & A_z \end{vmatrix}$	$\nabla\times\mathbf{A} = \begin{vmatrix} \dfrac{\mathbf{r}}{r^2\sin\theta} & \dfrac{\boldsymbol{\theta}}{r\sin\theta} & \dfrac{\boldsymbol{\phi}}{r} \\ \dfrac{\partial}{\partial r} & \dfrac{\partial}{\partial\theta} & \dfrac{\partial}{\partial\varphi} \\ A_r & rA_\theta & rA_\varphi\sin\theta \end{vmatrix}$
Laplacian	$\nabla^2\phi = \dfrac{\partial^2\phi}{\partial x^2} + \dfrac{\partial^2\phi}{\partial y^2} + \dfrac{\partial^2\phi}{\partial z^2}$	$\nabla^2\phi = \dfrac{1}{r}\dfrac{\partial}{\partial r}\left(r\dfrac{\partial\phi}{\partial r}\right) + \dfrac{1}{r^2}\dfrac{\partial^2\phi}{\partial\varphi^2} + \dfrac{\partial^2\phi}{\partial z^2}$	$\nabla^2\phi = \dfrac{1}{r^2}\dfrac{\partial}{\partial r}\left(r^2\dfrac{\partial\phi}{\partial r}\right) + \dfrac{1}{r^2\sin\theta}\dfrac{\partial}{\partial\theta}\left(\sin\theta\dfrac{\partial\phi}{\partial\theta}\right) + \dfrac{1}{r^2\sin^2\theta}\dfrac{\partial^2\phi}{\partial\varphi^2}$

Transformation of Integrals

$s\ $ = the distance along some curve "C" in space and is measured from some fixed point.

$S\ $ = a surface area

$V\ $ = a volume contained by a specified surface

$\hat{\mathbf{t}}\ $ = the unit tangent to C at the point P

$\hat{\mathbf{n}}\ $ = the unit outward pointing normal

$F\ $ = some vector function

ds = the vector element of curve ($= \hat{\mathbf{t}}\,ds$)

dS = the vector element of surface ($= \hat{\mathbf{n}}\,dS$)

Then

$$\int_{(c)} \mathbf{F} \cdot \hat{\mathbf{t}}\,ds = \int_{(c)} \mathbf{F} \cdot d\mathbf{s}$$

and when

$$\mathbf{F} = \nabla\phi$$

$$\int_{(c)} (\nabla\phi) \cdot \hat{\mathbf{t}}\,ds = \int_{(c)} d\phi$$

Gauss' Theorem (Green's Theorem)

When S defines a closed region having a volume V

$$\iiint_{(v)} (\nabla \cdot \mathbf{F})\,dV = \iint_{(s)} (\mathbf{F} \cdot \hat{\mathbf{n}})\,dS = \iint_{(s)} \mathbf{F} \cdot d\mathbf{S}$$

also

$$\iiint_{(v)} (\nabla\phi)\,dV = \iint_{(s)} \phi\hat{\mathbf{n}}\,dS$$

and

$$\iiint_{(v)} (\nabla \times \mathbf{F})\,dV = \iint_{(s)} (\hat{\mathbf{n}} \times \mathbf{F})\,dS$$

Stokes' Theorem

When C is closed and bounds the open surface S.

$$\iint_{(s)} \hat{\mathbf{n}} \cdot (\nabla \times \mathbf{F})\,dS = \int_{(c)} \mathbf{F} \cdot d\mathbf{s}$$

also

$$\iint_{(s)} (\hat{\mathbf{n}} \times \nabla\phi)\,dS = \int_{(c)} \phi\,d\mathbf{s}$$

Green's Theorem

$$\iint_{(s)} (\nabla\phi \cdot \nabla\theta)\,dS = \iint_{(s)} \phi\hat{\mathbf{n}} \cdot (\nabla\theta)\,dS = \iiint_{(v)} \phi(\nabla^2\theta)\,dV$$

$$= \iint_{(s)} \theta \cdot \hat{\mathbf{n}}(\nabla\phi)\,dS = \iiint_{(v)} \theta(\nabla^2\phi)\,dV$$

FINITE DIFFERENCES

For equi-spaced arguments x_i, and associated y_i, the successive **advancing y-differences** are $\Delta^0 y_i = y_i$, $\Delta y_i = y_{i+1} - y_i$, $\Delta^2 y_i = \Delta y_{i+1} - \Delta y_i = y_{i+2} - 2y_{i+1} + y_i$, ... , $\Delta^m y_i = \Delta^{m-1} y_{i+1} - \Delta^{m-1} y_i = \sum_r (-1)^r \binom{m}{r} y_{i+m-r}$. With arbitrary origin A and class-interval length, $x_{i+1} - x_i = h$, using $u_i = (x_i - A)/h$, write $y(u_i)$ for y_i. Then if for some fixed m, for the portion of the table considered, the values of $\Delta^{m+1} y_i$ be zero (or approximately, if these be regarded as negligible) **Newton's formula** gives

$$y(u) = \sum \frac{u^{(r)}}{r!} \Delta^r y(0) = y(0) + u\Delta y(0) + \frac{u(u-1)}{1 \cdot 2} \Delta^2 y(0) + \cdots$$

$$+ \frac{u(u-1) \cdots (u-m+1)}{m!} \Delta^m y(0).$$

This formula reduces to an identity for $u = u_0, u_1, \ldots, u_n$, $(u_i = i)$, and may be used to interpolate for intermediate values.

Example. Given

x	$-4, -2, 0, 2, 4, 6, 8, \ldots$
y	$10, 14, 30, 64, 122, 210, 334, \ldots$

to find a value for y when $x = 10$, and when $x = 1$. Suppose for some reason A has been taken at $x = 2$. The work may be arranged as follows:

u	x	y	Δ	Δ^2	Δ^3	Δ^4
-3	-4	10				
			4			
-2	-2	14		12		
			16		6	
-1	0	30		18		0
			34		6	
0	2	64		24		0
			58		6	
1	4	122		30		0
			88		6	
2	6	210		36		$-$
			124		$-$	
3	8	334		$-$		$-$
$-$	$-$	$-$	$-$	$-$	$-$	$-$

$$y(u) = 64 + 58u + 30\frac{u(u-1)}{1 \cdot 2} + 6\frac{u(u-1)(u-2)}{1 \cdot 2 \cdot 3},$$

$$= 64 + 58u + 15u(u-1) + u(u-1)(u-2).$$

At $x = 10$, $u = 4$. Substituting $u = 4$, one has $y\big|_{x=10} = 500$.

At $x = 1$, $u = -\frac{1}{2}$. Substituting $u = -\frac{1}{2}$, one has $y\big|_{x=1} = 44\frac{5}{8}$.

Note: This method is sometimes called Gregory–Newton interpolation.

Probability and Statistics

DESCRIPTIVE STATISTICS

a) Ungrouped Data

The formulas of this section designated as a) apply to a random sample of size n, denoted by x_i, $i = 1, 2, \ldots, n$.

b) Grouped Data

The formulas of this section designated as b) apply to data grouped into a frequency distribution having class marks x_i, $i = 1, 2, \ldots, k$, and corresponding class frequencies f_i, $i = 1, 2, \ldots, k$. The total number of observations given by

$$n = \sum_{i=1}^{k} f_i$$

In the formulas that follow, c denotes the width of the class interval, x_o denotes one of the class marks taken to be the computing origin, and $u_i = \dfrac{x_i - x_o}{c}$. Then coded class marks are obtained by replacing the original class marks with the integers $\ldots, -3, -2, -1, 0, 1, 2, 3, \ldots$ where 0 corresponds to class mark x_o in the original scale.

Mean (Arithmetic Mean)

a) $\bar{x} = \dfrac{1}{n} \sum_{i=1}^{n} x_i = \dfrac{x_1 + x_2 + \cdots + x_n}{n}$

b.1) $\bar{x} = \dfrac{1}{n} \sum_{i=1}^{k} f_i x_i = \dfrac{f_1 x_1 + f_2 x_2 + \cdots + f_k x_k}{n}$

If data is coded

b.2) $\bar{x} = x_o + c \dfrac{\displaystyle\sum_{i=1}^{k} f_i u_i}{n}$

Weighted Mean (Weighted Arithmetic Mean)

If with each value x_i is associated a weighting factor $w_i \geq 0$, then $\displaystyle\sum_{i=1}^{n} w_i$ is the total weight, and

a) $\bar{x} = \dfrac{\displaystyle\sum_{i=1}^{n} w_i x_i}{\displaystyle\sum_{i=1}^{n} w_i} = \dfrac{w_1 x_1 + w_2 x_2 + \cdots + w_n x_n}{w_1 + w_2 + \cdots + w_n}$

Geometric Mean

a) $\text{G.M.} = \sqrt[n]{x_1 \cdot x_2 \cdots x_n}$

570

In logarithmic form

$$\log (\text{G.M.}) = \frac{1}{n} \sum_{i=1}^{n} \log x_i = \frac{\log x_1 + \log x_2 + \cdots + \log x_n}{n}$$

b) $\text{G.M.} = \sqrt[n]{x_1^{f_1} \cdot x_2^{f_1} \cdots x_k^{f_k}}$

In logarithmic form

$$\log (\text{G.M.}) = \frac{1}{n} \sum_{i=1}^{k} f_i \log x_i = \frac{f_1 \log x_1 + f_2 \log x_2 + \cdots + f_k \log x_k}{n}$$

Harmonic Mean

a) $\text{H.M.} = \dfrac{n}{\displaystyle\sum_{i=1}^{n} \dfrac{1}{x_i}} = \dfrac{n}{\dfrac{1}{x_1} + \dfrac{1}{x_2} + \cdots + \dfrac{1}{x_n}}$

b) $\text{H.M.} = \dfrac{n}{\displaystyle\sum_{i=1}^{k} \dfrac{f_i}{x_i}} = \dfrac{n}{\dfrac{f_1}{x_1} + \dfrac{f_2}{x_2} + \cdots + \dfrac{f_k}{x_k}}$

Relation Between Arithmetic, Geometric, and Harmonic Mean

$\text{H.M.} \leq \text{G.M.} \leq \bar{x}$, (Equality sign holds only if all sample values are identical.)

Mode

a) A mode M_o of a sample of size n is a value which occurs with greatest frequency, i.e., it is the most common value. A mode may not exist, and even if it does exist it may not be unique.

b) $M_o = L + c \dfrac{\Delta_1}{\Delta_1 + \Delta_2}$,

where L is the lower class boundary of the modal class (class containing the mode),
$\quad \Delta_1$ is the excess of modal frequency over frequency of next lower class,
$\quad \Delta_2$ is the excess of modal frequency over frequency of next higher class.

Median

a) If the sample is arranged in ascending order of magnitude, then the median M_d is given by the $\dfrac{n+1}{2}$ nd value. When n is odd, the median is the middle value of the set of ordered data; when n is even, the median is usually taken as the mean of the two middle values of the set of ordered data.

b) $M_d = L + c \dfrac{\dfrac{n}{2} - F_c}{f_m}$,

where L is lower class boundary of median class (class containing the median),
$\quad F_c$ is the sum of the frequencies of all classes lower than the median class,
$\quad f_m$ is the frequency of the median class.

Empirical Relation Between Mean, Median, and Mode

$$\text{Mean} - \text{Mode} = 3 \, (\text{Mean} - \text{Median})$$

Quartiles

a) If the data is arranged in ascending order of magnitude, the jth quartile Q_j, $j = 1$, 2, or 3, is given by the $\dfrac{j(n + 1)}{4}$ th value. It may be necessary to interpolate between successive values.

b) The jth quartile Q_j, $j = 1$, 2, or 3, is obtained from formula b) for the median by counting $\dfrac{jn}{4}$ cases starting at the bottom of the distribution.

Deciles

a) If the sample is arranged in ascending order of magnitude, the jth decile D_j, $j = 1, 2, \ldots$, or 9, is given by the $\dfrac{j(n + 1)}{10}$ th value. It may be necessary to interpolate between successive values.

b) The jth decile D_j, $j = 1, 2, \ldots$, or 9, is obtained from formula b) for the median by counting $\dfrac{jn}{10}$ cases starting at the bottom of the distribution.

Percentiles

a) If the sample is arranged in ascending order of magnitude, the jth percentile P_j, $j = 1, 2, \ldots$, or 99 is given by the $\dfrac{j(n + 1)}{100}$ th value. It may be necessary to interpolate between successive values.

b) The jth percentile P_j, $j = 1, 2, \ldots$, or 99, is obtained from formulas b) for the median by counting $\dfrac{jn}{100}$ cases starting at the bottom of the distribution.

Mean Deviation

a) $\text{M.D.} = \dfrac{1}{n} \displaystyle\sum_{i=1}^{n} |x_i - \bar{x}|$

or

$\text{M.D.} = \dfrac{1}{n} \displaystyle\sum_{i=1}^{n} |x_i - M_d|$

where $\bar{x}$ is the mean and M_d is the median of the sample.

b) $\text{M.D.} = \dfrac{1}{n} \displaystyle\sum_{i=1}^{k} f_i |x_i - \bar{x}|$

or

$\text{M.D.} = \dfrac{1}{n} \displaystyle\sum_{i=1}^{k} f_i |x_i - M_d|$

where $\bar{x}$ is the mean and M_d the median of the sample.

Standard Deviation

a) $s = \sqrt{\dfrac{\sum\limits_{i=1}^{n} (x_i - \bar{x})^2}{n-1}}$, where $\bar{x}$ is the mean of the sample.

For computational purposes,

$$s = \sqrt{\dfrac{\sum\limits_{i=1}^{n} x_i^2 - n\bar{x}^2}{n-1}}$$

$$s = \sqrt{\dfrac{n\sum\limits_{i=1}^{n} x_i^2 - \left(\sum\limits_{i=1}^{n} x_i\right)^2}{n(n-1)}}$$

b) $s = \sqrt{\dfrac{\sum\limits_{i=1}^{k} f_i(x_i - \bar{x})^2}{n-1}}$, where $\bar{x}$ is the mean of the sample.

For computational purposes

$$s = \sqrt{\dfrac{\sum\limits_{i=1}^{k} f_i x_i^2 - n\bar{x}^2}{n-1}}$$

$$s = \sqrt{\dfrac{n\sum\limits_{i=1}^{k} f_i x_i^2 - \left(\sum\limits_{i=1}^{k} f_i x_i\right)^2}{n(n-1)}}$$

If data is coded,

$$s = c\sqrt{\dfrac{n\sum\limits_{i=1}^{k} f_i u_i^2 - \left(\sum\limits_{i=1}^{k} f_i u_i\right)^2}{n(n-1)}}$$

Variance

The variance is the square of the standard deviation.

Range

The range of a set of values is the difference between the largest and smallest values in the set.

Root Mean Square

a) $\text{R.M.S.} = \left[\dfrac{1}{n}\sum\limits_{i=1}^{n} x_i^2\right]^{\frac{1}{2}}$

b) $\text{R.M.S.} = \left[\dfrac{1}{n}\sum\limits_{i=1}^{k} f_i x_i^2\right]^{\frac{1}{2}}$

Interquartile Range

$$Q_3 - Q_1,$$

where Q_1 and Q_3 are the first and third quartiles.

Quartile Deviation (Semi-Interquartile Range)

$$\frac{Q_3 - Q_1}{2},$$

where Q_1 and Q_3 are the first and third quartiles.

Coefficient of Variation

$$V = \frac{100s}{\bar{x}},$$

where $\bar{x}$ is the mean and s the standard deviation of the sample.

Coefficient of Quartile Variation

$$V = 100 \frac{Q_3 - Q_1}{Q_3 + Q_1},$$

where Q_1 and Q_3 are the first and third quartiles.

Standardized Variable (Standard Scores)

$$z = \frac{x_i - \bar{x}}{s},$$

where $\bar{x}$ is the mean and s the standard deviation of the sample.

Moments

a) The rth moment about the origin is given by

$$m_r' = \frac{1}{n} \sum_{i=1}^{n} x_i^r$$

The rth moment about the mean $\bar{x}$ is given by

$$m_r = \frac{1}{n} \sum_{i=1}^{n} (x_i - \bar{x})^r$$

If $\sum_{i=1}^{n} (x_i - \bar{x})^r$ is expanded by use of the binomial theorem, moments about the mean may be expressed in terms of moments about the origin.

b) The rth moment about the origin is given by

$$m_r' = \frac{1}{n} \sum_{i=1}^{k} f_i x_i^r$$

The rth moment about the mean $\bar{x}$ is given by

$$m_r = \frac{1}{n} \sum_{i=1}^{k} f_i (x_i - \bar{x})^r$$

If $\sum_{i=1}^{k} f_i(x_i - \bar{x})^r$ is expanded by use of the binomial theorem, moments about the mean may be expressed in terms of moments about the origin.

If data is coded

$$m'_r = c^r \frac{\sum_{i=1}^{k} f_i u_i^r}{n}$$

Coefficient of Skewness

$$\alpha_3 = \frac{m_3}{(m_2)^{3/2}},$$

where m_2 and m_3 are the second and third moments about the mean of the sample.

Coefficient of Momental Skewness

$$\frac{\alpha_3}{2} = \frac{m_3}{2(m_2)^{3/2}},$$

where m_2 and m_3 are the second and third moments about the mean of the sample.

Pearson's First Coefficient of Skewness

$$S_{k_1} = \frac{3(\bar{x} - M_o)}{s},$$

where $\bar{x}$ is the mean, M_o the mode, and s the standard deviation of the sample.

Pearson's Second Coefficient of Skewness

$$S_{k_2} = \frac{3(\bar{x} - M_d)}{s},$$

where $\bar{x}$ is the mean, M_d the median, and s the standard deviation of the sample.

Quartile Coefficient of Skewness

$$S_{k_Q} = \frac{Q_3 - 2Q_2 + Q_1}{Q_3 - Q_1},$$

where Q_1, Q_2, and Q_3 are the first, second, and third quartiles.

Coefficient of Kurtosis

$$\alpha_4 = \frac{m_4}{(m_2)^2},$$

where m_2 and m_4 are the second and fourth moments about the mean of the sample.

Coefficient of Excess (Kurtosis)

$$\alpha_4 - 3 = \frac{m_4}{(m_2)^2} - 3,$$

where m_2 and m_4 are the second and fourth moments about the mean of the sample.

Sheppards Corrections for Grouping

Let all class intervals be of equal length c. If the distribution of x has a high order of contact with the x-axis at both tails, (i.e., if the distribution of x has tails which are very nearly tangent to the x-axis), one may improve the grouped data approximation to the variance by adding Sheppard's correction $-\dfrac{c^2}{12}$. Thus

$$\text{corrected variance} = \text{grouped data variance} - \frac{c^2}{12}$$

Analogous corrections for grouped data sample moments

$$m_r' = \frac{1}{n} \sum_{i=1}^{k} f_i x_i^r \quad \text{and} \quad m_r = \frac{1}{n} \sum_{i=1}^{k} f_i (x_i - \bar{x})^r$$

yield improved estimates m_{r_e}' and m_{r_e} given by

$$m_{1_e}' = m_1' \qquad\qquad m_{1_e} = m_1$$

$$m_{2_e}' = m_2' - \frac{c^2}{12} \qquad\qquad m_{2_e} = m_2 - \frac{c^2}{12}$$

$$m_{3_e}' = m_3' - \frac{c^2}{4} m_1' \qquad\qquad m_{3_e} = m_3$$

$$m_{4_e}' = m_4' - \frac{c^2}{2} m_1' + \frac{7c^4}{240} \qquad m_{4_e} = m_4 - \frac{c^2}{2} m_2 + \frac{7c^4}{240}$$

Curve Fitting, Regression, and Correlation

The following formulas apply to a set of n ordered pairs $\{(x_i, y_i)\}$, $i = 1, 2, \ldots, n$. The assumptions of normal regression analysis are that the x's are fixed variables, and the y's are independent random variables having normal distributions with common variance σ^2. The assumptions of normal correlation analysis are that $\{(x_i, y_i)\}$ constitute a random sample from a bivariate normal population.

Curve Fitting

1. Polynomial Function

$$y = b_0 + b_1 x + b_2 x^2 + \cdots + b_m x^m$$

For a polynomial function fit by the method of least squares, the values of $b_0, b_1, \ldots, b_m$ are obtained by solving the system of $m + 1$ normal equations

$$nb_0 + b_1 \Sigma x_i + b_2 \Sigma x_i^2 + \cdots + b_m \Sigma x_i^m = \Sigma y_i$$
$$b_0 \Sigma x_i + b_1 \Sigma x_i^2 + b_2 \Sigma x_i^3 + \cdots + b_m \Sigma x_i^{m+1} = \Sigma x_i y_i$$
$$\cdots\cdots\cdots\cdots\cdots\cdots\cdots\cdots\cdots\cdots\cdots\cdots$$
$$b_0 \Sigma x_i^m + b_1 \Sigma x_i^{m+1} + b_2 \Sigma x_i^{m+2} + \cdots + b_m \Sigma x_i^{2m} = \Sigma x_i^m y_i$$

2. Straight Line

$$y = b_0 + b_1 x$$

For a straight line fit by the method of least squares, the values b_0 and b_1 are obtained by solving the normal equations

$$nb_0 + b_1 \Sigma x_i = \Sigma y_i$$
$$b_0 \Sigma x_i + b_1 \Sigma x_i^2 = \Sigma x_i y_i$$

The solutions of these normal equations are

$$b_1 = \frac{n \Sigma x_i y_i - (\Sigma x_i)(\Sigma y_i)}{n \Sigma x_i^2 - (\Sigma x_i)^2}$$

$$b_0 = \frac{\Sigma y_i}{n} - b_1 \frac{\Sigma x_i}{n} = \bar{y} - b_1 \bar{x}$$

3. Exponential Curve

$$y = ab^x$$

or

$$\log y = \log a + (\log b)x$$

For an exponential curve fit by the method of least squares, the values $\log a$ and $\log b$ are obtained by fitting a straight line to the set of ordered pairs $\{(x_i, \log y_i)\}$.

4. Power Function

$$y = ax^b$$

or

$$\log y = \log a + b \log x$$

For a power function fit by the method of least squares, the values $\log a$ and b are obtained by fitting a straight line to the set of ordered pairs $\{(\log x_i, \log y_i)\}$.

Regression and Correlation

1. Simple Linear Regression.

For a regression of y on x

$$E(y/x) = b_0 + b_1 x,$$

where $E(y/x)$ is the mean of the distribution of y for a given x.

Standard Error of Estimate

$$s_e = \sqrt{\frac{\Sigma[y_i - (b_0 + b_1 x_i)]^2}{n - 2}},$$

where b_0 and b_1 are given by

$$b_1 = \frac{n\Sigma x_i y_i - (\Sigma x_i)(\Sigma y_i)}{n\Sigma x_i^2 - (\Sigma x_i)^2}$$

$$b_0 = \frac{\Sigma y_i}{n} - b_1 \frac{\Sigma x_i}{n} = \bar{y} - b_1 \bar{x}$$

2. Correlation.

An estimate of the population correlation coefficient ρ is given by

$$r = \frac{\Sigma(x_i - \bar{x})(y_i - \bar{y})}{\sqrt{[\Sigma(x_i - \bar{x})^2][\Sigma(y_i - \bar{y})^2]}}$$

or by the computing formula

$$r = \frac{n\Sigma x_i y_i - (\Sigma x_i)(\Sigma y_i)}{\sqrt{[n\Sigma x_i^2 - (\Sigma x_i)^2][n\Sigma y_i^2 - (\Sigma y_i)^2]}}$$

For grouped data

$$r = \frac{n\Sigma f x_i y_i - (\Sigma f_x x_i)(\Sigma f_y y_i)}{\sqrt{[n\Sigma f_x x_i^2 - (\Sigma f_x x_i)^2][n\Sigma f_y y_i^2 - (\Sigma f_y y_i)^2]}}$$

where f_x and f_y denote the frequencies corresponding to the class marks x and y, and f denotes the frequency of the corresponding cell of the correlation table.

If the data is coded

$$r = \frac{n\Sigma f uv - (\Sigma f_u u)(\Sigma f_v v)}{\sqrt{[n\Sigma f_u u^2 - (\Sigma f_u u)^2][n\Sigma f_v v^2 - (\Sigma f_v v)^2]}}$$

where the u's and v's are coded class marks. The frequencies f_u and f_v are defined analogous to f_x and f_y.

PROBABILITY

Definitions

A sample space S associated with an experiment is a set S of elements such that any outcome of the experiment corresponds to one and only one element of the set. An event E is a subset of a sample space S. An element in a sample space is called a sample point or a simple event (Unit subset of S).

Definition of Probability

If an experiment can occur in n mutually exclusive and equally likely ways, and if exactly m of these ways correspond to an event E, then the probability of E is given by

$$P(E) = \frac{m}{n}.$$

If E is a subset of S, and if to each unit subset of S, a non-negative number, called its probability, is assigned, and if E is the union of two or more different simple events, then the probability of E, denoted by $P(E)$, is the sum of the probabilities of those simple events whose union is E.

Marginal and Conditional Probability

Suppose a sample space S is partioned into rs disjoint subsets where the general subset is denoted by $E_i \cap F_j$. Then the marginal probability of E_i is defined as

$$P(E_i) = \sum_{j=1}^{s} P(E_i \cap F_j)$$

and the marginal probability of F_j is defined as

$$P(F_j) = \sum_{i=1}^{r} P(E_i \cap F_j)$$

The conditional probability of E_i, given that F_j has occurred, is defined as

$$P(E_i|F_j) = \frac{P(E_i \cap F_j)}{P(F_j)} , \qquad P(F_j) \neq 0$$

and that of F_j, given that E_i has occurred, is defined as

$$P(F_j|E_i) = \frac{P(E_i \cap F_j)}{P(E_i)} , \qquad P(E_i) \neq 0 .$$

Probability Theorems

1. If ϕ is the null set, $P(\phi) = 0$.
2. If S is the sample space, $P(S) = 1$.
3. If E and F are two events

$$P(E \cup F) = P(E) + P(F) - P(E \cap F).$$

4. If E and F are mutually exclusive events,

$$P(E \cup F) = P(E) + P(F).$$

5. If E and E' are complementary events,

$$P(E) = 1 - P(E').$$

6. The conditional probability of an event E, given an event F, is denoted by $P(E/F)$ and is defined as

$$P(E|F) = \frac{P(E \cap F)}{P(F)},$$

where $P(F) \neq 0$.

7. Two events E and F are said to be independent if and only if

$$P(E \cap F) = P(E) \cdot P(F).$$

E is said to be statistically independent of F if $P(E|F) = P(E)$ and $P(F/E) = P(F)$.

8. The events E_1, E_2, . . . , E_n are called mutually independent for all combinations if and only if every combination of these events taken any number at a time is independent.

9. *Bayes Theorem.*

If E_1, E_2, . . . , E_n are n mutually exclusive events whose union is the sample space S, and E is any arbitrary event of S such that $P(E) \neq 0$, then

$$P(E_k|E) = \frac{P(E_k) \cdot P(E|E_k)}{\sum_{j=1}^{n} [P(E_j) \cdot P(E|E_j)]}$$

EXAMPLE: Two unbiased six sided dice, one red and one green, are tossed and the number of dots appearing on their upper faces is observed.

The sample space S consists of 36 elements, i.e.

$$S = \{(1, 1), (1, 2), . . . , (6, 5), (6, 6)\} \ .$$

1. What is the probability of throwing a seven, denoted by the event A?

$$A = \{(1, 6)\} \cup \{(2, 5)\} \cup \{(3, 4)\} \cup \{(4, 3)\} \cup \{(5, 2)\} \cup \{(6, 1)\}$$
$$P(A) = \tfrac{1}{36} + \tfrac{1}{36} + \tfrac{1}{36} + \tfrac{1}{36} + \tfrac{1}{36} + \tfrac{1}{36} = \tfrac{1}{6}$$

2. What is the probability of throwing a seven or a ten? Denote by A the event "throwing a 7" and by B the event "throwing a ten" .

$$P(A) = \tfrac{1}{6} \qquad P(A \cup B) = P(A) + P(B)$$
$$P(B) = \tfrac{1}{12} \qquad\qquad = \tfrac{1}{6} + \tfrac{1}{12}$$
$$\qquad\qquad = \tfrac{1}{4}$$

3. What is the probability that the red die shows a number less than or equal to three and the green die shows a number greater than or equal to five? Denote by C the event "red die shows number ≤ 3" and by D the event "green die shows number ≥ 5" .

$$C \cap D = \{(1, 5), (2, 5), (3, 5), (1, 6), (2, 6), (3, 6)\}$$
$$P(C \cap D) = \tfrac{6}{36} = \tfrac{1}{6}$$

Note:
$$P(C) = \tfrac{18}{36} = \tfrac{1}{2}$$
$$P(D) = \tfrac{12}{36} = \tfrac{1}{3}$$
$$P(C) \cdot P(D) = \tfrac{1}{2} \cdot \tfrac{1}{3} = \tfrac{1}{6}$$

Thus $P(C \cap D) = P(C) \cdot P(D)$ and events C and D are independent.

4. What is the probability that the green die shows a one, given that the sum of the numbers on the two dice is less than four? Denote by E the event "green die shows 1" and by F the event "sum of numbers on dice <4".

$$E = \{(1, 1), (1, 2), (1, 3), (1, 4), (1, 5), (1, 6)\}$$
$$F = \{(1, 1), (1, 2), (\sim, 1)\}$$
$$E \cap F = \{(1, 1), (1, 2)\}$$
$$P(E \mid F) = \frac{P(E \cap F)}{P(F)} = \frac{\frac{2}{36}}{\frac{3}{36}} = \tfrac{2}{3}$$

5. What is the probability that the sum of the numbers on the two dice is not seven?

$$P(A) = \tfrac{1}{6}$$
$$P(A') = 1 - \tfrac{1}{6} = \tfrac{5}{6}$$

Random Variable

A function whose domain is a sample space S and whose range is some set of real numbers is called a random variable, denoted by $\mathbf{X}$. The function $\mathbf{X}$ transforms sample points of S into points on the x-axis. $\mathbf{X}$ will be called a discrete random variable if it is a random variable that assumes only a finite or denumerable number of values on the x-axis. $\mathbf{X}$ will be called a continuous random variable if it assumes a continuum of values on the x-axis.

Probability Function (Discrete Case)

The random variable $\mathbf{X}$ will be called a discrete random variable if there exists a function f such that $f(x_i) \geq 0$ and $\sum_i f(x_i) = 1$ for $i = 1, 2, 3, \ldots$ and such that for any event E,

$$P(E) = P[\mathbf{X} \text{ is in } E] = \sum_E f(x)$$

where $\sum_E$ means sum $f(x)$ over those values x_i that are in E and where $f(x) = P[\mathbf{X} = x]$. The probability that the value of $\mathbf{X}$ is some real number x, is given by $f(x) = P[\mathbf{X} = x]$, where f is called the probability function of the random variable $\mathbf{X}$.

Cumulative Distribution Function (Discrete Case)

The probability that the value of a random variable $\mathbf{X}$ is less than or equal to some real number x is defined as

$$F(x) = P(\mathbf{X} \leq x)$$
$$= \Sigma f(x_i), \qquad -\infty < x < \infty,$$

where the summation extends over those values of i such that $x_i \leq x$.

Probability Density (Continuous Case)

The random variable $\mathbf{X}$ will be called a continuous random variable if there exists a function f such that $f(x) \geq 0$ and $\int_{-\infty}^{\infty} f(x)\, dx = 1$ for all x in interval $-\infty < x < \infty$ and such that for any event E

$$P(E) = P(\mathbf{X} \text{ is in } E) = \int_E f(x)\, dx.$$

$f(x)$ is called the probability density of the random variable **X**. The probability that **X** assumes any given value of x is equal to zero and the probability that it assumes a value on the interval from a to b, including or excluding either end point, is equal to

$$\int_a^b f(x)\ dx.$$

Cumulative Distribution Function (Continuous Case)

The probability that the value of a random variable **X** is less than or equal to some real number x is defined as

$$F(x) = P(\mathbf{X} \le x), \qquad -\infty < x < \infty$$
$$= \int_{-\infty}^x f(x)\ dx.$$

From the cumulative distribution, the density, if it exists, can be found from

$$f(x) = \frac{dF(x)}{dx}.$$

From the cumulative distribution

$$P(a \le \mathbf{X} \le b) = P(\mathbf{X} \le b) - P(\mathbf{X} \le a)$$
$$= F(b) - F(a)$$

THE NORMAL PROBABILITY FUNCTION
AND RELATED FUNCTIONS

This table gives values of:

a) $f(x)$ = the probability density of a standardized random variable

$$= \frac{1}{\sqrt{2\pi}} e^{-\frac{1}{2}x^2}$$

For negative values of x, one uses the fact that $f(-x) = f(x)$.

b) $F(x)$ = the cumulative distribution function of a standardized normal random variable

$$= \int_{-\infty}^{x} \frac{1}{\sqrt{2\pi}} e^{-\frac{1}{2}t^2} dt$$

For negative values of x, one uses the relationship $F(-x) = 1 - F(x)$. Values of x corresponding to a few special values of $F(x)$ are given in a separate table following the main table.

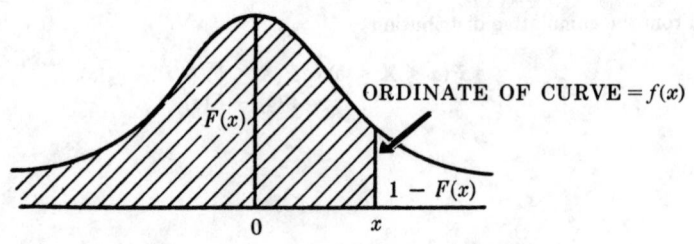

c) $f'(x)$ = the first derivative of $f(x)$ with respect to x

$$= -\frac{x}{\sqrt{2\pi}} e^{-\frac{1}{2}x^2} = -xf(x)$$

d) $f''(x)$ = the second derivative of $f(x)$ with respect to x

$$= \frac{(x^2 - 1)}{\sqrt{2\pi}} e^{-\frac{1}{2}x^2} = (x^2 - 1)f(x)$$

e) $f'''(x)$ = the third derivative of $f(x)$ with respect to x

$$= \frac{3x - x^3}{\sqrt{2\pi}} e^{-\frac{1}{2}x^2} = (3x - x^3)f(x)$$

f) $f^{iv}(x)$ = the fourth derivative of $f(x)$ with respect to x

$$= \frac{x^4 - 6x^2 + 3}{\sqrt{2\pi}} e^{-\frac{1}{2}x^2} = (x^4 - 6x^2 + 3)f(x)$$

582

THE NORMAL PROBABILITY FUNCTION AND
RELATED FUNCTIONS (Continued)

It should be noted that other probability integrals can be evaluated by the use of these tables. For example,

$$\int_0^z f(t)dt = \tfrac{1}{2}\,\mathrm{erf}\left(\frac{x}{\sqrt{2}}\right),$$

where $\mathrm{erf}\left(\dfrac{x}{\sqrt{2}}\right)$ represents the error function associated with the normal curve.

To evaluate erf (2.3) one proceeds as follows: Since $\dfrac{x}{\sqrt{2}} = 2.3$, one finds $x = (2.3)(\sqrt{2}) = 3.25$. In the entry opposite $x = 3.25$, the value 0.9994 is given. Subtracting 0.5000 from the tabular value, one finds the value 0.4994. Thus erf (2.3) = 2(0.4994) = 0.9988.

NORMAL PROBABILITY FUNCTION AND RELATED FUNCTIONS (Continued)

x	$F(x)$	$1 - F(x)$	$f(x)$	$f'(x)$	$f''(x)$	$f'''(x)$	$f^{\mathrm{iv}}(x)$
.00	.5000	.5000	.3989	− .0000	− .3989	.0000	1.1968
.01	.5040	.4960	.3989	− .0040	− .3989	.0120	1.1965
.02	.5080	.4920	.3989	− .0080	− .3987	.0239	1.1956
.03	.5120	.4880	.3988	− .0120	− .3984	.0359	1.1941
.04	.5160	.4840	.3986	− .0159	− .3980	.0478	1.1920
.05	.5199	.4801	.3984	− .0199	− .3975	.0597	1.1894
.06	.5239	.4761	.3982	− .0239	− .3968	.0716	1.1861
.07	.5279	.4721	.3980	− .0279	− .3960	.0834	1.1822
.08	.5319	.4681	.3977	− .0318	− .3951	.0952	1.1778
.09	.5359	.4641	.3973	− .0358	− .3941	.1070	1.1727
.10	.5398	.4602	.3970	− .0397	− .3930	.1187	1.1671
.11	.5438	.4562	.3965	− .0436	− .3917	.1303	1.1609
.12	.5478	.4522	.3961	− .0475	− .3904	.1419	1.1541
.13	.5517	.4483	.3956	− .0514	− .3889	.1534	1.1468
.14	.5557	.4443	.3951	− .0553	− .3873	.1648	1.1389
.15	.5596	.4404	.3945	− .0592	− .3856	.1762	1.1304
.16	.5636	.4364	.3939	− .0630	− .3838	.1874	1.1214
.17	.5675	.4325	.3932	− .0668	− .3819	.1986	1.1118
.18	.5714	.4286	.3925	− .0707	− .3798	.2097	1.1017
.19	.5753	.4247	.3918	− .0744	− .3777	.2206	1.0911
.20	.5793	.4207	.3910	− .0782	− .3754	.2315	1.0799
.21	.5832	.4168	.3902	− .0820	− .3730	.2422	1.0682
.22	.5871	.4129	.3894	− .0857	− .3706	.2529	1.0560
.23	.5910	.4090	.3885	− .0894	− .3680	.2634	1.0434
.24	.5948	.4052	.3876	− .0930	− .3653	.2737	1.0302
.25	.5987	.4013	.3867	− .0967	− .3625	.2840	1.0165
.26	.6026	.3974	.3857	− .1003	− .3596	.2941	1.0024
.27	.6064	.3936	.3847	− .1039	− .3566	.3040	0.9878
.28	.6103	.3897	.3836	− .1074	− .3535	.3138	0.9727
.29	.6141	.3859	.3825	− .1109	− .3504	.3235	0.9572
.30	.6179	.3821	.3814	− .1144	− .3471	.3330	0.9413
.31	.6217	.3783	.3802	− .1179	− .3437	.3423	0.9250
.32	.6255	.3745	.3790	− .1213	− .3402	.3515	0.9082
.33	.6293	.3707	.3778	− .1247	− .3367	.3605	0.8910
.34	.6331	.3669	.3765	− .1280	− .3330	.3693	0.8735
.35	.6368	.3632	.3752	− .1313	− .3293	.3779	0.8556
.36	.6406	.3594	.3739	− .1346	− .3255	.3864	0.8373
.37	.6443	.3557	.3726	− .1378	− .3216	.3947	0.8186
.38	.6480	.3520	.3712	− .1410	− .3176	.4028	0.7996
.39	.6517	.3483	.3697	− .1442	− .3135	.4107	0.7803
.40	.6554	.3446	.3683	− .1473	− .3094	.4184	0.7607
.41	.6591	.3409	.3668	− .1504	− .3051	.4259	0.7408
.42	.6628	.3372	.3653	− .1534	− .3008	.4332	0.7206
.43	.6664	.3336	.3637	− .1564	− .2965	.4403	0.7001
.44	.6700	.3300	.3621	− .1593	− .2920	.4472	0.6793
.45	.6736	.3264	.3605	− .1622	− .2875	.4539	0.6583
.46	.6772	.3228	.3589	− .1651	− .2830	.4603	0.6371
.47	.6808	.3192	.3572	− .1679	− .2783	.4666	0.6156
.48	.6844	.3156	.3555	− .1707	− .2736	.4727	0.5940
.49	.6879	.3121	.3538	− .1734	− .2689	.4785	0.5721
.50	.6915	.3085	.3521	− .1760	− .2641	.4841	0.5501

NORMAL PROBABILITY FUNCTION AND RELATED FUNCTIONS (Continued)

x	$F(x)$	$1 - F(x)$	$f(x)$	$f'(x)$	$f''(x)$	$f'''(x)$	$f^{iv}(x)$
.50	.6915	.3085	.3521	$-.1760$	$-.2641$	.4841	.5501
.51	.6950	.3050	.3503	$-.1787$	$-.2592$	.4895	.5279
.52	.6985	.3015	.3485	$-.1812$	$-.2543$	.4947	.5056
.53	.7019	.2981	.3467	$-.1837$	$-.2493$	.4996	.4831
.54	.7054	.2946	.3448	$-.1862$	$-.2443$	.5043	.4605
.55	.7088	.2912	.3429	$-.1886$	$-.2392$	.5088	.4378
.56	.7123	.2877	.3410	$-.1920$	$-.2341$	.5131	.4150
.57	.7157	.2843	.3391	$-.1933$	$-.2289$	.5171	.3921
.58	.7190	.2810	.3372	$-.1956$	$-.2238$	.5209	.3691
.59	.7224	.2776	.3352	$-.1978$	$-.2185$	.5245	.3461
.60	.7257	.2743	.3332	$-.1999$	$-.2133$	.5278	.3231
.61	.7291	.2709	.3312	$-.2020$	$-.2080$	.5309	.3000
.62	.7324	.2676	.3292	$-.2041$	$-.2027$	.5338	.2770
.63	.7357	.2643	.3271	$-.2061$	$-.1973$	.5365	.2539
.64	.7389	.2611	.3251	$-.2080$	$-.1919$	.5389	.2309
.65	.7422	.2578	.3230	$-.2099$	$-.1865$	.5411	.2078
.66	.7454	.2546	.3209	$-.2118$	$-.1811$	.5431	.1849
.67	.7486	.2514	.3187	$-.2136$	$-.1757$	.5448	.1620
.68	.7517	.2483	.3166	$-.2153$	$-.1702$	.5463	.1391
.69	.7549	.2451	.3144	$-.2170$	$-.1647$	.5476	.1164
.70	.7580	.2420	.3123	$-.2186$	$-.1593$	.5486	.0937
.71	.7611	.2389	.3101	$-.2201$	$-.1538$	.5495	.0712
.72	.7642	.2358	.3079	$-.2217$	$-.1483$	.5501	.0487
.73	.7673	.2327	.3056	$-.2231$	$-.1428$	.5504	.0265
.74	.7704	.2296	.3034	$-.2245$	$-.1373$	.5506	.0043
.75	.7734	.2266	.3011	$-.2259$	$-.1318$	.5505	$-.0176$
.76	.7764	.2236	.2989	$-.2271$	$-.1262$	.5502	$-.0394$
.77	.7794	.2206	.2966	$-.2284$	$-.1207$	.5497	$-.0611$
.78	.7823	.2177	.2943	$-.2296$	$-.1153$	.5490	$-.0825$
.79	.7852	.2148	.2920	$-.2307$	$-.1098$	.5481	$-.1037$
.80	.7881	.2119	.2897	$-.2318$	$-.1043$	.5469	$-.1247$
.81	.7910	.2090	.2874	$-.2328$	$-.0988$	.5456	$-.1455$
.82	.7939	.2061	.2850	$-.2337$	$-.0934$	.5440	$-.1660$
.83	.7967	.2033	.2827	$-.2346$	$-.0880$	.5423	$-.1862$
.84	.7995	.2005	.2803	$-.2355$	$-.0825$	.5403	$-.2063$
.85	.8023	.1977	.2780	$-.2363$	$-.0771$	.5381	$-.2260$
.86	.8051	.1949	.2756	$-.2370$	$-.0718$	.5358	$-.2455$
.87	.8079	.1921	.2732	$-.2377$	$-.0664$	.5332	$-.2646$
.88	.8106	.1894	.2709	$-.2384$	$-.0611$	.5305	$-.2835$
.89	.8133	.1867	.2685	$-.2389$	$-.0558$	.5276	$-.3021$
.90	.8159	.1841	.2661	$-.2395$	$-.0506$	.5245	$-.3203$
.91	.8186	.1814	.2637	$-.2400$	$-.0453$	.5212	$-.3383$
.92	.8212	.1788	.2613	$-.2404$	$-.0401$	.5177	$-.3559$
.93	.8238	.1762	.2589	$-.2408$	$-.0350$	.5140	$-.3731$
.94	.8264	.1736	.2565	$-.2411$	$-.0299$	.5102	$-.3901$
.95	.8289	.1711	.2541	$-.2414$	$-.0248$	.5062	$-.4066$
.96	.8315	.1685	.2516	$-.2416$	$-.0197$	.5021	$-.4228$
.97	.8340	.1660	.2492	$-.2417$	$-.0147$	.4978	$-.4387$
.98	.8365	.1635	.2468	$-.2419$	$-.0098$	.4933	$-.4541$
.99	.8389	.1611	.2444	$-.2420$	$-.0049$	.4887	$-.4692$
1.00	.8413	.1587	.2420	$-.2420$	.0000	.4839	$-.4839$

NORMAL PROBABILITY FUNCTION AND RELATED FUNCTIONS (Continued)

x	$F(x)$	$1 - F(x)$	$f(x)$	$f'(x)$	$f''(x)$	$f'''(x)$	$f^{\mathrm{iv}}(x)$
1.00	.8413	.1587	.2420	− .2420	.0000	.4839	− .4839
1.01	.8438	.1562	.2396	− .2420	.0048	.4790	− .4983
1.02	.8461	.1539	.2371	− .2419	.0096	.4740	− .5122
1.03	.8485	.1515	.2347	− .2418	.0143	.4688	− .5257
1.04	.8508	.1492	.2323	− .2416	.0190	.4635	− .5389
1.05	.8531	.1469	.2299	− .2414	.0236	.4580	− .5516
1.06	.8554	.1446	.2275	− .2411	.0281	.4524	− .5639
1.07	.8577	.1423	.2251	− .2408	.0326	.4467	− .5758
1.08	.8599	.1401	.2227	− .2405	.0371	.4409	− .5873
1.09	.8621	.1379	.2203	− .2401	.0414	.4350	− .5984
1.10	.8643	.1357	.2179	− .2396	.0458	.4290	− .6091
1.11	.8665	.1335	.2155	− .2392	.0500	.4228	− .6193
1.12	.8686	.1314	.2131	− .2386	.0542	.4166	− .6292
1.13	.8708	.1292	.2107	− .2381	.0583	.4102	− .6386
1.14	.8729	.1271	.2083	− .2375	.0624	.4038	− .6476
1.15	.8749	.1251	.2059	− .2368	.0664	.3973	− .6561
1.16	.8770	.1230	.2036	− .2361	.0704	.3907	− .6643
1.17	.8790	.1210	.2012	− .2354	.0742	.3840	− .6720
1.18	.8810	.1190	.1989	− .2347	.0780	.3772	− .6792
1.19	.8830	.1170	.1965	− .2339	.0818	.3704	− .6861
1.20	.8849	.1151	.1942	− .2330	.0854	.3635	− .6926
1.21	.8869	.1131	.1919	− .2322	.0890	.3566	− .6986
1.22	.8888	.1112	.1895	− .2312	.0926	.3496	− .7042
1.23	.8907	.1093	.1872	− .2303	.0960	.3425	− .7094
1.24	.8925	.1075	.1849	− .2293	.0994	.3354	− .7141
1.25	.8944	.1056	.1826	− .2283	.1027	.3282	− .7185
1.26	.8962	.1038	.1804	− .2273	.1060	.3210	− .7224
1.27	.8980	.1020	.1781	− .2262	.1092	.3138	− .7259
1.28	.8997	.1003	.1758	− .2251	.1123	.3065	− .7291
1.29	.9015	.0985	.1736	− .2240	.1153	.2992	− .7318
1.30	.9032	.0968	.1714	− .2228	.1182	.2918	− .7341
1.31	.9049	.0951	.1691	− .2216	.1211	.2845	− .7361
1.32	.9066	.0934	.1669	− .2204	.1239	.2771	− .7376
1.33	.9082	.0918	.1647	− .2191	.1267	.2697	− .7388
1.34	.9099	.0901	.1626	− .2178	.1293	.2624	− .7395
1.35	.9115	.0885	.1604	− .2165	.1319	.2550	− .7399
1.36	.9131	.0869	.1582	− .2152	.1344	.2476	− .7400
1.37	.9147	.0853	.1561	− .2138	.1369	.2402	− .7396
1.38	.9162	.0838	.1539	− .2125	.1392	.2328	− .7389
1.39	.9177	.0823	.1518	− .2110	.1415	.2254	− .7378
1.40	.9192	.0808	.1497	− .2096	.1437	.2180	− .7364
1.41	.9207	.0793	.1476	− .2082	.1459	.2107	− .7347
1.42	.9222	.0778	.1456	− .2067	.1480	.2033	− .7326
1.43	.9236	.0764	.1435	− .2052	.1500	.1960	− .7301
1.44	.9251	.0749	.1415	− .2037	.1519	.1887	− .7274
1.45	.9265	.0735	.1394	− .2022	.1537	.1815	− .7243
1.46	.9279	.0721	.1374	− .2006	.1555	.1742	− .7209
1.47	.9292	.0708	.1354	− .1991	.1572	.1670	− .7172
1.48	.9306	.0694	.1334	− .1975	.1588	.1599	− .7132
1.49	.9319	.0681	.1315	− .1959	.1604	.1528	− .7089
1.50	.9332	.0668	.1295	− .1943	.1619	.1457	− .7043

NORMAL PROBABILITY FUNCTION AND RELATED FUNCTIONS (Continued)

x	$F(x)$	$1 - F(x)$	$f(x)$	$f'(x)$	$f''(x)$	$f'''(x)$	$f^{\mathrm{iv}}(x)$
1.50	.9332	.0668	.1295	− .1943	.1619	.1457	− .7043
1.51	.9345	.0655	.1276	− .1927	.1633	.1387	− .6994
1.52	.9357	.0643	.1257	− .1910	.1647	.1317	− .6942
1.53	.9370	.0630	.1238	− .1894	.1660	.1248	− .6888
1.54	.9382	.0618	.1219	− .1877	.1672	.1180	− .6831
1.55	.9394	.0606	.1200	− .1860	.1683	.1111	− .6772
1.56	.9406	.0594	.1182	− .1843	.1694	.1044	− .6710
1.57	.9418	.0582	.1163	− .1826	.1704	.0977	− .6646
1.58	.9429	.0571	.1145	− .1809	.1714	.0911	− .6580
1.59	.9441	.0559	.1127	− .1792	.1722	.0846	− .6511
1.60	.9452	.0548	.1109	− .1775	.1730	.0781	− .6441
1.61	.9463	.0537	.1092	− .1757	.1738	.0717	− .6368
1.62	.9474	.0526	.1074	− .1740	.1745	.0654	− .6293
1.63	.9484	.0516	.1057	− .1723	.1751	.0591	− .6216
1.64	.9495	.0505	.1040	− .1705	.1757	.0529	− .6138
1.65	.9505	.0495	.1023	− .1687	.1762	.0468	− .6057
1.66	.9515	.0485	.1006	− .1670	.1766	.0408	− .5975
1.67	.9525	.0475	.0989	− .1652	.1770	.0349	− .5891
1.68	.9535	.0465	.0973	− .1634	.1773	.0290	− .5806
1.69	.9545	.0455	.0957	− .1617	.1776	.0233	− .5720
1.70	.9554	.0446	.0940	− .1599	.1778	.0176	− .5632
1.71	.9564	.0436	.0925	− .1581	.1779	.0120	− .5542
1.72	.9573	.0427	.0909	− .1563	.1780	.0065	− .5452
1.73	.9582	.0418	.0893	− .1546	.1780	.0011	− .5360
1.74	.9591	.0409	.0878	− .1528	.1780	− .0042	− .5267
1.75	.9599	.0401	.0863	− .1510	.1780	− .0094	− .5173
1.76	.9608	.0392	.0848	− .1492	.1778	− .0146	− .5079
1.77	.9616	.0384	.0833	− .1474	.1777	− .0196	− .4983
1.78	.9625	.0375	.0818	− .1457	.1774	− .0245	− .4887
1.79	.9633	.0367	.0804	− .1439	.1772	− .0294	− .4789
1.80	.9641	.0359	.0790	− .1421	.1769	− .0341	− .4692
1.81	.9649	.0351	.0775	− .1403	.1765	− .0388	− .4593
1.82	.9656	.0344	.0761	− .1386	.1761	− .0433	− .4494
1.83	.9664	.0336	.0748	− .1368	.1756	− .0477	− .4395
1.84	.9671	.0329	.0734	− .1351	.1751	− .0521	− .4295
1.85	.9678	.0322	.0721	− .1333	.1746	− .0563	− .4195
1.86	.9686	.0314	.0707	− .1316	.1740	− .0605	− .4095
1.87	.9693	.0307	.0694	− .1298	.1734	− .0645	− .3995
1.88	.9699	.0301	.0681	− .1281	.1727	− .0685	− .3894
1.89	.9706	.0294	.0669	− .1264	.1720	− .0723	− .3793
1.90	.9713	.0287	.0656	− .1247	.1713	− .0761	− .3693
1.91	.9719	.0281	.0644	− .1230	.1705	− .0797	− .3592
1.92	.9726	.0274	.0632	− .1213	.1697	− .0832	− .3492
1.93	.9732	.0268	.0620	− .1196	.1688	− .0867	− .3392
1.94	.9738	.0262	.0608	− .1179	.1679	− .0900	− .3292
1.95	.9744	.0256	.0596	− .1162	.1670	− .0933	− .3192
1.96	.9750	.0250	.0584	− .1145	.1661	− .0964	− .3093
1.97	.9756	.0244	.0573	− .1129	.1651	− .0994	− .2994
1.98	.9761	.0239	.0562	− .1112	.1641	− .1024	− .2895
1.99	.9767	.0233	.0551	− .1096	.1630	− .1052	− .2797
2.00	.9772	.0228	.0540	− .1080	.1620	− .1080	− .2700

NORMAL PROBABILITY FUNCTION AND RELATED FUNCTIONS (Continued)

x	$F(x)$	$1 - F(x)$	$f(x)$	$f'(x)$	$f''(x)$	$f'''(x)$	$f^{\text{iv}}(x)$
2.00	.9772	.0228	.0540	− .1080	.1620	− .1080	− .2700
2.01	.9778	.0222	.0529	− .1064	.1609	− .1106	− .2603
2.02	.9783	.0217	.0519	− .1048	.1598	− .1132	− .2506
2.03	.9788	.0212	.0508	− .1032	.1586	− .1157	− .2411
2.04	.9793	.0207	.0498	− .1016	.1575	− .1180	− .2316
2.05	.9798	.0202	.0488	− .1000	.1563	− .1203	− .2222
2.06	.9803	.0197	.0478	− .0985	.1550	− .1225	− .2129
2.07	.9808	.0192	.0468	− .0969	.1538	− .1245	− .2036
2.08	.9812	.0188	.0459	− .0954	.1526	− .1265	− .1945
2.09	.9817	.0183	.0449	− .0939	.1513	− .1284	− .1854
2.10	.9821	.0179	.0440	− .0924	.1500	− .1302	− .1765
2.11	.9826	.0174	.0431	− .0909	.1487	− .1320	− .1676
2.12	.9830	.0170	.0422	− .0894	.1474	− .1336	− .1588
2.13	.9834	.0166	.0413	− .0879	.1460	− .1351	− .1502
2.14	.9838	.0162	.0404	− .0865	.1446	− .1366	− .1416
2.15	.9842	.0158	.0396	− .0850	.1433	− .1380	− .1332
2.16	.9846	.0154	.0387	− .0836	.1419	− .1393	− .1249
2.17	.9850	.0150	.0379	− .0822	.1405	− .1405	− .1167
2.18	.9854	.0146	.0371	− .0808	.1391	− .1416	− .1086
2.19	.9857	.0143	.0363	− .0794	.1377	− .1426	− .1006
2.20	.9861	.0139	.0355	− .0780	.1362	− .1436	− .0927
2.21	.9864	.0136	.0347	− .0767	.1348	− .1445	− .0850
2.22	.9868	.0132	.0339	− .0754	.1333	− .1453	− .0774
2.23	.9871	.0129	.0332	− .0740	.1319	− .1460	− .0700
2.24	.9875	.0125	.0325	− .0727	.1304	− .1467	− .0626
2.25	.9878	.0122	.0317	− .0714	.1289	− .1473	− .0554
2.26	.9881	.0119	.0310	− .0701	.1275	− .1478	− .0484
2.27	.9884	.0116	.0303	− .0689	.1260	− .1483	− .0414
2.28	.9887	.0113	.0297	− .0676	.1245	− .1486	− .0346
2.29	.9890	.0110	.0290	− .0664	.1230	− .1490	− .0279
2.30	.9893	.0107	.0283	− .0652	.1215	− .1492	− .0214
2.31	.9896	.0104	.0277	− .0639	.1200	− .1494	− .0150
2.32	.9898	.0102	.0270	− .0628	.1185	− .1495	− .0088
2.33	.9901	.0099	.0264	− .0616	.1170	− .1496	− .0027
2.34	.9904	.0096	.0258	− .0604	.1155	− .1496	.0033
2.35	.9906	.0094	.0252	− .0593	.1141	− .1495	.0092
2.36	.9909	.0091	.0246	− .0581	.1126	− .1494	.0149
2.37	.9911	.0089	.0241	− .0570	.1111	− .1492	.0204
2.38	.9913	.0087	.0235	− .0559	.1096	− .1490	.0258
2.39	.9916	.0084	.0229	− .0548	.1081	− .1487	.0311
2.40	.9918	.0082	.0224	− .0538	.1066	− .1483	.0362
2.41	.9920	.0080	.0219	− .0527	.1051	− .1480	.0412
2.42	.9922	.0078	.0213	− .0516	.1036	− .1475	.0461
2.43	.9925	.0075	.0208	− .0506	.1022	− .1470	.0508
2.44	.9927	.0073	.0203	− .0496	.1007	− .1465	.0554
2.45	.9929	.0071	.0198	− .0486	.0992	− .1459	.0598
2.46	.9931	.0069	.0194	− .0476	.0978	− .1453	.0641
2.47	.9932	.0068	.0189	− .0467	.0963	− .1446	.0683
2.48	.9934	.0066	.0184	− .0457	.0949	− .1439	.0723
2.49	.9936	.0064	.0180	− .0448	.0935	− .1432	.0762
2.50	.9938	.0062	.0175	− .0438	.0920	− .1424	.0800

NORMAL PROBABILITY FUNCTION AND RELATED FUNCTIONS (Continued)

x	$F(x)$	$1 - F(x)$	$f(x)$	$f'(x)$	$f''(x)$	$f'''(x)$	$f^{iv}(x)$
2.50	.9938	.0062	.0175	− .0438	.0920	− .1424	.0800
2.51	.9940	.0060	.0171	− .0429	.0906	− .1416	.0836
2.52	.9941	.0059	.0167	− .0420	.0892	− .1408	.0871
2.53	.9943	.0057	.0163	− .0411	.0878	− .1399	.0905
2.54	.9945	.0055	.0158	− .0403	.0864	− .1389	.0937
2.55	.9946	.0054	.0155	− .0394	.0850	− .1380	.0968
2.56	.9948	.0052	.0151	− .0386	.0836	− .1370	.0998
2.57	.9949	.0051	.0147	− .0377	.0823	− .1360	.1027
2.58	.9951	.0049	.0143	− .0369	.0809	− .1350	.1054
2.59	.9952	.0048	.0139	− .0361	.0796	− .1339	.1080
2.60	.9953	.0047	.0136	− .0353	.0782	− .1328	.1105
2.61	.9955	.0045	.0132	− .0345	.0769	− .1317	.1129
2.62	.9956	.0044	.0129	− .0338	.0756	− .1305	.1152
2.63	.9957	.0043	.0126	− .0330	.0743	− .1294	.1173
2.64	.9959	.0041	.0122	− .0323	.0730	− .1282	.1194
2.65	.9960	.0040	.0119	− .0316	.0717	− .1270	.1213
2.66	.9961	.0039	.0116	− .0309	.0705	− .1258	.1231
2.67	.9962	.0038	.0113	− .0302	.0692	− .1245	.1248
2.68	.9963	.0037	.0110	− .0295	.0680	− .1233	.1264
2.69	.9964	.0036	.0107	− .0288	.0668	− .1220	.1279
2.70	.9965	.0035	.0104	− .0281	.0656	− .1207	.1293
2.71	.9966	.0034	.0101	− .0275	.0644	− .1194	.1306
2.72	.9967	.0033	.0099	− .0269	.0632	− .1181	.1317
2.73	.9968	.0032	.0096	− .0262	.0620	− .1168	.1328
2.74	.9969	.0031	.0093	− .0256	.0608	− .1154	.1338
2.75	.9970	.0030	.0091	− .0250	.0597	− .1141	.1347
2.76	.9971	.0029	.0088	− .0244	.0585	− .1127	.1356
2.77	.9972	.0028	.0086	− .0238	.0574	− .1114	.1363
2.78	.9973	.0027	.0084	− .0233	.0563	− .1100	.1369
2.79	.9974	.0026	.0081	− .0227	.0552	− .1087	.1375
2.80	.9974	.0026	.0079	− .0222	.0541	− .1073	.1379
2.81	.9975	.0025	.0077	− .0216	.0531	− .1059	.1383
2.82	.9976	.0024	.0075	− .0211	.0520	− .1045	.1386
2.83	.9977	.0023	.0073	− .0206	.0510	− .1031	.1389
2.84	.9977	.0023	.0071	− .0201	.0500	− .1017	.1390
2.85	.9978	.0022	.0069	− .0196	.0490	− .1003	.1391
2.86	.9979	.0021	.0067	− .0191	.0480	− .0990	.1391
2.87	.9979	.0021	.0065	− .0186	.0470	− .0976	.1391
2.88	.9980	.0020	.0063	− .0182	.0460	− .0962	.1389
2.89	.9981	.0019	.0061	− .0177	.0451	− .0948	.1388
2.90	.9981	.0019	.0060	− .0173	.0441	− .0934	.1385
2.91	.9982	.0018	.0058	− .0168	.0432	− .0920	.1382
2.92	.9982	.0018	.0056	− .0164	.0423	− .0906	.1378
2.93	.9983	.0017	.0055	− .0160	.0414	− .0893	.1374
2.94	.9984	.0016	.0053	− .0156	.0405	− .0879	.1369
2.95	.9984	.0016	.0051	− .0152	.0396	− .0865	.1364
2.96	.9985	.0015	.0050	− .0148	.0388	− .0852	.1358
2.97	.9985	.0015	.0048	− .0144	.0379	− .0838	.1352
2.98	.9986	.0014	.0047	− .0140	.0371	− .0825	.1345
2.99	.9986	.0014	.0046	− .0137	.0363	− .0811	.1337
3.00	.9987	.0013	.0044	− .0133	.0355	− .0798	.1330

NORMAL PROBABILITY FUNCTION AND RELATED FUNCTIONS (Continued)

x	$F(x)$	$1 - F(x)$	$f(x)$	$f'(x)$	$f''(x)$	$f'''(x)$	$f^{iv}(x)$
3.00	.9987	.0013	.0044	− .0133	.0355	− .0798	.1330
3.01	.9987	.0013	.0043	− .0130	.0347	− .0785	.1321
3.02	.9987	.0013	.0042	− .0126	.0339	− .0771	.1313
3.03	.9988	.0012	.0040	− .0123	.0331	− .0758	.1304
3.04	.9988	.0012	.0039	− .0119	.0324	− .0745	.1294
3.05	.9989	.0011	.0038	− .0116	.0316	− .0732	.1285
3.06	.9989	.0011	.0037	− .0113	.0309	− .0720	.1275
3.07	.9989	.0011	.0036	− .0110	.0302	− .0707	.1264
3.08	.9990	.0010	.0035	− .0107	.0295	− .0694	.1254
3.09	.9990	.0010	.0034	− .0104	.0288	− .0682	.1243
3.10	.9990	.0010	.0033	− .0101	.0281	− .0669	.1231
3.11	.9991	.0009	.0032	− .0099	.0275	− .0657	.1220
3.12	.9991	.0009	.0031	− .0096	.0268	− .0645	.1208
3.13	.9991	.0009	.0030	− .0093	.0262	− .0633	.1196
3.14	.9992	.0008	.0029	− .0091	.0256	− .0621	.1184
3.15	.9992	.0008	.0028	− .0088	.0249	− .0609	.1171
3.16	.9992	.0008	.0027	− .0086	.0243	− .0598	.1159
3.17	.9992	.0008	.0026	− .0083	.0237	− .0586	.1146
3.18	.9993	.0007	.0025	− .0081	.0232	− .0575	.1133
3.19	.9993	.0007	.0025	− .0079	.0226	− .0564	.1120
3.20	.9993	.0007	.0024	− .0076	.0220	− .0552	.1107
3.21	.9993	.0007	.0023	− .0074	.0215	− .0541	.1093
3.22	.9994	.0006	.0022	− .0072	.0210	− .0531	.1080
3.23	.9994	.0006	.0022	− .0070	.0204	− .0520	.1066
3.24	.9994	.0006	.0021	− .0068	.0199	− .0509	.1053
3.25	.9994	.0006	.0020	− .0066	.0194	− .0499	.1039
3.26	.9994	.0006	.0020	− .0064	.0189	− .0488	.1025
3.27	.9995	.0005	.0019	− .0062	.0184	− .0478	.1011
3.28	.9995	.0005	.0018	− .0060	.0180	− .0468	.0997
3.29	.9995	.0005	.0018	− .0059	.0175	− .0458	.0983
3.30	.9995	.0005	.0017	− .0057	.0170	− .0449	.0969
3.31	.9995	.0005	.0017	− .0055	.0166	− .0439	.0955
3.32	.9995	.0005	.0016	− .0054	.0162	− .0429	.0941
3.33	.9996	.0004	.0016	− .0052	.0157	− .0420	.0927
3.34	.9996	.0004	.0015	− .0050	.0153	− .0411	.0913
3.35	.9996	.0004	.0015	− .0049	.0149	− .0402	.0899
3.36	.9996	.0004	.0014	− .0047	.0145	− .0393	.0885
3.37	.9996	.0004	.0014	− .0046	.0141	− .0384	.0871
3.38	.9996	.0004	.0013	− .0045	.0138	− .0376	.0857
3.39	.9997	.0003	.0013	− .0043	.0134	− .0367	.0843
3.40	.9997	.0003	.0012	− .0042	.0130	− .0359	.0829
3.41	.9997	.0003	.0012	− .0041	.0127	− .0350	.0815
3.42	.9997	.0003	.0012	− .0039	.0123	− .0342	.0801
3.43	.9997	.0003	.0011	− .0038	.0120	− .0334	.0788
3.44	.9997	.0003	.0011	− .0037	.0116	− .0327	.0774
3.45	.9997	.0003	.0010	− .0036	.0113	− .0319	.0761
3.46	.9997	.0003	.0010	− .0035	.0110	− .0311	.0747
3.47	.9997	.0003	.0010	− .0034	.0107	− .0304	.0734
3.48	.9997	.0003	.0009	− .0033	.0104	− .0297	.0721
3.49	.9998	.0002	.0009	− .0032	.0101	− .0290	.0707
3.50	.9998	.0002	.0009	− .0031	.0098	− .0283	.0694

NORMAL PROBABILITY FUNCTION AND RELATED FUNCTIONS (Continued)

x	$F(x)$	$1 - F(x)$	$f(x)$	$f'(x)$	$f''(x)$	$f'''(x)$	$f^{iv}(x)$
3.50	.9998	.0002	.0009	− .0031	.0098	− .0283	.0694
3.51	.9998	.0002	.0008	− .0030	.0095	− .0276	.0681
3.52	.9998	.0002	.0008	− .0029	.0093	− .0269	.0669
3.53	.9998	.0002	.0008	− .0028	.0090	− .0262	.0656
3.54	.9998	.0002	.0008	− .0027	.0087	− .0256	.0643
3.55	.9998	.0002	.0007	− .0026	.0085	− .0249	.0631
3.56	.9998	.0002	.0007	− .0025	.0082	− .0243	.0618
3.57	.9998	.0002	.0007	− .0024	.0080	− .0237	.0606
3.58	.9998	.0002	.0007	− .0024	.0078	− .0231	.0594
3.59	.9998	.0002	.0006	− .0023	.0075	− .0225	.0582
3.60	.9998	.0002	.0006	− .0022	.0073	− .0219	.0570
3.61	.9998	.0002	.0006	− .0021	.0071	− .0214	.0559
3.62	.9999	.0001	.0006	− .0021	.0069	− .0208	.0547
3.63	.9999	.0001	.0005	− .0020	.0067	− .0203	.0536
3.64	.9999	.0001	.0005	− .0019	.0065	− .0198	.0524
3.65	.9999	.0001	.0005	− .0019	.0063	− .0192	.0513
3.66	.9999	.0001	.0005	− .0018	.0061	− .0187	.0502
3.67	.9999	.0001	.0005	− .0017	.0059	− .0182	.0492
3.68	.9999	.0001	.0005	− .0017	.0057	− .0177	.0481
3.69	.9999	.0001	.0004	− .0016	.0056	− .0173	.0470
3.70	.9999	.0001	.0004	− .0016	.0054	− .0168	.0460
3.71	.9999	.0001	.0004	− .0015	.0052	− .0164	.0450
3.72	.9999	.0001	.0004	− .0015	.0051	− .0159	.0440
3.73	.9999	.0001	.0004	− .0014	.0049	− .0155	.0430
3.74	.9999	.0001	.0004	− .0014	.0048	− .0150	.0420
3.75	.9999	.0001	.0004	− .0013	.0046	− .0146	.0410
3.76	.9999	.0001	.0003	− .0013	.0045	− .0142	.0401
3.77	.9999	.0001	.0003	− .0012	.0043	− .0138	.0392
3.78	.9999	.0001	.0003	− .0012	.0042	− .0134	.0382
3.79	.9999	.0001	.0003	− .0012	.0041	− .0131	.0373
3.80	.9999	.0001	.0003	− .0011	.0039	− .0127	.0365
3.81	.9999	.0001	.0003	− .0011	.0038	− .0123	.0356
3.82	.9999	.0001	.0003	− .0010	.0037	− .0120	.0347
3.83	.9999	.0001	.0003	− .0010	.0036	− .0116	.0339
3.84	.9999	.0001	.0003	− .0010	.0034	− .0113	.0331
3.85	.9999	.0001	.0002	− .0009	.0033	− .0110	.0323
3.86	.9999	.0001	.0002	− .0009	.0032	− .0107	.0315
3.87	.9999	.0001	.0002	− .0009	.0031	− .0104	.0307
3.88	.9999	.0001	.0002	− .0008	.0030	− .0100	.0299
3.89	1.0000	.0000	.0002	− .0008	.0029	− .0098	.0292
3.90	1.0000	.0000	.0002	− .0008	.0028	− .0095	.0284
3.91	1.0000	.0000	.0002	− .0008	.0027	− .0092	.0277
3.92	1.0000	.0000	.0002	− .0007	.0026	− .0089	.0270
3.93	1.0000	.0000	.0002	− .0007	.0026	− .0086	.0263
3.94	1.0000	.0000	.0002	− .0007	.0025	− .0084	.0256
3.95	1.0000	.0000	.0002	− .0006	.0024	− .0081	.0250
3.96	1.0000	.0000	.0002	− .0006	.0023	− .0079	.0243
3.97	1.0000	.0000	.0002	− .0006	.0022	− .0076	.0237
3.98	1.0000	.0000	.0001	− .0006	.0022	− .0074	.0230
3.99	1.0000	.0000	.0001	− .0006	.0021	− .0072	.0224
4.00	1.0000	.0000	.0001	− .0005	.0020	− .0070	.0218

x	1.282	1.645	1.960	2.326	2.576	3.090
$F(x)$	.90	.95	.975	.99	.995	.999
$2[1 - F(x)]$	.20	.10	.05	.02	.01	.002

INDIVIDUAL TERMS, BINOMIAL DISTRIBUTION

The $(x + 1)^{st}$ term in the expansion of the binomial $[\theta + (1 - \theta)]^n$ is given by

$$f(x;n,\theta) = \binom{n}{x} \theta^x (1 - \theta)^{n-x}, \qquad x = 0, 1, 2, \ldots, n.$$

This is the probability of exactly x successes in n independent binomial trials with probability of success on a single trial equal to θ. This table contains the individual terms of $f(x;n,\theta)$ for specified choices of x, n, and θ.

For $\theta > 0.5$, the value of $\binom{n}{x} \theta^x (1 - \theta)^{n-x}$ is found by using the table entry for $\binom{n}{n-x} (1 - \theta)^{n-x} \theta^x$.

INDIVIDUAL TERMS, BINOMIAL DISTRIBUTION (Continued)

| | | | | | | θ | | | | | |
n	x	.05	.10	.15	.20	.25	.30	.35	.40	45	.50
1	0	.9500	.9000	.8500	.8000	.7500	.7000	.6500	.6000	.5500	.5000
	1	.0500	.1000	.1500	.2000	.2500	.3000	.3500	.4000	.4500	.5000
2	0	.9025	.8100	.7225	.6400	.5625	.4900	.4225	.3600	.3025	.2500
	1	.0950	.1800	.2550	.3200	.3750	.4200	.4550	.4800	.4950	.5000
	2	.0025	.0100	.0225	.0400	.0625	.0900	.1225	.1600	.2025	.2500
3	0	.8574	.7290	.6141	.5120	.4219	.3430	.2746	.2160	.1664	.1250
	1	.1354	.2430	.3251	.3840	.4219	.4410	.4436	.4320	.4084	.3750
	2	.0071	.0270	.0574	.0960	.1406	.1890	.2389	.2880	.3341	.3750
	3	.0001	.0010	.0034	.0080	.0156	.0270	.0429	.0640	.0911	.1250
4	0	.8145	.6561	.5220	.4096	.3164	.2401	.1785	.1296	.0915	.0625
	1	.1715	.2916	.3685	.4096	.4219	.4116	.3845	.3456	.2995	.2500
	2	.0135	.0486	.0975	.1536	.2109	.2646	.3105	.3456	.3675	.3750
	3	.0005	.0036	.0115	.0256	.0469	.0756	.1115	.1536	.2005	.2500
	4	.0000	.0001	.0005	.0016	.0039	.0081	.0150	.0256	.0410	.0625
5	0	.7738	.5905	.4437	.3277	.2373	.1681	.1160	.0778	.0503	.0312
	1	.2036	.3280	.3915	.4096	.3955	.3602	.3124	.2592	.2059	.1562
	2	.0214	.0729	.1382	.2048	.2637	.3087	.3364	.3456	.3369	.3125
	3	.0011	.0081	.0244	.0512	.0879	.1323	.1811	.2304	.2757	.3125
	4	.0000	.0004	.0022	.0064	.0146	.0284	.0488	.0768	.1128	.1562
	5	.0000	.0000	.0001	.0003	.0010	.0024	.0053	.0102	.0185	.0312
6	0	.7351	.5314	.3771	.2621	.1780	.1176	.0754	.0467	.0277	.0156
	1	.2321	.3543	.3993	.3932	.3560	.3025	.2437	.1866	.1359	.0938
	2	.0305	.0984	.1762	.2458	.2966	.3241	.3280	.3110	.2780	.2344
	3	.0021	.0146	.0415	.0819	.1318	.1852	.2355	.2765	.3032	.3125
	4	.0001	.0012	.0055	.0154	.0330	.0595	.0951	.1382	.1861	.2344
	5	.0000	.0001	.0004	.0015	.0044	.0102	.0205	.0369	.0609	.0938
	6	.0000	.0000	.0000	.0001	.0002	.0007	.0018	.0041	.0083	.0156
7	0	.6983	.4783	.3206	.2097	.1335	.0824	.0490	.0280	.0152	.0078
	1	.2573	.3720	.3960	.3670	.3115	.2471	.1848	.1306	.0872	.0547
	2	.0406	.1240	.2097	.2753	.3115	.3177	.2985	.2613	.2140	.1641
	3	.0036	.0230	.0617	.1147	.1730	.2269	.2679	.2903	.2918	.2734
	4	.0002	.0026	.0109	.0287	.0577	.0972	.1442	.1935	.2388	.2734
	5	.0000	.0002	.0012	.0043	.0115	.0250	.0466	.0774	.1172	.1641
	6	.0000	.0000	.0001	.0004	.0013	.0036	.0084	.0172	.0320	.0547
	7	.0000	.0000	.0000	.0000	.0001	.0002	.0006	.0016	.0037	.0078
8	0	.6634	.4305	.2725	.1678	.1001	.0576	.0319	.0168	.0084	.0039
	1	.2793	.3826	.3847	.3355	.2670	.1977	.1373	.0896	.0548	.0312
	2	.0515	.1488	.2376	.2936	.3115	.2965	.2587	.2090	.1569	.1094
	3	.0054	.0331	.0839	.1468	.2076	.2541	.2786	.2787	.2568	.2188
	4	.0004	.0046	.0185	.0459	.0865	.1361	.1875	.2322	.2627	.2734
	5	.0000	.0004	.0026	.0092	.0231	.0467	.0808	.1239	.1719	.2188
	6	.0000	.0000	.0002	.0011	.0038	.0100	.0217	.0413	.0703	.1094
	7	.0000	.0000	.0000	.0001	.0004	.0012	.0033	.0079	.0164	.0312
	8	.0000	.0000	.0000	.0000	.0000	.0001	.0002	.0007	.0017	.0039

Linear interpolations with respect to p will in general be accurate at most to two decimal places.

Binomial Distribution

INDIVIDUAL TERMS, BINOMIAL DISTRIBUTION (Continued)

n	x	.05	.10	.15	.20	.25	.30	.35	.40	.45	.50
9	0	.6302	.3874	.2316	.1342	.0751	.0404	.0207	.0101	.0046	.0020
	1	.2985	.3874	.3679	.3020	.2253	.1556	.1004	.0605	.0339	.0176
	2	.0629	.1722	.2597	.3020	.3003	.2668	.2162	.1612	.1110	.0703
	3	.0077	.0446	.1069	.1762	.2336	.2668	.2716	.2508	.2119	.1641
	4	.0006	.0074	.0283	.0661	.1168	.1715	.2194	.2508	.2600	.2461
	5	.0000	.0008	.0050	.0165	.0389	.0735	.1181	.1672	.2128	.2461
	6	.0000	.0001	.0006	.0028	.0087	.0210	.0424	.0743	.1160	.1641
	7	.0000	.0000	.0000	.0003	.0012	.0039	.0098	.0212	.0407	.0703
	8	.0000	.0000	.0000	.0000	.0001	.0004	.0013	.0035	.0083	.0176
	9	.0000	.0000	.0000	.0000	.0000	.0000	.0001	.0003	.0008	.0020
10	0	.5987	.3487	.1969	.1074	.0563	.0282	.0135	.0060	.0025	.0010
	1	.3151	.3874	.3474	.2684	.1877	.1211	.0725	.0403	.0207	.0098
	2	.0746	.1937	.2759	.3020	.2816	.2335	.1757	.1209	.0763	.0439
	3	.0105	.0574	.1298	.2013	.2503	.2668	.2522	.2150	.1665	.1172
	4	.0010	.0112	.0401	.0881	.1460	.2001	.2377	.2508	.2384	.2051
	5	.0001	.0015	.0085	.0264	.0584	.1029	.1536	.2007	.2340	.2461
	6	.0000	.0001	.0012	.0055	.0162	.0368	.0689	.1115	.1596	.2051
	7	.0000	.0000	.0001	.0008	.0031	.0090	.0212	.0425	.0746	.1172
	8	.0000	.0000	.0000	.0001	.0004	.0014	.0043	.0106	.0229	.0439
	9	.0000	.0000	.0000	.0000	.0000	.0001	.0005	.0016	.0042	.0098
	10	.0000	.0000	.0000	.0000	.0000	.0000	.0000	.0001	.0003	.0010
11	0	.5688	.3138	1673	.0859	.0422	.0198	.0088	.0036	.0014	.0004
	1	.3293	.3835	.3248	.2362	.1549	.0932	.0518	.0266	.0125	.0055
	2	.0867	.2131	.2866	.2953	.2581	.1998	.1395	.0887	.0513	.0269
	3	.0137	.0710	.1517	.2215	.2581	.2568	.2254	.1774	.1259	.0806
	4	.0014	.0158	.0536	.1107	.1721	.2201	.2428	.2365	.2060	.1611
	5	.0001	.0025	.0132	.0388	.0803	.1321	.1830	.2207	.2360	.2256
	6	.0000	.0003	.0023	.0097	.0268	.0566	.0985	.1471	.1931	.2256
	7	.0000	.0000	.0003	.0017	.0064	.0173	.0379	.0701	.1128	.1611
	8	.0000	.0000	.0000	.0002	.0011	.0037	.0102	.0234	.0462	.0806
	9	.0000	.0000	.0000	.0000	.0001	.0005	.0018	.0052	.0126	.0269
	10	.0000	.0000	.0000	.0000	.0000	.0000	.0002	.0007	.0021	.0054
	11	.0000	.0000	.0000	.0000	.0000	.0000	.0000	.0000	.0002	.0005
12	0	.5404	.2824	.1422	.0687	.0317	.0138	.0057	.0022	.0008	.0002
	1	.3413	.3766	.3012	.2062	.1267	.0712	.0368	.0174	.0075	.0029
	2	.0988	.2301	.2924	.2835	.2323	.1678	.1088	.0639	.0339	.0161
	3	.0173	.0852	.1720	.2362	.2581	.2397	.1954	.1419	.0923	.0537
	4	.0021	.0213	.0683	.1329	.1936	.2311	.2367	.2128	.1700	.1208
	5	.0002	.0038	.0193	.0532	.1032	.1585	.2039	.2270	.2225	.1934
	6	.0000	.0005	.0040	.0155	.0401	.0792	.1281	.1766	.2124	.2256
	7	.0000	.0000	.0006	.0033	.0115	.0291	.0591	.1009	.1489	.1934
	8	.0000	.0000	.0001	.0005	.0024	.0078	.0199	.0420	.0762	.1208
	9	.0000	.0000	.0000	.0001	.0004	.0015	.0048	.0125	.0277	.0537
	10	.0000	.0000	.0000	.0000	.0000	.0002	.0008	.0025	.0068	.0161
	11	.0000	.0000	.0000	.0000	.0000	.0000	.0001	.0003	.0010	.0029
	12	.0000	.0000	.0000	.0000	.0000	.0000	.0000	.0000	.0001	.0002

INDIVIDUAL TERMS, BINOMIAL DISTRIBUTION (Continued)

n	x	.05	.10	.15	.20	θ .25	.30	.35	.40	.45	.50
13	0	.5133	.2542	.1209	.0550	.0238	.0097	.0037	.0013	.0004	.0001
	1	.3512	.3672	.2774	.1787	.1029	.0540	.0259	.0113	.0045	.0016
	2	.1109	.2448	.2937	.2680	.2059	.1388	.0836	.0453	.0220	.0095
	3	.0214	.0997	.1900	.2457	.2517	.2181	.1651	.1107	.0660	.0349
	4	.0028	.0277	.0838	.1535	.2097	.2337	.2222	.1845	.1350	.0873
	5	.0003	.0055	.0266	.0691	.1258	.1803	.2154	.2214	.1989	.1571
	6	.0000	.0008	.0063	.0230	.0559	.1030	.1546	.1968	.2169	.2095
	7	.0000	.0001	.0011	.0058	.0186	.0442	.0833	.1312	.1775	.2095
	8	.0000	.0000	.0001	.0011	.0047	.0142	.0336	.0656	.1089	.1571
	9	.0000	.0000	.0000	.0001	.0009	.0034	.0101	.0243	.0495	.0873
	10	.0000	.0000	.0000	.0000	.0001	.0006	.0022	.0065	.0162	.0349
	11	.0000	.0000	.0000	.0000	.0000	.0001	.0003	.0012	.0036	.0095
	12	.0000	.0000	.0000	.0000	.0000	.0000	.0000	.0001	.0005	.0016
	13	.0000	.0000	.0000	.0000	.0000	.0000	.0000	.0000	.0000	.0001
14	0	.4877	.2288	.1028	.0440	.0178	.0068	.0024	.0008	.0002	.0001
	1	.3593	.3559	.2539	.1539	.0832	.0407	.0181	.0073	.0027	.0009
	2	.1229	.2570	.2912	.2501	.1802	.1134	.0634	.0317	.0141	.0056
	3	.0259	.1142	.2056	.2501	.2402	.1943	.1366	.0845	.0462	.0222
	4	.0037	.0349	.0998	.1720	.2202	.2290	.2022	.1549	.1040	.0611
	5	.0004	.0078	.0352	.0860	.1468	.1963	.2178	.2066	.1701	.1222
	6	.0000	.0013	.0093	.0322	.0734	.1262	.1759	.2066	.2088	.1833
	7	.0000	.0002	.0019	.0092	.0280	.0618	.1082	.1574	.1952	.2095
	8	.0000	.0000	.0003	.0020	.0082	.0232	.0510	.0918	.1398	.1833
	9	.0000	.0000	.0000	.0003	.0018	.0066	.0183	.0408	.0762	.1222
	10	.0000	.0000	.0000	.0000	.0003	.0014	.0049	.0136	.0312	.0611
	11	.0000	.0000	.0000	.0000	.0000	.0002	.0010	.0033	.0093	.0222
	12	.0000	.0000	.0000	.0000	.0000	.0000	.0001	.0005	.0019	.0056
	13	.0000	.0000	.0000	.0000	.0000	.0000	.0000	.0001	.0002	.0009
	14	.0000	.0000	.0000	.0000	.0000	.0000	.0000	.0000	.0000	.0001
15	0	.4633	.2059	.0874	.0352	.0134	.0047	.0016	.0005	.0001	.0000
	1	.3658	.3432	.2312	.1319	.0668	.0305	.0126	.0047	.0016	.0005
	2	.1348	.2669	.2856	.2309	.1559	.0916	.0476	.0219	.0090	.0032
	3	.0307	.1285	.2184	.2501	.2252	.1700	.1110	.0634	.0318	.0139
	4	.0049	.0428	.1156	.1876	.2252	.2186	.1792	.1268	.0780	.0417
	5	.0006	.0105	.0449	.1032	.1651	.2061	.2123	.1859	.1404	.0916
	6	.0000	.0019	.0132	.0430	.0917	.1472	.1906	.2066	.1914	.1527
	7	.0000	.0003	.0030	.0138	.0393	.0811	.1319	.1771	.2013	.1964
	8	.0000	.0000	.0005	.0035	.0131	.0348	.0710	.1181	.1647	.1964
	9	.0000	.0000	.0001	.0007	.0034	.0116	.0298	.0612	.1048	.1527
	10	.0000	.0000	.0000	.0001	.0007	.0030	.0096	.0245	.0515	.0916
	11	.0000	.0000	.0000	.0000	.0001	.0006	.0024	.0074	.0191	.0417
	12	.0000	.0000	.0000	.0000	.0000	.0001	.0004	.0016	.0052	.0139
	13	.0000	.0000	.0000	.0000	.0000	.0000	.0001	.0003	.0010	.0032
	14	.0000	.0000	.0000	.0000	.0000	.0000	.0000	.0000	.0001	.0005
	15	.0000	.0000	.0000	.0000	.0000	.0000	.0000	.0000	.0000	.0000

INDIVIDUAL TERMS, BINOMIAL DISTRIBUTION (Continued)

n	x	.05	.10	.15	.20	.25	.30	.35	.40	.45	.50
16	0	.4401	.1853	.0743	.0281	.0100	.0033	.0010	.0003	.0001	.0000
	1	.3706	.3294	.2097	.1126	.0535	.0228	.0087	.0030	.0009	.0002
	2	.1463	.2745	.2775	.2111	.1336	.0732	.0353	.0150	.0056	.0018
	3	.0359	.1423	.2285	.2463	.2079	.1465	.0888	.0468	.0215	.0085
	4	.0061	.0514	.1311	.2001	.2252	.2040	.1553	.1014	.0572	.0278
	5	.0008	.0137	.0555	.1201	.1802	.2099	.2008	.1623	.1123	.0667
	6	.0001	.0028	.0180	.0550	.1101	.1649	.1982	.1983	.1684	.1222
	7	.0000	.0004	.0045	.0197	.0524	.1010	.1524	.1889	.1969	.1746
	8	.0000	.0001	.0009	.0055	.0197	.0487	.0923	.1417	.1812	.1964
	9	.0000	.0000	.0001	.0012	.0058	.0185	.0442	.0840	.1318	.1746
	10	.0000	.0000	.0000	.0002	.0014	.0056	.0167	.0392	.0755	.1222
	11	.0000	.0000	.0000	.0000	.0002	.0013	.0049	.0142	.0337	.0667
	12	.0000	.0000	.0000	.0000	.0000	.0002	.0011	.0040	.0115	.0278
	13	.0000	.0000	.0000	.0000	.0000	.0000	.0002	.0008	.0029	.0085
	14	.0000	.0000	.0000	.0000	.0000	.0000	.0000	.0001	.0005	.0018
	15	.0000	.0000	.0000	.0000	.0000	.0000	.0000	.0000	.0001	.0002
	16	.0000	.0000	.0000	.0000	.0000	.0000	.0000	.0000	.0000	.0000
17	0	.4181	.1668	.0631	.0225	.0075	.0023	.0007	.0002	.0000	.0000
	1	.3741	.3150	.1893	.0957	.0426	.0169	.0060	.0019	.0005	.0001
	2	.1575	.2800	.2673	.1914	.1136	.0581	.0260	.0102	.0035	.0010
	3	.0415	.1556	.2359	.2393	.1893	.1245	.0701	.0341	.0144	.0052
	4	.9076	.0605	.1457	.2093	.2209	.1868	.1320	.0796	.0411	.0182
	5	.0010	.0175	.0668	.1361	.1914	.2081	.1849	.1379	.0875	.0472
	6	.0001	.0039	.0236	.0680	.1276	.1784	.1991	.1839	.1432	.0944
	7	.0000	.0007	.0065	.0267	.0668	.1201	.1685	.1927	.1841	.1484
	8	.0000	.0001	.0014	.0084	.0279	.0644	.1134	.1606	.1883	.1855
	9	.0000	.0000	.0003	.0021	.0093	.0276	.0611	.1070	.1540	.1855
	10	.0000	.0000	.0000	.0004	.0025	.0095	.0263	.0571	.1008	.1484
	11	.0000	.0000	.0000	.0001	.0005	.0026	.0090	.0242	.0525	.0944
	12	.0000	.0000	.0000	.0000	.0001	.0006	.0024	.0081	.0215	.0472
	13	.0000	.0000	.0000	.0000	.0000	.0001	.0005	.0021	.0068	.0182
	14	.0000	.0000	.0000	.0000	.0000	.0000	.0001	.0004	.0016	.0052
	15	.0000	.0000	.0000	.0000	.0000	.0000	.0000	.0001	.0003	.0010
	16	.0000	.0000	.0000	.0000	.0000	.0000	.0000	.0000	.0000	.0001
	17	.0000	.0000	.0000	.0000	.0000	.0000	.0000	.0000	.0000	.0000
18	0	.3972	.1501	.0536	.0180	.0056	.0016	.0004	.0001	.0000	.0000
	1	.3763	.3002	.1704	.0811	.0338	.0126	.0042	.0012	.0003	.0001
	2	.1683	.2835	.2556	.1723	.0958	.0458	.0190	.0069	.0022	.0006
	3	.0473	.1680	.2406	.2297	.1704	.1046	.0547	.0246	.0095	.0031
	4	.0093	.0700	.1592	.2153	.2130	.1681	.1104	.0614	.0291	.0117
	5	.0014	.0218	.0787	.1507	.1988	.2017	.1664	.1146	.0666	.0327
	6	.0002	.0052	.0301	.0816	.1436	.1873	.1941	.1655	.1181	.0708
	7	.0000	.0010	.0091	.0350	.0820	.1376	.1792	.1892	.1657	.1214
	8	.0000	.0002	.0022	.0120	.0376	.0811	.1327	.1734	.1864	.1669
	9	.0000	.0000	.0004	.0033	.0139	.0386	.0794	.1284	.1694	.1855
	10	.0000	.0000	.0001	.0008	.0042	.0149	.0385	.0771	.1248	.1669
	11	.0000	.0000	.0000	.0001	.0010	.0046	.0151	.0374	.0742	.1214

INDIVIDUAL TERMS, BINOMIAL DISTRIBUTION (Continued)

n	x	θ .05	.10	.15	.20	.25	.30	.35	.40	.45	.50
18	12	.0000	.0000	.0000	.0000	.0002	.0012	.0047	.0145	.0354	.0708
	13	.0000	.0000	.0000	.0000	.0000	.0002	.0012	.0045	.0134	.0327
	14	.0000	.0000	.0000	.0000	.0000	.0000	.0002	.0011	.0039	.0117
	15	.0000	.0000	.0000	.0000	.0000	.0000	.0000	.0002	.0009	.0031
	16	.0000	.0000	.0000	.0000	.0000	.0000	.0000	.0000	.0001	.0006
	17	.0000	.0000	.0000	.0000	.0000	.0000	.0000	.0000	.0000	.0001
	18	.0000	.0000	.0000	.0000	.0000	.0000	.0000	.0000	.0000	.0000
19	0	.3774	.1351	.0456	.0144	.0042	.0011	.0003	.0001	.0000	.0000
	1	.3774	.2852	.1529	.0685	.0268	.0093	.0029	.0008	.0002	.0000
	2	.1787	.2852	.2428	.1540	.0803	.0358	.0138	.0046	.0013	.0003
	3	.0533	.1796	.2428	.2182	.1517	.0869	.0422	.0175	.0062	.0018
	4	.0112	.0798	.1714	.2182	.2023	.1491	.0909	.0467	.0203	.0074
	5	.0018	.0266	.0907	.1636	.2023	.1916	.1468	.0933	.0497	.0222
	6	.0002	.0069	.0374	.0955	.1574	.1916	.1844	.1451	.0949	.0518
	7	.0000	.0014	.0122	.0443	.0974	.1525	.1844	.1797	.1443	.0961
	8	.0000	.0002	.0032	.0166	.0487	.0981	.1489	.1797	.1771	.1442
	9	.0000	.0000	.0007	.0051	.0198	.0514	.0980	.1464	.1771	.1762
	10	.0000	.0000	.0001	.0013	.0066	.0220	.0528	.0976	.1449	.1762
	11	.0000	.0000	.0000	.0003	.0018	.0077	.0233	.0532	.0970	.1442
	12	.0000	.0000	.0000	.0000	.0004	.0022	.0083	.0237	.0529	.0961
	13	.0000	.0000	.0000	.0000	.0001	.0005	.0024	.0085	.0233	.0518
	14	.0000	.0000	.0000	.0000	.0000	.0001	.0006	.0024	.0082	.0222
	15	.0000	.0000	.0000	.0000	.0000	.0000	.0001	.0005	.0022	.0074
	16	.0000	.0000	.0000	.0000	.0000	.0000	.0000	.0001	.0005	.0018
	17	.0000	.0000	.0000	.0000	.0000	.0000	.0000	.0000	.0001	.0003
	18	.0000	.0000	.0000	.0000	.0000	.0000	.0000	.0000	.0000	.0000
	19	.0000	.0000	.0000	.0000	.0000	.0000	.0000	.0000	.0000	.0000
20	0	.3585	.1216	.0388	.0115	.0032	.0008	.0002	.0000	.0000	.0000
	1	.3774	.2702	.1368	.0576	.0211	.0068	.0020	.0005	.0001	.0000
	2	.1887	.2852	.2293	.1369	.0669	.0278	.0100	.0031	.0008	.0002
	3	.0596	.1901	.2428	.2054	.1339	.0716	.0323	.0123	.0040	.0011
	4	.0133	.0898	.1821	.2182	.1897	.1304	.0738	.0350	.0139	.0046
	5	.0022	.0319	.1028	.1746	.2023	.1789	.1272	.0746	.0365	.0148
	6	.0003	.0089	.0454	.1091	.1686	.1916	.1712	.1244	.0746	.0370
	7	.0000	.0020	.0160	.0545	.1124	.1643	.1844	.1659	.1221	.0739
	8	.0000	.0004	.0046	.0222	.0609	.1144	.1614	.1797	.1623	.1201
	9	.0000	.0001	.0011	.0074	.0271	.0654	.1158	.1597	.1771	.1602
	10	.0000	.0000	.0002	.0020	.0099	.0308	.0686	.1171	.1593	.1762
	11	.0000	.0000	.0000	.0005	.0030	.0120	.0336	.0710	.1185	.1602
	12	.0000	.0000	.0000	.0001	.0008	.0039	.0136	.0355	.0727	.1201
	13	.0000	.0000	.0000	.0000	.0002	.0010	.0045	.0146	.0366	.0739
	14	.0000	.0000	.0000	.0000	.0000	.0002	.0012	.0049	.0150	.0370
	15	.0000	.0000	.0000	.0000	.0000	.0000	.0003	.0013	.0049	.0148
	16	.0000	.0000	.0000	.0000	.0000	.0000	.0000	.0003	.0013	.0046
	17	.0000	.0000	.0000	.0000	.0000	.0000	.0000	.0000	.0002	.0011
	18	.0000	.0000	.0000	.0000	.0000	.0000	.0000	.0000	.0000	.0002
	19	.0000	.0000	.0000	.0000	.0000	.0000	.0000	.0000	.0000	.0000
	20	.0000	.0000	.0000	.0000	.0000	.0000	.0000	.0000	.0000	.0000

CUMULATIVE TERMS, BINOMIAL DISTRIBUTION

For the binomial probability function $f(z\,;n,\theta)$ the probability of observing x' or more successes is given by

$$\sum_{x=x'}^{n} \binom{n}{x} \theta^x (1-\theta)^{n-x},$$

This table contains the values of $\displaystyle\sum_{x=x'}^{n} \binom{n}{x} \theta^x (1-\theta)^{n-x}$ for specified values of n, x', and

θ. If $\theta > 0.5$, the values for $\displaystyle\sum_{x=x'}^{n} \binom{n}{x} \theta^x (1-\theta)^{n-x}$ are obtained using the corresponding

results obtained from

$$1 - \sum_{x=n-x'+1}^{n} \binom{n}{x} (1-\theta)^x \theta^{n-x}$$

The cumulative binomial distribution is related to the incomplete beta function as follows:

$$\sum_{x=x'}^{n} \binom{n}{x} \theta^x (1-\theta)^{n-x} = I_\theta(x',\, n-x'+1),$$

$$\sum_{x=0}^{x'-1} \binom{n}{x} \theta^x (1-\theta)^{n-x} = 1 - I_\theta(x',\, n-x'+1)$$

$$= 1 - \int_0^\theta u^{x'-1}(1-u)^{n-x'}\, du \Big/ \int_0^1 u^{x'-1}(1-u)^{n-x'}\, du\,.$$

The cumulative binomial distribution is related to the cumulative negative binomial distribution as follows:

$$1 - \sum_{x'=0}^{r-1} \binom{x+r}{x'} \theta^{x'}(1-\theta)^{x+r-x'} = \sum_{x'=0}^{x} \binom{x'+r-1}{r-1} \theta^r (1-\theta)^{x'}$$

or

$$\sum_{x'=r}^{x+r} \binom{x+r}{x'} \theta^{x'}(1-\theta)^{x+r-x'} = \sum_{x'=0}^{x} \binom{x'+r-1}{r-1} \theta^r (1-\theta)^{x'}.$$

CUMULATIVE TERMS, BINOMIAL DISTRIBUTION (Continued)

n	x'	.05	.10	.15	.20	θ .25	.30	.35	.40	.45	.50
2	1	.0975	.1900	.2775	.3600	.4375	.5100	.5775	.6400	.6975	.7500
	2	.0025	.0100	.0225	.0400	.0625	.0900	.1225	.1600	.2025	.2500
3	1	.1426	.2710	.3859	.4880	.5781	.6570	.7254	.7840	.8336	.8750
	2	.0072	.0280	.0608	.1040	.1562	.2160	.2818	.3520	.4252	.5000
	3	.0001	.0010	.0034	.0080	.0156	.0270	.0429	.0640	.0911	.1250
4	1	.1855	.3439	.4780	.5904	.6836	.7599	.8215	.8704	.9085	.9375
	2	.0140	.0523	.1095	.1808	.2617	.3483	.4370	.5248	.6090	.6875
	3	.0005	.0037	.0120	.0272	.0508	.0837	.1265	.1792	.2415	.3125
	4	.0000	.0001	.0005	.0016	.0039	.0081	.0150	.0256	.0410	.0625
5	1	.2262	.4095	.5563	.6723	.7627	.8319	.8840	.9222	.9497	.9688
	2	.0226	.0815	.1648	.2627	.3672	.4718	.5716	.6630	.7438	.8125
	3	.0012	.0086	.0266	.0579	.1035	.1631	.2352	.3174	.4069	.5000
	4	.0000	.0005	.0022	.0067	.0156	.0308	.0540	.0870	.1312	.1875
	5	.0000	.0000	.0001	.0003	.0010	.0024	.0053	.0102	.0185	.0312
6	1	.2649	.4686	.6229	.7379	.8220	.8824	.9246	.9533	.9723	.9844
	2	.0328	.1143	.2235	.3446	.4661	.5798	.6809	.7667·	.8364	.8906
	3	.0022	.0158	.0473	.0989	.1694	.2557	.3529	.4557	.5585	.6562
	4	.0001	.0013	.0059	.0170	.0376	.0705	.1174	.1792	.2553	.3438
	5	.0000	.0001	.0004	.0016	.0046	.0109	.0223	.0410	.0692	.1094
	6	.0000	.0000	.0000	.0001	.0002	.0007	.0018	.0041	.0083	.0156
7	1	.3017	.5217	.6794	.7903	.8665	.9176	.9510	.9720	.9848	.9922
	2	.0444	.1497	.2834	.4233	.5551	.6706	.7662	.8414	.8976	.9375
	3	.0038	.0257	.0738	.1480	.2436	.3529	.4677	.5801	.6836	.7734
	4	.0002	.0027	.0121	.0333	.0706	.1260	.1998	.2898	.3917	.5000
	5	.0000	.0002	.0012	.0047	.0129	.0288	.0556	.0963	.1529	.2266
	6	.0000	.0000	.0001	.0004	.0013	.0038	.0090	.0188	.0357	.0625
	7	.0000	.0000	.0000	.0000	.0001	.0002	.0006	.0016	.0037	.0078
8	1	.3366	.5695	.7275	.8322	.8999	.9424	.9681	.9832	.9916	.9961
	2	.0572	.1869	.3428	.4967	.6329	.7447	.8309	.8936	.9368	.9648
	3	.0058	.0381	.1052	.2031	.3215	.4482	.5722	.6846	.7799	.8555
	4	.0004	.0050	.0214	.0563	.1138	.1941	.2936	.4059	.5230	.6367
	5	.0000	.0004	.0029	.0104	.0273	.0580	.1061	.1737	.2604	.3633
	6	.0000	.0000	.0002	.0012	.0042	.0113	.0253	.0498	.0885	.1445
	7	.0000	.0000	.0000	.0001	.0004	.0013	.0036	.0085	.0181	.0352
	8	.0000	.0000	.0000	.0000	.0000	.0001	.0002	.0007	.0017	.0039
9	1	.3698	.6126	.7684	.8658	.9249	.9596	.9793	.9899	.9954	.9980
	2	.0712	.2252	.4005	.5638	.6997	.8040	.8789	.9295	.9615	.9805
	3	.0084	.0530	.1409	.2618	.3993	.5372	.6627	.7682	.8505	.9102
	4	.0006	.0083	.0339	.0856	.1657	.2703	.3911	.5174	.6386	.7461
	5	.0000	.0009	.0056	.0196	.0489	.0988	.1717	.2666	.3786	.5000
	6	.0000	.0001	.0006	.0031	.0100	.0253	.0536	.0994	.1658	.2539
	7	.0000	.0000	.0000	.0003	.0013	.0043	.0112	.0250	.0498	.0898
	8	.0000	.0000	.0000	.0000	.0001	.0004	.0014	.0038	.0091	.0195
	9	.0000	.0000	.0000	.0000	.0000	.0000	.0001	.0003	.0008	.0020

Linear interpolation will be accurate at most to two decimal places.

CUMULATIVE TERMS, BINOMIAL DISTRIBUTION (Continued)

n	x′	.05	.10	.15	.20	θ .25	.30	.35	.40	.45	.50
10	1	.4013	.6513	.8031	.8926	.9437	.9718	.9865	.9940	.9975	.9990
	2	.0861	.2639	.4557	.6242	.7560	.8507	.9140	.9536	.9767	.9893
	3	.0115	.0702	.1798	.3222	.4744	.6172	.7384	.8327	.9004	.9453
	4	.0010	.0128	.0500	.1209	.2241	.3504	.4862	.6177	.7340	.8281
	5	.0001	.0016	.0099	.0328	.0781	.1503	.2485	.3669	.4956	.6230
	6	.0000	.0001	.0014	.0064	.0197	.0473	.0949	.1662	.2616	.3770
	7	.0000	.0000	.0001	.0009	.0035	.0106	.0260	.0548	.1020	.1719
	8	.0000	.0000	.0000	.0001	.0004	.0016	.0048	.0123	.0274	.0547
	9	.0000	.0000	.0000	.0000	.0000	.0001	.0005	.0017	.0045	.0107
	10	.0000	.0000	.0000	.0000	.0000	.0000	.0000	.0001	.0003	.0010
11	1	.4312	.6862	.8327	.9141	.9578	.9802	.9912	.9964	.9986	.9995
	2	.1019	.3026	.5078	.6779	.8029	.8870	.9394	.9698	.9861	.9941
	3	.0152	.0896	.2212	.3826	.5448	.6873	.7999	.8811	.9348	.9673
	4	.0016	.0185	.0694	.1611	.2867	.4304	.5744	.7037	.8089	.8867
	5	.0001	.0028	.0159	.0504	.1146	.2103	.3317	.4672	.6029	.7256
	6	.0000	.0003	.0027	.0117	.0343	.0782	.1487	.2465	.3669	.5000
	7	.0000	.0000	.0003	.0020	.0076	.0216	.0501	.0994	.1738	.2744
	8	.0000	.0000	.0000	.0002	.0012	.0043	.0122	.0293	.0610	.1133
	9	.0000	.0000	.0000	.0000	.0001	.0006	.0020	.0059	.0148	.0327
	10	.0000	.0000	.0000	.0000	.0000	.0000	.0002	.0007	.0022	.0059
	11	.0000	.0000	.0000	.0000	.0000	.0000	.0000	.0000	.0002	.0005
12	1	.4596	.7176	.8578	.9313	.9683	.9862	.9943	.9978	.9992	.9998
	2	.1184	.3410	.5565	.7251	.8416	.9150	.9576	.9804	.9917	.9968
	3	.0196	.1109	.2642	.4417	.6093	.7472	.8487	.9166	.9579	.9807
	4	.0022	.0256	.0922	.2054	.3512	.5075	.6533	.7747	.8655	.9270
	5	.0002	.0043	.0239	.0726	.1576	.2763	.4167	.5618	.6956	.8062
	6	.0000	.0005	.0046	.0194	.0544	.1178	.2127	.3348	.4731	.6128
	7	.0000	.0001	.0007	.0039	.0143	.0386	.0846	.1582	.2607	.3872
	8	.0000	.0000	.0001	.0006	.0028	.0095	.0255	.0573	.1117	.1938
	9	.0000	.0000	.0000	.0001	.0004	.0017	.0056	.0153	.0356	.0730
	10	.0000	.0000	.0000	.0000	.0000	.0002	.0008	.0028	.0079	.0193
	11	.0000	.0000	.0000	.0000	.0000	.0000	.0001	.0003	.0011	.0032
	12	.0000	.0000	.0000	.0000	.0000	.0000	.0000	.0000	.0001	.0002
13	1	.4867	.7458	.8791	.9450	.9762	.9903	.9963	.9987	.9996	.9999
	2	.1354	.3787	.6017	.7664	.8733	.9363	.9704	.9874	.9951	.9983
	3	.0245	.1339	.3080	.4983	.6674	.7975	.8868	.9421	.9731	.9888
	4	.0031	.0342	.1180	.2527	.4157	.5794	.7217	.8314	.9071	.9539
	5	.0003	.0065	.0342	.0991	.2060	.3457	.4995	.6470	.7721	.8666
	6	.0000	.0009	.0075	.0300	.0802	.1654	.2841	.4256	.5732	.7095
	7	.0000	.0001	.0013	.0070	.0243	.0624	.1295	.2288	.3563	.5000
	8	.0000	.0000	.0002	.0012	.0056	.0182	.0462	.0977	.1788	.2905
	9	.0000	.0000	.0000	.0002	.0010	.0040	.0126	.0321	.0698	.1334
	10	.0000	.0000	.0000	.0000	.0001	.0007	.0025	.0078	.0203	.0461
	11	.0000	.0000	.0000	.0000	.0000	.0001	.0003	.0013	.0041	.0112
	12	.0000	.0000	.0000	.0000	.0000	.0000	.0000	.0001	.0005	.0017
	13	.0000	.0000	.0000	.0000	.0000	.0000	.0000	.0000	.0000	.0001

CUMULATIVE TERMS, BINOMIAL DISTRIBUTION (Continued)

n	x′	.05	.10	.15	.20	θ .25	.30	.35	.40	.45	.50
14	1	.5123	.7712	.8972	.9560	.9822	.9932	.9976	.9992	.9998	.9999
	2	.1530	.4154	.6433	.8021	.8990	.9525	.9795	.9919	.9971	.9991
	3	.0301	.1584	.3521	.5519	.7189	.8392	.9161	.9602	.9830	.9935
	4	.0042	.0441	.1465	.3018	.4787	.6448	.7795	.8757	.9368	.9713
	5	.0004	.0092	.0467	.1298	.2585	.4158	.5773	.7207	.8328	.9102
	6	.0000	.0015	.0115	.0439	.1117	.2195	.3595	.5141	.6627	.7880
	7	.0000	.0002	.0022	.0116	.0383	.0933	.1836	.3075	.4539	.6047
	8	.0000	.0000	.0003	.0024	.0103	.0315	.0753	.1501	.2586	.3953
	9	.0000	.0000	.0000	.0004	.0022	.0083	.0243	.0583	.1189	.2120
	10	.0000	.0000	.0000	.0000	.0003	.0017	.0060	.0175	.0426	.0898
	11	.0000	.0000	.0000	.0000	.0000	.0002	.0011	.0039	.0114	.0287
	12	.0000	.0000	.0000	.0000	.0000	.0000	.0001	.0006	.0022	.0065
	13	.0000	.0000	.0000	.0000	.0000	.0000	.0000	.0001	.0003	.0009
	14	.0000	.0000	.0000	.0000	.0000	.0000	.0000	.0000	.0000	.0001
15	1	.5367	.7941	.9126	.9648	.9866	.9953	.9984	.9995	.9999	1.0000
	2	.1710	.4510	.6814	.8329	.9198	.9647	.9858	.9948	.9983	.9995
	3	.0362	.1841	.3958	.6020	.7639	.8732	.9383	.9729	.9893	.9963
	4	.0055	.0556	.1773	.3518	.5387	.7031	.8273	.9095	.9576	.9824
	5	.0006	.0127	.0617	.1642	.3135	.4845	.6481	.7827	.8796	.9408
	6	.0001	.0022	.0168	.0611	.1484	.2784	.4357	.5968	.7392	.8491
	7	.0000	.0003	.0036	.0181	.0566	.1311	.2452	.3902	.5478	.6964
	8	.0000	.0000	.0006	.0042	.0173	.0500	.1132	.2131	.3465	.5000
	9	.0000	.0000	.0001	.0008	.0042	.0152	.0422	.0950	.1818	.3036
	10	.0000	.0000	.0000	.0001	.0008	.0037	.0124	.0338	.0769	.1509
	11	.0000	.0000	.0000	.0000	.0001	.0007	.0028	.0093	.0255	.0592
	12	.0000	.0000	.0000	.0000	.0000	.0001	.0005	.0019	.0063	.0176
	13	.0000	.0000	.0000	.0000	.0000	.0000	.0001	.0003	.0011	.0037
	14	.0000	.0000	.0000	.0000	.0000	.0000	.0000	.0000	.0001	.0005
	15	.0000	.0000	.0000	.0000	.0000	.0000	.0000	.0000	.0000	.0000
16	1	.5599	.8147	.9257	.9719	.9900	.9967	.9990	.9997	.9999	1.0000
	2	.1892	.4853	.7161	.8593	.9365	.9739	.9902	.9967	.9990	.9997
	3	.0429	.2108	.4386	.6482	.8029	.9006	.9549	.9817	.9934	.9979
	4	.0070	.0684	.2101	.4019	.5950	.7541	.8661	.9349	.9719	.9894
	5	.0009	.0170	.0791	.2018	.3698	.5501	.7108	.8334	.9147	.9616
	6	.0001	.0033	.0235	.0817	.1897	.3402	.5100	.6712	.8024	.8949
	7	.0000	.0005	.0056	.0267	.0796	.1753	.3119	.4728	.6340	.7228
	8	.0000	.0001	.0011	.0070	.0271	.0744	.1594	.2839	.4371	.5982
	9	.0000	.0000	.0002	.0015	.0075	.0257	.0671	.1423	.2559	.4018
	10	.0000	.0000	.0000	.0002	.0016	.0071	.0229	.0583	.1241	.2272
	11	.0000	.0000	.0000	.0000	.0003	.0016	.0062	.0191	.0486	.1051
	12	.0000	.0000	.0000	.0000	.0000	.0003	.0013	.0049	.0149	.0384
	13	.0000	.0000	.0000	.0000	.0000	.0000	.0002	.0009	.0035	.0106
	14	.0000	.0000	.0000	.0000	.0000	.0000	.0000	.0001	.0006	.0021
	15	.0000	.0000	.0000	.0000	.0000	.0000	.0000	.0000	.0001	.0003
	16	.0000	.0000	.0000	.0000	.0000	.0000	.0000	.0000	.0000	.0000

CUMULATIVE TERMS, BINOMIAL DISTRIBUTION (Continued)

n	x'	.05	.10	.15	.20	.25	.30	.35	.40	.45	.50
17	1	.5819	.8332	.9369	.9775	.9925	.9977	.9993	.9998	1.0000	1.0000
	2	.2078	.5182	.7475	.8818	.9499	.9807	.9933	.9979	.9994	.9999
	3	.0503	.2382	.4802	.6904	.8363	.9226	.9673	.9877	.9959	.9988
	4	.0088	.0826	.2444	.4511	.6470	.7981	.8972	.9536	.9816	.9936
	5	.0012	.0221	.0987	.2418	.4261	.6113	.7652	.8740	.9404	.9755
	6	.0001	.0047	.0319	.1057	.2347	.4032	.5803	.7361	.8529	.9283
	7	.0000	.0008	.0083	.0377	.1071	.2248	.3812	.5522	.7098	.8338
	8	.0000	.0001	.0017	.0109	.0402	.1046	.2128	.3595	.5257	.6855
	9	.0000	.0000	.0003	.0026	.0124	.0403	.0994	.1989	.3374	.5000
	10	.0000	.0000	.0000	.0005	.0031	.0127	.0383	.0919	.1834	.3145
	11	.0000	.0000	.0000	.0001	.0006	.0032	.0120	.0348	.0826	.1662
	12	.0000	.0000	.0000	.0000	.0001	.0007	.0030	.0106	.0301	.0717
	13	.0000	.0000	.0000	.0000	.0000	.0001	.0006	.0025	.0086	.0245
	14	.0000	.0000	.0000	.0000	.0000	.0000	.0001	.0005	.0019	.0064
	15	.0000	.0000	.0000	.0000	.0000	.0000	.0000	.0001	.0003	.0012
	16	.0000	.0000	.0000	.0000	.0000	.0000	.0000	.0000	.0000	.0001
	17	.0000	.0000	.0000	.0000	.0000	.0000	.0000	.0000	.0000	.0000
18	1	.6028	.8499	.9464	.9820	.9944	.9984	.9996	.9999	1.0000	1.0000
	2	.2265	.5497	.7759	.9009	.9605	.9858	.9954	.9987	.9997	.9999
	3	.0581	.2662	.5203	.7287	.8647	.9400	.9764	.9918	.9975	.9993
	4	.0109	.0982	.2798	.4990	.6943	.8354	.9217	.9672	.9880	.9962
	5	.0015	.0282	.1206	.2836	.4813	.6673	.8114	.9058	.9589	.9846
	6	.0002	.0064	.0419	.1329	.2825	.4656	.6450	.7912	.8923	.9519
	7	.0000	.0012	.0118	.0513	.1390	.2783	.4509	.6257	.7742	.8811
	8	.0000	.0002	.0027	.0163	.0569	.1407	.2717	.4366	.6085	.7597
	9	.0000	.0000	.0005	.0043	.0193	.0596	.1391	.2632	.4222	.5927
	10	.0000	.0000	.0001	.0009	.0054	.0210	.0597	.1347	.2527	.4073
	11	.0000	.0000	.0000	.0002	.0012	.0061	.0212	.0576	.1280	.2403
	12	.0000	.0000	.0000	.0000	.0002	.0014	.0062	.0203	.0537	.1189
	13	.0000	.0000	.0000	.0000	.0000	.0003	.0014	.0058	.0183	.0481
	14	.0000	.0000	.0000	.0000	.0000	.0000	.0003	.0013	.0049	.0154
	15	.0000	.0000	.0000	.0000	.0000	.0000	.0000	.0002	.0010	.0038
	16	.0000	.0000	.0000	.0000	.0000	.0000	.0000	.0000	.0001	.0007
	17	.0000	.0000	.0000	.0000	.0000	.0000	.0000	.0000	.0000	.0001
	18	.0000	.0000	.0000	.0000	.0000	.0000	.0000	.0000	.0000	.0000
19	1	.6226	.8649	.9544	.9856	.9958	.9989	.9997	.9999	1.0000	1.0000
	2	.2453	.5797	.8015	.9171	.9690	.9896	.9969	.9992	.9998	1.0000
	3	0.665	.2946	.5587	.7631	.8887	.9538	.9830	.9945	.9985	.9996
	4	.0132	.1150	.3159	.5449	.7369	.8668	.9409	.9770	.9923	.9978
	5	.0020	.0352	.1444	.3267	.5346	.7178	.8500	.9304	.9720	.9904
	6	.0002	.0086	.0537	.1631	.3322	.5261	.7032	.8371	.9223	.9682
	7	.0000	.0017	.0163	.0676	.1749	.3345	.5188	.6919	.8273	.9165
	8	.0000	.0003	.0041	.0233	.0775	.1820	.3344	.5122	.6831	.8204
	9	.0000	.0000	.0008	.0067	.0287	.0839	.1855	.3325	.5060	.6762
	10	.0000	.0000	.0001	.0016	.0089	.0326	.0875	.1861	.3290	.5000

CUMULATIVE TERMS, BINOMIAL DISTRIBUTION (Continued)

n	x'	.05	.10	.15	.20	.25	.30	.35	.40	.45	.50
19	11	.0000	.0000	.0000	.0003	.0023	.0105	.0347	.0885	.1841	.3238
	12	.0000	.0000	.0000	.0000	.0005	.0028	.0114	.0352	.0871	.1796
	13	.0000	.0000	.0000	.0000	.0001	.0006	.0031	.0116	.0342	.0835
	14	.0000	.0000	.0000	.0000	.0000	.0001	.0007	.0031	.0109	.0318
	15	.0000	.0000	.0000	.0000	.0000	.0000	.0001	.0006	.0028	.0096
	16	.0000	.0000	.0000	.0000	.0000	.0000	.0000	.0001	.0005	.0022
	17	.0000	.0000	.0000	.0000	.0000	.0000	.0000	.0000	.0001	.0004
	18	.0000	.0000	.0000	.0000	.0000	.0000	.0000	.0000	.0000	.0000
	19	.0000	.0000	.0000	.0000	.0000	.0000	.0000	.0000	.0000	.0000
20	1	.6415	.8784	.9612	.9885	.9968	.9992	.9998	1.0000	1.0000	1.0000
	2	.2642	.6083	.8244	.9308	.9757	.9924	.9979	.9995	.9999	1.0000
	3	.0755	.3231	.5951	.7939	.9087	.9645	.9879	.9964	.9991	.9998
	4	.0159	.1330	.3523	.5886	.7748	.8929	.9556	.9840	.9951	.9987
	5	.0026	.0432	.1702	.3704	.5852	.7625	.8818	.9490	.9811	.9941
	6	.0003	.0113	.0673	.1958	.3828	.5836	.7546	.8744	.9447	.9793
	7	.0000	.0024	.0219	.0867	.2142	.3920	.5834	.7500	.8701	.9423
	8	.0000	.0004	.0059	.0321	.1018	.2277	.3990	.5841	.7480	.8684
	9	.0000	.0001	.0013	.0100	.0409	.1133	.2376	.4044	.5857	.7483
	10	.0000	.0000	.0002	.0026	.0139	.0480	.1218	.2447	.4086	.5881
	11	.0000	.0000	.0000	.0006	.0039	.0171	.0532	.1275	.2493	.4119
	12	.0000	.0000	.0000	.0001	.0009	.0051	.0196	.0565	.1308	.2517
	13	.0000	.0000	.0000	.0000	.0002	.0013	.0060	.0210	.0580	.1316
	14	.0000	.0000	.0000	.0000	.0000	.0003	.0015	.0065	.0214	.0577
	15	.0000	.0000	.0000	.0000	.0000	.0000	.0003	.0016	.0064	.0207
	16	.0000	.0000	.0000	.0000	.0000	.0000	.0000	.0003	.0015	.0059
	17	.0000	.0000	.0000	.0000	.0000	.0000	.0000	.0000	.0003	.0013
	18	.0000	.0000	.0000	.0000	.0000	.0000	.0000	.0000	.0000	.0002
	19	.0000	.0000	.0000	.0000	.0000	.0000	.0000	.0000	.0000	.0000
	20	.0000	.0000	.0000	.0000	.0000	.0000	.0000	.0000	.0000	.0000

INDIVIDUAL TERMS, POISSON DISTRIBUTION

The Poisson probability function is given by

$$f(x;\lambda) = \frac{\lambda^x e^{-\lambda}}{x!}, \quad \lambda > 0, x = 0, 1, 2, \ldots .$$

This table contains the individual terms of $f(x;\lambda)$ for specified values of x and λ.

INDIVIDUAL TERMS, POISSON DISTRIBUTION (Continued)

x	0.1	0.2	0.3	0.4	0.5	0.6	0.7	0.8	0.9	1.0
0	.9048	.8187	.7408	.6703	.6065	.5488	.4966	.4493	.4066	.3679
1	.0905	.1637	.2222	.2681	.3033	.3293	.3476	.3595	.3659	.3679
2	.0045	.0164	.0333	.0536	.0758	.0988	.1217	.1438	.1647	.1839
3	.0002	.0011	.0033	.0072	.0126	.0198	.0284	.0383	.0494	.0613
4	.0000	.0001	.0003	.0007	.0016	.0030	.0050	.0077	.0111	.0153
5	.0000	.0000	.0000	.0001	.0002	.0004	.0007	.0012	.0020	.0031
6	.0000	.0000	.0000	.0000	.0000	.0000	.0001	.0002	.0003	.0005
7	.0000	.0000	.0000	.0000	.0000	.0000	.0000	.0000	.0000	.0001

x	1.1	1.2	1.3	1.4	1.5	1.6	1.7	1.8	1.9	2.0
0	.3329	.3012	.2725	.2466	.2231	.2019	.1827	.1653	.1496	.1353
1	.3662	.3614	.3543	.3452	.3347	.3230	.3106	.2975	.2842	.2707
2	.2014	.2169	.2303	.2417	.2510	.2584	.2640	.2678	.2700	.2707
3	.0738	.0867	.0998	.1128	.1255	.1378	.1496	.1607	.1710	.1804
4	.0203	.0260	.0324	.0395	.0471	.0551	.0636	.0723	.0812	.0902
5	.0045	.0062	.0084	.0111	.0141	.0176	.0216	.0260	.0309	.0361
6	.0008	.0012	.0018	.0026	.0035	.0047	.0061	.0078	.0098	.0120
7	.0001	.0002	.0003	.0005	.0008	.0011	.0015	.0020	.0027	.0034
8	.0000	.0000	.0001	.0001	.0001	.0002	.0003	.0005	.0006	.0009
9	.0000	.0000	.0000	.0000	.0000	.0000	.0001	.0001	.0001	.0002

x	2.1	2.2	2.3	2.4	2.5	2.6	2.7	2.8	2.9	3.0
0	.1225	.1108	.1003	.0907	.0821	.0743	.0672	.0608	.0550	.0498
1	.2572	.2438	.2306	.2177	.2052	.1931	.1815	.1703	.1596	.1494
2	.2700	.2681	.2652	.2613	.2565	.2510	.2450	.2384	.2314	.2240
3	.1890	.1966	.2033	.2090	.2138	.2176	.2205	.2225	.2237	.2240
4	.0992	.1082	.1169	.1254	.1336	.1414	.1488	.1557	.1622	.1680
5	.0417	.0476	.0538	.0602	.0668	.0735	.0804	.0872	.0940	.1008
6	.0146	.0174	.0206	.0241	.0278	.0319	.0362	.0407	.0455	.0504
7	.0044	.0055	.0068	.0083	.0099	.0118	.0139	.0163	.0188	.0216
8	.0011	.0015	.0019	.0025	.0031	.0038	.0047	.0057	.0068	.0081
9	.0003	.0004	.0005	.0007	.0009	.0011	.0014	.0018	.0022	.0027
10	.0001	.0001	.0001	.0002	.0002	.0003	.0004	.0005	.0006	.0008
11	.0000	.0000	.0000	.0000	.0000	.0001	.0001	.0001	.0002	.0002
12	.0000	.0000	.0000	.0000	.0000	.0000	.0000	.0000	.0000	.0001

x	3.1	3.2	3.3	3.4	3.5	3.6	3.7	3.8	3.9	4.0
0	.0450	.0408	.0369	.0334	.0302	.0273	.0247	.0224	.0202	.0183
1	.1397	.1304	.1217	.1135	.1057	.0984	.0915	.0850	.0789	.0733
2	.2165	.2087	.2008	.1929	.1850	.1771	.1692	.1615	.1539	.1465
3	.2237	.2226	.2209	.2186	.2158	.2125	.2087	.2046	.2001	.1954
4	.1734	.1781	.1823	.1858	.1888	.1912	.1931	.1944	.1951	.1954
5	.1075	.1140	.1203	.1264	.1322	.1377	.1429	.1477	.1522	.1563
6	.0555	.0608	.0662	.0716	.0771	.0826	.0881	.0936	.0989	.1042
7	.0246	.0278	.0312	.0348	.0385	.0425	.0466	.0508	.0551	.0595
8	.0095	.0111	.0129	.0148	.0169	.0191	.0215	.0241	.0269	.0298
9	.0033	.0040	.0047	.0056	.0066	.0076	.0089	.0102	.0116	.0132

INDIVIDUAL TERMS, POISSON DISTRIBUTION (Continued)

					λ					
x	3.1	3.2	3.3	3.4	3.5	3.6	3.7	3.8	3.9	4.0
10	.0010	.0013	.0016	.0019	.0023	.0028	.0033	.0039	.0045	.0053
11	.0003	.0004	.0005	.0006	.0007	.0009	.0011	.0013	.0016	.0019
12	.0001	.0001	.0001	.0002	.0002	.0003	.0003	.0004	.0005	.0006
13	.0000	.0000	.0000	.0000	.0001	.0001	.0001	.0001	.0002	.0002
14	.0000	.0000	.0000	.0000	.0000	.0000	.0000	.0000	.0000	.0001

					λ					
x	4.1	4.2	4.3	4.4	4.5	4.6	4.7	4.8	4.9	5.0
0	.0166	.0150	.0136	.0123	.0111	.0101	.0091	.0082	.0074	.0067
1	.0679	.0630	.0583	.0540	.0500	.0462	.0427	.0395	.0365	.0337
2	.1393	.1323	.1254	.1188	.1125	.1063	.1005	.0948	.0894	.0842
3	.1904	.1852	.1798	.1743	.1687	.1631	.1574	.1517	.1460	.1404
4	.1951	.1944	.1933	.1917	.1898	.1875	.1849	.1820	.1789	.1755
5	.1600	.1633	.1662	.1687	.1708	.1725	.1738	.1747	.1753	.1755
6	.1093	.1143	.1191	.1237	.1281	.1323	.1362	.1398	.1432	.1462
7	.0640	.0686	.0732	.0778	.0824	.0869	.0914	.0959	.1002	.1044
8	.0328	.0360	.0393	.0428	.0463	.0500	.0537	.0575	.0614	.0653
9	.0150	.0168	.0188	.0209	.0232	.0255	.0280	.0307	.0334	.0363
10	.0061	.0071	.0081	.0092	.0104	.0118	.0132	.0147	.0164	.0181
11	.0023	.0027	.0032	.0037	.0043	.0049	.0056	.0064	.0073	.0082
12	.0008	.0009	.0011	.0014	.0016	.0019	.0022	.0026	.0030	.0034
13	.0002	.0003	.0004	.0005	.0006	.0007	.0008	.0009	.0011	.0013
14	.0001	.0001	.0001	.0001	.0002	.0002	.0003	.0003	.0004	.0005
15	.0000	.0000	.0000	.0000	.0001	.0001	.0001	.0001	.0001	.0002

					λ					
x	5.1	5.2	5.3	5.4	5.5	5.6	5.7	5.8	5.9	6.0
0	.0061	.0055	.0050	.0045	.0041	.0037	.0033	.0030	.0027	.0025
1	.0311	.0287	.0265	.0244	.0225	.0207	.0191	.0176	.0162	.0149
2	.0793	.0746	.0701	.0659	.0618	.0580	.0544	.0509	.0477	.0446
3	.1348	.1293	.1239	.1185	.1133	.1082	.1033	.0985	.0938	.0892
4	.1719	.1681	.1641	.1600	.1558	.1515	.1472	.1428	.1383	.1339
5	.1753	.1748	.1740	.1728	.1714	.1697	.1678	.1656	.1632	.1606
6	.1490	.1515	.1537	.1555	.1571	.1584	.1594	.1601	.1605	.1606
7	.1086	.1125	.1163	.1200	.1234	.1267	.1298	.1326	.1353	.1377
8	.0692	.0731	.0771	.0810	.0849	.0887	.0925	.0962	.0998	.1033
9	.0392	.0423	.0454	.0486	.0519	.0552	.0586	.0620	.0654	.0688
10	.0200	.0220	.0241	.0262	.0285	.0309	.0334	.0359	.0386	.0413
11	.0093	.0104	.0116	.0129	.0143	.0157	.0173	.0190	.0207	.0225
12	.0039	.0045	.0051	.0058	.0065	.0073	.0082	.0092	.0102	.0113
13	.0015	.0018	.0021	.0024	.0028	.0032	.0036	.0041	.0046	.0052
14	.0006	.0007	.0008	.0009	.0011	.0013	.0015	.0017	.0019	.0022
15	.0002	.0002	.0003	.0003	.0004	.0005	.0006	.0007	.0008	.0009
16	.0001	.0001	.0001	.0001	.0001	.0002	.0002	.0002	.0003	.0003
17	.0000	.0000	.0000	.0000	.0000	.0000	.0001	.0001	.0001	.0001

INDIVIDUAL TERMS, POISSON DISTRIBUTION (Continued)

λ

x	6.1	6.2	6.3	6.4	6.5	6.6	6.7	6.8	6.9	7.0
0	.0022	.0020	.0018	.0017	.0015	.0014	.0012	.0011	.0010	.0009
1	.0137	.0126	.0116	.0106	.0098	.0090	.0082	.0076	.0070	.0064
2	.0417	.0390	.0364	.0340	.0318	.0296	.0276	.0258	.0240	.0223
3	.0848	.0806	.0765	.0726	.0688	.0652	.0617	.0584	.0552	.0521
4	.1294	.1249	.1205	.1162	.1118	.1076	.1034	.0992	.0952	.0912
5	.1579	.1549	.1519	.1487	.1454	.1420	.1385	.1349	.1314	.1277
6	.1605	.1601	.1595	.1586	.1575	.1562	.1546	.1529	.1511	.1490
7	.1399	.1418	.1435	.1450	.1462	.1472	.1480	.1486	.1489	.1490
8	.1066	.1099	.1130	.1160	.1188	.1215	.1240	.1263	.1284	.1304
9	.0723	.0757	.0791	.0825	.0858	.0891	.0923	.0954	.0985	.1014
10	.0441	.0469	.0498	.0528	.0558	.0588	.0618	.0649	.0679	.0710
11	.0245	.0265	.0285	.0307	.0330	.0353	.0377	.0401	.0426	.0452
12	.0124	.0137	.0150	.0164	.0179	.0194	.0210	.0227	.0245	.0264
13	.0058	.0065	.0073	.0081	.0089	.0098	.0108	.0119	.0130	.0142
14	.0025	.0029	.0033	.0037	.0041	.0046	.0052	.0058	.0064	.0071
15	.0010	.0012	.0014	.0016	.0018	.0020	.0023	.0026	.0029	.0033
16	.0004	.0005	.0005	.0006	.0007	.0008	.0010	.0011	.0013	.0014
17	.0001	.0002	.0002	.0002	.0003	.0003	.0004	.0004	.0005	.0006
18	.0000	.0001	.0001	.0001	.0001	.0001	.0001	.0002	.0002	.0002
19	.0000	.0000	.0000	.0000	.0000	.0000	.0000	.0001	.0001	.0001

λ

x	7.1	7.2	7.3	7.4	7.5	7.6	7.7	7.8	7.9	8.0
0	.0008	.0007	.0007	.0006	.0006	.0005	.0005	.0004	.0004	.0003
1	.0059	.0054	.0049	.0045	.0041	.0038	.0035	.0032	.0029	.0027
2	.0208	.0194	.0180	.0167	.0156	.0145	.0134	.0125	.0116	.0107
3	.0492	.0464	.0438	.0413	.0389	.0366	.0345	.0324	.0305	.0286
4	.0874	.0836	.0799	.0764	.0729	.0696	.0663	.0632	.0602	.0573
5	.1241	.1204	.1167	.1130	.1094	.1057	.1021	.0986	.0951	.0916
6	.1468	.1445	.1420	.1394	.1367	.1339	.1311	.1282	.1252	.1221
7	.1489	.1486	.1481	.1474	.1465	.1454	.1442	.1428	.1413	.1396
8	.1321	.1337	.1351	.1363	.1373	.1382	.1388	.1392	.1395	.1396
9	.1042	.1070	.1096	.1121	.1144	.1167	.1187	.1207	.1224	.1241
10	.0740	.0770	.0800	.0829	.0858	.0887	.0914	.0941	.0967	.0993
11	.0478	.0504	.0531	.0558	.0585	.0613	.0640	.0667	.0695	.0722
12	.0283	.0303	.0323	.0344	.0366	.0388	.0411	.0434	.0457	.0481
13	.0154	.0168	.0181	.0196	.0211	.0227	.0243	.0260	.0278	.0296
14	.0078	.0086	.0095	.0104	.0113	.0123	.0134	.0145	.0157	.0169
15	.0037	.0041	.0046	.0051	.0057	.0062	.0069	.0075	.0083	.0090
16	.0016	.0019	.0021	.0024	.0026	.0030	.0033	.0037	.0041	.0045
17	.0007	.0008	.0009	.0010	.0012	.0013	.0015	.0017	.0019	.0021
18	.0003	.0003	.0004	.0004	.0005	.0006	.0006	.0007	.0008	.0009
19	.0001	.0001	.0001	.0002	.0002	.0002	.0003	.0003	.0003	.0004
20	.0000	.0000	.0001	.0001	.0001	.0001	.0001	.0001	.0001	.0002
21	.0000	.0000	.0000	.0000	.0000	.0000	.0000	.0000	.0001	.0001

INDIVIDUAL TERMS, POISSON DISTRIBUTION (Continued)

λ

x	8.1	8.2	8.3	8.4	8.5	8.6	8.7	8.8	8.9	9.0
0	.0003	.0003	.0002	.0002	.0002	.0002	.0002	.0002	.0001	.0001
1	.0025	.0023	.0021	.0019	.0017	.0016	.0014	.0013	.0012	.0011
2	.0100	.0092	.0086	.0079	.0074	.0068	.0063	.0058	.0054	.0050
3	.0269	.0252	.0237	.0222	.0208	.0195	.0183	.0171	.0160	.0150
4	.0544	.0517	.0491	.0466	.0443	.0420	.0398	.0377	.0357	.0337
5	.0882	.0849	.0816	.0784	.0752	.0722	.0692	.0663	.0635	.0607
6	.1191	.1160	.1128	.1097	.1066	.1034	.1003	.0972	.0941	.0911
7	.1378	.1358	.1338	.1317	.1294	.1271	.1247	.1222	.1197	.1171
8	.1395	.1392	.1388	.1382	.1375	.1366	.1356	.1344	.1332	.1318
9	.1256	.1269	.1280	.1290	.1299	.1306	.1311	.1315	.1317	.1318
10	.1017	.1040	.1063	.1084	.1104	.1123	.1140	.1157	.1172	.1186
11	.0749	.0776	.0802	.0828	.0853	.0878	.0902	.0925	.0948	.0970
12	.0505	.0530	.0555	.0579	.0604	.0629	.0654	.0679	.0703	.0728
13	.0315	.0334	.0354	.0374	.0395	.0416	.0438	.0459	.0481	.0504
14	.0182	.0196	.0210	.0225	.0240	.0256	.0272	.0289	.0306	.0324
15	.0098	.0107	.0116	.0126	.0136	.0147	.0158	.0169	.0182	.0194
16	.0050	.0055	.0060	.0066	.0072	.0079	.0086	.0093	.0101	.0109
17	.0024	.0026	.0029	.0033	.0036	.0040	.0044	.0048	.0053	.0058
18	.0011	.0012	.0014	.0015	.0017	.0019	.0021	.0024	.0026	.0029
19	.0005	.0005	.0006	.0007	.0008	.0009	.0010	.0011	.0012	.0014
20	.0002	.0002	.0002	.0003	.0003	.0004	.0004	.0005	.0005	.0006
21	.0001	.0001	.0001	.0001	.0001	.0002	.0002	.0002	.0002	.0003
22	.0000	.0000	.0000	.0000	.0001	.0001	.0001	.0001	.0001	.0001

λ

x	9.1	9.2	9.3	9.4	9.5	9.6	9.7	9.8	9.9	10
0	.0001	.0001	.0001	.0001	.0001	.0001	.0001	.0001	.0001	.0000
1	.0010	.0009	.0009	.0008	.0007	.0007	.0006	.0005	.0005	.0005
2	.0046	.0043	.0040	.0037	.0034	.0031	.0029	.0027	.0025	.0023
3	.0140	.0131	.0123	.0115	.0107	.0100	.0093	.0087	.0081	.0076
4	.0319	.0302	.0285	.0269	.0254	.0240	.0226	.0213	.0201	.0189
5	.0581	.0555	.0530	.0506	.0483	.0460	.0439	.0418	.0398	.0378
6	.0881	.0851	.0822	.0793	.0764	.0736	.0709	.0682	.0656	.0631
7	.1145	.1118	.1091	.1064	.1037	.1010	.0982	.0955	.0928	.0901
8	.1302	.1286	.1269	.1251	.1232	.1212	.1191	.1170	.1148	.1126
9	.1317	.1315	.1311	.1306	.1300	.1293	.1284	.1274	.1263	.1251
10	.1198	.1210	.1219	.1228	.1235	.1241	.1245	.1249	.1250	.1251
11	.0991	.1012	.1031	.1049	.1067	.1083	.1098	.1112	.1125	.1137
12	.0752	.0776	.0799	.0822	.0844	.0866	.0888	.0908	.0928	.0948
13	.0526	.0549	.0572	.0594	.0617	.0640	.0662	.0685	.0707	.0729
14	.0342	.0361	.0380	.0399	.0419	.0439	.0459	.0479	.0500	.0521
15	.0208	.0221	.0235	.0250	.0265	.0281	.0297	.0313	.0330	.0347
16	.0118	.0127	.0137	.0147	.0157	.0168	.0180	.0192	.0204	.0217
17	.0063	.0069	.0075	.0081	.0088	.0095	.0103	.0111	.0119	.0128
18	.0032	.0035	.0039	.0042	.0046	.0051	.0055	.0060	.0065	.0071
19	.0015	.0017	.0019	.0021	.0023	.0026	.0028	.0031	.0034	.0037

INDIVIDUAL TERMS, POISSON DISTRIBUTION (Continued)

x	9.1	9.2	9.3	9.4	9.5 λ	9.6	9.7	9.8	9.9	10
20	.0007	.0008	.0009	.0010	.0011	.0012	.0014	.0015	.0017	.0019
21	.0003	.0003	.0004	.0004	.0005	.0006	.0006	.0007	.0008	.0009
22	.0001	.0001	.0002	.0002	.0002	.0002	.0003	.0003	.0004	.0004
23	.0000	.0001	.0001	.0001	.0001	.0001	.0001	.0001	.0002	.0002
24	.0000	.0000	.0000	.0000	.0000	.0000	.0000	.0001	.0001	.0001

x	11	12	13	14	15 λ	16	17	18	19	20
0	.0000	.0000	.0000	.0000	.0000	.0000	.0000	.0000	.0000	.0000
1	.0002	.0001	.0000	.0000	.0000	.0000	.0000	.0000	.0000	.0000
2	.0010	.0004	.0002	.0001	.0000	.0000	.0000	.0000	.0000	.0000
3	.0037	.0018	.0008	.0004	.0002	.0001	.0000	.0000	.0000	.0000
4	.0102	.0053	.0027	.0013	.0006	.0003	.0001	.0001	.0000	.0000
5	.0224	.0127	.0070	.0037	.0019	.0010	.0005	.0002	.0001	.0001
6	.0411	.0255	.0152	.0087	.0048	.0026	.0014	.0007	.0004	.0002
7	.0646	.0437	.0281	.0174	.0104	.0060	.0034	.0018	.0010	.0005
8	.0888	.0655	.0457	.0304	.0194	.0120	.0072	.0042	.0024	.0013
9	.1085	.0874	.0661	.0473	.0324	.0213	.0135	.0083	.0050	.0029
10	.1194	.1048	.0859	.0663	.0486	.0341	.0230	.0150	.0095	.0058
11	.1194	.1144	.1015	.0844	.0663	.0496	.0355	.0245	.0164	.0106
12	.1094	.1144	.1099	.0984	.0829	.0661	.0504	.0368	.0259	.0176
13	.0926	.1056	.1099	.1060	.0956	.0814	.0658	.0509	.0378	.0271
14	.0728	.0905	.1021	.1060	.1024	.0930	.0800	.0655	.0514	.0387
15	.0534	.0724	.0885	.0989	.1024	.0992	.0906	.0786	.0650	.0516
16	.0367	.0543	.0719	.0866	.0960	.0992	.0963	.0884	.0772	.0646
17	.0237	.0383	.0550	.0713	.0847	.0934	.0963	.0936	.0863	.0760
18	.0145	.0256	.0397	.0554	.0706	.0830	.0909	.0936	.0911	.0844
19	.0084	.0161	.0272	.0409	.0557	.0699	.0814	.0887	.0911	.0888
20	.0046	.0097	.0177	.0286	.0418	.0559	.0692	.0798	.0866	.0888
21	.0024	.0055	.0109	.0191	.0299	.0426	.0560	.0684	.0783	.0846
22	.0012	.0030	.0065	.0121	.0204	.0310	.0433	.0560	.0676	.0769
23	.0006	.0016	.0037	.0074	.0133	.0216	.0320	.0438	.0559	.0669
24	.0003	.0008	.0020	.0043	.0083	.0144	.0226	.0328	.0442	.0557
25	.0001	.0004	.0010	.0024	.0050	.0092	.0154	.0237	.0336	.0446
26	.0000	.0002	.0005	.0013	.0029	.0057	.0101	.0164	.0246	.0343
27	.0000	.0001	.0002	.0007	.0016	.0034	.0063	.0109	.0173	.0254
28	.0000	.0000	.0001	.0003	.0009	.0019	.0038	.0070	.0117	.0181
29	.0000	.0000	.0001	.0002	.0004	.0011	.0023	.0044	.0077	.0125
30	.0000	.0000	.0000	.0001	.0002	.0006	.0013	.0026	.0049	.0083
31	.0000	.0000	.0000	.0000	.0001	.0003	.0007	.0015	.0030	.0054
32	.0000	.0000	.0000	.0000	.0001	.0001	.0004	.0009	.0018	.0034
33	.0000	.0000	.0000	.0000	.0000	.0001	.0002	.0005	.0010	.0020
34	.0000	.0000	.0000	.0000	.0000	.0000	.0001	.0002	.0006	.0012
35	.0000	.0000	.0000	.0000	.0000	.0000	.0000	.0001	.0003	.0007
36	.0000	.0000	.0000	.0000	.0000	.0000	.0000	.0001	.0002	.0004
37	.0000	.0000	.0000	.0000	.0000	.0000	.0000	.0000	.0001	.0002
38	.0000	.0000	.0000	.0000	.0000	.0000	.0000	.0000	.0000	.0001
39	.0000	.0000	.0000	.0000	.0000	.0000	.0000	.0000	.0000	.0001

CUMULATIVE TERMS, POISSON DISTRIBUTION

This table contains the values of

$$\sum_{x = x'}^{\infty} \frac{e^{-\lambda}\lambda^x}{x'}$$

for specified values of x' and λ. The cumulative Poisson distribution and the cumulative chi-square (χ^2) distribution are related as follows:

$$\sum_{x = 0}^{x'-1} \frac{e^{-\lambda}\lambda^x}{x'} = 1 - F(\chi^2)$$

$$= \frac{1}{2^{\frac{n}{2}} \Gamma\left(\frac{n}{2}\right)} \int_{\chi^2}^{\infty} x^{\frac{n}{2}-1} e^{-\frac{x}{2}} \, dx$$

where $\lambda = \frac{1}{2}\chi^2$ and $x' = \frac{1}{2}n$.

CUMULATIVE TERMS, POISSON DISTRIBUTION (Continued)

x'	0.1	0.2	0.3	0.4	λ 0.5	0.6	0.7	0.8	0.9	1.0
0	1.0000	1.0000	1.0000	1.0000	1.0000	1.0000	1.0000	1.0000	1.0000	1.0000
1	.0952	.1813	.2592	.3297	.3935	.4512	.5034	.5507	.5934	.6321
2	.0047	.0175	.0369	.0616	.0902	.1219	.1558	.1912	.2275	.2642
3	.0002	.0011	.0036	.0079	.0144	.0231	.0341	.0474	.0629	.0803
4	.0000	.0001	.0003	.0008	.0018	.0034	.0058	.0091	.0135	.0190
5	.0000	.0000	.0000	.0001	.0002	.0004	.0008	.0014	.0023	.0037
6	.0000	.0000	.0000	.0000	.0000	.0000	.0001	.0002	.0003	.0006
7	.0000	.0000	.0000	.0000	.0000	.0000	.0000	.0000	.0000	.0001

x'	1.1	1.2	1.3	1.4	λ 1.5	1.6	1.7	1.8	1.9	2.0
0	1.0000	1.0000	1.0000	1.0000	1.0000	1.0000	1.0000	1.0000	1.0000	1.0000
1	.6671	.6988	.7275	.7534	.7769	.7981	.8173	.8347	.8504	.8647
2	.3010	.3374	.3732	.4082	.4422	.4751	.5068	.5372	.5663	.5940
3	.0996	.1205	.1429	.1665	.1912	.2166	.2428	.2694	.2963	.3233
4	.0257	.0338	.0431	.0537	.0656	.0788	.0932	.1087	.1253	.1429
5	.0054	.0077	.0107	.0143	.0186	.0237	.0296	.0364	.0441	.0527
6	.0010	.0015	.0022	.0032	.0045	.0060	.0080	.0104	.0132	.0166
7	.0001	.0003	.0004	.0006	.0009	.0013	.0019	.0026	.0034	.0045
8	.0000	.0000	.0001	.0001	.0002	.0003	.0004	.0006	.0008	.0011
9	.0000	.0000	.0000	.0000	.0000	.0000	.0001	.0001	.0002	.0002

x'	2.1	2.2	2.3	2.4	λ 2.5	2.6	2.7	2.8	2.9	3.0
0	1.0000	1.0000	1.0000	1.0000	1.0000	1.0000	1.0000	1.0000	1.0000	1.0000
1	.8775	.8892	.8997	.9093	.9179	.9257	.9328	.9392	.9450	.9502
2	.6204	.6454	.6691	.6916	.7127	.7326	.7513	.7689	.7854	.8009
3	.3504	.3773	.4040	.4303	.4562	.4816	.5064	.5305	.5540	.5768
4	.1614	.1806	.2007	.2213	.2424	.2640	.2859	.3081	.3304	.3528
5	.0621	.0725	.0838	.0959	.1088	.1226	.1371	.1523	.1682	.1847
6	.0204	.0249	.0300	.0357	.0420	.0490	.0567	.0651	.0742	.0839
7	.0059	.0075	.0094	.0116	.0142	.0172	.0206	.0244	.0287	.0335
8	.0015	.0020	.0026	.0033	.0042	.0053	.0066	.0081	.0099	.0119
9	.0003	.0005	.0006	.0009	.0011	.0015	.0019	.0024	.0031	.0038
10	.0001	.0001	.0001	.0002	.0003	.0004	.0005	.0007	.0009	.0011
11	.0000	.0000	.0000	.0000	.0001	.0001	.0001	.0002	.0002	.0003
12	.0000	.0000	.0000	.0000	.0000	.0000	.0000	.0000	.0001	.0001

x'	3.1	3.2	3.3	3.4	λ 3.5	3.6	3.7	3.8	3.9	4.0
0	1.0000	1.0000	1.0000	1.0000	1.0000	1.0000	1.0000	1.0000	1.0000	1.0000
1	.9550	.9592	.9631	.9666	.9698	.9727	.9753	.9776	.9798	.9817
2	.8153	.8288	.8414	.8532	.8641	.8743	.8838	.8926	.9008	.9084
3	.5988	.6201	.6406	.6603	.6792	.6973	.7146	.7311	.7469	.7619
4	.3752	.3975	.4197	.4416	.4634	.4848	.5058	.5265	.5468	.5665

CUMULATIVE TERMS, POISSON DISTRIBUTION (Continued)

λ

x'	3.1	3.2	3.3	3.4	3.5	3.6	3.7	3.8	3.9	4.0
5	.2018	.2194	.2374	.2558	.2746	.2936	.3128	.3322	.3516	.3712
6	.0943	.1054	.1171	.1295	.1424	.1559	.1699	.1844	.1994	.2149
7	.0388	.0446	.0510	.0579	.0653	.0733	.0818	.0909	.1005	.1107
8	.0142	.0168	.0198	.0231	.0267	.0308	.0352	.0401	.0454	.0511
9	.0047	.0057	.0069	.0083	.0099	.0117	.0137	.0160	.0185	.0214
10	.0014	.0018	.0022	.0027	.0033	.0040	.0048	.0058	.0069	.0081
11	.0004	.0005	.0006	.0008	.0010	.0013	.0016	.0019	.0023	.0028
12	.0001	.0001	.0002	.0002	.0003	.0004	.0005	.0006	.0007	.0009
13	.0000	.0000	.0000	.0001	.0001	.0001	.0001	.0002	.0002	.0003
14	.0000	.0000	.0000	.0000	.0000	.0000	.0000	.0000	.0001	.0001

λ

x'	4.1	4.2	4.3	4.4	4.5	4.6	4.7	4.8	4.9	5.0
0	1.0000	1.0000	1.0000	1.0000	1.0000	1.0000	1.0000	1.0000	1.0000	1.0000
1	.9834	.9850	.9864	.9877	.9889	.9899	.9909	.9918	.9926	.9933
2	.9155	.9220	.9281	.9337	.9389	.9437	.9482	.9523	.9561	.9596
3	.7762	.7898	.8026	.8149	.8264	.8374	.8477	.8575	.8667	.8753
4	.5858	.6046	.6228	.6406	.6577	.6743	.6903	.7058	.7207	.7350
5	.3907	.4102	.4296	.4488	.4679	.4868	.5054	.5237	.5418	.5595
6	.2307	.2469	.2633	.2801	.2971	.3142	.3316	.3490	.3665	.3840
7	.1214	.1325	.1442	.1564	.1689	.1820	.1954	.2092	.2233	.2378
8	.0573	.0639	.0710	.0786	.0866	.0951	.1040	.1133	.1231	.1334
9	.0245	.0279	.0317	.0358	.0403	.0451	.0503	.0558	.0618	.0681
10	.0095	.0111	.0129	.0149	.0171	.0195	.0222	.0251	.0283	.0318
11	.0034	.0041	.0048	.0057	.0067	.0078	.0090	.0104	.0120	.0137
12	.0011	.0014	.0017	.0020	.0024	.0029	.0034	.0040	.0047	.0055
13	.0003	.0004	.0005	.0007	.0008	.0010	.0012	.0014	.0017	.0020
14	.0001	.0001	.0002	.0002	.0003	.0003	.0004	.0005	.0006	.0007
15	.0000	.0000	.0000	.0001	.0001	.0001	.0001	.0001	.0002	.0002
16	.0000	.0000	.0000	.0000	.0000	.0000	.0000	.0000	.0001	.0001

λ

x'	5.1	5.2	5.3	5.4	5.5	5.6	5.7	5.8	5.9	6.0
0	1.0000	1.0000	1.0000	1.0000	1.0000	1.0000	1.0000	1.0000	1.0000	1.0000
1	.9939	.9945	.9950	.9955	.9959	.9963	.9967	.9970	.9973	.9975
2	.9628	.9658	.9686	.9711	.9734	.9756	.9776	.9794	.9811	.9826
3	.8835	.8912	.8984	.9052	.9116	.9176	.9232	.9285	.9334	.9380
4	.7487	.7619	.7746	.7867	.7983	.8094	.8200	.8300	.8396	.8488
5	.5769	.5939	.6105	.6267	.6425	.6579	.6728	.6873	.7013	.7149
6	.4016	.4191	.4365	.4539	.4711	.4881	.5050	.5217	.5381	.5543
7	.2526	.2676	.2829	.2983	.3140	.3297	.3456	.3616	.3776	.3937
8	.1440	.1551	.1665	.1783	.1905	.2030	.2159	.2290	.2424	.2560
9	.0748	.0819	.0894	.0974	.1056	.1143	.1234	.1328	.1426	.1528

CUMULATIVE TERMS, POISSON DISTRIBUTION (Continued)

x	5.1	5.2	5.3	5.4	λ 5.5	5.6	5.7	5.8	5.9	6.0
10	.0356	.0397	.0441	.0488	.0538	.0591	.0648	.0708	.0772	.0839
11	.0156	.0177	.0200	.0225	.0253	.0282	.0314	.0349	.0386	.0426
12	.0063	.0073	.0084	.0096	.0110	.0125	.0141	.0160	.0179	.0201
13	.0024	.0028	.0033	.0038	.0045	.0051	.0059	.0068	.0078	.0088
14	.0008	.0010	.0012	.0014	.0017	.0020	.0023	.0027	.0031	.0036
15	.0003	.0003	.0004	.0005	.0006	.0007	.0009	.0010	.0012	.0014
16	.0001	.0001	.0001	.0002	.0002	.0002	.0003	.0004	.0004	.0005
17	.0000	.0000	.0000	.0001	.0001	.0001	.0001	.0001	.0001	.0002
18	.0000	.0000	.0000	.0000	.0000	.0000	.0000	.0000	.0000	.0001

x'	6.1	6.2	6.3	6.4	λ 6.5	6.6	6.7	6.8	6.9	7.0
0	1.0000	1.0000	1.0000	1.0000	1.0000	1.0000	1.0000	1.0000	1.0000	1.0000
1	.9978	.9980	.9982	.9983	.9985	.9986	.9988	.9989	.9990	.9991
2	.9841	.9854	.9866	.9877	.9887	.9897	.9905	.9913	.9920	.9927
3	.9423	.9464	.9502	.9537	.9570	.9600	.9629	.9656	.9680	.9704
4	.8575	.8658	.8736	.8811	.8882	.8948	.9012	.9072	.9129	.9182
5	.7281	.7408	.7531	.7649	.7763	.7873	.7978	.8080	.8177	.8270
6	.5702	.5859	.6012	.6163	.6310	.6453	.6594	.6730	.6863	.6993
7	.4098	.4258	.4418	.4577	.4735	.4892	.5047	.5201	.5353	.5503
8	.2699	.2840	.2983	.3127	.3272	.3419	.3567	.3715	.3864	.4013
9	.1633	.1741	.1852	.1967	.2084	.2204	.2327	.2452	.2580	.2709
10	.0910	.0984	.1061	.1142	.1226	.1314	.1404	.1498	.1505	.1695
11	.0469	.0514	.0563	.0614	.0668	.0726	.0786	.0849	.0916	.0985
12	.0224	.0250	.0277	.0307	.0339	.0373	.0409	.0448	.0490	.0534
13	.0100	.0113	.0127	.0143	.0160	.0179	.0199	.0221	.0245	.0270
14	.0042	.0048	.0055	.0063	.0071	.0080	.0091	.0102	.0115	.0128
15	.0016	.0019	.0022	.0026	.0030	.0034	.0039	.0044	.0050	.0057
16	.0006	.0007	.0008	.0010	.0012	.0014	.0016	.0018	.0021	.0024
17	.0002	.0003	.0003	.0004	.0004	.0005	.0006	.0007	.0008	.0010
18	.0001	.0001	.0001	.0001	.0002	.0002	.0002	.0003	.0003	.0004
19	.0000	.0000	.0000	.0000	.0000	.0001	.0001	.0001	.0001	.0001

x'	7.1	7.2	7.3	7.4	λ 7.5	7.6	7.7	7.8	7.9	8.0
0	1.0000	1.0000	1.0000	1.0000	1.0000	1.0000	1.0000	1.0000	1.0000	1.0000
1	.9992	.9993	.9993	.9994	.9994	.9995	.9995	.9996	.9996	.9997
2	.9933	.9939	.9944	.9949	.9953	.9957	.9961	.9964	.9967	.9970
3	.9725	.9745	.9764	.9781	.9797	.9812	.9826	.9839	.9851	.9862
4	.9233	.9281	.9326	.9368	.9409	.9446	.9482	.9515	.9547	.9576
5	.8359	.8445	.8527	.8605	.8679	.8751	.8819	.8883	.8945	.9004
6	.7119	.7241	.7360	.7474	.7586	.7693	.7797	.7897	.7994	.8088
7	.5651	.5796	.5940	.6080	.6218	.6354	.6486	.6616	.6743	.6866
8	.4162	.4311	.4459	.4607	.4754	.4900	.5044	.5188	.5330	.5470
9	.2840	.2973	.3108	.3243	.3380	.3518	.3657	.3796	.3935	.4075
10	.1798	.1904	.2012	.2123	.2236	.2351	.2469	.2589	.2710	.2834
11	.1058	.1133	.1212	.1293	.1378	.1465	.1555	.1648	.1743	.1841
12	.0580	.0629	.0681	.0735	.0792	.0852	.0915	.0980	.1048	.1119
13	.0297	.0327	.0358	.0391	.0427	.0464	.0504	.0546	.0591	.0638
14	.0143	.0159	.0176	.0195	.0216	.0238	.0261	.0286	.0313	.0342

CUMULATIVE TERMS, POISSON DISTRIBUTION (Continued)

x'	7.1	7.2	7.3	7.4	7.5	7.6	7.7	7.8	7.9	8.0
15	.0065	.0073	.0082	.0092	.0103	.0114	.0127	.0141	.0156	.0173
16	.0028	.0031	.0036	.0041	.0046	.0052	.0059	.0066	.0074	.0082
17	.0011	.0013	.0015	.0017	.0020	.0022	.0026	.0029	.0033	.0037
18	.0004	.0005	.0006	.0007	.0008	.0009	.0011	.0012	.0014	.0016
19	.0002	.0002	.0002	.0003	.0003	.0004	.0004	.0005	.0006	.0006
20	.0001	.0001	.0001	.0001	.0001	.0001	.0002	.0002	.0002	.0003
21	.0000	.0000	.0000	.0000	.0000	.0000	.0001	.0001	.0001	.0001

x'	8.1	8.2	8.3	8.4	8.5	8.6	8.7	8.8	8.9	9.0
0	1.0000	1.0000	1.0000	1.0000	1.0000	1.0000	1.0000	1.0000	1.0000	1.0000
1	.9997	.9997	.9998	.9998	.9998	.9998	.9998	.9998	.9999	.9999
2	.9972	.9975	.9977	.9979	.9981	.9982	.9984	.9985	.9987	.9988
3	.9873	.9882	.9891	.9900	.9907	.9914	.9921	.9927	.9932	.9938
4	.9604	.9630	.9654	.9677	.9699	.9719	'.9738	.9756	.9772	.9788
5	.9060	.9113	.9163	.9211	.9256	.9299	.9340	.9379	.9416	.9450
6	.8178	.8264	.8347	.8427	.8504	.8578	.8648	.8716	.8781	.8843
7	.6987	.7104	.7219	.7330	.7438	.7543	.7645	.7744	.7840	.7932
8	.5609	.5746	.5881	.6013	.6144	.6272	.6398	.6522	.6643	.6761
9	.4214	.4353	.4493	.4631	.4769	.4906	.5042	.5177	.5311	.5443
10	.2959	.3085	.3212	.3341	.3470	.3600	.3731	.3863	.3994	.4126
11	.1942	.2045	.2150	.2257	.2366	.2478	.2591	.2706	.2822	.2940
12	.1193	.1269	.1348	.1429	.1513	.1600	.1689	.1780	.1874	.1970
13	.0687	.0739	.0793	.0850	.0909	.0971	.1035	.1102	.1171	.1242
14	.0372	.0405	.0439	.0476	.0514	.0555	.0597	.0642	.0689	.0739
15	.0190	.0209	.0229	.0251	.0274	.0299	.0325	.0353	.0383	.0415
16	.0092	.0102	.0113	.0125	.0138	.0152	.0168	.0184	.0202	.0220
17	.0042	.0047	.0053	.0059	.0066	.0074	.0082	.0091	.0101	.0111
18	.0018	.0021	.0023	.0027	.0030	.0034	.0038	.0043	.0048	.0053
19	.0008	.0009	.0010	.0011	.0013	.0015	.0017	.0019	.0022	.0024
20	.0003	.0003	.0004	.0005	.0005	.0006	.0007	.0008	.0009	.0011
21	.0001	.0001	.0002	.0002	.0002	.0002	.0003	.0003	.0004	.0004
22	.0000	.0000	.0001	.0001	.0001	.0001	.0001	.0001	.0002	.0002
23	.0000	.0000	.0000	.0000	.0000	.0000	.0000	.0000	.0001	.0001

x'	9.1	9.2	9.3	9.4	9.5	9.6	9.7	9.8	9.9	10
0	1.0000	1.0000	1.0000	1.0000	1.0000	1.0000	1.0000	1.0000	1.0000	1.0000
1	.9999	.9999	.9999	.9999	.9999	.9999	.9999	.9999	1.0000	1.0000
2	.9989	.9990	.9991	.9991	.9992	.9993	.9993	.9994	.9995	.9995
3	.9942	9947	.9951	.9955	.9958	.9962	.9965	.9967	.9970	.9972
4	.9802	.9816	.9828	.9840	.9851	.9862	.9871	.9880	.9889	.9897
5	.9483	.9514	.9544	.9571	.9597	.9622	.9645	.9667	.9688	.9707
6	.8902	.8959	.9014	.9065	.9115	.9162	.9207	.9250	.9290	.9329
7	.8022	.8108	.8192	.8273	.8351	.8426	.8498	.8567	.8634	.8699
8	.6877	.6990	.7101	.7208	.7313	.7416	.7515	.7612	.7706	.7798
9	.5574	.5704	.5832	.5958	.6082	.6204	.6324	.6442	.6558	.6672

CUMULATIVE TERMS, POISSON DISTRIBUTION (Continued)

λ

x'	9.1	9.2	9.3	9.4	9.5	9.6	9.7	9.8	9.9	10
10	.4258	.4389	.4521	.4651	.4782	.4911	.5040	.5168	.5295	.5421
11	.3059	.3180	.3301	.3424	.3547	.3671	.3795	.3920	.4045	.4170
12	.2068	.2168	.2270	.2374	.2480	.2588	.2697	.2807	.2919	.3032
13	.1316	.1393	.1471	.1552	.1636	.1721	.1809	.1899	.1991	.2084
14	.0790	.0844	.0900	.0958	.1019	.1081	.1147	.1214	.1284	.1355
15	.0448	.0483	.0520	.0559	.0600	.0643	.0688	.0735	.0784	.0835
16	.0240	.0262	.0285	.0309	.0335	.0362	.0391	.0421	.0454	.0487
17	.0122	.0135	.0148	.0162	.0177	.0194	.0211	.0230	.0249	.0270
18	.0059	.0066	.0073	.0081	.0089	.0098	.0108	.0119	.0130	.0143
19	.0027	.0031	.0034	.0038	.0043	.0048	.0053	.0059	.0065	.0072
20	.0012	.0014	.0015	.0017	.0020	.0022	.0025	.0028	.0031	.0035
21	.0005	.0006	.0007	.0008	.0009	.0010	.0011	.0013	.0014	.0016
22	.0002	.0002	.0003	.0003	.0004	.0004	.0005	.0005	.0006	.0007
23	.0001	.0001	.0001	.0001	.0001	.0002	.0002	.0002	.0003	.0003
24	.0000	.0000	.0000	.0000	.0001	.0001	.0001	.0001	.0001	.0001

λ

x'	11	12	13	14	15	16	17	18	19	20
0	1.0000	1.0000	1.0000	1.0000	1.0000	1.0000	1.0000	1.0000	1.0000	1.0000
1	1.0000	1.0000	1.0000	1.0000	1.0000	1.0000	1.0000	1.0000	1.0000	1.0000
2	.9998	.9999	1.0000	1.0000	1.0000	1.0000	1.0000	1.0000	1.0000	1.0000
3	.9988	.9995	.9998	.9999	1.0000	1.0000	1.0000	1.0000	1.0000	1.0000
4	.9951	.9977	.9990	.9995	.9998	.9999	1.0000	1.0000	1.0000	1.0000
5	.9849	.9924	.9963	.9982	9991	.9996	.9998	.9999	1.0000	1.0000
6	.9625	.9797	.9893	.9945	.9972	.9986	.9993	.9997	.9998	.9999
7	.9214	.9542	.9741	.9858	.9924	.9960	.9979	.9990	.9995	.9997
8	.8568	.9105	.9460	.9684	.9820	.9900	.9946	.9971	.9985	.9992
9	.7680	.8450	.9002	.9379	.9626	.9780	.9874	.9929	.9961	.9979
10	.6595	.7576	.8342	.8906	.9301	.9567	.9739	.9846	.9911	.9950
11	.5401	.6528	.7483	.8243	.8815	.9226	.9509	.9696	.9817	.9892
12	.4207	.5384	.6468	.7400	.8152	.8730	.9153	.9451	.9653	.9786
13	.3113	.4240	.5369	.6415	.7324	.8069	.8650	.9083	.9394	.9610
14	.2187	.3185	.4270	.5356	.6368	.7255	.7991	.8574	.9016	.9339
15	.1460	.2280	.3249	.4296	.5343	.6325	.7192	.7919	.8503	.8951
16	.0926	.1556	.2364	.3306	.4319	.5333	.6285	.7133	.7852	.8435
17	.0559	.1013	.1645	.2441	.3359	.4340	.5323	.6250	.7080	.7789
18	.0322	.0630	.1095	.1728	.2511	.3407	.4360	.5314	.6216	.7030
19	.0177	.0374	.0698	.1174	.1805	.2577	.3450	.4378	.5305	.6186
20	.0093	.0213	.0427	.0765	.1248	.1878	.2637	.3491	.4394	.5297
21	.0047	.0116	.0250	.0479	.0830	.1318	.1945	.2693	.3528	.4409
22	.0023	.0061	.0141	.0288	.0531	.0892	.1385	.2009	.2745	.3563
23	.0010	.0030	.0076	.0167	.0327	.0582	.0953	.1449	.2069	.2794
24	.0005	.0015	.0040	.0093	.0195	.0367	.0633	.1011	.1510	.2125
25	.0002	.0007	.0020	.0050	.0112	.0223	.0406	.0683	.1067	.1568
26	.0001	.0003	.0010	.0026	.0062	.0131	.0252	.0446	.0731	.1122
27	.0000	.0001	.0005	.0013	.0033	.0075	.0152	.0282	.0486	.0779
28	.0000	.0001	.0002	.0006	.0017	.0041	.0088	.0173	.0313	.0525
29	.0000	.0000	.0001	.0003	.0009	.0022	.0050	.0103	.0195	.0343

CUMULATIVE TERMS, POISSON DISTRIBUTION (Continued)

x'	λ 11	12	13	14	15	16	17	18	19	20
30	.0000	.0000	.0000	.0001	.0004	.0011	.0027	.0059	.0118	.0218
31	.0000	.0000	.0000	.0001	.0002	.0006	.0014	.0033	.0070	.0135
32	.0000	.0000	.0000	.0000	.0001	.0003	.0007	.0018	.0040	.0081
33	.0000	.0000	.0000	.0000	.0000	.0001	.0004	.0010	.0022	.0047
34	.0000	.0000	.0000	.0000	.0000	.0001	.0002	.0005	.0012	.0027
35	.0000	.0000	.0000	.0000	.0000	.0000	.0001	.0002	.0006	.0015
36	.0000	.0000	.0000	.0000	.0000	.0000	.0000	.0001	.0003	.0008
37	.0000	.0000	.0000	.0000	.0000	.0000	.0000	.0001	.0002	.0004
38	.0000	.0000	.0000	.0000	.0000	.0000	.0000	.0000	.0001	.0002
39	.0000	.0000	.0000	.0000	.0000	.0000	.0000	.0000	.0000	.0001
40	.0000	.0000	.0000	.0000	.0000	.0000	.0000	.0000	.0000	.0001

PERCENTAGE POINTS, STUDENT'S t-DISTRIBUTION

This table gives values of t such that

$$F(t) = \int_{-\infty}^{t} \frac{\Gamma\left(\frac{n+1}{2}\right)}{\sqrt{n\pi}\,\Gamma\left(\frac{n}{2}\right)} \left(1 + \frac{x^2}{n}\right)^{-\frac{n+1}{2}} dx$$

for n, the number of degrees of freedom, equal to 1, 2, . . . , 30, 40, 60, 120, ∞ ; and for $F(t) = 0.60, 0.75, 0.90, 0.95, 0.975, 0.99, 0.995,$ and 0.9995. The t-distribution is symmetrical, so that $F(-t) = 1 - F(t)$

n	.60	.75	.90	.95	.975	.99	.995	.9995
1	.325	1.000	3.078	6.314	12.706	31.821	63.657	636.619
2	.289	.816	1.886	2.920	4.303	6.965	9.925	31.598
3	.277	.765	1.638	2.353	3.182	4.541	5.841	12.924
4	.271	.741	1.533	2.132	2.776	3.747	4.604	8.610
5	.267	.727	1.476	2.015	2.571	3.365	4.032	6.869
6	.265	.718	1.440	1.943	2.447	3.143	3.707	5.959
7	.263	.711	1.415	1.895	2.365	2.998	3.499	5.408
8	.262	.706	1.397	1.860	2.306	2.896	3.355	5.041
9	.261	.703	1.383	1.833	2.262	2.821	3.250	4.781
10	.260	.700	1.372	1.812	2.228	2.764	3.169	4.587
11	.260	.697	1.363	1.796	2.201	2.718	3.106	4.437
12	.259	.695	1.356	1.782	2.179	2.681	3.055	4.318
13	.259	.694	1.350	1.771	2.160	2.650	3.012	4.221
14	.258	.692	1.345	1.761	2.145	2.624	2.977	4.140
15	.258	.691	1.341	1.753	2.131	2.602	2.947	4.073
16	.258	.690	1.337	1.746	2.120	2.583	2.921	4.015
17	.257	.689	1.333	1.740	2.110	2.567	2.898	3.965
18	.257	.688	1.330	1.734	2.101	2.552	2.878	3.922
19	.257	.688	1.328	1.729	2.093	2.539	2.861	3.883
20	.257	.687	1.325	1.725	2.086	2.528	2.845	3.850
21	.257	.686	1.323	1.721	2.080	2.518	2.831	3.819
22	.256	.686	1.321	1.717	2.074	2.508	2.819	3.792
23	.256	.685	1.319	1.714	2.069	2.500	2.807	3.767
24	.256	.685	1.318	1.711	2.064	2.492	2.797	3.745
25	.256	.684	1.316	1.708	2.060	2.485	2.787	3.725
26	.256	.684	1.315	1.706	2.056	2.479	2.779	3.707
27	.256	.684	1.314	1.703	2.052	2.473	2.771	3.690
28	.256	.683	1.313	1.701	2.048	2.467	2.763	3.674
29	.256	.683	1.311	1.699	2.045	2.462	2.756	3.659
30	.256	.683	1.310	1.697	2.042	2.457	2.750	3.646
40	.255	.681	1.303	1.684	2.021	2.423	2.704	3.551
60	.254	.679	1.296	1.671	2.000	2.390	2.660	3.460
120	.254	.677	1.289	1.658	1.980	2.358	2.617	3.373
∞	.253	.674	1.282	1.645	1.960	2.326	2.576	3.291

* This table is abridged from the "Statistical Tables" of R. A. Fisher and Frank Yates published by Oliver & Boyd, Ltd., Edinburgh and London, 1938. It is here published with the kind permission of the authors and their publishers.

PERCENTAGE POINTS, CHI-SQUARE DISTRIBUTION

This table gives values of χ^2 such that

$$F(\chi^2) = \int_0^{\chi^2} \frac{1}{2^{\frac{n}{2}} \, \Gamma\left(\frac{n}{2}\right)} \, x^{\frac{n-2}{2}} \, e^{-\frac{x}{2}} \, dx$$

for n, the number of degrees of freedom, equal to 1, 2, . . . , 30. For $n > 30$, a normal approximation is quite accurate. The expression $\sqrt{2\chi^2} - \sqrt{2n-1}$ is approximately normally distributed as the standard normal distribution. Thus χ_α^2, the α-point of the distribution, may be computed by the formula

$$\chi_\alpha^2 = \tfrac{1}{2}[x_\alpha + \sqrt{2n-1}]^2,$$

where x_α is the α-point of the cumulative normal distribution. For even values of n, $F(\chi^2)$ can be written as

$$1 - F(\chi^2) = \sum_{x=0}^{x'-1} \frac{e^{-\lambda} \lambda^x}{x!}$$

with $\lambda = \tfrac{1}{2}\chi^2$ and $x' = \tfrac{1}{2}n$. Thus the cumulative Chi-Square distribution is related to the cumulative Poisson distribution.

Another approximate formula for large n

$$\chi_\alpha^2 = n \left(1 - \frac{2}{9n} + z_\alpha \sqrt{\frac{2}{9n}} \right)^3$$

n = degrees of freedom
z_α = the normal deviate, (the value of x for which $F(x)$ = the desired percentile).

x	1.282	1.645	1.960	2.326	2.576	3.090
$F(x)$	.90	.95	.975	.99	.995	.999

$\chi_{.99}^2 = 60[1 - 0.00370 + 2.326(0.06086)]^3 = 88.4$ is the 99th percentile for 60 degrees of freedom.

PERCENTAGE POINTS, CHI-SQUARE DISTRIBUTION (Continued)

$$F(x^2) = \int_0^{x^2} \frac{1}{2^{\frac{n}{2}} \Gamma\left(\frac{n}{2}\right)} x^{\frac{n-2}{2}} e^{-\frac{x}{2}}\, dx$$

F \ n	.995	.990	.975	.950	.900	.750	.500	.250	.100	.050	.025	.010	.005
1	7.88	6.63	5.02	3.84	2.71	1.32	.455	.102	.0158	.00393	.000982	.000157	.0000393
2	10.6	9.21	7.38	5.99	4.61	2.77	1.39	.575	.211	.103	.0506	.0201	.0100
3	12.8	11.3	9.35	7.81	6.25	4.11	2.37	1.21	.584	.352	.216	.115	.0717
4	14.9	13.3	11.1	9.49	7.78	5.39	3.36	1.92	1.06	.711	.484	.297	.207
5	16.7	15.1	12.8	11.1	9.24	6.63	4.35	2.67	1.61	1.15	.831	.554	.412
6	18.5	16.8	14.4	12.6	10.6	7.84	5.35	3.45	2.20	1.64	1.24	.872	.676
7	20.3	18.5	16.0	14.1	12.0	9.04	6.35	4.25	2.83	2.17	1.69	1.24	.989
8	22.0	20.1	17.5	15.5	13.4	10.2	7.34	5.07	3.49	2.73	2.18	1.65	1.34
9	23.6	21.7	19.0	16.9	14.7	11.4	8.34	5.90	4.17	3.33	2.70	2.09	1.73
10	25.2	23.2	20.5	18.3	16.0	12.5	9.34	6.74	4.87	3.94	3.25	2.56	2.16
11	26.8	24.7	21.9	19.7	17.3	13.7	10.3	7.58	5.58	4.57	3.82	3.05	2.60
12	28.3	26.2	23.3	21.0	18.5	14.8	11.3	8.44	6.30	5.23	4.40	3.57	3.07
13	29.8	27.7	24.7	22.4	19.8	16.0	12.3	9.30	7.04	5.89	5.01	4.11	3.57
14	31.3	29.1	26.1	23.7	21.1	17.1	13.3	10.2	7.79	6.57	5.63	4.66	4.07
15	32.8	30.6	27.5	25.0	22.3	18.2	14.3	11.0	8.55	7.26	6.26	5.23	4.60
16	34.3	32.0	28.8	26.3	23.5	19.4	15.3	11.9	9.31	7.96	6.91	5.81	5.14
17	35.7	33.4	30.2	27.6	24.8	20.5	16.3	12.8	10.1	8.67	7.56	6.41	5.70
18	37.2	34.8	31.5	28.9	26.0	21.6	17.3	13.7	10.9	9.39	8.23	7.01	6.26
19	38.6	36.2	32.9	30.1	27.2	22.7	18.3	14.6	11.7	10.1	8.91	7.63	6.84
20	40.0	37.6	34.2	31.4	28.4	23.8	19.3	15.5	12.4	10.9	9.59	8.26	7.43
21	41.4	38.9	35.5	32.7	29.6	24.9	20.3	16.3	13.2	11.6	10.3	8.90	8.03
22	42.8	40.3	36.8	33.9	30.8	26.0	21.3	17.2	14.0	12.3	11.0	9.54	8.64
23	44.2	41.6	38.1	35.2	32.0	27.1	22.3	18.1	14.8	13.1	11.7	10.2	9.26
24	45.6	43.0	39.4	36.4	33.2	28.2	23.3	19.0	15.7	13.8	12.4	10.9	9.89
25	46.9	44.3	40.6	37.7	34.4	29.3	24.3	19.9	16.5	14.6	13.1	11.5	10.5
26	48.3	45.6	41.9	38.9	35.6	30.4	25.3	20.8	17.3	15.4	13.8	12.2	11.2
27	49.6	47.0	43.2	40.1	36.7	31.5	26.3	21.7	18.1	16.2	14.6	12.9	11.8
28	51.0	48.3	44.5	41.3	37.9	32.6	27.3	22.7	18.9	16.9	15.3	13.6	12.5
29	52.3	49.6	45.7	42.6	39.1	33.7	28.3	23.6	19.8	17.7	16.0	14.3	13.1
30	53.7	50.9	47.0	43.8	40.3	34.8	29.3	24.5	20.6	18.5	16.8	15.0	13.8

PERCENTAGE POINTS, F-DISTRIBUTION

This table gives values of F such that

$$F(F) = \int_0^F \frac{\Gamma\left(\dfrac{m+n}{2}\right)}{\Gamma\left(\dfrac{m}{2}\right)\Gamma\left(\dfrac{n}{2}\right)} m^{\frac{m}{2}} n^{\frac{n}{2}} x^{\frac{m-2}{2}} (n+mx)^{-\frac{m+n}{2}} dx$$

for selected values of m, the number of degrees of freedom of the numerator of F; and for selected values of n, the number of degrees of freedom of the denominator of F. The table also provides values corresponding to $F(F) = .10, .05, .025, .01, .005, .001$ since $F_{1-\alpha}$ for m and n degrees of freedom is the reciprocal of F_α for n and m degrees of freedom. Thus

$$F_{.05}(4, 7) = \frac{1}{F_{.95}(7, 4)} = \frac{1}{6.09} = .164 .$$

PERCENTAGE POINTS, *F*-DISTRIBUTION (Continued)

$$F(F) = \int_0^F \frac{\Gamma\left(\frac{m+n}{2}\right)}{\Gamma\left(\frac{m}{2}\right)\Gamma\left(\frac{n}{2}\right)} m^{\frac{m}{2}} n^{\frac{n}{2}} x^{\frac{m}{2}-1}(n+mx)^{-\frac{m+n}{2}}\, dx = .90$$

m \ n	1	2	3	4	5	6	7	8	9	10	12	15	20	24	30	40	60	120	∞
1	39.86	49.50	53.59	55.83	57.24	58.20	58.91	59.44	59.86	60.19	60.71	61.22	61.74	62.00	62.26	62.53	62.79	63.06	63.33
2	8.53	9.00	9.16	9.24	9.29	9.33	9.35	9.37	9.38	9.39	9.41	9.42	9.44	9.45	9.46	9.47	9.47	9.48	9.49
3	5.54	5.46	5.39	5.34	5.31	5.28	5.27	5.25	5.24	5.23	5.22	5.20	5.18	5.18	5.17	5.16	5.15	5.14	5.13
4	4.54	4.32	4.19	4.11	4.05	4.01	3.98	3.95	3.94	3.92	3.90	3.87	3.84	3.83	3.82	3.80	3.79	3.78	3.76
5	4.06	3.78	3.62	3.52	3.45	3.40	3.37	3.34	3.32	3.30	3.27	3.24	3.21	3.19	3.17	3.16	3.14	3.12	3.10
6	3.78	3.46	3.29	3.18	3.11	3.05	3.01	2.98	2.96	2.94	2.90	2.87	2.84	2.82	2.80	2.78	2.76	2.74	2.72
7	3.59	3.26	3.07	2.96	2.88	2.83	2.78	2.75	2.72	2.70	2.67	2.63	2.59	2.58	2.56	2.54	2.51	2.49	2.47
8	3.46	3.11	2.92	2.81	2.73	2.67	2.62	2.59	2.56	2.54	2.50	2.46	2.42	2.40	2.38	2.36	2.34	2.32	2.29
9	3.36	3.01	2.81	2.69	2.61	2.55	2.51	2.47	2.44	2.42	2.38	2.34	2.30	2.28	2.25	2.23	2.21	2.18	2.16
10	3.29	2.92	2.73	2.61	2.52	2.46	2.41	2.38	2.35	2.32	2.28	2.24	2.20	2.18	2.16	2.13	2.11	2.08	2.06
11	3.23	2.86	2.66	2.54	2.45	2.39	2.34	2.30	2.27	2.25	2.21	2.17	2.12	2.10	2.08	2.05	2.03	2.00	1.97
12	3.18	2.81	2.61	2.48	2.39	2.33	2.28	2.24	2.21	2.19	2.15	2.10	2.06	2.04	2.01	1.99	1.96	1.93	1.90
13	3.14	2.76	2.56	2.43	2.35	2.28	2.23	2.20	2.16	2.14	2.10	2.05	2.01	1.98	1.96	1.93	1.90	1.88	1.85
14	3.10	2.73	2.52	2.39	2.31	2.24	2.19	2.15	2.12	2.10	2.05	2.01	1.96	1.94	1.91	1.89	1.86	1.83	1.80
15	3.07	2.70	2.49	2.36	2.27	2.21	2.16	2.12	2.09	2.06	2.02	1.97	1.92	1.90	1.87	1.85	1.82	1.79	1.76
16	3.05	2.67	2.46	2.33	2.24	2.18	2.13	2.09	2.06	2.03	1.99	1.94	1.89	1.87	1.84	1.81	1.78	1.75	1.72
17	3.03	2.64	2.44	2.31	2.22	2.15	2.10	2.06	2.03	2.00	1.96	1.91	1.86	1.84	1.81	1.78	1.75	1.72	1.69
18	3.01	2.62	2.42	2.29	2.20	2.13	2.08	2.04	2.00	1.98	1.93	1.89	1.84	1.81	1.78	1.75	1.72	1.69	1.66
19	2.99	2.61	2.40	2.27	2.18	2.11	2.06	2.02	1.98	1.96	1.91	1.86	1.81	1.79	1.76	1.73	1.70	1.67	1.63
20	2.97	2.59	2.38	2.25	2.16	2.09	2.04	2.00	1.96	1.94	1.89	1.84	1.79	1.77	1.74	1.71	1.68	1.64	1.61
21	2.96	2.57	2.36	2.23	2.14	2.08	2.02	1.98	1.95	1.92	1.87	1.83	1.78	1.75	1.72	1.69	1.66	1.62	1.59
22	2.95	2.56	2.35	2.22	2.13	2.06	2.01	1.97	1.93	1.90	1.86	1.81	1.76	1.73	1.70	1.67	1.64	1.60	1.57
23	2.94	2.55	2.34	2.21	2.11	2.05	1.99	1.95	1.92	1.89	1.84	1.80	1.74	1.72	1.69	1.66	1.62	1.59	1.55
24	2.93	2.54	2.33	2.19	2.10	2.04	1.98	1.94	1.91	1.88	1.83	1.78	1.73	1.70	1.67	1.64	1.61	1.57	1.53
25	2.92	2.53	2.32	2.18	2.09	2.02	1.97	1.93	1.89	1.87	1.82	1.77	1.72	1.69	1.66	1.63	1.59	1.56	1.52
26	2.91	2.52	2.31	2.17	2.08	2.01	1.96	1.92	1.88	1.86	1.81	1.76	1.71	1.68	1.65	1.61	1.58	1.54	1.50
27	2.90	2.51	2.30	2.17	2.07	2.00	1.95	1.91	1.87	1.85	1.80	1.75	1.70	1.67	1.64	1.60	1.57	1.53	1.49
28	2.89	2.50	2.29	2.16	2.06	2.00	1.94	1.90	1.87	1.84	1.79	1.74	1.69	1.66	1.63	1.59	1.56	1.52	1.48
29	2.89	2.50	2.28	2.15	2.06	1.99	1.93	1.89	1.86	1.83	1.78	1.73	1.68	1.65	1.62	1.58	1.55	1.51	1.47
30	2.88	2.49	2.28	2.14	2.05	1.98	1.93	1.88	1.85	1.82	1.77	1.72	1.67	1.64	1.61	1.57	1.54	1.50	1.46
40	2.84	2.44	2.23	2.09	2.00	1.93	1.87	1.83	1.79	1.76	1.71	1.66	1.61	1.57	1.54	1.51	1.47	1.42	1.38
60	2.79	2.39	2.18	2.04	1.95	1.87	1.82	1.77	1.74	1.71	1.66	1.60	1.54	1.51	1.48	1.44	1.40	1.35	1.29
120	2.75	2.35	2.13	1.99	1.90	1.82	1.77	1.72	1.68	1.65	1.60	1.55	1.48	1.45	1.41	1.37	1.32	1.26	1.19
∞	2.71	2.30	2.08	1.94	1.85	1.77	1.72	1.67	1.63	1.60	1.55	1.49	1.42	1.38	1.34	1.30	1.24	1.17	1.00

$F = \dfrac{s_1^2}{s_2^2} = \dfrac{S_1/m}{S_2/n}$, where $s_1^2 = S_1/m$ and $s_2^2 = S_2/n$ are independent mean squares estimating a common variance σ^2 and based on m and n degrees of freedom, respectively.

PERCENTAGE POINTS, *F*-DISTRIBUTION (Continued)

$$F(F) = \int_0^F \frac{\Gamma\left(\dfrac{m+n}{2}\right)}{\Gamma\left(\dfrac{m}{2}\right)\Gamma\left(\dfrac{n}{2}\right)} m^{\frac{m}{2}} n^{\frac{n}{2}} x^{\frac{m}{2}-1} (n+mx)^{-\frac{m+n}{2}} \, dx = .95$$

m \ n	1	2	3	4	5	6	7	8	9	10	12	15	20	24	30	40	60	120	∞
1	161.4	199.5	215.7	224.6	230.2	234.0	236.8	238.9	240.5	241.9	243.9	245.9	248.0	249.1	250.1	251.1	252.2	253.3	254.3
2	18.51	19.00	19.16	19.25	19.30	19.33	19.35	19.37	19.38	19.40	19.41	19.43	19.45	19.45	19.46	19.47	19.48	19.49	19.50
3	10.13	9.55	9.28	9.12	9.01	8.94	8.89	8.85	8.81	8.79	8.74	8.70	8.66	8.64	8.62	8.59	8.57	8.55	8.53
4	7.71	6.94	6.59	6.39	6.26	6.16	6.09	6.04	6.00	5.96	5.91	5.86	5.80	5.77	5.75	5.72	5.69	5.66	5.63
5	6.61	5.79	5.41	5.19	5.05	4.95	4.88	4.82	4.77	4.74	4.68	4.62	4.56	4.53	4.50	4.46	4.43	4.40	4.36
6	5.99	5.14	4.76	4.53	4.39	4.28	4.21	4.15	4.10	4.06	4.00	3.94	3.87	3.84	3.81	3.77	3.74	3.70	3.67
7	5.59	4.74	4.35	4.12	3.97	3.87	3.79	3.73	3.68	3.64	3.57	3.51	3.44	3.41	3.38	3.34	3.30	3.27	3.23
8	5.32	4.46	4.07	3.84	3.69	3.58	3.50	3.44	3.39	3.35	3.28	3.22	3.15	3.12	3.08	3.04	3.01	2.97	2.93
9	5.12	4.26	3.86	3.63	3.48	3.37	3.29	3.23	3.18	3.14	3.07	3.01	2.94	2.90	2.86	2.83	2.79	2.75	2.71
10	4.96	4.10	3.71	3.48	3.33	3.22	3.14	3.07	3.02	2.98	2.91	2.85	2.77	2.74	2.70	2.66	2.62	2.58	2.54
11	4.84	3.98	3.59	3.36	3.20	3.09	3.01	2.95	2.90	2.85	2.79	2.72	2.65	2.61	2.57	2.53	2.49	2.45	2.40
12	4.75	3.89	3.49	3.26	3.11	3.00	2.91	2.85	2.80	2.75	2.69	2.62	2.54	2.51	2.47	2.43	2.38	2.34	2.30
13	4.67	3.81	3.41	3.18	3.03	2.92	2.83	2.77	2.71	2.67	2.60	2.53	2.46	2.42	2.38	2.34	2.30	2.25	2.21
14	4.60	3.74	3.34	3.11	2.96	2.85	2.76	2.70	2.65	2.60	2.53	2.46	2.39	2.35	2.31	2.27	2.22	2.18	2.13
15	4.54	3.68	3.29	3.06	2.90	2.79	2.71	2.64	2.59	2.54	2.48	2.40	2.33	2.29	2.25	2.20	2.16	2.11	2.07
16	4.49	3.63	3.24	3.01	2.85	2.74	2.66	2.59	2.54	2.49	2.42	2.35	2.28	2.24	2.19	2.15	2.11	2.06	2.01
17	4.45	3.59	3.20	2.96	2.81	2.70	2.61	2.55	2.49	2.45	2.38	2.31	2.23	2.19	2.15	2.10	2.06	2.01	1.96
18	4.41	3.55	3.16	2.93	2.77	2.66	2.58	2.51	2.46	2.41	2.34	2.27	2.19	2.15	2.11	2.06	2.02	1.97	1.92
19	4.38	3.52	3.13	2.90	2.74	2.63	2.54	2.48	2.42	2.38	2.31	2.23	2.16	2.11	2.07	2.03	1.98	1.93	1.88
20	4.35	3.49	3.10	2.87	2.71	2.60	2.51	2.45	2.39	2.35	2.28	2.20	2.12	2.08	2.04	1.99	1.95	1.90	1.84
21	4.32	3.47	3.07	2.84	2.68	2.57	2.49	2.42	2.37	2.32	2.25	2.18	2.10	2.05	2.01	1.96	1.92	1.87	1.81
22	4.30	3.44	3.05	2.82	2.66	2.55	2.46	2.40	2.34	2.30	2.23	2.15	2.07	2.03	1.98	1.94	1.89	1.84	1.78
23	4.28	3.42	3.03	2.80	2.64	2.53	2.44	2.37	2.32	2.27	2.20	2.13	2.05	2.01	1.96	1.91	1.86	1.81	1.76
24	4.26	3.40	3.01	2.78	2.62	2.51	2.42	2.36	2.30	2.25	2.18	2.11	2.03	1.98	1.94	1.89	1.84	1.79	1.73
25	4.24	3.39	2.99	2.76	2.60	2.49	2.40	2.34	2.28	2.24	2.16	2.09	2.01	1.96	1.92	1.87	1.82	1.77	1.71
26	4.23	3.37	2.98	2.74	2.59	2.47	2.39	2.32	2.27	2.22	2.15	2.07	1.99	1.95	1.90	1.85	1.80	1.75	1.69
27	4.21	3.35	2.96	2.73	2.57	2.46	2.37	2.31	2.25	2.20	2.13	2.06	1.97	1.93	1.88	1.84	1.79	1.73	1.67
28	4.20	3.34	2.95	2.71	2.56	2.45	2.36	2.29	2.24	2.19	2.12	2.04	1.96	1.91	1.87	1.82	1.77	1.71	1.65
29	4.18	3.33	2.93	2.70	2.55	2.43	2.35	2.28	2.22	2.18	2.10	2.03	1.94	1.90	1.85	1.81	1.75	1.70	1.64
30	4.17	3.32	2.92	2.69	2.53	2.42	2.33	2.27	2.21	2.16	2.09	2.01	1.93	1.89	1.84	1.79	1.74	1.68	1.62
40	4.08	3.23	2.84	2.61	2.45	2.34	2.25	2.18	2.12	2.08	2.00	1.92	1.84	1.79	1.74	1.69	1.64	1.58	1.51
60	4.00	3.15	2.76	2.53	2.37	2.25	2.17	2.10	2.04	1.99	1.92	1.84	1.75	1.70	1.65	1.59	1.53	1.47	1.39
120	3.92	3.07	2.68	2.45	2.29	2.17	2.09	2.02	1.96	1.91	1.83	1.75	1.66	1.61	1.55	1.50	1.43	1.35	1.25
∞	3.84	3.00	2.60	2.37	2.21	2.10	2.01	1.94	1.88	1.83	1.75	1.67	1.57	1.52	1.46	1.39	1.32	1.22	1.00

$F = \dfrac{s_1^2}{s_2^2} = \dfrac{S_1}{m} \Big/ \dfrac{S_2}{n}$, where $s_1^2 = S_1/m$ and $s_2^2 = S_2/n$ are independent mean squares estimating a common variance σ^2 and based on m and n degrees of freedom, respectively.

PERCENTAGE POINTS, *F*-DISTRIBUTION (Continued)

$$F(F) = \int_0^F \frac{\Gamma\left(\frac{m+n}{2}\right)}{\Gamma\left(\frac{m}{2}\right)\Gamma\left(\frac{n}{2}\right)} m^{\frac{m}{2}} n^{\frac{n}{2}} x^{\frac{m}{2}-1} (n+mx)^{-\frac{m+n}{2}}\, dx = .975$$

$m \backslash n$	∞	120	60	40	30	24	20	15	12	10	9	8	7	6	5	4	3	2	1
1	1018	1014	1010	1006	1001	997.2	993.1	984.9	976.7	968.6	963.3	956.7	948.2	937.1	921.8	899.6	864.2	799.5	647.8
2	39.50	39.49	39.48	39.47	39.46	39.46	39.45	39.43	39.41	39.40	39.39	39.37	39.36	39.33	39.30	39.25	39.17	39.00	38.51
3	13.90	13.95	13.99	14.04	14.08	14.12	14.17	14.25	14.34	14.42	14.47	14.54	14.62	14.73	14.88	15.10	15.44	16.04	17.44
4	8.26	8.31	8.36	8.41	8.46	8.51	8.56	8.66	8.75	8.84	8.90	8.98	9.07	9.20	9.36	9.60	9.98	10.65	12.22
5	6.02	6.07	6.12	6.18	6.23	6.28	6.33	6.43	6.52	6.62	6.68	6.76	6.85	6.98	7.15	7.39	7.76	8.43	10.01
6	4.85	4.90	4.96	5.01	5.07	5.12	5.17	5.27	5.37	5.46	5.52	5.60	5.70	5.82	5.99	6.23	6.60	7.26	8.81
7	4.14	4.20	4.25	4.31	4.36	4.42	4.47	4.57	4.67	4.76	4.82	4.90	4.99	5.12	5.29	5.52	5.89	6.54	8.07
8	3.67	3.73	3.78	3.84	3.89	3.95	4.00	4.10	4.20	4.30	4.36	4.43	4.53	4.65	4.82	5.05	5.42	6.06	7.57
9	3.33	3.39	3.45	3.51	3.56	3.61	3.67	3.77	3.87	3.96	4.03	4.10	4.20	4.32	4.48	4.72	5.08	5.71	7.21
10	3.08	3.14	3.20	3.26	3.31	3.37	3.42	3.52	3.62	3.72	3.78	3.85	3.95	4.07	4.24	4.47	4.83	5.46	6.94
11	2.88	2.94	3.00	3.06	3.12	3.17	3.23	3.33	3.43	3.53	3.59	3.66	3.76	3.88	4.04	4.28	4.63	5.26	6.72
12	2.72	2.79	2.85	2.91	2.96	3.02	3.07	3.18	3.28	3.37	3.44	3.51	3.61	3.73	3.89	4.12	4.47	5.10	6.55
13	2.60	2.66	2.72	2.78	2.84	2.89	2.95	3.05	3.15	3.25	3.31	3.39	3.48	3.60	3.77	4.00	4.35	4.97	6.41
14	2.49	2.55	2.61	2.67	2.73	2.79	2.84	2.95	3.05	3.15	3.21	3.29	3.38	3.50	3.66	3.89	4.24	4.86	6.30
15	2.40	2.46	2.52	2.59	2.64	2.70	2.76	2.86	2.96	3.06	3.12	3.20	3.29	3.41	3.58	3.80	4.15	4.77	6.20
16	2.32	2.38	2.45	2.51	2.57	2.63	2.68	2.79	2.89	2.99	3.05	3.12	3.22	3.34	3.50	3.73	4.08	4.69	6.12
17	2.25	2.32	2.38	2.44	2.50	2.56	2.62	2.72	2.82	2.92	2.98	3.06	3.16	3.28	3.44	3.66	4.01	4.62	6.04
18	2.19	2.26	2.32	2.38	2.44	2.50	2.56	2.67	2.77	2.87	2.93	3.01	3.10	3.22	3.38	3.61	3.95	4.56	5.98
19	2.13	2.20	2.27	2.33	2.39	2.45	2.51	2.62	2.72	2.82	2.88	2.96	3.05	3.17	3.33	3.56	3.90	4.51	5.92
20	2.09	2.16	2.22	2.29	2.35	2.41	2.46	2.57	2.68	2.77	2.84	2.91	3.01	3.13	3.29	3.51	3.86	4.46	5.87
21	2.04	2.11	2.18	2.25	2.31	2.37	2.42	2.53	2.64	2.73	2.80	2.87	2.97	3.09	3.25	3.48	3.82	4.42	5.83
22	2.00	2.08	2.14	2.21	2.27	2.33	2.39	2.50	2.60	2.70	2.76	2.84	2.93	3.05	3.22	3.44	3.78	4.38	5.79
23	1.97	2.04	2.11	2.18	2.24	2.30	2.36	2.47	2.57	2.67	2.73	2.81	2.90	3.02	3.18	3.41	3.75	4.35	5.75
24	1.94	2.01	2.08	2.15	2.21	2.27	2.33	2.44	2.54	2.64	2.70	2.78	2.87	2.99	3.15	3.38	3.72	4.32	5.72
25	1.91	1.98	2.05	2.12	2.18	2.24	2.30	2.41	2.51	2.61	2.68	2.75	2.85	2.97	3.13	3.35	3.69	4.29	5.69
26	1.88	1.95	2.03	2.09	2.16	2.22	2.28	2.39	2.49	2.59	2.65	2.73	2.82	2.94	3.10	3.33	3.67	4.27	5.66
27	1.85	1.93	2.00	2.07	2.13	2.19	2.25	2.36	2.47	2.57	2.63	2.71	2.80	2.92	3.08	3.31	3.65	4.24	5.63
28	1.83	1.91	1.98	2.05	2.11	2.17	2.23	2.34	2.45	2.55	2.61	2.69	2.78	2.90	3.06	3.29	3.63	4.22	5.61
29	1.81	1.89	1.96	2.03	2.09	2.15	2.21	2.32	2.43	2.53	2.59	2.67	2.76	2.88	3.04	3.27	3.61	4.20	5.59
30	1.79	1.87	1.94	2.01	2.07	2.14	2.20	2.31	2.41	2.51	2.57	2.65	2.75	2.87	3.03	3.25	3.59	4.18	5.57
40	1.64	1.72	1.80	1.88	1.94	2.01	2.07	2.18	2.29	2.39	2.45	2.53	2.62	2.74	2.90	3.13	3.46	4.05	5.42
60	1.48	1.58	1.67	1.74	1.82	1.88	1.94	2.06	2.17	2.27	2.33	2.41	2.51	2.63	2.79	3.01	3.34	3.93	5.29
120	1.31	1.43	1.53	1.61	1.69	1.76	1.82	1.94	2.05	2.16	2.22	2.30	2.39	2.52	2.67	2.89	3.23	3.80	5.15
∞	1.00	1.27	1.39	1.48	1.57	1.64	1.71	1.83	1.94	2.05	2.11	2.19	2.29	2.41	2.57	2.79	3.12	3.69	5.02

$F = \frac{s_1^2}{s_2^2} = \frac{S_1/m}{S_2/n}$, where $s_1^2 = S_1/m$ and $s_2^2 = S_2/n$ are independent mean squares estimating a common variance σ^2 and based on m and n degrees of freedom, respectively.

PERCENTAGE POINTS, *F*-DISTRIBUTION (Continued)

$$F(F) = \int_0^F \frac{\Gamma\left(\dfrac{m+n}{2}\right)}{\Gamma\left(\dfrac{m}{2}\right)\Gamma\left(\dfrac{n}{2}\right)} m^{\frac{m}{2}} n^{\frac{n}{2}} x^{\frac{m}{2}-1} (n+mx)^{-\frac{m+n}{2}}\, dx = .99$$

m / n	1	2	3	4	5	6	7	8	9	10	12	15	20	24	30	40	60	120	∞
1	4052	4999.5	5403	5625	5764	5859	5928	5982	6022	6056	6106	6157	6209	6235	6261	6287	6313	6339	6366
2	98.50	99.00	99.17	99.25	99.30	99.33	99.36	99.37	99.39	99.40	99.42	99.43	99.45	99.46	99.47	99.47	99.48	99.49	99.50
3	34.12	30.82	29.46	28.71	28.24	27.91	27.67	27.49	27.35	27.23	27.05	26.87	26.69	26.60	26.50	26.41	26.32	26.22	26.13
4	21.20	18.00	16.69	15.98	15.52	15.21	14.98	14.80	14.66	14.55	14.37	14.20	14.02	13.93	13.84	13.75	13.65	13.56	13.46
5	16.26	13.27	12.06	11.39	10.97	10.67	10.46	10.29	10.16	10.05	9.89	9.72	9.55	9.47	9.38	9.29	9.20	9.11	9.02
6	13.75	10.92	9.78	9.15	8.75	8.47	8.26	8.10	7.98	7.87	7.72	7.56	7.40	7.31	7.23	7.14	7.06	6.97	6.88
7	12.25	9.55	8.45	7.85	7.46	7.19	6.99	6.84	6.72	6.62	6.47	6.31	6.16	6.07	5.99	5.91	5.82	5.74	5.65
8	11.26	8.65	7.59	7.01	6.63	6.37	6.18	6.03	5.91	5.81	5.67	5.52	5.36	5.28	5.20	5.12	5.03	4.95	4.86
9	10.56	8.02	6.99	6.42	6.06	5.80	5.61	5.47	5.35	5.26	5.11	4.96	4.81	4.73	4.65	4.57	4.48	4.40	4.31
10	10.04	7.56	6.55	5.99	5.64	5.39	5.20	5.06	4.94	4.85	4.71	4.56	4.41	4.33	4.25	4.17	4.08	4.00	3.91
11	9.65	7.21	6.22	5.67	5.32	5.07	4.89	4.74	4.63	4.54	4.40	4.25	4.10	4.02	3.94	3.86	3.78	3.69	3.60
12	9.33	6.93	5.95	5.41	5.06	4.82	4.64	4.50	4.39	4.30	4.16	4.01	3.86	3.78	3.70	3.62	3.54	3.45	3.36
13	9.07	6.70	5.74	5.21	4.86	4.62	4.44	4.30	4.19	4.10	3.96	3.82	3.66	3.59	3.51	3.43	3.34	3.25	3.17
14	8.86	6.51	5.56	5.04	4.69	4.46	4.28	4.14	4.03	3.94	3.80	3.66	3.51	3.43	3.35	3.27	3.18	3.09	3.00
15	8.68	6.36	5.42	4.89	4.56	4.32	4.14	4.00	3.89	3.80	3.67	3.52	3.37	3.29	3.21	3.13	3.05	2.96	2.87
16	8.53	6.23	5.29	4.77	4.44	4.20	4.03	3.89	3.78	3.69	3.55	3.41	3.26	3.18	3.10	3.02	2.93	2.84	2.75
17	8.40	6.11	5.18	4.67	4.34	4.10	3.93	3.79	3.68	3.59	3.46	3.31	3.16	3.08	3.00	2.92	2.83	2.75	2.65
18	8.29	6.01	5.09	4.58	4.25	4.01	3.84	3.71	3.60	3.51	3.37	3.23	3.08	3.00	2.92	2.84	2.75	2.66	2.57
19	8.18	5.93	5.01	4.50	4.17	3.94	3.77	3.63	3.52	3.43	3.30	3.15	3.00	2.92	2.84	2.76	2.67	2.58	2.49
20	8.10	5.85	4.94	4.43	4.10	3.87	3.70	3.56	3.46	3.37	3.23	3.09	2.94	2.86	2.78	2.69	2.61	2.52	2.42
21	8.02	5.78	4.87	4.37	4.04	3.81	3.64	3.51	3.40	3.31	3.17	3.03	2.88	2.80	2.72	2.64	2.55	2.46	2.36
22	7.95	5.72	4.82	4.31	3.99	3.76	3.59	3.45	3.35	3.26	3.12	2.98	2.83	2.75	2.67	2.58	2.50	2.40	2.31
23	7.88	5.66	4.76	4.26	3.94	3.71	3.54	3.41	3.30	3.21	3.07	2.93	2.78	2.70	2.62	2.54	2.45	2.35	2.26
24	7.82	5.61	4.72	4.22	3.90	3.67	3.50	3.36	3.26	3.17	3.03	2.89	2.74	2.66	2.58	2.49	2.40	2.31	2.21
25	7.77	5.57	4.68	4.18	3.85	3.63	3.46	3.32	3.22	3.13	2.99	2.85	2.70	2.62	2.54	2.45	2.36	2.27	2.17
26	7.72	5.53	4.64	4.14	3.82	3.59	3.42	3.29	3.18	3.09	2.96	2.81	2.66	2.58	2.50	2.42	2.33	2.23	2.13
27	7.68	5.49	4.60	4.11	3.78	3.56	3.39	3.26	3.15	3.06	2.93	2.78	2.63	2.55	2.47	2.38	2.29	2.20	2.10
28	7.64	5.45	4.57	4.07	3.75	3.53	3.36	3.23	3.12	3.03	2.90	2.75	2.60	2.52	2.44	2.35	2.26	2.17	2.06
29	7.60	5.42	4.54	4.04	3.73	3.50	3.33	3.20	3.09	3.00	2.87	2.73	2.57	2.49	2.41	2.33	2.23	2.14	2.03
30	7.56	5.39	4.51	4.02	3.70	3.47	3.30	3.17	3.07	2.98	2.84	2.70	2.55	2.47	2.39	2.30	2.21	2.11	2.01
40	7.31	5.18	4.31	3.83	3.51	3.29	3.12	2.99	2.89	2.80	2.66	2.52	2.37	2.29	2.20	2.11	2.02	1.92	1.80
60	7.08	4.98	4.13	3.65	3.34	3.12	2.95	2.82	2.72	2.63	2.50	2.35	2.20	2.12	2.03	1.94	1.84	1.73	1.60
120	6.85	4.79	3.95	3.48	3.17	2.96	2.79	2.66	2.56	2.47	2.34	2.19	2.03	1.95	1.86	1.76	1.66	1.53	1.38
∞	6.63	4.61	3.78	3.32	3.02	2.80	2.64	2.51	2.41	2.32	2.18	2.04	1.88	1.79	1.70	1.59	1.47	1.32	1.00

$F = \dfrac{s_1^2}{s_2^2} = \dfrac{S_1/m}{S_2/n}$ where $s_1^2 = S_1/m$ and $s_2^2 = S_2/n$ are independent mean squares estimating a common variance σ^2 and based on m and n degrees of freedom, respectively.

PERCENTAGE POINTS, *F*-DISTRIBUTION (Continued)

$$F(F) = \int_0^F \frac{\Gamma\left(\frac{m+n}{2}\right)}{\Gamma\left(\frac{m}{2}\right)\Gamma\left(\frac{n}{2}\right)} m^{\frac{m}{2}} n^{\frac{n}{2}} x^{\frac{m}{2}-1} (n+mx)^{-\frac{m+n}{2}} \, dx = .995$$

m \ n	1	2	3	4	5	6	7	8	9	10	12	15	20	24	30	40	60	120	∞
1	16211	20000	21615	22500	23056	23437	23715	23925	24091	24224	24426	24630	24836	24940	25044	25148	25253	25359	25465
2	198.5	199.0	199.2	199.2	199.3	199.3	199.4	199.4	199.4	199.4	199.4	199.4	199.4	199.5	199.5	199.5	199.5	199.5	199.5
3	55.55	49.80	47.47	46.19	45.39	44.84	44.43	44.13	43.88	43.69	43.39	43.08	42.78	42.62	42.47	42.31	42.15	41.99	41.83
4	31.33	26.28	24.26	23.15	22.46	21.97	21.62	21.35	21.14	20.97	20.70	20.44	20.17	20.03	19.89	19.75	19.61	19.47	19.32
5	22.78	18.31	16.53	15.56	14.94	14.51	14.20	13.96	13.77	13.62	13.38	13.15	12.90	12.78	12.66	12.53	12.40	12.27	12.14
6	18.63	14.54	12.92	12.03	11.46	11.07	10.79	10.57	10.39	10.25	10.03	9.81	9.59	9.47	9.36	9.24	9.12	9.00	8.88
7	16.24	12.40	10.88	10.05	9.52	9.16	8.89	8.68	8.51	8.38	8.18	7.97	7.75	7.65	7.53	7.42	7.31	7.19	7.08
8	14.69	11.04	9.60	8.81	8.30	7.95	7.69	7.50	7.34	7.21	7.01	6.81	6.61	6.50	6.40	6.29	6.18	6.06	5.95
9	13.61	10.11	8.72	7.96	7.47	7.13	6.88	6.69	6.54	6.42	6.23	6.03	5.83	5.73	5.62	5.52	5.41	5.30	5.19
10	12.83	9.43	8.08	7.34	6.87	6.54	6.30	6.12	5.97	5.85	5.66	5.47	5.27	5.17	5.07	4.97	4.86	4.75	4.64
11	12.23	8.91	7.60	6.88	6.42	6.10	5.86	5.68	5.54	5.42	5.24	5.05	4.86	4.76	4.65	4.55	4.44	4.34	4.23
12	11.75	8.51	7.23	6.52	6.07	5.76	5.52	5.35	5.20	5.09	4.91	4.72	4.53	4.43	4.33	4.23	4.12	4.01	3.90
13	11.37	8.19	6.93	6.23	5.79	5.48	5.25	5.08	4.94	4.82	4.64	4.46	4.27	4.17	4.07	3.97	3.87	3.76	3.65
14	11.06	7.92	6.68	6.00	5.56	5.26	5.03	4.86	4.72	4.60	4.43	4.25	4.06	3.96	3.86	3.76	3.66	3.55	3.44
15	10.80	7.70	6.48	5.80	5.37	5.07	4.85	4.67	4.54	4.42	4.25	4.07	3.88	3.79	3.69	3.58	3.48	3.37	3.26
16	10.58	7.51	6.30	5.64	5.21	4.91	4.69	4.52	4.38	4.27	4.10	3.92	3.73	3.64	3.54	3.44	3.33	3.22	3.11
17	10.38	7.35	6.16	5.50	5.07	4.78	4.56	4.39	4.25	4.14	3.97	3.79	3.61	3.51	3.41	3.31	3.21	3.10	2.98
18	10.22	7.21	6.03	5.37	4.96	4.66	4.44	4.28	4.14	4.03	3.86	3.68	3.50	3.40	3.30	3.20	3.10	2.99	2.87
19	10.07	7.09	5.92	5.27	4.85	4.56	4.34	4.18	4.04	3.93	3.76	3.59	3.40	3.31	3.21	3.11	3.00	2.89	2.78
20	9.94	6.99	5.82	5.17	4.76	4.47	4.26	4.09	3.96	3.85	3.68	3.50	3.32	3.22	3.12	3.02	2.92	2.81	2.69
21	9.83	6.89	5.73	5.09	4.68	4.39	4.18	4.01	3.88	3.77	3.60	3.43	3.24	3.15	3.05	2.95	2.84	2.73	2.61
22	9.73	6.81	5.65	5.02	4.61	4.32	4.11	3.94	3.81	3.70	3.54	3.36	3.18	3.08	2.98	2.88	2.77	2.66	2.55
23	9.63	6.73	5.58	4.95	4.54	4.26	4.05	3.88	3.75	3.64	3.47	3.30	3.12	3.02	2.92	2.82	2.71	2.60	2.48
24	9.55	6.66	5.52	4.89	4.49	4.20	3.99	3.83	3.69	3.59	3.42	3.25	3.06	2.97	2.87	2.77	2.66	2.55	2.43
25	9.48	6.60	5.46	4.84	4.43	4.15	3.94	3.78	3.64	3.54	3.37	3.20	3.01	2.92	2.82	2.72	2.61	2.50	2.38
26	9.41	6.54	5.41	4.79	4.38	4.10	3.89	3.73	3.60	3.49	3.33	3.15	2.97	2.87	2.77	2.67	2.56	2.45	2.33
27	9.34	6.49	5.36	4.74	4.34	4.06	3.85	3.69	3.56	3.45	3.28	3.11	2.93	2.83	2.73	2.63	2.52	2.41	2.29
28	9.28	6.44	5.32	4.70	4.30	4.02	3.81	3.65	3.52	3.41	3.25	3.07	2.89	2.79	2.69	2.59	2.48	2.37	2.25
29	9.23	6.40	5.28	4.66	4.26	3.98	3.77	3.61	3.48	3.38	3.21	3.04	2.86	2.76	2.66	2.56	2.45	2.33	2.24
30	9.18	6.35	5.24	4.62	4.23	3.95	3.74	3.58	3.45	3.34	3.18	3.01	2.82	2.73	2.63	2.52	2.42	2.30	2.18
40	8.83	6.07	4.98	4.37	3.99	3.71	3.51	3.35	3.22	3.12	2.95	2.78	2.60	2.50	2.40	2.30	2.18	2.06	1.93
60	8.49	5.79	4.73	4.14	3.76	3.49	3.29	3.13	3.01	2.90	2.74	2.57	2.39	2.29	2.19	2.08	1.96	1.83	1.69
120	8.18	5.54	4.50	3.92	3.55	3.28	3.09	2.93	2.81	2.71	2.54	2.37	2.19	2.09	1.98	1.87	1.75	1.61	1.43
∞	7.88	5.30	4.28	3.72	3.35	3.09	2.90	2.74	2.62	2.52	2.36	2.19	2.00	1.90	1.79	1.67	1.53	1.36	1.00

$F = \dfrac{s_1^2}{s_2^2} = \dfrac{S_1/m}{S_2/n}$, where $s_1^2 = S_1/m$ and $s_2^2 = S_2/n$ are independent mean squares estimating a common variance σ^2 and based on m and n degrees of freedom, respectively.

PERCENTAGE POINTS, F-DISTRIBUTION (Continued)

$$F(F) = \int_0^F \frac{\Gamma\left(\frac{m+n}{2}\right)}{\Gamma\left(\frac{m}{2}\right)\Gamma\left(\frac{n}{2}\right)}\, m^{\frac{m}{2}} n^{\frac{n}{2}} x^{\frac{m}{2}-1}\,(n+mx)^{-\frac{m+n}{2}}\,dx = .999$$

m \ n	1	2	3	4	5	6	7	8	9	10	12	15	20	24	30	40	60	120	∞
1	4053*	5000*	5404*	5625*	5764*	5859*	5929*	5981*	6023*	6056*	6107*	6158*	6209*	6235*	6261*	6287*	6313*	6340*	6366*
2	998.5	999.0	999.2	999.2	999.3	999.3	999.4	999.4	999.4	999.4	999.4	999.4	999.4	999.5	999.5	999.5	999.5	999.5	999.5
3	167.0	148.5	141.1	137.1	134.6	132.8	131.6	130.6	129.9	129.2	128.3	127.4	126.4	125.9	125.4	125.0	124.5	124.0	123.5
4	74.14	61.25	56.18	53.44	51.71	50.53	49.66	49.00	48.47	48.05	47.41	46.76	46.10	45.77	45.43	45.09	44.75	44.40	44.05
5	47.18	37.12	33.20	31.09	29.75	28.84	28.16	27.64	27.24	26.92	26.42	25.91	25.39	25.14	24.87	24.60	24.33	24.06	23.79
6	35.51	27.00	23.70	21.92	20.81	20.03	19.46	19.03	18.69	18.41	17.99	17.56	17.12	16.89	16.67	16.44	16.21	15.99	15.75
7	29.25	21.69	18.77	17.19	16.21	15.52	15.02	14.63	14.33	14.08	13.71	13.32	12.93	12.73	12.53	12.33	12.12	11.91	11.70
8	25.42	18.49	15.83	14.39	13.49	12.86	12.40	12.04	11.77	11.54	11.19	10.84	10.48	10.30	10.11	9.92	9.73	9.53	9.33
9	22.86	16.39	13.90	12.56	11.71	11.13	10.70	10.37	10.11	9.89	9.57	9.24	8.90	8.72	8.55	8.37	8.19	8.00	7.81
10	21.04	14.91	12.55	11.28	10.48	9.92	9.52	9.20	8.96	8.75	8.45	8.13	7.80	7.64	7.47	7.30	7.12	6.94	6.76
11	19.69	13.81	11.56	10.35	9.58	9.05	8.66	8.35	8.12	7.92	7.63	7.32	7.01	6.85	6.68	6.52	6.35	6.17	6.00
12	18.64	12.97	10.80	9.63	8.89	8.38	8.00	7.71	7.48	7.29	7.00	6.71	6.40	6.25	6.09	5.93	5.76	5.59	5.42
13	17.81	12.31	10.21	9.07	8.35	7.86	7.49	7.21	6.98	6.80	6.52	6.23	5.93	5.78	5.63	5.47	5.30	5.14	4.97
14	17.14	11.78	9.73	8.62	7.92	7.43	7.08	6.80	6.58	6.40	6.13	5.85	5.56	5.41	5.25	5.10	4.94	4.77	4.60
15	16.59	11.34	9.34	8.25	7.57	7.09	6.74	6.47	6.26	6.08	5.81	5.54	5.25	5.10	4.95	4.80	4.64	4.47	4.31
16	16.12	10.97	9.00	7.94	7.27	6.81	6.46	6.19	5.98	5.81	5.55	5.27	4.99	4.85	4.70	4.54	4.39	4.23	4.06
17	15.72	10.66	8.73	7.68	7.02	6.56	6.22	5.96	5.75	5.58	5.32	5.05	4.78	4.63	4.48	4.33	4.18	4.02	3.85
18	15.38	10.39	8.49	7.46	6.81	6.35	6.02	5.76	5.56	5.39	5.13	4.87	4.59	4.45	4.30	4.15	4.00	3.84	3.67
19	15.08	10.16	8.28	7.26	6.62	6.18	5.85	5.59	5.39	5.22	4.97	4.70	4.43	4.29	4.14	3.99	3.84	3.68	3.51
20	14.82	9.95	8.10	7.10	6.46	6.02	5.69	5.44	5.24	5.08	4.82	4.56	4.29	4.15	4.00	3.86	3.70	3.54	3.38
21	14.59	9.77	7.94	6.95	6.32	5.88	5.56	5.31	5.11	4.95	4.70	4.44	4.17	4.03	3.88	3.74	3.58	3.42	3.26
22	14.38	9.61	7.80	6.81	6.19	5.76	5.44	5.19	4.99	4.83	4.58	4.33	4.06	3.92	3.78	3.63	3.48	3.32	3.15
23	14.19	9.47	7.67	6.69	6.08	5.65	5.33	5.09	4.89	4.73	4.48	4.23	3.96	3.82	3.68	3.53	3.38	3.22	3.05
24	14.03	9.34	7.55	6.59	5.98	5.55	5.23	4.99	4.80	4.64	4.39	4.14	3.87	3.74	3.59	3.45	3.29	3.14	2.97
25	13.88	9.22	7.45	6.49	5.88	5.46	5.15	4.91	4.71	4.56	4.31	4.06	3.79	3.66	3.52	3.37	3.22	3.06	2.89
26	13.74	9.12	7.36	6.41	5.80	5.38	5.07	4.83	4.64	4.48	4.24	3.99	3.72	3.59	3.44	3.30	3.15	2.99	2.82
27	13.61	9.02	7.27	6.33	5.73	5.31	5.00	4.76	4.57	4.41	4.17	3.92	3.66	3.52	3.38	3.23	3.08	2.92	2.75
28	13.50	8.93	7.19	6.25	5.66	5.24	4.93	4.69	4.50	4.35	4.11	3.86	3.60	3.46	3.32	3.18	3.02	2.86	2.69
29	13.39	8.85	7.12	6.19	5.59	5.18	4.87	4.64	4.45	4.29	4.05	3.80	3.54	3.41	3.27	3.12	2.97	2.81	2.64
30	13.29	8.77	7.05	6.12	5.53	5.12	4.82	4.58	4.39	4.24	4.00	3.75	3.49	3.36	3.22	3.07	2.92	2.76	2.59
40	12.61	8.25	6.60	5.70	5.13	4.73	4.44	4.21	4.02	3.87	3.64	3.40	3.15	3.01	2.87	2.73	2.57	2.41	2.23
60	11.97	7.76	6.17	5.31	4.76	4.37	4.09	3.87	3.69	3.54	3.31	3.08	2.83	2.69	2.55	2.41	2.25	2.08	1.89
120	11.38	7.32	5.79	4.95	4.42	4.04	3.77	3.55	3.38	3.24	3.02	2.78	2.53	2.40	2.26	2.11	1.95	1.76	1.54
∞	10.83	6.91	5.42	4.62	4.10	3.74	3.47	3.27	3.10	2.96	2.74	2.51	2.27	2.13	1.99	1.84	1.66	1.45	1.00

* Multiply these entries by 100.

TABLE OF BINOMIAL COEFFICIENTS

n	$\binom{n}{0}$	$\binom{n}{1}$	$\binom{n}{2}$	$\binom{n}{3}$	$\binom{n}{4}$	$\binom{n}{5}$	$\binom{n}{6}$	$\binom{n}{7}$	$\binom{n}{8}$	$\binom{n}{9}$	$\binom{n}{10}$
0	1										
1	1	1									
2	1	2	1								
3	1	3	3	1							
4	1	4	6	4	1						
5	1	5	10	10	5	1					
6	1	6	15	20	15	6	1				
7	1	7	21	35	35	21	7	1			
8	1	8	28	56	70	56	28	8	1		
9	1	9	36	84	126	126	84	36	9	1	
10	1	10	45	120	210	252	210	120	45	10	1
11	1	11	55	165	330	462	462	330	165	55	11
12	1	12	66	220	495	792	924	792	495	220	66
13	1	13	78	286	715	1287	1716	1716	1287	715	286
14	1	14	91	364	1001	2002	3003	3432	3003	2002	1001
15	1	15	105	455	1365	3003	5005	6435	6435	5005	3003
16	1	16	120	560	1820	4368	8008	11440	12870	11440	8008
17	1	17	136	680	2380	6188	12376	19448	24310	24310	19448
18	1	18	153	816	3060	8568	18564	31824	43758	48620	43758
19	1	19	171	969	3876	11628	27132	50388	75582	92378	92378
20	1	20	190	1140	4845	15504	38760	77520	125970	167960	184756

NOTE: $\binom{n}{m} = \dfrac{n(n-1)(n-2) \cdots (n-m+1)}{m(m-1)(m-2) \cdots 3.2.1}$; $\binom{n}{0} = 1$; $\binom{n}{1} = n$.

For coefficients missing from the above table, use the relation

$$\binom{n}{m} = \binom{n}{n-m}, \text{ e.g. } \binom{20}{11} = \binom{20}{9} = 167960.$$

RANDOM UNITS

Use of Table. If one wishes to select a random sample of N items from a universe of M items, the following procedure may be applied. ($M > N$.)

1. Decide upon some arbitrary scheme of selecting entries from the table. For example, one may decide to use the entries in the first line, second column; second line, third column; third line, fourth column; etc.

2. Assign numbers to each of the items in the universe from 1 to M. Thus, if $M = 500$, the items would be numbered from 001 to 500, and therefore, each designated item is associated with a three digit number.

3. Decide upon some arbitrary scheme of selecting positional digits from each entry chosen according to Step 1. Thus, if $M = 500$, one may decide to use the first, third, and fourth digit of each entry selected, and as a consequence a three digit number is created for each entry choice.

4. If the number formed is $\leq M$, the correspondingly designated item in the universe is chosen for the random sample of N items. If a number formed is $> M$ or is a repeated number of one already chosen, it is passed over and the next desirable number is taken. This process is continued until the random sample of N items is selected.

A TABLE OF 14,000 RANDOM UNITS

ne/Col.	(1)	(2)	(3)	(4)	(5)	(6)	(7)	(8)	(9)	(10)	(11)	(12)	(13)	(14)
1	10480	15011	01536	02011	81647	91646	69179	14194	62590	36207	20969	99570	91291	90700
2	22368	46573	25595	85393	30995	89198	27982	53402	93965	34095	52666	19174	39615	99505
3	24130	48360	22527	97265	76393	64809	15179	24830	49340	32081	30680	19655	63348	58629
4	42167	93093	06243	61680	07856	16376	39440	53537	71341	57004	00849	74917	97758	16379
5	37570	39975	81837	16656	06121	91782	60468	81305	49684	60672	14110	06927	01263	54613
6	77921	06907	11008	42751	27756	53498	18602	70659	90655	15053	21916	81825	44394	42880
7	99562	72905	56420	69994	98872	31016	71194	18738	44013	48840	63213	21069	10634	12952
8	96301	91977	05463	07972	18876	20922	94595	56869	69014	60045	18425	84903	42508	32307
9	89579	14342	63661	10281	17453	18103	57740	84378	25331	12566	58678	44947	05585	56941
10	85475	36857	43342	53988	53060	59533	38867	62300	08158	17983	16439	11458	18593	64952
11	28918	69578	88231	33276	70997	79936	56865	05859	90106	31595	01547	85590	91610	78188
12	63553	40961	48235	03427	49626	69445	18663	72695	52180	20847	12234	90511	33703	90322
13	09429	93969	52636	92737	88974	33488	36320	17617	30015	08272	84115	27156	30613	74952
14	10365	61129	87529	85689	48237	52267	67689	93394	01511	26358	85104	20285	29975	89868
15	07119	97336	71048	08178	77233	13916	47564	81056	97735	85977	29372	74461	28551	90707
16	51085	12765	51821	51259	77452	16308	60756	92144	49442	53900	70960	63990	75601	40719
17	02368	21382	52404	60268	89368	19885	55322	44819	01188	65255	64835	44919	05944	55157
18	01011	54092	33362	94904	31273	04146	18594	29852	71585	85030	51132	01915	92747	64951
19	52162	53916	46369	58586	23216	14513	83149	98736	23495	64350	94738	17752	35156	35749
20	07056	97628	33787	09998	42698	06691	76988	13602	51851	46104	88916	19509	25625	58104
21	48663	91245	85828	14346	09172	30168	90229	04734	59193	22178	30421	61666	99904	32812
22	54164	58492	22421	74103	47070	25306	76468	26384	58151	06646	21524	15227	96909	44592
23	32639	32363	05597	24200	13363	38005	94342	28728	35806	06912	17012	64161	18296	22851
24	29334	27001	87637	87308	58731	00256	45834	15398	46557	41135	10367	07684	36188	18510
25	02488	33062	28834	07351	19731	92420	60952	61280	50001	67658	32586	86679	50720	94953
26	81525	72295	04839	96423	24878	82651	66566	14778	76797	14780	13300	87074	79666	95725
27	29676	20591	68086	26432	46901	20849	89768	81536	86645	12659	92259	57102	80428	25280
28	00742	57392	39064	66432	84673	40027	32832	61362	98947	96067	64760	64584	96096	98253
29	05366	04213	25669	26422	44407	44048	37937	63904	45766	66134	75470	66520	34693	90449
30	91921	26418	64117	94305	26766	25940	39972	22209	71500	64568	91402	42416	07844	69618
31	00582	04711	87917	77341	42206	35126	74087	99547	81817	42607	43808	76655	62028	76630
32	00725	69884	62797	56170	86324	88072	76222	36086	84637	93161	76038	65855	77919	88006
33	69011	65797	95876	55293	18988	27354	26575	08625	40801	59920	29841	80150	12777	48501
34	25976	57948	29888	88604	67917	48708	18912	82271	65424	69774	33611	54262	85963	03547
35	09763	83473	73577	12908	30883	18317	28290	35797	05998	41688	34952	37888	38917	88050
36	91567	42595	27958	30134	04024	86385	29880	99730	55536	84855	29080	09250	79656	73211
37	17955	56349	90999	49127	20044	59931	06115	20542	18059	02008	73708	83517	36103	42791
38	46503	18584	18845	49618	02304	51038	20655	58727	28168	15475	56942	53389	20562	87338
39	92157	89634	94824	78171	84610	82834	09922	25417	44137	48413	25555	21246	35509	20468
40	14577	62765	35605	81263	39667	47358	56873	56307	61607	49518	89656	20103	77490	18062
41	98427	07523	33362	64270	01638	92477	66969	98420	04880	45585	46565	04102	46880	45709
42	34914	63976	88720	82765	34476	17032	87589	40836	32427	70002	70663	88863	77775	69348
43	70060	28277	39475	46473	23219	53416	94970	25832	69975	94884	19661	72828	00102	66794
44	53976	54914	06990	67245	68350	82948	11398	42878	80287	88267	47363	46634	06541	97809
45	76072	29515	40980	07391	58745	25774	22987	80059	39911	96189	41151	14222	60697	59583
46	90725	52210	83974	29992	65831	38857	50490	83765	55657	14361	31720	57375	56228	41546
47	64364	67412	33339	31926	14883	24413	59744	92351	97473	89286	35931	04110	23726	51900
48	08962	00358	31662	25388	61642	34072	81249	35648	56891	69352	48373	45578	78547	81788
49	95012	68379	93526	70765	10593	04542	76463	54328	02349	17247	28865	14777	62730	92277
50	15664	10493	20492	38391	91132	21999	59516	81652	27195	48223	46751	22923	32261	85653

A TABLE OF 14,000 RANDOM UNITS (Continued)

Line/Col.	(1)	(2)	(3)	(4)	(5)	(6)	(7)	(8)	(9)	(10)	(11)	(12)	(13)
51	16408	81899	04153	53381	79401	21438	83035	92350	36693	31238	59649	91754	72772
52	18629	81953	05520	91962	04739	13092	97662	24822	94730	06496	35090	04822	86772
53	73115	35101	47498	87637	99016	71060	88824	71013	18735	20286	23153	72924	35165
54	57491	16703	23167	49323	45021	33132	12544	41035	80780	45393	44812	12515	98931
55	30405	83946	23792	14422	15059	45799	22716	19792	09983	74353	68668	30429	70735
56	16631	35006	85900	98275	32388	52390	16815	69298	82732	38480	73817	32523	41961
57	96773	20206	42559	78985	05300	22164	24369	54224	35083	19687	11052	91491	60383
58	38935	64202	14349	82674	66523	44133	00697	35552	35970	19124	63318	29686	03387
59	31624	76384	17403	53363	44167	64486	64758	75366	76554	31601	12614	33072	60332
60	78919	19474	23632	27889	47914	02584	37680	20801	72152	39339	34806	08930	85001
61	03931	33309	57047	74211	63445	17361	62825	39908	05607	91284	68833	25570	38818
62	74426	33278	43972	10119	89917	15665	52872	73823	73144	88662	88970	74492	51805
63	09066	00903	20795	95452	92648	45454	09552	88815	16553	51125	79375	97596	16296
64	42238	12426	87025	14267	20979	04508	64535	31355	86064	29472	47689	05974	52468
65	16153	08002	26504	41744	81959	65642	74240	56302	00033	67107	77510	70625	28725
66	21457	40742	29820	96783	29400	21840	15035	34537	33310	06116	95240	15957	16572
67	21581	57802	02050	89728	17937	37621	47075	42080	97403	48626	68995	43805	33386
68	55612	78095	83197	33732	05810	24813	86902	60397	16489	03264	88525	42786	05269
69	44657	66999	99324	51281	84463	60563	79312	93454	68876	25471	93911	25650	12682
70	91340	84979	46949	81973	37949	61023	43997	15263	80644	43942	89203	71795	99533
71	91227	21199	31935	27022	84067	05462	35216	14486	29891	68607	41867	14951	91696
72	50001	38140	66321	19924	72163	09538	12151	06878	91903	18749	34405	56087	82790
73	65390	05224	72958	28609	81406	39147	25549	48542	42627	45233	57202	94617	23772
74	27504	96131	83944	41575	10573	08619	64482	73923	36152	05184	94142	25299	84387
75	37169	94851	39117	89632	00959	16487	65536	49071	39782	17095	02330	74301	00275
76	11508	70225	51111	38351	19444	66499	71945	05422	13442	78675	84081	66938	93654
77	37449	30362	06694	54690	04052	53115	62757	95348	78662	11163	81651	50245	34971
78	46515	70331	85922	38329	57015	15765	97161	17869	45349	61796	66345	81073	49106
79	30986	81223	42416	58353	21532	30502	32305	86482	05174	07901	54339	58861	74818
80	63798	64995	46583	09765	44160	78128	83991	42865	92520	83531	80377	35909	81250
81	82486	84846	99254	67632	43218	50076	21361	64816	51202	88124	41870	52689	51275
82	21885	32906	92431	09060	64297	51674	64126	62570	26123	05155	59194	52799	28225
83	60336	98782	07408	53458	13564	59089	26445	29789	85205	41001	12535	12133	14645
84	43937	46891	24010	25560	86355	33941	25786	54990	71899	15475	95434	98227	21824
85	97656	63175	89303	16275	07100	92063	21942	18611	47348	20203	18534	03862	78095
86	03299	01221	05418	38982	55758	92237	26759	86367	21216	98442	08303	56613	91511
87	79626	06486	03574	17668	07785	76020	79924	25651	83325	88428	85076	72811	22717
88	85636	68335	47539	03129	65651	11977	02510	26113	99447	68645	34427	15152	55230
89	18039	14367	61337	06177	12143	46609	32989	74014	64708	00533	35398	58408	13261
90	08362	15656	60627	36478	65648	16764	53412	09013	07832	41574	17639	82163	60859
91	79556	29068	04142	16268	15387	12856	66227	38358	22478	73373	88732	09443	82558
92	92608	82674	27072	32534	17075	27698	98204	63863	11951	34648	88022	56148	34925
93	23982	25835	40055	67006	12293	02753	14827	22235	35071	99704	37543	11601	35503
94	09915	96306	05908	97901	28395	14186	00821	80703	70426	75647	76310	88717	37890
95	50937	33300	26695	62247	69927	76123	50842	43834	86654	70959	79725	93872	28117
96	42488	78077	69882	61657	34136	79180	97526	43092	04098	73571	80799	76536	71255
97	46764	86273	63003	93017	31204	36692	40202	33275	57306	55543	53203	18098	47625
98	03237	45430	55417	63282	90816	17349	88298	90183	36600	78406	06216	95787	42579
99	86591	81482	52667	61583	14972	90053	89534	76036	49199	43716	97548	04379	46370
100	38534	01715	94964	87288	65680	43772	39560	12918	86537	62738	19636	51132	25739

A TABLE OF 14,000 RANDOM UNITS (Continued)

Line/Col.	(1)	(2)	(3)	(4)	(5)	(6)	(7)	(8)	(9)	(10)	(11)	(12)	(13)	(14)
101	13284	16834	74151	92027	24670	36665	00770	22878	02179	51602	07270	76517	97275	45960
102	21224	00370	30420	03883	96648	89428	41583	17564	27395	63904	41548	49197	82277	24120
103	99052	47887	81085	64933	66279	80432	65793	83287	34142	13241	30590	97760	35848	91983
104	00199	50993	98603	38452	87890	94624	69721	57484	67501	77638	44331	11257	71131	11059
105	60578	06483	28733	37867	07936	98710	98539	27186	31237	80612	44488	97819	70401	95419
106	91240	18312	17441	01929	18163	69201	31211	54288	39296	37318	65724	90401	79017	62077
107	97458	14229	12063	59611	32249	90466	33216	19358	02591	54263	88449	01912	07436	50813
108	35249	38646	34475	72417	60514	69257	12489	51924	86871	92446	36607	11458	30440	52639
109	38980	46600	11759	11900	46743	27860	77940	39298	97838	95145	32378	68038	89351	37005
110	10750	52745	38749	87365	58959	53731	89295	59062	39404	13198	59960	70408	29812	83126
111	36247	27850	73958	20673	37800	63835	71051	84724	52492	22342	78071	17456	96104	18327
112	70994	66986	99744	72438	01174	42159	11392	20724	54322	36923	70009	23233	65438	59685
113	99638	94702	11463	18148	81386	80431	90628	52506	02016	85151	88598	47821	00265	82525
114	72055	15774	43857	99805	10419	76939	25993	03544	21560	83471	43989	90770	22965	44247
115	24038	65541	85788	55835	38835	59399	13790	35112	01324	39520	76210	22467	83275	32286
116	74976	14631	35908	28221	39470	91548	12854	30166	09073	75887	36782	00268	97121	57676
117	35553	71628	70189	26436	63407	91178	90348	55359	80392	41012	36270	77786	89578	21059
118	35676	12797	51434	82976	42010	26344	92920	92155	58807	54644	58581	95331	78629	73344
119	74815	67523	72985	23183	02446	63594	98924	20633	58842	85961	07648	70164	34994	67662
120	45246	88048	65173	50989	91060	89894	36063	32819	68559	99221	49475	50558	34698	71800
121	76509	47069	86378	41797	11910	49672	88575	97966	32466	10083	54728	81972	58975	30761
122	19689	90332	04315	21358	97248	11188	39062	63312	52496	07349	79178	33692	57352	72862
123	42751	35318	97513	61537	54955	08159	00337	80778	27507	95478	21252	12746	37554	97775
124	11946	22681	45045	13964	57517	59419	58045	44067	58716	58840	45557	96345	33271	53464
125	96518	48688	20996	11090	48396	57177	83867	86464	14342	21545	46717	72364	86954	55580
126	35726	58643	76869	84622	39098	36083	72505	92265	23107	60278	05822	46760	44294	07672
127	39737	42750	48968	70536	84864	64952	38404	94317	65402	13589	01055	79044	19308	83623
128	97025	66492	56177	04049	80312	48028	26408	43591	75528	65341	49044	95495	81256	53214
129	62814	08075	09788	56350	76787	51591	54509	49295	85830	59860	30883	89660	96142	18354
130	25578	22950	15227	83291	41737	79599	96191	71845	86899	70694	24290	01551	80092	82118
131	68763	69576	88991	49662	46704	63362	56625	00481	73323	91427	15264	06969	57048	54149
132	17900	00813	64361	60725	88974	61005	99709	30666	26451	11528	44323	34778	60342	60388
133	71944	60227	63551	71109	05624	43836	58254	26160	32116	63403	35404	57146	10909	07346
134	54684	93691	85132	64399	29182	44324	14491	55226	78793	34107	30374	48429	51376	09559
135	25946	27623	11258	65204	52832	50880	22273	05554	99521	73791	85744	29276	70326	60251
136	01353	39318	44961	44972	91766	90262	56073	06606	51826	18893	83448	31915	97764	75091
137	99083	88191	27662	99113	57174	35571	99884	13951	71057	53961	61448	74909	07322	80960
138	52021	45406	37945	75234	24327	86978	22644	87779	23753	99926	63898	54886	18051	96314
139	78755	47744	43776	83098	03225	14281	83637	55984	13300	52212	58781	14905	46502	04472
140	25282	69106	59180	16257	22810	43609	12224	25643	89884	31149	85423	32581	34374	70873
141	11959	94202	02743	86847	79725	51811	12998	76844	05320	54236	53891	70226	38632	84776
142	11644	13792	98190	01424	30078	28197	55583	05197	47714	68440	22016	79204	06862	94451
143	06307	97912	68110	59812	95448	43244	31262	88880	13040	16453	43813	89416	42482	33939
144	76285	75714	89585	99296	52640	46518	55486	90754	88932	19937	57119	23251	55619	23679
145	55322	07589	39600	60866	63007	20007	66819	84164	61131	81429	60676	42807	78286	29015
146	78017	90928	90220	92503	83375	26986	74399	30885	88567	29169	72816	53357	15428	86932
147	44768	43342	20696	26331	43140	69744	82928	24988	94237	46138	77426	39039	55596	12655
148	25100	19336	14605	86603	51680	97678	24261	02464	86563	74812	60069	71674	15478	47642
149	83612	46623	62876	85197	07824	91392	58317	37726	84628	42221	10268	20692	15699	29167
150	41347	81666	82961	60413	71020	83658	02415	33322	66036	98712	46795	16308	28413	05417

A TABLE OF 14,000 RANDOM UNITS (Continued)

Line/Col.	(1)	(2)	(3)	(4)	(5)	(6)	(7)	(8)	(9)	(10)	(11)	(12)	(13)	(14)
151	38128	51178	75096	13609	16110	73533	42564	59870	29399	67834	91055	89917	51096	89
152	60950	00455	73254	96067	50717	13878	03216	78274	65863	37011	91283	33914	91303	49
153	90524	17320	29832	96118	75792	25326	22940	24904	80523	38928	91374	55597	97567	38
154	49897	18278	67160	39408	97056	43517	84426	59650	20247	19293	02019	14790	02852	05
155	18494	99209	81060	19488	65596	59787	47939	91225	98768	43688	00438	05548	09443	82
156	65373	72984	30171	37741	70203	94094	87261	30056	58124	70133	18936	02138	59372	09
157	40653	12843	04213	70925	95360	55774	76439	61768	52817	81151	52188	31940	54273	49
158	51638	22238	56344	44587	83231	50317	74541	07719	25472	41602	77318	15145	57515	07
159	69742	99303	62578	83575	30337	07488	51941	84316	42067	49692	28616	29101	03013	73
160	58012	74072	67488	74580	47992	69482	58624	17106	47538	13452	22620	24260	40155	74
161	18348	19855	42887	08279	43206	47077	42637	45606	00011	20662	14642	49984	94509	56
162	59614	09193	58064	29086	44385	45740	70752	05663	49081	26960	57454	99264	24142	74
163	75688	28630	39210	52897	62748	72658	98059	67202	72789	01869	13496	14663	87645	89
164	13941	77802	69101	70061	35460	34576	15412	81304	58757	35498	94830	75521	00603	97
165	96656	86420	96475	86458	54463	96419	55417	41375	76886	19008	66877	35934	59801	00
166	03363	82042	15942	14549	38324	87094	19069	67590	11087	68570	22591	65232	85915	91
167	70366	08390	69155	25496	13240	57407	91407	49160	07379	34444	94567	66035	38918	65
168	47870	36605	12927	16043	53257	93796	52721	73120	48025	76074	95605	67422	41646	14
169	79504	77606	22761	30518	28373	73898	30550	76684	77366	32276	04690	61667	64798	66
170	46967	74841	50923	15339	37755	98995	40162	89561	69199	42257	11647	47603	48779	97
171	14558	50769	35444	59030	87516	48193	02945	00922	48189	04724	21263	20892	92955	90
172	12440	25057	01132	38611	28135	68089	10954	10097	54243	06460	50856	65435	79377	53
173	32293	29938	68653	10497	98919	46587	77701	99119	93165	67788	17638	23097	21468	36
174	10640	21875	72462	77981	56550	55999	87310	69643	45124	00349	25748	00844	96831	30
175	47615	23169	39571	56972	20628	21788	51736	33133	72696	32605	41569	76148	91544	21
176	16948	11128	71624	72754	49084	96303	27830	45817	67867	18062	87453	17226	72904	71
177	21258	61092	66634	70335	92448	17354	83432	49608	66520	06442	59664	20420	39201	69
178	15072	48853	15178	30730	47481	48490	41436	25015	49932	20474	53821	51015	79841	32
179	99154	57412	09858	65671	70655	71479	63520	31357	56968	06729	34465	70685	04184	25
180	08759	61089	23706	32994	35426	36666	63988	98844	37533	08269	27021	45886	22835	78
181	67323	57839	61114	62192	47547	58023	64630	34886	98777	75442	95592	06141	45096	73
182	09255	13986	84834	20764	72206	89393	34548	93438	88730	61805	78955	18952	46436	58
183	36304	74712	00374	10107	85061	69228	81969	92216	03568	39630	81869	52824	50937	27
184	15884	67429	86612	47367	10242	44880	12060	44309	46629	55105	66793	93173	00480	13
185	18745	32031	35303	08134	33925	03044	59929	95418	04917	57596	24878	61733	92834	64
186	72934	40086	88292	65728	38300	42323	64068	98373	48971	09049	59943	36538	05976	82
187	17626	02944	20910	57662	80181	38579	24580	90529	52303	50436	29401	57824	86039	81
188	27117	61399	50967	41399	81636	16663	15634	79717	94696	59240	25543	97989	63306	90
189	93995	18678	90012	63645	85701	85269	62263	68331	00389	72571	15210	20769	44686	96
190	67392	89421	09623	80725	62620	84162	87368	29560	00519	84545	08004	24526	41252	14
191	04910	12261	37566	80016	21245	69377	50420	85658	55263	68667	78770	04533	14513	18
192	81453	20283	79929	59839	23875	13245	46808	74124	74703	35769	95588	21014	37078	39
193	19480	75790	48539	23703	15537	48885	02861	86587	74539	65227	90799	58789	96257	02
194	21456	13162	74608	81011	55512	07481	93551	72189	76261	91206	89941	15132	37738	59
195	89406	20912	46189	76376	25538	87212	20748	12831	57166	35026	16817	79121	18929	40
196	09866	07414	55977	16419	01101	69343	13305	94302	80703	57910	36933	57771	42546	03
197	86541	24681	23421	13521	28000	94917	07423	57523	97234	63951	42876	46829	09781	58
198	10414	96941	06205	72222	57167	83902	07460	69507	10600	08858	07685	44472	64220	27
199	49942	06683	41479	58982	56288	42853	92196	20632	62045	78812	35895	51851	83534	10
200	23995	68882	42291	23374	24299	27024	67460	94783	40937	16961	26053	78749	46704	21

THE NUMBER OF EACH DAY OF THE YEAR

Day of Mo.	Jan.	Feb.	Mar.	Apr.	May	Jun.	Jul.	Aug.	Sep.	Oct.	Nov.	Dec.	Day of Mo.
1	1	32	60	91	121	152	182	213	244	274	305	335	1
2	2	33	61	92	122	153	183	214	245	275	306	336	2
3	3	34	62	93	123	154	184	215	246	276	307	337	3
4	4	35	63	94	124	155	185	216	247	277	308	338	4
5	5	36	64	95	125	156	186	217	248	278	309	339	5
6	6	37	65	96	126	157	187	218	249	279	310	340	6
7	7	38	66	97	127	158	188	219	250	280	311	341	7
8	8	39	67	98	128	159	189	220	251	281	312	342	8
9	9	40	68	99	129	160	190	221	252	282	313	343	9
10	10	41	69	100	130	161	191	222	253	283	314	344	10
11	11	42	70	101	131	162	192	223	254	284	315	345	11
12	12	43	71	102	132	163	193	224	255	285	316	346	12
13	13	44	72	103	133	164	194	225	256	286	317	347	13
14	14	45	73	104	134	165	195	226	257	287	318	348	14
15	15	46	74	105	135	166	196	227	258	288	319	349	15
16	16	47	75	106	136	167	197	228	259	289	320	350	16
17	17	48	76	107	137	168	198	229	260	290	321	351	17
18	18	49	77	108	138	169	199	230	261	291	322	352	18
19	19	50	78	109	139	170	200	231	262	292	323	353	19
20	20	51	79	110	140	171	201	232	263	293	324	354	20
21	21	52	80	111	141	172	202	233	264	294	325	355	21
22	22	53	81	112	142	173	203	234	265	295	326	356	22
23	23	54	82	113	143	174	204	235	266	296	327	357	23
24	24	55	83	114	144	175	205	236	267	297	328	358	24
25	25	56	84	115	145	176	206	237	268	298	329	359	25
26	26	57	85	116	146	177	207	238	269	299	330	360	26
27	27	58	86	117	147	178	208	239	270	300	331	361	27
28	28	59	87	118	148	179	209	240	271	301	332	362	28
29	29	*	88	119	149	180	210	241	272	302	333	363	29
30	30		89	120	150	181	211	242	273	303	334	364	30
31	31		90		151		212	243		304		365	31

* In leap years, after February 28, add 1 to the tabulated number.

INTEREST TABLES FROM ¼% TO 20%

SIMPLE INTEREST

If P is the principal placed at interest at a rate i (expressed as a decimal), for a period of n years

The **amount,**

$$A = P (1 + ni)$$

Present value,

$$P = \frac{A}{1 + ni}$$

COMPOUND INTEREST

At interest compounded annually the **amount,**—

$$A = P (1 + i)^n$$

At interest compounded q times per year,—

$$A = P \left(1 + \frac{i}{q}\right)^{nq}$$

At interest compounded annually the **present value,**—

$$P = \frac{A}{(1 + i)^n} = A (1 + i)^{-n} = Av^n. \quad v = \frac{1}{1 + i}$$

At interest compounded q times per year,—

$$P = A \left(1 + \frac{i}{q}\right)^{-nq}$$

* The **amount of an annuity of 1 per annum,**—

$$s_{\overline{n}|i} = \frac{(1 + i)^n - 1}{i}$$

* The **present value of an annuity,**—

$$a_{\overline{n}|i} = \frac{1 - (1 + i)^{-n}}{i}$$

The **annuity whose present value is 1,**—

$$\frac{1}{a_{\overline{n}|i}} = \frac{1}{s_{\overline{n}|i}} + i = \frac{i}{(1 - v^n)}$$

Compound amount of 1 for fractional periods,—$(1+i)^{1/p}$

* This information can be constructed by use of tables $(1 + i)^n$ and $(1 + i)^{-n}$ as may be observed from the formula structures. For example $s_{\overline{50}|.07} = \frac{(1.07)^{50} - 1}{.07}$. Here $(1.07)^{50}$ is obtained from the entries under $(1 + i)^n$, where $i = .07$ and $n = 50$ and is equal to 29.45702506. Accordingly $s_{\overline{50}|.07} = \frac{28.45702506}{.07} = 406.528929$ Similarly $a_{\overline{n}|i}$ may be evaluated by use of entries for $(1 + i)^{-n}$ and carrying out the appropriate arithmetic.

AMOUNT AT COMPOUND INTEREST $(1 + i)^{n}$*

ᵉ following table gives the amount after a term of n periods on unit original principal at rate of interest i.

Periods			Rate i		
n	0.0025(1/4%)	0.004167(5/12%)	0.005(1/2%)	0.005833(7/12%)	0.0075(3/4%)
1	1.00250000	1.00416667	1.00500000	1.00583333	1.00750000
2	1.00500625	1.00835069	1.01002500	1.01170069	1.01505625
3	1.00751877	1.01255216	1.01507513	1.01760228	1.02266917
4	1.01003756	1.01677112	1.02015050	1.02353830	1.03033919
5	1.01256266	1.02100767	1.02525125	1.02950894	1.03806673
6	1.01509406	1.02526187	1.03037751	1.03551440	1.04585224
7	1.01763180	1.02953379	1.03552940	1.04155490	1.05369613
8	1.02017588	1.03382352	1.04070704	1.04763064	1.06159885
9	1.02272632	1.03813111	1.04591058	1.05374182	1.06956084
10	1.02528313	1.04245666	1.05114013	1.05988865	1.07758255
11	1.02784634	1.04680023	1.05639583	1.06607133	1.08566441
12	1.03041596	1.05116190	1.06167781	1.07229008	1.09380690
13	1.03299200	1.05554174	1.06698620	1.07854511	1.10201045
14	1.03557448	1.05993983	1.07232113	1.08483662	1.11027553
15	1.03816341	1.06435625	1.07768274	1.09116483	1.11860259
16	1.04075882	1.06879106	1.08307115	1.09752996	1.12699211
17	1.04336072	1.07324436	1.08848651	1.10393222	1.13544455
18	1.04596912	1.07771621	1.09392894	1.11037182	1.14396039
19	1.04858404	1.08220670	1.09939858	1.11684899	1.15254009
20	1.05120550	1.08671589	1.10489558	1.12336395	1.16118414
21	1.05383352	1.09124387	1.11042006	1.12991690	1.16989302
22	1.05646810	1.09579072	1.11597216	1.13650808	1.17866722
23	1.05910927	1.10035652	1.12155202	1.14313771	1.18750723
24	1.06175704	1.10494134	1.12715978	1.14980602	1.19641353
25	1.06441144	1.10954526	1.13279558	1.15651322	1.20538663
26	1.06707247	1.11416836	1.13845955	1.16325955	1.21442703
27	1.06974015	1.11881073	1.14415185	1.17004523	1.22353523
28	1.07241450	1.12347244	1.14987261	1.17687049	1.23271175
29	1.07509553	1.12815358	1.15562197	1.18373557	1.24195709
30	1.07778327	1.13285422	1.16140008	1.19064069	1.25127176
31	1.08047773	1.13757444	1.16720708	1.19758610	1.26065630
32	1.08317892	1.14231434	1.17304312	1.20457202	1.27011122
33	1.08588687	1.14707398	1.17890833	1.21159869	1.27963706
34	1.08860159	1.15185346	1.18480288	1.21866634	1.28923434
35	1.09132309	1.15665284	1.19072689	1.22577523	1.29890359
36	1.09405140	1.16147223	1.19668052	1.23292559	1.30864537
37	1.09678653	1.16631170	1.20266393	1.24011765	1.31846021
38	1.09952850	1.17117133	1.20867725	1.24735167	1.32834866
39	1.10227732	1.17605121	1.21472063	1.25462789	1.33831128
40	1.10503301	1.18095142	1.22079424	1.26194655	1.34834861
41	1.10779559	1.18587206	1.22689821	1.26930791	1.35846123
42	1.11056508	1.19081319	1.23303270	1.27671220	1.36864969
43	1.11334149	1.19577491	1.23919786	1.28415969	1.37891456
44	1.11612485	1.20075731	1.24539385	1.29165062	1.38925642
45	1.11891516	1.20576046	1.25162082	1.29918525	1.39967584
46	1.12171245	1.21078446	1.25787892	1.30676383	1.41017341
47	1.12451673	1.21582940	1.26416832	1.31438662	1.42074971
48	1.12732802	1.22089536	1.27048916	1.32205388	1.43140533
49	1.13014634	1.22598242	1.27684161	1.32976586	1.44214087
50	1.13297171	1.23109068	1.28322581	1.33752283	1.45295693

*The $\mathcal{A}\,_{\overline{n}|i}$ table may be constructed from this table by use of the formula $\dfrac{(1 + i)^{n} - 1}{i}$.
See page 634.

AMOUNT AT COMPOUND INTEREST $(1 + i)^n$ (Continued)

Periods			Rate i		
n	0.0025(1/4%)	0.004167(5/12%)	0.005(1/2%)	0.005833(7/12%)	0.0075(3/4%)
51	1.13580414	1.23622022	1.28964194	1.34532504	1.4638541
52	1.23864365	1.24137114	1.29609014	1.35317277	1.4748330
53	1.14149026	1.24654352	1.30257060	1.36106628	1.4858942
54	1.14434398	1.25173745	1.30908346	1.36900583	1.4970384
55	1.14720484	1.25695302	1.31562887	1.37699170	1.5082662
56	1.15007285	1.26219033	1.32220702	1.38502415	1.5195782
57	1.15294804	1.26744946	1.32881805	1.39310346	1.530975C
58	1.15583041	1.27273050	1.33546214	1.40122990	1.5424574
59	1.15871998	1.27803354	1.34213946	1.40940374	1.5540258
60	1.16161678	1.28335868	1.34885015	1.41762526	1.5656810
61	1.16452082	1.28870601	1.35559440	1.42589474	1.5774236
62	1.16743213	1.29407561	1.36237238	1.43421246	1.5892543
63	1.17035071	1.29946760	1.36918424	1.44257870	1.6011737
64	1.17327658	1.30488204	1.37603016	1.45099374	1.6131825
65	1.17620977	1.31031905	1.38291031	1.45945787	1.6252813
66	1.17915030	1.31577872	1.38982486	1.46797138	1.6374710
67	1.18209817	1.32126113	1.39677399	1.47653454	1.6497520
68	1.18505342	1.32676638	1.40375785	1.48514766	1.6621251
69	1.18801605	1.33229458	1.41077664	1.49381102	1.6745911
70	1.19098609	1.33784580	1.41783053	1.50252492	1.6871505
71	1.19396356	1.34342016	1.42491968	1.51128965	1.6998041
72	1.19694847	1.34901774	1.43204428	1.52010550	1.7125527
73	1.19994084	1.35463865	1.43920450	1.52897279	1.7253968
74	1.20294069	1.36028298	1.44640052	1.53789179	1.7383373
75	1.20594804	1.36595082	1.45363252	1.54686283	1.7513748
76	1.20896291	1.37164229	1.46090069	1.55588620	1.7645101
77	1.21198532	1.37735746	1.46820519	1.56496220	1.7777440
78	1.21501528	1.38309645	1.47554622	1.57409115	1.7910770
79	1.21805282	1.38885935	1.48292395	1.58327334	1.8045191
80	1.22109795	1.39464627	1.49033857	1.59250910	1.8180439
81	1.22415070	1.40045729	1.49779026	1.60179874	1.8316793
82	1.22721108	1.40629253	1.50527921	1.61114257	1.8454169
83	1.23027910	1.41215209	1.51280561	1.62054090	1.8592575
84	1.23335480	1.41803605	1.52036964	1.62999405	1.8732019
85	1.23643819	1.42394454	1.52797148	1.63950235	1.8872509
86	1.23952928	1.42987764	1.53561134	1.64906612	1.9014053
87	1.24262811	1.43583546	1.54328940	1.65868567	1.9156659
88	1.24573468	1.44181811	1.55100585	1.66836134	1.9300333
89	1.24884901	1.44782568	1.55876087	1.67809344	1.9445086
90	1.25197114	1.45385829	1.56655468	1.68788232	1.9590924
91	1.25510106	1.45991603	1.57438745	1.69772830	1.9737856
92	1.25823882	1.46599902	1.58225939	1.70763172	1.9885890
93	1.26138441	1.47210735	1.59017069	1.71759290	2.0035034
94	1.26453787	1.47824113	1.59812154	1.72761219	2.0185297
95	1.26769922	1.48440047	1.60611215	1.73768993	2.0336687
96	1.27086847	1.49058547	1.61414271	1.74782646	2.0489212
97	1.27404564	1.49679624	1.62221342	1.75802211	2.0642881
98	1.27723075	1.50303289	1.63032449	1.76827724	2.0797703C
99	1.28042383	1.50929553	1.63847611	1.77859219	2.0953685
100	1.28362489	1.51558426	1.64666849	1.78896731	2.1110838

AMOUNT AT COMPOUND INTEREST $(1 + i)^n$ (Continued)

Periods	Rate i				
n	0.01(1%)	0.001125(1 1/8%)	0.0125(1 1/4%)	0.015(1 1/2%)	0.0175(1 3/4%)
1	1.01000000	1.01125000	1.01250000	1.01500000	1.01750000
2	1.02010000	1.02262656	1.02515625	1.03022500	1.03530625
3	1.03030100	1.03413111	1.03797070	1.04567838	1.05342411
4	1.04060401	1.04576509	1.05094534	1.06136355	1.07185903
5	1.05101005	1.05752994	1.06408215	1.07728400	1.09061656
6	1.06152015	1.06942716	1.07738318	1.09344326	1.10970235
7	1.07213535	1.08145821	1.09085047	1.10984491	1.12912215
8	1.08285671	1.09362462	1.10448610	1.12649259	1.14888178
9	1.09368527	1.10592789	1.11829218	1.14338998	1.16898721
10	1.10462213	1.11836958	1.13227083	1.16054083	1.18944449
11	1.11566835	1.13095124	1.14642422	1.17794894	1.21025977
12	1.12682503	1.14367444	1.16075452	1.19561817	1.23143931
13	1.13809328	1.15654078	1.17526395	1.21355244	1.25298950
14	1.14947421	1.16955186	1.18995475	1.23175573	1.27491682
15	1.16096896	1.18270932	1.20482918	1.25023207	1.29722786
16	1.17257864	1.19601480	1.21988955	1.26898555	1.31992935
17	1.18430443	1.20946997	1.23513817	1.28802033	1.34302811
18	1.19614748	1.22307650	1.25057739	1.30734064	1.36653111
19	1.20810895	1.23683611	1.26620961	1.32695075	1.39044540
20	1.22019004	1.25075052	1.28203723	1.34685501	1.41477820
21	1.23239194	1.26482146	1.29806270	1.36705783	1.43953681
22	1.24471586	1.27905071	1.31428848	1.38756370	1.46472871
23	1.25716302	1.29344003	1.33071709	1.40837715	1.49036146
24	1.26973465	1.30799123	1.34735105	1.42950281	1.51644279
25	1.28243200	1.32270613	1.36419294	1.45094535	1.54298054
26	1.29525631	1.33758657	1.38124535	1.47270953	1.56998269
27	1.30820888	1.35263442	1.39851092	1.49480018	1.59745739
28	1.32129097	1.46785156	1.41599230	1.51722218	1.62541290
29	1.33450388	1.38323989	1.43369221	1.53998051	1.65385762
30	1.34784892	1.39880134	1.45161336	1.56308022	1.68280013
31	1.36132740	1.41453785	1.46975853	1.58652642	1.71224913
32	1.37494068	1.43045140	1.48813051	1.61032432	1.74221349
33	1.38869009	1.44654398	1.50673214	1.63447918	1.77270223
34	1.40257699	1.46281760	1.52556629	1.65899637	1.80372452
35	1.41660276	1.47927430	1.54463587	1.68388132	1.83528970
36	1.43076878	1.49591613	1.56394382	1.70913954	1.86740727
37	1.44507647	1.51274519	1.58349312	1.73479663	1.90008689
38	1.45952724	1.52976357	1.60328678	1.76079828	1.93333841
39	1.47412251	1.54697341	1.62332787	1.78721025	1.96717184
40	1.48886373	1.56437687	1.64361946	1.81401841	2.00159734
41	1.50375237	1.58197611	1.66416471	1.84122868	2.03662530
42	1.51878989	1.59977334	1.68496677	1.86884712	2.07226624
43	1.53397779	1.61777079	1.70602885	1.89687982	2.10853090
44	1.54931757	1.63597071	1.72735421	1.92533302	2.14543019
45	1.56481075	1.65437538	1.74894614	1.95421301	2.18297522
46	1.58045885	1.67298710	1.77080797	1.98352621	2.22117728
47	1.59626344	1.69180821	1.79294306	2.01327910	2.26004789
48	1.61222608	1.71084105	1.81535485	2.04347829	2.29959872
49	1.62834834	1.73008801	1.83804679	2.07413046	2.33984170
50	1.64463182	1.74955150	1.86102237	2.10524242	2.38078893

AMOUNT AT COMPOUND INTEREST $(1 + i)^n$ (Continued)

Periods *n*	0.01(1%)	0.001125(1 1/8%)	0.0125(1 1/4%)	0.015(1 1/2%)	0.0175(1 3/
				Rate *i*	
51	1.66107814	1.76923395	1.88428515	2.13682106	2.4224527
52	1.67768892	1.78913784	1.90783872	2.16887337	2.4648456
53	1.69446581	1.80926564	1.93168670	2.20140647	2.5079804
54	1.71141047	1.82961988	1.95583279	2.23442757	2.5518701
55	1.72852457	1.85020310	1.98028070	2.26794398	2.5965278
56	1.74580982	1.87101788	2.00503420	2.30196314	2.6419670
57	1.76326792	1.89206684	2.03009713	2.33649259	2.6882015
58	1.78090060	1.91335259	2.05547335	2.37153998	2.7352450
59	1.79870960	1.93487780	2.08116676	2.40711308	2.7831118
60	1.81669670	1.95664518	2.10718135	2.44321978	2.8318162
61	1.83486367	1.97865744	2.13352111	2.47986807	2.8813730
62	1.85321230	2.00091733	2.16019013	2.51706609	2.9317970
63	1.87174443	2.02342765	2.18719250	2.55482208	2.9831035
64	1.89046187	2.04619121	2.21453241	2.59314442	3.0353078
65	1.90936649	2.06921087	2.24221407	2.63204158	3.0884257
66	1.92846015	2.09248949	2.27024174	2.67152221	3.1424731
67	1.94774475	2.11602999	2.29861976	2.71159504	3.1974664
68	1.96722220	2.13983533	2.32735251	2.75226896	3.2534221
69	1.98689442	2.16390848	2.35644442	2.79355300	3.3103570
70	2.00676337	2.18825245	2.38589997	2.83545629	3.3682882
71	2.02683100	2.21287029	2.41572372	2.87798814	3.4272333
72	2.04709931	2.23776508	2.44592027	2.92115696	3.4872099
73	2.06757031	2.26293994	2.47649427	2.96497533	3.5482360
74	2.08824601	2.28839801	2.50745045	3.00944996	3.6103302
75	2.10912847	2.31414249	2.53879358	3.05459171	3.6735109
76	2.13021975	2.34017659	2.57052850	3.10041059	3.7377974
77	2.15152195	2.36650358	2.60266011	3.14691674	3.8032088
78	2.17303717	2.39312675	2.63519336	3.19412050	3.8697650
79	2.19476754	2.42004942	2.66813327	3.24203230	3.9374850
80	2.21671522	2.44727498	2.70148494	3.29066279	4.0063919
81	2.23888237	2.47480682	2.73525350	3.34002273	4.0765037
82	2.26127119	2.50264840	2.76944417	3.39012307	4.1478426
83	2.28388390	2.53080319	2.80406222	3.44097492	4.2204298
84	2.30672274	2.55927473	2.83911300	3.49258954	4.2942873
85	2.32978997	2.58806657	2.87460191	3.54497838	4.3694374
86	2.35308787	2.61718232	2.91053444	3.59815306	4.4459025
87	2.37661875	2.64662562	2.94691612	3.65212535	4.5237058
88	2.40038494	2.67640016	2.98375257	3.70690723	4.6028707
89	2.42438879	2.70650966	3.02104948	3.76251084	4.6834209
90	2.44863267	2.73695789	3.05881260	3.81894851	4.7653808
91	2.47311900	2.76774867	3.09704775	3.87623273	4.8487749
92	2.49785019	2.79888584	3.13576085	3.93437622	4.9336285
93	2.52282869	2.83037331	3.17495786	3.99339187	5.0199670
94	2.54805698	2.86221501	3.21464483	4.05329275	5.1078164
95	2.57353755	2.89441492	3.25482789	4.11409214	5.1972032
96	2.59927293	2.92697709	3.29551324	4.17580352	5.2881542
97	2.62526565	2.95990559	3.33670716	4.23844057	5.3806969
98	2.65151831	2.99320452	3.37841600	4.30201718	5.4748591
99	2.67803349	3.02687807	3.42064620	4.36654744	5.5706692
100	2.70481383	3.06093045	3.46340427	4.43204565	5.6681559

AMOUNT AT COMPOUND INTEREST $(1 + i)^n$ (Continued)

Periods n	Rate i 0.02(2%)	0.0225(2 1/4%)	0.025(2 1/2%)	0.0275(2 3/4%)
1	1.02000000	1.02250000	1.02500000	1.02750000
2	1.04040000	1.04550625	1.05062500	1.05575625
3	1.06120800	1.06903014	1.07689063	1.08478955
4	1.08243216	1.09308332	1.10381289	1.11462126
5	1.10408080	1.11767769	1.13140821	1.14527334
6	1.12616242	1.14282544	1.15969342	1.17676836
7	1.14868567	1.16853901	1.18868575	1.20912949
8	1.17165938	1.19483114	1.21840290	1.24238055
9	1.19509257	1.22171484	1.24886297	1.27654602
10	1.21899442	1.24920343	1.28008454	1.31165103
11	1.24337431	1.27731050	1.31208666	1.34772144
12	1.26824179	1.30604999	1.34488882	1.38478378
13	1.29360663	1.33543611	1.37851104	1.42286533
14	1.31947876	1.36548343	1.41297382	1.46199413
15	1.34586834	1.39620680	1.44829817	1.50219896
16	1.37278571	1.42762146	1.48450562	1.54350944
17	1.40024142	1.45974294	1.52161826	1.58595595
18	1.42824625	1.49258716	1.55965872	1.62956973
19	1.45681117	1.52617037	1.59865019	1.67438290
20	1.48594740	1.56050920	1.63861644	1.72042843
21	1.51566634	1.59562066	1.67958185	1.76774021
22	1.54597967	1.63152212	1.72157140	1.81635307
23	1.57689926	1.66823137	1.76461068	1.86630278
24	1.60843725	1.70576658	1.80872595	1.91762610
25	1.64060599	1.74414632	1.85394410	1.97036082
26	1.67341811	1.78338962	1.90029270	2.02454575
27	1.70688648	1.82351588	1.94780002	2.08022075
28	1.74102421	1.86454499	1.99649602	2.13742682
29	1.77584469	1.90649725	2.04640739	2.19620606
30	1.81136158	1.94939344	2.09756758	2.25660173
31	1.84758882	1.99325479	2.15000677	2.31865828
32	1.88454059	2.03810303	2.20375694	2.38242138
33	1.92223140	2.08396034	2.25885086	2.44793797
34	1.96067603	2.13084945	2.31532213	2.51525626
35	1.99988955	2.17879356	2.37320519	2.58442581
36	2.03988734	2.22781642	2.43253532	2.65549752
37	2.08068509	2.27794229	2.49334870	2.72852370
38	2.12229879	2.32919599	2.55568242	2.80355810
39	2.16474477	2.38160290	2.61957448	2.88065595
40	2.20803966	2.43518897	2.68506384	2.95987399
41	2.25220046	2.48998072	2.75219043	3.04127052
42	2.29724447	2.54600528	2.82099520	3.12490546
43	2.34318936	2.60329040	2.89152008	3.21084036
44	2.39005214	2.66186444	2.96380808	3.29913847
45	2.43785421	2.72175639	3.03790328	3.38986478
46	2.48661129	2.78299590	3.11385086	3.48308606
47	2.53634352	2.84561331	3.19169713	3.57887093
48	2.58707039	2.90963961	3.27148956	3.67728988
49	2.63881179	2.97510650	3.35327680	3.77841535
50	2.69158803	3.04204640	3.43710872	3.88232177

AMOUNT AT COMPOUND INTEREST $(1 + i)^n$ (Continued)

Periods	Rate i			
n	0.02(2%)	0.0225(2 1/4%)	0.025(2 1/2%)	0.0275(2 3/4%)
51	2.74541979	3.11049244	3.52303644	3.98908562
52	2.80032819	3.18047852	3.61111235	4.09878547
53	2.85633475	3.25203929	3.70139016	4.21150208
54	2.91346144	3.32521017	3.79392491	4.32721838
55	2.97173067	3.40002740	3.88877303	4.44631964
56	3.03116529	3.47652802	3.98599236	4.56859343
57	3.09178859	3.55474990	4.08564217	4.69422975
58	3.15362436	3.63473177	4.18778322	4.82332107
59	3.21669685	3.71651324	4.29247780	4.95596239
60	3.28103079	3.80013479	4.39978975	5.09225136
61	3.34665140	3.88563782	4.50978449	5.23228827
62	3.41358443	3.97306467	4.62252910	5.37617620
63	3.48185612	4.06245862	4.73809233	5.52402105
64	3.55149324	4.15386394	4.85654464	5.67593162
65	3.62252311	4.24732588	4.97795826	5.83201974
66	3.69497357	4.34289071	5.10240721	5.99240029
67	3.76887304	4.44060576	5.22996739	6.15719130
68	3.84425050	4.54051939	5.36071658	6.32651406
69	3.92113551	4.64268107	5.49473449	6.50049319
70	3.99955822	4.74714140	5.63210286	6.67925676
71	4.07954939	4.85395208	5.77290543	6.86293632
72	4.16114038	4.96316600	5.91722806	7.05166706
73	4.24436318	5.07483723	6.06515876	7.24558791
74	4.32925045	5.18902107	6.21678773	7.44484158
75	4.41583546	5.30577405	6.37220743	7.64957472
76	4.50415216	5.42515396	6.53151261	7.85993802
77	4.59423521	5.54721993	6.69480043	8.07608632
78	4.68611991	5.67203237	6.86217044	8.29817869
79	4.77984231	5.79965310	7.03372470	8.52637861
80	4.87543916	5.93014530	7.20956782	8.76085402
81	4.97294794	6.06357357	7.38980701	9.00177751
82	5.07240690	6.20000397	7.57455219	9.24932639
83	5.17385504	6.33950406	7.76391599	9.50368286
84	5.27733214	6.48214290	7.95801389	9.76503414
85	5.38287878	6.62799112	8.15695424	10.03357258
86	5.49053636	6.77712092	8.36088834	10.30949583
87	5.60034708	6.92960614	8.56991055	10.59300696
88	5.71235402	7.08552228	8.78415832	10.88421465
89	5.82660110	7.24494653	9.00376228	11.18363331
90	5.94313313	7.40795782	9.22885633	11.49118322
91	6.06199579	7.57463688	9.45957774	11.80719076
92	6.18323570	7.74506621	9.69606718	12.13188851
93	6.30690042	7.91933020	9.93846886	12.46551544
94	6.43303843	8.09751512	10.18693058	12.80831711
95	6.56169920	8.27970921	10.44160385	13.16054584
96	6.69293318	8.46600267	10.70264395	13.52246085
97	6.82679184	8.65648773	10.97021004	13.89432852
98	6.96332768	8.85125871	11.24446530	14.27642255
99	7.10359423	9.05041203	11.52557693	14.66902417
100	7.24464612	9.25404630	11.81371635	15.07242234

AMOUNT AT COMPOUND INTEREST $(1 + i)^n$ (Continued)

Periods		Rate i		
n	0.03(3%)	0.0325(3 1/4%)	0.035(3 1/2%)	0.0375(3 3/4%)
1	1.03000000	1.03250000	1.03500000	1.03750000
2	1.06090000	1.06605625	1.07122500	1.07640625
3	1.09272700	1.10070308	1.10871788	1.11677148
4	1.12550881	1.13647593	1.14752300	1.15865042
5	1.15927407	1.17341140	1.18768631	1.20209981
6	1.19405230	1.21154727	1.22925533	1.24717855
7	1.22987387	1.25092255	1.27227926	1.29394774
8	1.26677008	1.29157754	1.31680904	1.34247078
9	1.30477318	1.33355381	1.36289735	1.39281344
10	1.34391638	1.37689430	1.41059876	1.44504394
11	1.38423387	1.42164337	1.45996972	1.49923309
12	1.42576089	1.46784678	1.51106866	1.55545433
13	1.46853371	1.51555180	1.56395606	1.61378387
14	1.51258972	1.56480723	1.61869452	1.67430076
15	1.55796742	1.61566347	1.67534883	1.73708704
16	1.60470644	1.66817253	1.73398604	1.80222781
17	1.65284763	1.72238814	1.79467555	1.86981135
18	1.70243306	1.77836575	1.85748920	1.93992927
19	1.75350605	1.83616264	1.92250132	2.01267662
20	1.80611123	1.89583792	1.98978886	2.08815200
21	1.86029457	1.95745266	2.05943147	2.16645770
22	1.91610341	2.02106987	2.13151158	2.24769986
23	1.97358651	2.08675464	2.20611448	2.33198860
24	2.03279411	2.15457416	2.28332849	2.41943818
25	2.09377793	2.22459782	2.36324498	2.51016711
26	2.15659127	2.29689725	2.44595856	2.60429838
27	2.22128901	2.37154641	2.53156711	2.70195956
28	2.28792768	2.44862167	2.62017196	2.80328305
29	2.35656551	2.52820188	2.71187798	2.90840616
30	2.42726247	2.61036844	2.80679370	3.01747139
31	2.50008035	2.69520541	2.90503148	3.13062657
32	2.57508276	2.78279959	2.00670759	3.24802507
33	2.65233524	2.87324058	3.11194235	3.36982601
34	2.73190530	2.96662089	3.22086033	3.49619448
35	2.81386245	3.06303607	3.33359045	3.62730178
36	2.89827833	2.16258475	3.45026611	3.76332559
37	2.98522668	3.26536875	3.57102543	3.90445030
38	3.07478348	3.37149323	3.69601132	4.05086719
39	3.16702698	3.48106676	3.82537171	4.20277471
40	3.26203779	3.59420143	3.95925972	4.36037876
41	3.35989893	3.71101298	4.09783381	4.52389296
42	3.46069589	3.83162090	4.24125799	4.69353895
43	3.56451677	3.95614858	4.38970202	4.86954666
44	3.67145227	4.08472341	4.54334160	5.05215466
45	3.78159584	4.21747692	4.70235855	5.24161046
46	3.89504372	4.35454492	4.86694110	5.43817085
47	4.01189503	4.49606763	5.03728404	5.64210226
48	4.13225188	4.64218983	5.21358898	5.85368109
49	4.25621944	4.79306100	5.39606459	6.07319413
50	4.38390602	4.94883548	5.58492686	6.30093891

Financial Tables

AMOUNT AT COMPOUND INTEREST $(1 + i)^n$ (Continued)

Periods	Rate i			
n	0.04(4%)	0.0425(4 1/4%)	0.045(4 1/2%)	0.0475(4 3/4%)
1	1.04000000	1.04250000	1.04500000	1.04750000
2	1.08160000	1.08680625	1.09202500	1.09725625
3	1.12486400	1.13299552	1.14116613	1.14937592
4	1.16985856	1.18114783	1.19251860	1.20397128
5	1.21665290	1.23134661	1.24618194	1.26115991
6	1.26531902	1.28367884	1.30226012	1.32106501
7	1.31593178	1.33823519	1.36086183	1.38381560
8	1.36856905	1.39511018	1.42210061	1.44954684
9	1.42331181	1.45440237	1.48609514	1.51840031
10	1.48024428	1.51621447	1.55296942	1.59052433
11	1.53945406	1.58065358	1.62285305	1.66607423
12	1.60103222	1.64783136	1.69588143	1.74521276
13	1.66507351	1.71786419	1.77219610	1.82811037
14	1.73167645	1.79087342	1.85194492	1.91494561
15	1.80094351	1.86698554	1.93528244	2.00590552
16	1.87298125	1.94633243	2.02237015	2.10118604
17	1.94790050	2.02905156	2.11337681	2.20099237
18	2.02581652	2.11528625	2.20847877	2.30553951
19	2.10684918	2.20518591	2.30786031	2.41505264
20	2.19112314	2.29890631	2.41171402	2.52976764
21	2.27876807	2.39660983	2.52024116	2.64993160
22	2.36991879	2.49846575	2.63365201	2.77580335
23	2.46471554	2.60465054	2.75216635	2.90765401
24	2.56330416	2.71534819	2.87601383	2.04576758
25	2.66583633	2.83075049	3.00543446	3.19044154
26	2.77246978	2.95105739	3.14067901	3.34198751
27	2.88336858	3.07647732	3.28200956	3.50073192
28	2.99870332	3.20722761	3.42969999	3.66701668
29	3.11865145	3.34353478	3.58403649	3.84119998
30	3.24339751	3.48563501	3.74531813	4.02365698
31	3.37313341	3.63377450	3.91385745	4.21478068
32	3.50805875	3.78820992	4.08998104	4.41498276
33	3.64838110	3.94920884	4.27403018	4.62469445
34	3.79431634	4.11705021	4.46636154	4.84436743
35	3.94608899	4.29202485	4.66734781	5.07447488
36	4.10393255	4.47443590	4.87737846	5.31551244
37	4.26808986	4.66459943	5.09686049	5.56799928
38	4.43881345	4.86284491	5.32621921	5.83247925
39	4.61636599	5.06951581	5.56589908	6.10952201
40	4.80102063	5.28497024	5.81636454	6.39972431
41	4.99306145	5.50958147	6.07810094	6.70371121
42	5.19278391	5.74373868	6.35161548	7.02213750
43	5.40049527	5.98784758	6.63743818	7.35568903
44	5.61651508	6.24233110	6.93612290	7.70508426
45	5.84117568	6.50763017	7.24824843	8.07107576
46	6.07482271	6.78420445	7.57441961	8.45445186
47	6.31781562	7.07253314	7.91526849	8.85603832
48	6.57052824	7.37311580	8.27145557	9.27670014
49	6.83334937	7.68647322	8.64367107	9.71734340
50	7.10668335	8.01314834	9.03263627	10.17891721

AMOUNT AT COMPOUND INTEREST $(1 + i)^n$ (Continued)

Periods n	Rate i			
	0.05(5%)	0.0525(5 1/4%)	0.055(5 1/2%)	0.0575(5 3/4%)
1	1.05000000	1.05250000	1.05500000	1.05750000
2	1.10250000	1.10775625	1.11302500	1.11830625
3	1.15762500	1.16591345	1.17424138	1.18260886
4	1.21550625	1.22712391	1.23882465	1.25060887
5	1.27628156	1.29154791	1.30696001	1.32251888
6	1.34009564	1.35935418	1.37884281	1.39856371
7	1.40710042	1.43072027	1.45467916	1.47898113
8	1.47745544	1.50583309	1.53468651	1.56402254
9	1.55132822	1.58488933	1.61909427	1.65395384
10	1.62889463	1.66809602	1.70814446	1.74905618
11	1.71033936	1.75567106	1.80209240	1.84962692
12	1.79585633	1.84784379	1.90120749	1.95598046
13	1.88564914	1.94485559	2.00577390	2.06844934
14	1.97993160	2.04696050	2.11609146	2.18738518
15	2.07892818	2.15442593	2.23247649	2.31315982
16	2.18287459	2.26753329	2.35526270	2.44616651
17	2.29201832	2.38657879	2.48480215	2.58682109
18	2.40661923	2.51187418	2.62146627	2.73556330
19	2.52695020	2.64374757	2.76564691	2.89285819
20	2.65329771	2.78254432	2.91775749	3.05919754
21	2.78596259	2.92862789	3.07823415	3.23510140
22	2.92526072	2.08238086	3.24753703	3.42111973
23	3.07152376	3.24420585	3.42615157	3.61783411
24	3.22509994	3.41452666	3.61458990	3.82585957
25	3.38635494	3.59378931	3.81339235	4.04584650
26	3.55567269	3.78246325	4.02312893	4.27848267
27	3.73345632	3.98104257	4.24440102	4.52449542
28	3.92012914	4.19004731	4.47784307	4.78465391
29	4.11613560	4.41002479	4.72412444	5.05977151
30	4.32194238	4.64155109	4.98395129	5.35070837
31	4.53803949	4.88523252	5.25806861	5.65837410
32	4.76494147	5.14170723	5.54726238	5.98373061
33	5.00318854	5.41164686	5.85236181	6.32779512
34	5.25334797	5.69575832	6.17424171	6.69164334
35	5.51601537	5.99478563	6.51382501	7.07641284
36	5.79181614	6.30951188	6.87208538	7.48330657
37	6.08140694	6.64076125	7.25005008	7.91359670
38	6.38547729	6.98940122	7.64880283	8.36862851
39	6.70475115	7.35634478	8.06948699	8.84982465
40	7.03998871	7.74255288	8.51330877	9.35868957
41	7.39198815	8.14903691	8.98154076	9.89681422
42	7.76158756	8.57686135	9.47552550	10.46588104
43	8.14966693	9.02714657	9.99667940	11.06766920
44	8.55715028	9.50107176	10.54649677	11.70406018
45	8.98500779	9.99987803	11.12655409	12.37704364
46	9.43425818	10.52487163	11.73851456	13.08872365
47	9.90597109	11.07742739	12.38413287	13.84132526
48	10.40126965	11.65899232	13.06526017	14.63720146
49	10.92133313	12.27108942	13.78384948	15.47884054
50	11.46739979	12.91532162	14.54196120	16.36887387

Financial Tables

AMOUNT AT COMPOUND INTEREST $(1 + i)^n$ (Continued)

Periods	Rate i			
n	0.06(6%)	0.0625(6 1/4%)	0.065(6 1/2%)	0.0675(6 3/4%)
1	1.06000000	1.06250000	1.06500000	1.06750000
2	1.12360000	1.12890625	1.13422500	1.13955625
3	1.19101600	1.19946289	1.20794963	1.21647630
4	1.26247696	1.27442932	1.28646635	1.29858845
5	1.33822558	1.35408115	1.37008666	1.38624317
6	1.41851911	1.43871123	1.45914230	1.47981458
7	1.50363026	1.52863068	1.55398655	1.57970207
8	1.59384807	1.62417009	1.65499567	1.68633195
9	1.68947896	1.72568073	1.76257039	1.80015936
10	1.79084770	1.83353577	1.87713747	1.92167012
11	1.89829856	1.94813176	1.99915140	2.05138285
12	2.01219647	2.06988999	2.12909624	2.18985119
13	2.13292826	2.19925812	2.26748750	2.33766615
14	2.26090396	2.33671175	2.41487418	2.49545861
15	2.39655819	2.48275623	2.57184101	2.66390207
16	2.54035168	2.63792850	2.73901067	2.84371546
17	2.69277279	2.80279903	2.91704637	3.03566625
18	2.85433915	2.97797397	3.10665438	3.24057373
19	3.02559950	3.16409734	3.30858691	3.45931245
20	3.20713547	3.36185342	3.52364506	3.69281604
21	3.39956360	3.57196926	3.75268199	3.94208113
22	3.60353742	3.79521734	3.99660632	4.20817160
23	3.81974966	4.03241843	4.25638573	4.49222319
24	4.04893464	4.28444458	4.53305081	4.79544825
25	4.29187072	4.55222236	4.82769911	5.11914101
26	4.54938296	4.83673626	5.14149955	5.46468303
27	4.82234594	5.13903228	5.47569702	5.83354913
28	5.11168670	5.46022180	5.83161733	6.22731370
29	5.41838790	5.80148566	6.21067245	6.64765737
30	5.74349117	6.16407851	6.61436616	7.90637424
31	6.08810064	6.54933342	7.04429996	7.57537950
32	6.45338668	6.95866676	7.50217946	8.08671762
33	6.84058988	7.39358343	7.98982113	8.63257106
34	7.25102528	7.85568239	8.50915950	9.21526961
35	7.68608679	8.34666254	9.06225487	9.83730031
36	8.14725200	8.86832895	9.65130143	10.50131808
37	8.63608712	9.42259951	10.27863603	11.21015705
38	9.15425235	10.01151198	10.94674737	11.96684265
39	9.70350749	10.63723148	11.65828595	12.77460453
40	10.28571794	11.30205845	12.41607453	13.63689033
41	10.90286101	12.00843710	13.22311938	14.55738043
42	11.55703267	12.75896442	14.08262214	15.54000361
43	12.25045463	13.55639970	14.99799258	16.58895385
44	12.98548191	14.40367468	15.97286209	17.70870824
45	13.76461083	15.30390434	17.01109813	18.90404604
46	14.59048748	16.26039837	18.11681951	20.18006915
47	15.46591673	17.27667326	19.29441278	21.54222382
48	16.39387173	18.35646534	20.54854961	22.99632392
49	17.37750403	19.50374443	21.88420533	24.54857579
50	18.42015427	20.72272845	23.30667868	26.20560466

AMOUNT AT COMPOUND INTEREST $(1 + i)^n$ (Continued)

Periods		Rate i		
n	0.07(7%)	0.0725(7 1/4%)	0.075(7 1/2%)	0.0775(7 3/4%)
1	1.07000000	1.07250000	1.07500000	1.07750000
2	1.14490000	1.15025625	1.15562500	1.16100625
3	1.22504300	1.23364983	1.24229687	1.25098423
4	1.31079601	1.32308944	1.33546914	1.34793551
5	1.40255173	1.41901343	1.43562933	1.45240051
6	1.50073035	1.52189190	1.54330153	1.56496155
7	1.60578148	1.63222906	1.65904914	1.68624608
8	1.71818618	1.75056567	1.78347783	1.81693015
9	1.83845921	1.87748168	1.91723866	1.95774223
10	1.96715136	2.01359910	2.06103156	2.10946726
11	2.10485195	2.15958504	2.21560893	2.27295097
12	2.25219159	2.31615495	2.38177960	2.44910467
13	2.40984500	2.48407618	2.56041307	2.63891028
14	2.57853415	2.66417171	2.75244405	2.84342583
15	2.75903154	2.85732416	2.95887735	3.06379133
16	2.95216375	3.06448016	3.18079315	3.30123516
17	3.15881521	3.28665497	3.41935264	3.55708088
18	3.37993228	3.52493745	3.67580409	3.83275465
19	3.61652754	3.78049542	3.95148940	4.12979313
20	3.86968446	4.05458134	4.24785110	4.44985210
21	4.14056237	4.34853849	4.56643993	4.79471564
22	4.43040174	4.66380753	4.90892293	5.16630610
23	4.74052986	5.00193357	5.27709215	5.56669482
24	5.07236695	5.36457375	5.67287406	5.99811367
25	5.42743264	5.75350535	6.09833961	6.46296748
26	5.80735292	6.17063449	6.55571508	6.96384746
27	6.21386763	6.61800549	7.04739371	7.50354564
28	6.64883836	7.09781089	7.57594824	8.08507043
29	7.11425705	7.61240218	8.14414436	8.71166339
30	7.61225504	8.16430134	8.75495519	9.38681730
31	8.14511290	8.75621318	9.41157683	10.11429564
32	8.71527080	9.39103864	10.11744509	10.89815355
33	9.32533975	10.07188894	10.87625347	11.74276045
34	9.97811354	10.80210089	11.69197248	12.65282439
35	10.67658148	11.58525320	12.56887042	13.63341828
36	11.42394219	12.42518406	13.51153570	14.69000819
37	12.22361814	13.32600990	14.52490088	15.82848383
38	13.07927141	14.29214562	15.61426844	17.05519132
39	13.99482041	15.32832618	16.78533858	18.37696865
40	14.97445784	16.43962983	18.04423897	19.80118372
41	16.02266989	17.63150299	19.39755689	21.33577546
42	17.14425678	18.90978696	20.85237366	22.98929806
43	18.34435475	20.28074651	22.41630168	24.77096866
44	19.62845959	21.75110063	24.09752431	26.69071873
45	21.00245176	23.32805543	25.90483863	28.75924943
46	22.47262338	25.01933945	27.84770153	30.98809126
47	24.04570702	26.83324156	29.93627915	33.38966833
48	25.72890651	28.77865157	32.18150008	35.97736763
49	27.52992997	30.86510381	34.59511259	38.76561362
50	29.45702506	33.10282384	37.18974603	41.76994868

AMOUNT AT COMPOUND INTEREST $(1 + i)^n$ (Continued)

Periods		Rate i		
n	0.08(8%)	0.0825(8 1/4%)	0.085(8 1/2%)	0.0875(8 3/4%)
1	1.08000000	1.08250000	1.08500000	1.08750000
2	1.16640000	1.17180625	1.17722500	1.18265625
3	1.25971200	1.26848027	1.27728912	1.28613867
4	1.36048896	1.37312989	1.38585870	1.39867581
5	1.46932808	1.48641310	1.50365669	1.52105994
6	1.58687432	1.60904218	1.63146751	1.65415268
7	1.71382427	1.74178816	1.77014225	1.79889104
8	1.85093021	1.88548569	1.92060434	1.95629401
9	1.99900463	2.04103826	2.08385571	2.12746974
10	2.15892500	2.20942391	2.26098344	2.31362334
11	2.33163900	2.39170139	2.45316703	2.51606538
12	2.51817012	2.58901675	2.66168623	2.73622110
13	2.71962373	2.80261063	2.88792956	2.97564045
14	2.93719362	3.03382601	3.13340357	3.23600898
15	3.17216911	3.28411666	3.39974288	3.51915977
16	3.42594264	3.55505628	3.68872102	3.82708625
17	3.70001805	3.84834842	4.00226231	4.16195630
18	3.99601950	4.16583717	4.34245461	4.52612747
19	4.31570106	4.50951873	4.71156325	4.92216363
20	4.66095714	4.88155403	5.11204612	5.35285295
21	5.03383372	5.28428224	5.54657005	5.82122758
22	5.43654041	5.72023552	6.01802850	6.33058499
23	5.87146365	6.19215495	6.52956092	6.88451118
24	6.34118074	6.70300774	7.08457360	7.48690591
25	6.84847520	7.25600587	7.68676236	8.14201017
26	7.39635321	7.85462636	8.34013716	8.85443606
27	7.98806147	8.50263303	9.04904881	9.62919922
28	8.62710639	9.20410026	9.81821796	10.47175415
29	9.31727490	9.96343853	10.65276649	11.38803264
30	10.06265689	10.78542221	11.55825164	12.38448549
31	10.86766944	11.67521954	12.54070303	13.46812797
32	11.73708300	12.63842515	13.60666279	14.64658917
33	12.67604964	13.68109523	14.76322913	15.92816573
34	13.69013361	14.80978558	16.01810360	17.32188023
35	14.78534429	16.03159290	17.37964241	18.83754475
36	15.96817184	17.35419931	18.85691201	20.48582991
37	17.24562558	18.78592075	20.45974953	22.27834003
38	18.62527563	20.33575921	22.19882824	24.22769478
39	20.11529768	22.01345935	24.08572865	26.34761807
40	21.72452150	23.82956975	26.13301558	28.65303466
41	23.46248322	25.79550925	28.35432190	31.16017519
42	25.33948187	27.92363876	30.76443927	33.88669052
43	27.36664042	30.22733896	33.37941660	36.85177594
44	29.55597166	32.72109442	36.21666702	40.07630633
45	31.92044939	35.42058471	39.29508371	43.58298314
46	34.47408534	38.34278295	42.63516583	47.39649416
47	37.23201217	41.50606255	46.25915492	51.54368740
48	40.21057314	44.93031271	50.19118309	56.05376005
49	43.42741899	48.63706351	54.45743365	60.95846405
50	46.90161251	52.64962124	59.08631551	66.29232966

AMOUNT AT COMPOUND INTEREST $(1 + i)^n$ (Continued)

Periods *n*	0.09(9%)	0.0925(9 1/4%)	0.095(9 1/2%)	0.0975(9 3/4%)
			Rate *i*	
1	1.09000000	1.09250000	1.09500000	1.09750000
2	1.18810000	1.19355625	1.19902500	1.20450625
3	1.29502900	1.30396020	1.31293237	1.32194561
4	1.41158161	1.42457652	1.43766095	1.45083531
5	1.53862395	1.55634985	1.57423874	1.59229175
6	1.67710011	1.70031221	1.72379142	1.74754019
7	1.82803912	1.85759109	1.88755161	1.91792536
8	1.99256264	2.02941827	2.06686901	2.10492309
9	2.17189328	2.21713946	2.26322156	2.31015309
10	2.36736367	2.42222486	2.47822761	2.53539301
11	2.58042641	2.64628066	2.71365924	2.78259383
12	2.81266478	2.89106162	2.97145686	3.05389673
13	3.06580461	3.15848482	3.25374527	3.35165166
14	3.34172703	3.45064466	3.56285107	3.67843770
15	3.64248246	3.76982929	3.90132192	4.03708537
16	3.97030588	4.11853850	4.27194750	4.43070120
17	4.32763341	4.49950331	4.67778251	4.86269456
18	4.71712042	4.91570737	5.12217185	5.33680728
19	5.14166125	5.37041030	5.60877818	5.85714599
20	5.60441077	5.86717325	6.14161210	6.42821773
21	6.10880774	6.40988678	6.72506525	7.05496896
22	6.65860043	7.00280131	7.36394645	7.74282843
23	7.25787447	7.65056043	8.06352137	8.49775420
24	7.91108317	8.35823727	8.82955590	9.32628524
25	8.62308066	9.13137421	9.66836371	10.23559805
26	9.39915792	9.97602633	10.58685826	11.23356886
27	10.24508213	10.89880877	11.59260979	12.32884182
28	11.16713952	11.90694858	12.69390772	13.53090390
29	12.17218208	13.00834132	13.89982896	14.85016703
30	13.26767847	14.21161289	15.22031271	16.29805832
31	14.46176953	15.52618708	16.66624241	17.88711900
32	15.76332879	16.96235939	18.24953544	19.63111310
33	17.18202838	18.53137763	19.98324131	21.54514663
34	18.72841093	20.24553006	21.88164924	23.64579843
35	20.41396792	22.11824159	23.96040591	25.95126378
36	22.25122503	24.16417894	26.23664448	28.48151199
37	24.25383528	26.39936549	28.72912570	31.25845941
38	26.43668046	28.84130680	31.45839264	34.30615921
39	28.81598170	31.50912768	34.44693994	37.65100973
40	31.40942005	34.42372199	37.71939924	41.32198318
41	34.23626786	37.60791628	41.30274216	45.35087654
42	37.31753197	41.08664853	45.22650267	49.77258700
43	40.67610984	44.88716352	49.52302042	54.62541423
44	44.33695973	49.03922615	54.22770736	59.95139212
45	48.32728610	53.57535456	59.37933956	65.79665285
46	52.67674185	58.53107486	65.02037682	72.21182650
47	57.41764862	63.94519929	71.19731262	79.25247959
48	62.58523700	69.86013022	77.96105732	86.97959635
49	68.21790833	76.32219227	85.36735777	95.46010699
50	74.35752008	83.38199505	93.47725675	104.76746742

AMOUNT AT COMPOUND INTEREST $(1 + i)^n$ (Continued)

Periods n	0.10(10%)	0.1025(10 1/4%)	0.105(10 1/2%)	0.1075(10 3/4%)
			Rate i	
1	1.10000000	1.10250000	1.10500000	1.10750000
2	1.21000000	1.21550625	1.22102500	1.22655625
3	1.33100000	1.34009564	1.34923262	1.35841105
4	1.46410000	1.47745544	1.49090205	1.50444023
5	1.61051000	1.62889463	1.64744677	1.66616756
6	1.77156100	1.79585633	1.82042868	1.84528057
7	1.94871710	1.97993160	2.01157369	2.04364823
8	2.14358881	2.18287459	2.22278892	2.26334042
9	2.35794769	2.40661923	2.45618176	2.50664951
10	2.59374246	2.65329771	2.71408085	2.77611434
11	2.85311671	2.92526072	2.99905934	3.07454663
12	3.13842838	3.22509994	3.31396057	3.40506039
13	3.45227121	3.55567269	3.66192643	3.77110438
14	3.79749834	3.92012914	4.04642870	4.17649810
15	4.17724817	4.32194238	4.47130371	4.62547165
16	4.59497299	4.76494147	4.94079060	5.12270985
17	5.05447028	5.25334797	5.45957362	5.67340116
18	5.55991731	5.79181614	6.03282885	6.28329179
19	6.11590904	6.38547729	6.66627588	6.95874565
20	6.72749995	7.03998871	7.36623484	7.70681081
21	7.40024994	7.76158756	8.13968950	8.53529297
22	8.14027494	8.55715028	8.99435690	9.45283697
23	8.95430243	9.43425818	9.93876437	10.46901694
24	9.84973268	10.40126965	10.98233463	11.59443626
25	10.83470594	11.46739979	12.13547977	12.84083816
26	11.91817654	12.64280826	13.40970514	14.22122826
27	13.10999419	13.93869611	14.81772418	15.75001030
28	14.42099361	15.36741246	16.37358522	17.44313641
29	15.86309297	16.94257224	18.09281167	19.31827357
30	17.44940227	18.67918589	19.99255690	21.39498798
31	19.19434250	20.59380245	22.09177537	23.69494919
32	21.11377675	22.70466720	24.41141178	26.24215623
33	23.22515442	25.03189559	26.97461002	29.06318802
34	25.54766986	27.59766488	29.80694407	32.18748073
35	28.10243685	30.42642554	32.93667320	35.64763491
36	30.91268053	33.54513415	36.39502389	39.47975567
37	34.00394859	36.98351040	40.21650140	43.72382940
38	37.40434344	40.77432022	44.43923404	48.42414106
39	41.14477779	44.95368804	49.10535362	53.62973622
40	45.25925557	49.56144107	54.26141575	59.39493287
41	49.78518112	54.64148878	59.95886440	65.77988815
42	54.76369924	60.24224138	66.25454516	72.85122613
43	60.24006916	66.41707112	73.21127240	80.68273294
44	66.26407608	73.22482091	80.89845601	89.35612673
45	72.89048369	80.73036505	89.39279389	98.96191035
46	80.17953205	89.00522747	98.77903724	109.60031571
47	88.19748526	98.12826328	109.15083616	121.38234965
48	97.01723378	108.18641027	120.61167395	134.43095224
49	106.71895716	119.27551732	133.27589972	148.88227961
50	117.39085288	131.50125785	147.26986919	164.88712466

AMOUNT AT COMPOUND INTEREST $(1 + i)^n$ (Continued)

Periods	Rate i			
n	0.11(11%)	0.1125(11 1/4%)	0.115(11 1/2%)	0.1175(11 3/4%)
1	1.11000000	1.11250000	1.11500000	1.11750000
2	1.23210000	1.23765625	1.24322500	1.24880625
3	1.36763100	1.37689258	1.38619587	1.39554098
4	1.51807041	1.53179299	1.54560840	1.55951705
5	1.68505816	1.70411970	1.72335337	1.74276030
6	1.87041455	1.89583317	1.92153900	1.94753464
7	2.07616015	2.10911440	2.14251599	2.17636996
8	2.30453777	2.34638977	2.38890533	2.43209343
9	2.55803692	2.61035862	2.66362944	2.71786441
10	2.83942099	2.90402397	2.96994683	3.03721348
11	3.15175729	3.23072667	3.31149071	3.39408606
12	3.49845060	3.59418341	3.69231214	3.79289117
13	3.88328016	3.99852905	4.11692804	4.23855588
14	4.31044098	4.44836357	4.59037476	4.73658620
15	4.78458949	4.94880447	5.11826786	5.29313508
16	5.31089433	5.50554497	5.70686867	5.91507845
17	5.89509271	6.12491878	6.36315856	6.61010017
18	6.54355291	6.81397214	7.09492180	7.38678694
19	7.26334373	7.58054401	7.91083780	8.25473440
20	8.06231154	8.43335521	8.82058415	9.22466569
21	8.94916581	9.38210767	9.83495133	10.30856391
22	9.93357404	10.43759478	10.96597073	11.51982017
23	11.02626719	11.61182420	12.22705737	12.87339904
24	12.23915658	12.91815442	13.63316896	14.38602343
25	13.58546380	14.37144679	15.20098340	16.07638118
26	15.07986482	15.98823456	16.94909649	17.96535597
27	16.73864995	17.78691094	18.89824258	20.07628530
28	18.57990145	19.78793843	21.07154048	22.43524882
29	20.62369061	22.01408150	23.49476763	25.07139056
30	22.89229657	24.49066567	26.19666591	28.01727895
31	25.41044919	27.24586555	29.20928249	31.30930923
32	28.20559861	30.31102543	32.56834998	34.98815306
33	31.30821445	33.72101579	36.31371022	39.09926104
34	34.75211804	37.51463007	40.48978690	43.69342422
35	38.57485103	41.73502595	45.14611239	48.82740156
36	42.81808464	46.43021637	50.33791532	54.56462125
37	47.52807395	51.65361571	56.12677558	60.97596424
38	52.75616209	57.46464748	62.58135477	68.14064004
39	58.55933991	63.92942032	69.77821057	76.14716525
40	65.00086731	71.12148010	77.80270479	85.09445716
41	72.15096271	79.12264661	86.75001584	95.09305588
42	80.08756861	88.02394436	96.72626766	106.26648994
43	88.89720115	97.92663810	107.84978844	118.75280251
44	98.67589328	108.94338488	120.25251411	132.70625681
45	109.53024154	121.19951568	134.08155323	148.29924198
46	121.57856811	134.83446120	149.50093186	165.72440292
47	134.95221060	150.00333808	166.69353902	185.19702026
48	149.79695377	166.87871362	185.86329601	206.95767014
49	166.27461868	185.65256890	207.23757505	231.27519638
50	184.56482674	206.53848290	231.06989618	258.45003195

Financial Tables

AMOUNT AT COMPOUND INTEREST $(1 + i)^n$ (Continued)

Periods		Rate i		
n	0.12(12%)	0.1225(12 1/4%)	0.125(12 1/2%)	0.1275(12 3/4%)
1	1.12000000	1.12250000	1.12500000	1.12750000
2	1.25440000	1.26000625	1.26562500	1.27125625
3	1.40492800	1.41435702	1.42382812	1.43334142
4	1.57351936	1.58761575	1.60180664	1.61609245
5	1.76234168	1.78209868	1.80203247	1.82214424
6	1.97382269	2.00040577	2.02728653	2.05446763
7	2.21068141	2.24545547	2.28069735	2.31641225
8	2.47596318	2.52052377	2.56578451	2.61175482
9	2.77307876	2.82928793	2.88650758	2.94475356
10	3.10584821	3.17587570	3.24732103	3.32020963
11	3.47854999	3.56492048	3.65323615	3.74353636
12	3.89597599	4.00162324	4.10989067	4.22083725
13	4.36349311	4.49182208	4.62362701	4.75899400
14	4.88711229	5.04207029	5.20158038	5.36576573
15	5.47356576	5.65972390	5.85177793	6.04990086
16	6.13039365	6.35304007	6.58325017	6.82126323
17	6.86604089	7.13128748	7.40615644	7.69097429
18	7.68996580	8.00487020	8.33192600	8.67157351
19	8.61276169	8.98546608	9.37341675	9.77719913
20	9.64629309	10.08618648	10.54509384	11.02379202
21	10.80384826	11.32174433	11.86323057	12.42932550
22	12.10031006	12.70865801	13.34613439	14.01406450
23	13.55234726	14.26546861	15.01440119	15.80085773
24	15.17862893	16.01298852	16.89120134	17.81546709
25	17.00006441	17.97457961	19.00260151	20.08693914
26	19.04007214	20.17646561	21.37792670	22.64802388
27	21.32488079	22.64808265	24.05016754	25.53564693
28	23.88386649	25.42247277	27.05643848	28.79144191
29	26.74993047	28.53672569	30.43849329	32.46235075
30	29.95992212	32.03247459	34.24330495	36.60130047
31	33.55511278	35.95645272	38.52371807	41.26796628
32	37.58172631	40.36111818	43.33918283	46.52963199
33	42.09153347	45.30535516	48.75658068	52.46216006
34	47.14251748	50.85526117	54.85115327	59.15108547
35	52.79961958	57.08503066	61.70754742	66.69284887
36	59.13557393	64.07794691	69.42099085	75.19618710
37	66.23184280	71.92749541	78.09861471	84.78370095
38	74.17966394	80.73861360	87.86094155	95.59362283
39	83.08122361	90.62909377	98.84355924	107.78180974
40	93.05097044	101.73115775	111.19900415	121.52399048
41	104.21708689	114.19322458	125.09887966	137.01829926
42	116.72313732	128.18189459	140.73623962	154.48813242
43	130.72991380	143.88417667	158.32826958	174.18536930
44	146.41750346	161.50998832	178.11930327	196.39400389
45	163.98760387	181.29496188	200.38421618	221.43423939
46	183.66611634	203.50359472	225.43224320	249.66710491
47	205.70605030	228.43278507	253.61127360	281.49966078
48	230.39077633	256.41580124	285.31268280	317.39086753
49	258.03766949	287.82673689	320.97676816	357.85820315
50	289.00218983	323.08551216	361.09886417	403.48512405

AMOUNT AT COMPOUND INTEREST $(1 + i)^n$ (Continued)

Periods n	0.13(13%)	0.1325(13 1/4%)	0.135(13 1/2%)	0.1375(13 3/4%)
			Rate i	
1	1.13000000	1.13250000	1.13500000	1.13750000
2	1.27690000	1.28255625	1.28822500	1.29390625
3	1.44289700	1.45249495	1.46213537	1.47181836
4	1.63047361	1.64495053	1.65952365	1.67419338
5	1.84243518	1.86290648	1.88355934	1.90439497
6	2.08195175	2.10974159	2.13783985	2.16624928
7	2.35260548	2.38928235	2.42644824	2.46410856
8	2.65844419	2.70586226	2.75401875	2.80292349
9	3.00404194	3.06438901	3.12581128	3.18832547
10	3.39456739	3.47042055	3.54779580	3.62672022
11	3.83586115	3.93025128	4.02674823	4.12539425
12	4.33452310	4.45100957	4.57035924	4.69263596
13	4.89801110	5.04076834	5.18735774	5.33787340
14	5.53475255	5.70867015	5.88765104	6.07183099
15	6.25427038	6.46506894	6.68248393	6.90670775
16	7.06732553	7.32169057	7.58461926	7.85638007
17	7.98607785	8.29181457	8.60854286	8.93663233
18	9.02426797	9.39048001	9.77069614	10.16541928
19	10.19742280	10.63471861	11.08974012	11.56316443
20	11.52308776	12.04381882	12.58685504	13.15309953
21	13.02108917	13.63962482	14.28608047	14.96165072
22	14.71383077	15.44687510	16.21470134	17.01887769
23	16.62662877	17.49358606	18.40368602	19.35897338
24	18.78809051	19.81148621	20.88818363	22.02083222
25	21.23054227	22.43650813	23.70808842	25.04869665
26	23.99051277	25.40934546	26.90868035	28.49289243
27	27.10927943	28.77608373	30.54135220	32.41066514
28	30.63348575	32.58891482	34.66443475	36.86713160
29	34.61583890	36.90694604	39.34413344	41.93636220
30	39.11589796	41.79711639	44.65559145	47.70261200
31	44.20096469	47.33523431	50.68409630	54.26172115
32	49.94709010	53.60715286	57.52644930	61.72270781
33	.56.44021181	60.71010061	65.29251996	70.20958013
34	63.77743935	68.75418894	74.10701015	79.86339740
35	72.06850647	77.86411898	84.11145652	90.84461454
36	81.43741231	88.18111474	95.46650315	103.33574904
37	92.02427591	99.86511244	108.35448108	117.54441453
38	103.98743178	113.09723984	122.98233602	133.70677153
39	117.50579791	128.08262412	139.58495138	152.09145262
40	132.78155163	145.05357182	158.42891982	173.00402735
41	150.04315335	164.27317008	179.81682400	196.79208111
42	169.54876328	186.03936512	204.09209523	223.85099227
43	191.59010251	210.68958100	231.64452809	254.63050370
44	216.49681583	238.60595048	262.91653938	289.64219796
45	244.64140189	270.22123892	298.41027220	329.46800018
46	276.44478414	306.02555308	338.69565895	374.76985021
47	312.38260608	346.57393886	384.41957291	426.30070461
48	352.99234487	392.49498576	436.31621525	484.91705149
49	398.88134970	444.50057137	495.21890431	551.59314607
50	450.73592516	503.39689708	562.07345639	627.43720366

Financial Tables

AMOUNT AT COMPOUND INTEREST $(1 + i)^n$ (Continued)

Periods	Rate i			
n	0.14(14%)	0.1425(14 1/4%)	0.145(14 1/2%)	0.1475(14 3/4%)
1	1.14000000	1.14250000	1.14500000	1.14750000
2	1.29960000	1.30530625	1.31102500	1.31675625
3	1.48154400	1.49131239	1.50112362	1.51097780
4	1.68896016	1.70382441	1.71878655	1.73384702
5	1.92541458	1.94661938	1.96801060	1.98958946
6	2.19497262	2.22401265	2.25337214	2.28305390
7	2.50226879	2.54093445	2.58011110	2.61980435
8	2.85258642	2.90301761	2.95422721	3.00622550
9	3.25194852	3.31669762	3.38259015	3.44964376
10	3.70722131	3.78932703	3.87306572	3.95846621
11	4.22623230	4.32930613	4.43466025	4.54233998
12	4.81790482	4.94623225	5.07768599	5.21233512
13	5.49241149	5.65107035	5.81395046	5.98115455
14	6.26134910	6.45634787	6.65697328	6.86337485
15	7.13793798	7.37637744	7.62223440	7.87572264
16	8.13724930	8.42751123	8.72745839	9.03739173
17	9.27646420	9.62843158	9.99293985	10.37040701
18	10.57516918	11.00048308	11.44191613	11.90004204
19	12.05569287	12.56805192	13.10099397	13.65529824
20	13.74348987	14.35899932	15.00063810	15.66945474
21	15.66757845	16.40515672	17.17573062	17.98069931
22	17.86103944	18.74289155	19.66621156	20.63285246
23	20.36158496	21.41375360	22.51781224	23.67619819
24	23.21220685	24.46521349	25.78289502	27.16843743
25	26.46191581	27.95150641	29.52141479	31.17578195
26	30.16658403	31.93459607	33.80201994	35.77420979
27	34.38990579	36.48527601	38.70331283	41.05090573
28	39.20449260	41.68442784	44.31529319	47.10591432
29	44.69312156	47.62445881	50.74101070	54.05403669
30	50.95015858	54.41094419	58.09845725	62.02700710
31	58.08318078	62.16450374	66.52273355	71.17599065
32	66.21482609	71.02294552	76.16852992	81.67444927
33	75.48490175	81.14371526	87.21296676	93.72143053
34	86.05278799	92.70669468	99.85884694	107.54534154
35	98.10017831	105.91739867	114.33837974	123.40827941
36	111.83420328	121.01062798	130.91744481	141.61100063
37	127.49099173	138.25464247	149.90047430	162.49862322
38	145.33973058	157.95592902	171.63604308	186.46717015
39	165.68729286	180.46464891	196.52326932	213.97107774
40	188.88351386	206.18086138	225.01914337	245.53181171
41	215.32720580	235.56163412	257.64691916	281.74775394
42	245.47301461	269.12916699	295.00572244	323.30554764
43	279.83923665	307.48007328	337.78155220	370.99311592
44	319.01672979	351.29598372	386.75987726	425.71460052
45	363.67907196	401.35566140	442.84005947	488.50750409
46	414.59414203	458.54884315	507.05186809	560.56236095
47	472.63732191	523.89205330	580.57438896	643.24530919
48	538.80654698	598.54667090	664.75767536	738.12399229
49	614.23946356	683.83957150	761.14753829	846.99728115
50	700.23298846	781.28671044	871.51393134	971.92938012

AMOUNT AT COMPOUND INTEREST $(1 + i)^n$ (Continued)

Periods	Rate i			
n	0.15(15%)	0.1525(15 1/4%)	0.155(15 1/2%)	0.1575(15 3/4%)
1	1.15000000	1.15250000	1.15500000	1.15750000
2	1.32250000	1.32825625	1.33402500	1.33980625
3	1.52087500	1.53081533	1.54079887	1.55082573
4	1.74900625	1.76426467	1.77962270	1.79508079
5	2.01135719	2.03331503	2.05546422	2.07780601
6	2.31306077	2.34339557	2.37406117	2.40506046
7	2.66001988	2.70076339	2.74204066	2.78385748
8	3.05902286	3.11262981	3.16705696	3.22231503
9	3.51787629	3.58730586	3.65795078	3.72982965
10	4.04555774	4.13437000	4.22493316	4.31727782
11	4.65239140	4.76486142	4.87979780	4.99724908
12	5.35025011	5.49150279	5.63616645	5.78431581
13	6.15278762	6.32895697	6.50977225	6.69534555
14	7.07570576	7.29412291	7.51878695	7.74986247
15	8.13706163	8.40647665	8.68419893	8.97046581
16	9.35762087	9.68846434	10.03024977	10.38331418
17	10.76126400	11.16595515	11.58493848	12.01868616
18	12.37545361	12.86876331	13.38060394	13.91162923
19	14.23177165	14.83124971	15.45459756	16.10271083
20	16.36653739	17.09301529	17.85006018	18.63888779
21	18.82151800	19.69970013	20.61681950	21.57451262
22	21.64474570	22.70390440	23.81242653	24.97249835
23	24.89145756	26.16624982	27.50335264	28.90566685
24	28.62517619	30.15660291	31.76637230	33.45830937
25	32.91895262	34.75548486	36.69016000	38.72799310
26	37.85679551	40.05569630	42.37713481	44.82765201
27	43.53531484	46.16418999	48.94559070	51.88800720
28	50.06561207	53.20422896	56.53215726	60.06036834
29	57.57545388	61.31787387	65.29464163	69.51987635
30	66.21177196	70.66884964	75.41531109	80.46925688
31	76.14353775	81.44584921	87.10468431	93.14316484
32	87.56506841	93.86634121	100.60591037	107.81321330
33	100.69982867	108.18095825	116.19982648	124.79379439
34	115.80480298	124.67855438	134.21079959	144.44881701
35	133.17552342	143.69203393	155.01347352	167.19950569
36	153.15185194	165.60506910	179.04056192	193.53342783
37	176.12462973	190.85984214	206.79184901	224.01494272
38	202.54332419	219.96596806	238.84458561	259.29729620
39	232.92482281	253.51077819	275.86549638	300.13662035
40	267.86354623	292.17117187	318.62464832	347.40813805
41	308.04307817	336.72727558	368.01146881	402.12491980
42	354.24953990	388.07818510	425.05324647	465.45959466
43	407.38697088	447.26010833	490.93649968	538.76948082
44	468.49501651	515.46727485	567.03165713	623.62567405
45	538.76926899	594.07603427	654.92156398	721.84671772
46	619.58465934	684.67262949	756.43440640	835.53757576
47	712.52235824	789.08520549	873.68173939	967.13474394
48	819.40071197	909.42069933	1009.10240900	1119.45846611
49	942.31081877	1048.10735598	1165.51328239	1295.77317452
50	1083.65744158	1207.94372776	1346.16784116	1499.85744951

Financial Tables

AMOUNT AT COMPOUND INTEREST $(1 + i)^n$ (Continued)

Periods	Rate i			
n	0.16(16%)	0.1625(16 1/4%)	0.165(16 1/2%)	0.1675(16 3/4%)
1	1.16000000	1.16250000	1.16500000	1.16750000
2	1.34560000	1.35140625	1.35722500	1.36305625
3	1.56089600	1.57100977	1.58116712	1.59136817
4	1.81063936	1.82629885	1.84205970	1.85792234
5	2.10034166	2.12307242	2.14599955	2.16912433
6	2.43639632	2.46807168	2.50008948	2.53245266
7	2.82621973	2.86913333	2.91260424	2.95663848
8	3.27841489	3.33536750	3.39318394	3.45187542
9	3.80296127	3.87736472	3.95305929	4.03006456
10	4.41143508	4.50743648	4.60531407	4.70510037
11	5.11726469	5.23989491	5.36519090	5.49320468
12	5.93602704	6.09137784	6.25044739	6.41331647
13	6.88579137	7.08122673	7.28177121	7.48754698
14	7.98751799	8.23192608	8.48326346	8.74171109
15	9.26552087	9.56961407	9.88300194	10.20594770
16	10.74800420	11.12467635	11.51369726	11.91544394
17	12.46768488	12.93243626	13.41345730	13.91128080
18	14.46251446	15.03395715	15.62667776	16.24142034
19	16.77651677	17.47697519	18.20507959	18.96185824
20	19.46075945	20.31698366	21.20891772	22.13796950
21	22.57448097	23.61849350	24.70838914	25.84607939
22	26.18639792	27.45649869	28.78527335	30.17529769
23	30.37622159	31.91817973	33.53484345	35.22966005
24	35.23641704	37.10488394	39.06809262	41.13062811
25	40.87424377	43.13442758	45.51432791	48.02000832
26	47.41412277	50.14377206	53.02419201	56.06335971
27	55.00038241	58.29213502	61.77318369	65.45397246
28	63.80044360	67.76460696	71.96575900	76.41751285
29	74.00851458	78.77635559	83.84010924	89.21744625
30	85.84987691	91.57751338	97.67372726	104.16136850
31	99.58585721	106.45885930	113.78989226	121.60839773
32	115.51959437	123.75842394	132.56522448	141.97780434
33	134.00272947	143.86916783	154.43848652	165.75908657
34	155.44316618	167.24790760	179.92083680	193.52373357
35	180.31407277	194.42569258	209.60777487	225.93895895
36	209.16432441	226.01986763	244.19305773	263.78373457
37	242.63061632	262.74809612	284.48491225	307.96751011
38	281.45151493	305.44466173	331.42492277	359.55206805
39	326.48375732	355.07941927	386.11003503	419.77703945
40	378.72115849	412.77982490	449.81819081	490.08969356
41	439.31654385	479.85654644	524.03819230	572.17971723
42	509.60719087	557.83323524	610.50449402	668.01981987
43	591.14434141	648.48113596	711.23773554	779.91313970
44	685.72743603	753.85932056	828.59196190	910.54859060
45	795.44382580	876.36146015	965.30963562	1063.06547952
46	922.71483793	1018.77019742	1124.58572549	1241.12894734
47	1070.34921199	1184.32035451	1310.14237020	1449.01804602
48	1241.60508591	1376.77241211	1526.31586128	1691.72856873
49	1440.26189966	1600.49792908	1778.15797839	1975.09310399
50	1670.70380360	1860.57884256	2071.55404483	2305.92119891

AMOUNT AT COMPOUND INTEREST $(1 + i)^n$ (Continued)

Periods	Rate i			
n	0.17(17%)	0.1725(17 1/4%)	0.175(17 1/2%)	0.1775(17 3/4%)
1	1.17000000	1.17250000	1.17500000	1.17750000
2	1.36890000	1.37475625	1.38062500	1.38650625
3	1.60161300	1.61190170	1.62223437	1.63261111
4	1.87388721	1.88995475	1.90612539	1.92239958
5	2.19244804	2.21597194	2.23969733	2.26362551
6	2.56516420	2.59822710	2.63164437	2.66541903
7	3.00124212	3.04642128	3.09218213	3.13853091
8	3.51145328	3.57192895	3.63331400	3.69562015
9	4.10840033	4.18808669	4.26914396	4.35159273
10	4.80682839	4.91053164	5.01624415	5.12400044
11	5.62398922	5.75759835	5.89408687	6.03351051
12	6.58006738	6.75078407	6.92555208	7.10445863
13	7.69867884	7.91529432	8.13752369	8.36550004
14	9.00745424	9.28068259	9.56159034	9.85037629
15	10.53872146	10.88160033	11.23486864	11.59881808
16	12.33030411	12.75867639	13.20097066	13.65760829
17	14.42645581	14.95954807	15.51114052	16.08183377
18	16.87895329	17.54007011	18.22559011	18.93635926
19	19.74837535	20.56573220	21.41506838	22.29756303
20	23.10559916	24.11332101	25.16270535	26.25538047
21	27.03355102	28.27286888	29.56617879	30.91561050
22	31.62925470	33.14993877	34.74026008	36.40324911
23	37.00622799	38.86830320	40.81980559	42.86482583
24	43.29728675	45.57308551	47.96327157	50.47333241
25	50.65782550	53.43444275	56.35684409	59.43234892
26	59.26965584	62.65188413	66.21929181	69.98159085
27	69.34549733	73.45933414	77.80766787	82.40332323
28	81.13423187	86.13106928	91.42400975	94.02991310
29	94.92705129	100.98867873	107.42321146	114.25272268
30	111.06465001	118.40922581	126.22227346	134.53258095
31	129.94564051	138.83481727	148.31117132	158.41211407
32	152.03639940	162.78382325	174.26562630	186.53026432
33	177.88258730	190.86403276	204.76211090	219.63938623
34	208.12262714	223.78807841	240.59548031	258.62537729
35	243.50347375	262.39152193	282.69968936	304.53138176
36	284.89906429	307.65405947	332.17213500	358.58570202
37	333.33190522	360.72438472	390.30225862	422.23466413
38	389.99832910	422.94934109	458.60515388	497.18131701
39	456.29804505	495.90810243	538.86105581	585.43100078
40	533.86871271	581.45225010	633.16174058	689.34500342
41	624.62639387	681.75276324	743.96504518	811.70374152
42	730.81288083	799.35511490	874.15892808	955.78115564
43	855.05107057	937.24387221	1027.13674050	1125.43231077
44	1000.40975257	1098.91844017	1206.88567009	1325.19654593
45	1170.47941051	1288.48187110	1418.09066235	1560.41893283
46	1369.46091029	1510.74499387	1666.25652826	1837.39329341
47	1602.26926504	1771.34850531	1957.85142071	2163.53060299
48	1874.65504010	2076.90612247	2300.47541933	2547.55728502
49	2193.34639691	2435.17242860	2703.05861771	2999.74870311
50	2566.21528439	2855.23967253	3176.09387581	3532.20409792

Financial Tables

AMOUNT AT COMPOUND INTEREST $(1 + i)^n$ (Continued)

Periods	Rate i			
n	0.18(18%)	0.1825(18 1/4%)	0.185(18 1/2%)	0.1875(18 3/4%)
1	1.18000000	1.18250000	1.18500000	1.18750000
2	1.39240000	1.39830625	1.40422500	1.41015625
3	1.64303200	1.65349714	1.66400662	1.67456055
4	1.93877776	1.95526037	1.97184785	1.98854065
5	2.28775776	2.31209539	2.33663970	2.36139202
6	2.69955415	2.73405279	2.76891805	2.80415303
7	3.18547390	3.23301743	3.28116789	3.32993172
8	3.75885920	3.82304311	3.88818395	3.95429391
9	4.43545386	4.52074848	4.60749798	4.69572402
10	5.23383555	5.34578507	5.45988510	5.57617228
11	6.17592595	6.32139085	6.46996385	6.62170458
12	7.28759263	7.47504468	7.66690716	7.86327419
13	8.59935930	8.83924033	9.08528498	9.33763810
14	10.14724397	10.45240170	10.76606270	11.08844524
15	11.97374789	12.35996501	12.75778430	13.16752873
16	14.12902251	14.61565862	15.11797440	15.63644036
17	16.67224656	17.28301632	17.91479966	18.56827293
18	19.67325094	20.43716679	21.22903760	22.04982410
19	23.21443611	24.16694973	25.15640955	26.18416612
20	27.39303460	28.57741806	29.81034532	31.09369727
21	32.32378083	33.79279686	35.32525921	36.92376551
22	38.14206138	39.95998228	41.86043216	43.84697154
23	45.00763243	47.25267905	49.60461211	52.06827871
24	53.10900627	55.87629298	58.78146535	61.83108096
25	62.66862740	66.07371645	69.65603644	73.42440864
26	73.94898033	78.13216970	82.54240318	87.19148526
27	87.25979679	92.39129067	97.81274777	103.53988875
28	102.96656021	109.25270122	115.90810611	122.95361789
29	121.50054105	129.19131919	137.35110574	146.00742125
30	143.37063844	152.76873494	162.76106030	173.38381273
31	169.17735336	180.64902906	192.87185646	205.89327762
32	199.62927696	213.61747687	228.55314990	244.49826717
33	235.56254681	252.60266640	270.83548263	290.34169227
34	277.96380524	298.70265302	320.94004692	344.78075956
35	327.99729018	353.21588719	380.31395560	409.42715198
36	387.03680242	417.67778660	450.67203738	486.19474298
37	456.70342685	493.90398266	534.04636430	577.35625729
38	538.91004369	584.04145949	632.84494170	685.61055553
39	635.91385155	690.62902585	749.92125591	814.16253469
40	750.37834483	816.66882307	888.65668825	966.81800995
41	885.44644690	965.71088328	1053.05817558	1148.09638681
42	1044.82680734	1141.95311948	1247.87393806	1363.36445934
43	1232.89563266	1350.35956378	1478.73061660	1618.99529547
44	1454.81684654	1596.80018417	1752.29578067	1922.55691337
45	1716.68387891	1888.21621778	2076.47050010	2283.03633462
46	2025.68697712	2232.81567753	2460.61754262	2711.10564736
47	2390.31063300	2640.30453867	2915.83178800	3219.43795624
48	2820.56654694	3122.16011698	3455.26006878	3823.08257304
49	3328.26852539	3691.95433833	4094.48389250	4539.91055548
50	3927.35685996	4365.73600508	4851.96341262	5391.14378464

AMOUNT AT COMPOUND INTEREST $(1 + i)^n$ (Continued)

Periods			Rate i		
n	0.19(19%)	0.1925(19 1/4%)	0.195(19 1/2%)	0.1975(19 3/4%)	0.20(20%)
1	1.19000000	1.19250000	1.19500000	1.19750000	1.20000000
2	1.41610000	1.42205625	1.42802500	1.43400625	1.44000000
3	1.68515900	1.69580208	1.70648987	1.71722248	1.72800000
4	2.00533921	2.02224398	2.03925540	2.05637393	2.07360000
5	2.38635366	2.41152594	2.43691020	2.46250778	2.48832000
6	2.83976086	2.87574469	2.91210769	2.94885306	2.98598400
7	3.37931542	3.42932554	3.47996869	3.53125154	3.58318080
8	4.02138535	4.08947071	4.15856259	4.22867372	4.29981696
9	4.78544856	4.87669382	4.96948229	5.06383678	5.15978035
10	5.69468379	5.81545738	5.93853134	6.06394454	6.19173642
11	6.77667371	6.93493292	7.09654495	7.26157359	7.43008371
12	8.06424172	8.26990751	8.48037122	8.69573437	8.91610045
13	9.59644764	9.86186471	10.13404361	10.41314191	10.69932054
14	11.41977269	11.76027366	12.11018211	12.46973744	12.83918465
15	13.58952950	14.02412634	14.47166762	14.93251059	15.40702157
16	16.17154011	16.72377067	17.29364281	17.88168143	18.48842589
17	19.24413273	19.94309652	20.66590315	21.41331351	22.18611107
18	22.90051795	23.78214260	24.69575427	25.64244293	26.62333328
19	27.25161636	28.36020505	29.51142635	30.70682540	31.94799994
20	32.42942347	33.81954452	35.26615449	36.77142342	38.33759992
21	38.59101393	40.32980684	42.14305461	44.03377955	46.00511991
22	45.92330658	48.09329466	50.36095026	52.73045101	55.20614389
23	54.64873482	57.35125388	60.18133557	63.14471508	66.24737267
24	65.03199444	68.39137025	71.91669600	75.61579631	79.49684720
25	77.38807338	81.55670902	85.94045172	90.54991608	95.39621664
26	92.09180733	97.25637551	102.69883981	108.43352451	114.47545997
27	109.58925072	115.97822780	122.72511357	129.84914560	137.37055197
28	130.41120836	138.30403665	146.65651072	155.49435185	164.84466236
29	155.18933794	164.92756370	175.25453031	186.20448635	197.81359483
30	184.67531215	196.67611971	209.42916372	222.97987240	237.37631380
31	219.76362146	234.53627276	250.26785064	267.01839720	284.85157656
32	261.51870954	279.68450526	299.07008152	319.75453064	341.82189187
33	311.20726435	333.52377253	357.38874741	382.90605045	410.18627025
34	370.33664458	397.72709874	427.07955316	458.52999541	492.22352430
35	440.70060705	474.28956524	510.36006602	549.08966950	590.66822915
36	524.43372239	565.59030655	609.88027890	657.53487923	708.80187499
37	624.07612965	674.46644056	728.80693328	787.39801788	850.56224998
38	742.65059428	804.30123037	870.92428527	942.90912641	1020.67469998
39	883.75420719	959.12921722	1040.75452090	1129.13367888	1224.80963997
40	1051.66750656	1143.76159154	1243.70165248	1352.13758046	1469.77156797
41	1251.48433281	1363.93569791	1486.22347471	1619.18475260	1763.72588156
42	1489.26635604	1626.49331975	1776.03705228	1938.97374123	2116.47105788
43	1772.22696369	1939.59328381	2122.36427748	2321.92105513	2539.76526945
44	2108.95008679	2312.96499094	2536.22531159	2780.50046351	3047.71832334
45	2509.65060328	2758.21075169	3030.78924734	3329.64930506	3657.26198801
46	2986.48421790	3289.16632140	3621.79315058	3987.25504281	4388.71438561
47	3553.91621930	3922.33083826	4328.04281494	4774.73791376	5266.45726273
48	4229.16030097	4677.37952463	5172.01116385	5717.74865173	6319.74871528
49	5032.70075815	5577.77508312	6180.55334080	6847.00401044	7583.69845834
50	5988.91390220	6651.49678662	7385.76124226	8199.28730251	9100.43815000

PRESENT VALUE $1/(1+i)^{n}$*

The following table gives the value of unit amount due in n years at rate of interest i, compounded annually, $1/(1+i)^{n} = v^{n}$

Periods			Rate i		
n	0.0025(1/4%)	0.004167(5/12%)	0.005(1/2%)	0.005833(7/12%)	0.0075(3/4%)
1	0.99750623	0.99585062	0.99502488	0.99420050	0.99255583
2	0.99501869	0.99171846	0.99007450	0.98843463	0.98516708
3	0.99253734	0.98760345	0.98514876	0.98270220	0.97783333
4	0.99006219	0.98350551	0.98024752	0.97700301	0.97055417
5	0.98759321	0.97942457	0.97537067	0.97133688	0.96332920
6	0.98513038	0.97536057	0.97051808	0.96570361	0.95615802
7	0.98267370	0.97131343	0.96568963	0.96010301	0.94904022
8	0.98022314	0.96728308	0.96088520	0.95453489	0.94197540
9	0.97777869	0.96326946	0.95610468	0.94899906	0.93496318
10	0.97534034	0.95927249	0.95134794	0.94349534	0.92800315
11	0.97290807	0.95529211	0.94661487	0.93802354	0.92109494
12	0.97048187	0.95132824	0.94190534	0.93258347	0.91423815
13	0.96806171	0.94738082	0.93721924	0.92717495	0.90743241
14	0.96564759	0.94344978	0.93255646	0.92179779	0.90067733
15	0.96323949	0.93953505	0.92791688	0.91645182	0.89397254
16	0.96083740	0.93563657	0.92330037	0.91113686	0.88731766
17	0.95844130	0.93175426	0.91870684	0.90585272	0.88071231
18	0.95605117	0.92788806	0.91413616	0.90059922	0.87415614
19	0.95366700	0.92403790	0.90958822	0.89537619	0.86764878
20	0.95128878	0.92020372	0.90506290	0.89018346	0.86118985
21	0.94891649	0.91638544	0.90056010	0.88502084	0.85477901
22	0.94655011	0.91258301	0.89607971	0.87988815	0.84841589
23	0.94418964	0.90879636	0.89162160	0.87478524	0.84210014
24	0.94183505	0.90502542	0.88718567	0.86971192	0.83583140
25	0.93948634	0.90127013	0.88277181	0.86466802	0.82960933
26	0.93714348	0.89753042	0.87837991	0.85965338	0.82343358
27	0.93480646	0.89380623	0.87400986	0.85466782	0.81730380
28	0.93247527	0.89009749	0.86966155	0.84971117	0.81121966
29	0.93014990	0.88640414	0.86533488	0.84478327	0.80518080
30	0.92783032	0.88272611	0.86102973	0.83988394	0.79918690
31	0.92551653	0.87906335	0.85674600	0.83501303	0.79323762
32	0.92320851	0.87541578	0.85248358	0.83017037	0.78733262
33	0.92090624	0.87178335	0.84824237	0.82535580	0.78147158
34	0.91860972	0.86816599	0.84402226	0.82056914	0.77565418
35	0.91631892	0.86456365	0.83982314	0.81581025	0.76988008
36	0.91403384	0.86097624	0.83564492	0.81107896	0.76414896
37	0.91175445	0.85740373	0.83148748	0.80637510	0.75846051
38	0.90948075	0.85384604	0.82735073	0.80169853	0.75281440
39	0.90721272	0.85030311	0.82323455	0.79704907	0.74721032
40	0.90495034	0.84677488	0.81913886	0.79242659	0.74164796
41	0.90269361	0.84326129	0.81506354	0.78783091	0.73612701
42	0.90044250	0.83976228	0.81100850	0.78326188	0.73064716
43	0.89819701	0.83627779	0.80697363	0.77871935	0.72520809
44	0.89595712	0.83280776	0.80295884	0.77420316	0.71980952
45	0.89372281	0.82935212	0.79896402	0.76971317	0.71445114
46	0.89149407	0.82591083	0.79498907	0.76524922	0.70913264
47	0.88927090	0.82248381	0.79103390	0.76081115	0.70385374
48	0.88705326	0.81907102	0.78709841	0.75639883	0.69861414
49	0.88484116	0.81567238	0.78318250	0.75201209	0.69341353
50	0.88263457	0.81228785	0.77928607	0.74765079	0.68825165

*$a_{\overline{n}|i}$ may be constructed from these tables by use of the formula $\dfrac{1-(1+i)^{-n}}{i}$.
See page 634.

PRESENT VALUE $1/(1 + i)^n$ (Continued)

eriods			Rate i		
n	0.0025(1/4%)	0.004167(5/12%)	0.005(1/2%)	0.005833(7/12%)	0.0075(3/4%)
51	0.88043349	0.80891736	0.77540902	0.74331479	0.68312819
52	0.87823790	0.80556086	0.77155127	0.73900393	0.67804286
53	0.87604778	0.80221828	0.76771270	0.73471808	0.67299540
54	0.87386312	0.79888957	0.76389324	0.73045708	0.66798551
55	0.87168391	0.79557468	0.76009277	0.72622079	0.66301291
56	0.86951013	0.79227354	0.75631122	0.72200907	0.65807733
57	0.86734178	0.78898610	0.75254847	0.71782178	0.65317849
58	0.86517883	0.78571230	0.74880445	0.71365877	0.64831612
59	0.86302128	0.78245208	0.74507906	0.70951990	0.64348995
60	0.86086911	0.77920539	0.74137220	0.70540504	0.63869970
61	0.85872230	0.77597217	0.73768378	0.70131404	0.63394511
62	0.85658085	0.77275237	0.73401371	0.69724677	0.62922592
63	0.85444474	0.76954593	0.73036190	0.69320308	0.62454185
64	0.85231395	0.76635279	0.72672826	0.68918285	0.61989266
65	0.85018848	0.76317291	0.72311269	0.68518593	0.61527807
66	0.84806831	0.76000621	0.71951512	0.68121219	0.61069784
67	0.84595343	0.75685266	0.71593544	0.67726150	0.60615170
68	0.84384382	0.75371219	0.71237357	0.67333372	0.60163940
69	0.84173947	0.75058476	0.70882943	0.66942872	0.59716070
70	0.83964037	0.74747030	0.70530291	0.66554637	0.59271533
71	0.83754650	0.74436876	0.70179394	0.66168653	0.58830306
72	0.83545786	0.74128009	0.69830243	0.65784908	0.58392363
73	0.83337442	0.73820424	0.69482829	0.65403388	0.57957681
74	0.83129618	0.73514115	0.69137143	0.65024081	0.57526234
75	0.82922312	0.73209078	0.68793177	0.64646973	0.57097999
76	0.82715523	0.72905306	0.68450923	0.64272053	0.56672952
77	0.82509250	0.72602794	0.68110371	0.63899306	0.56251069
78	0.82303491	0.72301537	0.67771513	0.63528723	0.55832326
79	0.82098246	0.72001531	0.67434342	0.63160288	0.55416701
80	0.81893512	0.71702770	0.67098847	0.62793989	0.55004170
81	0.81689289	0.71405248	0.66765022	0.62429816	0.54594710
82	0.81485575	0.71108960	0.66432858	0.62067754	0.54188297
83	0.81282369	0.70813902	0.66102346	0.61707792	0.53784911
84	0.81079670	0.70520069	0.65773479	0.61349917	0.53384527
85	0.80877476	0.70227454	0.65446248	0.60994118	0.52987123
86	0.80675787	0.69936054	0.65120644	0.60640382	0.52592678
87	0.80474600	0.69645863	0.64796661	0.60288698	0.52201169
88	0.80273915	0.69356876	0.64474290	0.59939054	0.51812575
89	0.80073731	0.69069088	0.64153522	0.59591437	0.51426873
90	0.79874046	0.68782495	0.63834350	0.59245836	0.51044043
91	0.79674859	0.68497090	0.63516766	0.58902240	0.50664063
92	0.79476168	0.68212870	0.63200763	0.58560636	0.50286911
93	0.79277973	0.67929829	0.62886331	0.58221014	0.49912567
94	0.79080273	0.67647962	0.62573464	0.57883361	0.49541009
95	0.78883065	0.67367265	0.62262153	0.57547666	0.49172217
96	0.78686349	0.67087733	0.61952391	0.57213918	0.48806171
97	0.78490124	0.66809361	0.61644170	0.56882106	0.48442850
98	0.78294388	0.66532143	0.61337483	0.56552218	0.48082233
99	0.78099140	0.66256076	0.61032321	0.56224243	0.47724301
00	0.77904379	0.65981155	0.60728678	0.55898171	0.47369033

Financial Tables

PRESENT VALUE $1/(1 + i)^n$ (Continued)

Rate i

Periods n	0.01(1%)	0.001125(1 1/8%)	0.0125(1 1/4%)		0.0175(1 3/4%)
1	0.99009901	0.98887515	0.98765432	0.98522167	0.98280098
2	0.98029605	0.97787407	0.97546106	0.97066175	0.96589777
3	0.97059015	0.96699537	0.96341833	0.95631699	0.94928528
4	0.96098034	0.95623770	0.95152428	0.94218423	0.93295851
5	0.95146569	0.94559970	0.93977706	0.92826033	0.91691254
6	0.94204524	0.93508005	0.92817488	0.91454219	0.90114254
7	0.93271805	0.92467743	0.91671593	0.90102679	0.88564378
8	0.92348322	0.91439054	0.90539845	0.88771112	0.87041157
9	0.91433982	0.90421808	0.89422069	0.87459224	0.85544135
10	0.90528695	0.89415880	0.88318093	0.86166723	0.84072860
11	0.89632372	0.88421142	0.87227746	0.84893323	0.82626889
12	0.88744923	0.87437470	0.86150860	0.83638742	0.81205788
13	0.87866260	0.86464742	0.85087269	0.82402702	0.79809128
14	0.86996297	0.85502835	0.84036809	0.81184928	0.78436490
15	0.86134947	0.84551629	0.82999318	0.79985150	0.77087459
16	0.85282126	0.83611005	0.81974635	0.78803104	0.75761631
17	0.84437749	0.82680846	0.80962602	0.77638526	0.74458605
18	0.83601731	0.81761034	0.79963064	0.76491159	0.73177990
19	0.82773992	0.80851455	0.78975866	0.75360747	0.71919401
20	0.81954447	0.79951995	0.78000855	0.74247042	0.70682458
21	0.81143017	0.79062542	0.77037881	0.73149795	0.69466789
22	0.80339621	0.78182983	0.76086796	0.72068763	0.68272028
23	0.79544179	0.77313210	0.75147453	0.71003708	0.67097817
24	0.78756613	0.76453112	0.74219707	0.69954392	0.65943800
25	0.77976844	0.75602583	0.73303414	0.68920583	0.64809632
26	0.77204796	0.74761516	0.72398434	0.67092052	0.63694970
27	0.76440392	0.73929806	0.71504626	0.66898574	0.62599479
28	0.75683557	0.73107348	0.70621853	0.65909925	0.61522829
29	0.74934215	0.72294040	0.69749978	0.64935887	0.60464697
30	0.74192292	0.71489780	0.68888867	0.63976243	0.59424764
31	0.73457715	0.70694467	0.68038387	0.63030781	0.58402716
32	0.72730411	0.69908002	0.67198407	0.62099292	0.57398247
33	0.72010307	0.69130287	0.66368797	0.61181568	0.56411053
34	0.71297334	0.68361223	0.65549429	0.60277407	0.55440839
35	0.70591420	0.67600715	0.64740177	0.59386608	0.54487311
36	0.69892495	0.66848667	0.63940916	0.58508974	0.53550183
37	0.69200490	0.66104986	0.63151522	0.57644309	0.52629172
38	0.68515337	0.65369578	0.62371873	0.56792423	0.51724002
39	0.67836967	0.64642352	0.61601850	0.55953126	0.50834400
40	0.67165314	0.63923216	0.60841334	0.55126232	0.49960098
41	0.66500311	0.63212080	0.60090206	0.54311559	0.49100834
42	0.65841892	0.62508855	0.59348352	0.53508925	0.48256348
43	0.65189992	0.61813454	0.58615656	0.52718153	0.47426386
44	0.64544546	0.61125789	0.57892006	0.51939067	0.46610699
45	0.63905492	0.60445774	0.57177290	0.51171494	0.45809040
46	0.63272764	0.59773324	0.56471397	0.50415265	0.45021170
47	0.62646301	0.59108355	0.55774219	0.49670212	0.44246850
48	0.62026041	0.58450784	0.55085649	0.48936170	0.43485848
49	0.61411921	0.57800528	0.54405579	0.48212975	0.42737934
50	0.60803882	0.57157506	0.53733905	0.47500468	0.42002883

PRESENT VALUE $1/(1 + i)^n$ (Continued)

Periods n	0.01(1%)	0.001125(1 1/8%)	0.0125(1 1/4%)	0.0175(1 3/4%)	
51	0.60201864	0.56521637	0.53070524	0.46798491	0.41280475
52	0.59605806	0.55892843	0.52415332	0.46106887	0.40570492
53	0.59015649	0.55271044	0.51768229	0.45425505	0.39872719
54	0.58431336	0.54656162	0.51129115	0.44754192	0.39186947
55	0.57852808	0.54048120	0.50497892	0.44092800	0.38512970
56	0.57280008	0.53446843	0.49874461	0.43441182	0.37850585
57	0.56712879	0.52852256	0.49258727	0.42799194	0.37199592
58	0.56151365	0.52264282	0.48650594	0.42166694	0.36559796
59	0.55595411	0.51682850	0.48049970	0.41543541	0.35931003
60	0.55044962	0.51107887	0.47456760	0.40929597	0.35313025
61	0.54499962	0.50539319	0.46870874	0.40324726	0.34705676
62	0.53960358	0.49977077	0.46292222	0.39728794	0.34108772
63	0.53426097	0.49421090	0.45720713	0.39141669	0.33522135
64	0.52897126	0.48871288	0.45156259	0.38563221	0.32945587
65	0.52373392	0.48327602	0.44598775	0.37993321	0.32378956
66	0.51854844	0.47789965	0.44048173	0.37431843	0.31822069
67	0.51341429	0.47258309	0.43504368	0.36878663	0.31274761
68	0.50833099	0.46732568	0.42967277	0.36333658	0.30736866
69	0.50329801	0.46212675	0.42436817	0.35796708	0.30208222
70	0.49831486	0.45698566	0.41912905	0.35267692	0.29688670
71	0.49338105	0.45190177	0.41395462	0.34746495	0.29178054
72	0.48849609	0.44687443	0.40884407	0.34233000	0.28676221
73	0.48365949	0.44190302	0.40379661	0.33727093	0.28183018
74	0.47887078	0.43698692	0.39881147	0.33228663	0.27698298
75	0.47412949	0.43212551	0.39388787	0.32737599	0.27221914
76	0.46943514	0.42731818	0.38902506	0.32253793	0.26753724
77	0.46478726	0.42256433	0.38422228	0.31777136	0.26293586
78	0.46018541	0.41786337	0.37947879	0.31307523	0.25841362
79	0.45562912	0.41321470	0.37479387	0.30844850	0.25396916
80	0.45111794	0.40861775	0.37016679	0.30389015	0.24960114
81	0.44665142	0.40407194	0.36559683	0.29939916	0.24530825
82	0.44222913	0.39957670	0.36108329	0.29497454	0.24108919
83	0.43785063	0.39513148	0.35662547	0.29061531	0.23694269
84	0.43351547	0.39073570	0.35222268	0.28632050	0.23286751
85	0.42922324	0.38638882	0.34787426	0.28208917	0.22886242
86	0.42497350	0.38209031	0.34357951	0.27792036	0.22492621
87	0.42076585	0.37783961	0.33933779	0.27381316	0.22105770
88	0.41659985	0.37363621	0.33514843	0.26976666	0.21725572
89	0.41247510	0.36947956	0.33101080	0.26577996	0.21351914
90	0.40839119	0.36536916	0.32692425	0.26185218	0.20984682
91	0.40434771	0.36130448	0.32288814	0.25798245	0.20623766
92	0.40034427	0.35728503	0.31890187	0.25416990	0.20269057
93	0.39638046	0.35331029	0.31496481	0.25041369	0.19920450
94	0.39245590	0.34937976	0.31107636	0.24671300	0.19577837
95	0.38857020	0.34549297	0.30723591	0.24306699	0.19241118
96	0.38472297	0.34164941	0.30344287	0.23947487	0.18910190
97	0.38091383	0.33784861	0.29969666	0.23593583	0.18584953
98	0.37714241	0.33409010	0.29599670	0.23244909	0.18265310
99	0.37340832	0.33037340	0.29234242	0.22901389	0.17951165
100	0.36971121	0.32669805	0.28873326	0.22562944	0.17642422

PRESENT VALUE $1/(1 + i)^n$ (Continued)

Periods		Rate i		
n	0.02(2%)	0.0225(2 1/4%)	0.025(2 1/2%)	0.0275(2 3/4%)
1	0.98039216	0.97799511	0.97560976	0.97323601
2	0.96116878	0.95647444	0.95181440	0.94718833
3	0.94232233	0.93542732	0.92859941	0.92183779
4	0.92384543	0.91484335	0.90595064	0.89716573
5	0.90573081	0.89471232	0.88385429	0.87315400
6	0.88797138	0.87502427	0.86229687	0.84978491
7	0.87056018	0.85576946	0.84126524	0.82704128
8	0.85349037	0.83693835	0.82074657	0.80490635
9	0.83675527	0.81852161	0.80072836	0.78336385
10	0.82034830	0.80051013	0.78119840	0.76239791
11	0.80426304	0.78289499	0.76214478	0.74199310
12	0.78849318	0.76566748	0.74355589	0.72213440
13	0.77303253	0.74881905	0.72542038	0.70280720
14	0.75787502	0.73234137	0.70772720	0.68399728
15	0.74301473	0.71622628	0.69046556	0.66569078
16	0.72844581	0.70046580	0.67362493	0.64787424
17	0.71416256	0.68505212	0.65719506	0.63053454
18	0.70015937	0.66997763	0.64115691	0.61365892
19	0.68643076	0.65523484	0.62552772	0.59723496
20	0.67297133	0.64081647	0.61027094	0.58125057
21	0.65977582	0.62671538	0.59538629	0.56569398
22	0.64683904	0.61292457	0.58086467	0.55055375
23	0.63415592	0.59943724	0.56669724	0.53581874
24	0.62172149	0.58624668	0.55287535	0.52147809
25	0.60953087	0.57334639	0.53939059	0.50752126
26	0.59757928	0.56072997	0.52623472	0.49393796
27	0.58586204	0.54839117	0.51339973	0.48071821
28	0.57437455	0.53632388	0.50087778	0.46785227
29	0.56311231	0.52452213	0.48866125	0.45533068
30	0.55207089	0.51298008	0.47674269	0.44314421
31	0.54124597	0.50169201	0.46511481	0.43128391
32	0.53063330	0.49065233	0.45377055	0.41974103
33	0.52022873	0.47985558	0.44270298	0.40850708
34	0.51002817	0.46929641	0.43190534	0.39757380
35	0.50002761	0.45896960	0.42137107	0.38693314
36	0.49022315	0.44887002	0.41109372	0.37657727
37	0.48061093	0.43899268	0.40106705	0.36649856
38	0.47118719	0.42933270	0.39128492	0.35668959
39	0.46194822	0.41988528	0.38174139	0.34714316
40	0.45289042	0.41064575	0.37243062	0.33785222
41	0.44401021	0.40160954	0.36334695	0.32880995
42	0.43530413	0.39277216	0.35448483	0.32000968
43	0.42676875	0.38412925	0.34583886	0.31144495
44	0.41840074	0.37567653	0.33740376	0.30310944
45	0.41019680	0.36740981	0.32917440	0.29499702
46	0.40215373	0.35932500	0.32114576	0.28710172
47	0.39426836	0.35141809	0.31331294	0.27941773
48	0.38653761	0.34368518	0.30567116	0.27193940
49	0.37895844	0.33612242	0.29821576	0.26466122
50	0.37152788	0.32872608	0.29094221	0.25757783

PRESENT VALUE $1/(1 + i)^n$ (Continued)

Periods n	Rate i			
	0.02(2%)	0.0225(2 1/4%)	0.025(2 1/2%)	0.0275(2 3/4%)
51	0.36424302	0.32149250	0.28384606	0.25068402
52	0.35710100	0.31441810	0.27692298	0.24397471
53	0.35009902	0.30749936	0.27016876	0.23744497
54	0.34323433	0.30073287	0.26357928	0.23109000
55	0.33650425	0.29411528	0.25715052	0.22490511
56	0.32990613	0.28764330	0.25087855	0.21888575
57	0.32343738	0.28131374	0.24475956	0.21302749
58	0.31709547	0.27512347	0.23878982	0.20732603
59	0.31087791	0.26906940	0.23296568	0.20177716
60	0.30478227	0.26314856	0.22728359	0.19637679
61	0.29880614	0.25735801	0.22174009	0.19112097
62	0.29294720	0.25169487	0.21633179	0.18600581
63	0.28720314	0.24615635	0.21105541	0.18102755
64	0.28157170	0.24073971	0.20590771	0.17618253
65	0.27605069	0.23544226	0.20088557	0.17146718
66	0.27063793	0.23026138	0.19598593	0.16687804
67	0.26533130	0.22519450	0.19120578	0.16241172
68	0.26012873	0.22023912	0.18654223	0.15806493
69	0.25502817	0.21539278	0.18199241	0.15383448
70	0.25002761	0.21065309	0.17755358	0.14971726
71	0.24512511	0.20601769	0.17322300	0.14571023
72	0.24031874	0.20148429	0.16899805	0.14181044
73	0.23560661	0.19705065	0.16487615	0.13801503
74	0.23098687	0.19271458	0.16085478	0.13432119
75	0.22645771	0.18847391	0.15693149	0.13072622
76	0.22201737	0.18432657	0.15310389	0.12722747
77	0.21766408	0.18027048	0.14936965	0.12382235
78	0.21339616	0.17630365	0.14572649	0.12050837
79	0.20921192	0.17242411	0.14217218	0.11728309
80	0.20510973	0.16862993	0.13870457	0.11414412
81	0.20108797	0.16491925	0.13532153	0.11108917
82	0.19714507	0.16129022	0.13202101	0.10811598
83	0.19327948	0.15774105	0.12880098	0.10522237
84	0.18948968	0.15426997	0.12565949	0.10240620
85	0.18577420	0.15087528	0.12259463	0.09966540
86	0.18213157	0.14755528	0.11960452	0.09699795
87	0.17856036	0.14430835	0.11668733	0.09440190
88	0.17505918	0.14113286	0.11384130	0.09187533
89	0.17162665	0.13802724	0.11106468	0.08941638
90	0.16826142	0.13498997	0.10835579	0.08702324
91	0.16496217	0.13201953	0.10571296	0.08469415
92	0.16172762	0.12911445	0.10313460	0.08242740
93	0.15855649	0.12627331	0.10061912	0.08022131
94	0.15544754	0.12349468	0.09816500	0.07807427
95	0.15239955	0.12077719	0.09577073	0.07598469
96	0.14941132	0.11811950	0.09343486	0.07395104
97	0.14648169	0.11552029	0.09115596	0.07197181
98	0.14360950	0.11297828	0.08893264	0.07004556
99	0.14079363	0.11049221	0.08676355	0.06817086
100	0.13803297	0.10806084	0.08464737	0.06634634

Financial Tables

PRESENT VALUE $1/(1 + i)^n$ (Continued)

Periods		Rate i		
n	0.03(3%)	0.0325(3 1/4%)	0.035(3 1/2%)	0.0375(3 3/4%)
1	0.97087379	0.96852300	0.96618357	0.96385542
2	0.94259591	0.93803681	0.93351070	0.92901727
3	0.91514166	0.90851022	0.90194271	0.89543834
4	0.88848705	0.87991305	0.87144223	0.86307310
5	0.86260878	0.85221603	0.84197317	0.83187768
6	0.83748426	0.82539083	0.81350064	0.80180981
7	0.81309151	0.79941000	0.78599096	0.77282874
8	0.78940923	0.77424698	0.75941156	0.74489517
9	0.76641673	0.74987601	0.73373097	0.71797125
10	0.74409391	0.72627216	0.70891881	0.69202048
11	0.72242128	0.70341129	0.68494571	0.66700769
12	0.70137988	0.68127002	0.66178330	0.64289898
13	0.68095134	0.65982568	0.63940415	0.61966167
14	0.66111781	0.63905635	0.61778179	0.59726426
15	0.64186195	0.61894078	0.59689062	0.57567639
16	0.62316694	0.59945838	0.57670591	0.55486881
17	0.60501645	0.58058923	0.55720378	0.53481331
18	0.58739461	0.56231402	0.53836114	0.51548271
19	0.57028603	0.54461407	0.52015569	0.49685080
20	0.55367575	0.52747125	0.50256588	0.47889234
21	0.53754928	0.51086804	0.48557090	0.46158298
22	0.52189250	0.49478745	0.46915063	0.44489926
23	0.50669175	0.47921302	0.45328563	0.42881856
24	0.49193374	0.46412884	0.43795713	0.41331910
25	0.47760557	0.44951945	0.42314699	0.39837985
26	0.46369473	0.43536993	0.40883767	0.38398058
27	0.45018906	0.42166579	0.39501224	0.37010176
28	0.43707675	0.40839302	0.38165434	0.35672459
29	0.42434636	0.39553803	0.36874815	0.34389093
30	0.41198676	0.38308768	0.35627841	0.33140331
31	0.39998715	0.37102923	0.34423035	0.31942487
32	0.38833703	0.35935035	0.33258971	0.30787940
33	0.37702625	0.34803908	0.32134271	0.29675123
34	0.36604490	0.33708385	0.31047605	0.28602528
35	0.35538340	0.32647346	0.29997686	0.27568702
36	0.35503243	0.31619706	0.28983272	0.26572242
37	0.33498294	0.30624413	0.28003161	0.25611800
38	0.32522615	0.29660448	0.27056194	0.24686072
39	0.31575355	0.28726826	0.26141250	0.23793805
40	0.30655684	0.27822592	0.25257247	0.22933788
41	0.29762800	0.26946820	0.24403137	0.22104855
42	0.28895922	0.26098615	0.23577910	0.21305885
43	0.28054294	0.25277109	0.22780590	0.20535793
44	0.27237178	0.24481462	0.22010231	0.19793535
45	0.26443862	0.23710859	0.21265924	0.19078106
46	0.25673653	0.22964512	0.20546787	0.18388536
47	0.24925876	0.22241658	0.19851968	0.17723890
48	0.24199880	0.21541558	0.19180645	0.17083268
49	0.23495029	0.20863494	0.18532024	0.16465800
50	0.22810708	0.20206774	0.17905337	0.15870651

PRESENT VALUE $1/(1 + i)^n$ (Continued)

Periods n	Rate i			
	0.04(4%)	0.0425(4 1/4%)	0.045(4 1/2%)	0.0475(4 3/4%)
1	0.96153846	0.95923261	0.95693780	0.95465894
2	0.92455621	0.92012721	0.91572995	0.91136414
3	0.88899636	0.88261603	0.87629660	0.87003737
4	0.85480419	0.84663408	0.83856134	0.83058460
5	0.82192711	0.81211902	0.80245105	0.79292086
6	0.79031453	0.77901105	0.76789574	0.75696502
7	0.75991781	0.74725281	0.73482846	0.72263964
8	0.73069021	0.71678926	0.70318513	0.68987077
9	0.70258674	0.68756764	0.67290443	0.65858785
10	0.67556417	0.65953730	0.64392768	0.62872349
11	0.64958093	0.63264969	0.61619874	0.60021335
12	0.62459705	0.60685822	0.58966386	0.57299604
13	0.60057409	0.58211819	0.56427164	0.54701293
14	0.57747508	0.55838676	0.53997286	0.52220804
15	0.55526450	0.53562279	0.51672044	0.49852797
16	0.53390818	0.51378685	0.49446932	0.47592169
17	0.51337325	0.49284110	0.47317639	0.45434051
18	0.49362812	0.47274926	0.45280037	0.43373796
19	0.47464242	0.45347650	0.43330179	0.41406965
20	0.45638695	0.43498945	0.41464286	0.39529322
21	0.43883360	0.41725607	0.39678743	0.37736823
22	0.41295539	0.40024563	0.37970089	0.36025607
23	0.40572633	0.38392866	0.36335013	0.34391987
24	0.39012147	0.36827689	0.34770347	0.32832446
25	0.37511680	0.35326321	0.33273060	0.31343624
26	0.36068923	0.33886159	0.31840248	0.29922314
27	0.34681657	0.32504709	0.30469137	0.28565455
28	0.33347747	0.31179577	0.29157069	0.27270124
29	0.32065141	0.29908467	0.27901502	0.26033531
30	0.30831867	0.28689177	0.26700002	0.24853013
31	0.29646026	0.27519594	0.25550241	0.23726027
32	0.28505794	0.26397692	0.24449991	0.22650145
33	0.27409417	0.25321527	0.23397121	0.21623050
34	0.26355209	0.24289235	0.22389589	0.20642530
35	0.25341547	0.23299026	0.21425444	0.19706473
36	0.24366872	0.22349186	0.20502817	0.18812862
37	0.23429685	0.21438068	0.19619921	0.17959772
38	0.22528543	0.20564094	0.18775044	0.17134367
39	0.21662061	0.19725750	0.17966549	0.16367893
40	0.20828904	0.18921582	0.17192870	0.17145367
41	0.20027793	0.18150199	0.16452507	0.14917110
42	0.19257493	0.17410263	0.15744026	0.14240678
43	0.18516820	0.16700492	0.15066054	0.13594919
44	0.17804635	0.16019657	0.14417276	0.12978443
45	0.17119841	0.15366577	0.13796437	0.12389922
46	0.16461386	0.14740122	0.13202332	0.11828088
47	0.15828256	0.14139206	0.12633810	0.11291731
48	0.15219476	0.13562787	0.12089771	0.10779695
49	0.14634112	0.13009868	0.11569158	0.10290878
50	0.14071262	0.12479489	0.11070965	0.09824228

Financial Tables

PRESENT VALUE $1/(1 + i)^n$ (Continued)

Periods n	Rate i			
	0.05(5%)	0.0525(5 1/4%)	0.055(5 1/2%)	0.0575(5 3/4%)
1	0.95238095	0.95011876	0.94786730	0.94562648
2	0.90702948	0.90272567	0.89845242	0.89420944
3	0.86383760	0.85769660	0.85161366	0.84558812
4	0.82270247	0.81491363	0.80721674	0.79961051
5	0.78352617	0.77426473	0.76513434	0.75613287
6	0.74621540	0.73564345	0.72524583	0.71501927
7	0.71068133	0.69894865	0.68743681	0.67614115
8	0.67683936	0.66408423	0.65159887	0.63937697
9	0.64460892	0.63095888	0.61762926	0.60461180
10	0.61391325	0.59948588	0.58543058	0.57173692
11	0.58467929	0.56958278	0.55491050	0.54064957
12	0.55683742	0.54117129	0.52598152	0.51125255
13	0.53032135	0.51417699	0.49856068	0.48345395
14	0.50506795	0.48852921	0.47256937	0.45716685
15	0.48101710	0.46416077	0.44793305	0.43230908
16	0.45811152	0.44100786	0.42458109	0.40880291
17	0.43629669	0.41900984	0.40244653	0.38657486
18	0.41552065	0.39810911	0.38146590	0.36555542
19	0.39573396	0.37825094	0.36157906	0.34567889
20	0.37688948	0.35938331	0.34272896	0.32688311
21	0.35894236	0.34145683	0.32486158	0.30910932
22	0.34184987	0.32442454	0.30792567	0.29230196
23	0.32557131	0.30824185	0.29187267	0.27640847
24	0.31006791	0.29286636	0.27665656	0.26137917
25	0.29530277	0.27825783	0.26223370	0.24716706
26	0.28124073	0.26437798	0.24856275	0.23372772
27	0.26784832	0.25119048	0.23560450	0.22101912
28	0.25509364	0.23866079	0.22332181	0.20900153
29	0.24294632	0.22675609	0.21167944	0.19763738
30	0.23137745	0.21544522	0.20064402	0.18689114
31	0.22035947	0.20469855	0.19018390	0.17672921
32	0.20986617	0.19448793	0.18026910	0.16711982
33	0.19987254	0.18478663	0.17087119	0.15803293
34	0.19035480	0.17556925	0.16196321	0.14944012
35	0.18129029	0.16681164	0.15341963	0.14131454
36	0.17265741	0.15849087	0.14551624	0.13363077
37	0.16443563	0.15058515	0.13793008	0.12636479
38	0.15660536	0.14307377	0.13073941	0.11949389
39	0.14914797	0.13593708	0.12392362	0.11299659
40	0.14204568	0.12915637	0.11746314	0.10685257
41	0.13528160	0.12271389	0.11133947	0.10104262
42	0.12883962	0.11659277	0.10553504	0.09554857
43	0.12270440	0.11077698	0.10003322	0.09035326
44	0.11686133	0.10525128	0.09481822	0.08544044
45	0.11129651	0.10000122	0.08987509	0.08079474
46	0.10599668	0.09501304	0.08518965	0.07640164
47	0.10094921	0.09027367	0.08074849	0.07224742
48	0.09614211	0.08577071	0.07653885	0.06831907
49	0.09156391	0.08149236	0.07254867	0.06460432
50	0.08720373	0.07742742	0.06876652	0.06109156

PRESENT VALUE $1/(1 + i)^n$ (Continued)

Rate i

Periods n	0.06(6%)	0.0625(6 1/4%)	0.065(6 1/2%)	0.0675(6 3/4%)
1	0.94339623	0.94117647	0.93896714	0.93676815
2	0.88999644	0.88581315	0.88165928	0.87753457
3	0.83961928	0.83370649	0.82784909	0.82204643
4	0.79209366	0.78466493	0.77732309	0.77006692
5	0.74725817	0.73850817	0.72988084	0.72137416
6	0.70496054	0.69506652	0.68533412	0.67576034
7	0.66505711	0.65418025	0.64350621	0.63303076
8	0.62741237	0.61569906	0.60423119	0.59300305
9	0.59189846	0.57948147	0.56735323	0.55550637
10	0.55839478	0.54539432	0.53272604	0.52038068
11	0.52678753	0.51331230	0.50021224	0.48747605
12	0.49696936	0.48311746	0.46968285	0.45665203
13	0.46883902	0.45469879	0.44101676	0.42777708
14	0.44230096	0.42795180	0.41410025	0.40072794
15	0.41726506	0.40277817	0.38882652	0.37538917
16	0.39364628	0.37908533	0.36509533	0.35165262
17	0.37136442	0.35678619	0.34281251	0.32941698
18	0.35034379	0.33579877	0.32188969	0.30858733
19	0.33051301	0.31604590	0.30224384	0.28907478
20	0.31180473	0.29745497	0.28379703	0.27079605
21	0.29415540	0.27995762	0.26647608	0.25367312
22	0.27750510	0.26348952	0.25021228	0.23763289
23	0.26179726	0.24799014	0.23494111	0.22260693
24	0.24697855	0.23340248	0.22060198	0.20853108
25	0.23299863	0.21967202	0.20713801	0.19534527
26	0.21981003	0.20675099	0.19449579	0.18299323
27	0.20736795	0.19458917	0.18262515	0.17142223
28	0.19563014	0.18314274	0.17147902	0.16058289
29	0.18455674	0.17236964	0.16101316	0.15042893
30	0.17411013	0.16223025	0.15118607	0.14091703
31	0.16425484	0.15268729	0.14195875	0.13200659
32	0.15495740	0.14370569	0.13329460	0.12365957
33	0.14618622	0.13525241	0.12515925	0.11584034
34	0.13791153	0.12729639	0.11752042	0.10851554
35	0.13010522	0.11980837	0.11034781	0.10165391
36	0.12274077	0.11276081	0.10361297	0.09522614
37	0.11579318	0.10612783	0.09728917	0.08920482
38	0.10923885	0.09988501	0.09135134	0.08356423
39	0.10305552	0.09400942	0.08577590	0.07828031
40	0.09722219	0.08847946	0.08054075	0.07333050
41	0.09171905	0.08327478	0.07562512	0.06869368
42	0.08652740	0.07837627	0.07100950	0.06435005
43	0.08162962	0.07376590	0.06667559	0.06028108
44	0.07700908	0.06942673	0.06260619	0.05646939
45	0.07265007	0.06534280	0.05878515	0.05289873
46	0.06853781	0.06149911	0.05519733	0.04955384
47	0.06465831	0.05788151	0.05182848	0.04642046
48	0.06099840	0.05447672	0.04866524	0.04348521
49	0.05754566	0.05127221	0.04569506	0.04073556
50	0.05428836	0.04825619	0.04290616	0.03815978

PRESENT VALUE $1/(1 + i)^n$ (Continued)

Periods n	Rate i 0.07(7%)	0.0725(7 1/4%)	0.075(7 1/2%)	0.0775(7 3/4%)
1	0.93457944	0.93240093	0.93023256	0.92807425
2	0.87343873	0.86937150	0.86533261	0.86132181
3	0.81629788	0.81060280	0.80496057	0.79937059
4	0.76289521	0.75580680	0.74880053	0.74187525
5	0.71298618	0.70471497	0.69655863	0.68851532
6	0.66634222	0.65707689	0.64796152	0.63899333
7	0.62274974	0.61265911	0.60275490	0.59303326
8	0.58200910	0.57124392	0.56070223	0.55037889
9	0.54393374	0.53262837	0.52158347	0.51079247
10	0.50834929	0.49662319	0.48519393	0.47405334
11	0.47509280	0.46305192	0.45134319	0.43995670
12	0.44401196	0.43175004	0.41985413	0.40831248
13	0.41496445	0.40256414	0.39056198	0.37894430
14	0.38781724	0.37535118	0.36331347	0.35168844
15	0.36244602	0.34997779	0.33796602	0.32639299
16	0.33873460	0.32631962	0.31438699	0.30291692
17	0.31657439	0.30426072	0.29245302	0.28112940
18	0.29586392	0.28369298	0.27204932	0.26090895
19	0.27650833	0.26451560	0.25306913	0.24214288
20	0.25841900	0.24663459	0.23541315	0.22472657
21	0.24151309	0.22996232	0.21898897	0.20856294
22	0.22571317	0.21441708	0.20371067	0.19356190
23	0.21094688	0.19992269	0.18949830	0.17963981
24	0.19714662	0.18640810	0.17627749	0.16671908
25	0.18424918	0.17380709	0.16397906	0.15472769
26	0.17219549	0.16205789	0.15253866	0.14359878
27	0.16093037	0.15110293	0.14189643	0.13327033
28	0.15040221	0.14088851	0.13199668	0.12368476
29	0.14056282	0.13136458	0.12278761	0.11478864
30	0.13136712	0.12248446	0.11422103	0.10653238
31	0.12277301	0.11420462	0.10625212	0.09886996
32	0.11474113	0.10648449	0.09883918	0.09175866
33	0.10723470	0.09928624	0.09194343	0.08515885
34	0.10021934	0.09257458	0.08552877	0.07903374
35	0.09366294	0.08631663	0.07956164	0.07334918
36	0.08753546	0.08048171	0.07401083	0.06807348
37	0.08180884	0.07504122	0.06884729	0.06317724
38	0.07645686	0.06996850	0.06404399	0.05863317
39	0.07145501	0.06523870	0.05957580	0.05441594
40	0.06678038	0.06082862	0.05541935	0.05050203
41	0.06241157	0.05671666	0.05155288	0.04686963
42	0.05832857	0.05288267	0.04795617	0.04349850
43	0.05451268	0.04930785	0.04461039	0.04036984
44	0.05094643	0.04597468	0.04149804	0.03746621
45	0.04761349	0.04286684	0.03860283	0.03477142
46	0.04449859	0.03996908	0.03590961	0.03227046
47	0.04158747	0.03726721	0.03340428	0.02994938
48	0.03886679	0.03474798	0.03107375	0.02779525
49	0.03632410	0.03239905	0.02890582	0.02579606
50	0.03394776	0.03020890	0.02688913	0.02394066

PRESENT VALUE $1/(1 + i)^n$ (Continued)

Periods		Rate i		
n	0.08(8%)	0.0825(8 1/4%)	0.085(8 1/2%)	0.0875(8 3/4%)
1	0.92592593	0.92378753	0.92165899	0.91954023
2	0.85733882	0.85338340	0.84945529	0.84555423
3	0.79383224	0.78834494	0.78290810	0.77752114
4	0.73502985	0.72826322	0.72157428	0.71496196
5	0.68058320	0.67276048	0.66504542	0.65743629
6	0.63016963	0.62148775	0.61294509	0.60453912
7	0.58349040	0.57412263	0.56492635	0.55589804
8	0.54026888	0.53036732	0.52066945	0.51117061
9	0.50024897	0.48994672	0.47987968	0.47004194
10	0.46319349	0.45260667	0.44228542	0.43222247
11	0.42888286	0.41811240	0.40763633	0.39744595
12	0.39711376	0.38624702	0.37570168	0.36546754
13	0.36769792	0.35681018	0.34626883	0.33606211
14	0.34046104	0.32961679	0.31914178	0.30902263
15	0.31524170	0.30449588	0.29413989	0.28415874
16	0.29189047	0.28128950	0.27109667	0.26129539
17	0.27026895	0.25985173	0.24985869	0.24027162
18	0.25024903	0.24004779	0.23028450	0.22093942
19	0.23171206	0.22175315	0.21224378	0.20316269
20	0.21454821	0.20485280	0.19561639	0.18681627
21	0.19865575	0.18924046	0.18029160	0.17178507
22	0.18394051	0.17481798	0.16616738	0.15796328
23	0.17031528	0.16149467	0.15314965	0.14525360
24	0.15769934	0.14918676	0.14115176	0.13356652
25	0.14601790	0.13781687	0.13009378	0.12281979
26	0.13520176	0.12731350	0.11990210	0.11293774
27	0.12518682	0.11761063	0.11050885	0.10385080
28	0.11591372	0.10864723	0.10185148	0.09549498
29	0.10732752	0.10036696	0.09387233	0.08781148
30	0.09937733	0.09271774	0.08651828	0.08074619
31	0.09201605	0.08565149	0.07974035	0.07424937
32	0.08520005	0.07912378	0.07349341	0.06827528
33	0.07888893	0.07309356	0.06773586	0.06278187
34	0.07304531	0.06752292	0.06242936	0.05773045
35	0.06763454	0.06237683	0.05753858	0.05308547
36	0.06262458	0.05762294	0.05303095	0.04881423
37	0.05798572	0.05323135	0.04887645	0.04488665
38	0.05369048	0.04917446	0.04504742	0.04127508
39	0.04971341	0.04542675	0.04151836	0.03795410
40	0.04603093	0.04196467	0.03826577	0.03490032
41	0.04262123	0.03876644	0.03526799	0.03209225
42	0.03946411	0.03581195	0.03250506	0.02951011
43	0.03654084	0.03308263	0.02995858	0.02713573
44	0.03383411	0.03056132	0.02761160	0.02495240
45	0.03132788	0.02823217	0.02544848	0.02294474
46	0.02900730	0.02608053	0.02345482	0.02109861
47	0.02685861	0.02409287	0.02161734	0.01940102
48	0.02486908	0.02225669	0.01992382	0.01784002
49	0.02302693	0.02056045	0.01836297	0.01640461
50	0.02132123	0.01899349	0.01692439	0.01508470

Financial Tables

PRESENT VALUE $1/(1 + i)^n$ (Continued)

Periods		Rate i		
n	0.09(9%)	0.0925(9 1/4%)	0.095(9 1/2%)	0.0975(9 3/4%)
1	0.91743119	0.91533181	0.91324201	0.91116173
2	0.84167999	0.83783232	0.83401097	0.83021570
3	0.77218348	0.76689457	0.76165385	0.75646077
4	0.70842521	0.70196299	0.69557429	0.68925811
5	0.64993139	0.64252906	0.63522767	0.62802561
6	0.59626733	0.58812728	0.58011659	0.57223290
7	0.54703424	0.53833161	0.52978684	0.52139672
8	0.50186628	0.49275204	0.48382360	0.47507674
9	0.46042778	0.45103162	0.44184803	0.43287175
10	0.42241081	0.41284359	0.40351419	0.39441617
11	0.38753285	0.37788887	0.36850611	0.35937692
12	0.35553473	0.34589370	0.33653626	0.32745050
13	0.32617865	0.31660751	0.30733813	0.29836036
14	0.29924647	0.28980092	0.28067410	0.27185454
15	0.27453804	0.26526400	0.25632337	0.24770346
16	0.25186976	0.24280458	0.23408527	0.22569791
17	0.23107318	0.22224675	0.21377651	0.20564730
18	0.21199374	0.20342952	0.19522969	0.18737795
19	0.19448967	0.18620551	0.17829195	0.17073162
20	0.17843089	0.17043983	0.16282370	0.15556411
21	0.16369806	0.15600900	0.14869744	0.14174407
22	0.15018171	0.14280000	0.13579675	0.12915177
23	0.13778139	0.13070938	0.12401530	0.11767815
24	0.12640044	0.11964245	0.11325598	0.10722383
25	0.11596784	0.10951254	0.10343012	0.09769825
26	0.10639251	0.10024031	0.09445673	0.08901891
27	0.09760781	0.09175315	0.08626185	0.08111062
28	0.08954845	0.08398457	0.07877795	0.07390489
29	0.08215454	0.07687375	0.07194333	0.06733931
30	0.07537114	0.07036499	0.06570167	0.06135700
31	0.06914783	0.06440731	0.06000153	0.05590615
32	0.06343838	0.05895406	0.05479592	0.05093955
33	0.05820035	0.05396253	0.05004193	0.04641417
34	0.05339481	0.04939362	0.04570039	0.04229081
35	0.04898607	0.04521155	0.04173552	0.03853377
36	0.04494135	0.04138357	0.03811463	0.03511050
37	0.04123059	0.03787970	0.03480788	0.03199134
38	0.03782623	0.03467249	0.03178802	0.02914928
39	0.03470296	0.03173684	0.02903015	0.02655971
40	0.03183758	0.02904973	0.02651156	0.02420019
41	0.02920879	0.02659015	0.02421147	0.02205029
42	0.02679706	0.02433881	0.02211093	0.02009138
43	0.02458446	0.02227808	0.02019263	0.01830650
44	0.02255455	0.02039184	0.01844076	0.01668018
45	0.02069224	0.01866530	0.01684087	0.01519834
46	0.01898371	0.01708494	0.01537979	0.01384815
47	0.01741625	0.01563839	0.01404547	0.01261790
48	0.01597821	0.01431432	0.01282692	0.01149695
49	0.01465891	0.01310235	0.01171408	0.01047558
50	0.01344854	0.01199300	0.01069779	0.00954495

PRESENT VALUE $1/(1 + i)^n$ (Continued)

Periods n	Rate i			
	0.10(10%)	0.1025(10 1/4%)	0.105(10 1/2%)	0.1075(10 3/4%)
1	0.90909091	0.90702948	0.90497738	0.90293454
2	0.82644628	0.82270247	0.81898405	0.81529078
3	0.75131480	0.74621540	0.74116204	0.73615420
4	0.68301346	0.67683936	0.67073487	0.66469905
5	0.62092132	0.61391325	0.60699989	0.60017973
6	0.56447393	0.55683742	0.54932116	0.54192301
7	0.51315812	0.50506795	0.49712323	0.48932100
8	0.46650738	0.45811152	0.44988527	0.44182483
9	0.42409762	0.41552065	0.40713599	0.39893890
10	0.38554329	0.37688948	0.36844886	0.36021571
11	0.35049390	0.34184987	0.33343788	0.32525121
12	0.31863082	0.31006791	0.30175374	0.29368055
13	0.28966438	0.28124073	0.27308031	0.26517431
14	0.26333125	0.25509364	0.24713150	0.23943504
15	0.23939205	0.23137745	0.22364842	0.21619417
16	0.21762914	0.20986617	0.20239676	0.19520918
17	0.19784467	0.19035480	0.18316449	0.17626111
18	0.17985879	0.17265741	0.16575972	0.15915225
19	0.16350799	0.15660536	0.15000879	0.14370406
20	0.14864363	0.14204568	0.13575456	0.12975536
21	0.13513057	0.12883962	0.12285481	0.11716059
22	0.12284597	0.11686133	0.11118082	0.10578835
23	0.11167816	0.10599668	0.10061613	0.09551995
24	0.10152560	0.09614211	0.09105532	0.08624826
25	0.09229600	0.08720373	0.08240301	0.07787654
26	0.08390545	0.07909635	0.07457286	0.07031741
27	0.07627768	0.07174272	0.06748675	0.06349202
28	0.06934335	0.06507276	0.06107398	0.05732914
29	0.06303941	0.05902291	0.05527057	0.05176446
30	0.05730855	0.05353552	0.05001861	0.04673992
31	0.05209868	0.04855830	0.04526571	0.04220309
32	0.04736244	0.04404381	0.04096445	0.03810662
33	0.04305676	0.03994903	0.03707190	0.03440779
34	0.03914251	0.03623495	0.03354923	0.03106798
35	0.03558410	0.03286617	0.03036129	0.02805235
36	0.03234918	0.20981058	0.02747628	0.02532944
37	0.02940835	0.02703908	0.02486542	0.02287082
38	0.02673486	0.02452524	0.02250264	0.02065086
39	0.02430442	0.02224512	0.02036438	0.01864637
40	0.02209493	0.02017698	0.01842930	0.01683645
41	0.02008630	0.01830111	0.01667810	0.01520221
42	0.01826027	0.01659965	0.01509330	0.01372660
43	0.01660025	0.01505637	0.01365910	0.01239423
44	0.01509113	0.01365657	0.01236118	0.01119117
45	0.01371921	0.01238691	0.01118658	0.01010490
46	0.01247201	0.01123530	0.01012361	0.00912406
47	0.01133819	0.01019074	0.00916163	0.00823843
48	0.01030745	0.00924331	0.00829107	0.00743876
49	0.00937041	0.00838395	0.00750323	0.00671672
50	0.00851855	0.00760449	0.00679026	0.00606475

Financial Tables

PRESENT VALUE $1/(1 + i)^n$ (Continued)

Periods n	Rate i			
	0.11(11%)	0.1125(11 1/4%)	0.115(11 1/2%)	0.1175(11 3/4%)
1	0.90090090	0.89887640	0.89686099	0.89485459
2	0.81162243	0.80797879	0.80435963	0.80076473
3	0.73119138	0.72627307	0.72139877	0.71656799
4	0.65873097	0.65282973	0.64699441	0.64122415
5	0.59345133	0.58681324	0.58026405	0.57380237
6	0.53464084	0.52747257	0.52041619	0.51346969
7	0.48165841	0.47413265	0.46674097	0.45948070
8	0.43392650	0.42618665	0.41860177	0.41116841
9	0.39092477	0.38308912	0.37542760	0.36793594
10	0.35218448	0.34434977	0.33670636	0.32924916
11	0.31728331	0.30952789	0.30197880	0.29463013
12	0.28584082	0.27822731	0.27083301	0.26365112
13	0.25751426	0.25009197	0.24289956	0.23592941
14	0.23199482	0.22480177	0.21784714	0.21112252
15	0.20900435	0.20206901	0.19537860	0.18892395
16	0.18829220	0.18163506	0.17522744	0.16905947
17	0.16963262	0.16326747	0.15715466	0.15128364
18	0.15282218	0.14675728	0.14094588	0.13537686
19	0.13767764	0.13191665	0.12640886	0.12114260
20	0.12403391	0.11857677	0.11337118	0.10840501
21	0.11174226	0.10658586	0.10167818	0.09700672
22	0.10066870	0.09580751	0.09119120	0.08680691
23	0.09069252	0.08611911	0.08178583	0.07767956
24	0.08170498	0.07741044	0.07335052	0.06951191
25	0.07360809	0.06958242	0.06578522	0.06220305
26	0.06631359	0.06254599	0.05900020	0.05566269
27	0.05974197	0.05622112	0.05291497	0.04981001
28	0.05382160	0.05053584	0.04745738	0.04457272
29	0.04848793	0.04542547	0.04256267	0.03988610
30	0.04368282	0.04083188	0.03817280	0.03569226
31	0.03935389	0.03670282	0.03423569	0.03193938
32	0.03545395	0.03299130	0.03070466	0.02858110
33	0.03194050	0.02965510	0.02753781	0.02557593
34	0.02877522	0.02665627	0.02469759	0.02288674
35	0.02592363	0.02396069	0.02215030	0.02048030
36	0.02335462	0.02153770	0.01986574	0.01832689
37	0.02104020	0.01935973	0.01781681	0.01639990
38	0.01895513	0.01740200	0.01597920	0.01467553
39	0.01707670	0.01564225	0.01433112	0.01313247
40	0.01538441	0.01406045	0.01285302	0.01175165
41	0.01385983	0.01263861	0.01152738	0.01051601
42	0.01248633	0.01136055	0.01033845	0.00941030
43	0.01124895	0.01021173	0.00927216	0.00842085
44	0.01013419	0.00917908	0.00831583	0.00753544
45	0.00912990	0.00825086	0.00745815	0.00674312
46	0.00822513	0.00741650	0.00668892	0.00603411
47	0.00741005	0.00666652	0.00599903	0.00539965
48	0.00667570	0.00599238	0.00538030	0.00483191
49	0.00601415	0.00538641	0.00482538	0.00432385
50	0.00541815	0.00484171	0.00432769	0.00386922

PRESENT VALUE $1/(1 + i)^n$ (Continued)

Periods n	Rate i			
	0.12(12%)	0.1225(12 1/4%)	0.125(12 1/2%)	0.1275(12 3/4%)
1	0.89285714	0.89086860	0.88888889	0.88691796
2	0.79719388	0.79364686	0.79012346	0.78662347
3	0.71178025	0.70703506	0.70233196	0.69767048
4	0.63551808	0.62987533	0.62429508	0.61877648
5	0.56742686	0.56113615	0.55492896	0.54880397
6	0.50663112	0.49989858	0.49327018	0.48674410
7	0.45234922	0.44534395	0.43846239	0.43170208
8	0.40388323	0.39674294	0.38974434	0.38288433
9	0.36061002	0.35344582	0.34643942	0.33958699
10	0.32197324	0.31487378	0.30794615	0.30118580
11	0.28747610	0.28051117	0.27372991	0.26712710
12	0.25667509	0.24989859	0.24331547	0.23691982
13	0.22917419	0.22262681	0.21628042	0.21012844
14	0.20461981	0.19833123	0.19224926	0.18636669
15	0.18269626	0.17668706	0.17088823	0.16529196
16	0.16312166	0.15740496	0.15190065	0.14660041
17	0.14564434	0.14022713	0.13502280	0.13002254
18	0.13003959	0.12492395	0.12002027	0.11531932
19	0.11610678	0.11129082	0.10668468	0.10227878
20	0.10366677	0.09914550	0.09483083	0.09071289
21	0.09255961	0.08832561	0.08429407	0.08045489
22	0.08264251	0.07868651	0.07492806	0.07135689
23	0.07378796	0.07009934	0.06660272	0.06328770
24	0.06588210	0.06244930	0.05920242	0.05613100
25	0.05882331	0.05563412	0.05262437	0.04978359
26	0.05252081	0.04956269	0.04677722	0.04415396
27	0.04689358	0.04415385	0.04157975	0.03916094
28	0.04186927	0.03933528	0.03695978	0.03473254
29	0.03738327	0.03504256	0.03285314	0.03080492
30	0.03337792	0.03121832	0.02920279	0.02732143
31	0.02980172	0.02781142	0.02595803	0.02423187
32	0.02660868	0.02477632	0.02307381	0.02149168
33	0.02375775	0.02207245	0.02051005	0.01906136
34	0.02121227	0.01966365	0.01823116	0.01690586
35	0.01893953	0.01751773	0.01620547	0.01499411
36	0.01691029	0.01560599	0.01440486	0.01329855
37	0.01509848	0.01390289	0.01280432	0.01179472
38	0.01348078	0.01238565	0.01138162	0.01046095
39	0.01203641	0.01103398	0.01011700	0.00927800
40	0.01074680	0.00982983	0.00899289	0.00822883
41	0.00959536	0.00875709	0.00799368	0.00729830
42	0.00856728	0.00780141	0.00710549	0.00647299
43	0.00764936	0.00695003	0.00631599	0.00574101
44	0.00682978	0.00619157	0.00561421	0.00509181
45	0.00609802	0.00551587	0.00499041	0.00451601
46	0.00544466	0.00491392	0.00443592	0.00400533
47	0.00486131	0.00437766	0.00394304	0.00355240
48	0.00434045	0.00389992	0.00350493	0.00315069
49	0.00387540	0.00347431	0.00311549	0.00279440
50	0.00346018	0.00309516	0.00276932	0.00247841

Financial Tables

PRESENT VALUE $1/(1 + i)^n$ (Continued)

Periods	Rate i			
n	0.13(13%)	0.1325(13 1/4%)	0.135(13 1/2%)	0.1375(13 3/4%)
1	0.88495575	0.88300221	0.88105727	0.87912088
2	0.78314668	0.77969290	0.77626191	0.77285352
3	0.69305016	0.68847055	0.68393120	0.67943167
4	0.61331873	0.60792102	0.60258255	0.59730256
5	0.54275994	0.53679560	0.53090974	0.52510115
6	0.48031853	0.47399170	0.46776188	0.46162739
7	0.42506064	0.41853572	0.41212501	0.40582628
8	0.37615986	0.36956796	0.36310573	0.35677035
9	0.33288483	0.32632933	0.31991695	0.31364427
10	0.29458835	0.28814952	0.28186515	0.27573122
11	0.26069765	0.25443666	0.24833934	0.24240107
12	0.23070589	0.22466813	0.21880118	0.21309985
13	0.20416450	0.19838246	0.19277637	0.18734052
14	0.18067655	0.17517215	0.16984702	0.16469497
15	0.15989075	0.15467739	0.14964495	0.14478678
16	0.14149624	0.13658048	0.13184577	0.12728508
17	0.12521791	0.12060086	0.11616368	0.11189898
18	0.11081231	0.10649083	0.10234685	0.09837273
19	0.09806399	0.09403164	0.09017344	0.08648152
20	0.08678229	0.08303014	0.07944796	0.07602771
21	0.07679849	0.07331580	0.06999821	0.06683754
22	0.06796327	0.06473801	0.06167243	0.05875828
23	0.06014448	0.05716381	0.05433694	0.05165563
24	0.05322521	0.05047577	0.04787396	0.04541154
25	0.04710195	0.04457022	0.04217970	0.03992224
26	0.04168314	0.03935560	0.03716273	0.03509647
27	0.03688774	0.03475108	0.03274249	0.03085404
28	0.03264402	0.03068528	0.02884801	0.02712443
29	0.02888851	0.02709517	0.02541675	0.02384565
30	0.02556505	0.02392510	0.02239361	0.02096321
31	0.02262394	0.02112591	0.01973005	0.01842920
32	0.02002119	0.01865423	0.01738331	0.01620149
33	0.01771786	0.01647172	0.01531569	0.01424307
34	0.01567953	0.01454457	0.01349400	0.01252138
35	0.01387569	0.01284289	0.01188899	0.01100781
36	0.01227937	0.01134030	0.01047488	0.00967719
37	0.01086670	0.01001351	0.00922897	0.00850742
38	0.00961655	0.00884195	0.00813125	0.00747905
39	0.00851022	0.00780746	0.00716410	0.00657499
40	0.00753117	0.00689400	0.00631198	0.00578021
41	0.00666475	0.00608742	0.00556121	0.00508151
42	0.00589801	0.00537521	0.00489975	0.00446726
43	0.00521948	0.00474632	0.00431696	0.00392726
44	0.00461901	0.00419101	0.00380349	0.00345254
45	0.00408762	0.00370067	0.00335109	0.00303520
46	0.00361736	0.00326770	0.00295250	0.00266830
47	0.00320120	0.00288539	0.00260132	0.00234576
48	0.00283292	0.00254780	0.00229192	0.00206221
49	0.00250701	0.00224972	0.00201931	0.00181293
50	0.00221859	0.00198650	0.00177913	0.00159378

PRESENT VALUE $1/(1 + i)^n$ (Continued)

Rate i

Periods n	0.14(14%)	0.1425(14 1/4%)	0.145(14 1/2%)	0.1475(14 3/4%)
1	0.87719298	0.87527352	0.87336245	0.87145969
2	0.76946753	0.76610374	0.76276196	0.75944200
3	0.67497152	0.67055032	0.66616765	0.66182309
4	0.59208028	0.58691494	0.58180581	0.57675215
5	0.51936866	0.51371111	0.50812734	0.50261625
6	0.45558655	0.44963773	0.44377934	0.43800981
7	0.39963732	0.39355600	0.38758021	0.38170789
8	0.35055905	0.34446915	0.33849800	0.33264304
9	0.30750794	0.30150472	0.29563144	0.28988501
10	0.26974381	0.26389910	0.25819340	0.25262310
11	0.23661738	0.23098390	0.22549642	0.22015085
12	0.20755910	0.20217409	0.19694010	0.19185259
13	0.18206939	0.17695763	0.17200009	0.16719180
14	0.15970999	0.15488633	0.15021842	0.14570092
15	0.14009648	0.13556790	0.13119513	0.12697248
16	0.12289165	0.11865899	0.11458090	0.11065139
17	0.10779969	0.10385908	0.10007065	0.09642823
18	0.09456113	0.09090510	0.08739795	0.08403332
19	0.08294836	0.07956683	0.07633009	0.07323165
20	0.07276172	0.06964274	0.06666383	0.06381843
21	0.06382607	0.06095644	0.05822169	0.05561519
22	0.05598778	0.05335356	0.05084863	0.04846640
23	0.04911209	0.04669896	0.04440929	0.04223651
24	0.04308078	0.04087436	0.03878640	0.03680742
25	0.03779016	0.03577625	0.03387372	0.03207618
26	0.03314926	0.03131400	0.02958403	0.02795310
27	0.02907830	0.02740832	0.02583758	0.02436000
28	0.02550728	0.02398977	0.02256557	0.02122876
29	0.02237481	0.02099761	0.01970792	0.01850001
30	0.01962702	0.01837866	0.01721216	0.01612201
31	0.01721669	0.01608635	0.01503246	0.01404968
32	0.01510236	0.01407996	0.01312878	0.01224373
33	0.01324768	0.01232381	0.01146618	0.01066992
34	0.01162077	0.01078671	0.01001414	0.00929840
35	0.01019366	0.00944132	0.00874597	0.00810318
36	0.00894181	0.00826374	0.00763840	0.00706160
37	0.00784369	0.00723303	0.00667109	0.00615390
38	0.00688043	0.00633088	0.00582628	0.00536287
39	0.00603547	0.00554125	0.00508846	0.00467353
40	0.00529427	0.00485011	0.00444407	0.00407279
41	0.00464410	0.00424517	0.00388128	0.00354927
42	0.00407377	0.00371569	0.00338976	0.00309305
43	0.00357348	0.00325224	0.00296049	0.00269547
44	0.00313463	0.00284660	0.00258558	0.00234899
45	0.00274968	0.00249156	0.00225815	0.00204705
46	0.00241200	0.00218079	0.00197218	0.00178392
47	0.00211579	0.00190879	0.00172243	0.00155462
48	0.00185595	0.00167071	0.00150431	0.00135479
49	0.00162803	0.00146233	0.00131381	0.00118064
50	0.00142810	0.00127994	0.00114743	0.00102888

PRESENT VALUE $1/(1 + i)^n$ (Continued)

Periods		Rate i		
n	0.15(15%)	0.1525(15 1/4%)	0.155(15 1/2%)	0.1575(15 3/4%)
1	0.86956522	0.86767896	0.86580087	0.86393089
2	0.75614367	0.75286678	0.74961114	0.74637657
3	0.65751623	0.65324666	0.64901397	0.64481778
4	0.57175325	0.56680838	0.56191686	0.55707799
5	0.49717674	0.49180771	0.48650810	0.48127688
6	0.43232760	0.42673120	0.42121914	0.41578996
7	0.37593704	0.37026568	0.36469189	0.35921379
8	0.32690177	0.32127174	0.31575056	0.31033589
9	0.28426241	0.27876073	0.27337711	0.26810876
10	0.24718471	0.24187482	0.23669014	0.23162744
11	0.21494322	0.20986969	0.20492652	0.20011010
12	0.18690715	0.18209952	0.17742556	0.17288129
13	0.16252796	0.15800392	0.15361521	0.14935749
14	0.14132866	0.13709668	0.13300018	0.12903455
15	0.12289449	0.11895590	0.11515167	0.11147693
16	0.10686477	0.10321553	0.09969841	0.09630836
17	0.09292589	0.08955795	0.08631897	0.08320377
18	0.08080512	0.07770754	0.07473504	0.07188231
19	0.07026532	0.06742520	0.06470566	0.06210134
20	0.06110028	0.05850343	0.05602222	0.05365127
21	0.05313068	0.05076219	0.04850409	0.04635099
22	0.04620059	0.04404529	0.04199488	0.04004405
23	0.04017443	0.03821717	0.03635920	0.03459529
24	0.03493428	0.03316023	0.03147983	0.02988794
25	0.03037764	0.02877244	0.02725526	0.02582112
26	0.02641534	0.02496524	0.02359763	0.02230766
27	0.02296986	0.02166181	0.02043085	0.01927228
28	0.01997379	0.01879550	0.01768905	0.01664991
29	0.01736851	0.01630846	0.01531519	0.01438438
30	0.01510305	0.01415051	0.01325991	0.01242711
31	0.01313309	0.01227810	0.01148044	0.01073616
32	0.01142008	0.01065345	0.00993977	0.00927530
33	0.00993050	0.00924377	0.00860586	0.00801322
34	0.00863522	0.00802063	0.00745097	0.00692287
35	0.00750889	0.00695933	0.00645105	0.00598088
36	0.00652947	0.00603846	0.00558533	0.00516707
37	0.00567780	0.00523945	0.00483578	0.00446399
38	0.00493722	0.00454616	0.00418682	0.00385658
39	0.00429323	0.00394461	0.00362495	0.00333182
40	0.00373324	0.00342265	0.00313849	0.00287846
41	0.00324630	0.00296976	0.00271731	0.00248679
42	0.00282287	0.00257680	0.00235265	0.00214841
43	0.00245467	0.00223584	0.00203692	0.00185608
44	0.00213449	0.00193999	0.00176357	0.00160353
45	0.00185608	0.00168329	0.00152690	0.00138534
46	0.00161398	0.00146055	0.00132199	0.00080244
47	0.00140346	0.00126729	0.00114458	0.00103398
48	0.00122040	0.00109960	0.00099098	0.00089329
49	0.00106122	0.00095410	0.00085799	0.00077174
50	0.00092280	0.00082785	0.00074285	0.00066673

PRESENT VALUE $1/(1 + i)^n$ (Continued)

Rate i

Periods n	0.16(16%)	0.1625(16 1/4%)	0.165(16 1/2%)	0.1675(16 3/4%)
1	0.86206897	0.86021505	0.85836910	0.85653105
2	0.74316290	0.73996994	0.73679751	0.73364544
3	0.64065767	0.63653328	0.63244421	0.62839020
4	0.55229110	0.54755551	0.54287057	0.53823563
5	0.47611302	0.47101549	0.46598332	0.46101553
6	0.41044225	0.40517462	0.39998568	0.39487411
7	0.35382953	0.34853731	0.34333535	0.33822194
8	0.30502546	0.29981704	0.29470846	0.28969759
9	0.26295298	0.25790713	0.25296863	0.24713498
10	0.22668360	0.22185559	0.21714046	0.21253532
11	0.19541690	0.19084352	0.18638666	0.18204310
12	0.16846284	0.16416647	0.15998855	0.15592557
13	0.14522659	0.14121847	0.13732923	0.13355509
14	0.12519534	0.12147825	0.11787916	0.11438408
15	0.10792701	0.10449742	0.10118383	0.09798208
16	0.09304053	0.08989026	0.08685307	0.08392470
17	0.08020735	0.07732495	0.07455199	0.07188411
18	0.06914427	0.06651609	0.06399313	0.06157097
19	0.05960713	0.05721814	0.05492972	0.05273745
20	0.05138546	0.04921990	0.04714998	0.04517126
21	0.04429781	0.04233970	0.04047208	0.03869059
22	0.03818776	0.03642125	0.03473999	0.03313969
23	0.03292049	0.03133011	0.02981973	0.02838517
24	0.02837973	0.02695063	0.02559634	0.02431278
25	0.02446528	0.02318334	0.02197110	0.02082465
26	0.02109076	0.01994266	0.01885932	0.01783696
27	0.01818169	0.01715497	0.01618825	0.01527791
28	0.01567387	0.01475697	0.01389550	0.01308601
29	0.01351196	0.01269416	0.01192747	0.01120857
30	0.01164824	0.01091971	0.01023817	0.00960049
31	0.01004159	0.00939330	0.00878813	0.00822312
32	0.00865654	0.00808026	0.00754346	0.00704335
33	0.00746253	0.00695076	0.00647507	0.00603285
34	0.00643322	0.00597915	0.00555800	0.00516732
35	0.00554588	0.00514335	0.00477082	0.00442597
36	0.00478093	0.00442439	0.00409512	0.00379098
37	0.00412149	0.00380593	0.00351512	0.00324710
38	0.00355301	0.00327392	0.00201727	0.00278124
39	0.00306294	0.00281627	0.00258994	0.00238222
40	0.00264047	0.00242260	0.00222312	0.00204044
41	0.00227626	0.00208396	0.00190826	0.00174770
42	0.00196230	0.00179265	0.00163799	0.00149696
43	0.00169163	0.00154206	0.00140600	0.00128219
44	0.00145831	0.00132651	0.00120687	0.00109824
45	0.00125716	0.00114108	0.00103594	0.00094068
46	0.00109376	0.00098158	0.00088922	0.00090572
47	0.00093427	0.00084437	0.00076328	0.00069012
48	0.00080541	0.00072643	0.00065517	0.00059111
49	0.00069432	0.00062481	0.00056238	0.00050631
50	0.00059855	0.00053747	0.00048273	0.00043367

PRESENT VALUE $1/(1 + i)^n$ (Continued)

Periods	Rate i			
n	0.17(17%)	0.1725(17 1/4%)	0.175(17 1/2%)	0.1775(17 3/4%)
1	0.85470085	0.85287846	0.85106383	0.72123728
2	0.73051355	0.72740168	0.72430964	0.72123728
3	0.62437056	0.62038522	0.61643374	0.61251574
4	0.53365005	0.52911320	0.52462446	0.52018322
5	0.45611115	0.45126925	0.44648890	0.44176919
6	0.38983859	0.38487783	0.37999055	0.37517553
7	0.33319538	0.32825401	0.32339622	0.31862041
8	0.28478237	0.27996078	0.27523082	0.27059058
9	0.24340374	0.23877252	0.23423900	0.22980092
10	0.20803738	0.20364394	0.19935234	0.19156001
11	0.17780973	0.17368353	0.16966156	0.16574099
12	0.15197413	0.14813094	0.14439282	0.10485668
13	0.12989242	0.12633769	0.12288751	0.11953858
14	0.11101916	0.10775070	0.10458511	0.10151896
15	0.09488817	0.09189825	0.08900861	0.08621568
16	0.08110100	0.07837804	0.07575201	0.07321926
17	0.06931709	0.06684694	0.06446979	0.06219196
18	0.05924538	0.05701231	0.05486791	0.05280846
19	0.05063708	0.04862458	0.04669609	0.04484795
20	0.04327955	0.04147085	0.03974135	0.03808743
21	0.03699107	0.03536960	0.03382243	0.03234601
22	0.03161630	0.03016597	0.02878505	0.02747008
23	0.02702248	0.02572790	0.02449791	0.02332915
24	0.02309614	0.02194278	0.02084929	0.01981244
25	0.01974029	0.01871452	0.01774407	0.01682585
26	0.01687204	0.01596121	0.01510134	0.01428947
27	0.01442055	0.01361297	0.01285220	0.01213543
28	0.01232525	0.01161021	0.01093805	0.01030610
29	0.01053440	0.00990210	0.00930898	0.00875253
30	0.00900376	0.00844529	0.00792253	0.00743314
31	0.00769553	0.00720280	0.00674258	0.00631265
32	0.00657737	0.00614312	0.00573837	0.00536106
33	0.00562169	0.00523933	0.00488372	0.00455292
34	0.00480486	0.00446851	0.00415635	0.00386660
35	0.00410672	0.00381110	0.00353732	0.00328373
36	0.00351002	0.00325040	0.00301049	0.00279973
37	0.00300001	0.00277220	0.00256212	0.00236835
38	0.00256411	0.00236435	0.00218052	0.00201134
39	0.00219155	0.00201650	0.00185577	0.00170814
40	0.00187312	0.00171983	0.00157938	0.00145065
41	0.00160096	0.00146681	0.00134415	0.00123198
42	0.00136834	0.00125101	0.00114396	0.00104626
43	0.00116952	0.00106696	0.00097358	0.00088855
44	0.00099959	0.00090999	0.00082858	0.00075461
45	0.00085435	0.00077611	0.00070517	0.00064085
46	0.00073021	0.00066193	0.00060015	0.00054425
47	0.00062411	0.00056454	0.00051076	0.00046221
48	0.00053343	0.00048149	0.00043469	0.00039253
49	0.00045592	0.00041065	0.00036995	0.00033336
50	0.00038968	0.00035023	0.00031485	0.00028311

PRESENT VALUE $1/(1 + i)^n$ (Continued)

Rate i

Periods n	0.18(18%)	0.1825(18 1/4%)	0.185(18 1/2%)	0.1875(18 3/4%)
1	0.84745763	0.84566596	0.84388186	0.84210526
2	0.71818443	0.71515092	0.71213659	0.70914127
3	0.60863087	0.60477879	0.60095915	0.59717160
4	0.51578888	0.51144084	0.50713852	0.50288135
5	0.43710922	0.43250811	0.42796500	0.42347903
6	0.37043154	0.36575738	0.36115189	0.35661392
7	0.31392503	0.30930857	0.30476953	0.30030646
8	0.26603816	0.26157173	0.25718948	0.25288965
9	0.22545607	0.22120231	0.21703753	0.21295970
10	0.19106447	0.18706326	0.18315404	0.17933449
11	0.16191904	0.15819303	0.15456037	0.15101852
12	0.13721953	0.13377846	0.13043069	0.12717349
13	0.11628773	0.11313189	0.11006809	0.10709346
14	0.09854893	0.09567179	0.09288447	0.09018397
15	0.08351604	0.08090638	0.07838352	0.07594439
16	0.07077630	0.06841977	0.06614643	0.06395317
17	0.05997992	0.05786027	0.05581977	0.05385530
18	0.05083044	0.04893046	0.04710529	0.04535184
19	0.04307664	0.04137883	0.03975130	0.03819102
20	0.03650563	0.03499266	0.03354540	0.03216086
21	0.03093698	0.02959211	0.02830836	0.02708283
22	0.02621778	0.02502504	0.02388891	0.02280659
23	0.02221845	0.02116282	0.02015942	0.01920555
24	0.01882920	0.01789668	0.01701217	0.01617310
25	0.01595695	0.01513461	0.01435626	0.01361945
26	0.01352284	0.01279883	0.01211499	0.01146901
27	0.01146003	0.01082353	0.01022362	0.00965811
28	0.00971189	0.00915309	0.00862752	0.00813315
29	0.00823042	0.00774046	0.00728061	0.00684897
30	0.00697493	0.00654584	0.00614398	0.00576755
31	0.00591096	0.00553560	0.00518479	0.00485689
32	0.00500929	0.00468126	0.00437535	0.00409001
33	0.00424516	0.00395879	0.00369228	0.00344422
34	0.00359759	0.00334781	0.00311585	0.00290039
35	0.00304881	0.00283113	0.00262941	0.00244244
36	0.00258373	0.00239419	0.00221891	0.00205679
37	0.00218960	0.00202469	0.00187250	0.00173203
38	0.00185560	0.00171221	0.00158017	0.00145855
39	0.00157254	0.00144796	0.00133347	0.00122826
40	0.00133266	0.00122449	0.00112529	0.00103432
41	0.00112937	0.00103551	0.00094962	0.00087101
42	0.00095710	0.00087569	0.00080136	0.00073348
43	0.00081110	0.00074054	0.00067626	0.00061767
44	0.00068737	0.00062625	0.00057068	0.00052014
45	0.00058252	0.00052960	0.00048159	0.00043801
46	0.00049366	0.00044787	0.00040640	0.00036885
47	0.00041836	0.00037874	0.00034296	0.00031061
48	0.00035454	0.00032029	0.00028941	0.00026157
49	0.00030046	0.00027086	0.00024423	0.00022027
50	0.00025462	0.00022906	0.00020610	0.00018549

Financial Tables

PRESENT VALUE $1/(1 + i)^n$ (Continued)

Periods			Rate i		
n	0.19(19%)	0.1925(19 1/4%)	0.195(19 1/2%)	0.1975(19 3/4%)	0.20(20%)
1	0.84033613	0.83857442	0.83682008	0.83507307	0.83333333
2	0.70616482	0.70320706	0.70026785	0.69734703	0.69444444
3	0.59341581	0.58969146	0.58599820	0.58233572	0.57870370
4	0.49866875	0.49450017	0.49037507	0.48629288	0.48225309
5	0.41904937	0.41467520	0.41035570	0.40609009	0.40187757
6	0.35214233	0.34773602	0.34339389	0.33911490	0.33489798
7	0.29591792	0.29160253	0.28735891	0.28318572	0.27908165
8	0.24867052	0.24453042	0.24046770	0.23648077	0.23256804
9	0.20896683	0.20505696	0.20122820	0.19747872	0.19380670
10	0.17560238	0.17195552	0.16839180	0.16490916	0.16150558
11	0.14756502	0.14419750	0.14091364	0.13771120	0.13458799
12	0.12400422	0.12092034	0.11791937	0.11499891	0.11215665
13	0.10420523	0.10140070	0.09867729	0.09603250	0.09346388
14	0.08756742	0.08503203	0.08257514	0.08019415	0.07788657
15	0.07358606	0.07130569	0.06910054	0.06696798	0.06490547
16	0.06183703	0.05979513	0.05782472	0.05592315	0.05408789
17	0.05196389	0.05014266	0.04838888	0.04669992	0.04507324
18	0.04366713	0.04204836	0.04049279	0.03899784	0.03756104
19	0.03669507	0.03526068	0.03388518	0.03256605	0.03130086
20	0.03083619	0.02956870	0.02835580	0.02719503	0.02608405
21	0.02591277	0.02479556	0.02372870	0.02270984	0.02173671
22	0.02177544	0.02079292	0.01985665	0.01896437	0.01811393
23	0.01829869	0.01743641	0.01661645	0.01583664	0.01509494
24	0.01537705	0.01462173	0.01390498	0.01322475	0.01257912
25	0.01292189	0.01226141	0.01163596	0.01104363	0.01048260
26	0.01085873	0.01028210	0.00973721	0.00922224	0.00873550
27	0.00912498	0.00862231	0.00814829	0.00770124	0.00727958
28	0.00766805	0.00723045	0.00681865	0.00643110	0.00606632
29	0.00644374	0.00606327	0.00570599	0.00537044	0.00505526
30	0.00541491	0.00508450	0.00477488	0.00448471	0.00421272
31	0.00455034	0.00426373	0.00399572	0.00374506	0.00351060
32	0.00382382	0.00357546	0.00334370	0.00312740	0.00292550
33	0.00321329	0.00299829	0.00279807	0.00261161	0.00243792
34	0.00270025	0.00251429	0.00234148	0.00218088	0.00203160
35	0.00226911	0.00210842	0.00195940	0.00182120	0.00169300
36	0.00190682	0.00176806	0.00163967	0.00152083	0.00141083
37	0.00160237	0.00148265	0.00137211	0.00127001	0.00117569
38	0.00134653	0.00124332	0.00114821	0.00106055	0.00097974
39	0.00113154	0.00104261	0.00096084	0.00088563	0.00081645
40	0.00095087	0.00087431	0.00080405	0.00073957	0.00068038
41	0.00079905	0.00073317	0.00067285	0.00061759	0.00056698
42	0.00067147	0.00061482	0.00056305	0.00051574	0.00047248
43	0.00056426	0.00051557	0.00047117	0.00043068	0.00039374
44	0.00047417	0.00043235	0.00039429	0.00035965	0.00032811
45	0.00039846	0.00036255	0.00032995	0.00030033	0.00027343
46	0.00033484	0.00030403	0.00027611	0.00025080	0.00022786
47	0.00028138	0.00025495	0.00023105	0.00020944	0.00018988
48	0.00023645	0.00021379	0.00019335	0.00017489	0.00015823
49	0.00019870	0.00017928	0.00016180	0.00014605	0.00013186
50	0.00016698	0.00015034	0.00013540	0.00012196	0.00010988

ANNUITY WHOSE PRESENT VALUE IS 1

$$\frac{1}{a_{\overline{n}|i}} = \frac{i}{1 - (1 + i)^{-n}} = \frac{i}{1 - v^n} = \frac{1}{s_{\overline{n}|i}} + i$$

Periods			Rate i		
n	0.0025(1/4%)	0.004167(5/12%)	0.005(1/2%)	0.005833(7/12%)	0.0075(3/4%)
1	1.00250000	1.00416667	1.00500000	1.00583333	1.00750000
2	0.50187578	0.50312717	0.50375312	0.50437924	0.50563200
3	0.33500139	0.33611496	0.33667221	0.33722976	0.33834579
4	0.25156445	0.25260958	0.25313279	0.25365644	0.25470501
5	0.20150250	0.20250693	0.20300997	0.20351357	0.20452242
6	0.16812803	0.16910564	0.16959546	0.17008594	0.17106891
7	0.14428928	0.14524800	0.14572854	0.14620986	0.14717488
8	0.12641035	0.12735512	0.12782886	0.12830352	0.12925552
9	0.11250462	0.11343876	0.11390736	0.11437698	0.11531929
10	0.10138015	0.10230596	0.10277057	0.10323632	0.10417123
11	0.09227840	0.09319757	0.09365903	0.09412175	0.09505094
12	0.08469370	0.08560748	0.08606643	0.08652675	0.08745148
13	0.07827595	0.07918532	0.07964224	0.08010064	0.08102188
14	0.07277510	0.07368082	0.07413609	0.07459295	0.07551146
15	0.06800777	0.06891045	0.06936436	0.06982000	0.07073639
16	0.06383642	0.06473655	0.06518937	0.06564401	0.06655879
17	0.06015587	0.06105387	0.06150579	0.06195966	0.06287321
18	0.05688433	0.05778053	0.05823173	0.05868499	0.05959766
19	0.05395722	0.05485191	0.05530253	0.05575532	0.05666740
20	0.05132288	0.05221630	0.05266645	0.05311889	0.05403063
21	0.04893947	0.04983183	0.05028163	0.05073383	0.05164543
22	0.04677278	0.04766427	0.04811380	0.04856585	0.04947748
23	0.04479455	0.04568531	0.04613465	0.04658663	0.04749846
24	0.04298121	0.04387139	0.04432061	0.04477258	0.04568474
25	0.04131298	0.04220270	0.04265186	0.04310388	0.04401650
26	0.03977312	0.04066247	0.04111163	0.04156376	0.04247693
27	0.03834736	0.03923645	0.03968565	0.04013793	0.04105176
28	0.03702347	0.03791239	0.03836167	0.03881415	0.03972871
29	0.03579093	0.03667974	0.03712914	0.03758186	0.03849723
30	0.03464059	0.03552936	0.03597892	0.03643191	0.03734816
31	0.03356440	0.03445330	0.03490304	0.03535633	0.03627352
32	0.03255569	0.03344458	0.03389453	0.03434815	0.03526634
33	0.03160806	0.03249708	0.03294727	0.03340124	0.03432048
34	0.03071620	0.03160540	0.03205586	0.03251020	0.03343053
35	0.02987533	0.03076476	0.03121550	0.03167024	0.03259170
36	0.02908121	0.02997090	0.03042194	0.03087710	0.03179973
37	0.02833004	0.02922003	0.02967139	0.03012698	0.03105082
38	0.02761843	0.02850875	0.02896045	0.02941649	0.03034157
39	0.02694335	0.02783402	0.02828607	0.02874258	0.02966893
40	0.02630204	0.02719310	0.02764552	0.02810251	0.02903016
41	0.02569204	0.02658352	0.02703631	0.02749379	0.02842276
42	0.02511112	0.02600303	0.02645622	0.02691420	0.02784452
43	0.02455724	0.02544961	0.02590320	0.02636170	0.02729338
44	0.02402855	0.02492141	0.02537541	0.02583443	0.02676751
45	0.02352339	0.02441675	0.02487117	0.02533073	0.02626521
46	0.02304022	0.02393409	0.02438894	0.02484905	0.02578495
47	0.02257762	0.02347204	0.02392733	0.02438798	0.02532532
48	0.02213433	0.02302929	0.02348503	0.02394624	0.02488504
49	0.02170915	0.02260468	0.02306087	0.02352265	0.02446292
50	0.02130099	0.02219711	0.02265376	0.02311612	0.02405787

ANNUITY WHOSE PRESENT VALUE IS 1

$$a_{\overline{n}|i}^{-1} = \frac{i}{1 - v^n} = s_{\overline{n}|i}^{-1} + i \text{ (Continued)}$$

Periods			Rate i		
n	0.0025(1/4%)	0.004167(5/12%)	0.005(1/2%)	0.005833(7/12%)	0.0075(3/4
51	0.02090886	0.02180557	0.02226269	0.02272563	0.023668
52	0.02053184	0.02142916	0.02188675	0.02235027	0.023295
53	0.02016906	0.02106700	0.02152507	0.02198919	0.022935
54	0.01981974	0.02071830	0.02117686	0.02164157	0.022589
55	0.01948314	0.02038234	0.02081439	0.02130671	0.022256
56	0.01915858	0.02005843	0.02051797	0.02098390	0.021934
57	0.01884542	0.01974593	0.02020598	0.02067251	0.021624
58	0.01854308	0.01944426	0.01990481	0.02037196	0.021325
59	0.01825101	0.01915287	0.01961392	0.02008170	0.021037
60	0.01796869	0.01887123	0.01933280	0.01980120	0.020758
61	0.01769564	0.01859888	0.01906096	0.01952999	0.020488
62	0.01743142	0.01833536	0.01879796	0.01926762	0.020227
63	0.01717561	0.01808025	0.01854337	0.01901366	0.019975
64	0.01692780	0.01783315	0.01829681	0.01876773	0.019731
65	0.01668764	0.01759371	0.01805789	0.01852946	0.019494
66	0.01645476	0.01736156	0.01782627	0.01829848	0.019265
67	0.01622886	0.01713639	0.01760163	0.01807449	0.019042
68	0.01600961	0.01691788	0.01738366	0.01785716	0.018827
69	0.01579674	0.01670574	0.01717206	0.01764622	0.018617
70	0.01558996	0.01649971	0.01696657	0.01744138	0.018414
71	0.01538902	0.01629952	0.01676693	0.01724239	0.018217
72	0.01519368	0.01610493	0.01657289	0.01704901	0.018025
73	0.01500370	0.01591572	0.01638422	0.01686100	0.017839
74	0.01481887	0.01573165	0.01620070	0.01667814	0.017657
75	0.01463898	0.01555253	0.01602214	0.01650024	0.017481
76	0.01446385	0.01537816	0.01584832	0.01632709	0.017310
77	0.01429327	0.01520836	0.01567908	0.01615851	0.017143
78	0.01412708	0.01504295	0.01551423	0.01599432	0.016980
79	0.01396511	0.01488177	0.01535360	0.01583436	0.016822
80	0.01380721	0.01472464	0.01519704	0.01567847	0.016668
81	0.01365321	0.01457144	0.01504439	0.01552650	0.016517
82	0.01350298	0.01442200	0.01489552	0.01537830	0.016371
83	0.01335639	0.01427620	0.01475028	0.01523373	0.016228
84	0.01321330	0.01413391	0.01460855	0.01509268	0.016089
85	0.01307359	0.01399500	0.01447021	0.01495501	0.015953
86	0.01293714	0.01385935	0.01433513	0.01482060	0.015820
87	0.01280384	0.01372685	0.01420320	0.01468935	0.015690
88	0.01267357	0.01359740	0.01407431	0.01456115	0.015564
89	0.01254625	0.01347088	0.01394837	0.01443588	0.015440
90	0.01242177	0.01334721	0.01382527	0.01431347	0.015319
91	0.01230004	0.01322629	0.01370493	0.01409380	0.015201
92	0.01218096	0.01310803	0.01358724	0.01407679	0.015086
93	0.01206446	0.01299234	0.01347213	0.01396236	0.014973
94	0.01195044	0.01287915	0.01335950	0.01385042	0.014863
95	0.01183884	0.01276836	0.01324930	0.01374090	0.014755
96	0.01172957	0.01265992	0.01314143	0.01363372	0.014650
97	0.01162257	0.01255374	0.01303583	0.01352880	0.014546
98	0.01151776	0.01244976	0.01293242	0.01342608	0.014445
99	0.01141508	0.01234790	0.01283115	0.01332549	0.014347
100	0.01131446	0.01224811	0.01273194	0.01322696	0.014250

ANNUITY WHOSE PRESENT VALUE IS 1

$$a_{\overline{n}|i}^{-1} = \frac{i}{1 - v^n} = \mathit{a}\,_{\overline{n}|i}^{-1} + i \text{ (Continued)}$$

Periods			Rate i		
n	0.01(1%)	0.001125(1 1/8%)	0.0125(1 1/4%)	0.015(1 1/2%)	0.0175(1 3/4%)
1	1.01000000	1.01125000	1.01250000	0.01500000	1.01750000
2	0.50751244	0.50845323	0.50939441	0.51127792	0.51316295
3	0.34002211	0.34086130	0.34170117	0.34338296	0.34506746
4	0.25628109	0.25707058	0.25786102	0.25944479	0.26103237
5	0.20603980	0.20680034	0.20756211	0.20908932	0.21062142
6	0.17254837	0.17329034	0.17403381	0.17552521	0.17702256
7	0.14862828	0.14935762	0.15008872	0.15155616	0.15303059
8	0.13069029	0.13141071	0.13213314	0.13358402	0.13504292
9	0.11674036	0.11745432	0.11817055	0.11960982	0.12105813
10	0.10558208	0.10629131	0.10700307	0.10843418	0.10987534
11	0.09645408	0.09715984	0.09786839	0.09929384	0.10073038
12	0.08884879	0.08955203	0.09025831	0.09167999	0.09311377
13	0.08241482	0.08311626	0.08382100	0.08524036	0.08667283
14	0.07690117	0.07760138	0.07830515	0.07972332	0.08115562
15	0.07212378	0.07282321	0.07352646	0.07494436	0.07637739
16	0.06794460	0.06864363	0.06934672	0.07076508	0.07219958
17	0.06425806	0.06495698	0.06566023	0.06707966	0.06851623
18	0.06098205	0.06168113	0.06238479	0.06380578	0.06524492
19	0.05805175	0.05875120	0.05945548	0.06087847	0.06232061
20	0.05541531	0.05611531	0.05682039	0.05824574	0.05969122
21	0.05303075	0.05373145	0.05443749	0.05586550	0.05731464
22	0.05086372	0.05156525	0.05227238	0.05370332	0.05515638
23	0.04888584	0.04958833	0.05029666	0.05173075	0.05318796
24	0.04707347	0.04777701	0.04848665	0.04992410	0.05138565
25	0.04540675	0.04611144	0.04682247	0.04826345	0.04972952
26	0.04386888	0.04457479	0.04528729	0.04673196	0.04820269
27	0.04244553	0.04315273	0.04386677	0.04531527	0.04679079
28	0.04112444	0.04183299	0.04254863	0.04400108	0.04548151
29	0.03989502	0.04060498	0.04132228	0.04277878	0.04426424
30	0.03874811	0.03945953	0.04017854	0.04163919	0.04312975
31	0.03767573	0.03838866	0.03910942	0.04057430	0.04207005
32	0.03667089	0.03738535	0.03810791	0.03957710	0.04107812
33	0.03572744	0.03644349	0.03716786	0.03864144	0.04014779
34	0.03483997	0.03555763	0.03628387	0.03776189	0.03927363
35	0.03400368	0.03472299	0.03545111	0.03693363	0.03845082
36	0.03321431	0.03393529	0.03466533	0.03615240	0.03767507
37	0.03246805	0.03319072	0.03392270	0.03541437	0.03694257
38	0.03176150	0.03248589	0.03321983	0.03471613	0.03624990
39	0.03109160	0.03181773	0.03255365	0.03405463	0.03559399
40	0.03045560	0.03118349	0.03192141	0.03342710	0.03497209
41	0.02985102	0.03058069	0.03132063	0.03283106	0.03438170
42	0.02927563	0.03000709	0.03074906	0.03226426	0.03382057
43	0.02872737	0.02946064	0.03020466	0.03172465	0.03328666
44	0.02820441	0.02893949	0.02968557	0.03121038	0.03277810
45	0.02770505	0.02844197	0.02919012	0.03071976	0.03229321
46	0.02722775	0.02796652	0.02871675	0.03025125	0.03183043
47	0.02677111	0.02751173	0.02826406	0.02980342	0.03138836
48	0.02633384	0.02707632	0.02783075	0.02937500	0.03096569
49	0.02591474	0.02665910	0.02741563	0.02896478	0.03056124
50	0.02551273	0.02625898	0.02701763	0.02857168	0.03017391

ANNUITY WHOSE PRESENT VALUE IS 1

$$a_{\overline{n}|i}^{-1} = \frac{i}{1 - v^n} = s_{\overline{n}|i}^{-1} + i \text{ (Continued)}$$

Periods			Rate i		
n	0.01(1%)	0.001125(1 1/8%)	0.0125(1 1/4%)	0.015(1 1/2%)	0.0175(1 3/4%)
51	0.02512680	0.02587494	0.02663571	0.02819469	0.02980269
52	0.02475603	0.02550606	0.02626897	0.02783287	0.02944665
53	0.02439956	0.02515149	0.02591653	0.02748537	0.02910492
54	0.02405658	0.02481043	0.02557760	0.02715138	0.02877672
55	0.02372637	0.02448213	0.02525145	0.02683018	0.02846129
56	0.02340824	0.02416592	0.02493739	0.02652106	0.02815795
57	0.02310156	0.02386116	0.02463478	0.02622341	0.02786606
58	0.02280573	0.02356726	0.02434303	0.02593661	0.02758503
59	0.02252020	0.02328366	0.02406158	0.02566012	0.02731430
60	0.02224445	0.02300985	0.02378993	0.02539343	0.02705336
61	0.02197800	0.02274534	0.02352758	0.02513604	0.02680172
62	0.02172041	0.02248969	0.02327410	0.02488751	0.02655892
63	0.02147125	0.02224247	0.02302904	0.02464741	0.02632455
64	0.02123013	0.02200329	0.02279203	0.02441534	0.02609821
65	0.02099667	0.02177178	0.02256268	0.02419094	0.02587952
66	0.02077052	0.02154758	0.02234065	0.02397386	0.02566813
67	0.02055136	0.02133037	0.02212560	0.02376376	0.02546372
68	0.02033889	0.02111985	0.02191724	0.02356033	0.02526597
69	0.02013280	0.02091571	0.02171527	0.02336329	0.02507459
70	0.01993282	0.02071769	0.02151941	0.02317235	0.02488930
71	0.01973870	0.02052552	0.02132941	0.02298727	0.02470985
72	0.01955019	0.02033896	0.02114501	0.02280779	0.02453600
73	0.01936706	0.02015779	0.02096600	0.02263368	0.02436750
74	0.01918910	0.01998177	0.02079215	0.02246473	0.02420413
75	0.01901609	0.01981072	0.02062325	0.02230072	0.02404570
76	0.01884784	0.01964442	0.02045910	0.02214146	0.02389200
77	0.01868416	0.01948269	0.02029953	0.02198676	0.02374285
78	0.01852488	0.01932536	0.02014436	0.02183645	0.02359806
79	0.01836983	0.01917226	0.01999341	0.02169036	0.02345748
80	0.01821885	0.01902323	0.01984652	0.02154832	0.02332093
81	0.01807179	0.01887812	0.01970356	0.02141019	0.02318828
82	0.01792851	0.01873678	0.01956437	0.02127583	0.02305936
83	0.01778887	0.01859908	0.01942881	0.02114509	0.02293406
84	0.01765273	0.01846489	0.01929675	0.02101784	0.02281223
85	0.01751998	0.01833409	0.01916808	0.02089396	0.02269375
86	0.01739050	0.01820654	0.01904267	0.02077333	0.02257850
87	0.01726418	0.01808215	0.01892041	0.02065584	0.02246636
88	0.01714089	0.01796081	0.01880119	0.02054138	0.02235724
89	0.01702056	0.01784240	0.01868491	0.02042984	0.02225102
90	0.01690306	0.01772684	0.01857146	0.02032113	0.02214760
91	0.01678832	0.01761403	0.01846076	0.02021516	0.02204690
92	0.01667624	0.01750387	0.01835272	0.02011182	0.02194882
93	0.01656673	0.01739629	0.01824724	0.02001104	0.02185327
94	0.01645971	0.01729119	0.01814425	0.01991273	0.02176017
95	0.01635511	0.01718851	0.01804366	0.01981681	0.02166944
96	0.01625284	0.01708816	0.01794541	0.01972321	0.02158101
97	0.01615284	0.01699007	0.01784941	0.01963186	0.02149480
98	0.01605503	0.01689418	0.01775560	0.01954268	0.02141074
99	0.01595936	0.01680041	0.01766391	0.01945560	0.02132876
100	0.01586574	0.01670870	0.01757428	0.01937057	0.02124880

ANNUITY WHOSE PRESENT VALUE IS 1

$$a_{\overline{n}|i}^{-1} = \frac{i}{1 - v^n} = a_{\overline{n}|i}^{-1} + i \text{ (Continued)}$$

Rate i

Periods n	0.02(2%)	0.0225(2 1/4%)	0.025(2 1/2%)	0.0275(2 3/4%)
1	1.02000000	1.02250000	1.02500000	1.02750000
2	0.51504950	0.51693758	0.51882716	0.52071825
3	0.34675467	0.34844458	0.35013717	0.35183243
4	0.26262375	0.26421893	0.26581788	0.26742059
5	0.21215839	0.21370021	0.21524686	0.21679832
6	0.17852581	0.18003496	0.18154997	0.18307083
7	0.15451196	0.15600025	0.15749543	0.15899747
8	0.13650980	0.13798462	0.13946735	0.14095795
9	0.12251544	0.12398170	0.12545689	0.12694095
10	0.11132653	0.11278768	0.11425876	0.11573972
11	0.10217794	0.10363649	0.10510596	0.10658629
12	0.09455960	0.09601740	0.09748713	0.09896871
13	0.08811835	0.08957686	0.09104827	0.09253252
14	0.08260197	0.08406230	0.08553652	0.08702457
15	0.07782547	0.07928852	0.08076646	0.08225917
16	0.07365013	0.07511663	0.07659899	0.07809710
17	0.06996984	0.07144039	0.07292777	0.07443186
18	0.06670210	0.06817720	0.06967008	0.07118063
19	0.06378177	0.06526182	0.06676062	0.06827802
20	0.06115672	0.06264207	0.06414713	0.06567173
21	0.05878477	0.06027572	0.06178733	0.06331941
22	0.05663140	0.05812821	0.05964661	0.06118640
23	0.05466810	0.05617097	0.05769638	0.05924410
24	0.05287110	0.05438023	0.05591282	0.05746863
25	0.05122044	0.05273599	0.05427592	0.05583997
26	0.04969923	0.05122134	0.05276875	0.05434116
27	0.04829309	0.04982188	0.05137687	0.05295776
28	0.04698967	0.04852525	0.05008793	0.05167738
29	0.04577836	0.04732081	0.04889127	0.05048935
30	0.04464992	0.04619934	0.04777764	0.04938442
31	0.04359635	0.04515280	0.04673900	0.04835453
32	0.04261061	0.04417415	0.04576831	0.04739263
33	0.04168653	0.04325722	0.04485938	0.04649253
34	0.04081867	0.04239655	0.04400675	0.04564875
35	0.04000221	0.04158731	0.04320558	0.04485645
36	0.03923285	0.04082522	0.04245158	0.04411132
37	0.03850678	0.04010643	0.04174090	0.04340953
38	0.03782057	0.03942753	0.04107012	0.04274764
39	0.03717114	0.03878543	0.04043615	0.04212256
40	0.03655575	0.03817738	0.03983623	0.04153151
41	0.03597188	0.03760087	0.03926786	0.04097200
42	0.03541729	0.03705364	0.03872876	0.04044175
43	0.03488993	0.03653364	0.03821688	0.03993871
44	0.03438794	0.03603901	0.03773037	0.03946100
45	0.03390962	0.03556805	0.03726751	0.03900693
46	0.03345342	0.03511921	0.03682676	0.03857493
47	0.03301792	0.03469107	0.03640669	0.03816358
48	0.03260184	0.03428233	0.03600599	0.03777158
49	0.03220396	0.03389179	0.03562348	0.03739773
50	0.03182321	0.03351836	0.03525806	0.03704092

ANNUITY WHOSE PRESENT VALUE IS 1

$$a_{\overline{n}|i}^{-1} = \frac{i}{1 - v^n} = a_{\overline{n}|i}^{-1} + i \text{ (Continued)}$$

Periods n	Rate i			
	0.02(2%)	0.0225(2 1/4%)	0.025(2 1/2%)	0.0275(2 3/4%)
51	0.03145856	0.03316102	0.03490870	0.03670014
52	0.03110909	0.03281884	0.03457446	0.03637444
53	0.03077392	0.03249094	0.03425449	0.03606297
54	0.03045226	0.03217654	0.03394799	0.03576491
55	0.03014337	0.03187489	0.03365419	0.03547953
56	0.02984656	0.03158530	0.03337243	0.03520612
57	0.02956120	0.03130712	0.03310204	0.03494404
58	0.02928667	0.03103977	0.03284244	0.03469270
59	0.02902243	0.03078268	0.03259307	0.03445153
60	0.02876797	0.03053533	0.03235340	0.03422002
61	0.02852278	0.03029724	0.03212294	0.03399767
62	0.02828643	0.03006795	0.03190126	0.03378402
63	0.02805848	0.02984704	0.03168790	0.03357866
64	0.02783855	0.02963411	0.03148249	0.03338118
65	0.02762624	0.02942878	0.03128463	0.03319120
66	0.02742122	0.02923070	0.03109398	0.03300837
67	0.02722316	0.02903955	0.03091021	0.03283236
68	0.02703173	0.02885500	0.03073300	0.03266285
69	0.02684665	0.02867677	0.03056206	0.03249955
70	0.02666765	0.02850458	0.03039712	0.03234218
71	0.02649446	0.02833816	0.03023790	0.03219048
72	0.02632683	0.02817728	0.03008417	0.03204420
73	0.02616454	0.02802169	0.02993568	0.03190311
74	0.02600736	0.02787118	0.02979222	0.03176698
75	0.02585508	0.02772554	0.02965358	0.03163560
76	0.02570751	0.02758457	0.02951956	0.03150878
77	0.02556447	0.02744808	0.02938997	0.03138633
78	0.02542576	0.02731589	0.02926463	0.03126806
79	0.02529123	0.02718784	0.02914338	0.03115382
80	0.02516071	0.02706376	0.02902605	0.03104342
81	0.02503405	0.02694350	0.02891248	0.03093674
82	0.02491110	0.02682692	0.02880254	0.03083361
83	0.02479173	0.02671387	0.02869608	0.03073389
84	0.02467581	0.02660423	0.02859298	0.03063747
85	0.02456321	0.02649787	0.02849310	0.03054420
86	0.02445381	0.02639467	0.02839633	0.03045397
87	0.02434750	0.02629452	0.02830255	0.03036667
88	0.02424416	0.02619730	0.02821165	0.03028219
89	0.02414370	0.02610291	0.02812353	0.03020041
90	0.02404602	0.02601126	0.02803809	0.03012125
91	0.02395101	0.02592224	0.02795523	0.03004460
92	0.02385859	0.02583577	0.02787486	0.02997038
93	0.02376868	0.02575176	0.02779690	0.02989850
94	0.02368118	0.02567012	0.02772126	0.02982887
95	0.02359602	0.02559078	0.02764786	0.02976141
96	0.02351313	0.02551366	0.02757662	0.02969605
97	0.02343242	0.02543868	0.02750747	0.02963272
98	0.02335383	0.02536578	0.02744034	0.02957134
99	0.02327729	0.02529489	0.02737517	0.02951185
100	0.02320274	0.02522594	0.02731188	0.02945418

ANNUITY WHOSE PRESENT VALUE IS 1

$$a_{\overline{n}|i}^{-1} = \frac{i}{1 - v^n} = s_{\overline{n}|i}^{-1} + i \text{ (Continued)}$$

Periods n	0.03(3%)	0.0325(3 1/4%)	0.035(3 1/2%)	0.0375(3 3/4%)
1	1.03000000	1.03250000	1.03500000	1.03750000
2	0.52261084	0.52450492	0.52640049	0.52829755
3	0.35353036	0.35523095	0.35693418	0.35864005
4	0.26902705	0.27063723	0.27225114	0.27386875
5	0.21835457	0.21991560	0.22148137	0.22305189
6	0.18459750	0.18612997	0.18766821	0.18921219
7	0.16050635	0.16202204	0.16354449	0.16507370
8	0.14245639	0.14396263	0.14547665	0.14699839
9	0.12843386	0.12993555	0.13144601	0.13296517
10	0.11723051	0.11873107	0.12024137	0.12176134
11	0.10807745	0.10957936	0.11109197	0.11261521
12	0.10046209	0.10196719	0.10348395	0.10501230
13	0.09402954	0.09553925	0.09706157	0.09859642
14	0.08852634	0.09004176	0.09157073	0.09311317
15	0.08376658	0.08528858	0.08682507	0.08837595
16	0.07961085	0.08114013	0.08268483	0.08424483
17	0.07595253	0.07748966	0.07904313	0.08061280
18	0.07270870	0.07425415	0.07581684	0.07739662
19	0.06981388	0.07136804	0.07294033	0.07453058
20	0.06721571	0.06877888	0.07036108	0.07196210
21	0.06487178	0.06644424	0.06803659	0.06964862
22	0.06274739	0.06432936	0.06593207	0.06755531
23	0.06081390	0.06240555	0.06401880	0.06565339
24	0.05904742	0.06064891	0.06227283	0.06391890
25	0.05742787	0.05903933	0.06067404	0.06233169
26	0.05593829	0.05755981	0.05920540	0.06087470
27	0.05456421	0.05619588	0.05785241	0.05953343
28	0.05329323	0.05493512	0.05660265	0.05829540
29	0.05211467	0.05376682	0.05544538	0.05714991
30	0.05101926	0.05268172	0.05437133	0.05608762
31	0.04999893	0.05167172	0.05337240	0.05510046
32	0.04904662	0.05072976	0.05244150	0.05418131
33	0.04815612	0.04984961	0.05157242	0.05332395
34	0.04732196	0.04902581	0.05075966	0.05252287
35	0.04653929	0.04825348	0.04999835	0.05177320
36	0.04580379	0.04752831	0.04928416	0.05107060
37	0.04511162	0.04684645	0.04861325	0.05041122
38	0.04445934	0.04620445	0.04798214	0.04979159
39	0.04384385	0.04559920	0.04738775	0.04920860
40	0.04326238	0.04502794	0.04682728	0.04865946
41	0.04271241	0.04448814	0.04629822	0.04814164
42	0.04219167	0.04397753	0.04579828	0.04765286
43	0.04169811	0.04349403	0.04532539	0.04719106
44	0.04122985	0.04303579	0.04487768	0.04675434
45	0.04078518	0.04260108	0.04445343	0.04634098
46	0.04036254	0.04218835	0.04405108	0.04594943
47	0.03996051	0.04179616	0.04366919	0.04557824
48	0.03957777	0.04142320	0.04330646	0.04522609
49	0.03921314	0.04106828	0.04296167	0.04489179
50	0.03886549	0.04073027	0.04263371	0.04457422

Financial Tables

ANNUITY WHOSE PRESENT VALUE IS 1

$$a_{\overline{n}|i}^{-1} = \frac{i}{1 - v^n} = a_{\overline{n}|i}^{-1} + i \text{ (Continued)}$$

Periods n	0.04(4%)	0.0425(4 1/4%)	0.045(4 1/2%)	0.0475(4 3/4%)
			Rate *i*	
1	1.04000000	1.04250000	1.04500000	1.04750000
2	0.53019608	0.53209608	0.53399756	0.53590049
3	0.36034854	0.36205965	0.36377336	0.36548967
4	0.27549005	0.27711502	0.27874365	0.28037592
5	0.22462711	0.22620704	0.22779164	0.22938090
6	0.19076190	0.19231731	0.19387839	0.19544512
7	0.16660961	0.16815221	0.16970147	0.17125735
8	0.14852783	0.15006493	0.15160965	0.15316196
9	0.13449299	0.13602944	0.13757447	0.13912803
10	0.12329094	0.12483012	0.12637882	0.12793699
11	0.11414904	0.11569338	0.11724818	0.11881337
12	0.10655217	0.10810349	0.10966619	0.11124019
13	0.10014373	0.10170340	0.10327535	0.10485950
14	0.09466897	0.09623806	0.09782032	0.09941565
15	0.08994110	0.09152043	0.09311381	0.09472113
16	0.08582000	0.08741022	0.08901537	0.09063531
17	0.08219852	0.08380017	0.08541758	0.08705063
18	0.07899333	0.08060681	0.08223690	0.08388343
19	0.07613862	0.07776427	0.07940734	0.08106766
20	0.07358175	0.07521983	0.07687614	0.07855047
21	0.07128011	0.07293083	0.07460057	0.07628907
22	0.06919881	0.07086234	0.07254565	0.07424846
23	0.06730906	0.06898552	0.07068249	0.07239969
24	0.06558683	0.06727631	0.06898703	0.07071867
25	0.06401196	0.06571452	0.06743903	0.06918513
26	0.06256738	0.06428306	0.06602137	0.06778192
27	0.06123854	0.06296736	0.06471946	0.06649444
28	0.06001298	0.06175492	0.06352081	0.06531016
29	0.05887993	0.06063500	0.06241461	0.06421829
30	0.05783010	0.05959825	0.06139154	0.06320945
31	0.05685535	0.05863654	0.06044345	0.06227550
32	0.05594859	0.05774275	0.05956320	0.06140929
33	0.05510357	0.05691064	0.05874453	0.06060455
34	0.05431477	0.05613469	0.05798191	0.05985574
35	0.05357732	0.05540999	0.05727045	0.05915794
36	0.05288688	0.05473220	0.05660578	0.05850680
37	0.05223957	0.05409745	0.05598402	0.05789843
38	0.05163192	0.05350225	0.05540169	0.05732932
39	0.05106083	0.05294350	0.05485567	0.05679637
40	0.05052349	0.05241839	0.05434315	0.05629675
41	0.05001738	0.05192438	0.05386158	0.05582791
42	0.04954020	0.05145918	0.05340868	0.05538756
43	0.04908989	0.05102071	0.05298235	0.05497362
44	0.04866454	0.05060708	0.05258071	0.05458418
45	0.04826246	0.05021657	0.05220202	0.05421751
46	0.04788205	0.04984760	0.05184471	0.05387203
47	0.04752189	0.04949873	0.05150734	0.05354630
48	0.04718065	0.04916864	0.05118858	0.05323900
49	0.04685712	0.04885612	0.05088722	0.05294891
50	0.04655020	0.04856005	0.05060215	0.05267490

ANNUITY WHOSE PRESENT VALUE IS 1

$$a_{\overline{n}|i}^{-1} = \frac{i}{1 - v^n} = \text{\it o } {}_{\overline{n}|i}^{-1} + i \text{ (Continued)}$$

Periods		Rate i		
n	0.05(5%)	0.0525(5 1/4%)	0.055(5 1/2%)	0.0575(5 3/4%)
1	1.05000000	1.05250000	1.05500000	1.05750000
2	0.53780488	0.53971072	0.54161800	0.54352673
3	0.36720856	0.36893004	0.37065407	0.37238067
4	0.28201183	0.28365136	0.28529449	0.28694120
5	0.23097480	0.23257332	0.23417644	0.23578414
6	0.19701747	0.19859542	0.20017895	0.20176803
7	0.17281982	0.17438885	0.17596442	0.17754648
8	0.15472181	0.15628918	0.15786401	0.15944628
9	0.14069008	0.14226057	0.14383946	0.14542670
10	0.12950457	0.13108152	0.13266777	0.13426327
11	0.12038889	0.12197467	0.12357065	0.12517676
12	0.11282541	0.11442178	0.11602923	0.11764767
13	0.10645577	0.10806405	0.10968426	0.11131631
14	0.10102397	0.10264516	0.10427912	0.10592574
15	0.09634229	0.09797715	0.09962560	0.10128751
16	0.09226991	0.09391903	0.09558254	0.09726029
17	0.08869914	0.09036298	0.09204197	0.09373597
18	0.08554622	0.08722511	0.08891992	0.09063045
19	0.08274501	0.08443921	0.08615006	0.08787734
20	0.08024259	0.08195228	0.08367933	0.08542350
21	0.07799611	0.07972143	0.08146478	0.08322590
22	0.07597051	0.07771153	0.07947123	0.08124934
23	0.07413682	0.07589358	0.07766965	0.07946472
24	0.07247090	0.07424339	0.07603580	0.07784779
25	0.07095246	0.07274066	0.07454935	0.07637817
26	0.06956432	0.07136817	0.07319307	0.07503860
27	0.06829186	0.07011129	0.07195228	0.07381439
28	0.06712253	0.06895744	0.07081440	0.07269293
29	0.06604551	0.06789578	0.06976857	0.07166336
30	0.06505144	0.06691693	0.06880539	0.07071624
31	0.06413212	0.06601270	0.06791665	0.06984336
32	0.06328042	0.06517593	0.06709519	0.06903754
33	0.06249004	0.06440032	0.06633469	0.06829246
34	0.06175545	0.06368030	0.06562958	0.06760253
35	0.06107171	0.06301096	0.06497493	0.06696282
36	0.06043446	0.06238791	0.06436635	0.06636893
37	0.05983979	0.06180725	0.06379993	0.06581694
38	0.05928423	0.06126548	0.06327217	0.06530335
39	0.05876462	0.06075946	0.06277991	0.06482500
40	0.05827816	0.06028637	0.06232034	0.06437907
41	0.05782229	0.05984365	0.06189090	0.06396299
42	0.05739471	0.05942899	0.06148927	0.06357445
43	0.05699333	0.05904031	0.06111337	0.06321135
44	0.05661625	0.05867569	0.06076128	0.06287179
45	0.05626173	0.05833341	0.06043127	0.06255404
46	0.05592820	0.05801189	0.06012175	0.06225650
47	0.05561421	0.05770966	0.05983129	0.06197773
48	0.05531843	0.05742542	0.05955854	0.06171641
49	0.05503965	0.05715793	0.05930230	0.06147131
50	0.05477674	0.05690609	0.05906145	0.06124133

ANNUITY WHOSE PRESENT VALUE IS 1

$$a_{\overline{n}|i}^{-1} = \frac{i}{1 - v^n} = s_{\overline{n}|i}^{-1} + i \text{ (Continued)}$$

Periods	Rate i			
n	0.06(6%)	0.0625(6 1/4%)	0.065(6 1/2%)	0.0675(6 3/4%)
1	1.06000000	1.06250000	1.06500000	1.06750000
2	0.54543689	0.54734848	0.54926150	0.55117594
3	0.37410981	0.37584149	0.37757570	0.37931243
4	0.28859149	0.29024534	0.29190274	0.29356367
5	0.23739640	0.23901321	0.24063454	0.24226037
6	0.20336263	0.20496273	0.20656831	0.20817934
7	0.17913502	0.18072999	0.18233137	0.18393912
8	0.16103594	0.16263296	0.16423730	0.16584891
9	0.14702224	0.14862603	0.15023803	0.15185820
10	0.13586796	0.13748179	0.13910469	0.14073662
11	0.12679294	0.12841911	0.13005521	0.13170116
12	0.11927703	0.12091722	0.12256817	0.12422978
13	0.11296011	0.11461555	0.11628256	0.11796102
14	0.10758491	0.10925653	0.11094048	0.11263666
15	0.10296276	0.10465123	0.10635278	0.10806729
16	0.09895214	0.10065795	0.10237757	0.10411086
17	0.09544480	0.09716831	0.09890633	0.10065868
18	0.09235654	0.09409799	0.09585461	0.09762621
19	0.08962086	0.09138040	0.09315575	0.09494670
20	0.08718456	0.08896227	0.09075640	0.09256670
21	0.08500045	0.08680045	0.08861333	0.09044294
22	0.08304557	0.08485962	0.08669120	0.08854002
23	0.08127848	0.08311061	0.08496078	0.08682866
24	0.07967900	0.08152909	0.08339770	0.08528446
25	0.07822672	0.08009462	0.08198148	0.08388691
26	0.07690435	0.07878989	0.08069480	0.08261865
27	0.07569717	0.07760015	0.07952288	0.08146489
28	0.07459255	0.07651276	0.07845305	0.08041294
29	0.07357961	0.07551680	0.07747440	0.07945186
30	0.07264891	0.07460284	0.07657744	0.07857215
31	0.07179222	0.07376261	0.07575393	0.07776557
32	0.07100234	0.07298892	0.07499665	0.07702486
33	0.07027293	0.07227543	0.07429924	0.07634368
34	0.06959843	0.07161653	0.07365610	0.07571641
35	0.06897386	0.07100726	0.07306226	0.07513808
36	0.06839483	0.07044324	0.07251332	0.07460428
37	0.06785743	0.06992051	0.07200534	0.07411106
38	0.06735812	0.06943557	0.07153480	0.07365492
39	0.06689377	0.06898526	0.07109854	0.07323268
40	0.06646154	0.06856675	0.07069373	0.07284150
41	0.06605886	0.06817746	0.07031779	0.07247884
42	0.06568342	0.06781509	0.06996842	0.07214236
43	0.06533312	0.06747754	0.06964352	0.07182999
44	0.06500606	0.06716290	0.06934119	0.07153981
45	0.06470050	0.06686944	0.06905968	0.07127010
46	0.06441485	0.06659557	0.06879743	0.07101928
47	0.06414768	0.06633985	0.06855300	0.07078591
48	0.06389765	0.06610096	0.06832505	0.07056869
49	0.06366356	0.06587769	0.06811240	0.07036642
50	0.06344429	0.06566893	0.06791393	0.07017798

ANNUITY WHOSE PRESENT VALUE IS 1

$$a_{\overline{n}|i}^{-1} = \frac{i}{1 - v^n} = s_{\overline{n}|i}^{-1} + i \text{ (Continued)}$$

Rate i

Periods

n	0.07(7%)	0.0725(7 1/4%)	0.075(7 1/2%)	0.0775(7 3/4%)
1	1.07000000	1.07250000	1.07500000	1.07750000
2	0.55309179	0.55500905	0.55692771	0.55884777
3	0.38105167	0.38279340	0.38453763	0.38628434
4	0.29522812	0.29689607	0.29856751	0.30024243
5	0.24389069	0.24552548	0.24716472	0.24880838
6	0.20979580	0.21141766	0.21304489	0.21467748
7	0.18555322	0.18717363	0.18880032	0.19043325
8	0.16746776	0.16909381	0.17072702	0.17236735
9	0.15348647	0.15512281	0.15676716	0.15841948
10	0.14237750	0.14402729	0.14568593	0.14735335
11	0.13335690	0.13502237	0.13669747	0.13838216
12	0.12590199	0.12758470	0.12927783	0.13098130
13	0.11965085	0.12135194	0.12306420	0.12478752
14	0.11434494	0.11606522	0.11779737	0.11954129
15	0.10979462	0.11153465	0.11328724	0.11505225
16	0.10585765	0.10761780	0.10939116	0.11117757
17	0.10242519	0.10420570	0.10600003	0.10780800
18	0.09941260	0.10121358	0.10302896	0.10485853
19	0.09675301	0.09857449	0.10041090	0.10226202
20	0.09439293	0.09623484	0.09809219	0.09996473
21	0.09228900	0.09415124	0.09602937	0.09792314
22	0.09040577	0.09228816	0.09418687	0.09610161
23	0.08871393	0.09061624	0.09253528	0.09447070
24	0.08718902	0.08911101	0.09105008	0.09300585
25	0.08581052	0.08775190	0.08971067	0.09168643
26	0.08456103	0.08652149	0.08849961	0.09049497
27	0.08342573	0.08540494	0.08740204	0.08941658
28	0.08239193	0.08438951	0.08640520	0.08843849
29	0.08144865	0.08346425	0.08549811	0.08754971
30	0.08058640	0.08261962	0.08467124	0.08674069
31	0.07979691	0.08184734	0.08391628	0.08600313
32	0.07907292	0.08114017	0.08322599	0.08532974
33	0.07840807	0.08049172	0.08259397	0.08471416
34	0.07779674	0.07989637	0.08201461	0.08415075
35	0.07723396	0.07934915	0.08148291	0.08363452
36	0.07671531	0.07884563	0.08099447	0.08316106
37	0.07623685	0.07838187	0.08054533	0.08272643
38	0.07579505	0.07795435	0.08013197	0.08232710
39	0.07538676	0.07755991	0.07975124	0.08195993
40	0.07500914	0.07719571	0.07940031	0.08162208
41	0.07465962	0.07685920	0.07907663	0.08131102
42	0.07433591	0.07654807	0.07877789	0.08102444
43	0.07403590	0.07626023	0.07850201	0.08076028
44	0.07375769	0.07599379	0.07824710	0.08051665
45	0.07349957	0.07574704	0.07801146	0.08029186
46	0.07325996	0.07551840	0.07779354	0.08008436
47	0.07303744	0.07530646	0.07759190	0.07989274
48	0.07283070	0.07510992	0.07740527	0.07971572
49	0.07263853	0.07492758	0.07723247	0.07955213
50	0.07245985	0.07475837	0.07707241	0.07940091

Financial Tables

ANNUITY WHOSE PRESENT VALUE IS 1

$$a_{\overline{n}|i}^{-1} = \frac{i}{1 - v^n} = \mathbf{\mathit{o}} \; _{\overline{n}|i}^{-1} + i \; \text{(Continued)}$$

Rate i

Periods n	0.08(8%)	0.0825(8 1/4%)	0.085(8 1/2%)	0.0875(8 3/4%)
1	1.08000000	1.08250000	1.08500000	1.08750000
2	0.56076923	0.56269208	0.56461631	0.56654192
3	0.38803351	0.38978515	0.39153925	0.39329579
4	0.30192080	0.30360263	0.30528789	0.30697657
5	0.25045645	0.25210892	0.25376575	0.25542694
6	0.21631539	0.21795860	0.21960708	0.22126082
7	0.19207240	0.19371774	0.19536922	0.19702683
8	0.17401476	0.17566921	0.17733065	0.17899906
9	0.16007971	0.16174781	0.16342372	0.16510740
10	0.14902949	0.15071430	0.15240771	0.15410966
11	0.14007634	0.14177996	0.14349293	0.14521519
12	0.13269502	0.13441890	0.13615286	0.13789681
13	0.12652181	0.12826696	0.13002287	0.13178944
14	0.12129685	0.12306394	0.12484244	0.12663222
15	0.11682954	0.11861900	0.12042046	0.12223380
16	0.11297687	0.11478892	0.11661354	0.11845059
17	0.10962943	0.11146415	0.11331198	0.11517274
18	0.10670210	0.10855946	0.11043041	0.11231476
19	0.10412763	0.10600750	0.10790140	0.10980912
20	0.10185221	0.10375437	0.10567097	0.10760176
21	0.09983225	0.10175643	0.10369541	0.10564890
22	0.09803207	0.09997794	0.10193892	0.10391471
23	0.09642217	0.09838936	0.10037193	0.10236954
24	0.09497796	0.09696605	0.09896975	0.10098871
25	0.09367878	0.09568733	0.09771168	0.09975145
26	0.09250713	0.09453567	0.09658017	0.09864020
27	0.09144810	0.09349614	0.09556025	0.09763999
28	0.09048891	0.09255595	0.09463914	0.09673799
29	0.08961854	0.09170406	0.09380577	0.09592315
30	0.08882743	0.09093091	0.09305058	0.09518590
31	0.08810728	0.09022818	0.09236524	0.09451789
32	0.08745081	0.08958859	0.09174247	0.09391186
33	0.08685163	0.08900575	0.09117588	0.09336140
34	0.08630411	0.08847402	0.09065984	0.09286090
35	0.08580326	0.08798844	0.09018937	0.09240538
36	0.08534467	0.08754458	0.08976006	0.09199044
37	0.08492440	0.08713850	0.08936799	0.09161216
38	0.08453894	0.08676671	0.08900966	0.09126705
39	0.08418513	0.08642606	0.08868193	0.09095200
40	0.08386016	0.08611373	0.08838201	0.09066421
41	0.08356149	0.08582722	0.08810737	0.09040118
42	0.08328684	0.08556422	0.08785576	0.09016065
43	0.08303414	0.08532270	0.08762512	0.08994060
44	0.08280152	0.08510079	0.08741363	0.08973921
45	0.08258728	0.08489682	0.08721961	0.08955481
46	0.08238991	0.08470926	0.08704154	0.08938592
47	0.08220799	0.08453673	0.08687807	0.08923118
48	0.08204027	0.08437797	0.08672795	0.08908936
49	0.08188557	0.08423184	0.08659005	0.08895934
50	0.08174286	0.08409730	0.08646334	0.08884013

ANNUITY WHOSE PRESENT VALUE IS 1

$$a_{\overline{n}|i}^{-1} = \frac{i}{1 - v^n} = a_{\overline{n}|i}^{-1} + i \text{ (Continued)}$$

Periods	Rate i			
n	0.09(9%)	0.0925(9 1/4%)	0.095(9 1/2%)	0.0975(9 3/4%)
1	1.09000000	1.09250000	1.09500000	1.09750000
2	0.56846890	0.57039725	0.57232697	0.57425805
3	0.39505476	0.39681615	0.39857997	0.40034619
4	0.30866866	0.31036414	0.31206300	0.31376523
5	0.25709246	0.25876229	0.26043642	0.26211482
6	0.22291978	0.22458395	0.22625328	0.22792777
7	0.19869052	0.20036026	0.20203603	0.20371779
8	0.18067438	0.18235658	0.18404561	0.18574144
9	0.16679880	0.16849786	0.17020454	0.17191878
10	0.15582009	0.15753894	0.15926615	0.16100166
11	0.14694666	0.14868726	0.15043693	0.15219558
12	0.13965066	0.14141432	0.14318771	0.14497074
13	0.13356656	0.13535414	0.13715206	0.13896022
14	0.12843317	0.13024517	0.13206809	0.13390182
15	0.12405888	0.12589556	0.12774370	0.12960315
16	0.12029991	0.12216133	0.12403470	0.12591985
17	0.11704625	0.11893232	0.12083078	0.12274145
18	0.11421229	0.11612281	0.11804610	0.11998198
19	0.11173041	0.11366506	0.11561284	0.11757352
20	0.10954648	0.11150487	0.11347670	0.11546170
21	0.10761663	0.10959832	0.11159370	0.11360248
22	0.10590499	0.10790947	0.10992784	0.11195981
23	0.10438188	0.10640860	0.10844938	0.11050389
24	0.10302256	0.10507095	0.10713351	0.10920990
25	0.10180625	0.10387569	0.10595939	0.10805698
26	0.10071536	0.10280523	0.10490940	0.10702747
27	0.09973491	0.10184456	0.10396852	0.10610635
28	0.09885205	0.10098083	0.10312389	0.10528076
29	0.09805572	0.10020298	0.10236444	0.10453963
30	0.09733635	0.09950142	0.10168058	0.10387336
31	0.09668560	0.09886781	0.10106399	0.10327363
32	0.09609619	0.09829488	0.10050739	0.10273318
33	0.09556173	0.09777625	0.10000441	0.10224565
34	0.09507660	0.09730631	0.09954945	0.10180543
35	0.09463584	0.09688010	0.09913756	0.10140762
36	0.09423505	0.09649323	0.09876437	0.10104784
37	0.09387033	0.09614182	0.09842600	0.10072224
38	0.09353820	0.09582240	0.09811901	0.10042739
39	0.09323555	0.09553188	0.09784032	0.10016023
40	0.09295961	0.09526750	0.09758719	0.09991804
41	0.09270789	0.09502678	0.09735716	0.09969838
42	0.09247814	0.09480750	0.09714803	0.09949907
43	0.09226837	0.09460768	0.09695783	0.09931817
44	0.09207675	0.09442551	0.09678478	0.09915390
45	0.09190165	0.09425938	0.09662729	0.09900471
46	0.09174160	0.09410783	0.09648390	0.09886915
47	0.09159525	0.09396953	0.09635333	0.09874597
48	0.09146139	0.09384330	0.09623439	0.09863399
49	0.09133893	0.09372806	0.09612603	0.09853218
50	0.09122687	0.09362282	0.09602728	0.09843960

ANNUITY WHOSE PRESENT VALUE IS 1

$$a_{\overline{n}|i}^{-1} = \frac{i}{1 - v^n} = s_{\overline{n}|i}^{-1} + i \text{ (Continued)}$$

Rate i

Periods n	0.10(10%)	0.1025(10 1/4%)	0.105(10 1/2%)	0.1075(10 3/4%)
1	1.10000000	1.10250000	1.10500000	1.10750000
2	0.57619048	0.57812426	0.58005938	0.58199585
3	0.40211480	0.40388581	0.40565920	0.40743495
4	0.31547080	0.31717972	0.31889196	0.32060751
5	0.26379748	0.26548438	0.26717550	0.26887081
6	0.22960738	0.23129209	0.23298187	0.23467671
7	0.20540550	0.20709914	0.20879867	0.21050405
8	0.18744402	0.18915331	0.19086928	0.19259187
9	0.17364054	0.17536976	0.17710638	0.17885037
10	0.16274539	0.16449730	0.16625732	0.16802538
11	0.15396314	0.15573954	0.15752470	0.15931855
12	0.14676332	0.14856535	0.15037675	0.15219742
13	0.14077852	0.14260686	0.14444512	0.14629320
14	0.13574622	0.13760119	0.13946659	0.14134230
15	0.13147378	0.13335544	0.13524800	0.13715131
16	0.12781662	0.12972486	0.13164440	0.13357508
17	0.12466413	0.12659866	0.12854485	0.13050252
18	0.12193022	0.12389064	0.12586302	0.12784716
19	0.11954687	0.12153267	0.12353069	0.12554071
20	0.11745962	0.11947023	0.12149327	0.12352848
21	0.11562439	0.11765916	0.11970652	0.12176620
22	0.11400506	0.11606331	0.11813426	0.12021762
23	0.11257181	0.11465282	0.11674659	0.11885282
24	0.11129978	0.11340278	0.11551858	0.11764684
25	0.11016807	0.11229231	0.11442932	0.11657875
26	0.10915904	0.11130372	0.11346112	0.11563086
27	0.10825764	0.11042197	0.11259894	0.11478813
28	0.10745101	0.10963420	0.11182990	0.11403768
29	0.10672807	0.10892933	0.11114293	0.11336846
30	0.10607925	0.10829778	0.11052848	0.11277090
31	0.10549621	0.10773125	0.10997824	0.11223674
32	0.10497172	0.10722249	0.10948499	0.11175875
33	0.10449941	0.10676517	0.10904241	0.11133064
34	0.10407371	0.10635372	0.10864495	0.11094690
35	0.10368971	0.10598326	0.10828776	0.11060266
36	0.10334306	0.10564947	0.10796652	0.11029368
37	0.10302994	0.10534853	0.10767744	0.11001616
38	0.10274692	0.10507704	0.10741717	0.10976678
39	0.10249098	0.10483200	0.10718271	0.10954257
40	0.10225941	0.10461073	0.10697141	0.10934091
41	0.10204980	0.10441083	0.10678090	0.10915947
42	0.10185999	0.10423018	0.10660908	0.10899615
43	0.10168805	0.10406687	0.10645407	0.10884910
44	0.10153224	0.10391918	0.10631417	0.10871667
45	0.10139100	0.10378558	0.10618788	0.10859737
46	0.10126295	0.10366470	0.10607385	0.10848987
47	0.10114682	0.10355531	0.10597087	0.10839299
48	0.10104148	0.10345628	0.10587784	0.10830566
49	0.10094590	0.10336662	0.10579380	0.10822693
50	0.10085917	0.10328543	0.10571785	0.10815594

ANNUITY WHOSE PRESENT VALUE IS 1

$$a_{\overline{n}|i}^{-1} = \frac{i}{1 - v^n} = s_{\overline{n}|i}^{-1} + i \text{ (Continued)}$$

Rate i

Periods				
n	0.11(11%)	0.1125(11 1/4%)	0.115(11 1/2%)	0.1175(11 3/4%)
1	1.11000000	1.11250000	1.11500000	1.11750000
2	0.58393365	0.58587278	0.58781324	0.58975502
3	0.40921307	0.41099354	0.41277636	0.41456150
4	0.32232635	0.32404848	0.32577388	0.32750254
5	0.27057031	0.27227397	0.27398177	0.27569370
6	0.23637656	0.23808142	0.23979125	0.24150602
7	0.21221527	0.21393228	0.21565505	0.21738354
8	0.19432105	0.19605678	0.19779902	0.19954772
9	0.18060166	0.18236022	0.18412597	0.18589888
10	0.16980143	0.17158539	0.17337721	0.17517682
11	0.16112101	0.16293200	0.16475144	0.16657927
12	0.15402729	0.15586625	0.15771422	0.15957110
13	0.14815099	0.15001840	0.15189530	0.15378160
14	0.14322820	0.14512417	0.14703008	0.14894582
15	0.13906524	0.14098964	0.14292436	0.14486928
16	0.13551675	0.13746923	0.13943238	0.14140603
17	0.13247148	0.13445157	0.13644259	0.13844437
18	0.12984287	0.13184994	0.13386817	0.13589736
19	0.12756250	0.12959585	0.13164053	0.13369632
20	0.12557564	0.12763448	0.12970478	0.13178629
21	0.12383793	0.12592145	0.12801648	0.13012278
22	0.12231310	0.12442041	0.12653927	0.12866939
23	0.12097118	0.12310138	0.12524311	0.12739607
24	0.11978721	0.12193938	0.12410302	0.12627781
25	0.11874024	0.12091345	0.12309803	0.12529365
26	0.11781258	0.12000589	0.12221044	0.12442588
27	0.11698916	0.11920165	0.12142521	0.12365948
28	0.11625715	0.11848788	0.12072951	0.12298163
29	0.11560547	0.11785355	0.12011230	0.12238131
30	0.11502460	0.11728914	0.11956410	0.12184907
31	0.11450627	0.11678639	0.11907667	0.12137670
32	0.11404329	0.11633815	0.11864289	0.12095709
33	0.11362938	0.11593816	0.11825653	0.12058405
34	0.11325905	0.11558096	0.11791215	0.12025218
35	0.11292749	0.11526175	0.11760499	0.11995675
36	0.11263044	0.11497633	0.11733086	0.11969361
37	0.11236416	0.11472097	0.11708610	0.11945912
38	0.11212535	0.11449240	0.11686745	0.11925006
39	0.11191107	0.11428872	0.11667204	0.11906360
40	0.11171873	0.11428772	0.11649734	0.11889724
41	0.11154601	0.11410436	0.11634111	0.11874876
42	0.11139086	0.11379275	0.11620134	0.11861621
43	0.11125146	0.11366067	0.11607628	0.11849785
44	0.11112617	0.11354221	0.11596434	0.11839214
45	0.11101354	0.11343594	0.11586413	0.11829770
46	0.11091227	0.11334059	0.11577441	0.11821331
47	0.11082119	0.11325502	0.11569405	0.11813790
48	0.11073926	0.11317821	0.11562208	0.11807051
49	0.11066556	0.11310925	0.11555761	0.11801026
50	0.11059924	0.11304734	0.11549985	0.11795640

Financial Tables

ANNUITY WHOSE PRESENT VALUE IS 1

$$a_{\overline{n}|i}^{-1} = \frac{i}{1 - v^n} = \measuredangle\,_{\overline{n}|i}^{-1} + i \text{ (Continued)}$$

Rate *i*

Periods n	0.12(12%)	0.1225(12 1/4%)	0.125(12 1/2%)	0.1275(12 3/4%)
1	1.12000000	1.12250000	1.12500000	1.12750000
2	0.59169811	0.59364252	0.59558824	0.59753525
3	0.41634898	0.41813877	0.41993088	0.42172528
4	0.32923444	0.33096957	0.33270791	0.33444946
5	0.27740973	0.27912985	0.28085404	0.28258228
6	0.24322572	0.24495031	0.24667978	0.24841410
7	0.21911774	0.22085759	0.22260308	0.22435416
8	0.20130284	0.20306434	0.20483219	0.20660632
9	0.18767889	0.18946595	0.19126000	0.19306101
10	0.17698416	0.17879917	0.18062178	0.18245193
11	0.16841540	0.17025977	0.17211228	0.17397287
12	0.16143681	0.16331125	0.16519434	0.16708598
13	0.15567720	0.15758197	0.15949582	0.16141865
14	0.15087125	0.15280625	0.15475071	0.15670450
15	0.14682424	0.14878911	0.15076375	0.15274802
16	0.14339002	0.14538419	0.14738839	0.14940246
17	0.14045673	0.14247949	0.14451248	0.14655552
18	0.13793731	0.13998783	0.14204873	0.14411980
19	0.13576300	0.13784037	0.13992820	0.14202627
20	0.13387878	0.13598200	0.13809573	0.14021974
21	0.13224009	0.13436815	0.13650671	0.13865551
22	0.13081051	0.13296234	0.13512463	0.13729709
23	0.12955996	0.13173450	0.13391940	0.13611437
24	0.12846344	0.13065960	0.13286599	0.13508230
25	0.12749997	0.12971667	0.13194344	0.13417996
26	0.12665186	0.12888804	0.13113409	0.13338968
27	0.12590409	0.12815870	0.13042295	0.13269652
28	0.12524387	0.12751587	0.12979728	0.13208774
29	0.12466021	0.12694860	0.12924614	0.13155246
30	0.12414366	0.12644748	0.12876016	0.13108133
31	0.12368606	0.12600436	0.12833123	0.13066629
32	0.12328033	0.12561221	0.12795235	0.13030037
33	0.12292031	0.12526490	0.12761744	0.12997755
34	0.12260064	0.12495711	0.12732121	0.12969256
35	0.12231662	0.12468418	0.12705905	0.12944085
36	0.12206414	0.12444204	0.12682692	0.12921842
37	0.12183959	0.12422712	0.12662130	0.12902178
38	0.12163980	0.12403627	0.12643908	0.12884787
39	0.12146197	0.12386674	0.12627755	0.12869402
40	0.12130363	0.12371611	0.12613431	0.12855788
41	0.12116260	0.12358222	0.12600726	0.12843737
42	0.12103696	0.12346319	0.12589454	0.12833068
43	0.12092500	0.12335734	0.12579452	0.12823621
44	0.12082521	0.12326319	0.12570574	0.12815253
45	0.12073625	0.12317944	0.12562693	0.12807840
46	0.12065694	0.12310493	0.12555696	0.12801273
47	0.12058621	0.12303862	0.12549483	0.12795455
48	0.12052312	0.12297961	0.12543966	0.12790298
49	0.12046686	0.12292709	0.12539065	0.12785728
50	0.12041666	0.12288033	0.12534713	0.12781678

ANNUITY WHOSE PRESENT VALUE IS 1

$$a_{\overline{n}|i}^{-1} = \frac{i}{1 - v^n} = o_{\overline{n}|i}^{-1} + i \text{ (Continued)}$$

Rate i

Periods

n	0.13(13%)	0.1325(13 1/4%)	0.135(13 1/2%)	0.1375(13 3/4%)
1	1.13000000	1.13250000	1.13500000	1.13750000
2	0.59948357	0.60143318	0.60338407	0.60533626
3	0.42352197	0.42533095	0.42712219	0.42892571
4	0.33619420	0.33794211	0.33969319	0.34144742
5	0.28431454	0.28605082	0.28779110	0.28953534
6	0.25015323	0.25189717	0.25364587	0.25539932
7	0.22611080	0.22787298	0.22964066	0.23141380
8	0.20838672	0.21017333	0.21196611	0.21376502
9	0.19486890	0.19668364	0.19850517	0.20033343
10	0.18428956	0.18613459	0.18798698	0.18984665
11	0.17584145	0.17771797	0.17960232	0.18149445
12	0.16898608	0.17089456	0.17281132	0.17473627
13	0.16335034	0.16529079	0.16723990	0.16919756
14	0.15866750	0.16063958	0.16262063	0.16461052
15	0.15474178	0.15674489	0.15875722	0.16077862
16	0.15142624	0.15345958	0.15550232	0.15755431
17	0.14860844	0.15067106	0.15274321	0.15482473
18	0.14620085	0.14829171	0.15039216	0.15250204
19	0.14413439	0.14625235	0.14837993	0.15051693
20	0.14235379	0.14449766	0.14665113	0.14881399
21	0.14081433	0.14298291	0.14516101	0.14734841
22	0.13947948	0.14167153	0.14387300	0.14608362
23	0.13831913	0.14053343	0.14275698	·0.14498953
24	0.13730826	0.13954357	0.14178795	0.14404113
25	0.13642593	0.13868104	0.14094502	0.14321757
26	0.13565451	0.13792825	0.14021061	0.14250129
27	0.13497907	0.13727029	0.13956987	0.14187749
28	0.13438693	0.13669451	0.13901017	0.14133359
29	0.13386722	0.13619009	0.13852075	0.14085887
30	0.13341065	0.13574778	0.13809239	0.14044416
31	0.13300919	0.13535959	0.13771717	0.14008159
32	0.13265593	0.13501867	0.13738826	0.13976439
33	0.13234487	0.13471906	0.13709978	0.13948672
34	0.13207081	0.13445560	0.13684661	0.13924352
35	0.13182922	0.13422382	0.13662432	0.13903042
36	0.13161616	0.13401982	0.13642908	0.13884362
37	0.13142819	0.13384021	0.13625752	0.13867981
38	0.13126229	0.13368201	0.13610672	0.13853612
39	0.13111582	0.13354263	0.13597413	0.13841004
40	0.13098648	0.13341980	0.13585753	0.13829940
41	0.13087223	0.13331152	0.13575496	0.13820228
42	0.13077129	0.13321606	0.13566472	0.13811700
43	0.13068209	0.13313189	0.13558532	0.13804213
44	0.13060326	0.13305765	0.13551543	0.13797637
45	0.13053357	0.13299216	0.13545392	0.13791861
46	0.13047196	0.13293439	0.13539977	0.13786787
47	0.13041749	0.13288342	0.13535209	0.13782330
48	0.13036933	0.13283845	0.13531012	0.13778414
49	0.13032673	0.13279876	0.13527316	0.13774973
50	0.13028906	0.13276374	0.13524061	0.13771950

ANNUITY WHOSE PRESENT VALUE IS 1

$$a_{\overline{n}|i}^{-1} = \frac{i}{1 - v^n} = s_{\overline{n}|i}^{-1} + i \text{ (Continued)}$$

Rate i

Periods n	0.14(14%)	0.1425(14 1/4%)	0.145(14 1/2%)	0.1475(14 3/4%)
1	1.14000000	1.14250000	1.14500000	1.14750000
2	0.60728972	0.60924446	0.61120047	0.61315774
3	0.43073148	0.43253950	0.43434976	0.43616225
4	0.34320478	0.34496527	0.34672887	0.34849557
5	0.29128355	0.29303569	0.29479175	0.29655171
6	0.25715750	0.25892037	0.26068791	0.26246010
7	0.23319238	0.23497635	0.23676570	0.23856038
8	0.21557002	0.21738107	0.21919813	0.22102115
9	0.20216838	0.20400997	0.20585814	0.20771284
10	0.19171354	0.19358759	0.19546874	0.19735692
11	0.18339427	0.18530171	0.18721669	0.18913914
12	0.17666933	0.17861039	0.18055938	0.18251621
13	0.17116366	0.17313811	0.17512079	0.17711161
14	0.16660914	0.16861637	0.17063208	0.17265616
15	0.16280896	0.16484811	0.16689593	0.16895229
16	0.15961540	0.16168543	0.16376426	0.16585172
17	0.15691544	0.15901517	0.16112376	0.16324105
18	0.15462115	0.15674931	0.15888634	0.16103206
19	0.15266316	0.15481841	0.15698249	0.15915520
20	0.15098600	0.15316697	0.15535667	0.15755491
21	0.14954486	0.15175015	0.15396405	0.15618633
22	0.14830317	0.15053139	0.15276805	0.15501292
23	0.14723081	0.14948059	0.15173360	0.15400462
24	0.14630284	0.14857282	0.15085081	0.15313656
25	0.14549841	0.14778727	0.15008390	0.15238803
26	0.14480001	0.14710649	0.14942046	0.15174165
27	0.14419288	0.14651575	0.14884582	0.15118281
28	0.14366449	0.14600257	0.14834755	0.15069916
29	0.14320417	0.14555634	0.14791510	0.15028018
30	0.14280279	0.14516799	0.14753947	0.14991696
31	0.14245256	0.14482978	0.14721297	0.14960186
32	0.14214675	0.14453505	0.14692900	0.14932834
33	0.14187958	0.14427806	0.14668188	0.14909079
34	0.14164604	0.14405387	0.14646674	0.14888439
35	0.14144181	0.14385821	0.14627935	0.14870498
36	0.14126315	0.14368739	0.14611609	0.14854899
37	0.14110680	0.14353822	0.14597380	0.14841332
38	0.14096993	0.14340790	0.14584976	0.14829529
39	0.14085010	0.14329403	0.14574160	0.14819258
40	0.14074514	0.14319451	0.14564727	0.14810319
41	0.14065321	0.14310752	0.14556498	0.14802538
42	0.14057266	0.14303146	0.14549319	0.14795764
43	0.14050208	0.14296496	0.14543055	0.14789866
44	0.14044023	0.14290680	0.14537588	0.14784729
45	0.14038602	0.14285593	0.14532817	0.14780256
46	0.14033850	0.14281144	0.14528653	0.14776360
47	0.14029684	0.14277252	0.14525018	0.14772966
48	0.14026032	0.14273848	0.14521845	0.14770010
49	0.14022830	0.14270869	0.14519075	0.14767435
50	0.14020022	0.14268263	0.14516657	0.14765192

ANNUITY WHOSE PRESENT VALUE IS 1

$$a_{\overline{n}|i}^{-1} = \frac{i}{1 - v^n} = \wp \ _{\overline{n}|i}^{-1} + i \ \text{(Continued)}$$

Rate i

Periods

n	0.15(15%)	0.1525(15 1/4%)	0.155(15 1/2%)	0.1575(15 3/4%)
1	1.15000000	1.15250000	1.15500000	1.15750000
2	0.61511628	0.61707607	0.61903712	0.62099942
3	0.43797696	0.43979389	0.44161302	0.44343435
4	0.35026535	0.35203821	0.35381412	0.35559308
5	0.29831555	0.30008326	0.30185481	0.30363019
6	0.26423691	0.26601831	0.26780429	0.26959482
7	0.24036036	0.24216562	0.24397611	0.24579181
8	0.22285009	0.22468491	0.22652558	0.22837204
9	0.20957402	0.21144162	0.21331560	0.21519591
10	0.19925206	0.20115412	0.20306301	0.20497869
11	0.19106898	0.19300614	0.19495054	0.19690210
12	0.18448078	0.18645300	0.18843279	0.19042007
13	0.17911046	0.18111723	0.18313183	0.18515416
14	0.17468849	0.17672895	0.17877743	0.18083381
15	0.17101705	0.17309009	0.17517126	0.17726045
16	0.16794769	0.17005201	0.17216453	0.17428511
17	0.16536686	0.16750105	0.16964345	0.17179390
18	0.16318629	0.16534885	0.16751958	0.16969831
19	0.16133635	0.16352576	0.16572323	0.16792859
20	0.15976147	0.16197616	0.16419878	0.16642913
21	0.15841679	0.16065521	0.16290138	0.16515510
22	0.15726577	0.15952639	0.16179454	0.16407003
23	0.15627839	0.15855970	0.16084832	0.16314401
24	0.15542983	0.15773038	0.16003797	0.16235238
25	0.15469940	0.15701778	0.15934293	0.16167462
26	0.15406981	0.15640468	0.15874603	0.16109362
27	0.15352648	0.15587657	0.15823283	0.16059503
28	0.15305713	0.15542122	0.15779118	0.16016676
29	0.15265133	0.15502827	0.15741078	0.15979860
30	0.15230020	0.15468893	0.15708290	0.15948190
31	0.15199618	0.15439569	0.15680013	0.15920930
32	0.15173280	0.15414215	0.15655613	0.15897454
33	0.15150452	0.15392283	0.15634549	0.15877228
34	0.15130675	0.15373304	0.15616357	0.15859795
35	0.15113485	0.15356874	0.15600641	0.15844766
36	0.15098586	0.15342646	0.15587059	0.15831804
37	0.15085653	0.15330322	0.15575319	0.15820623
38	0.15074426	0.15319646	0.15565169	0.15810976
39	0.15064676	0.15310393	0.15556391	0.15802652
40	0.15056209	0.15302375	0.15548800	0.15795467
41	0.15048853	0.15295424	0.15542233	0.15789265
42	0.15042463	0.15289398	0.15536552	0.15783910
43	0.15036911	0.15284173	0.15531637	0.15779288
44	0.15032086	0.15279642	0.15527384	0.15775296
45	0.15027893	0.15275713	0.15523703	0.15771849
46	0.15024249	0.15272306	0.15520518	0.15768873
47	0.15021082	0.15269351	0.15517761	0.15766302
48	0.15018328	0.15266787	0.15515375	0.15764082
49	0.15015935	0.15264564	0.15513310	0.15762164
50	0.15013855	0.15262635	0.15511523	0.15760508

Financial Tables

ANNUITY WHOSE PRESENT VALUE IS 1

$$a_{\overline{n}|i}^{-1} = \frac{i}{1 - v^n} = a_{\overline{n}|i}^{-1} + i \text{ (Continued)}$$

Rate i

Periods				
n	0.16(16%)	0.1625(16 1/4%)	0.165(16 1/2%)	0.1675(16 3/4%)
1	1.16000000	1.16250000	1.16500000	1.16750000
2	0.62296296	0.62492775	0.62689376	0.62886101
3	0.44525787	0.44708357	0.44891145	0.45074149
4	0.35737507	0.35916008	0.36094810	0.36273912
5	0.30540938	0.30719236	0.30897911	0.31076962
6	0.27138987	0.27318942	0.27499344	0.27680191
7	0.24761268	0.24943869	0.25126981	0.25310600
8	0.23022426	0.23208220	0.23394581	0.23581505
9	0.21708249	0.21897529	0.22087426	0.22277935
10	0.20690108	0.20883013	0.21076578	0.21270795
11	0.19886075	0.20082642	0.20279903	0.20477852
12	0.19241473	0.19441670	0.19642589	0.19844221
13	0.18718411	0.18922158	0.19126648	0.19331870
14	0.18289797	0.18496981	0.18704920	0.18913604
15	0.17935752	0.18146235	0.18357480	0.18569476
16	0.17641362	0.17854990	0.18069381	0.18284523
17	0.17395225	0.17611834	0.17829203	0.18047315
18	0.17188485	0.17407906	0.17628076	0.17848979
19	0.17014166	0.17236225	0.17459019	0.17682532
20	0.16866703	0.17091229	0.17316471	0.17542413
21	0.16741617	0.16968439	0.17195956	0.17424151
22	0.16635264	0.16864216	0.17093840	0.17324116
23	0.16544658	0.16775581	0.17007149	0.17239342
24	0.16467339	0.16700078	0.16933434	0.17167387
25	0.16401262	0.16635670	0.16870667	0.17106231
26	0.16344723	0.16580662	0.16817160	0.17054195
27	0.16296294	0.16533634	0.16771501	0.17009875
28	0.16254775	0.16493392	0.16732506	0.16972097
29	0.16219153	0.16458932	0.16699179	0.16939872
30	0.16188568	0.16429404	0.16670677	0.16912367
31	0.16162295	0.16404089	0.16646290	0.16888879
32	0.16139714	0.16382374	0.16625413	0.16868813
33	0.16120298	0.16363740	0.16607535	0.16851664
34	0.16103598	0.16347746	0.16592220	0.16837002
35	0.16089229	0.16334012	0.16579096	0.16824465
36	0.16076862	0.16322216	0.16567847	0.16813741
37	0.16066217	0.16312083	0.16558204	0.16804566
38	0.16057051	0.16303376	0.16549936	0.16796716
39	0.16049158	0.16295894	0.16542845	0.16789997
40	0.16042359	0.16289463	0.16536763	0.16584247
41	0.16036503	0.16283935	0.16531546	0.16779325
42	0.16031458	0.16279183	0.16527071	0.16775112
43	0.16027112	0.16275097	0.16523232	0.16771504
44	0.16023367	0.16271584	0.16519937	0.16768416
45	0.16020140	0.16268564	0.16517111	0.16765771
46	0.16017359	0.16265966	0.16514685	0.16763507
47	0.16014962	0.16263733	0.16512604	0.16761568
48	0.16012897	0.16261812	0.16510817	0.16759907
49	0.16011117	0.16260159	0.16509284	0.16758485
50	0.16009583	0.16258739	0.16507969	0.16757267

ANNUITY WHOSE PRESENT VALUE IS 1

$$a_{\overline{n}|i}^{-1} = \frac{i}{1 - v^n} = \! \backslash\, \overline{n}|i^{-1} + i \text{ (Continued)}$$

Rate *i*

Periods				
n	0.17(17%)	0.1725(17 1/4%)	0.175(17 1/2%)	0.1775(17 3/4%)
1	0.17000000	1.17250000	1.17500000	1.17750000
2	0.63082949	0.63279919	0.63477011	0.63674225
3	0.45257368	0.45440802	0.45624451	0.45808312
4	0.36453311	0.36633008	0.36813000	0.36993287
5	0.31256386	0.31436183	0.31616349	0.31796883
6	0.27861480	0.28043210	0.28225376	0.28407978
7	0.25494724	0.25679349	0.25864473	0.26050090
8	0.23768989	0.23957028	0.24145618	0.24334756
9	0.22469051	0.22660769	0.22853083	0.23045990
10	0.21465660	0.21661165	0.21857305	0.22054073
11	0.20676479	0.20875779	0.21075744	0.21276366
12	0.20046558	0.20249591	0.20453311	0.20657711
13	0.19537814	0.19744471	0.19951831	0.20159884
14	0.19123022	0.19333162	0.19544013	0.19755564
15	0.18782209	0.18995669	0.19209841	0.19424715
16	0.18500401	0.18717002	0.18934312	0.19152319
17	0.18266157	0.18485713	0.18705970	0.18926913
18	0.18070600	0.18292922	0.18515930	0.18739610
19	0.17906745	0.18131643	0.18357210	0.18583429
20	0.17769036	0.17996323	0.18224257	0.18452821
21	0.17653004	0.17882497	0.18112613	0.18343334
22	0.17555025	0.17786548	0.18018668	0.18251366
23	0.17472141	0.17705526	0.17939480	0.18173984
24	0.17401917	0.17637005	0.17872632	0.18108779
25	0.17342343	0.17578982	0.17816131	0.18053770
26	0.17291747	0.17529797	0.17768326	0.18007315
27	0.17248736	0.17488065	0.17727842	0.17968050
28	0.17212144	0.17452629	0.17693533	0.17934838
29	0.17180992	0.17422520	0.17664438	0.17906729
30	0.17154455	0.17396922	0.17639751	0.17882926
31	0.17131839	0.17375150	0.17618796	0.17862761
32	0.17112556	0.17356624	0.17601001	0.17845672
33	0.17096109	0.17340864	0.17585884	0.17831184
34	0.17082077	0.17327428	0.17573040	0.17818898
35	0.17070102	0.17315993	0.17562123	0.17808478
36	0.17059880	0.17306252	0.17552843	0.17799638
37	0.17051154	0.17297953	0.17544952	0.17792138
38	0.17043702	0.17290882	0.17538243	0.17785773
39	0.17037338	0.17284855	0.17532536	0.17780371
40	0.17031903	0.17279718	0.17527683	0.17775786
41	0.17027260	0.17275340	0.17523554	0.17771895
42	0.17023294	0.17271607	0.17520042	0.17768591
43	0.17019905	0.17268425	0.17517054	0.17765786
44	0.17017010	0.17265712	0.17514512	0.17763404
45	0.17014536	0.17263398	0.17512349	0.17761382
46	0.17012423	0.17261426	0.17510509	0.17759666
47	0.17010617	0.17259744	0.17508943	0.17758208
48	0.17009073	0.17258310	0.17507610	0.17756970
49	0.17007754	0.17257087	0.17506477	0.17755919
50	0.17006627	0.17256044	0.17505512	0.17755027

Financial Tables

ANNUITY WHOSE PRESENT VALUE IS 1

$$a_{\overline{n}|i}^{-1} = \frac{i}{1 - v^n} = a_{\overline{n}|i}^{-1} + i \text{ (Continued)}$$

Rate *i*

Periods				
n	0.18(18%)	0.1825(18 1/4%)	0.185(18 1/2%)	0.1875(18 3/4%)
1	1.18000000	1.18250000	1.18500000	1.18750000
2	0.63871560	0.64069015	0.64266590	0.64464286
3	0.45992386	0.46176672	0.46361168	0.46545874
4	0.37173867	0.37354739	0.37535902	0.37717354
5	0.31977784	0.32159050	0.32340678	0.32522668
6	0.28591013	0.28774478	0.28958370	0.29142688
7	0.26236200	0.26422798	0.26609881	0.26797446
8	0.24524436	0.24714655	0.24905409	0.25096694
9	0.23239482	0.23433557	0.23628208	0.23823431
10	0.22251464	0.22449471	0.22648089	0.22847311
11	0.21477639	0.21679555	0.21882106	0.22085287
12	0.20862781	0.21068513	0.21274900	0.21481932
13	0.20368621	0.20578032	0.20788107	0.20998838
14	0.19967806	0.20180726	0.20394315	0.20608562
15	0.19640278	0.19856519	0.20073426	0.20290987
16	0.19371008	0.19590369	0.19810386	0.20031049
17	0.19148527	0.19370800	0.19593717	0.19817265
18	0.18963946	0.19188923	0.19414527	0.19640744
19	0.18810284	0.19037760	0.19265842	0.19494515
20	0.18681998	0.18911773	0.19142130	0.19373054
21	0.18574643	0.18806525	0.19038962	0.19271939
22	0.18484626	0.18718429	0.18952761	0.19187604
23	0.18409020	0.18644572	0.18880622	0.19117156
24	0.18345430	0.18582566	0.18820172	0.19058231
25	0.18291883	0.18530451	0.18769459	0.19008891
26	0.18246748	0.18486607	0.18726876	0.18967539
27	0.18208672	0.18449691	0.18691091	0.18932856
28	0.18176528	0.18418587	0.18660998	0.18903747
29	0.18149377	0.18392365	0.18635679	0.18879304
30	0.18126431	0.18370249	0.18614366	0.18858769
31	0.18107030	0.18351587	0.18596419	0.18841511
32	0.18090621	0.18335835	0.18581300	0.18827003
33	0.18076739	0.18322535	0.18568560	0.18814802
34	0.18064990	0.18311303	0.18557823	0.18804541
35	0.18055046	0.18301815	0.18548772	0.18795908
36	0.18046628	0.18293799	0.18541141	0.18788644
37	0.18039499	0.18287025	0.18534706	0.18782532
38	0.18033463	0.18281301	0.18529279	0.18777388
39	0.18028350	0.18276464	0.18524702	0.18773058
40	0.18024020	0.18272374	0.18520841	0.18769414
41	0.18020352	0.18268918	0.18517585	0.18766346
42	0.18017244	0.18265995	0.18514837	0.18763763
43	0.18014612	0.18263525	0.18512519	0.18761588
44	0.18012381	0.18261436	0.18510564	0.18759758
45	0.18010491	0.18259670	0.18508914	0.18758216
46	0.18008890	0.18258177	0.18507521	0.18756919
47	0.18007534	0.18256915	0.18506347	0.18755826
48	0.18006384	0.18225847	0.18505356	0.18754906
49	0.18005410	0.18254945	0.18504519	0.18754131
50	0.18004584	0.18254181	0.18503814	0.18753479

ANNUITY WHOSE PRESENT VALUE IS 1

$$a_{\overline{n}|i}^{-1} = \frac{i}{1 - v^n} = s_{\overline{n}|i}^{-1} + i \text{ (Continued)}$$

Rate i

Periods n	0.19(19%)	0.1925(19 1/4%)	0.195(19 1/2%)	0.1975(19 3/4%)	0.20(20%)
1	1.19000000	1.19250000	1.19500000	1.19750000	1.20000000
2	0.64662100	0.64860034	0.65058087	0.65256257	0.65454545
3	0.46730789	0.46915913	0.47101245	0.47286783	0.47472527
4	0.37899094	0.38081121	0.38263434	0.38446031	0.38628912
5	0.32705017	0.32887723	0.33070785	0.33254202	0.33437970
6	0.29327429	0.29512591	0.29698170	0.29884166	0.30070575
7	0.26985490	0.27174010	0.27363002	0.27552464	0.27742393
8	0.25288506	0.25480841	9.25673694	0.25867063	0.26060942
9	0.24019220	0.24215571	0.24412479	0.24609939	0.24807946
10	0.23047131	0.23247543	0.23448542	0.23650122	0.23852276
11	0.22289090	0.22493508	0.22698533	0.22904159	0.23110379
12	0.21689602	0.21897902	0.22106822	0.22316357	0.22526496
13	0.21210215	0.21422229	0.21634870	0.21848130	0.22062000
14	0.20823456	0.21038988	0.21255147	0.21471923	0.21689306
15	0.20509191	0.20728026	0.20947482	0.21167548	0.21388212
16	0.20252345	0.20474261	0.20696786	0.20919907	0.21143614
17	0.20041431	0.20266201	0.20491564	0.20717506	0.20944015
18	0.19867559	0.20094960	0.20322932	0.20551463	0.20780539
19	0.19723765	0.19953577	0.20183936	0.20414830	0.20646245
20	0.19604529	0.19836345	0.20069075	0.20302117	0.20535653
21	0.19505440	0.19739451	0.19973956	0.20208942	0.20444394
22	0.19422943	0.19658763	0.19895049	0.20131787	0.20368962
23	0.19354156	0.19591607	0.19829496	0.20067807	0.20306526
24	0.19296727	0.19535645	0.19774971	0.20014689	0.20254787
25	0.19248730	0.19488962	0.19729573	0.19970547	0.20211873
26	0.19208581	0.19449987	0.19691743	0.19933835	0.20176250
27	0.19174971	0.19417423	0.19660197	0.19903280	0.20146659
28	0.19146819	0.19390200	0.19633877	0.19877836	0.20122067
29	0.19123225	0.19367430	0.19611905	0.19856639	0.20101619
30	0.19103443	0.19348377	0.19593557	0.19838972	0.20084611
31	0.19086852	0.19332428	0.19578229	0.19824243	0.20070459
32	0.19072931	0.19319075	0.19565421	0.19811960	0.20058682
33	0.19061249	0.19307891	0.19554716	0.19801714	0.20048877
34	0.19051444	0.19298522	0.19545766	0.19793167	0.20040715
35	0.19043211	0.19290673	0.19538283	0.19786034	0.20033917
36	0.19036299	0.19284096	0.19532026	0.19780082	0.20028256
37	0.19030494	0.19278583	0.19526793	0.19775115	0.20023542
38	0.19025619	0.19273964	0.19522416	0.19770968	0.20019614
39	0.19021524	0.19270091	0.19518754	0.19767507	0.20016342
40	0.19018084	0.19266845	0.19515692	0.19764617	0.20013617
41	0.19015194	0.19264124	0.19513129	0.19762205	0.20011346
42	0.19012767	0.19261843	0.19510986	0.19760191	0.20009454
43	0.19010727	0.19259930	0.19509192	0.19758510	0.20007878
44	0.19009013	0.19258326	0.19507692	0.19757106	0.20006564
45	0.19007574	0.19256982	0.19506436	0.19755933	0.20005470
46	0.19006364	0.19255854	0.19505386	0.19754955	0.20004558
47	0.19005348	0.19254909	0.19504507	0.19754137	0.20003798
48	0.19004494	0.19254116	0.19503771	0.19753455	0.20003165
49	0.19003776	0.19253452	0.19503156	0.19752885	0.20002638
50	0.19003173	0.19252895	0.19502641	0.19752409	0.20002198

Financial Tables

COMPOUND AMOUNT OF 1 FOR FRACTIONAL PERIODS,

$$(1 + i)^{1/p}$$

p	i = ¼%	5/12%	1/2%	7/12%	3/4%
2	1.0012492	1.0020812	1.0024969	1.0029124	1.0037430
3	1.0008326	1.0013870	1.0016639	1.0019407	1.0024938
4	1.0006244	1.0010400	1.0012477	1.0014552	1.0018697
6	1.0004162	1.0006932	1.0008316	1.0009699	1.0012461
12	1.0002089	1.0003466	1.0004157	1.0004848	1.0006229
13	1.0001921	1.0003199	1.0003837	1.0004475	1.0005749
26	1.0000960	1.0001599	1.0001919	1.0002237	1.0002874
52	1.0000480	1.0000800	1.0000959	1.0001119	1.0001437
365	1.0000068	1.0000114	1.0000137	1.0000159	1.0000205

p	1%	1 1/8%	1 1/4%	1 1/2%	1 3/4%
2	1.0049876	1.0056093	1.0062306	1.0074721	1.0087121
3	1.0033223	1.0037360	1.0041494	1.0049752	1.0057996
4	1.0024907	1.0028008	1.0031105	1.0037291	1.0043466
6	1.0016598	1.0018663	1.0020726	1.0024845	1.0028956
12	1.0008295	1.0009327	1.0010357	1.0012415	1.0014468
13	1.0007657	1.0008609	1.0009560	1.0011459	1.0013354
26	1.0003828	1.0004304	1.0004779	1.0005728	1.0006675
52	1.0001914	1.0002152	1.0002389	1.0002864	1.0003337
365	1.0000273	1.0000307	1.0000340	1.0000408	1.0000475

p	2%	2 1/4%	2 1/2%	2 3/4%	3%
2	1.0099505	1.0111874	1.0124228	1.0136568	1.01488916
3	1.0066227	1.0074444	1.0082648	1.0090839	1.00990163
4	1.0049629	1.0055782	1.0061922	1.0068052	1.00741707
6	1.0033059	1.0037153	1.0041239	1.0045317	1.00493862
12	1.0016516	1.0018559	1.0020598	1.0022633	1.00246627
13	1.0015244	1.0017130	1.0019012	1.0020890	1.00227634
26	1.0007619	1.0008562	1.0009502	1.0010440	1.00113752
52	1.0003809	1.0004280	1.0004750	1.0005218	1.00056860
365	1.0000543	1.0000610	1.0000676	1.0000743	1.00008099

p	3 1/4%	3 1/2%	3 3/4%	4%	4 1/4%
2	1.01612007	1.01734950	1.01857744	1.01980390	1.02102889
3	1.01071805	1.01153314	1.01234693	1.01315940	1.01397058
4	1.00802781	1.00863745	1.00924598	1.00985341	1.01045974
6	1.00534474	1.00575004	1.00615452	1.00655820	1.00696106
12	1.00266881	1.00287090	1.00307254	1.00327374	1.00347450
13	1.00246326	1.00264977	1.00283586	1.00302153	1.00320680
26	1.00123087	1.00132401	1.00141692	1.00150963	1.00160212
52	1.00061525	1.00066178	1.00070821	1.00075453	1.00080074
365	1.00008763	1.00009425	1.00010087	1.00010746	1.00011404

p	4 1/2%	4 3/4%	5%	5 1/4%	5 1/2%
2	1.02225242	1.02347447	1.02469508	1.02591423	1.02713193
3	1.01478046	1.01558905	1.01639636	1.01720238	1.01800713
4	1.01106499	1.01166915	1.01227223	1.01287424	1.01347517
6	1.00736312	1.00776438	1.00816485	1.00856452	1.00896339
12	1.00367481	1.00387468	1.00407412	1.00427313	1.00447170
13	1.00339165	1.00357610	1.00376014	1.00394378	1.00412701
26	1.00169439	1.00178645	1.00187831	1.00196995	1.00206138
52	1.00084684	1.00089283	1.00093871	1.00098449	1.00103016
365	1.00012060	1.00012715	1.00013368	1.00014020	1.00014670

COMPOUND AMOUNT OF 1 FOR FRACTIONAL PERIODS

$$(1 + i)^{1/p} \text{ (Continued)}$$

p	5 3/4%	6%	6 1/4%	6 1/2%	6 3/4%
2	1.02834819	1.02956301	1.03077641	1.03198837	1.03319892
3	1.01881061	1.01961282	1.02041378	1.02121347	1.02201192
4	1.01407504	1.01467385	1.01527159	1.01586828	1.01646393
6	1.00936149	1.00975879	1.01015532	1.01055107	1.01094605
12	1.00466984	1.00486755	1.00506483	1.00526169	1.00545813
13	1.00430985	1.00449228	1.00467432	1.00485597	1.00503722
26	1.00215261	1.00224363	1.00233444	1.00242504	1.00251545
52	1.00107572	1.00112118	1.00116654	1.00121179	1.00125693
365	1.00015318	1.00015965	1.00016611	1.00017255	1.00017897

p	7%	7 1/4%	7 1/2%	7 3/4%	8%
2	1.03440804	1.03561576	1.03682207	1.03802697	1.03923048
3	1.02280912	1.02360508	1.02439981	1.02519330	1.02598557
4	1.01705853	1.01765208	1.01824460	1.01883609	1.01942655
6	1.01134026	1.01173370	1.01212638	1.01251830	1.01290946
12	1.00565415	1.00584974	1.00604492	1.00623968	1.00643403
13	1.00521808	1.00539855	1.00557863	1.00575833	1.00593764
26	1.00260564	1.00269564	1.00278544	1.00287503	1.00296443
52	1.00130197	1.00134691	1.00139175	1.00143648	1.00148112
365	1.00018538	1.00019178	1.00019816	1.00020452	1.00021087

p	8 1/4%	8 1/2%	8 3/4%	9%	9 1/4%
2	1.04043260	1.04163333	1.04283268	1.04403065	1.04522725
3	1.02677661	1.02756644	1.02835506	1.02914247	1.02992867
4	1.02001598	1.02060440	1.02119179	1.02177818	1.02236356
6	1.01329986	1.01368952	1.01407843	1.01446659	1.01485402
12	1.00662797	1.00682149	1.00701461	1.00720732	1.00739963
13	1.00611657	1.00629512	1.00647328	1.00665107	1.00682849
26	1.00305362	1.00314262	1.00323142	1.00332003	1.00340844
52	1.00152565	1.00157008	1.00161441	1.00165864	1.00170277
365	1.00021721	1.00022353	1.00022984	1.00023613	1.00024241

p	9 1/2%	9 3/4%	10%	10 1/4%	10 1/2%
2	1.04642248	1.04761634	1.04880885	1.05000000	1.05118980
3	1.03071368	1.03149749	1.03228012	1.03306155	1.03384181
4	1.02294793	1.02353131	1.02411369	1.02469508	1.02527548
6	1.01524070	1.01562665	1.01601187	1.01639636	1.01678012
12	1.00759153	1.00778304	1.00797414	1.00816485	1.00835516
13	1.00700553	1.00718220	1.00735849	1.00753442	1.00770998
26	1.00349665	1.00358467	1.00367250	1.00376014	1.00384759
52	1.00174680	1.00179073	1.00183457	1.00187831	1.00192195
365	1.00024867	1.00025492	1.00026116	1.00026738	1.00027359

p	10 3/4%	11%	11 1/4%	11 1/2%	11 3/4%
2	1.05237826	1.05356538	1.05475116	1.05593560	1.05711873
3	1.03462089	1.03539881	1.03617555	1.03695113	1.03772555
4	1.02585489	1.02643333	1.02701079	1.02758727	1.02816279
6	1.01716316	1.01754548	1.01792708	1.01830797	1.01868815
12	1.00854507	1.00873459	1.00892373	1.00911247	1.00930082
13	1.00788517	1.00806000	1.00823447	1.00840857	1.00858231
26	1.00393485	1.00402191	1.00410879	1.00419548	1.00428199
52	1.00196549	1.00200894	1.00205229	1.00209555	1.00213871
365	1.00027978	1.00028596	1.00029212	1.00029828	1.00030441

Financial Tables

COMPOUND AMOUNT OF 1 FOR FRACTIONAL PERIODS
$(1 + i)^{1/p}$ (Continued)

p	12%	12 1/4%	12 1/2%	12 3/4%	13%
2	1.05830052	1.05948101	1.06066017	1.06183803	1.06301458
3	1.03849882	1.03927094	1.04004191	1.04081174	1.04158044
4	1.02873734	1.02931094	1.02988357	1.03045525	1.03102598
6	1.01906762	1.01944639	1.01982445	1.02020181	1.02057848
12	1.00948879	1.00967638	1.00986358	1.01005040	1.01023684
13	1.00875570	1.00892873	1.00910140	1.00927372	1.00944569
26	1.00436831	1.00445444	1.00454039	1.00462616	1.00471174
52	1.00218177	1.00222475	1.00226763	1.00231041	1.00235310
365	1.00031054	1.00031665	1.00032275	1.00032883	1.00033490

p	13 1/4%	13 1/2%	13 3/4%	14%	14 1/4%
2	1.06418983	1.06536379	1.06653645	1.06770783	1.06887792
3	1.04234800	1.04311443	1.04387974	1.04464393	1.04540700
4	1.03159577	1.03216461	1.03273252	1.03329948	1.03386552
6	1.02095445	1.02132974	1.02170433	1.02207824	1.02245146
12	1.01042291	1.01060860	1.01079391	1.01097885	1.01116342
13	1.00961730	1.00978857	1.00995949	1.01013006	1.01030029
26	1.00479715	1.00488237	1.00496741	1.00505227	1.00513695
52	1.00239570	1.00243821	1.00248063	1.00252295	1.00256519
365	1.00034096	1.00034700	1.00035303	1.00035905	1.00036505

p	14 1/2%	14 3/4%	15%	15 1/4%	15 1/2%
2	1.07004673	1.07121426	1.07238053	1.07354553	1.07470926
3	1.04616896	1.04692981	1.04768955	1.04844820	1.04920575
4	1.03443063	1.03499481	1.03555808	1.03612042	1.03668185
6	1.02282401	1.02319588	1.02356707	1.02393760	1.02430745
12	1.01134762	1.01153145	1.01171492	1.01189802	1.01208075
13	1.01047017	1.01063972	1.01080892	1.01097778	1.01114630
26	1.00522146	1.00530578	1.00538993	1.00547391	1.00555771
52	1.00260733	1.00264938	1.00269134	1.00273322	1.00277500
365	1.00037104	1.00037702	1.00038298	1.00038893	1.00039487

p	15 3/4%	16%	16 1/4%	16 1/2%	16 3/4%
2	1.07587174	1.07703296	1.07819293	1.07935166	1.08050914
3	1.04996221	1.05071757	1.05147186	1.05222506	1.05297719
4	1.03724237	1.03780199	1.03836069	1.03891850	1.03947542
6	1.02467663	1.02504516	1.02541302	1.02578022	1.02614677
12	1.01226313	1.01244514	1.01262679	1.01280809	1.01298903
13	1.01131449	1.01148235	1.01164986	1.01181705	1.01198391
26	1.00564133	1.00572479	1.00580807	1.00589117	1.00597411
52	1.00281670	1.00285831	1.00289983	1.00294126	1.00298261
365	1.00040080	1.00040671	1.00041261	1.00041850	1.00042438

p	17%	17 1/4%	17 1/2%	17 3/4%	18%
2	1.08166538	1.08282039	1.08397417	1.08512672	1.08627805
3	1.05372824	1.05447823	1.05522715	1.05597501	1.05672181
4	1.04003143	1.04058656	1.04114080	1.04169416	1.04224664
6	1.02651266	1.02687790	1.02724250	1.02760644	1.02796975
12	1.01316961	1.01334984	1.01352972	1.01370925	1.01388843
13	1.01215044	1.01231663	1.01248251	1.01264805	1.01281328
26	1.00605687	1.00613947	1.00622190	1.00630416	1.00638625
52	1.00302387	1.00306504	1.00310612	1.00314713	1.00318804
365	1.00043024	1.00043609	1.00044193	1.00044775	1.00045357

COMPOUND AMOUNT OF 1 FOR FRACTIONAL PERIODS

$$(1 + i)^{1/p} \text{ (Continued)}$$

p	18 1/4%	18 1/2%	18 3/4%	19%
2	1.08742816	1.08857705	1.08972474	1.09087121
3	1.05746755	1.05821225	1.05895590	1.05969850
4	1.04279823	1.04334896	1.04389881	1.04444780
6	1.02833241	1.02869444	1.02905583	1.02941658
12	1.01406726	1.01424575	1.01442389	1.01460169
13	1.01297817	1.01314275	1.01330701	1.01347095
26	1.00646817	1.00654993	1.00663152	1.00671294
52	1.00322887	1.00326962	1.00331028	1.00335086
365	1.00045937	1.00046516	1.00047093	1.00047670

p	19 1/4%	19 1/2%	19 3/4%	20%
2	1.09201648	1.09316056	1.09430343	1.09544512
3	1.06044007	1.06118060	1.06192010	1.06265857
4	1.04499593	1.04554319	1.04608959	1.04663514
6	1.02977671	1.03013620	1.03049507	1.03085332
12	1.01477914	1.01495626	1.01513303	1.01530947
13	1.01363457	1.01379788	1.01396087	1.01412354
26	1.00679421	1.00687530	1.00695624	1.00703701
52	1.00339135	1.00343176	1.00347209	1.00351234
365	1.00048245	1.00048819	1.00049392	1.00049964

COMMISSIONERS 1941 STANDARD ORDINARY MORTALITY TABLE*

x	l_x	d_x	p_x	$\overset{\circ}{e}_x$	x	l_x	d_x	p_x	$\overset{\circ}{e}_x$
0	1 023 102	23 102	.977 42	62.33	50	810 900	9 990	.987 68	21.37
1	1 000 000	5 770	.994 23	62.76	51	800 910	10 628	.986 73	20.64
2	994 230	4 116	.995 86	62.12	52	790 282	11 301	.985 70	19.91
3	990 114	3 347	.996 62	61.37	53	778 981	12 020	.984 57	19.19
4	986 767	2 950	.997 01	60.58	54	766 961	12 770	.983 35	18.48
5	983 817	2 715	.997 24	59.76	55	754 191	13 560	.982 02	17.78
6	981 102	2 561	.997 39	58.92	56	740 631	14 390	.980 57	17.10
7	978 541	2 417	.997 53	58.08	57	726 241	15 251	.979 00	16.43
8	976 124	2 255	.997 69	57.22	58	710 990	16 147	.977 29	15.77
9	973 869	2 065	.997 88	56.35	59	694 843	17 072	.975 43	15.13
10	971 804	1 914	.998 03	55.47	60	677 771	18 022	.973 41	14.50
11	969 890	1 852	.998 09	54.58	61	659 749	18 988	.971 22	13.88
12	968 038	1 859	.998 08	53.68	62	640 761	19 979	.968 82	13.27
13	966 179	1 913	.998 02	52.78	63	620 782	20 958	.966 24	12.69
14	964 266	1 996	.997 93	51.89	64	599 824	21 942	.963 42	12.11
15	962 270	2 069	.997 85	50.99	65	577 882	22 907	.960 36	11.55
16	960 201	2 103	.997 81	50.10	66	554 975	23 842	.957 04	11.01
17	958 098	2 156	.997 75	49.21	67	531 133	24 730	.953 44	10.48
18	955 942	2 199	.997 70	48.32	68	506 403	25 553	.949 54	9.97
19	953 743	2 260	.997 63	47.43	69	480 850	26 302	.945 30	9.47
20	951 483	2 312	.997 57	46.54	70	454 548	26 955	.940 70	8.99
21	949 171	2 382	.997 49	45.66	71	427 593	27 481	.935 73	8.52
22	946 789	2 452	.997 41	44.77	72	400 112	27 872	.930 34	8.08
23	944 337	2 531	.997 32	43.88	73	372 240	28 104	.924 50	7.64
24	941 806	2 609	.997 23	43.00	74	344 136	28 154	.918 19	7.23
25	939 197	2 705	.997 12	42.12	75	315 982	28 009	.911 36	6.82
26	936 492	2 800	.997 01	41.24	76	287 973	27 651	.903 98	6.44
27	933 692	2 904	.996 89	40.36	77	260 322	27 071	.896 01	6.07
28	930 788	3 025	.996 75	39.49	78	233 251	26 262	.887 41	5.72
29	927 763	3 154	.996 60	38.61	79	206 989	25 224	.878 14	5.38
30	924 609	3 292	.996 44	37.74	80	181 765	23 966	.868 15	5.06
31	921 317	3 437	.996 27	36.88	81	157 799	22 502	.857 40	4.75
32	917 880	3 598	.996 08	36.01	82	135 297	20 857	.845 84	4.46
33	914 282	3 767	.995 88	35.15	83	114 440	19 062	.833 43	4.18
34	910 515	3 961	.995 65	34.29	84	95 378	17 157	.820 12	3.91
35	906 554	4 161	.995 41	33.44	85	78 221	15 185	.805 87	3.66
36	902 393	4 386	.995 14	32.59	86	63 036	13 198	.790 63	3.42
37	898 007	4 625	.994 85	31.75	87	49 838	11 245	.774 37	3.19
38	893 382	4 878	.994 54	30.91	88	38 593	9 378	.757 00	2.98
39	888 504	5 162	.994 19	30.08	89	29 215	7 638	.738 56	2.77
40	883 342	5 459	.993 82	29.25	90	21 577	6 063	.719 01	2.58
41	877 883	5 785	.993 41	28.43	91	15 514	4 681	.698 27	2.39
42	872 098	6 131	.992 97	27 62	92	10 833	3 506	.676 36	2.21
43	865 967	6 503	.992 49	26.81	93	7 327	2 540	.653 34	2.03
44	859 464	6 910	.991 96	26.01	94	4 787	1 776	.629 00	1.84
45	852 554	7 340	.991 39	25.21	95	3 011	1 193	.603 79	1.63
46	845 214	7 801	.990 77	24.43	96	1 818	813	.552 81	1.37
47	837 413	8 299	.990 09	23.65	97	1 005	551	.451 74	1.08
48	829 114	8 822	.989 36	22.88	98	454	329	.275 33	.78
49	820 292	9 392	.988 55	22.12	99	125	125	.000 00	.50

* Reproduced by permission of the Actuarial Society of America.

COMMUTATION COLUMNS 2 1/2%
Commissioners 1941 Standard Ordinary Mortality Table*

x	D_x	N_x	C_x	M_x	$1 + a_x$	A_x
0	1 023 102.00	31 374 230	22 538.536 6	257 876.88	30.665 8	0.252 054
1	975 609.76	30 351 128	5 491.969 1	235 338.35	31.109 9	.241 222
2	946 322.43	29 375 518	3 822.115 2	229 846.38	31.041 8	.242 884
3	919 419.28	28 429 196	3 032.216 8	226 024.26	30.920 8	.245 834
4	893 962.20	27 509 776	2 607.370 2	222 992.05	30.772 9	.249 442
5	869 550.88	26 615 814	2 341.136 0	220 384.68	30.608 7	.253 447
6	846 001.18	25 746 263	2 154.480 3	218 043.54	30.432 9	.257 734
7	823 212.53	24 900 262	1 983.744 5	215 889.06	30.247 7	.262 252
8	801 150.42	24 077 050	1 805.642 5	213 905.32	30.053 1	.266 998
9	779 804.53	23 275 899	1 613.174 7	212 099.67	29.848 4	.271 991
10	759 171.73	22 496 095	1 458.745 1	210 486.50	29.632 4	.277 258
11	739 196.60	21 736 923	1 377.065 5	209 027.75	29.406 1	.282 777
12	719 790.36	20 997 726	1 348.556 5	207 650 69	29.172 0	.288 488
13	700 885.94	20 277 936	1 353.882 1	206 302.13	28.931 9	.294 345
14	682 437.28	19 577 050	1 378.169 3	204 948.25	28.687 0	.300 318
15	664 414.29	18 894 613	1 393.730 0	203 570.08	28.438 0	.306 390
16	646 815.33	18 230 198	1 382.081 2	202 176.35	28.184 5	.312 572
17	629 657.27	17 583 383	1 382.353 7	200 794.27	27.925 3	.318 895
18	612 917.42	16 953 726	1 375.535 5	199 411.91	27.660 7	.325 349
19	596 592.68	16 340 808	1 379.212 3	198 036.38	27.390 2	.331 946
20	580 662.42	15 744 216	1 376.533 1	196 657.17	27.114 2	.338 677
21	565 123.40	15 163 553	1 383.619 6	195 280.63	26.832 3	.345 554
22	549 956.28	14 598 430	1 389.541 6	193 897 01	25.544 7	.352 568
23	535 153.17	14 048 474	1 399.327 5	192 507.47	26.251 3	.359 724
24	520 701.32	13 513 320	1 407.270 0	191 108.14	25.952 2	.367 021
25	506 594.02	12 992 619	1 423.464 9	189 700.88	25.647 0	.374 463
26	492 814.61	12 486 025	1 437.519 2	188 277.41	25.336 2	.382 045
27	479 357.22	11 993 210	1 454.549 1	186 839.89	25.019 4	.389 772
28	466 211.03	11 513 853	1 478.200 3	185 385.34	24.696 7	.397 643
29	453 361.83	11 047 642	1 503.646 4	183 907.14	24.368 3	.405 652
30	440 800.58	10 594 280	1 531.158 0	182 403.50	24.034 2	.413 800
31	428 518.18	10 153 480	1 559.609 4	180 872.34	23.694 4	.422 088
32	416 506.91	9 724 962	1 592.845 3	179 312.73	23.348 9	.430 516
33	404 755.37	9 308 455	1 626.987 4	177 719.88	22.997 7	.439 080
34	393 256.29	8 903 699	1 669.050 8	176 092.90	22.641 0	.447 781
35	381 995.63	8 510 443	1 710.561 0	174 423.84	22.278 9	.456 612
36	370 968.10	8 128 447	1 759.080 1	172 713.28	21.911 4	.465 574
37	360 161.02	7 757 479	1 809.692 8	170 954.20	21.538 9	.474 660
38	349 566.90	7 397 318	1 862.134 5	169 144.51	21.161 4	.483 869
39	339 178.75	7 047 751	1 922.486 9	167 282.38	20.778 9	.493 198
40	328 983.61	6 708 573	1 983.511 0	165 359.89	20.391 8	.502 639
41	318 976.11	6 379 589	2 050.694 7	163 376.38	20.000 2	.512 190
42	309 145.51	6 060 613	2 120.338 1	161 325.68	19.604 4	.521 844
43	299 485.04	5 751 467	2 194.136 7	159 205.35	19.204 5	.531 597
44	289 986.39	5 451 982	2 274.595 1	157 011.21	18.800 8	.541 443
45	280 638.95	5 161 996	2 357.209 9	154 736.61	18.393 7	.551 373
46	271 436.89	4 881 357	2 444.154 2	152 379.40	17.983 4	.561 381
47	262 372.33	4 609 920	2 536.765 0	149 935.25	17.570 1	.571 460
48	253 436.24	4 347 548	2 630.859 4	147 398.48	17.154 4	.581 600
49	244 624.00	4 094 112	2 732.529 2	144 767.62	16.736 3	.591 796
50	235 925.04	3 849 488	2 835.622 1	142 035.10	16.316 6	.602 035

Financial Tables

COMMUTATION COLUMNS 2 1/2% (Continued)
Commissioners 1941 Standard Ordinary Mortality Table*

x	D_x	N_x	C_x	M_x	$1 + a_x$	A_x
51	227 335.15	3 613 563	2 943.137 4	139 199.47	15.895 3	.612 310
52	218 847.25	3 386 227	3 053.177 2	136 256.34	15.473 0	.622 609
53	210 456.33	3 167 380	3 168.222 9	133 203.16	15.050 1	.632 925
54	202 155.03	2 956 924	3 283.812 1	130 034.94	14.627 0	.643 244
55	193 940.61	2 754 769	3 401.913 1	126 751.12	14.204 2	.653 556
56	185 808.43	2 560 828	3 522.090 1	123 349.21	13.782 1	.663 852
57	177 754.43	2 375 020	3 641.783 5	119 827.12	13 361 2	.674 116
58	169 777.17	2 197 265	3 761.696 8	116 185.34	12.942 1	.684 340
59	161 874.57	2 027 488	3 880.185 4	112 423.64	12.525 1	.694 511
60	154 046.23	1 865 614	3 996.199 9	108 543.46	12.110 7	.704 616
61	146 292.80	1 711 567	4 107.708 0	·104 547.26	11.699 6	.714 644
62	138 616.97	1 565 275	4 216.676 0	100 439.55	11.292 1	.724 583
63	131 019.40	1 426 658	4 315.413 8	96 222.87	10.888 9	.734 417
64	123 508.39	1 295 638	4 407.831 2	91 907.46	10.490 3	.744 139
65	116 088.15	1 172 130	4 489.449 7	87 499.63	10.096 9	.753 734
66	108 767.29	1 056 042	4 558.728 2	83 010.18	9.709 2	.763 191
67	101 555.70	947 274.4	4 613.189 3	78 451.45	9.327 6	.772 497
68	94 465.545	845 718.7	4 650.452 1	73 838.26	8.952 7	.781 642
69	87 511.050	751 253.1	4 670.014 3	69 187.81	8.584 7	.790 618
70	80 706.625	663 742.1	4 669.226 0	64 517.79	8.224 1	.799 411
71	74 068.942	583 035.4	4 644.235 4	59 848.57	7.871 5	.808 012
72	67 618.148	508 966.5	4 595.428 1	55 204.33	7.527 1	.816 413
73	61 373.498	441 348.3	4 520.662 7	50 608.90	7.191 2	.824 605
74	55 355.921	379 974.8	4 418.249 2	46 088.24	6.864 2	.832 580
75	49 587.526	324 618.9	4 288.286 9	41 669.99	6.546 4	.840 332
76	44 089.787	275 031.4	4 130.220 2	37 381.70	6.238 0	.847 854
77	38 884.206	230 941.6	3 944.961 8	33 251.48	5.939 2	.855 141
78	33 990.850	192 057.4	3 733.725 8	29 306.52	5.650 3	.862 189
79	29 428.077	158 066.6	3 498.684 1	25 572.80	5.371 3	.868 993
80	25 211.636	128 638.5	3 243.115 8	22 074.11	5.102 3	.875 553
81	21 353.602	103 426.8	2 970.736 8	18 831.00	4.843 5	.881 865
82	17 862.047	82 073.24	2 686.402 0	15 860.26	4.594 8	.887 931
83	14 739.984	64 211.19	2 395.321 2	13 173.86	4.356 3	.893 750
84	11 985.151	49 471.21	2 103.356 1	10 778.54	4.127 7	.899 324
85	9 589.474 6	37 486.06	1 816.194 6	8 675.180	3.909 1	.904 656
86	7 539.390 5	27 896.58	1 540.039 4	6 858.986	3.700 1	.909 753
87	5 815.463 2	20 357.19	1 280.145 4	5 318.946	3.500 5	.914 621
88	4 393.477 3	14 541.73	1 041.564 6	038.801	3.309 8	.919 272
89	3 244.754 6	10 148.25	827.621 52	2 997.236	3.127 6	.923 717
90	2 337.992 9	6 903.496	640.937 68	2 169.615	2.952 7	.927 982
91	1 640.030 9	4 565.503	482.773 06	1 528.677	2.783 8	.932 103
92	1 117.257 1	2 925.472	352.770 63	1 045.904	2.618 4	.936 136
93	737.236 29	1 808.215	249.339 10	693.133 5	2.452 7	.940 178
94	469.915 86	1 070.979	170.088 82	443.794 4	2.279 1	.944 413
95	288.365 67	601.062 8	111.467 79	273.705 6	2.084 4	.949 162
96	169.864 58	312.697 2	74.109 795	162.237 8	1.840 9	.955 101
97	91.611 740	142.832 6	49.001 885	88.128 0	1.559 1	.961 973
98	40.375 419	51.220 9	28.545 208	39.126 1	1.268 6	.969 058
99	10.845 444	10.845 4	10.580 921	10.580 9	1.000 0	.975 610

* Reproduced by permission of the Actuarial Society of America.

COMMISSIONERS 1958 STANDARD ORDINARY
MORTALITY TABLE*

Age, x	Number Living l_x	Number Dying d_x	Deaths per 1,000	Age, x	Number Living l_x	Number Dying d_x	Deaths per 1,000
0	10,000,000	70,800	7.08	**50**	8,762,306	72,902	8.32
1	9,929,200	17,475	1.76	51	8,689,404	79,160	9.11
2	9,911,725	15,066	1.52	52	8,610,244	85,758	9.96
3	9,896,659	14,449	1.46	53	8,524,486	92,832	10.89
4	9,882,210	13,835	1.40	54	8,431,654	100,337	11.90
5	9,868,375	13,322	1.35	**55**	8,331,317	108,307	13.00
6	9,855,053	12,812	1.30	56	8,223,010	116,849	14.21
7	9,842,241	12,401	1.26	57	8,106,161	125,970	15.54
8	9,829,840	12,091	1.23	58	7,980,191	135,663	17.00
9	9,817,749	11,879	1.21	59	7,844,528	145,830	18.59
10	9,805,870	11,865	1.21	**60**	7,698,698	156,592	20.34
11	9,794,005	12,047	1.23	61	7,542,106	167,736	22.24
12	9,781,958	12,325	1.26	62	7,374,370	179,271	24.31
13	9,769,633	12,896	1.32	63	7,195,099	191,174	26.57
14	9,756,737	13,562	1.39	64	7,003,925	203,394	29.04
15	9,743,175	14,225	1.46	**65**	6,800,531	215,917	31.75
16	9,728,950	14,983	1.54	66	6,584,614	228,749	34.74
17	9,713,967	15,737	1.62	67	6,355,865	241,777	38.04
18	9,698,230	16,390	1.69	68	6,114,088	254,835	41.68
19	9,681,840	16,846	1.74	69	5,859,253	267,241	45.61
20	9,664,994	17,300	1.79	**70**	5,592,012	278,426	49.79
21	9,647,694	17,655	1.83	71	5,313,586	287,731	54.15
22	9,630,039	17,912	1.86	72	5,025,855	294,766	58.65
23	9,612,127	18,167	1.89	73	4,731,089	299,289	63.26
24	9,593,960	18,324	1.91	74	4,431,800	301,894	68.12
25	9,575,636	18,481	1.93	**75**	4,129,906	303,011	73.37
26	9,557,155	18,732	1.96	76	3,826,895	303,014	79.18
27	9,538,423	18,981	1.99	77	3,523,881	301,997	85.70
28	9,519,442	19,324	2.03	78	3,221,884	299,829	93.06
29	9,500,118	19,760	2.08	79	2,922,055	295,683	101.19
30	9,480,358	20,193	2.13	**80**	2,626,372	238,848	109.98
31	9,460,165	20,718	2.19	81	2,337,524	278,983	119.35
32	9,439,447	21,239	2.25	82	2,058,541	265,902	129.17
33	9,418,208	21,850	2.32	83	1,792,639	249,858	139.38
34	9,396,358	22,551	2.40	84	1,542,781	231,433	150.01
35	9,373,807	23,528	2.51	**85**	1,311,348	211,311	161.14
36	9,350,279	24,685	2.64	86	1,100,037	190,108	172.82
37	9,325,594	26,112	2.80	87	909,929	168,455	185.13
38	9,299,482	27,991	3.01	88	741,474	146,997	198.25
39	9,271,491	30,132	3.25	89	594,477	126,303	212.46
40	9,241,359	32,622	3.53	**90**	468,174	106,809	228.14
41	9,208,737	35,362	3.84	91	361,365	88,813	245.77
42	9,173,375	38,253	4.17	92	272,552	72,480	265.93
43	9,135,122	41,382	4.53	93	200,072	57,881	289.30
44	9,093,740	44,741	4.92	94	142,191	45,026	316.66
45	9,048,999	48,412	5.35	**95**	97,165	34,128	351.24
46	9,000,587	52,473	5.83	96	63,037	25,250	400.56
47	8,948,114	56,910	6.36	97	37,787	18,456	488.42
48	8,891,204	61,794	6.95	98	19,331	12,916	668.15
49	8,829,410	67,104	7.60	99	6,415	6,415	1,000.00

* Reproduced by permission of the Actuarial Society of America.

COMMUTATION COLUMNS 2 1/2%*
Commissioners 1958 Standard Ordinary Mortality Table

Age, x	D_x	N_x	C_x	M_x
0	10,000,000.0000	324,850,104.9680	69,073.1710	2,076,826.7172
1	9,687,024.4290	314,850,104.9680	16,632.9566	2,007,753.5462
2	9,434,122.5838	305,163,080.5390	13,990.2787	1,991,120.5896
3	9,190,031.7084	295,728,957.9552	13,090.0808	1,977,130.3109
4	8,952,794.4741	286,538,926.2468	12,228.1241	1,964,040.2301
5	8,722,205.5791	277,586,131.7727	11,487.5189	1,951,812.1060
6	8,497,981.3556	268,863,926.1936	10,778.2903	1,940,324.5871
7	8,279,935.2370	260,365,944.8380	10,178.0782	1,929,546.2968
8	8,067,807.4636	252,086,009.6010	9,681.6066	1,919,368.2186
9	7,861,350.0557	244,018,202.1374	9,279.8558	1,909,686.6120
10	7,660,329.9546	236,156,852.0817	9,042.8478	1,900,406.7562
11	7,464,449.7860	228,496,522.1271	8,957.6178	1,891,363.9084
12	7,273,432.4866	221,032,072.3411	8,940.8062	1,882,406.2906
13	7,087,090.8833	213,758,639.8545	9,126.8500	1,873,465.4844
14	6,905,108.1581	206,671,548.9712	9,364.0939	1,864,338.6344
15	6,727,326.7826	199,766,440.8131	9,582.3146	1,854,974.5405
16	6,553,663.2627	193,039,114.0305	9,846.7536	1,845,392.2259
17	6,383,971.1254	186,485,450.7678	10,090.0279	1,835,545.4723
18	6,218,174.4633	180,101,479.6424	10,252.3993	1,825,455.4444
19	6,056,259.3006	173,883,305.1791	10,280.6243	1,815,203.0451
20	5,898,264.9735	167,827,045.8785	10,300.1828	1,804,922.4208
21	5,744,104.7377	161,928,780.9050	10,255.1657	1,794,622.2380
22	5,593,749.4258	156,184,676.1673	10,150.6810	1,784,367.0723
23	5,447,165.8414	150,590,926.7415	10,044.0865	1,774,216.3913
24	5,304,263.9929	145,143,760.9001	9,883.7932	1,764,172.3048
25	5,165,007.9517	139,839,496.9072	9,725.3439	1,754,288.5116
26	5,029,306.7854	134,674,488.9555	9,617.0037	1,744,563.1677
27	4,897,023.7928	129,645,182.1701	9,507.1611	1,734,946.1640
28	4,768,076.9758	124,748,158.3773	9,442.8900	1,725,439.0029
29	4,642,339.5370	119,980,081.4015	9,420.4356	1,715,996.1129
30	4,519,691.3751	115,337,741.8645	9,392.0634	1,706,575.6773
31	4,400,062.8465	110,818,050.4894	9,401.2183	1,697,183.6139
32	4,283,343.0569	106,417,987.6429	9,402.5686	1,687,782.3956
33	4,169,468.7479	102,134,644.5860	9,437.1317	1,678,379.8270
34	4,058,337.1968	97,965,175.8381	9,502.3390	1,668,942.6953
35	3,949,851.0856	93,906,838.6413	9,672.2130	1,659,440.3563
36	3,843,840.9771	89,956,987.5557	9,900.3401	1,649,768.1433
37	3,740,188.4751	86,113,146.5786	10,217.2318	1,639,867.8032
38	3,638,747.0704	82,372,958.1035	10,685.3232	1,629,650.5714
39	3,539,311.8617	78,734,211.0331	11,222.0794	1,618,965.2482
40	3,441,765.0620	75,194,899.1714	11,853.1042	1,607,743.1688
41	3,345,966.5023	71,753,134.1094	12,535.2926	1,595,890.0646
42	3,251,822.2774	68,407,167.6071	13,229.3739	1,583,354.7720
43	3,159,280.1784	65,155,345.3297	13,962.4424	1,570,125.3981
44	3,068,262.0685	61,996,065.1513	14,727.5918	1,556,162.9557
45	2,978,698.8164	58,927,803.0828	15,547.3085	1,541,435.3639
46	2,890,500.3526	55,949,104.2664	16,440.4699	1,525,888.0554
47	2,803,559.9048	53,058,603.9138	17,395.7457	1,509,447.5855
48	2,717,784.6405	50,255,044.0090	18,427.9447	1,492,051.8398
49	2,633,069.2135	47,537,259.3685	19,523.3861	1,473,623.8951

* Reproduced by permission of the Actuarial Society of America.

COMMUTATION COLUMNS 2 1/2%* (Continued)
Commissioners 1958 Standard Ordinary Mortality Table

Age, x	D_x	N_x	C_x	M_x
50	2,549,324.6723	44,904,190.1550	20,692.9455	1,454,100.5090
51	2,466,453.0891	42,354,865.4827	21,921.2231	1,433,407.5635
52	2,384,374.4270	39,888,412.3936	23,169.1325	1,411,486.3404
53	2,303,049.8123	37,504,037.9666	24,468.5917	1,388,317.2079
54	2,222,409.2905	35,200,988.1543	25,801.7117	1,363,848.6162
55	2,142,402.4988	32,978,578.8638	27,171.9031	1,338,046.9045
56	2,062,976.8254	30,836,176.3650	28,599.9098	1,310,875.0014
57	1,984,060.3996	28,773,199.5396	30,080.3536	1,282,275.0916
58	1,905,588.3725	26,789,139.1400	31,604.8230	1,252,194.7380
59	1,827,505.7998	24,883,550.7675	33,144.7659	1,220,589.9150
60	1,749,787.7198	23,056,044.9677	34,722.7242	1,187,445.1491
61	1,672,387.2632	21,306,257.2479	36,286.6291	1,152,722.4249
62	1,595,310.6622	19,633,869.9847	37,836.1144	1,116,435.7958
63	1,518,564.5694	18,038,559.3225	39,364.2006	1,078,599.6814
64	1,442,162.1578	16,519,994.7531	40,858.9196	1,039,235.4808
65	1,366,128.5462	15,077,832.5953	42,316.6940	998,376.5612
66	1,290,491.6985	13,711,704.0491	43,738.1310	956,059.8672
67	1,215,278.1249	12,421,212.3506	45,101.6207	912,321.7362
68	1,140,535.6099	11,205,934.2257	46,378.0358	867,220.1155
69	1,066,339.5743	10,065,398.6158	47,449.5963	820,842.0797
70	992,881.7500	8,999,059.0415	48,229.7870	773,392.4834
71	920,435.3077	8,006,177.2915	48,625.9779	725,162.6964
72	849,359.6946	7,085,741.9838	48,599.8832	676,536.7185
73	780,043.7396	6,236,382.2892	48,142.0663	627,936.8353
74	712,876.2140	5,456,338.5496	47,376.6752	579,794.7690
75	648,112.3021	4,743,462.3356	46,392.1628	532,418.0938
76	585,912.5111	4,095,350.0335	45,261.0951	486,025.9310
77	526,360.8716	3,509,437.5224	44,008.9628	440,764.8359
78	469,513.8465	2,983,076.6508	42,627.3426	396,755.8731
79	415,434.9294	2,513,562.8043	41,012.5834	354,128.5305
80	364,289.7989	2,098,127.8749	39,087.3533	313,115.9471
81	316,317.3241	1,733,838.0760	36,831.6174	274,028.5938
82	271,770.6619	1,417,520.7519	34,248.4382	237,196.9764
83	230,893.6600	1,145,750.0900	31,397.0289	202,948.5382
84	193,865.0736	914,856.4300	28,372.4430	171,551.5093
85	160,764.2229	720,991.3564	25,273.7507	143,179.0663
86	131,569.3974	560,227.1335	22,183.1949	117,905.3156
87	106,177.1855	428,657.7361	19,177.1362	95,722.1207
88	84,410.3641	322,480.5506	16,326.1748	76,544.9845
89	66,025.3978	238,070.1865	13,685.6613	60,218.8097
90	50,729.3636	172,044.7887	11,291.0955	46,533.1484
91	38,200.9638	121,315.4251	9,159.6932	35,242.0529
92	28,109.5415	83,114.4613	7,292.8738	26,082.3597
93	20,131.0686	55,004.9198	5,681.8884	18,789.4859
94	13,958.1795	34,873.8512	4,312.1729	13,107.5975
95	9,305.5630	20,915.6717	3,188.7449	8,795.4246
96	5,889.8533	11,610.1087	2,301.6880	5,606.6797
97	3,444.5103	5,720.2554	1,641.3408	3,304.9917
98	1,719.1569	2,275.7451	1,120.6380	1,663.6509
99	556.5882	556.5882	543.0129	543.0129

* Reproduced by permission of the Actuarial Society of America.

MATHEMATICAL SYMBOLS AND ABBREVIATIONS

Symbols and Abbreviations of Commercial Arithmetic

#	Number (if written before a numeral); pounds (weight), lb. (if written after a numeral.)	Apr.	April	Dr.	Debit, debtor, doctor
		a/s	Account sales		
		Aug.	August	E	East
		av.	Average	ea.	Each
@	At, as "@ 5¢ per C," for "at 5 cents per hundred."	avoir.	Avoirdupois	e.g.	(exempli gratia) for example
		bal.	Balance		
		bbl. or brl.	Barrel	etc.	And so forth
				ex.	Example, exercise, express
		bk.	Bank, book		
		bl.	Bale	exch.	Exchange
%	Per cent; per hundred.	B/L	Bill of lading	exp.	Expense
		bu.	Bushel	F	Fahrenheit
		bx.	Box	Feb.	February
¢	Cents (placed after figures)	C	(centum) hundred	f.o.b.	Free on board
				Fri.	Friday
$	Dollars, (prefixed before figures).	cd.	Cord	frt.	Freight
		cg.	Centigram	ft. or f.	Foot
		ch.	Chain	gal.	Gallon
£	Pounds (British currency)	chg.	Charge	gi.	Gill
		c.i.f.	Carriage and insurance free.	gr.	Grain
✓	Check mark			gro.	Gross
&	And, as in "Smith, Jones & Co."	ck.	Check	gr. gro.	Great gross
		cm.	Centimeter	guar.	Guarantee
		cml.	Commercial	hf.	Half
c/o	Care of	Co.	Company, county	hhd.	Hogshead
A	Acre			hr.	Hour
a/c	Account	c.o.d.	Cash on delivery	i.e.	(id est) that is
acct.	Account	coll.	Collection	in.	Inch, inches
ad val	(ad valorem), according to value	com.	Commission	ins.	Insurance
		cr.	Credit, creditor, crate	inst.	(instant) the present month
A.M. or a.m.	(ante meridiem) in the morning, between midnight and the following noon. 12:00 A.M. is noon, better 12:00 M, 12:01 A.M. is one minute after midnight.	cs.	Case	int.	Interest
		c. or ct.	Cent	inv.	Invoice
				inv'y	Inventory
		cu.	Cubic	Jan.	January
		cwt.	Hundredweight	kg.	Keg, kilogram
		d	Pence (British currency)	km.	Kilometer
				lb. lbs.	Pound, pounds
		da.	Day	lp	List price
		Dec.	December	ltd.	Limited
		dept.	Department	L.S.	(locus sigillis) place for the seal
		dft.	Draft		
amt.	Amount	disc.	Discount		
ans.	Answer	dm.	Decimeter	M	(mille) thousand; meridiem as in 12:00 M
ap	Apothecaries' weight or measure	do.	Ditto		
		doz.	Dozen		
		dr.	Dram	m.	Mill, meter

MATHEMATICAL SYMBOLS AND ABBREVIATIONS (Continued)

Symbols and Abbreviations of Commercial Arithmetic

Mar.	March	P.M.	(post meridiem)	Sat.	Saturday
mdsc.	Merchandise	*or*	in the after-	sec.	Second
mi.	Mile	p.m.	noon, between	sec'y	Secretary
min.	Minute		noon and the	Sept.	September
mm.	Millimeter		following mid-	set.	Settlement
mo.	Month		night. 12:00	sig.	Signed, signa-
Mon.	Monday		P.M. is mid-		ture
mortg.	Mortgage		night, 12:01	sq.	Square
N, NE,	North, North-		P.M. is one	stk.	Stock
NW,	east, North-		minute after	Sun,	Sunday
etc.	west, etc.		noon.	T.	Ton
no. *or*	Number	pp.	Pages	temp.	Temperature
numb.		pr.	Pair	Thu.	Thursday
Nov.	November	*prox.*	(proximo) in the	treas.	Treasurer,
Oct.	October		following		treasury
O.K.	Correct		month	Tues.	Tuesday
oz.	Ounce	pt.	Pint, point	*ult.*	(ultimo) in the
p.	Page	pwt.	Pennyweight		last month
par.	Paragraph	(*or*		*via*	By way of
pay't	Payment	dwt.)		viz.	(videlicet)
pc.	Piece	qr.	Quire		namely
pd.	Paid	qt.	Quart	vol.	Volume
per	By, by the, as in	rd.	Rod, road	W	West
	"per C," "per	rec'd	Received	Wed.	Wednesday
	M," "per doz."	rec't	Receipt	wk.	Week
pfd.	Preferred	rm.	Ream	wt.	Weight
pk.	Peck, pecks	S, SE,	South, South-	yd.	Yard
pkg.	Package	SW,	east, South-	yr.	Year
		etc.	west, etc.		

Symbols Belonging to Plane Geometry

In blackboard presentation combined with oral discussion a variety of informal abbreviations is acceptable. But in written reports it is best to use only standard abbreviations, preferably those which are found on a typewriter. Avoid characters not sufficiently distinctive as to remain legible and unambiguous when written hurriedly. When used as nouns, the plural may be indicated by adding "s"; when used as relations the copula "is" and preposition "to" may be deleted.

A°	*Angle* associated with the point or vector A. Use "rt°" for "right angle," and "st°" for "straight angle." Avoid $\angle$ which resembles symbol for "less than." Use "arc" rather than "⌒" to avoid confusion with bar for "line segment."
$\angle$	Angle
$\measuredangle$	Angles

MATHEMATICAL SYMBOLS AND ABBREVIATIONS (Continued)

⊙	Circle. ⊙ A(B) designates the circle with center A passing through B. ⊙ (AB) has AB as diameter, and ⊙ (ABC) circumscribes △ABC. ⊙A, r has center A, radius r.
Ⓢ	Circles.
A:B(S)	Collinear. The line AB passes through the point S. Use $\overline{AB}$(S) for "S lies between A and B."
≅	Congruent. (Same shape and same size).
A:B(S,r)	Point of division. "S divides AB in the ratio AS:BS = r." Use (S, −) for internal division, and (S, +) for external division.
=	Equal, equivalent. The quantity measured may be indicated in parenthesis at the right of the statement, as "(area)," "(vol.)," "(angle)." Avoid pictogram ≏.
$\overline{\barwedge}$	Perspective. See ABC:DEF(S) below.
$\barwedge$	Projective. See ABC::DEF below.
a/b	Fraction (with numerator a, denominator b). Same meaning as quotient "a ÷ b" (with dividend a, divisor b) and ratio a:b (with antecedent a, consequent b).
$\dot{\sim}$	Homothetic (Similar and perspective). "ABC $\dot{\sim}$ DEF" indicates that corresponding lines, such as BC and EF, are parallel. Use "$\dot{\sim}$ (S, r)" for "the homothecy with center S and ratio r."
AB	Line, segment, vector. When further distinctions are desired, use $\overline{AB}$ (or AB) for the length of the line segment (distance between A and B), use $\overrightarrow{AB}$ for the vector (displacement from A toward B), and use A:B for the infinite line (determined by the two points).
∥	Parallel.
▱	Parallelogram (vertices are named in counterclockwise order).
⊥	Perpendicular.
ABC::DEF	Projective (related by a sequence of perspectivities). Same meaning as pictogram "$\barwedge$."
ABC:DEF(S)	Perspective. The lines A:D and B:E and C:F are concurrent at the point S (center of perspectivity). Same meaning as pictogram "$\overline{\barwedge}$."
QED	End of proof.
QEF	End of construction.
℞	Cross ratio, anharmonic ratio ℞(AC, BD) = AB · CD/ AD · CB. ℞ = −1 means "harmonic" and may be used for collinear points (range), concurrent lines (pencil), or cyclic quadrangle. ℞(CA, BD) = 1/℞(AC, BD) = ℞(AC, DB). Also ℞(AB, CD) = 1 − ℞(AC, BD).
~	Similar. △ABC ~ △DEF means that A corresponds to D, B to E, and C to F, respectively.
□	Square. Use "rect" for "rectangle," "quad" for

MATHEMATICAL SYMBOLS AND ABBREVIATIONS (Continued)

"quadrilateral" (or quadrangle), and "trap" for "trapezoid" rather than pictograms.

ABC $\sim$ DEF(r = 1) Displaced by translation. (The triangles are congruent and similarly placed).

$\triangle$ Triangle. Use "isos" for "isosceles triangle" (naming vertex opposite base first).

$\dot{B}$ Vertex. In using triliteral symbol ABC, A is on the initial side, B is the vertex, C is on the terminal side. The vertex may be marked with a caret "AB̂C" or by superscript position "A^{B}C."

General Mathematical Symbols and Abbreviations

"Bold-face" or gothic type—To indicate vectors corresponding italic type indicates magnitude of the vector. In manuscript and at the blackboard, bold-faced type is variously indicated by wavy underscoring, or enclosure in a circle, or even by wavy overscoring. Some persons use German type.

Half-spaces—In writing numbers with many recorded digits, half-spaces (rather than commas or other marks) may well be used to separate convenient groups of digits. Thus $\pi = 3.14159\ 26536 -$.

Superscripts—To indicate: **1.** powers, as in x^2, $(a - x)^n$, etc. In modern practice $a^0 = 1$ always by definition (except for $a = 0$). Also in ∞', ∞^2, etc., indicating number of degrees of freedom. Wherever the context restricts the value of a to non-negative (real) values and n to positive integers, $a^{1/n}$ means the non-negative (real) nth root of a. For complex numbers, x^y is defined as $e^{y\ (\log\ x)}$, where the principal value of $\log x$ is to be taken. In tables 0.0^5314 may be used to indicate 0.00000314. Note special use of $\sin^n x$ for $(\sin x)^n$ except for $n = -1$, also for $\cos^n x$, etc. **2.** symbolic powers, or order of iteration, as in T^n or in D^n $(= d^n/dx^n)$, or in inverse functions as in $\sin^{-1}$, $\cos^{-1}$, $\sinh^{-1}$, etc. **3.** order of differentiation, as in y' ("y prime"), y'' ("y second," or "y double prime"), $\cdots$, $y^{(N)}$, $\cdots$ **4.** feet and inches, as in $3'4''$. **5.** degrees, minutes, seconds, as in $34°5'17''$. Do not omit ° for common angles. Write $0°$, $30°$, $45°$, $60°$, etc., not 0, 30, 45, 60, etc. Do not use superscript, ^{r}, for radians. Write $180° = \pi$ rad, but write $\cos (\pi/3)$ for $\cos 60°$. **6.** days, hours, minutes, seconds, as in $10^d3^h27^m5.3^s$. **7.** degrees of temperature as in $104°$. Where C (for Centigrade) or F (for Fahrenheit) is given, recent usage approves the omission of the °, thus $100C = 212F$, and $-40C = -40F$. **8.** For use with integral sign $\int$, and with vertical bar $|$, see these symbols. **9.** Vertex, as in A^BC.

Dot-accents—To indicate derivatives with respect to time, (Newton's notation), as in $\dot{x}$ for x-component of velocity, and $\ddot{x}$ for x-component of acceleration.

Subscripts—To indicate: **1.** position in a sequence, set, or matrix, as in a_1, a_2, a_3, $\cdots a_n$, $\cdots$, or $a_0x^n + a_1x^{n-1} + \cdots + a_rx^{n-r} + \cdots a_n$ or in $\begin{pmatrix} a_{11}a_{12}a_{13} \\ a_{21}a_{22}a_{23} \end{pmatrix}$. **2.** general distinguishing mark. Two subscripts may be written adjacently without commas as a_{11} and to be read "a sub one one," not "a sub eleven." A subscript is sometimes enclosed in parentheses as in $F_{(0)1}$ where such distinction seems demanded. For special uses see associated symbols.

MATHEMATICAL SYMBOLS AND ABBREVIATIONS (Continued)

Juxtaposition—To indicate: **1.** the algebraic product, as in $2bxy$. **2.** the logical product as in AB where A and B are given classes, and in symbolic logic. Also written with centrally placed dot as $A \cdot B$. **3.** the group product, as in ST (the result of performing first S, then T, or in aH, the co-set consisting for given a of all operations ah, where h is in H. **4.** general operational or functional combination as in dy/dx, $\sin x$, $\log x$, $\max y$, $\lim x_n$, etc. **5.** sequence of points or other elements determining a geometric figure, as line AB, parallelogram $ABCD$, angle ABC, etc. **6.** sum of products (in tensor notation) when index appears as subscript for one factor and superscript for another. Thus $a_i x^i$ means $\Sigma a_i x^i$, in tensor notation.

( )—Parentheses ("round brackets") to indicate: **1.** aggregation, as in $(a + b) \cdot (a - b) = a^2 - b^2$. **2.** argument of function, as in $f(x)$, $g(x,y)$, etc. **3.** sequence or set, as in $a = (a_i)$, $x = (x_{ij})$, (x,y,z), etc. **4.** matrix, as in $\begin{pmatrix} a_{11}a_{12}a_{13} \\ a_{21}a_{22}a_{23} \end{pmatrix}$ also written as $\begin{Vmatrix} a_{11}a_{12}a_{13} \\ a_{21}a_{22}a_{23} \end{Vmatrix}$. **5.** permutation (or substitution) in group theory as in $\begin{pmatrix} a_1 a_2 a_3 \\ b_1 b_2 b_3 \end{pmatrix}$ where a_i is replaced by $b_i (i = 1,2,3)$. **6.** binomial coefficient, as in $\begin{pmatrix} n \\ r \end{pmatrix} = n!/[r!(n - r)!]$. This is also designated by $C_{n,r}$ or $_nC_r$. For n,r, positive integers, $\begin{pmatrix} -n \\ r \end{pmatrix} = (-1)^r \begin{pmatrix} n + r - 1 \\ r \end{pmatrix}$, $\begin{pmatrix} n \\ -r \end{pmatrix} = 0$, by definition. **7.** cycle or cylic permutation (in group theory) as in (a_1, a_2, a_3) for $\begin{pmatrix} a_1 a_2 a_3 \\ a_2 a_3 a_1 \end{pmatrix}$. **8.** greatest common divisor, as in $(30,42) = 6$, $(7,5) = 1$. **9.** inner product as in $(ab) = \Sigma_i a_i b_i$. **10.** segment or open interval, as in (a,b), for system of values of x, where $a < x < b$.

Superscript $^{(\ )}$—To indicate: **1.** general index as distinguished from exponent. **2.** index of order of derivative as in y, y', $\cdots$, $y^{(n)}$, $\cdots$. **3.** "factorial," as in $x^{(r)} = x(x - 1) \cdots (x - r + 1)$. By definition $x^{(-r)} = 1/[(x + 1) \cdot (x + 2) \cdots (x + r)]$.

[ ]—Brackets ("square brackets"), to indicate: **1.** aggregation. **2.** argument of function as with ( ). **3.** greatest integer in, as $[2] = 2$, $[-7/3] = -3$. **4.** inner product (for coefficients in normal equations in the method of least squares), as in $[aa]$, $[XY]$, etc. **5.** outer product of vectors. Other notations are $V\ ab$ and $a \times b$. **6.** divided difference (in formal interpolation). $[x_i] = y_i$, $[x_i, x_{i+1}] = (y_{i+1} - y_i)/(x_{i+1} - x_i)$, $\cdots$ $[x_i, x_{i+1}, \cdots, x_{i+r}] = ([x_{i+1}, \cdots, x_{i+r}] - [x_i, \cdots, x_{i+r-1}])/(x_{i+r} - x_i)$. **7.** range of points (in projective geometry) as in $[P]$. **8.** base (basis) of Abelian group, as in $[a,b, \cdots, k]$. **9.** module or ideal, as $[2] = [0, \pm2, \pm4, \cdots, \pm 2n, \cdots]$. **10.** Christoffel symbol, as in $\begin{bmatrix} mn \\ p \end{bmatrix} = \frac{1}{2}\left(\frac{\partial g_{pm}}{\partial x^n} + \frac{\partial g_{pn}}{\partial x^m} = \frac{\partial g_{mn}}{\partial x^p}\right)$. **11.** closed interval, as in $[a,b]$ for system of values of x where $a \leqq x \leqq b$.

Subscript note. The use of adjacent subscripts, rather than of indices placed directly below is recommended on account of its availability for running text, and its economy of space and of expense in type setting. Thus use $\sum_i$ rather than $\sum_i$, $\int_a^b$ rather than $\int_a^b$, etc.

MATHEMATICAL SYMBOLS AND ABBREVIATIONS (Continued)

{ }—Braces ("curly brackets") to indicate: **1.** aggregation, as in $\{(x - a)(x - b)\}^2$. **2.** class of (in theory of aggregates), where the general element only is mentioned, as in $\{a_i\} = [a_1, a_2, a_3], (i = 1,2,3)$. **3.** Christoffel symbol, as in $\left\{ \begin{matrix} m\ n \\ p \end{matrix} \right\} = g^{rp} \left[\begin{matrix} m\ n \\ p \end{matrix} \right]$. **4.** the members in a uniquely determined set, as in $\{x_1, x_2, \cdots x_n\}$.

< >—Angle brackets to indicate: **1.** aggregation. **2.** closed interval as with [ ]. **3.** Angle between as in $A \cdot B = AB \cos <A, B>$. Use sparingly because of ambiguity with signs of inequality.

| |—Vertical bars, to indicate: **1.** absolute value (modulus of complex number). as $|a + ib|^2 = a^2 + b^2$. **2.** magnitude of (for vectors) as $a = |a|$. **3.** determinant, as in $\begin{matrix} a\ b \\ c\ d \end{matrix} = ad - bc$. The use of the notation $|a_{ij}|$ for the determinant of the matrix (a_{ij}), is common but is ambiguous. The notation det (a_{ij}) may be used for this determinant.

‖ ‖—Double bars, to indicate: **1.** matrix as in $\left\| \begin{matrix} a_{11}a_{12}a_{13} \\ a_{21}a_{22}a_{23} \end{matrix} \right\|$ or in $\|a_{ij}\|$. **2.** generalized length (for metrical spaces), as in $\|f\|^2 = \int f^2(x)dx$. **3.** To indicate the length of a vector, as in $\|X\|$.

(], [).—For intervals, as $(a,b]$, for system of values of x for which $a < x \leq b$, and $[a,b)$, for system of values of x for which $a \leq x < b$. Similarly $(a,b >$, and $< a,b)$ are sometimes used for these respectively.

⟨ ⟩—Brackets ("bent brackets"), to indicate an ordered set of objects, as in $\langle x, y, z \rangle$.

⊢—Is deducible from.

⊨—Is valid, or is a tautology (in logic), as in $\models A$ (A is valid).

∪—(is) the union, or sum or join (of), as in $A \cup B$.

∩—(is) the intersection, or product (of), as in $A \cap B$.

⊃—**1.** contains (or containing) as proper sub-class. **2.** implies (or implying).

⊇—contains (or containing) as sub-class. (Some writers use, ⊃, for this.)

⊂—(is) contained as proper sub-class within.

⊆—(is) contained as sub-class within. (Some writers use, ⊂, for this.)

≡—**1.** (is) identical with. $\equiv_x$ indicates (is) identical with for all values of x for which both members are defined. **2.** (is) congruent to (with respect to indicated modulus) as in $a \equiv b \pmod{m}$. **3.** (is) equivalent to (in formal logic).

=—(is) equal (to).

∧—and (in logic).

∨—or (in logic), as in $p \vee q$ (p or q), and/or

⊻—exclusive or, as in $p \veebar q$ (p or q, but not both).

<—(is) less than.

>—(is greater than). Use "less than" preferably as in "$a < x < b$" rather than "$b > x > a$" since former corresponds to order of real numbers on x-axis.

≦ *or* ≤—(is) less than or equal to. Sometimes read (in the case of real numbers) as "(is) not greater than."

≧ *or* ≥—(is) greater than or equal to. Sometimes read (in the case of real numbers) as "(is) not less than."

MATHEMATICAL SYMBOLS AND ABBREVIATIONS (Continued)

$\not\equiv$—**1.** (is) not identically equal (to). (Not "identically unequal **to**"), is unequal to for at least one value. **2.** (is) not congruent (to).

$\neq$—(is) not equal (to).

$\lessgtr$—**1.** (is) not equal (to), (for real quantities). **2.** (Sometimes when explained by context) less than or greater than respectively.

$\sim$—**1.** (is) formally, asymptotically, or approximately equal to. (The context should make the meaning specific.) Do not use $\doteq$ for "approximately equal to." **2.** (is) similar (to). **3.** not (in some works on formal logic). **4.** used to indicate the equivalence of two matrices.

Use "iff" for "if and only if." Alternately "$^{(n)}$ as" (read "as" may be used for "necessary and sufficient."

$\rightarrow$—**1.** approaches (as a limit), as in $\lim\limits_{x \to a} f(x) = b$, $f(x) \to b$, as $x \to a$, etc. (Do not use $\doteq$). Not usually employed with long expressions. **2.** leads to, validates, implies (in logic). **3.** corresponds to. **4.** "if . . . , then . . . " relation (in logic).

$\leftrightarrow$—**1.** mutually implies (in logic). **2.** in one-to-one correspondence with, corresponds reciprocally to. **3.** if and only if, also iff.

$\downarrow$—decreases monotonically to a limit.

$\uparrow$—increases monotonically to a limit.

Superscript $\rightarrow$—directed line as $\overrightarrow{AB}$.

$|$—Vertical bar, to indicate: **1.** value at, as in $f(x)|_a = f(a)$, or $f(x)|_{x=a} = f(a)$. **2.** value between as in $f(x)|_a^b = f(b) - f(a)$. **3.** is a divisor of, divides (in number theory) as $3|6$, $3\underline{/6}$ for "3 divides 6" or use solidus $6/3$ to indicate that this quotient is an integer, or $(x - a)|(x^2 - a^2)$. **4.** inner product (with parentheses) as $(a|b) = \Sigma_i a_i b_i$.

$\backslash$ or $/$—Stroke, mark of cancellation as in $3x = \overset{2}{\cancel{6}}$, $x + 3 = \overset{4}{\cancel{7}}$.

$/$—Solidus, or oblique rule, to indicate: **1.** actual or symbolic division, as in $3/7$, $(x - a)/(x - b)$, d/dx, dy/dx, d^2y/dx^2. Do not write ambiguously $a - b/c - d$, but $(a - b)/(c - d)$ or $a - (b/c) - d$, as may be intended. Do not write a/bc but $(a/b)c$ or $a/(bc)$ as intended. Write a proportion as $a/b = c/d$ not $a:b::c:d$. Where A, B, C, D designate displayed expressions, write the proportion as $\dfrac{A}{B} = \dfrac{C}{D}$. In commercial typing in place of $8\tfrac{5}{12}$, it is usual to write 8-5/12. The solidus form a/b, adapted to running text should be used where conveniently possible, rather than the displayed form $\dfrac{a}{b}$. **2.** quotient or factor group (in group theory) as G/H, (where H is a normal subgroup of G). **3.** per, as in ft/sec. **4.** discount symbol, as in Cash 6, 4/5, 2/30, n/90 indicating 6% discount for immediate payment, 4% discount if paid within 5 days, 2% discount if paid within 30 days, no discount thereafter, but face amount of bill is due (net) not later than the 90th day. **5.** shilling, (in British currency) as 3/6d, or 10/ $-$.

Superscript——Vinculium. This may be regarded as obsolescent for general use as a mark of aggregation due to its unsuitability for monotype setting. In conjunction with the radical sign it is widely used, but may often be avoided. There is little logical or historical basis for using $\sqrt{2}$ rather than

MATHEMATICAL SYMBOLS AND ABBREVIATIONS (Continued)

$\sqrt{}$ 2. For a longer expression, one may write $\sqrt{(x^2 + a^2)}$ rather than $\sqrt{x^2 + a^2}$. Instead of $\sqrt{x - a} \, (x - b)$, one might write $(x - b)\sqrt{(x - a)}$. In geometry, the vinculum may be used for line segments as in $\overline{AB}$.

Superscript ⎺⎺—Bar. To indicate: **1.** complex conjugate of, as $\bar{z}$. This is somewhat inconvenient for "upper extended" letters and capitals as, $\bar{b}$, $\bar{h}$, $\bar{X}$, etc. Also indicated by *conj*, as $conj \, (x + iy) = x - iy$ or by use of a "star" as in z^*. **2.** arithmetic mean value of, as in $\bar{x}$, $= \sum_i x_i/n$. **3.** closure of (in topology), as in $\bar{E}$ (the closure of E). **4.** "least upper," as in $\overline{\lim}$, and $\bar{B}$ for least upper limit and least upper bound, respectively. See "sup." **5.** repeating decimal, as in $1.\overline{14} = 1.141414 \cdots$.

Subscript ⎽⎽—To indicate: **1.** italics (in manuscript). **2.** "greatest lower," as in $\underline{\lim}$, and $\underline{B}$, for greatest lower limit, and greatest lower bound respectively. See "inf."

⎯⎯ —horizontal rule, sign of division, as in $\dfrac{x - a}{x + a}$. Ordinarily the solidus form, adapted to running text, is preferred, as in $(x - a)/(x + a)$. When numerator and denominator are both complicated, the displayed form using horizontal rule may be avoided by writing "A/B, where $A = \cdots$, and $B = \cdots$."

− (centrally placed)—Minus sign. To indicate: **1.** subtraction as in $7 - 2 = 5$, $a^2 - b^2 = (a - b)(a + b)$. **2.** overestimate, as in 3.5−. **3.** approach through negative values as in $-\infty$ and -0. **4.** region where variable indicated by context is negative (in graphs). **5.** logical difference (in theory of classes). **6.** in $(-)^n$, the sign expressed by $(-1)^n$.

·—(on line)—**1.** decimal point. In the decimal representation of a number between 0 and 1, the cipher, 0, should (except in tables) appear before the decimal point. Thus 0.314 not .314. Notation by powers of 10, ("scientific notation") is recommended, especially when recording approximate values; thus to four significant figures, 3.140×10^9 and 3.140×10^{-6}. **2.** (sometimes used in quoting bond prices) as in 95.17 for $95^{17}\!/_{32}$. **3.** (sometimes used in recording mental age) as in 12.3 for 12 yr. 3 mo. **4.** (in symbolic logic) as mark of punctuation separating terms, also as, "and."

:—Colon. To indicate: **1.** hours, in recording time, as in 4:10 p.m. **2.** ratio (an obsolescent form) as in $a:b$. The form a/b is preferred. **3.** (in symbolic logic) as mark of punctuation separating groups of terms, as in $p \cdot p \supset q \supset \cdot q$. **4.** Indicates infinite line $A:B$, collinearity $A:B(S)$, and perspectivity. **5.** such that (in logic). · (centrally placed)—**1.** mark of algebraic multiplication, particularly where mere juxtaposition would be ambiguous, as in $\overline{AB} \cdot \overline{CD}$. **2.** (for vectors), the mark of inner or dot multiplication as in $a \cdot b = ab \cos \angle \, ab$. Other notations are (ab) and $S \, ab$.

⎴ (placed above line)—to indicate repeating decimal, used in pairs, as in $1.\overline{735} = 1.735735735 \cdots$.

$\cdots$ (preferably centrally placed)—"three dots" meaning "and so forth," or "and so forth up to." Particularly when the reader knows what has been omitted, as in the sequence of natural integers, etc. as in $1, 2 \cdots, n, \cdots$; or $a_0, a_1, \cdots, a_n, \cdots$, or $1, \cdots, m$.

.MATHEMATICAL SYMBOLS AND ABBREVIATIONS (Continued)

$\therefore$—hence, therefore. Inverted $\because$ since.

$:.,\ ::,\ ::.,$ etc.—(in symbolic logic), marks of punctuation stronger than and $:$

$,,$—ditto.

$\circ$ (centrally placed)—indicates (in classes or sets) the composite of functions, as in $g \circ f$.

$+$ plus sign. To indicate: **1.** addition, as in $2 + 3$, $a + b$, 10^{a+1}. **2.** underestimate, as in $3.5+$. **3.** continued fraction as in $a_0 + \dfrac{1}{a_1 +} \dfrac{1}{a_2 +} \cdots$ for $a_0 + \dfrac{1}{a_1 + \dfrac{1}{a_2 +}} \cdot$ **4.** approach through positive values as in $+\infty$, and in $+0$

5. region where variable indicated by the context is positive, (in graphs). **6.** logical addition (in theory of classes). **7.** " $.\,.$ or $.\,.$ or both," (in formal logic). Note: In writing series indicate sign before and after dots of omission, as $a_0 + a_1 + \cdots + a_n$, or $1 - \dfrac{1}{2} + \dfrac{1}{3} + \cdots + (-1)^{n-1}\dfrac{1}{n}$.

8. in abstract group theory a group or co-set may be expressed as the sum of its elements.

$\oplus$—denoting a logical operation of summation between elements of a set, such as the sum of vectors.

$\pm$—**1.** "plus or minus." The repeated appearance of $\pm$ as in $\pm a \pm b \pm c$ is ambiguous. In many cases the sign $\pm$ before a term which appears repeatedly is intended to indicate the systematic use of the positive determination or of the negative determination throughout. Thus one may write $(a \pm b)^3 = a^3 \pm 3a^2b + 3ab^2 \pm b^3$. Where the context restricts the value of a to non-negative (real) values, $\sqrt{a}$ means the non-negative (real) square root of a. Hence when both signs are desired, write $\pm$ before the radical. For roots of a quadratic equation $ax^2 + bx + c = 0$, use $\pm$ as in $\dfrac{-b \pm \sqrt{b^2 - 4ac}}{2a}$. **2.** (in theory of observation), "with a probable error of." As in 17.2 ± 0.5 cm.

$\mp$—"minus or plus respectively." Used in context where $\pm$ has appeared previously, as in $a^3 \pm b^3 = (a \pm b)(a^2 \mp ab + b^2)$. Here upper signs are to be taken throughout, or else lower signs. The notation $\pm a \mp b \pm c$ is ambiguous, meaning perhaps one of the four values $\pm(a - b) \pm c$, or one of the two values $\pm(a - b + c)$.

$\times$—**1.** times, (sign of algebraic multiplication). Used chiefly in arithmetic, as in $2 \times 2 = 4$, 7.3×10^4. **2.** (for vectors) the sign of outer or cross multiplication. **3.** (for classes) the Cartesian product. Thus $A \times B$ is the class of all ordered pairs (a,b) where a is an element of A, and b of B.

$\otimes$—denoting a logical operation of multiplication between elements of a set, such as the product of vectors.

$\div$—sign of division. Used chiefly in arithmetic. Should be replaced by solidus, $/$, where convenient.

$\sqrt{}\ \sqrt[n]{}$—square root of, nth root of. (See discussion under "superscript," and under "vinculum"). By custom, for a positive, $\sqrt{(-a)}$ means usually $i\sqrt{a}$, rather than $-i\sqrt{a}$, but the latter unambiguous forms are preferred.

$!$—"factorial," as in $3! = 1 \cdot 2 \cdot 3 = 6$. $0! = 1$, (by definition). The ele-

MATHEMATICAL SYMBOLS AND ABBREVIATIONS (Continued)

mentary arithmetic definition of factorial n, may be replaced in favor of the definition as a special case of the Gamma function $\Gamma(x)$. For $-1 < n$, $n! = \Gamma(n+1), = \int_0^\infty x^n e^{-x} dx$. For n a large natural number, Stirling's asymptotic formula (extended) yields $n! \sim \sqrt{2n\pi}\,(n/e)^n \left(1 + \dfrac{1}{12n} + \dfrac{1}{288n^2} - \dfrac{139}{51840n^3} - \cdots \right)$. Note: Do not use the obsolescent form $\lfloor n$ for $n!$

$\int, \int_a^b, \int_a^x, \int\int, \int_c$ —Integral signs. (use preferably bold-face type)

$\int_a^b \int_c^d f(x,y)dxdy$ denotes $\int_a^b \left(\int_c^d f(x,y)dx \right)dy, = \int_a^b dy \int_c^d dx f(x,y)$.

$\oint$ —curvilinear integral over closed path free from singularities. (Use preferably bold-face type.)

§—section, or article.

¶ *or* ¶—paragraph.

$\propto$ —varies as. Instead of $y \propto x$ one may write $y = kx$, k being the constant factor of proportionality.

∇ —nabla—To indicate: **1.** linear vector operator $\left(\dfrac{\partial}{\partial x}, \dfrac{\partial}{\partial y}, \dfrac{\partial}{\partial z} \right)$ as used also in divergence, gradient, and curl (or rotation). **2.** backward difference (in interpolation theory) $\nabla a_n = a_n - a_{n-1}$.

∇^2 —Laplace operator. Sometimes written Δ.

$\boxdot$ —Four dimensional differential operator of D'Alembert and Poincare [= point carré].

$°, ', '', ''', \cdots, (N) \cdots$, (superscript)—superscript numbers. See "superscripts."

∞ —infinity. Use $+\infty$ or $-\infty$ respectively, where direction of approach along real numbers is to be indicated. Otherwise use ∞ rather than $\pm\infty$. Note: "$n \to \infty$," may be read "as n increases without bound." Lim $f(x) = \infty$ means "Lim $1/f(x) = 0$," so that whenever one variable "becomes infinite" the meaning is that its reciprocal "becomes zero."

$\in$ —(is) a member (of), as in $x \in A$. Several objects can be denoted as members in a set A by $x_1, x_2, \cdots x_n \in A$.

$\notin$ —(is) not a member (of).

$\mathcal{P}$ —denotes a power set, as in $\mathcal{P}(A)$ which denotes the set of all subsets of a set A.

$\aleph$ —Aleph (initial Hebrew letter) transfinite cardinal number, in particular that of all real numbers. $\aleph_0$ (aleph null) first transfinite cardinal. Use of Hebrew letters for transfinite numerals is recommended: "aleph" (omit the null) for the cardinal of the set of integers; ℶ "beth" for the cardinal of the continuum (number of points on a line); and ℷ "gimel" for the cardinal of functions of a real variable.

$\mathfrak{F}$ —the Farey sequence. $\mathfrak{F}_n$ denotes the Farey sequence of order n.

α —Alpha. To indicate: **1.** (in analytic geometry of 3 dimensions). direction angle with X-axis. **2.** angular acceleration. **3.** (in statistics) $\alpha_0 = 1$, $\alpha_1 = 0$, $\alpha_2 = 1$, $\alpha_3 = \mu_3/\sigma^3$, $\alpha_4 = \mu_4/\sigma^4 = \mu_4/\mu_2^2$. **4.** (in mathematical astronomy), right ascension (also indicated by R.A.) **5.** angle of triangle

MATHEMATICAL SYMBOLS AND ABBREVIATIONS (Continued)

at A, opposite side a. **6.** root of algebraic equation as in $a(x - \alpha)(x - \beta)(x - \gamma) = 0$.

B—(Greek Beta)—$B(m,n) = \Gamma(m)\Gamma(n)/\Gamma(m + n)$, (Eulerian Beta-function).

β—Beta. To indicate: **1.** (in analytic geometry of 3 dimensions), direction angle with Y-axis. **2.** (in statistics), $\beta_1 = \alpha_3{}^2 = \mu_3{}^2/\mu_2{}^3$, $\beta_2 = \alpha_4 = \mu_4/\mu_2{}^2$. **3.** angle of triangle at B, opposite side b. **4.** root of algebraic equation. See α.

Γ—$\Gamma(x)$ Gamma-function. See "!" Among numerous definitions equivalent for positive real values of x, are the two following: (i) $\Gamma(x) = \lim\limits_{n \to \infty}$

$$\frac{1 \cdot 2 \cdots n}{x(x + 1) \cdots (x + n - 1)} n^{x-1}, x > 0. \quad \text{(ii) } \Gamma(x) = \int_0^\infty e^{-t}t^{x-1}dt, R(x) > 0.$$

γ—Gamma. To indicate: **1.** (in analytic geometry of 3 dimensions) direction angle with Z-axis. **2.** Euler or Mascheroni constant. (Also indicated by C.) $\gamma = \lim\limits_{n \to \infty} \left(\frac{1}{1} + \frac{1}{2} + \cdots + \frac{1}{n} - \log n\right) = 0.57721\ 56649\ 01532$

86060 65120 $\cdots$ **3.** angle of triangle at C, opposite side c. **4.** radius of geodesic curvature. **5.** universal constant of gravitation $= 6.670 \times 10^{-8}$ cm³/(gm. sec²). **6.** root of algebraic equation, see α.

Δ—Delta. To indicate: **1.** triangle (in plane geometry). (For right triangle, write rtΔ, not $\angle$). Also area of triangle. **2.** increment, as in Δx, Δf, $f(x + \Delta x)$, etc. **3.** forward difference (interpolation theory). $\Delta a_n = a_{n+1} - a_n$. **4.** Laplacian operator $\frac{\partial^2}{\partial x^2} + \frac{\partial^2}{\partial y^2}$, or $\frac{\partial^2}{\partial x^2} + \frac{\partial^2}{\partial y^2} + \frac{\partial^2}{\partial z^2}$, also designated by ∇^2. **5.** selected square root of the discriminant of a given polynomial, as in $\Delta^2 = b^2 - 4ac$ for the polynomial $ax^2 + bx + c$. **6.** triangular number, (of form $(n^2 - n)/2$). **7.** Legendre's radical, $\Delta(\varphi)^2 = 1 - k^2 \sin^2 \varphi$.

δ—Delta. To indicate: **1.** positive constant dependent upon ϵ that may be chosen initially as near to zero as desired. (In theory of limits, of continuity, etc.) **2.** variation of. **3.** (in interpolational theory) central difference $\delta y_{c+i+\frac{1}{2}} = y_{c+i+1} - y_{c+i}$. **4.** (in mathematical astronomy) apparent declination. **5.** number of double points, or nodes (Plücker number). **6.** (in statistics) deviation. **7.** force of interest, $e^\delta = 1 + i$, (in mathematics of finance). **8.** Kronecker Delta, $\delta_{ij} = 0$ for $i \neq j$, $= 1$ for $i = j$. In tensor notation, also $\delta_i{}^j$. One has $\delta_{ij} = \begin{pmatrix} o \\ i - j \end{pmatrix}$ or $C_{0,i-i}$. **9.** unit elongation (in strength of materials).

∂—curly d. To indicate: **1.** partial differentiation as in $\partial f(x,y)/\partial x$. **2.** The Jacobian operator, as in $\partial(u,v,w)/\partial(x,y,z)$. This is variously represented, sometimes as $J\left(\frac{u,v,w}{x,y,z}\right)$ etc. **3.** a specified square root of the discriminant D. (also sometimes as Δ.)

ϵ—Epsilon. To indicate: **1.** positive constant, that may be chosen initially as near to zero as desired. (In theory of limits, of continuity etc.) **2.** primitive root of unity. **3.** (is) member of, (relation of element to containing class). **4.** eccentricity of conic section, usually better designated by e. **5.** (in mathematical astronomy) obliquity of ecliptic. **6.** an ϵ-number is a transfinite ordinal or a certain limiting type. Note: Do not use ϵ or ε for Napierian base except in engineering. See e.

MATHEMATICAL SYMBOLS AND ABBREVIATIONS (Continued)

$\ni$—(Reversed Epsilon). Such that.

$\notin$—(is not a member of.)

ζ—Zeta. To indicate: **1.** Riemann Zeta-function $\zeta(s) = \Sigma_{n=1}^{\infty} n^{-s}$ (for $s > 1$). **2.** (in statistics) a test of linearity. $\zeta = \eta^2 - r^2$.

η—Eta. To indicate: **1.** general variable or unknown constant, analogous to y as in case of moving system of coordinates, etc. Used in ordered set (ξ, η, ζ). **2.** a confocal coordinate. See ξ. **3.** (in statistics), correlation ratio. **4.** order-type of the aggregate of all rational numbers.

Θ—Theta. To indicate: **1.** Theta-function. See ϑ. **2.** absolute temperature (where t is used for time).

θ—Theta. To indicate: **1.** general angular displacement (in trigonometry and analytic geometry). **2.** (in plane polar coordinates (r cis θ)) angle from initial ray to radius vector, $x = r \cos \theta$, $y = r \sin \theta$. **3.** (in cylindrical coordinates ($r\,\theta\,z$)) angle from initial radial half-plane to radial half-plane containing radius vector. **4.** (in spherical coordinates (r,θ,φ)) co-latitude (measured from zenith) and (in astronomy) zenith distance. This notation is traditional in mathematical physics. In texts on analytic geometry, usage varies, θ being employed frequently for the longitude. See φ. **5.** Theta-function. See ϑ. **6.** (in formal theory of operations) a displacement operator. **7.** ordinary temperature (when t is used for time).

ϑ—Theta-function. Definitions and notations vary widely. For elliptic Theta-functions the notation given here is that followed by Whittaker and Watson. Here $\vartheta_i(o,q)$, ϑ_i', the value of $d\vartheta_i(z,q)/dz$. ($i = 1,2,3,4$). These are defined by $\vartheta_1(z,q) = 2q^{\frac{1}{4}} \sin Z - 2q^{\frac{9}{4}} \sin 3z + 2q^{\frac{25}{4}}$ $\sin 5z - \cdots \vartheta_2(z,q) = 2q^{\frac{1}{4}} \sin z + 2q^{\frac{9}{4}} \sin 3z + 2q^{\frac{25}{4}} \sin 5z + \cdots \vartheta_3(z,q)$ $= 1 + 2q \cos 2z + 2q^4 \cos 4z + 2q^9 \cos 6z + \cdots \vartheta_4(z,q) = 1 - 2q \cos$ $2z + 2q^4 \cos 4z - 2q^9 \cos 6z + \cdots$.

ι—Iota, number of inflexions (a Plücker number).

$\overline{\iota}$—inverted Iota, (in formal logic) the unique element fulfilling description stated.

κ—Kappa, number of cusps. (A Plücker number).

Λ—Lambda, sometimes used for null-class.

λ—Lambda. To indicate: **1.** general linear parameter (e.g., in a pencil), as in $F + \lambda G$. **2.** running index, as in $x_\lambda (\lambda = 1, 2, \cdots)$. **3.** longitude (in mathematical astronomy). **4.** characteristic value (as in λ_i) in theory of linear differential equations of second order, linear integral equations, etc. **5.** order-type of the aggregate of all real numbers. **6.** In solid analytic geometry (λ, μ, ν) are direction cosines.

μ—Mu. To indicate: **1.** running index, usually used with λ, as in $x_\lambda y_\mu$. **2.** general linear parameter, when used with λ, as in $\lambda F + \mu G$. **3.** (in statistics) moment, about the arithmetic mean, as in $\mu_k = \Sigma_i f_i(x_i - \bar{x})^k$, $\mu_2 = \sigma^2 =$ variance. **4.** μ_x, force of mortality $= -d(\log_e l_x)/dx$. **5.** (in number theory) inversion function of Moebius and Mertens. **6.** Various physical constants such as permeability, reduced mass. **7.** Integrating factor which converts integrable expression into exact differential form.

ν—Nu. To indicate: **1.** running index, usually with λ and μ. **2.** (in statistics) moment about arbitrary origin A (in "short method") as in $\nu_k = \Sigma_i f_i(x_i - A)^k$. **3.** Frequency.

ξ—Xi. To indicate: **1.** general variable, or unknown constant analogous to

MATHEMATICAL SYMBOLS AND ABBREVIATIONS (Continued)

x, as in moving systems of coordinates, etc.   **2.** a confocal coordinate as in
(i) confocal ellipses and hyperbolas, $\dfrac{x^2}{a^2 - \lambda} + \dfrac{y^2}{b^2 - \lambda} = 1, \ -\infty < \xi < b^2 <$

$\eta < a^2$.   (ii) confocal ellipsoids and hyperboloids of revolution, $\dfrac{x^2}{a^2 - \lambda} +$

$\dfrac{y^2 + z^2}{b^2 - \lambda} = 1, \ -\infty < \xi < b^2 < \eta < a^2$.   (iii) confocal parabolas, $y^2 + 2\lambda$.

$(x - \lambda) = 0, -\infty < \xi < 0 < \eta < +\infty$.   (iv) confocal paraboloids of revolution, $y^2 + z^2 + 2\lambda(x - \lambda) = 0, \ -\infty < \xi < 0 < \eta < +\infty$.   (v) confocal
ellipsoids and hyperboloids, $\dfrac{x^2}{a^2 - \lambda} + \dfrac{y^2}{b^2 - \lambda} + \dfrac{z^2}{c^2 - \lambda} = 1, \ -\infty < \xi <$

$c^2 < \eta < b^2 < \zeta < a^2$.   (vi) confocal paraboloids, $\dfrac{x^2}{a^2 - \lambda} + \dfrac{y^2}{b^2 - \lambda} = 2z - \lambda,$

$-\infty < \xi < b^2 < \eta < a^2 < \zeta < +\infty$. (ξ, η, ζ), Xi, eta, zeta, are used as
alternates for rectangular coordinates (x,y,z).

$\Pi, \ \Pi_i\Pi_{i-m}^n, \ \Pi_{(R)} \text{ or } \Pi$—**1.** product of terms with index i, or j, etc. ranging from

m to n, or over R. Do not use $\Pi, \ \underset{i=m}{\overset{n}{\underset{i}{\Pi}}}$, etc.   (Bold-faced type preferred.)

2. (in some formal logical treatments) "for every."

$\Pi_{ij}, \ \Pi_{ijk}, \ \cdots -\Pi_i\Pi_j, \ \Pi_i\Pi_j\Pi_k$, etc.

π—Pi.   **1.** the ratio of the length of circumference of a circle, to the diameter.
$\pi = 3.14159 \ 26535 \ 89793 \ 23846 \cdots$ **2.** general notation for plane,
projectivity, projective, period, etc.

ρ—Rho.   **1.** radius of geodesic curvature.   **2.** proportionality factor, as in
$\rho X_i = \Sigma_j a_{ij} x_j$.

$\sum, \ \sum_i, \ \sum_{i-m}^n, \ \sum_{(R)} \text{ or } \sum_{(R)}$—Sigma.   **1.** summation, sum of terms of index i,

or j, etc., ranging from m to n, or over range R. Do not use $\underset{i}{\sum}, \ \underset{i=m}{\overset{n}{\sum}}$, etc.

(bold-faced type preferred).   **2.** (on some formal logical treatments) "for
at least one."   **3.** (in number theory) $\Sigma_{d/n}$ summation extended over all
divisors of n.   **4.** (in mathematical astronomy) Σ-pt is the intersection of the
meridian with the equator.

$\Sigma_{ij}, \ \Sigma_{ijk} \cdots -\Sigma_i\Sigma_j, \ \Sigma_i\Sigma_j\Sigma_k$, etc.

σ—Sigma.   To indicate: **1.** radius of torsion.   **2.** (in statistics) standard
deviation $\sigma^2 N = \Sigma_i(x_i - \bar{x})^2 f_i$.   **3.** (in number theory), $\sigma_k(n) =$ sum of
kth powers of divisors of n.   **4.** any one of several analogous Sigma-func-
tions.   The simplest elliptic Sigma-function $\sigma(x)$ is related to the Weier-

strassian $\wp$ function by $\wp u = -d^2 \log \sigma u / du^2$.   One has $\sigma u = u\left\{ 1 - \dfrac{g_2}{2} \dfrac{u^4}{5!} \right.$

$\left. - 6g_3\dfrac{u^6}{7!} - \dfrac{9}{4}g_2{}^2\dfrac{u^8}{9!} - 18g_2g_3\dfrac{u^{10}}{11!} - \cdots \right\}$ **5.** proportionality factor, usually
used with ρ.

τ—Tau.   To indicate: **1.** number of bitangents (a Plücker number).   **2.** time
(when t is used for temperature).   **3.** torsion (of curve in space).

Υ—Upsilon.   (In mathematical astronomy) vernal equinox.

ϕ—Phi.   **1.** Used to indicate the Golden Ratio or Section, $\phi = 1.61803 \ 39887$
$49894 \cdots$.   **2.** Used to denote Euler's function, where $\phi(m)$ is the number

MATHEMATICAL SYMBOLS AND ABBREVIATIONS (Continued)

of positive integers not greater than and prime to m. **3.** The null (or empty) set containing no elements.

φ—Phi. To indicate: **1.** general functional symbol, especially for polynomials. **2.** (in spherical coordinates, (r,θ,φ), longitude from x to y in right-handed system. In some astronomical work the z-axis points to the zenith, θ is the zenith-distance, and φ is the latitude. In some works on analytic geometry the roles of θ and φ are interchanged, although the system given is traditional mathematical physics. $x = r \sin \theta \cos \varphi$, $y = r \sin \theta \sin \varphi$, $z = r \cos \theta$. **3.** (in geocentric coordinates, (r,φ,λ), φ = latitude (not co-latitude as with spherical coordinates). **4.** (in plane polar coordinates (r,φ).) Used chiefly as specialized case of spherical coordinates $(r,\pi/2,\varphi)$. See θ. **5.** inclination of plane curve, $\tan \varphi = dy/dx = m$. **6.** (in number theory.) Euler's function or indicatrix. $\varphi(n)$ is the number of positive integers not exceeding n and prime to n. **7.** $\varphi_i(x)$, characteristic function, see λ_i. **8.** argument in Legendre's elliptic integrals. $E(k,\varphi) = \int_0^\varphi \Delta(\varphi)d\varphi$, $F(k,\varphi) = \int_0^\varphi d\varphi/\Delta(\varphi)$. **9.** the normal probability function of Laplace and Gauss in the form $\varphi(t) = \dfrac{1}{\sqrt{2\pi}}e^{\frac{-t^2}{2}}$. **10.** $\varphi_n(x)$, sometimes used for Bernoulli polynomial. See $B_n(x)$.

χ—Chi. (In statistical theory) χ^2 is a measure of goodness of fit, devised by Karl Pearson. $\chi^2 = \Sigma(f_i - Np_i)^2/(Np_i)$ for N items, with p_i the probability of appearances and f_i the frequency for items in an ith class.

ψ—Psi. To indicate: **1.** general functional symbol (usually with φ). **2.** angle from radius vector to tangent of plane curve. **3.** (with geocentric coordinates in mathematical astronomy), co-latitude. See φ.

Ω—Omega. To indicate: **1.** a certain annihilator in the theory of binary concomitants. **2.** (with subscript) transfinite ordinals of certain minimal type. **3.** (in geometry of the triangle) Ω,Ω', the Brocard points.

ω—Omega. To indicate: **1.** angular velocity. **2.** first transfinite ordinal, order-type of the aggregate of all natural numbers. **3.** imaginary cube root of unity, related to i, by $\omega = (-1 + i\sqrt{3})/2$. **4.** ω_1, ω_2, ω_3, half-periods of Weierstrassian $\wp$-function. **5.** (in geometry of the triangle) Brocard angle. $\cot \omega = \cot A + \cot B + \cot C$.

A—**1.** A vertex, and the associated angle of $\triangle ABC$. See α. **2.** A_{ij}, algebraic complement of a_{ij} in determinant, D. $A_{ij} = dD/da_{ij}$. **3.** (in astronomy) azimuth. **4.** (in astronomy) astronomical unit, mean geocentric distance to the sun. **5.** acres. **6.** area.

$\mathring{A}$—ångstrom.

$\forall_x$—For every x.

AM—arithmetic mean. See also superscript ⁻.

Ans.—answer.

AP—arithmetic progression.

Ax—axiom.

a—**1.** (in elementary algebra) initial term in arithmetic or geometric progression. **2.** (with subscript) coefficient in Fourier series, $(a_0/2) + \Sigma_{n=1}^{\infty}(a_n \cos nx + b_n \sin nx)$. **3.** (with two indices) element in matrix or determinant, as in $\begin{pmatrix} a_{11}\ a_{12}\ a_{13} \\ a_{21}\ a_{22}\ a_{23} \end{pmatrix}$ or $\begin{vmatrix} a_{11}\ a_{12} \\ a_{21}\ a_{22} \end{vmatrix}$. **4.** (in elementary geometry) apothegm. **5.** (in

MATHEMATICAL SYMBOLS AND ABBREVIATIONS (Continued)

geometry or triangle) first side-line, also length of first side of the triangle.
6. (in elementary analytic geometry) x-intercept. **7.** (in elementary analytic geometry) semi-major axis of ellipse or semi-transverse axis of hyperbola, etc. Thus latus rectum of central conic is $2p = 2b^2/a$, eccentricity $e = c/a$. For central conics and quadrics the a is sometimes associated with x, as in $(x^2/a^2) + (y^2/b^2) = 1$, even when a may be less than b, or as in $-(x^2/a^2) + (y^2/b^2) = 1$, where a is the semi-conjugate axis.

abs—absolute value of.

acc—acceleration.

am—amplitude function. $\varphi = $ am u, where $u = F = \int_0^\varphi d\varphi/\Delta(\varphi)$.

amp—amplitude of vibration.

antilog—antilogarithm.

approx—approximate(ly).

arc (in "arc sin" etc.)—inverse. Also written $\sin^{-1}$ etc. Do not use "arc" for inverse of hyperbolic functions. Write $\sinh^{-1}$, etc.

arg—argument. Angle in polar coordinates r cis θ, and in complex number. $re^{i\theta}$ for r and θ real. Better than "arc" and more legible than superscript -1 to indicate inverse hyperbolic functions, though "$\sinh^{-1} x$" is often used.

av—average.

B—**1.** (With subscripts) Bernoulli numbers and polynomials. To indicate what usage among many is being followed in any given case, authors would do well to list the values of the first few Bernoulli numbers as for example, $B_1 = \frac{1}{2}$, $B_2 = \frac{1}{6}$, $B_3 = 0$, $B_4 = -\frac{1}{30}$, etc. The Bernoulli polynomials, are defined as $B_n(x) = \Sigma_{r=0}^n \binom{n}{r} B_r x^{n-r}$, and satisfy $B_n(x + 1) - B_n(x) = nx^{n-1}$ with the choice of notation for Bernoulli numbers given above. (Also designated by $\varphi_n(x)$.) See page 466 for a second definition of Bernoulli numbers. **2.** bound (general symbol). $\bar{B}$, $\underline{B}$ designate least upper, and greatest lower bound respectively. Preferred notations are "sup" and "inf" respectively. **3.** a vertex and the associated angle of $\triangle ABC$. See β. **4.** (in elementary solid geometry), area of base of a solid.

b—**1.** (in elementary geometry) length of base of plane figure. b,b', parallel bases of trapezoid. **2.** (in elementary analytic geometry) y-intercept. **3.** (in elementary analytic geometry) semi-axis. See a. **4.** (in geometry of the triangle) second side-line, also length of second side of the triangle.

bei(z)—Thomson-Bessel function, bei(z) $= \dfrac{(\frac{1}{2}z)^2}{(2!)^2} - \dfrac{(\frac{1}{2}z)^6}{(6!)^2} + \dfrac{(\frac{1}{2}z)^{10}}{(10!)^2} - \cdots$

ber(z) $\pm i$ bei(z) $= J_0(zi\sqrt{} \pm i) = I_0(z\sqrt{} \pm i)$.

ber(z)—Thomson-Bessel function. (See bei(z).) ber(z) $= 1 - \dfrac{(\frac{1}{2}z)^4}{(4!)^2} + \dfrac{(\frac{1}{2}z)^8}{(8!)^2} - \cdots$

(B)-space—A Banach space.

B_m^s—An s-dimensional Betti group modulo m (m prime).

B_0^s—An s-dimensional Betti group relative to the group of integers.

C—**1.** arbitrary constant of integration. **2.** (in elementary geometry) circumference of circle; also, circle. **3.** general symbol for curve. **4.** (with subscripts) combination, as in $C_{n,r}$ or $_nC_r$, the number of combinations of n things taken r at a time (without repetitions). The form $_nC_r$ or even ^nC_r is

MATHEMATICAL SYMBOLS AND ABBREVIATIONS (Continued)

widely used but the notation $C_{n,r}$ or $C(n,r)$ or $\binom{n}{r}$ is to be preferred. **5.** Roman numeral for "hundred." **6.** Euler or Mascheroni constant. Also designated by γ. (See γ.) **7.** (chiefly as subscript) contour of integration. **8.** Centigrade, degree Centigrade, as $-52C$.

C_I—(in topology) class of spaces satisfying first axiom of countability, or property of satisfying first axiom of countability.

C_{II}—Same as above for second axiom of countability.

$\underline{C}$—(underlined) the set of complex numbers.

$\underset{\sim}{C}$—(wavy underline) indicates congruence of two n-square matrices.

Ci—cosine integral function, $Ci(x) = \int_{\infty}^{x} (\cos u/u)du$.

c—**1.** (in geometry of triangle) third side-line, also length of third side of triangle. **2.** (in elementary analytic geometry), z-intercept. **3.** (in elementary analytic geometry) semi-axis. (See a.)

cis—cis $\theta = \cos \theta + i \sin \theta = e^{i\theta} = exp(i\theta)$. Used to distinguish polar coordinates r cis θ from rectangular coordinates. Using Gaussian coordinates, r cis $\theta = x + iy$. In de Moivres' formula cis$^n \theta = $ cis $n\theta$.

cn—cosine amplitude function. (Jacobian elliptic function.)

colog—cologarithm, $=$ log of reciprocal $=$ negative of log (especially with base 10).

conj—(complex) conjugate (of). See superscript —.

cos—cosine $=$ sine of the complementary angle.

$\cos^{-1}$—inverse cosine (of). Also written arc cos. $\theta = \cos^{-1} x$ means cos $\theta = x$. Arc cos x (with capital A) indicates principal value, $0 < \theta < \pi$.

cosh—hyperbolic cosine (of). Do not write Cos nor $\mathfrak{Cof}$ (in German letters).

$\cosh^{-1}$—inverse hyperbolic cosine of. Also written as arg cosh.

covers—coversed sine or coversine.

csc—cosecant (of). Reciprocal of sine.

$\csc^{-1}$—inverse cosecant (of). Also written arc csc.

ctn also cot—cotangent (of). Reciprocal of tangent.

ctn^{-1}—inverse cotangent (of). Also written as $\cot^{-1}$, arc cot, or arc ctn.

ctnh—hyperbolic cotangent (of). Also written as coth.

ctnh^{-1}—inverse hyperbolic cotangent of. Also written as arg coth or arg ctnh.

cu—cubic. In arithmetic "cubic feet" is written "cu ft" but "ft^3" is better.

cum—cumulative.

D—**1.** differential operator, as in $Dy = y'$, $d_x f(x,y) = \partial f/\partial x$. **2.** Roman numeral for "five hundred." **3.** general symbol for denominator, or for determinant. **4.** discriminant of binary form, or of polynomial. **5.** (in statistical theory), (with subscripts 0, 1, $\cdots$, 10), decile marks. **6.** $D(a_1, a_1, \cdots, a_n)$ sometimes designates the Vandermonde determinant.

$$\begin{vmatrix} 1a_1 & \cdots & a_1^{n-1} \\ \cdot & \cdots & \cdot \\ 1a_n & \cdots & a_n^{n-1} \end{vmatrix}$$

Def—definition.

Dem—demonstration, proof.

d—**1.** (in elementary algebra), common difference in arithmetic progression. **2.** differential operator, as in d^2y/dx^2. **3.** (in elementary geometry) diameter. **4.** (as superscript) days, as in $2^d3^h17^m$. **5.** (British currency) pence.

MATHEMATICAL SYMBOLS AND ABBREVIATIONS (Continued)

deg—degree, degrees. In navigation use 3 digits measured clockwise from north, so that 090 is due east. In trigonometry use cis θ to indicate direction measured counterclockwise from the positive x-axis, so that cis 90 is the direction of the positive y-axis.

det—determinant of, as in det (a_{ii}).

div—divergence of, also indicated by $\nabla\cdot$ (with nabla and dot).

dn—dn(z), a Jacobian elliptic function.

$\exists$—(there) exists.

$\exists\,|$—there exist uniquely.

E—**1.** E,F,G fundamental differential quantities of first order for surfaces. **2.** $E(k,\varphi)$, Legendre's normal elliptic integral, of the second kind, $E = E(k,\varphi)$ $\int_0^\varphi \Delta(\varphi)d\varphi$. **3.** east. **4.** (in Euler's polyhedral formula) number of edges of polyhedron. **5.** displacement operator, $E(f(x)) = f(x + 1)$. **6.** (in mathematical astronomy) equation of time.

Ei—exponential integral function $Ei(x) = \int_{-\infty}^{x} \frac{e^v dv}{v}$.

Eq—equation.

Ex—exercise.

e—**1.** base of natural (or Napierian) logarithms. In place of e^A one may write $\exp A$. $e = 2.71828\ 18284\ 59045\ 23536\ \cdots \log_{10} e = M = 0.43429\ 44819\ 03251\ 82765\ \cdots \log_e 10 = 1/M = 2.30258\ 50929\ 94045\ 68402$. In some engineering work, where e is used otherwise, the base of natural logarithms is designated by ϵ. **2.** eccentricity of a conic. **3.** $e_1 = \wp(\omega_1)$, $e_2 = \wp(\omega_2)$, $e_3 = \wp(\omega_3)$, for Weierstrassian elliptic functions. **4.** (in mathematical astronomy) eccentricity of earth's orbit. **5.** (in elementary solid geometry) length of lateral edge (of right pyramid, prism, etc.).

eq—equivalent to.

erf—error function, $\text{erf}(x) = \frac{2}{\sqrt{\pi}} \int_0^x e^{-v^2} dv$.

erfc—complementary function to error function, $\text{erfc}(x) = 1 - \text{erf}(x) = \frac{2}{\sqrt{\pi}} \int_x^\infty e^{-v^2} dv$.

exp—exponential function of, as in $\exp(a^2 + b^2)$ for $e^{a^2+b^2}$. One could also write this "e^u where $u = a^2 + b^2$."

exsec—Exsecant

$\mathbf{F}$—Force.

F—**1.** general symbol for function or functional. **2.** the second fundamental differential quantity of first order for surfaces. See E. **3.** (in Euler's polyhedral formula) number of faces of polyhedron. **4.** $F(k,\varphi)$, Legendre's normal elliptic integral of the first kind, $F = F(k,\varphi) \int_0^\varphi d\varphi/\Delta(\varphi)$. See Δ and E. φ is here the amplitude of F, $\varphi = \text{am } F$. **5.** $F(a, b; c: x)$, hypergeometric function. **6.** Fahrenheit, degree Fahrenheit, as in 70F. **7.** falsity (in logic).

FS—Fourier series.

Fig.—figure.

Fr—frontier set of.

f—**1.** general symbol for function or functional. **2.** f_i, frequency of X_i in

MATHEMATICAL SYMBOLS AND ABBREVIATIONS (Continued)

univariate table. **3.** frequency of vibration. **4.** feet as in f/s, feet per second. Preferably ft/sec.

ft—feet. See also f and $'$.

G—**1.** general symbol for group. **2.** the third fundamental differential quantity of first order for surfaces. **3.** $G(x_1, \cdots, x_n; \xi_1, \cdots, \xi_n)$ Green's function for two points in n-space. **4.** (constant) linear group of points on an algebraic curve. See g. **5.** gravitational constant.

G.C.T.—Greenwich civil time.

GCD—greatest common divisor.

GCS—greatest common subgroup.

GF—Galois field, as in GF(p^n).

GM—geometric mean.

GP—geometric progression.

g—**1.** general function symbol, used with f. **2.** (terrestrial) gravitational attraction. **3.** (variable) linear group of points on an algebraic curve. See G. **4.** g_i, frequency of y_i in bivariate table. **5.** general coefficient in tensor, as in $g_{i,j}^{k} x^i y^i z_k$.

gd—Gudermannian. $e^u = \tan\left(\dfrac{\pi}{4} + \dfrac{1}{2} \text{ gd } u\right)$. If $\theta = $ gd u then

$$\sin \theta = \tanh u, \qquad \cos \theta = \text{sech } u$$
$$\tan \theta = \sinh u, \qquad \cot \theta = \text{csch } u$$
$$\sec \theta = \cosh u, \qquad \csc \theta = \coth u$$

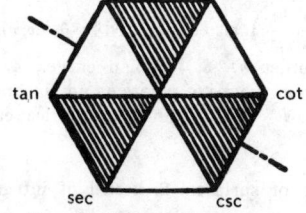

and corresponds to flipping the trigonometric hexagon on an axis perpendicular to cos-sec diagonal. Every vertex of the hexagon is the product of its adjacent vertices, (exhibiting 6 products, and 12 quotients, such as tan/sec = sin) opposite vertices are reciprocals, and in each shaded sector the Pythagorean identity holds. These identities also hold for hyperbolic functions except that Pythagorean sum is at right (so that $\tanh^2 + \text{sech}^2 = 1$).

grad—gradient of. Also written ∇.

H—**1.** general symbol for subgroup, as in G/H, particularly for normal (or self-conjugate) subgroup. **2.** Hessian, as $H(f) = \det \dfrac{\partial^2 f}{\partial x_i \partial x_j}$. **3.** $H_n(x)$, nth Hermite polynomial, $H_n(x) = e^{x^2} D^n e^{-x^2}$. **4.** $H(P_1, P_3; P_2, P_4)$ is the proposition that P_1 and P_3 separate harmonically P_2 and P_4. **5.** orthocenter of triangle where altitudes meet. **6.** $H(q_1, \cdots, q_n, t, p_1, \cdots, p_n)$ Hamiltonian function (in mathematical physics). **7.** mean curvature of surface, $H = EG - F^2$. **8.** (in mathematical astronomy) hour-angle. Also designated by t. **9.** Hilbert space, also $\mathfrak{H}$.

$\mathfrak{H}$—Hilbert space.

HCF—highest common factor.

MATHEMATICAL SYMBOLS AND ABBREVIATIONS (Continued)

HM—harmonic mean.

HP—(in elementary algebra) harmonic progression.

Hyp.—hypothesis.

h—**1.** (in interpolation theory), distance, between uniformly spaced ordinates. **2.** class interval, in x. **3.** increment of x. Also Δx. **4.** (as superscript) hours as in 8^h15^m. **5.** (terminal) hyperbolic, as in $\sinh$, $\tanh^{-1}$, etc. **6.** altitude ("height").

hav—haversine (of). hav $x = (\text{vers } x)/2 = (1 - \cos x)/2$.

I—**1.** general symbol for interval, and for definite integral. **2.** Roman numeral for "one." Write IV not IIII, IX not VIIII. **3.** $I(\ )$, imaginary part of, also designated by $\Im(\ )$, or $\text{Im}(\ )$. **4.** $I_n(z)$, the Bessel function "of imaginary argument," $I_n(z) = \sum_{m=0}^{\infty} \frac{(\frac{1}{2})z^{n+2m}}{m!\Gamma(n+m+1)}$. **5.** (in geometry) of triangle) in center where angle bisectors meet. **6.** sometimes used for the identity as an operation in a group.

$\Im$—(Black letter) imaginary part of. See I.

Im—imaginary part of. See I.

i—**1.** running index, as in a_i, $i = 1, \cdots, n$. **2.** one of the two imaginary square roots of -1. (In electrical engineering, when it is used for the current, j is used for this imaginary unit.)

i—i, j, k, unit vectors in a right-handed rectangular system. $i \times j = k$, $j \times k = i$, $k \times i = j$.

inf.—("infimum") greatest lower bound.

J—**1.** Jacobian as in $J\left(\dfrac{u,v,w}{x,y,z,}\right)$, also designated by $\partial(u,v,w)/\partial(x,y,z)$. **2.** $J_n(z)$, Bessel coefficient of order n. **3.** Jacobian curve. **4.** Jacobian group of points in a linear series of groups of points on an algebraic curve.

j—**1.** running index, with i. **2.** (sometimes in electrical engineering) $\sqrt{(-1)}$. See i.

j—a unit vector. See i.

K—**1.** specific curvature of surface. **2.** kernel of integral equation, as in $u(x) = f(x) + \lambda \int_a^b \bar{K}(x,t)u(t)dt$. K_n, the nth iterated kernel is then defined recursively by $K_1 \equiv K$, $K_n(x,y) = \int_a^b K_{n-1}(x,t)K(t,y)dt$. Also designated by $K^{(n)}$. **3.** K, iK', periods for Jacobian elliptic functions. **4.** Symmedian (Lemoine) center of triangle. **5.** $K_n(z)$, the Bessel function ("second solution") $\lim_{\nu \to n} \frac{(-1)^n}{2}\left[\frac{I_{-\nu}(z) - I_\nu(z)}{\nu - n}\right]$

k—**1.** proportionality factor for variation. Do not use $y \propto x$. **2.** running index, used with h. **3.** k,k', modulus and complementary modulus respectively of Jacobian elliptic functions. **4.** class interval, in y. **5.** increment in y. Also Δy.

k—a unit vector. See i.

kei, ker—Bessel functions defined as real for real z and satisfying, $\ker(z) + i \, \text{kei}(z) = K_0(z\sqrt{\pm i})$.

L—**1.** general symbol for linear function. **2.** general symbol for linear system, or linear space. **3.** limit, as in $\underset{n \to \infty}{L} e^{-n} = 0$. See "lim." **4.** Roman nu-

MATHEMATICAL SYMBOLS AND ABBREVIATIONS (Continued)

meral for "fifty." **5.** length. Also designated by l. **6.** first fundamental differential quantity of second order for surfaces. **7.** Lexis ratio, $\sigma \sqrt{pq/s}$, for sets of s objects each. **8.** $L_n(x)$, nth Laguerre polynomial, $L_n(x)e^{-x}n! = D^n(e^{-x}x^n)$.

LCD—lowest common denominator.

LCM—lowest (or least) common multiple.

l—**1.** running index. **2.** (in elementary algebra) last term (of arithmetic or geometric progression). **3.** $l = \cos\alpha$, directional cosine, (with x-axis). **4.** length. Also designated by L.

lat.—latitude.

li—logarithmic integral or integral logarithm function, $li(x) = \displaystyle\int_0^x du/\log u$.

lim—limit ( ), lim, least upper limit, $\underline{\lim}$, greatest lower limit.

ln—(Sometimes) natural logarithm of.

log—logarithm (of). In theoretical work, the natural base, e, is understood; in numerical computation with tables, the base 10 is understood unless otherwise specified. Some writers use "ln" for natural logarithm of. Where ambiguity is otherwise likely, indicate the base, thus $\log_b x$, $\log_{10} x$.

long—longitude.

M—**1.** Roman numeral, thousand. **2.** arithmetic mean. Also designated by superscript bar, as X, or by AM. **3.** centroid (in geometry of triangle) where medians meet. **4.** second fundamental differential quantity of second order for surfaces.

M.D.—mean deviation.

Md—median.

Mm—mid-mean, arithmetic mean of data in range Q_1 to Q_3.

Mo—mode.

m—**1.** general symbol for natural number, or integer, usually used with n. **2.** slope of line, dy/dx. **3.** $m = \cos\beta$, directional cosine (with y-axis). **4.** m_a, m_b, m_c, median lines, lengths of medians of triangle. **5.** (as subscript) meridian measurement. **6.** class of an algebraic plane curve (a Plücker number). **7.** (superscript) minutes, as in $10^d13^h5^m$. **8.** meters.

max—maximum (of).

meas—measure (of).

mi—miles.

min—**1.** minimum (of). **2.** minutes. **3.** mi. n. = nautical miles (at equator each minute of longitude corresponds to one nautical mile).

mod—**1.** modulus (of), as in $\mod(re^{i\theta}) = r$. **2.** modulo as in $7 \equiv -3(\mod 5)$.

N—**1.** third fundamental differential quantity of second order for surfaces. **2.** north. **3.** total frequency in a statistical distribution.

n—**1.** general symbol for natural number or integer. **2.** $n = \cos\gamma$, directional cosine (with z-axis). **3.** order or degree of plane algebraic curve (a Plücker number). **4.** (in elementary algebra) number of terms in finite progression. **5.** (sometimes) total frequency. See N. **6.** outward normal to surface, as in $\cos(\theta, n)$.

O—**1.** origin of coordinates. **2.** circumcenter of triangle where the perpendicular bisectors of the sides meet. **3.** of comparable order with, as $\Sigma_{n=0}^N n = O(N)^2$.

o—of inferior order to, as $\log n = o(n)$.

MATHEMATICAL SYMBOLS AND ABBREVIATIONS (Continued)

ord—order.

P—**1.** general symbol for polynomial, in particular the interpolational polynomial. **2.** product moment. Also expressed by p. **3.** general symbol for point. The common notation indicating the coordinate system used as $P(x,y,z)$, $P(r,\theta,\varphi)$, etc., is not recommended. **4.** general probability distribution function, in particular any one of Pearson's standard types, or Poisson's forms. **5.** $P_n(x)$, Legendre polynomial, $2^n n! P_n(x) = D^n(x^2 - 1)^n$. **6.** total force due to pressure. **7.** function, as in $Pdx + Qdy$, and in $y' + P(x)y = Q(x)$. **8.** $P_{n,r}$ or $_nP_r$, or $P(n,r)$, number of permutations of n distinct things taken r at a time (without repetitions), $n!/(n - r)!$. **9.** general potential due to finite number of particles. In Newtonian case $P = \Sigma_i m_i/r_i$. See U and W. **10.** horizontal parallax. **11.** north celestial pole.

PE—probable error. See $\pm$.

$P(E)$—Probability of E.

$P(E \wedge F)$—Probability of both E and F.

$P(E|F)$—Probability of E, given F.

$P(E \veebar F)$—Probability of E or F, but not both.

$P(E \vee F)$—Probability of E or F or both.

Post.—postulate.

Prob.—**1.** problem. **2.** probability.

Prop.—proposition.

PS—power series.

Pt.—point.

$\wp$—Weierstrassian elliptic function.

p—**1.** general symbol for prime number. **2.** semi-latus rectum. **3.** probability ratio. **4.** genus (or deficiency) of a plane algebraic curve (a Plücker number). **5.** perpendicular distance from origin to given line or plane.

6. p_n, numerator of nth convergent of continued fraction $a_0 + \dfrac{1}{a_1+} \dfrac{1}{a_2+}$ $\cdots$ $(p_{-1} = 0,\ p_0 = 1)$, $p_1 = a_0$, $p_{n+1} = a_n p_n + p_{n-1}$. **7.** p_{12}, p_{13}, p_{14}, p_{23}, p_{24}, p_{34}, line coordinates (point system). **8.** sometimes "per," as in "rpm," revolutions per minute. This use is not recommended. **9.** perimeter. Use s for semiperimeter. **10.** $p(n)$, total number of partitions of n. **11.** p_i, impulse component. **12.** the genus of an orientable surface.

p—page. pp—pages.

pos.—positive.

Q—**1.** general symbol for quadratic form or quadratic manifold. **2.** Q_1, Q_3 first and third quartile marks. (Q_2 is the median, Md.) **3.** function, as in $Pdx + Qdy$, and in $y' + P(x)y = Q(x)$. **4.** $Q(P_1, P_2, P_3; P_4, P_5, P_6)$, quadrangular set of six points.

$\underline{Q}$—(underlined) the set of rational numbers.

$\underline{Q}^+$—(underlined) the set of positive rational numbers.

QD—quartile deviation.

Q.E.D.—("Quod erat demonstrandum") which was to be proved.

Q.E.F.—("Quod erat faciendum") which was to be constructed.

q—**1.** complementary probability, $q = 1 - p$. **2.** q_n, denominator of nth convergent of continued fraction, $a_0 + \dfrac{1}{a_1+} \dfrac{1}{a_2+} \cdots$ $(q_0 = 0)$, $q_1 = 1$, $q_{n+1} = a_n q_n + q_{n-1}$. **3.** q_{12}, q_{13}, q_{14}, q_{23}, q_{24}, q_{34}, line coordinates (plane sys-

MATHEMATICAL SYMBOLS AND ABBREVIATIONS (Continued)

tem). **4.** q_1, q_2, quartile distances from the median. **5.** q_i, force component. **6.** the number of cross-caps on a non-orientable surface.

R—**1.** general symbol for remainder. $R_n(x)$, remainder after n terms in power-series in x. **2.** radius, in particular circumradius of triangle. **3.** real part of. Also indicated by $\Re$ (Black letter), and Re. **4.** general symbol for range of variable, as in $\displaystyle\int_{(R)}$.

$\underline{R}$—(underlined) the set of real numbers.

$\underline{R}^+$—(underlined) the set of positive real numbers.

$\Re$ —(Black letter) real value of. See R.

R. A.—right ascension. Also designated by α.

R_m^s—An s-dimensional Betti number modulo m (m prime).

R_0^s—An s-dimensional Betti number relative to the group of integers.

Re—real value of. See R.

RMS—root-mean-square. $\sqrt{(\Sigma_{i=1}^n x^2/n)}$.

r—**1.** general running index, as in rth term. **2.** radius (see R), in particular in radius of triangle. **3.** coefficient of linear correlation, correlation coefficient. **4.** (in elementary algebra) common ratio between successive terms in a geometric progression. **5.** distance, in polar and in spherical coordinates; projected distances in cylindrical coordinates. **6.** (sometimes) revolutions, as in r.p.m. (revolutions per minute). **7.** (sometimes) (superscript) radians, as in $2\pi^{(r)}$. (This usage is not recommended.) **8.** the number of boundary curves on a surface.

rad—**1.** radius. **2.** radians. Where no units are indicated angles are measured in radians, sin 30 means "sine of 30 radians," not sin 30°. Do not write sin a^r or sin $a^{(r)}$ for sin a (where a is measured in radians), since superscript r is sometimes interpreted as "revolutions."

rot—rotation or curl of vector. Also designated by $\nabla \times$ (nabla and cross).

S—**1.** general symbol for space, as S_n, space of n dimension. See L. **2.** general symbol for sum, as in S_n, sum of first n terms of given sequence or series. See s. **3.** south. **4.** standard error of estimate. **5.** radius of spherical curvature of curve. **6.** a set (any collection of distinguishable objects).

∂S—Boundary of a set S.

Si—1st sine-integral function $\mathrm{Si}(x) = \displaystyle\int_0^x (\sin u/u)du$. See si.

S.T.—sidereal time.

s.—**1.** general running index. Used with r. **2.** general symbol for sum, as in s_n sum of first n terms of sequence or series. See S. **3.** (in elementary algebra), sum of arithmetic or of geometric progression. **4.** $s_k(n)$, sum of kth powers of first n natural numbers. **5.** s_k, sum of the kth powers of the roots of an algebraic equation. **6.** arc length. **7.** slant height. **8.** (usually as superscript) seconds. **9.** semi-interquartile range. **10.** semi-perimeter of triangle, $s = (a + b + c)/2$. **11.** (sometimes) number of individuals in sample. **12.** root-mean-square deviation about arbitrarily assumed origin, (in "short method").

sec—secant (of). Reciprocal of cosine.

$\sec^{-1}$—inverse secant (of). Also designated by arc sec.

sech—hyperbolic secant (of). Do not use Sec or $\mathfrak{Sec}$ (in German letters).

sech^{-1}—inverse hyperbolic secant of. Also written as arg sech.

MATHEMATICAL SYMBOLS AND ABBREVIATIONS (Continued)

si—2nd sine-integral function, $\beta_i(x) = \int_\infty^x (\sin u/u)du$. See Si.

sgn—(signum) sign (of), more generally for z complex sgn $z = z/|z|$.

Use $\sigma_1 = \begin{pmatrix} + & + \\ - & - \end{pmatrix}$ for the signum of the sine (in the corresponding quadrant).

Use $\sigma_2 = \begin{pmatrix} - & + \\ - & + \end{pmatrix}$ for the signum of the cosine.

and $\sigma_3 = \begin{pmatrix} - & + \\ + & - \end{pmatrix}$ for the signum of the tangent.

Thus $d(\text{arc sin } x)/dx = \sigma_2/\sqrt{1 - x^2}$;
$\qquad d(\text{arc cos } x)/dx = -\sigma_1/\sqrt{1 - x^2}$
and $\sigma_1/\sigma_2 = \sigma_1\sigma_2 = \sigma_3$.

sin—sine (of). Do not use Sin. In general triangle sin $A = a/d$ where d is circumdiameter. Identity $d = a/\sin A = b/\sin B = c/\sin C$ is the "law of sines."

$\sin^{-1}$—inverse sine (of). Also designated arc sin.

sinh—hyperbolic sine (of).

$\sinh^{-1}$—inverse hyperbolic sine of—also written as arg sinh.

sk—skewness of frequency distribution.

sn—(Jacobian elliptic function), sine amplitude.

sq—square.

sup—(supremum) least upper bound. Sometimes designated by L.U.B., or l.u.b.

T—1. total time, (as in time of flight of projectile). 2. clock time. 3. general symbol for transformation, T^n, nth iterate of T. 4. tons. 5. (in logic), true or truth. 6. absolute temperature.

Th—theorem.

t—1. general variable or parameter. 2. time. (In navigation) use 4 digits 0230 for 2:30 a.m., and 1430 for 2:30 p.m. See τ. See "dot accent." 3. ordinary temperature. See T, τ, θ.

tan—tangent (of).

$\tan^{-1}$—inverse tangent (of). Also designated by arc tan.

tanh—hyperbolic tangent (of). Do not use Tan or $\mathfrak{Tan}$ (in German letters).

$\tanh^{-1}$—inverse hyperbolic tangent (of). Do not use arc tanh. Also written as arg tanh.

T_0-space—A topological space such that for distinct x and y there is either a neighborhood of x not containing y or a neighborhood of y not containing x.

T_1-space—A topological space such that for distinct x and y there is a neighborhood of x not containing y.

T_2-space—A Hausdorff topological space.

T_3-space—A T_2-space which is regular.

T_4-space—A T_2-space which is normal.

U-general (line surface or volume) potential. In Newtonian case, $U = \int_{(L)} \frac{\mu dL}{r}$, or $\int_{(S)} \frac{\mu dS}{r}$, or $\int_{(V)} \frac{\mu dV}{r}$. See P and W.

u—1. general variable, especially dependent variable or real part thereof. See w. 2. u_n, Lucas' function $u_n = (\alpha^n - \beta^n)/(\alpha - \beta)$, α, β, roots of given quadratic.

V—1. Roman numeral, five. 2. (in Euler's polyhedral formula) number of

MATHEMATICAL SYMBOLS AND ABBREVIATIONS (Continued)

vertices. **3.** general harmonic function. **4.** volume. **5.** coefficient of variation.

v—(linear) velocity.

v—**1.** general variable, especial dependent variable, used with u, or coefficient of pure imaginary part thereof. See w. **2.** v_n, Lucas' function $\alpha^n + \beta^n$, α, β, roots of given quadratic. See u_n. **3.** speed.

vers—versed sine or versine.

W—**1.** west. **2.** general potential of double layer. In Newtonian case,

$$W = \int_{(S)} v \frac{\partial}{\partial n}\left(\frac{1}{r}\right) dS, = -\int_{(S)} \frac{v}{r^2} \cos (r,n)\, dS.$$ See P and U. **3.** Wronskian,

$$W = \begin{vmatrix} y_1 & y_1' & \cdots & y_1^{(n-1)} \\ \cdots & \cdots & \cdots & \cdots \\ y_n & y_n' & \cdots & y_n^{(n-1)} \end{vmatrix}.$$

4. total weight. Also designated by Wt. **5.** work (or energy). Also designated by Wk.

Wt.—weight. See W.

w—**1.** general symbol for variable, particularly dependent variable. Used with u and v as in $J\left(\dfrac{u,v,w}{x,y,z}\right)$, etc. **2.** dependent complex variable, $w = u + iv$, or $w(z) = u(x,y) + iv(x,y)$ where $z = x + iy$, x,y,u,v, real.

X—**1.** Roman numeral, ten; as in XCIII, etc. **2.** X_i, original numerical data for x-variates, (previous to change of origin or scale). **3.** general symbol for variable point, particularly on x-axis. **4.** function, as in $Xdx + Ydy + Zdz$ or $\dfrac{dx}{X} = \dfrac{dy}{Y} = \dfrac{dz}{Z}$.

x—**1.** general symbol for independent variable or unknown. **2.** first rectangular coordinate. In space a right-handed coordinate system such as indicated

by 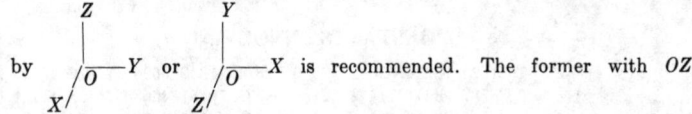 is recommended. The former with OZ directed to the zenith is more common. **3.** real part of independent complex variable $z = x + iy$.

Y—**1.** Y_i, original numerical data for y-variates (previous to change of origin or scale). **2.** function as in $Xdx + Ydy + Zdz$, or $\dfrac{dx}{X} = \dfrac{dy}{Y} = \dfrac{dz}{Z}$.

y—**1.** general symbol for dependent (real) variable. **2.** general symbol for second independent variable, r unknown. **3.** second rectangular coordinate. See x. **4.** pure imaginary coefficient, in independent complex variable, $z = x + iy$.

Z—zenith.

$\underline{Z}$—(underlined) the set of integers.

$\underline{Z}^+$—(underlined) the set of positive integers.

Z.T.—zone time.

z—**1.** independent complex variable, $z = x + iy$. **2.** general symbol for third independent variable or unknown. **3.** third rectangular coordinate. See x. **4.** axial coordinate in cylindrical coordinates (r, θ, z). **5.** zenith distance, $(90^0 - h)$. **6.** Fisher's z statistic.

GREEK ALPHABET

Greek letter	Greek name	English equivalent	Greek letter	Greek name	English equivalent
A α	Alpha	a	N ν	Nu	n
B β	Beta	b	Ξ ξ	Xi	x
Γ γ	Gamma	g	O o	Omicron	ŏ
Δ δ	Delta	d	Π π	Pi	p
E ε	Epsilon	ĕ	P ρ	Rho	r
Z ζ	Zeta	z	Σ σ ς	Sigma	s
H η	Eta	ē	T τ	Tau	t
Θ θ ϑ	Theta	th	Υ υ	Upsilon	u
I ι	Iota	i	Φ φ φ	Phi	ph
K κ	Kappa	k	X χ	Chi	ch
Λ λ	Lambda	l	Ψ ψ	Psi	ps
M μ	Mu	m	Ω ω	Omega	ō

MISCELLANEOUS CONSTANTS

π CONSTANTS

$$\pi = 3.14159\ 26535\ 89793\ 23846\ 26433\ 83279\ 50288\ 41971\ 69399\ 37511$$
$$1/\pi = 0.31830\ 98861\ 83790\ 67153\ 77675\ 26745\ 02872\ 40689\ 19291\ 48091$$
$$\pi^2 = 9.86960\ 44010\ 89358\ 61883\ 44909\ 99876\ 15113\ 53136\ 99407\ 24079$$
$$\log_e \pi = 1.14472\ 98858\ 49400\ 17414\ 34273\ 51353\ 05871\ 16472\ 94812\ 91531$$
$$\log_{10} \pi = 0.49714\ 98726\ 94133\ 85435\ 12682\ 88290\ 89887\ 36516\ 78324\ 38044$$
$$\log_{10} \sqrt{2\pi} = 0.39908\ 99341\ 79057\ 52478\ 25035\ 91507\ 69595\ 02099\ 34102\ 92128$$

CONSTANTS INVOLVING e

$$e = 2.71828\ 18284\ 59045\ 23536\ 02874\ 71352\ 66249\ 77572\ 47093\ 69996$$
$$1/e = 0.36787\ 94411\ 71442\ 32159\ 55237\ 70161\ 46086\ 74458\ 11131\ 03177$$
$$e^2 = 7.38905\ 60989\ 30650\ 22723\ 04274\ 60575\ 00781\ 31803\ 15570\ 55185$$
$$M = \log_{10} e = 0.43429\ 44819\ 03251\ 82765\ 11289\ 18916\ 60508\ 22943\ 97005\ 80367$$
$$1/M = \log_e 10 = 2.30258\ 50929\ 94045\ 68401\ 79914\ 54684\ 36420\ 76011\ 01488\ 62877$$
$$\log_{10} M = 9.63778\ 43113\ 00536\ 78912\ 29674\ 98645 - 10$$

π^e AND e^π CONSTANTS

$$\pi^e = 22.45915\ 77183\ 61045\ 47342\ 71522$$
$$e^\pi = 23.14069\ 26327\ 79269\ 00572\ 90864$$
$$e^{-\pi} = 0.04321\ 39182\ 63772\ 24977\ 44177$$
$$e^{\frac{1}{2}\pi} = 4.81047\ 73809\ 65351\ 65547\ 30357$$
$$i^i = e^{-\frac{1}{2}\pi} = 0.20787\ 95763\ 50761\ 90854\ 69556$$

NUMERICAL CONSTANTS

$$\sqrt{2} = 1.41421\ 35623\ 73095\ 04880\ 16887\ 24209\ 69807\ 85696\ 71875\ 37695$$
$$\sqrt[3]{2} = 1.25992\ 10498\ 94873\ 16476\ 72106\ 07278\ 22835\ 05702\ 51464\ 70151$$
$$\log_e 2 = 0.69314\ 71805\ 59945\ 30941\ 72321\ 21458\ 17656\ 80755\ 00134\ 36026$$
$$\log_{10} 2 = 0.30102\ 99956\ 63981\ 19521\ 37388\ 94724\ 49302\ 67681\ 89881\ 46211$$
$$\sqrt{3} = 1.73205\ 08075\ 68877\ 29352\ 74463\ 41505\ 87236\ 69428\ 05253\ 81039$$
$$\sqrt[3]{3} = 1.44224\ 95703\ 07408\ 38232\ 16383\ 10780\ 10958\ 83918\ 69253\ 49935$$
$$\log_e 3 = 1.09861\ 22886\ 68109\ 69139\ 52452\ 36922\ 52570\ 46474\ 90557\ 82275$$
$$\log_{10} 3 = 0.47712\ 12547\ 19662\ 43729\ 50279\ 03255\ 11530\ 92001\ 28864\ 19070$$

OTHER CONSTANTS

$$\text{Euler's Constant } \gamma = 0.57721\ 56649\ 01532\ 86061$$
$$\log_e \gamma = -0.54953\ 93129\ 81644\ 82234$$
$$\text{Golden Ratio } \phi = 1.61803\ 39887\ 49894\ 84820\ 45868\ 34365\ 63811\ 77203\ 09180$$

INDEX

A

B

C

G

H

I

J

K

L

M

N

Q

R

S

U

V

W

X Y Z